The ARRL Antenna Book

FOR RADIO COMMUNICATIONS

ARRL The National Association for Amateur Radio®

Twenty-Fifth Edition

Editor
Ward Silver, NØAX

Production Editor
Mark Derks, KC1RVQ

Production
Chris Dunham
Jodi Morin, KA1JPA
David F. Pingree, N1NAS

Editorial Assistant
Maty Weinberg, KB1EIB

Contributors to the Twenty-Fifth Edition
Alan Applegate, KØBG
Jim Breakall, WA3FET
Jim Brown, K9YC
Wyatt Dirks, ACØRA
Frank Donovan, W3LPL
James Duffey, KK6MC
Peter East
Doug Grant, K1DG
Rus Healy, K2UA
Matt Heere, N3NWV
Wolfgang Herrmann
Chuck Higgins
Martin Huml, OK1FUA
Dale Hunt, WB6BYU
Justin Johnson, GØKSC
Al Katz, K2UYH
Hal Kennedy, N4GG
Pete Kobak, KØBAK
Steve Kostro, N2CEI
Sean Kutzko, KX9X
Greg Lapin, N9GL
Dan Layne, ADØCY
Roy Lewellan, W7EL
Fred Maas, KT5X
Richard Marsden
Eduard Mol
Dave Mueller, N2NL
Mario Natali, IØNAA
Ron Ochu, KOØZ
Dave Olean, K1WHS
Steve Olney, VK2XV
Charles Osborne, K4CSO
Jonathan Pettingale
Alex Pettit, KK4VB
John Portune, W6NBC
Bruce Randall, NT4RT
Whitman Reeve
Rick Rosen, K1DS
Rich Russell, ACØUB
Charles Scharlau, NZØI
Tom Schiller, N6BT
Rudy Severns, N6LF
Lowell Silver, WW7SAR
Andrea Slack, K2EZ
Jim Smith, KKØU
John Stanley, K4ERO
Steve Stearns, K6OIK
Patrick Stoddard, WD9EWK
Chip Sufitchi, N2YO
Dave Typinkski, AJ4CO
Ray Uberecken, AAØL
Paul Wade, W1GHZ
Bill Wortman, N6MW
Ken Wyatt, KX7KW

Printed in the USA

ISBN: 978-1-62595-175-5 Hardcover
978-1-62595-176-2 Softcover
978-1-62595-183-0 Four-Volume Set

Kindle eBook Editions
ISBN: 978-1-62595-177-9 — Volume 1
ISBN: 978-1-62595-179-3 — Volume 2
ISBN: 978-1-62595-180-9 — Volume 3
ISBN: 978-1-62595-182-3 — Volume 4

Twenty-Fifth Edition, Second Printing

We strive to produce books without errors. Sometimes mistakes do occur, however. When we become aware of problems in our books (other than obvious typographical errors), we post corrections on the ARRL website. If you think you have found an error, please check **www.arrl.org/arrl-antenna-book-reference** for corrections. If you don't find a correction there, please let us know by sending an email to **pubsfdbk@arrl.org**.

Table of Contents

A detailed Table of Contents is included at the beginning of each chapter.
See the **Project Index** for a complete list of projects.

VOLUME 2

Basic Antenna Types and MF and HF Antennas

VOLUME 3

VHF, UHF, and Microwave Antennas and Specialty Applications

VOLUME 4

Building and Maintaining Antenna Systems and Index

TABLE OF CONTENTS

Chapter 15 — Online Material

Articles

- "2 x 3 = 6" by L.B. Cebik, W4RNL
- "A 6 Meter Moxon Antenna" by Allen Baker, KG4JJH
- "A 902-MHz Loop Yagi Antenna" by Don Hilliard, WØPW
- "A Short Boom, Wideband 3 Element Yagi for 6 Meters" by L.B. Cebik, W4RNL
- "A VHF/UHF Discone Antenna" by Bob Patterson, K5DZE
- "An Optimum Design for 432 MHz Yagis — Parts 1 and 2" by Steve Powlishen, K1FO
- "Building a Medium-Gain, Wide-Band, 2 Meter Yagi" by L.B. Cebik, W4RNL
- "Development and Real World Replication of Modern Yagi Antennas (III) — Manual Optimisation of Multiple Yagi Arrays" by Justin Johnson, GØKSC
- "High-Performance 'Self-Matched' Yagi Antennas" by Justin Johnson, GØKSC
- "High-Performance Yagis for 144, 222 and 432 MHz" by Steve Powlishen, K1FO
- "LPDA for 2 Meters Plus" by L.B. Cebik, W4RNL
- "Making the LFA Loop" by Justin Johnson, GØKSC
- "Microwavelengths — Microwave Transmission Lines" by Paul Wade, W1GHZ
- "RF — A Small 70-cm Yagi" by Zack Lau, W1VT
- "The Helical Antenna — Description and Design" by David Conn, VE3KL
- "Three-Band Log-Periodic Antenna" by Robert Heslin, K7RTY/2
- "Using LPDA TV Antennas for the VHF Ham Bands" by John Stanley, K4ERO
- "V-Shaped Elements versus Straight Elements" by John Stanley, K4ERO
- "Corner and Trough Reflector Antennas"
- "Focusing a Parabolic Dish" by Paul Wade, W1GHZ
- "A New Horizontal Polarized High Gain Omni-Directional Antenna" by Tom Apel, K5TRA
- "Horn Construction and Templates"
- "A 6 Meter Moxon Antenna" by Allen Baker, KG4JJH
- "A Moxon Antenna for 220 MHz" by Glenn Morrison, WB6RLC
- "Moxon Mighty Mite" by J. Barry Shackleford, W6YE
- "A Compact Two-Element, 2-Meter Beam" by Lee Lumpkin, KB8WEV, and Bob Cerreto, WA1FXT
- "Quagi Antennas"

Support Files

- Model files and sample radiation patterns for Yagi designs by Justin Johnson, GØKSC (will work with the free version of EZNEC Pro/4+)

Chapter 15

VHF, UHF, and Microwave Antennas

A good antenna system is one of the most valuable assets available to the VHF/UHF/microwave enthusiast. Compared to an antenna of lesser quality, an antenna that is well designed, is built of good quality materials, and is well maintained, will increase transmitting range, enhance reception of weak signals and reduce interference problems. The work itself building antennas is by no means the least attractive part of the job. Even with high-gain antennas, experimentation is greatly simplified at and above VHF because the antennas are a physically manageable size. Setting up a home antenna range is within the means of most amateurs, and much can be learned about the nature and adjustment of antennas. No large investment in test equipment is necessary.

Antenna design at VHF and higher frequencies has seen much innovation since the advent of cellular telephony and wireless data. The twin frontiers of miniaturization and higher frequencies have driven much research into novel forms for the antennas themselves and the associated feed line and matching structures.

Amateurs will benefit from technology developed to support consumer microwave equipment now operating at 75 GHz (vehicle navigation) and millimeter-wave technology for 5G wireless systems. There are many opportunities for amateur innovation in circuit and antenna design at microwave frequencies because of the excellent tools available to them at low cost, including modeling and simulation software.

The article "Antenna Technologies for the Future" by Patrick Hindle in the January 2018 issue of *Microwave Journal* explores 3D-printed antennas, metamaterials, fractal antenna structures, and other innovations. (The article is available online with free registration at **microwavejournal.com/articles/29572-antenna-technologies-for-the-future**.) Amateurs would do well to pay close attention to these interesting developments!

15.1 Design Factors At And Above VHF

The fundamental principles of antenna systems are the same at VHF and UHF as at HF. There is no magic dividing line at 50 MHz that suddenly changes the way antenna system components operate. However, factors that may be insignificant at HF must be taken into account at higher frequencies as the wavelength of the signals drops, dielectric loss increases, and skin depth shrinks. Similarly, techniques that may be impractical at HF such as dishes and long-boom Yagis with 20 elements can be put to work at VHF and higher frequencies. Instead of repeating the theory presented in other chapters, this section will identify areas that must be treated differently than at HF and give guidelines for how to approach the problem.

As on HF, the first step in choosing the right antenna is figuring out what you want it to do. Weak-signal operating on CW, SSB, and increasingly various digital modes, benefits from horizontally polarized, rotatable antennas with narrow beamwidths and minimum sidelobes. Satellite operation on CW and SSB goes farther and adds elevation control and circular polarization to the list. FM repeater and simplex operation uses vertical polarization for both directional and omnidirectional antennas. Simple ground-plane and low-gain omnidirectional antennas are common.

Just the polarization issue alone can have a dramatic effect as an antenna cross-polarized to an incoming signal receives up to 20 dB less signal than if the antenna and signal polarization are the same. Similarly, a narrow-beamwidth rotatable antenna can be a poor choice if the goal is to use several nearby repeaters that are located in different directions from the station. As a result, it is not uncommon for an amateur station to include both types — a horizontally polarized beam and a vertically polarized omnidirectional antenna — for VHF and UHF operation.

GAIN

At VHF and UHF, it is possible to build Yagi antennas with very high gain — 15 to 20 dBi — on a physically manageable boom. Such antennas then can be combined in arrays of two, four, six, eight or more antennas. These arrays are attractive for EME, tropospheric scatter or other weak-signal communications modes where the path loss is very high.

Collinear antennas such as Franklin arrays become much more manageable at and above 2 meters with gains of 6 to 12 dBi in a single, vertical package similar in size to a 10 meter ground plane antenna. The collinear dipole array is very popular as a repeater antenna (see the Repeater Antenna Systems article in the online content) with potential gains of up to 9 dBd for eight dipole arrays as described by Belrose (see Bibliography).

Reflectors, horns and dishes offer even higher gains (and narrower patterns) at UHF and microwave frequencies. A medium-sized dish can develop up to 30 dBi gain at 10 GHz, for example, turning 1 W of power into an EIRP of 1 kW!

RADIATION PATTERNS

Antenna radiation can be made omnidirectional, bidirectional, practically unidirectional, or anything between these configurations. A VHF net operator may find an omnidirectional system almost a necessity, but it may be a poor choice otherwise. Noise pickup and other interference problems are greater with such omnidirectional antennas, and omnidirectional antennas having some gain are especially bad in these respects. Maximum gain and low radiation angle are usually prime interests of the weak-signal DX aspirant. A clean pattern, with lowest possible pickup and radiation off the sides and back, may be important in high-activity areas, or where the noise level is high.

OPERATING BANDWIDTH

Most amateur communications use narrow bandwidths so that antenna bandwidth does not matter above 54 MHz. Some modes, like ATV and high-speed data networks, require wider bandwidth so that antenna bandwidth becomes a consideration.

For ATV at UHF, a 6 MHz bandwidth is common. Traditional Yagi designs only have good performance over a narrower bandwidth, so specialized designs like collinear arrays or skeleton-slot Yagis were popular. Modern Yagi designs like LFA or OWL provide very good performance with adequate bandwidth, are simpler, and readily available commercially. See "High Performance Yagi Design" in the Yagis and Quads at VHF and UHF section.

Horns and dishes used at microwave frequencies are inherently broadband. For amateur mesh networks, commercial "wireless network" antennas are convenient and frequently used.

HEIGHT GAIN

In general, higher is better in VHF and UHF antenna installations. Raising the antenna over nearby obstructions may make dramatic improvements in coverage. Within reason, greater height is almost always worth its cost, but height gain (see the **Radio Wave Propagation** chapter) must be balanced against increased transmission line loss. This loss can be considerable, and it increases with frequency. The best available line may not be very good if the run is long in terms of wavelengths. Line loss considerations as discussed in the **Transmission Lines** chapter are important in antenna planning.

> **Conference Proceedings and Presentations Online**
>
> Don't forget that more and more microwave and VHF/UHF conferences post papers and presentation videos online. Instead of having to order a printed book, you can now download a PDF or watch and listen to the presenter discuss the subject. YouTube is the most popular platform for videos. Just enter the conference name into the search window. Search engines will easily find conference proceedings, as well.

PHYSICAL SIZE

A given antenna design for 432 MHz has the same gain as the same design for 144 MHz, but being only one third as large intercepts only one-ninth as much energy in receiving. In other words, the antenna has less pickup efficiency at 432 MHz. To be equal in communication effectiveness, the 432-MHz array should be at least equal in *size* to the 144-MHz antenna, which requires roughly three times as many elements. With all the extra difficulties involved in using the higher frequencies effectively for weak-signal operation, it is best to keep antennas as large as possible for these bands.

POLARIZATION

Whether to position antenna elements vertically or horizontally has been widely debated since early VHF pioneering days. Tests have shown little evidence about which polarization sense is most desirable. On long propagation paths there is no consistent advantage either way. Shorter paths tend to yield higher signal levels with horizontally polarized antennas over some kinds of terrain. Man-made noise, especially ignition interference, also tends to be lower with horizontal antennas. These factors make horizontal polarization somewhat more desirable for weak-signal communications. On the other hand, vertically polarized antennas are much simpler to use in omnidirectional systems and in mobile operation. Circular polarization is commonly used for satellite and EME communication with antenna systems that can switch between right-hand and left-hand orientation.

Vertical polarization was widely used in early VHF operation, but horizontal polarization gained favor when directional arrays started to become widely used. The widespread use of FM and repeaters, particularly in the VHF/UHF bands, has tipped the balance in favor of vertical antennas in mobile and repeater use. Horizontal polarization predominates in other communication on 50 MHz and higher frequencies. An additional loss of up to 20 dB can be expected when cross-polarized antennas are used over direct paths.

15.2 Basic Antennas For VHF And UHF

Local operation with mobile stations and handheld radios requires an antenna with wide coverage capabilities and a generally omnidirectional pattern. Most mobile operation uses FM and the polarization used with this mode is generally vertical. Some simple vertical systems for fixed or base station use are described below. Additional material on antennas of this type is presented in the **Mobile VHF and UHF Antennas** chapter.

15.2.1 PROJECT: VHF/UHF Ground-Planes And Dipoles

For the FM operator living in the primary coverage area of a repeater, the ease of construction and low cost of a ¼ λ ground-plane antenna make it an ideal choice. Three different types of construction are detailed in the following section; the choice of construction method depends upon the materials at hand and the desired style of antenna mounting. (Note that while UHF connectors are not generally recommended for use on the upper VHF bands and at UHF, they will work fine as a base for ground-plane antennas. It is their uncontrolled impedance above 100 MHz that causes problems in transmission lines but as part of an antenna, their impedance is accounted for when trimming the antenna for minimum SWR.)

The 144-MHz model shown in **Figure 15.1** uses a flat piece of sheet aluminum, to which radials are connected with machine screws. A 45° bend is made in each of the radials. This bend can be made with an ordinary bench vise. An SO-239 chassis connector is mounted at the center of the aluminum plate with the threaded part of the connector facing down. The vertical portion of the antenna is made of #12 AWG copper wire soldered directly to the center pin of the SO-239 connector.

The 222-MHz version, **Figure 15.2**, uses a slightly different technique for mounting and sloping the radials. In this case the corners of the aluminum plate are bent down at a 45° angle with respect to the remainder of the plate. The four radials are held to the plate with machine screws, lock washers, and nuts. A mounting tab is included in the design of this antenna as part of the aluminum base. A compression type of hose clamp could be used to secure the antenna to a mast. As with the 144-MHz version, the vertical portion of the antenna is soldered directly to the SO-239 connector.

A very simple method of construction, shown in **Figure 15.3**, requires nothing more than an SO-239 connector and some #4-40 hardware. A small loop formed at the inside end of each radial is used to attach the radial directly to the mounting holes of the coaxial connector. After the radial is fastened to the SO-239 with #4-40 hardware, a large soldering iron or propane torch can be used to solder the radial and the mounting hardware to the coaxial connector. The radials are bent to a 45° angle and the vertical portion is soldered to the center pin to complete the antenna. The antenna can be mounted by passing the feed line through a mast of ¾-inch ID plastic or aluminum tubing. A compression hose clamp can be used to secure the PL-259 connector, attached to the feed line, in the end of the mast. Dimensions for the 144-, 222- and 440-MHz bands are given in Figure 15.3.

Dipole antennas are used frequently above the HF bands because horizontally polarized gain antennas are fairly small and easy to construct. Nevertheless, a rotatable dipole is very inexpensive and can be used for weak-signal operating when

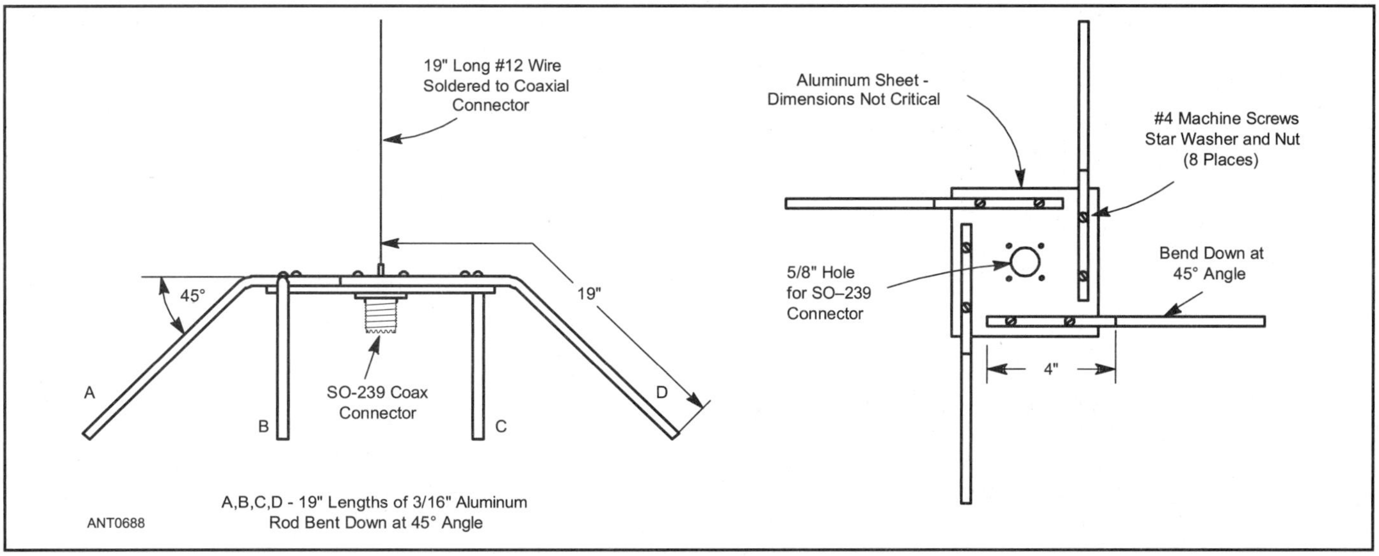

Figure 15.1 — These drawings illustrate the dimensions for the 144-MHz ground-plane antenna. The radials are bent down at a 45° angle.

a beam isn't practical. A dipole may actually be better than a beam when a very broad pattern is needed, such as for meteor scatter when the direction of propagation isn't known until a station is heard.

The rotatable dipole shown in **Figure 15.4** can be made of copper or aluminum tube or rod. The mounting plate can be made of almost any non-conductive plastic material such as thick plastic kitchen cutting boards. The simplicity of the antenna lends itself to experimenting or scrounging. (This design is from the ARRL book *Magic Band Antennas for Ham Radio* by Bruce Walker, N3JO — see the Bibliography.)

If these antennas are to be permanently mounted outside, waterproof the antenna by applying a small amount of sealant around the areas of the center pin of the connector to prevent the entry of water into the connector and coax line. The coax connector should be waterproofed as well. Techniques and materials for waterproofing are described in the **Building Antenna Systems and Towers** chapter.

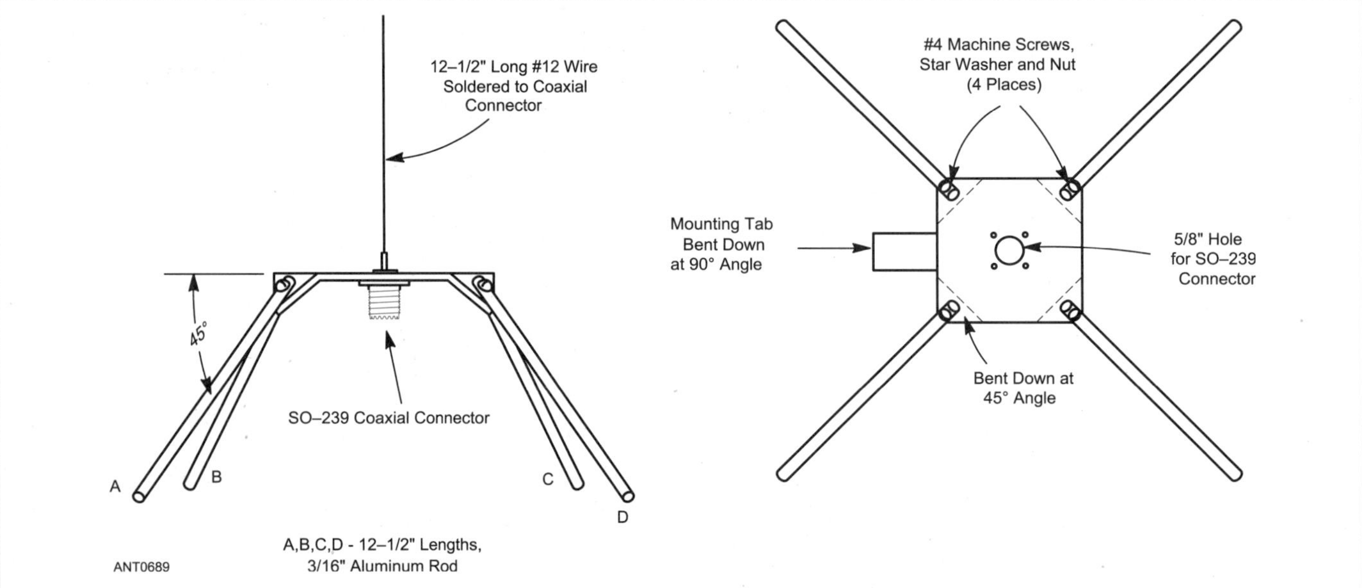

Figure 15.2 — Dimensional information for the 222-MHz ground-plane antenna. Lengths for A, B, C and D are the total distances measured from the center of the SO-239 connector. The corners of the aluminum plate are bent down at a 45° angle rather than bending the aluminum rod as in the 144-MHz model. Either method is suitable for these antennas.

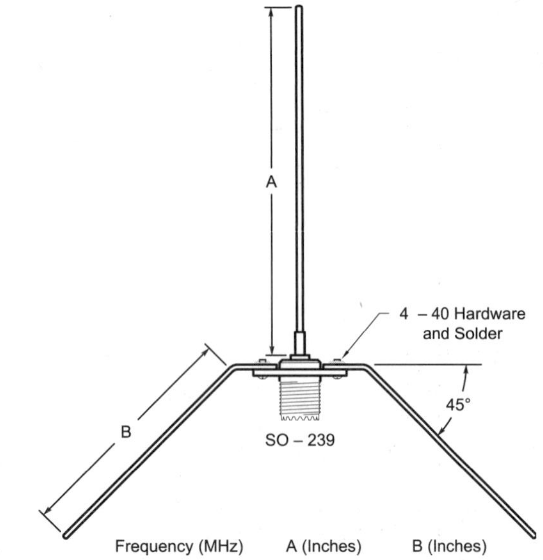

Frequency (MHz)	A (Inches)	B (Inches)
146	19 – 5/16"	18 – 11/16"
225	12 – 5/8"	12"
445	6 – 3/8"	5 – 3/4"

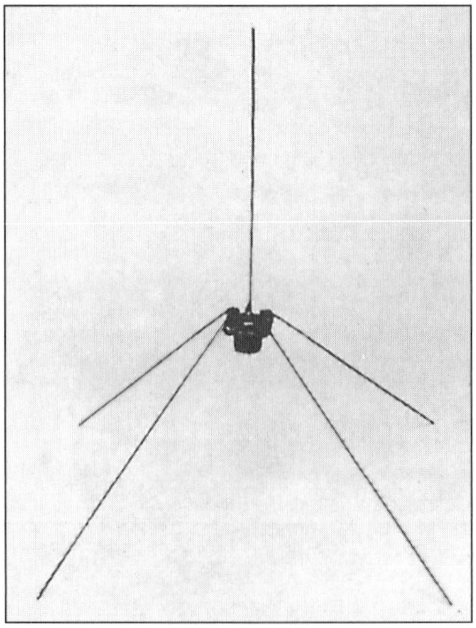

Figure 15.3 — Simple ground-plane antenna dimensions for the 144-, 222- and 440-MHz bands. (A) The vertical element and radials are 3⁄32- or 1⁄16-inch brass welding rod. Although 3⁄32-inch rod is preferred for the 144-MHz antenna, #10 or #12 AWG copper wire can also be used. The photograph (B) shows a 440-MHz ground-plane constructed using only an SO-239 connector, #4-40 hardware and 1/16-inch brass welding rod.

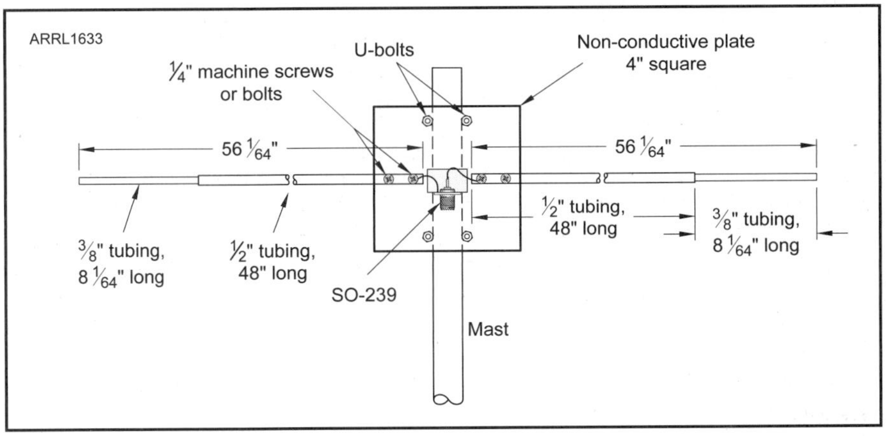

Figure 15.4 — Dimensions for a simple rotatable 6 meter dipole.

15.2.2 The J-Pole Antenna

The J-Pole is a half-wave antenna that is end-fed at its bottom. Since the radiator is longer than that of a ¼-wave ground-plane antenna, the vertical lobe is compressed down toward the horizon and it has about 1.5 dB of gain compared to the ground-plane configuration. The stub-matching section used to transform the high impedance at the end of a half-wave antenna to 50 Ω is shorted at the bottom, making the antenna look like the letter "J," and giving the antenna its name.

Rigid copper tubing, fittings and assorted hardware can be used to make a rugged J-pole antenna for the VHF bands through 440 MHz. (A flexible "roll-up" J-pole is described in the **Mobile and Portable Antennas** chapter.) When copper tubing is used, the entire assembly can be soldered together, ensuring electrical integrity, and making the whole antenna weatherproof. A general-purpose set of dimensions for the J-pole is provided in **Figure 15.5** along with a table of dimensions for 53 MHz, 146 MHz, 223 MHz, and 440 MHz. MHz. The dimensions assume ½-inch copper pipe is used to construct the antenna. The 53-MHz version is somewhat large for this construction method and the 440 MHz version a little small. Note that the inside dimensions of the matching section are between the outside surfaces of the tubing, not center-to-center. For placing the feed point, start with the feed point approximately as high above the bottom of the matching section as the tubing spacing.

The J-Pole can be fed directly from 50-Ω coax through a choke balun. A choke balun can be made by coiling the feed line or by using ferrite beads or cores as described in the **Transmission Line System Techniques** chapter. If the balun is not used, the outer surface of the coaxial cable will become part of the antenna, making tuning difficult and highly dependent on cable placement. In addition, radiation from the current flowing on the feed line can distort the pattern of the antenna, leading to poor performance by breaking up the low-elevation main lobe expected from this design.

PROJECT: 2 METER ALL-COPPER J-POLE

There are many J-pole designs available online and in the ARRL's online archive of *QST* articles at **arrl.org**. One of the more popular variants is known as the "Copper Cactus" (see Bibliography) and has been adapted to dual- and tri-band designs.

F (MHz)	A (ft)	B (ft)	C (ft)
53	13.3	4.42	0.42
146	4.83	1.6	0.15
223	3.16	1.05	0.10
440	1.6	0.53	0.05

Dimensions assume 1/2-inch copper pipe.

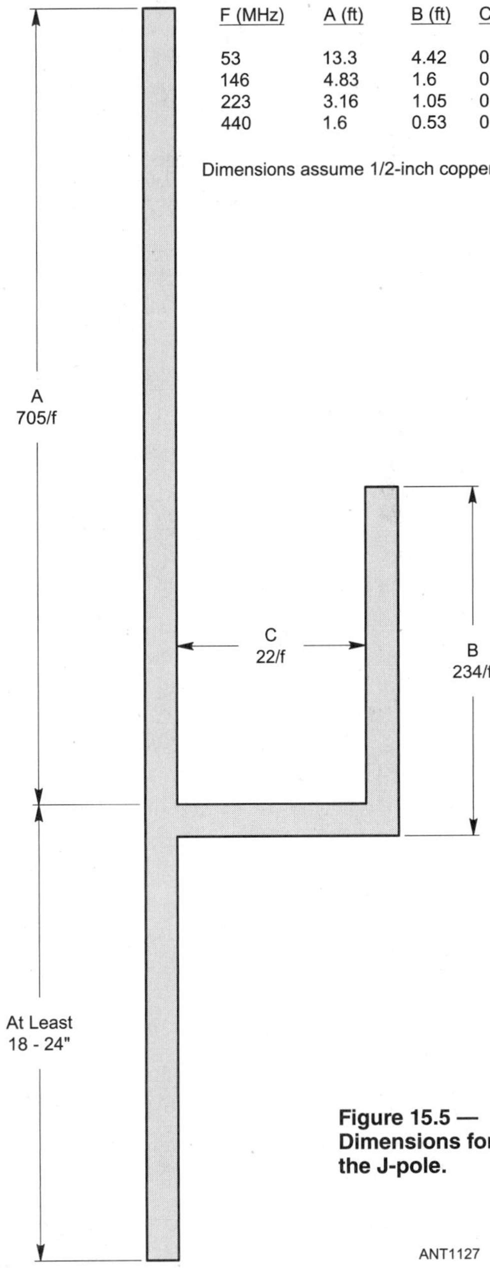

Figure 15.5 — Dimensions for the J-pole.

CONSTRUCTION

No special hardware or machined parts are used in this antenna, nor are insulating materials needed. If mounted on a metal mast the antenna is grounded, as well. The following 2 meter J-pole design came from an article by Michael Hood, KD8JB, in *The ARRL Antenna Compendium, Vol. 4*.

Copper and brass is used exclusively in this antenna. These metals get along together, so dissimilar metal corrosion is eliminated. Both metals solder well, too. See **Figure 15.6**. Cut the copper tubing to the lengths indicated. Item 9 is a 1¼-inch nipple cut from the 20-inch length of ½-inch tubing. This leaves 18¾ inches for the ¼-λ matching stub. Item 10 is a 3¼-inch long nipple cut from the 60-inch length of ¾-inch tubing. The ¾-wave element should measure 56¾ inches long. Remove burrs from the ends of the tubing after cutting, and clean the mating surfaces with sandpaper, steel wool or emery cloth.

After cleaning, apply a very thin coat of flux to the mating elements and assemble the tubing, elbow, tee, end caps and stubs. Solder the assembled parts with a propane torch and rosin-core solder. Wipe off excess solder with a damp cloth,

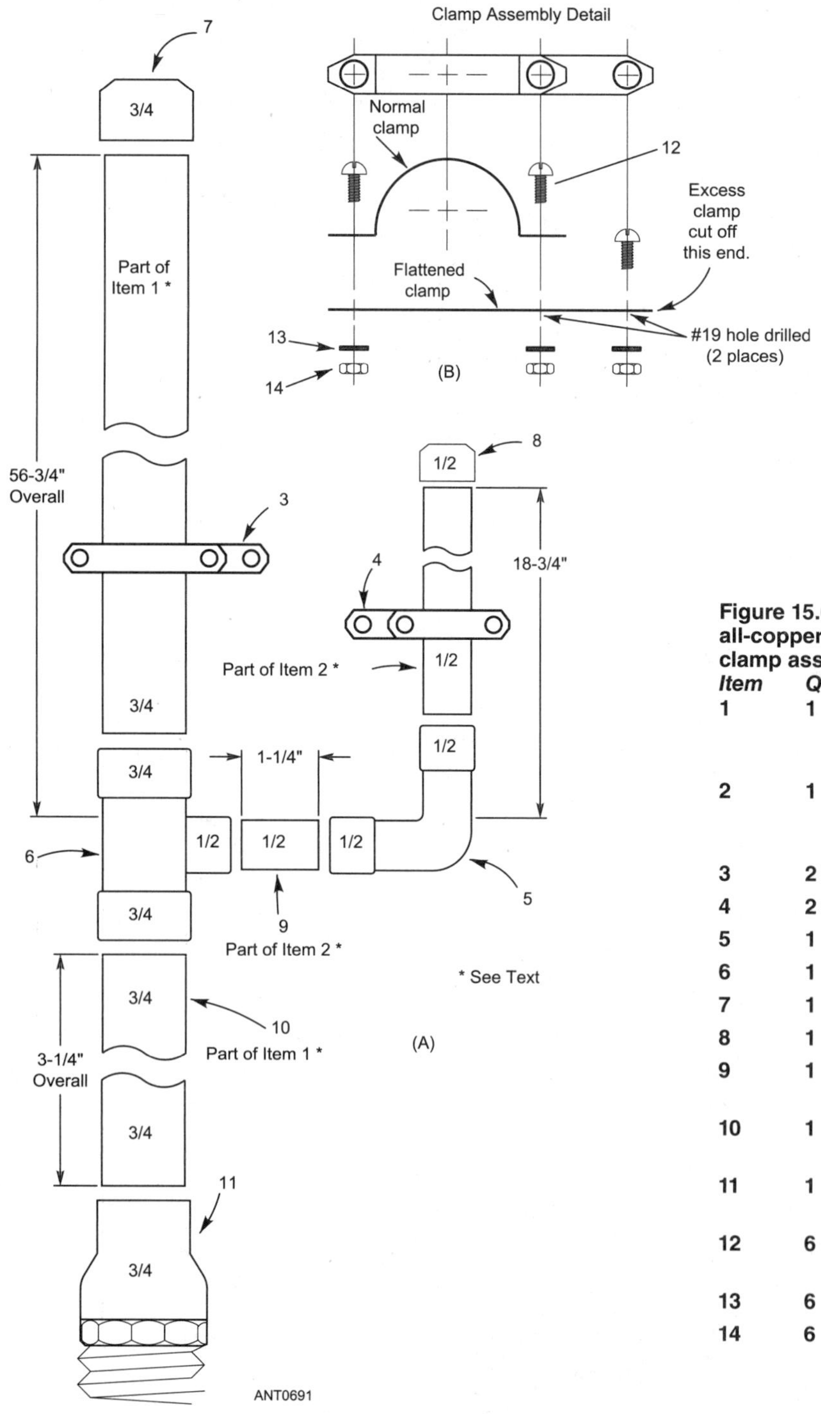

Figure 15.6 — At A, exploded assembly diagram of all-copper J-Pole antenna for 2 meters. At B, detail of clamp assemblies. Both clamp assemblies are the same.

Item	*Qty*	*Part or Material Name*
1	1	¾-inch × 10 foot length of rigid copper tubing (enough for 2 antennas, 60 inches per antenna)
2	1	½-inch × 10 ft length of rigid copper tubing (enough for 6 antennas, 20 inches per antenna)
3	2	¾-inch copper pipe clamps
4	2	½-inch copper pipe clamps
5	1	½-inch copper elbow
6	1	¾ × ½-inch copper tee
7	1	¾-inch copper end cap
8	1	½-inch copper end cap
9	1	½ × 1¼-inch copper nipple (Make from item 2. See text)
10	1	¾ × 3¼-inch copper nipple (Make from item 1. See text)
11	1	Your choice of coupling to mast fitting (¾ × 1 inch NPT used at KD8JB)
12	6	#8-32 × ½-inch brass machine screws (round, pan, or binder head)
13	6	#8 brass flat washers
14	6	#8-32 brass hex nuts

being careful not to burn yourself. The copper tubing will hold heat for a long time after you've finished soldering. After soldering, set the assembly aside to cool.

Flatten one each of the ½-inch and ¾-inch pipe clamps. Drill a hole in the flattened clamp as shown in Figure 15.6A. Assemble the clamps and cut off the excess metal from the flattened clamp using the unmodified clamp as a template. Disassemble the clamps.

Assemble the ½-inch clamp around the ¼-wave element and secure with two of the screws, washers, and nuts as shown in Figure 15.6B. Do the same with the ¾-inch clamp around the ¾-wave element. Initially set the clamps to a spot about 4 inches above the bottom of the "J" on their respective elements. Tighten the clamps only finger tight, since you'll need to move them when tuning.

TUNING

Before tuning, mount the antenna vertically, about 5 to 10 feet from the ground. A short TV mast on a tripod works well for this purpose. When tuning VHF antennas, keep in mind that they are sensitive to nearby objects — such as your body. Attach the feed line to the clamps on the antenna, and make sure all the nuts and screws are at least finger tight. It really doesn't matter to which element (¾-wave element or stub) you attach the coaxial center lead. KD8JB has done it both ways with no variation in performance. Tune the antenna by moving the two feed point clamps equal distances a small amount each time until the SWR is a minimum at the desired frequency. The SWR will be close to 1:1. (Stand clear of the antenna when measuring the SWR and include the choke balun in the feed line when making measurements.)

FINAL ASSEMBLY

The final assembly of the antenna will determine its long-term survivability. Perform the following steps with care. After adjusting the clamps for minimum SWR, mark the clamp positions with a pencil and then remove the feed line and clamps. Apply a very thin coating of flux to the inside of the clamp and the corresponding surface of the antenna element where the clamp attaches. Install the clamps and tighten the clamp screws.

Solder the feed line clamps where they are attached to the antenna elements. Now, apply a small amount of solder around the screw heads and nuts where they contact the clamps. Don't get solder on the screw threads! Clean away excess flux with a noncorrosive solvent. After final assembly and erecting/mounting the antenna in the desired location, attach the feed line and secure with the remaining washer and nut. Weatherproof this joint as described in the **Building Antenna Systems and Towers** chapter.

15.2.3 Collinear and Curtain Arrays

The information given earlier in this chapter pertains mainly to parasitic arrays, but the collinear array is worthy of consideration in VHF/UHF operation. Two types of collinear arrays are commonly used by amateurs; the *transposed-coaxial array* and the *collinear dipole array*.

Collinear arrays tend to be tolerant of construction tolerances, making them easy to build and adjust for VHF and UHF applications. The use of many collinear driven elements was once popular in very large phased arrays, such as those required in moonbounce (EME) communications, but computer-optimized Yagi arrays have largely replaced them. A collinear array of four dipoles is a popular repeater antenna as described in the Repeater Antenna Systems article included with this book's downloadable content.

COLLINEAR TRANSPOSED-COAX ARRAYS

The most popular collinear array is the omnidirectional array of half-wave dipoles constructed of transposed sections of coaxial cable as shown in **Figure 15.7**. The original array of this type is the Franklin array shown in Figure 15.7A. The phase-reversing stubs allow multiple half-wave sections to operate in phase, creating gain at right angles to the antenna. An example of this array is the popular Cushcraft Ringo Ranger series of omnidirectional VHF and UHF antennas.

While the phasing stubs make the Franklin array inconvenient for vertical stacking of more than two elements, a derivative of this array uses transposed sections of coaxial cable as in Figure 15.7B. The phasing stub is created by the inside of each coaxial section. The outer surface of the coaxial shield forms the radiating element. The resulting antenna can be enclosed in a PVC or fiberglass tube, such as the Comet GP-series of VHF/UHF omnidirectional antennas. Numerous examples of this design are available online. An article by WA6SVT in *73* magazine was the initial description of these antennas in the amateur literature. (See **repeater-builder.com/antenna/wa6svt.html** and this chapter's References and Bibliography section — see the entries for Collis and Belrose.) Gains claimed for this antenna may be optimistic (**owenduffy.net/antenna/WA6SVT/index.htm**) but the basic design is quite serviceable.

Another method of creating the phase reversal between radiating sections is the *meander line* shown in Figure 15.7C. The meander line is a coil of wire that forms a delay line of 180 degrees. The pitch (turns per unit length) and overall length are the important characteristics of the meander line. There are several designs for meander line collinear arrays online such as from WA3AYW at **hamuniverse.com/wb3aywcollinear.html**.

The practical limit for gain in this type of array is about 10 dBi. A choke balun or other method of decoupling such as a set of $\lambda/4$ radials is required at the feed point of the array to prevent current from being induced on the outer surface of the coaxial feed line. Feed line current would both upset the radiation pattern, reducing gain, and affect the feed point impedance in unpredictable ways.

COLLINEAR OMNIDIRECTIONAL ARRAY FOR 70 CM

Figure 15.8 shows the basic construction of a transposed-coax array for the 70 cm band with dimensions in millimeters for accuracy. The $\lambda/4$ whip at the end of the array is optional. The gain of this array is approximately 9 dBi (slightly less without the whip). The original design of this antenna is credited to the Radio Amateur Society of Norwich (**rason.org**). More information is available via the "Projects" page of the RASON website.

The physical length of each λ/2 section of coax must account for the velocity factor of the cable which should be measured accurately before cutting any cable. Once the physical length of λ/2 has been determined, add 8 mm to allow for creating the 4 mm connecting surfaces on each end. For a VF = 0.66, the λ/2 sections should be 223 mm long plus 8 mm for a total of 231 mm. RG-58, RG-8, RG-8X or RG-213 can be used for this antenna. Do not remove the outer jacket from the cable other than at the connecting ends as this will allow the individual braid strands to loosen, reducing the shield's effectiveness as a continuous conductor.

Use a 169 mm segment of #16 AWG copper wire for the top whip section. A λ/4 coaxial sleeve balun is attached at the feed point of the antenna. (See the **Transmission Line System Techniques** chapter.) The balun is made from copper tubing that is soldered to the shield of the feed line using strips of brass or copper shim. If ⅝-inch tubing is used, the length should be 160 mm. The feed line should be centered in the balun tubing by using small pieces of plastic inserted between the coax jacket and the tubing's inner surface. Approximately λ/4 beyond the end of the balun's closed end add an additional choke balun of three type #43 ferrite beads (choose the ID to fit the feed line coax). The entire antenna should be enclosed in a length of PVC or fiberglass tubing to protect it from the weather. If necessary for mechanical stability, support the antenna sections with a length of wooden dowel or plastic rod, secured with electrical tape.

COLLINEAR DIPOLE ARRAY

The vertical four-dipole collinear array in **Figure 15.9** is a very common repeater antenna, giving an omnidirectional pattern. Gain can be from 3 to 7.5 dBd depending on the dipoles vertical spacing and whether all of the dipoles are mounted on the same side of the supporting mast. Arrays of two to eight dipoles are practical. (See the Repeater Antenna Systems article in the online material.)

KG4JJH has published a very detailed article on the design and construction of 2-element and 4-element arrays for 2 meters using single-conductor dipole elements (available from

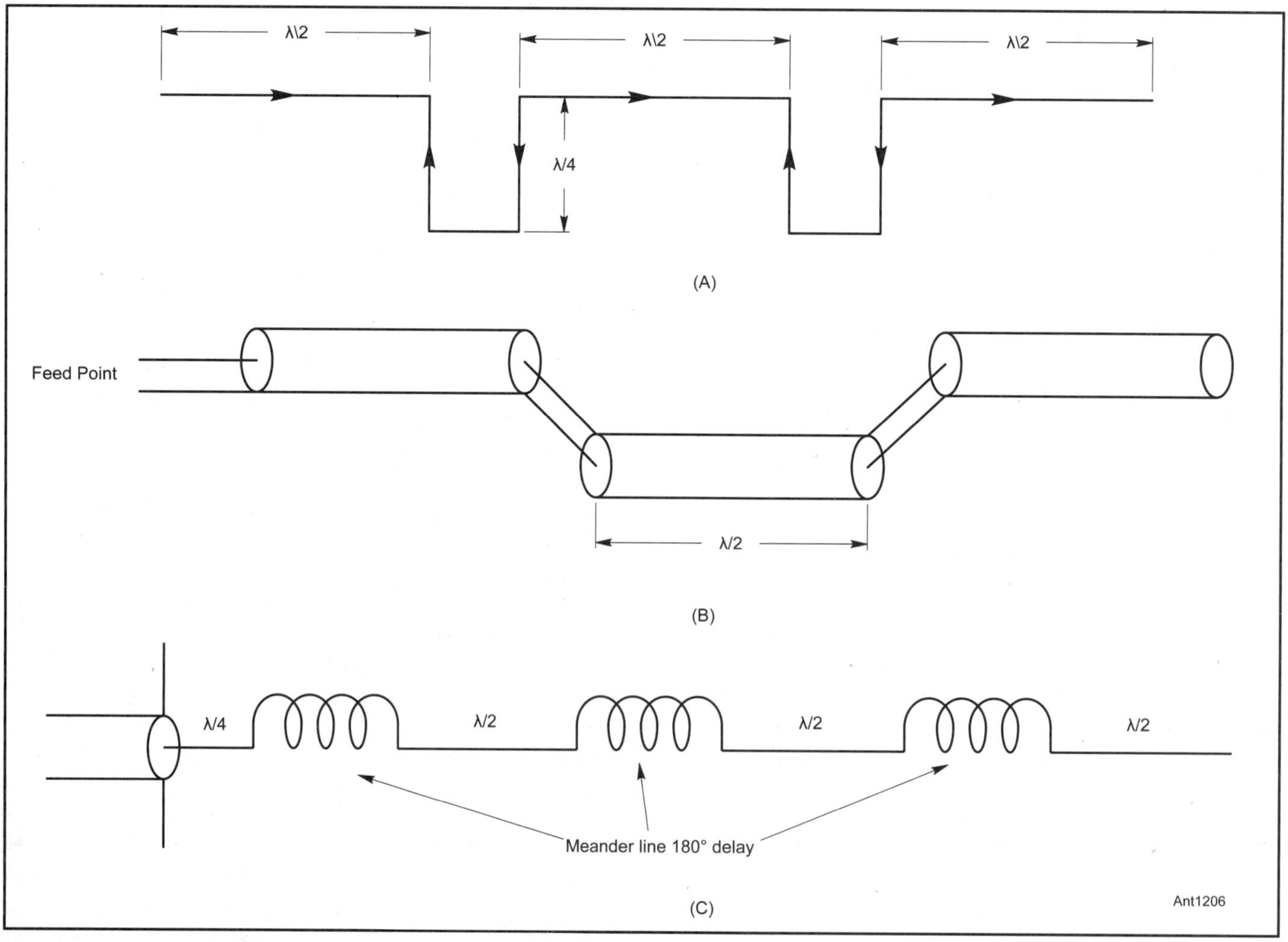

Figure 15.7 — The most popular collinear array is the Franklin array of half-wave dipoles (A) oriented vertically for an omnidirectional pattern. B shows the usual construction of transposed half-wavelength sections of coaxial cable for use at VHF and UHF. An alternative design (C) uses meander lines to create the 180° phase reversal.

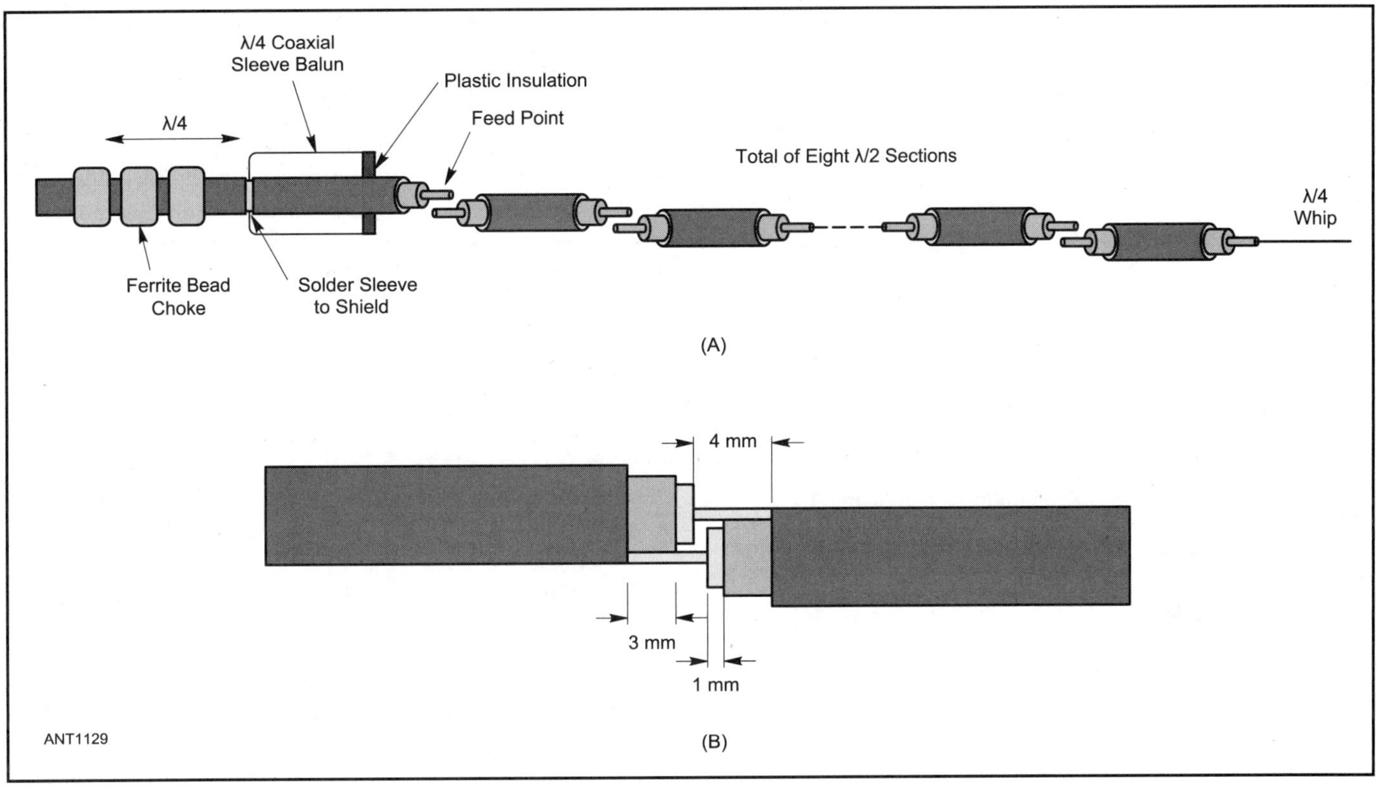

Figure 15.8 — Basic construction of a transposed-coax array for the 70 cm band. Dimensions are given in millimeters for accuracy.

kg4jjh.com). Most commercial versions use folded dipoles so that all antenna elements can be maintained at dc ground.

The phasing lines used to connect the individual dipoles must be of the correct length within a few electrical degrees in order to present a 50 Ω impedance to the main feed line. Individual phasing line segments may be of 50, 75, or some other impedance so be careful when repairing or replacing a phasing line or harness so that the antenna's radiation pattern and feed point impedance are correct.

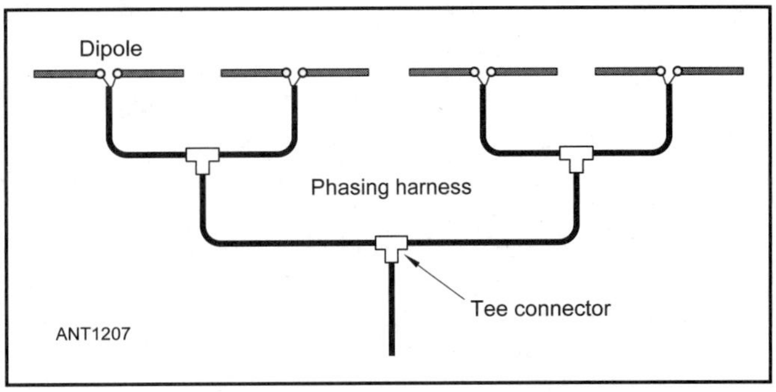

Figure 15.9 — A four-dipole collinear array fed with a phasing harness so that all of the dipoles are in-phase. Most commercial models use folded dipoles.

DIPOLE CURTAIN ARRAYS

Collinear dipole arrays were popular in the past because of simplicity, before computer modeling of antennas. Modern optimized Yagi antennas offer higher performance in terms of gain, cost, size, weight, and wind loading. Still, there are possibly applications where collinear arrays might be useful. Strictly speaking, the antennas discussed here are broadside arrays and not true collinear arrays since the antennas are not aligned along a single line. Nevertheless, they are often referred to as collinear arrays and included here for convenient reference.

Bidirectional curtain arrays of four, six and eight half waves in phase are shown in **Figure 15.10**. Usually reflector elements are added, normally at about 0.2 λ behind each driven element, for more gain and a unidirectional pattern. Such parasitic elements are omitted from the sketch in the interest of clarity.

The feed point impedance of two half waves in phase is high, typically 1000 Ω or more. When they are combined in parallel and parasitic elements are added, the feed impedance is low enough for direct connection to open wire line or twin-lead, connected at the points indicated by black dots. With coaxial line and a balun, it is suggested that the universal stub match (see the **VHF-UHF Antenna System Design** chapter) be used at the feed point. All elements should be mounted at their electrical centers, as indicated by open circles in Figure 15.10. The framework can be metal or insulating material. The metal supporting structure is entirely behind the plane of the reflector elements. Sheet-metal clamps can be cut from scraps of aluminum for this kind of assembly. Collinear elements of this type should be mounted at their centers (where the RF voltage is a minimum), rather than at their ends, where the voltage is high and insulation losses and detuning can be harmful.

A reflecting plane, which may be sheet metal, wire mesh,

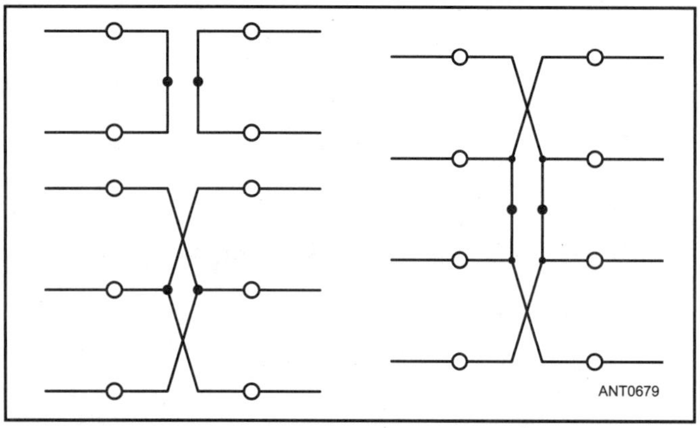

Figure 15.10 — Element arrangements for 8-, 12- and 16-element collinear arrays. Elements are λ/2 long and spaced λ/2. Parasitic reflectors, omitted here for clarity, are 5% longer and 0.2 λ behind the driven elements. Feed points are indicated by black dots. Open circles show recommended support points. The elements can run through wood or metal booms, without insulation, if supported at their centers in this way. Insulators at the element ends (points of high RF voltage) detune and unbalance the system.

or even closely spaced elements of tubing or wire, can be used in place of parasitic reflectors. To be effective, the plane reflector must extend on all sides to at least ¼ λ beyond the area occupied by the driven elements. The plane reflector provides high F/B ratio, a clean pattern, and somewhat more gain than parasitic elements, but large physical size limits it to use above 420 MHz. An interesting space-saving possibility lies in using a single plane reflector with elements for two different bands mounted on opposite sides. Reflector spacing from the driven element is not critical — about 0.2 λ is common.

The German antenna reference text, *Rothammel*, (see References and Bibliography for the **Antenna Fundamentals** chapter). gives the following guidelines for the reflecting plane:

- For the best F/B ratio, the reflecting plane should extend at least λ/2 beyond the perimeter of the curtain on all sides.
- If made of wire or mesh instead of solid sheet metal to reduce wind loading surface area, the wire pitch should be 0.1 λ or less.
- A reflecting plane spaced 5/8 λ behind the radiators adds a maximum gain of up to 7 dB, but a spacing of 0.1 to 0.3 λ provides a better F/B ratio.
- If spaced at least 0.3 λ behind the curtain, the reflecting plane does not affect the feed point impedance of the array.

15.3 Yagis And Quads At VHF And UHF

Without doubt, the Yagi is king of home-station VHF and UHF antennas for weak-signal operating and for long-distance repeater and simplex operation. Today's best designs are computer optimized. The **HF Yagi and Quad Antennas** chapter describes the parameters associated with Yagi antennas. Due to the shorter wavelengths above 50 MHz, high-performance designs that would be impractical at HF are easily achievable at VHF and UHF. A variety of designs are presented for 50 through 432 MHz.

15.3.1 Constructing VHF And UHF Yagis

Before discussing materials, it is important to note that high-performance, especially at and above 144 MHz, requires that design specifications be followed very closely. Measurement or machining errors that can be ignored at HF become more significant at short wavelengths. The antenna designs in this chapter are fairly tolerant of deviations in the final assembly dimensions from those specified by the model and in the dimension tables. Good performance will be obtained using standard building practices and paying attention to details. However, accurate assembly is required if maximum performance is required or to duplicate the modeled performance.

MATERIALS

Normally, aluminum tubing or rod is used for Yagi elements. Brass tubing is also used and has the additional advantage of being solderable. Hard-drawn copper wire can also be used on Yagis above 420 MHz. Resistive losses are inversely proportional to the square of the element diameter and the square root of its conductivity.

Element diameters of less than 3⁄16 inch or 4 mm should not be used on any band. The size should be chosen for reasonable strength. Half-inch diameter elements are the minimum suitable for 50 MHz (use a tempered alloy) and should be used at 144 MHz. One-quarter to three-sixteenths inch elements are acceptable for higher frequencies. Steel, including stainless steel and unprotected brass or copper wire, should not be used for elements.

When developing a Yagi at VHF and up, it is important to make the driven elements adjustable. This allows the builder to compensate for minor variations in feed line attachments and slight variations in element placement. See the note regarding connections in the section on Feed Point Construction below.

Boom material may be aluminum tubing, either square or round. High-strength aluminum alloys such as 6061-T6 or 6063-T651 offer the best strength-to-weight advantages. If the original design uses a metal boom, use the same size and shape metal boom when you duplicate it. Larger or smaller conductive booms may require an adjustment in element length. If the design calls for a wood boom, use a nonconductive material. Fiberglass tubes or poles are also good for booms but may need painting for UV protection.

Wood is popular for temporary or portable antennas, such as those in the section Cheap Yagis by WA5VJB later in this chapter. Suitable sizes of lumber include 1 × 3 (up to 15 feet long), 1 × 2 or ¾ × 1¼ pine molding stock, or even strips of ½-inch exterior plywood for very short antennas. The wood should be well seasoned and free from knots. Clear pine, spruce and Douglas fir are often used. The wood should be well treated to avoid water absorption and warping. If varnished well, wood can outlast aluminum in salt air and marine environments.

INSULATED AND NON-INSULATED ELEMENTS

Elements may be mounted insulated or non-insulated, above or through the boom. Insulating the elements from the boom reduces interaction between the elements and boom which becomes increasingly important in high-performance designs.

Non-insulated elements as in **Figure 15.11** are mechanically convenient and are at dc ground, assuming the boom of the antenna is also grounded. Two muffler clamps hold each aluminum plate to the boom, and two U-bolts fasten each element to the plate, which is 0.25 inch thick and 4 × 4 inches square. Stainless steel is the best choice for hardware, but galvanized hardware can be substituted. Plated muffler clamps do not work well in this application because they are not galvanized and quickly rust once exposed to the weather.

Computer modeling can apply a correction for the connection of the element with the boom — make sure you account for that interaction when designing the antenna as it is significant at VHF and higher frequencies! (Correction tables are available on the DG7YBN and YU7EF websites referenced in the sidebar "Yagi Designs Online" later in this chapter.)

Insulated elements can be mounted on shoulder insulators and run through the boom as in **Figure 15.12**. The stainless-steel element retainers are usually referred to as push-on retainers or "pushnuts" such as those made by Auveco Products (**auveco.com**). The insulating shoulder washers should be UV-resistant Teflon or Delrin, such as are available from Unicorp (**unicorpinc.com**). Directive Systems & Engineering (**directivesystems.com**) can supply small quantities of both parts.

Mounting non-insulated elements through a metal boom is the least desirable method unless the elements are welded in place. The Yagi elements will oscillate, even in moderate winds. Over several years this element oscillation will work open the boom holes or loosen connecting hardware. This will allow the elements to move in the boom, creating noise (in the receiver) when the wind blows, as the element contact changes. (Rope or string inside the element helps damp this movement.) Eventually the element-to-boom junction will corrode (aluminum oxide is a good insulator). This loss of electrical contact between the boom and element will reduce the boom's effect and change the resonant frequency of the Yagi.

One of the most popular construction methods for insulated elements is to mount the elements through the boom using insulating shoulder washers. This method is lightweight and durable. Its main disadvantage is difficult disassembly, making this method impractical for portable antennas.

Stauff clamps (**us.stauff.com**) can be used to hold the elements on the boom as shown in **Figure 15.13**. These clamps are relatively new to US antenna builders but solve several problems with the traditional plate-and-U-bolt construction and are rated for industrial and outdoor use. The clamps for reflector and director elements are typically mounted directly to the boom. Various brackets and supports are also available from Stauff. Be sure to use clamps with polypropylene (PP) insulation at VHF and above as other plastics exhibit excessive loss.

If a conductive boom is used, element lengths must be corrected for the mounting method used. The amount of correction is dependent upon the boom diameter in wavelengths. (A change in boom diameter also requires element length adjustment.) See **Figure 15.14** for an example of the effect of element mounting. Elements mounted through the boom and not insulated require the greatest correction. Mounting on top of the boom or through the boom on insulated shoulder wash-

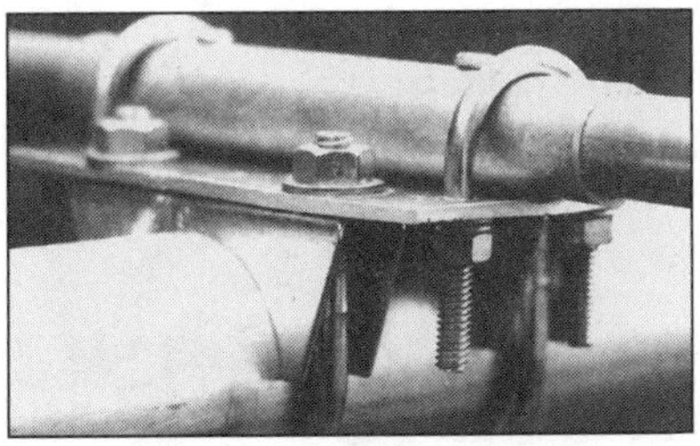

Figure 15.11 — The element to boom clamp. U bolts are used to hold the element to the plate, and 2-inch galvanized muffler clamps hold the plates to the boom.

Figure 15.12 — Insulated elements up to ⅜ inch in diameter can be mounted through the boom using plastic insulators. Stainless-steel push-nut retaining rings hold the element in place.

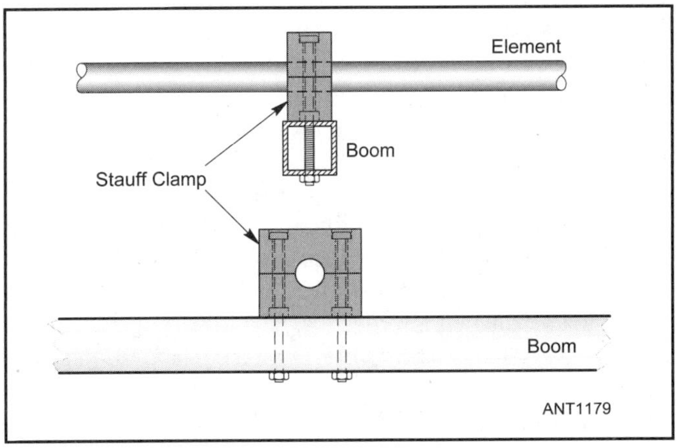

Figure 15.13 — Using a Stauff clamp to mount an insulated element on a square boom.

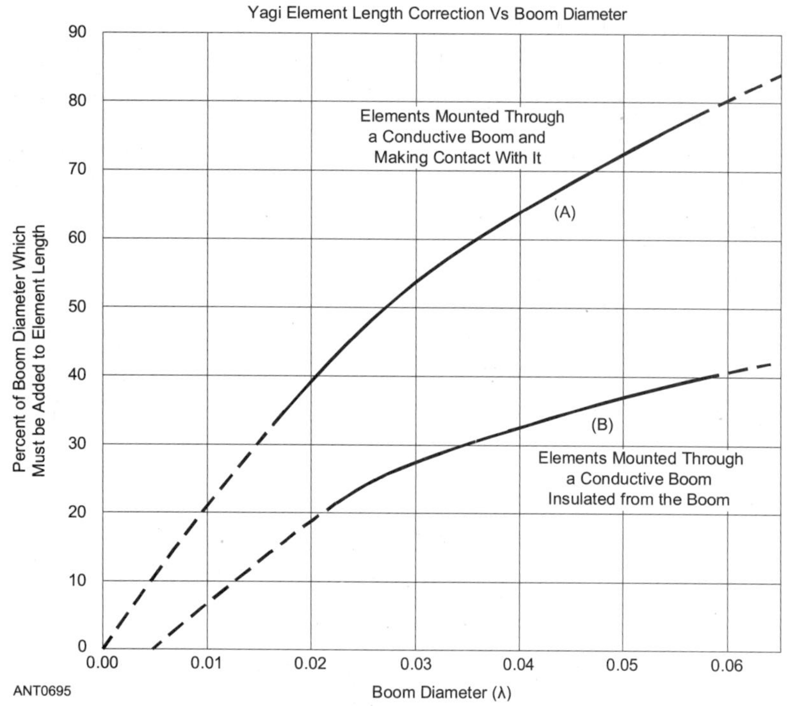

Figure 15.14 — Typical Yagi element correction vs boom diameter. Curve A is for elements mounted through a round or square conductive boom, with the elements in mechanical contact with the boom. Curve B is for insulated elements mounted through a conductive boom, and for elements mounted on top of a conductive boom (elements make electrical contact with the boom). The patterns were corrected to computer simulations to determine Yagi tuning. The amount of element correction is not affected by element diameter. This graph is an example of typical element length corrections and should not be applied in all circumstances.

ers requires about half of the through-the-boom correction. When using a model or design plans for a Yagi, be sure to note whether the elements are in contact with a conductive boom and whether corrections are incorporated into the model and design.

FEED POINT CONSTRUCTION

The following applies especially to high-performance antennas at VHF and above. Modeling software assumes that at the antenna feed point, the coax stops and the driven element starts and there are no wires or pigtails or connectors between them. This means that when an antenna is built from a software model, the driven element will need to be shorter than the model suggests when built, in order to account for the connections that will indeed need to exist between the coax and the antenna feed point in the real world.

RF does not wait until it arrives at the element itself to radiate. At the exact point at which the coax cable is no longer coaxial, the radiating element begins and this includes any wires or pigtails. It is for this reason that a driven element must usually be a bit shorter than modeled, assuming that the antenna is built correctly and any correction factors have been appropriately applied. Additionally, this highlights the fact that tail length should be reduced to an absolute minimum and more T-shaped across the feed point as in **Figure 15.15** rather than Y-shaped in order for the software model can be replicated as closely as possible. Similar considerations apply to the use of connectors. The higher the frequency, the more relevant this rule becomes.

Leads from a feed line or balun to the feed point (or coax pigtails) should be as short as possible and spread apart parallel to the driven element. Once no longer inside the coaxial cable, the leads form part of the driven element and if they are excessively long it will affect antenna performance.

Weatherproofing a coax pigtail can be a challenge, especially for VHF/UHF antennas where the length of the connections must be short. John Portune, W6NBC, designed a 3D-printed housing for these pigtails that makes the job easier. The March 2019 *QST* article, "3D-Printed Coax-to-Wire Connection Blocks" is included in the online content for the chapter **Building Antenna Systems and Towers** and is listed in this chapter's References and Bibliography.

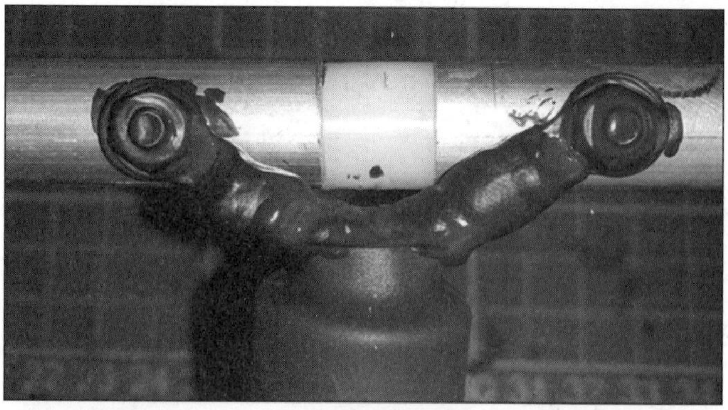

Figure 15.15 — A close-up of the feed line connection showing proper technique for creating and attaching coaxial cable to a driven element. The configuration should be as close to T-shaped as possible and in line with the element to avoid affecting performance at VHF and higher frequencies.

CHOKE BALUNS FOR VHF/UHF YAGIS

A choke balun should be used at the feed point to prevent interaction between the antenna and the feed line shield's outer surface. Alternately, resonant transmission line baluns are commonly used at VHF and UHF. See the **Transmission Line System Techniques** chapter for design and construction information on choke and transmission line baluns. At VHF and UHF, the most consistent performance from bead baluns requires using an appropriate ferrite mix such as #43 or #61.

If a choke balun at the feed point is used, feed line length between the balun and the feed point should be as short as possible to limit interaction between the feed line's outer surface and the antenna.

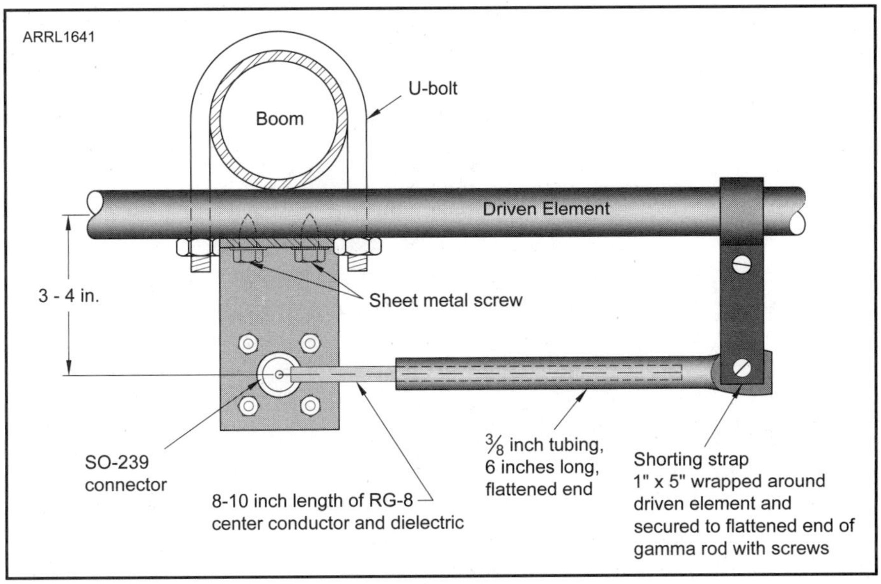

Figure 15.16 — A general-purpose gamma match for 6 meter beams.

GAMMA MATCH FOR 6 METER YAGIS

The drawing in **Figure 15.16** shows a gamma match design in the ARRL book *Magic Band Antennas for Ham Radio* by Bruce Walker, N3JO (see the References and Bibliography). The full article goes into some detail about the construction but the basic idea is well-illustrated here. Be sure to use anti-oxidation compound for all metal-to-metal connections, including the sheet metal screws holding the bracket to the driven element. For additional support of the gamma match, UV-resistant cable ties can be used.

Tune the gamma match by adjusting the position of the shorting strap connecting the driven element and ⅜-inch tubing. If the minimum obtainable SWR remains too high, shorten the length of the driven element by ½ inch and readjust the strap. If minimum SWR has decreased, continue to shorten the driven element and adjust the strap position. If minimum SWR has increased, the driven element needs to be lengthened, instead.

15.3.2 PROJECT: Yagis for 50 MHz

Boom length often proves to be the deciding factor when one selects a Yagi design. **Table 15.1** shows three 6 meter Yagis designed for convenient boom lengths (6, 12 and 22 feet). The 3-element, 6-foot boom design has 8.0 dBi gain in free space; the 12 foot boom, 5-element version has 10.1 dBi gain, and the 22-foot, 7 element Yagi has a gain of 11.3 dBi. All antennas exhibit better than 22 dB front-to-rear ratio and cover 50 to 51 MHz with better than 1.7:1 SWR. A high-performance OWL (Optimized Wideband Low Impedance) design for 50 MHz by Justin Johnson, GØKSC, is included in the High-Performance Yagi Design section of this chapter.

A beam designed for FM operation higher in the band is described by the August 2007 *QST* article "A Short Boom, Wideband 3 Element Yagi for 6 Meters," by L.B. Cebik, W4RNL. Cebik describes two additional 3-element Yagis for 6 meters — one optimized for gain and F/B and the other optimized for bandwidth — in the February 2000 *QST* article, "2 x 3 = 6." Both articles are included with this book's online material.

Half-element lengths and spacings are given in the table. Elements can be mounted to the boom as shown in Figure 15.13. Please note that the element lengths shown in Table 15.1 are half the overall element lengths. See the **Antenna**

Table 15.1
Optimized 6 Meter Yagi Designs

(Lengths are for half elements)

	Spacing Between Elements (inches)	*Seg1 OD Length (inches)*	*Seg2 OD Length (inches)*	*Midband Gain F/R*
306-06				
OD		0.750	0.625	
Refl.	0	36	23.500	7.9 dBi
D.E.	24	36	16.000	27.2 dB
Dir. 1	42	36	15.500	
506-12				
OD		0.750	0.625	
Refl.	0	36	24.000	10.1 dBi
D.E.	24	36	17.125	24.7 dB
Dir. 1	12	36	19.375	
Dir. 2	44	36	18.250	
Dir. 3	58	36	15.375	
706-22				
OD		0.750	0.625	
Refl.	0	36	25.000	11.3 dBi
D.E.	27	36	17.250	29.9 dB
Dir. 1	16	36	18.500	
Dir. 2	51	36	15.375	
Dir. 3	54	36	15.875	
Dir. 4	53	36	16.500	
Dir. 5	58	36	12.500	

Materials and Construction chapter for practical details of telescoping aluminum elements.

The driven element is mounted to the boom on a Bakelite or G-10 fiberglass plate of similar dimension to the other mounting plates. A 12-inch piece of Plexiglas rod is inserted into the driven element halves. The Plexiglas allows the use of a single clamp on each side of the element and also seals the center of the elements against moisture. Self-tapping screws are used for electrical connection to the driven element.

Refer to **Figure 15.17** for driven-element and hairpin match details. A bracket made from a piece of aluminum is used to mount the three SO-239 connectors to the driven element plate. A 4:1 transmission line balun connects the two element halves, transforming the 200 Ω resistance at the hairpin match to 50 Ω at the center connector. Note that the electrical length of the balun is λ/2, but the physical length will be shorter due to the velocity factor of the particular coaxial cable used. The hairpin is connected directly across the element halves. The exact center of the hairpin is electrically neutral and should be fastened to the boom. This has the advantage of placing the driven element at dc ground potential.

The hairpin match requires no adjustment as such. However, you may have to change the length of the driven element slightly to obtain the best match in your preferred portion of the band. Changing the driven-element length will not adversely affect antenna performance. *Do not adjust the lengths or spacings of the other elements — they are optimized already.* If you decide to use a gamma match, add 3 inches to each side of the driven element lengths given in the table for all antennas.

15.3.3 PROJECT: Utility Yagis for 144 MHz and 432 MHz

There are many applications for Yagis on 144 MHz that do not require high gain or tightly-controlled pattern. In fact, for casual operating, a beamwidth that is too narrow can actually prevent a station from hearing weak signals not in the main lobe of the antenna. For meteor scatter and other applications (see the sidebar, "Meteor Scatter: How Much Antenna is Too Much?") where the opening comes from an unknown azimuth, a wider beamwidth is preferred. Rover and portable stations often find the lighter weight and shorter boom length of the smaller antennas easier to handle.

UTILITY YAGI FOR 144 MHZ

The following material is a summary of the design presented by L.B. Cebik, W4RNL in the December 2004 *QST* article "Building a Medium-Gain, Wide-Band, 2 Meter Yagi." (The complete article is included with this book's online material.)

The 6-element Yagi presented here is a derivative of the "optimized wideband antenna" (OWA) designs developed for HF use by NW3Z and WA3FET. **Figure 15.18** shows the general structure of the beam and **Figure 15.19** gives the free-space E-plane pattern. If mounted with the elements horizontal, the E-plane pattern would be the azimuthal pattern.

Oversimplifying the design somewhat, the reflector and first director largely set the feed point impedance. The next two directors contribute to setting the operating bandwidth. The final director sets the gain.

Designed using *NEC-4*, the antenna's six elements are

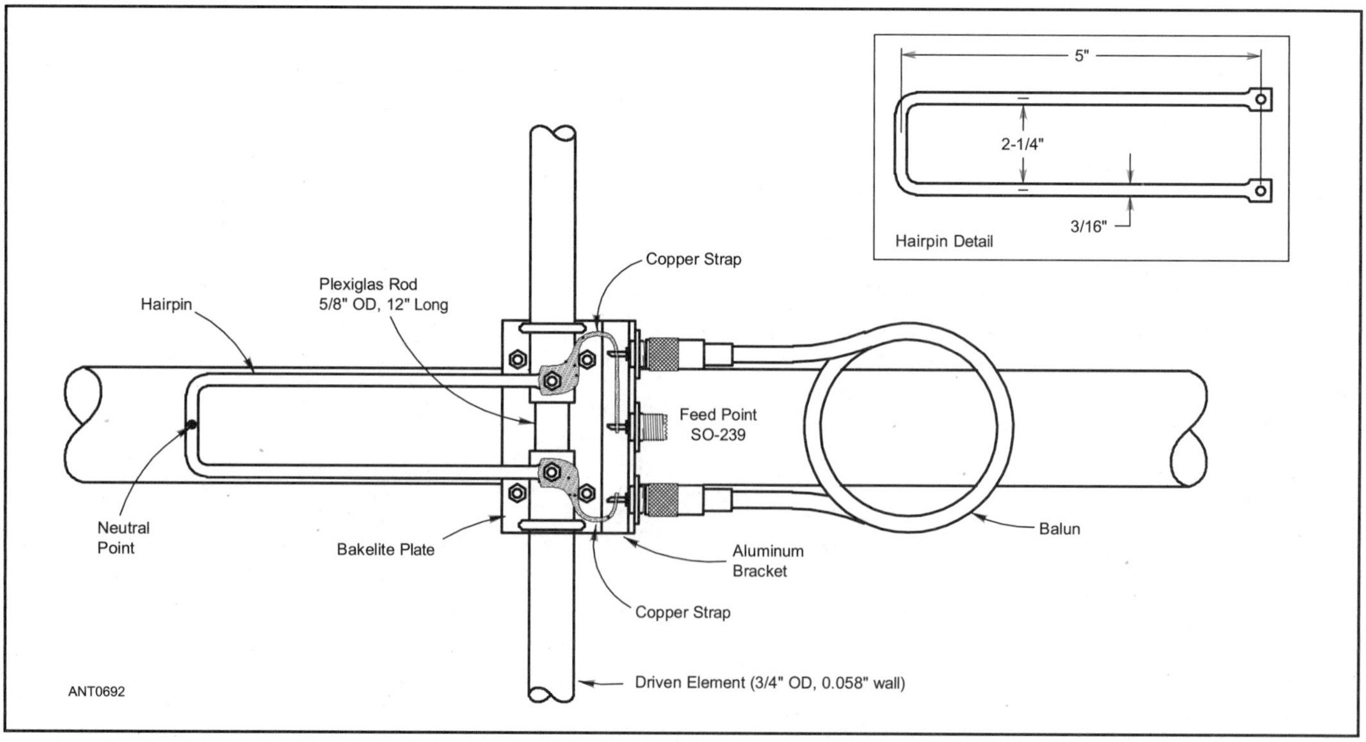

Figure 15.17 — This shows how the driven element and feed system are attached to the boom. The balun is coiled and taped to the boom. The center of the hairpin loop may be connected to the boom electrically and mechanically if desired.
Balun coax lengths:
For cable with 0.80 velocity factor — 7 ft, 10⅜ inches
For cable with 0.66 velocity factor — 6 ft, 5¾ inches

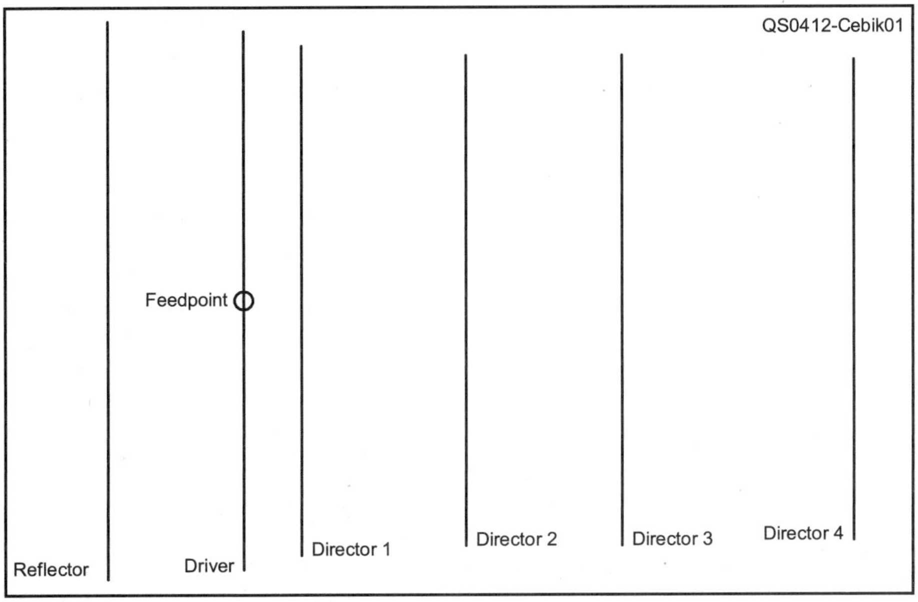

Figure 15.18 — The general structure of the 2 meter, 6-element OWA Yagi. See Table 15.2 for dimensions.

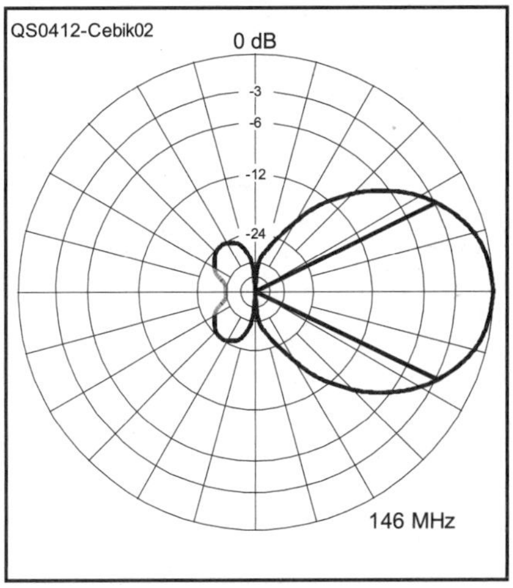

Figure 15.19 — E-plane (horizontal azimuth) pattern of the 2 meter, 6-element OWA Yagi in free space at mid-band — 146 MHz. The antenna exhibits a gain of about 10.2 dBi, consistent across the 2 meter band.

arranged on a 56-inch boom **Table 15.2** gives the specific dimension for the antenna. The parasitic elements are all 3⁄16-inch aluminum rod while the driver uses ½-inch aluminum tubing for reasons of construction. Dimensions for the beam with an alternate driver or the use of ⅛-inch elements is given in the original article.

The OWA design provides about 10.2 dBi of free-space gain with better than 20 dB F/B across the entire 2 meter band. The horizontal beamwidth is considerably wider if the beam is mounted with the elements vertical for use on FM.

One significant feature of the OWA design is its direct 50-Ω feed point impedance that requires no matching network.

Meteor Scatter: How Much Antenna is Too Much?

Can an antenna be too big or have too much gain? Perhaps surprisingly, in some circumstances the answer is a definite "Yes."

High gain means narrow beamwidth. Even supposing that a sharp beam can be directed just as desired, you may sometimes want your transmitter to illuminate a larger range of directions, or to receive signals with reasonable gain over a larger range. Such situations can exist even for point-to-point communication — for example, when station A tries to work station B, at a known location some 800 to 1200 km away, on a VHF band using meteor scatter.

The most probable path geometries for random meteor scatter are offset by angles of about 8° to 16° either side of the great circle path. Smaller offsets apply to the longest paths, on the order of 2200 to 2400 km; paths less than 1000 km have optimum offsets near the high end of the range. The largest number of meteor-scatter reflections will occur when stations A and B use antenna beamwidths that overlap throughout most of the potentially useful scattering volume. This implies beamwidths at least twice the offset angle: around 32° for 800 km paths, or 16° for the longest feasible paths. Of course, antennas with higher gain and narrower beams may yield stronger signals, when they produce any at all; but for efficient completion of their desired contact, A and B may be interested in getting *more* meteor reflections, rather than *stronger* ones.

A Yagi antenna with 30° beamwidth has boom length of about 3 wavelengths and gain of 13 dBd. Three wavelengths at 50 MHz is nearly 60 feet, so few if any amateur antennas for this band are likely to be "too large" for effective meteor-scatter use. At 144 MHz, however, Yagis of 5 wavelengths and more are quite practical. Their beamwidths will be significantly less than 30°, so they will be sub-optimal for meteor-scatter contacts at moderate distances.

Real-world amateur meteor scatter experience confirms the picture outlined above. For meteor scatter out to 1600 km on the 2 meter band, an optimized 10 to 12 element Yagi (length 1.8 to 2.5 λ) is probably close to the optimum antenna. Takeoff angles for meteor scatter are no more than about 15°, so a vertical stack of two such Yagis (which would have the same beamwidth in azimuth) would be even better. Horizontal stacking of a pair, or a 2 × 2 box of four such Yagis, would work well beyond about 1600 km, but would be sub-optimal at shorter distances. On the longest feasible meteor-scatter paths, beyond about 1800 km, the rule-of-thumb once again becomes "bigger is better." Note that for these long paths the optimum takeoff angle has fallen to less than 3°, so antenna height in excess of 5 λ (about 35 feet at 144 MHz) is also important. — *Joe Taylor, K1JT*

Table 15.2
2 Meter OWA Yagi Dimensions
(Lengths are for full elements)

Element	*Element Length (inches)*	*Spacing from Reflector (inches)*	*Element Diameter (inches)*
Reflector	40.52	—	3⁄16
Driven Ele.	39.70	10.13	½
Director 1	37.36	14.32	3⁄16
Director 2	36.32	25.93	3⁄16
Director 3	36.32	37.28	3⁄16
Director 4	34.96	54.22	3⁄16

Of course, a common-mode choke balun (see the **Transmission Line System Techniques** chapter) is desirable. The SWR as shown in **Figure 15.20** is very flat across the band and never exceeds 1.3:1. The SWR and pattern consistency together create a very useful utility antenna for 2 meters.

UTILITY YAGI FOR 432 MHZ

The following design was developed by Zack Lau, W1VT and described in his "RF" column "A Small 70-cm Yagi" in the July/August 2001 *QEX*. The complete article is included with this book's online material.

This six-element Yagi was designed for a wide bandwidth — in gain, F/B and SWR. Its gain was measured at 8.5 dBd during the 1995 Eastern States VHF/UHF Conference — with little gain variation between 417 and 446 MHz. The SWR is almost as broad, with better than 1.4:1 SWR between 422 and 446 MHz. The measured gain and return loss curves are shown in **Figure 15.21**. The short 30-inch boom is small enough to fit in the trunk of a compact sedan, perfect for portable or emergency operation. The F/B bandwidth is also very good, with over 20 dB of F/B between 424 and 450 MHz, according to a *Yagi Analyzer* computer model.

Even if you only intend to use this antenna for 432-MHz SSB or 436-MHz satellite operation, the extra bandwidth is useful when it rains. Heavy rain causes antenna elements to

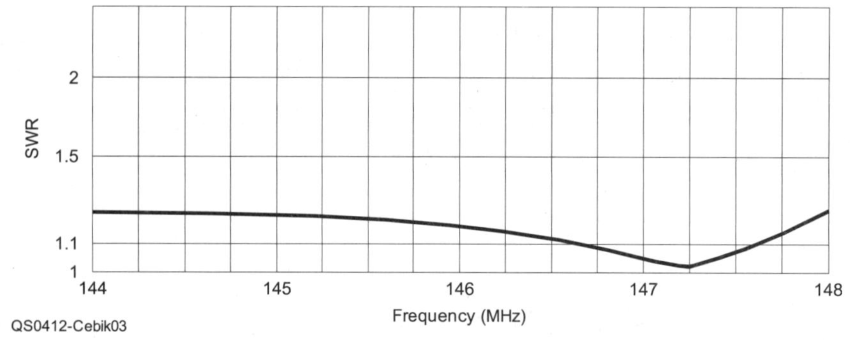

Figure 15.20 — The SWR for the OWA 2 meter Yagi from 144 to 148 MHz as modeled by *NEC-4*.

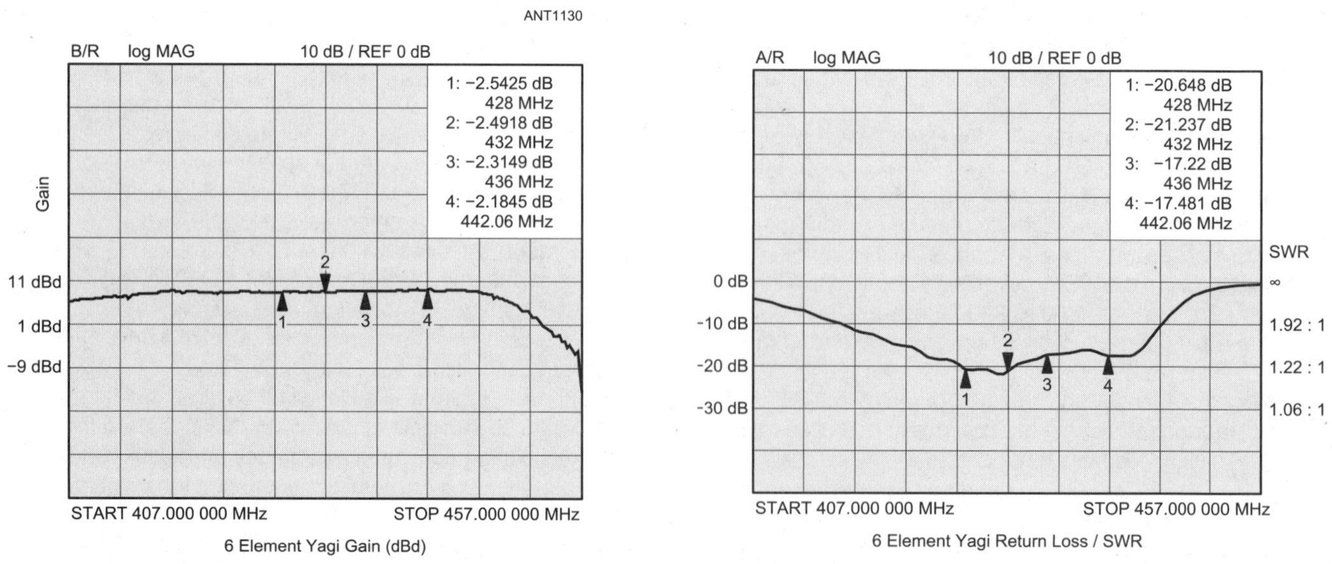

Figure 15.21 — Gain and SWR measurements for the 70 cm utility Yagi.

resonate lower in frequency. This is much worse if the antenna is tweaked for maximum gain. Yagis typically have a low-pass gain response. The gain falls off rapidly past the maximum-gain point. Thus, while the maximum gain is around 442 MHz, the gain is significantly lower at 457 MHz, while only a little bit lower at 427 MHz.

The optimized design is shown in **Figure 15.22** and the element lengths and placement are given in **Table 15.3**. The element lengths are adjusted to work with a particular boom and mounting arrangement. Changing the boom or element mounting may require adjusting the element lengths. The antenna uses a simple T-match, as simpler gamma matches have a poor reputation on this band. A T-matched Yagi is more likely to have a symmetrical radiation pattern. The feed system shown in the complete article included with this book's online material is a copy of that used in the K2RIW Yagi. A half-wave balun made out of semi-rigid UT-141 coax steps up the impedance to 200 Ω. Similarly, the T match steps up the impedance of the driven element to 200 Ω.

Table 15.3
432-MHz Yagi Dimensions

	Spacing Between Ele. (inches)	*Spacing from Reflector (inches)*	*Full Element Length (inches)*
Reflector	0	—	13.83
Driven Ele.	2.39	2.39	11.97
Dir. 1	2.72	5.11	12.28
Dir. 2	6.53	11.64	11.91
Dir. 3	7.91	19.54	11.81
Dir. 4	7.55	27.10	11.01

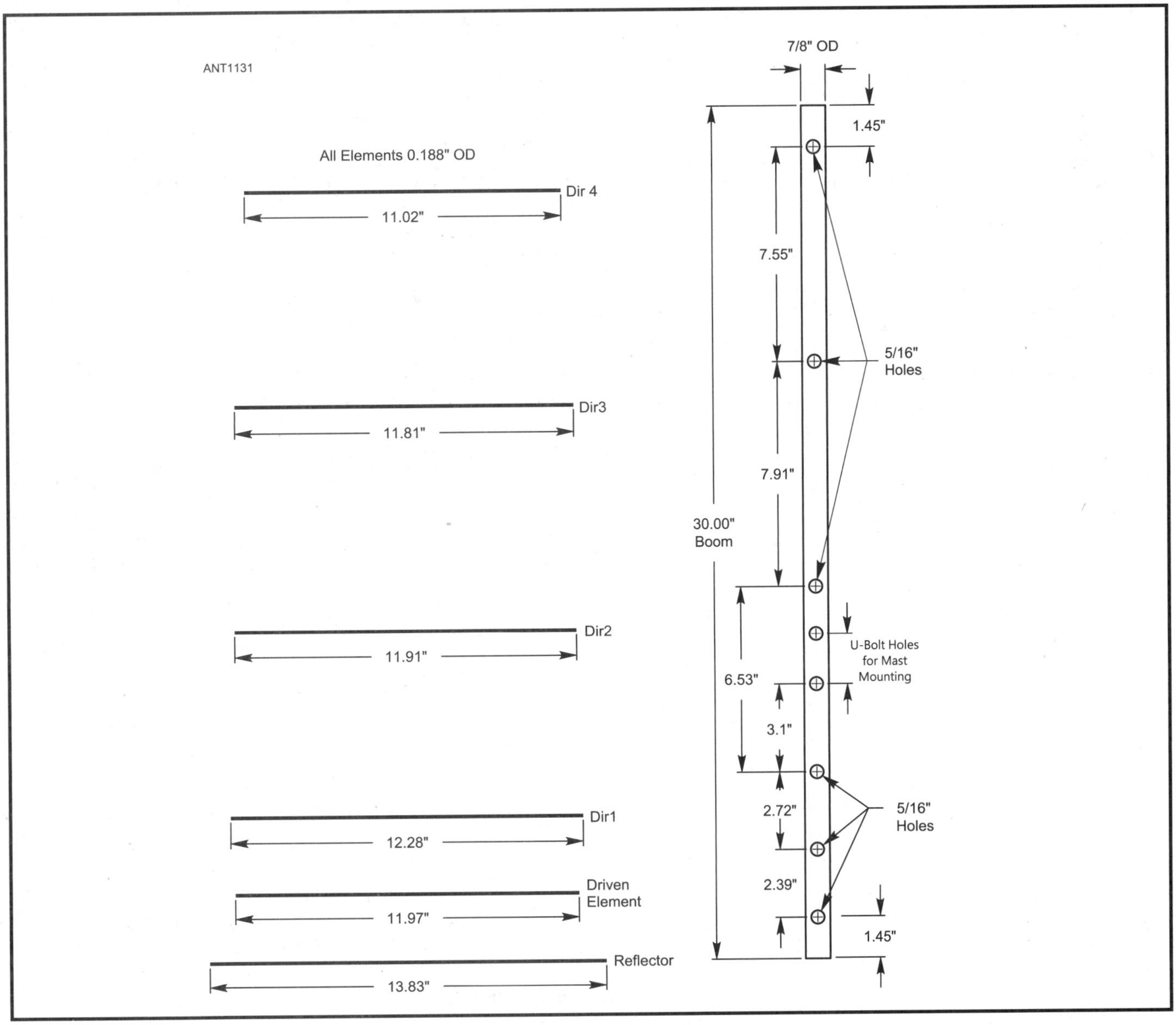

Figure 15.22 — Rough scale drawing of the 70 cm utility Yagi boom and elements.

15.3.4 PROJECT: Cheap Yagis By WA5VJB

The following material is adapted from an online paper by Kent Britain, WA5VJB, entitled "Controlled Impedance 'Cheap' Antennas." The paper is available from **wa5vjb.com/references.html**. The simplified feed uses the structure of the antenna itself for impedance matching. The antennas were designed with *YagiMax*, tweaked in *NEC*, and the driven elements experimentally determined on the antenna range. The result is a family of Yagis with good performance that can be built very inexpensively.

Construction of the antennas is straightforward. The boom is ¾-inch square, or ½-inch by ¾-inch wood. To install an element, drill a hole through the boom and insert the element. A drop of cyanoacrylate "super glue," epoxy, or silicone adhesive is used to hold the elements in place. There is no boom-to-mast plate — drill holes in the boom and use a U-bolt to attach it to the mast! The life of the antenna is determined by what you coat it with. The author had a 902-MHz version in the air varnished with polyurethane for two years with little deterioration.

The parasitic elements on prototypes have been made from silicon-bronze welding rod, aluminum rod, brass hobby tubing, and #10 or #12 AWG solid copper ground wire. So that you can solder to the driven element, use the welding rod, hobby tubing or copper wire. The driven element is folded at one end with its ends inserted through the boom.

Figure 15.23 shows the basic plan for the antenna and labels the dimensions that are given in the table for each band. All table dimensions are given in inches.

Figure 15.24 shows how the driven element is constructed for each antenna. Trim the free end of the driven element to tune it for minimum SWR at the desired frequency. **Figure 15.25** shows how to attach coaxial cable to the feed point. Sliding a quarter-wave sleeve along the coax had little effect, so there's not much RF on the outside of the coax. You may use a ferrite bead choke balun if you like, but these antennas are designed for minimum expense!

144 MHz Yagi: While others have reported good luck with 16-element long-boom wood antennas, six elements was about the maximum for most rovers. The design is peaked at 144.2 MHz, but performance is still good at 146.5 MHz. All parasitic elements are made from 3⁄16-inch aluminum rod and the driven element is made from ⅛-inch rod. Lengths and spacings are given in **Table 15.4**.

222 MHz Yagi: This antenna is peaked at 222.1 MHz, but performance has barely changed at 223.5 MHz. You can drill the mounting holes to mount it with the elements horizontal or vertical. All parasitic elements are made from 3⁄16-inch aluminum rod and the driven element is made from ⅛-inch rod. Lengths and spacings are given in Table 15.4.

432 MHz Yagi: At this band the antenna is getting very practical and easy to build. All parasitic elements are made from ⅛-inch diameter rod and the driven element is made from #10 AWG solid copper wire. Lengths and spacings are given in **Table 15.5**.

435 MHz Yagi for AMSAT: Ed Krome, K9EK, provided help and motivation for these antennas. A high front-to-back ratio (F/B) was a major design consideration of all versions. The model predicts 30 dB F/B for the six-element and over 40 dB for the others. For gain, *NEC* predicts 11.2 dBi for the six-element, 12.6 dBi for the eight-element, and 13.5 dBi for the 10-element, and 13.8 dBi for the 11-element.

Using ¾-inch square wood for the boom makes it easy to build two antennas on the same boom for cross-polarization. Offset the two antennas 6½ inch along the boom and feed them in-phase for circular polarization, or just use one for portable operations. All parasitic elements are made from ⅛-inch diameter rod and the driven element is made from #10 AWG solid copper wire. Lengths and spacings are given in **Table 15.6**. The same element spacing is used for all four versions of the antenna.

450 MHz Yagi for FM: this six-element Yagi is a good, cheap antenna to get a newcomer into a repeater or make a simplex-FM QSO during a contest. Aluminum ground wire, typically ⅛-inch diameter, was used in the prototype for all the elements except the driven element, which is made from #10 AWG solid copper wire. Other ⅛-inch diameter material could be used. Lengths and spacings are given in **Table 15.7**.

902 MHz Yagi: The 2.5-ft length has proven very practical. All parasitic elements are made from ⅛-inch-diameter rod and the driven element

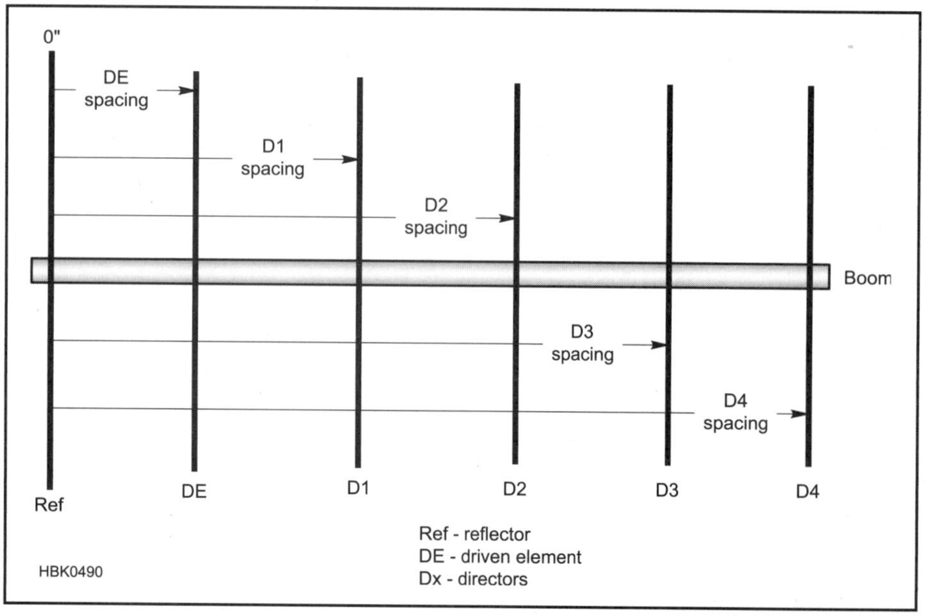

Figure 15.23 — Element spacing for the Cheap Yagis. Refer to Tables 15.4 to 15.10 for exact dimensions for the various bands.

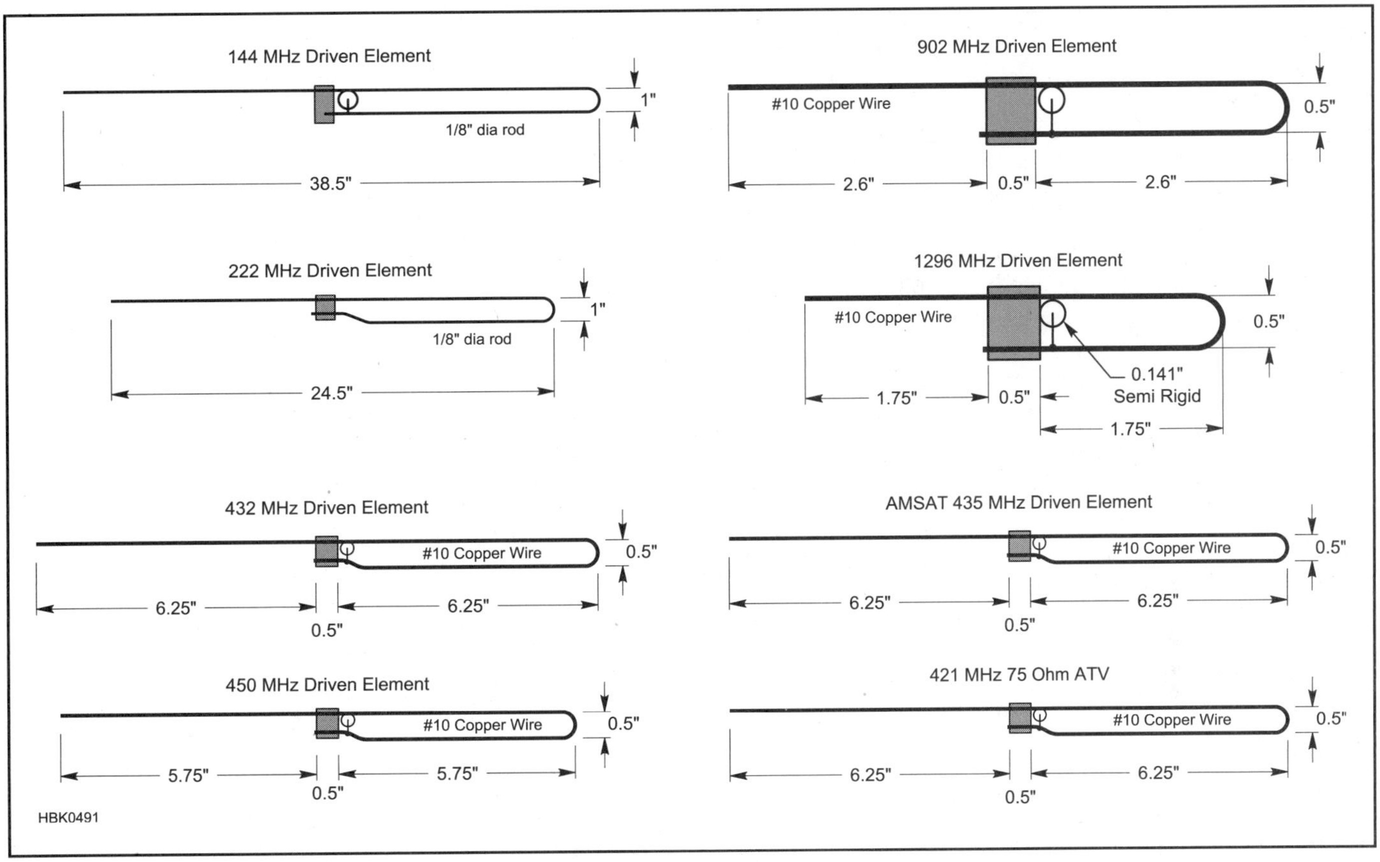

Figure 15.24 — Driven element dimensions for the Cheap Yagis. Attaching the coax shield to the center of the driven element is appropriate because that is the lowest impedance point of the element.

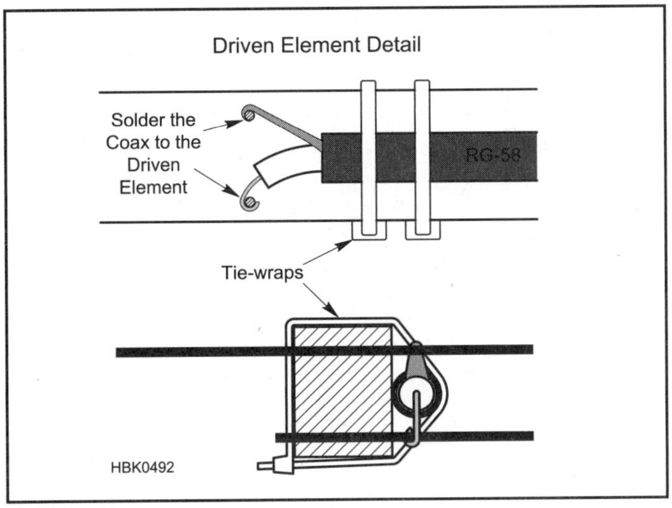

Figure 15.25 — Construction details and feed line attachment for the Cheap Yagi driven element.

is made from #10 AWG solid copper wire. Lengths and spacings are given in **Table 15.8**.

1296 MHz Yagi: This antenna is the veteran of several "Grid-peditions" and has measured 13.5 dBi on the Central States VHF Society antenna range. Dimensions must be followed with great care. The driven element is small enough to allow 0.141-inch semi-rigid coax to be used. The prototype antennas use ⅛-inch silicon-bronze welding rod for the elements, but any ⅛-inch-diameter material can be used. The driven element is made from #10 AWG solid copper wire. Lengths and spacings are given in **Table 15.9**.

421.25 MHz 75-Ω Yagi for ATV: 421 MHz vestigial sideband video is popular in North Texas for receiving the FM video input repeaters. These antennas are made for 421 MHz use and the driven element is designed for 75 Ω. RG-59 or an F adapter to RG-6 can be directly connected to a cable-TV converter or cable-ready TV on channel 57. All parasitic elements are made from ⅛-inch diameter rod and the driven element is made from #10 AWG solid copper wire. Lengths and spacings are given in **Table 15.10**. The same spacing is used for all versions.

Table 15.4
WA5VJB 144 and 222 MHz Yagi Dimensions

144 MHz Yagi

		Ref	*DE*	*D1*	*D2*	*D3*	*D4*
3-element	Length	41.0	—	37.0			
	Spacing	0	8.5	20.0			
4-element	Length	41.0	—	37.5	33.0		
	Spacing	0	8.5	19.25	40.5		
6-element	Length	40.5	—	37.5	36.5	36.5	32.75
	Spacing	0	7.5	16.5	34.0	52.0	70.0

222 MHz Yagi

		Ref	*DE*	*D1*	*D2*	*D3*	*D4*
3-element	Length	26.0	—	23.75			
	Spacing	0	5.5	13.5			
4-element	Length	26.25	—	24.1	22.0		
	Spacing	0	5.0	11.75	23.5		
6-element	Length	26.25	—	24.1	23.5	23.5	21.0
	Spacing	0	5.0	10.75	22.0	33.75	45.5

Dimensions in inches.

Table 15.5
WA5VJB 432 MHz Yagi Dimensions

		Ref	*DE*	*D1*	*D2*	*D3*	*D4*	*D5*	*D6*	*D7*	*D8*	*D9*
6-element	Length	13.5	—	12.5	12.0	12.0	11.0					
	Spacing	0	2.5	5.5	11.25	17.5	24.0					
8-element	Length	13.5	—	12.5	12.0	12.0	12.0	12.0	11.25			
	Spacing	0	2.5	5.5	11.25	17.5	24.0	30.75	38.0			
11-element	Length	13.5	—	12.5	12.0	12.0	12.0	12.0	12.0	11.75	11.75	11.0
	Spacing	0	2.5	5.5	11.25	17.5	24.0	30.75	38.0	45.5	53.0	59.5

Dimensions in inches.

Table 15.6
WA5VJB 435 MHz Yagi Dimensions

		Ref	*DE*	*D1*	*D2*	*D3*	*D4*	*D5*	*D6*	*D7*	*D8*	*D9*
6-element	Length	13.4	—	12.4	12.0	12.0	11.0					
8-element	Length	13.4	—	12.4	12.0	12.0	12.0	12.0	11.1			
10-element	Length	13.4	—	12.4	12.0	12.0	12.0	12.0	11.75	11.75	11.1	
11-element	Length	13.4	—	12.4	12.0	12.0	12.0	12.0	11.75	11.75	11.75	11.1
	Spacing	0	2.5	5.5	11.25	17.5	24.0	30.5	37.75	45.0	52.0	59.5

Dimensions in inches.

Table 15.7
WA5VJB 450 MHz Yagi Dimensions

		Ref	*DE*	*D1*	*D2*	*D3*	*D4*
6-element	Length	13.0	—	12.1	11.75	11.75	10.75
	Spacing	0	2.5	5.5	11.0	18.0	28.5

Dimensions in inches.

Table 15.8
WA5VJB 902 MHz Yagi Dimensions

		Ref	*DE*	*D1*	*D2*	*D3*	*D4*	*D5*	*D6*	*D7*	*D8*
10-element	Length	6.2	—	5.6	5.5	5.5	5.4	5.3	5.2	5.1	5.1
	Spacing	0	2.4	3.9	5.8	9.0	12.4	17.4	22.4	27.6	33.0

Dimensions in inches.

Table 15.9
WA5VJB 1296 MHz Yagi Dimensions

		Ref	DE	D1	D2	D3	D4	D5	D6	D7	D8
10-element	Length	4.3	—	3.9	3.8	3.75	3.75	3.65	3.6	3.6	3.5
	Spacing	0	1.7	2.8	4.0	6.3	8.7	12.2	15.6	19.3	23.0

Dimensions in inches.

Table 15.10
WA5VJB 421.25 MHz 75-Ω Yagi Dimensions

		Ref	DE	D1	D2	D3	D4	D5	D6	D7	D8	D9
6-element	Length	14.0	—	12.5	12.25	12.25	11.0					
9-element	Length	14.0	—	12.5	12.25	12.25	12.0	12.0	11.25			
11-element	Length	14.0	—	12.5	12.25	12.25	12.0	12.0	12.0	11.75	11.75	11.5
	Spacing	0	3.0	6.5	12.25	17.75	24.5	30.5	36.0	43.0	50.25	57.25

Dimensions in inches.

15.3.5 High-Performance Yagi Design

This section was primarily updated and extended by Justin Johnson, GØKSC, based on his articles in *DUBUS* and from material on his website at **g0ksc.co.uk**. In addition to the summarized information here, several articles by Justin are included with this book's online content. The online content also includes the classic Yagi designs by Steve Powlishen, K1FO, featured in several recent editions of this book. For those who wish to construct antennas based on DL6WU's work, a family of designs is available at the article referenced in the References and Bibliography.

The treatment of high-performance Yagi design in this edition takes advantage of high-precision modeling developed over the past few years to achieve better control of antenna pattern through manual and automatic optimization. In addition, construction techniques that can have a significant effect on performance across a band and susceptibility to noise pickup are discussed.

New techniques pioneered by YU7EF, DG7YBN, UA9TC, RA3AQ, and others (see the sidebar Yagi Designs Online) have contributed to the development of Yagis optimized for wideband (flat) performance, consideration of elevation plane lobes, self-matching radiating elements, close-spaced "driver

Yagi Designs Online

Many designers have been creating high-performance Yagis for EME and VHF+ contesting. Here are a few of the active designers websites:

DG7YBN — **dg7ybn.de/index.htm**
DK7ZB — **qsl.net/d/dk7zb**
GØKSC — **g0ksc.co.uk**
G4CQM — **g4cqm.www.idnet.com**
UA9TC — **vhfdx.ru/faylyi/view-details/shemyi-i-opisaniya/ant-ua9tc**
YU7EF — **yu7ef.com**
YU7XL— **qslnet.de/member/yu7xl**
DUBUS Magazine — **dubus.org**

Gain/Noise Temperature (G/T)

This parameter is a figure of merit for evaluating the antenna's ability to receive weak signals. That ability is particularly important at VHF/UHF/microwave where signals can be very weak, such as for EME operation and in contests. G represents the antenna gain in dB and T_a is the equivalent noise temperature of the antenna in degrees Kelvin. (See T. Milligan, *Modern Antenna Design, 2nd Edition,* IEEE Press, p. 32.)

For the purposes of this discussion:

$$G/T = (G + 2.15) - (10 \log T_a)$$

where more positive values indicate better performance. T_a includes noise received from all directions including side lobes. A clean radiation pattern reduces noise and increases G/T.

An alternative calculation of G/T for the entire receiving system includes the noise produced by the antenna and receiving system, which includes the feed line, any preamplifiers, and the receiver itself.

Optimizing G/T is similar to optimizing signal-to-noise ratio (SNR) in that the goal is optimizing the quality of the received signal and not necessarily absolute signal level or noise level.

G/T may be calculated directly from the Far Field radiation pattern tables produced by *EZNEC* or *4nec2* by using *TANT*, a DOS utility program developed by Sinisa Miloskjovic, YU1NT, originally for use in developing EME antenna systems. It imports the far field data from the file and computes G/T in 5-degree increments from elevation angles of 0 to 90 degrees. *TANT* may be downloaded at **dg7ybn.de/Ant_Temp/Ant_Temp.htm#TANT** with instructions for use and sample input and output files.

It is important to note that while this is a good method of comparison between antennas, it is intended for use in EME systems and the calculations are performed assuming an antenna elevation fixed at 30°. With any given set of Yagis pointed at the horizon or at elevation angles greater than 30° very different comparative results may be seen.

cell" (first three elements), and other key performance indicators, particularly gain/noise temperature performance as described in the sidebar Gain/Noise Temperature (G/T). It should be understood that not all of the antenna designs found online take into account the entire set of considerations in the following discussion while being optimized.

Building on the current state of computer-optimized antenna design, this section details some additional attributes that contribute to the "ideal" Yagi. In addition, reasons are presented and discussed as to why Yagis for UHF and microwave bands sometimes do not perform at the level predicted by software models.

On a philosophical note, recent advances in modeling and optimization of antenna performance have led to some exciting new advances, all pioneered by amateurs. The combination of sophisticated design tools, inexpensive materials, and the manageable weight and size for Yagis above 50 MHz, make it possible for any amateur so inclined to construct their own state of the art antennas.

HIGH-PERFORMANCE AT AND ABOVE 144 MHZ

At 144 MHz and above, most high-performance operation requires Yagi antennas two or more wavelengths in length. Before computer-based optimization became practical for amateurs, a boom length of 2 wavelengths was the point at which classic Yagi performance started to fall apart in terms of gain per boom length, bandwidth, and pattern quality. Careful optimization techniques have extended the range of high-performance Yagi designs considerably beyond the 2-wavelength limit. This is discussed in the sections Optimization and Bandwidth followed by Optimizing to Minimize Real-World Noise.

The Classic Design Approach

As described in previous editions of this book, classic high-performance Yagi design approaches start with closely spaced directors. The spacings gradually increase until a constant spacing of about 0.4 λ is reached. Conversely, the director lengths start out longest with the first director and decrease in length in a decreasing rate of change until they are virtually constant in length. This method of construction results in a wide gain bandwidth. A bandwidth of 7% of the center frequency at the –1 dB forward-gain points is typical for these Yagis even when they are longer than 10 λ. The driven-element impedance also changes moderately with boom length.

The actual rate of change in element lengths is determined by the diameter of the elements (in wavelengths). The spacings can be optimized for an individual boom length or chosen as a best compromise for most boom lengths.

Measurements and computer analysis by both amateurs and professionals indicates that given an optimum classic design, doubling a Yagi's boom length will result in a maximum theoretical gain increase of about 2.6 dB. (This value is not exact and varies with optimization technique and element construction.) In practice, the real gain increase may be less because of escalating resistive losses and the greater possibility of construction error. **Figure 15.26** shows the maximum theoretically possible gain per boom length expressed in decibels, referenced to an isotropic radiator. The actual number of directors does not play an important part in determining the gain vs boom length as long as a reasonable number of directors are used. The use of more directors per boom length will normally give a wider gain bandwidth, but a point exists where too many directors will adversely affect all performance aspects.

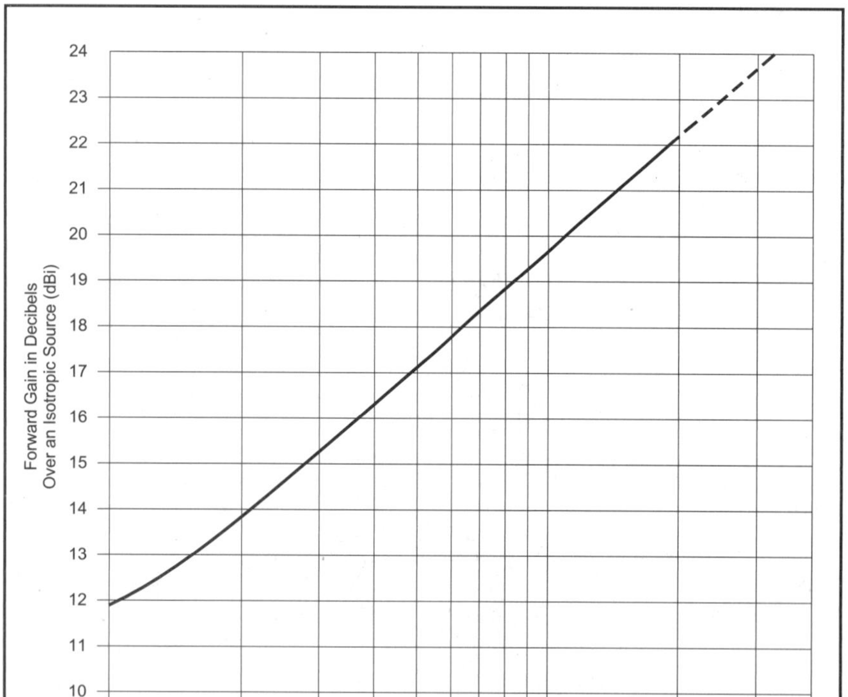

Figure 15.26 — This chart shows maximum gain per boom length for optimally designed long Yagi antennas using the classic design approach.

While short antennas (< 1.5 λ) may show increased gain with the use of quad or loop elements, long Yagis (> 2 λ) will not exhibit measurably greater forward gain or pattern integrity with loop-type elements. Similarly, loops used as driven elements and reflectors will not significantly change the properties of a long log-taper Yagi. Multiple-dipole driven-element assemblies will also not result in any significant gain increase per given boom length when compared to single-dipole feeds.

Once a long-Yagi director string is properly tuned, the reflector becomes relatively non-critical. Reflector spacings between 0.15 λ and 0.2 λ are preferred. The spacing can be chosen for best pattern and driven element impedance. Multiple-reflector arrangements will not significantly increase the forward gain of a Yagi which has its directors properly optimized for forward gain.

Bent-Element Yagis

By bending elements in the most active part of the Yagi (the reflector, driven element, and first director) a variety of improvements can be made to antenna performance with a variety of additional construction complexity.

UA9TC first experimented with bending the reflector in a right angle at the ends, similar to the Moxon designs, resulting in improved bandwidth and less noise pickup but gain was reduced. GØKSC then changed the design to bend the tips of the driven element back toward the reflector. (OP-DES designs)

Another early experimenter was K6STI who developed designs with V-shaped driven elements to raise the feed point impedance. (The V opens rearward toward the reflector.) A five-element version of this design for FM broadcast has been published at **ham-radio.com/k6sti/five.htm**. This approach was extended by DG7YBN and others.

LFA Yagis

The LFA Yagi (Loop Fed Array) replaces the bent tips of the driven element with an extended folded-dipole type feed laid flat on the boom. Thus, both sides of the driven loop are in line with the parasitic elements, rather than extending above or below the boom. Unlike a traditional folded dipole driven element, the feed point of the LFA design is in line with the boom and all elements as shown in **Figure 15.27** with the feed point toward the front of the antenna.

The LFA design leads to a symmetrical pattern in both the E and H planes. However, this mechanical arrangement adds certain construction complications. With all elements in line, the feed point lies at the boom, centered on its axis. Workable construction options include using a metallic boom, although for optimum long-term performance the elements must be welded to the boom. Insulated elements passing through a metallic boom are another option, but this practice can lead to eddy currents in the boom, detuning the antenna and causing deterioration of both pattern and system temperature. With these problems in mind, a hollow fiberglass boom is recommended.

OWA, OWL, and OWM Yagis

Optimized Wideband Low Impedance (OWL) Yagis are a modification of the Optimized Wideband Array (OWA) Yagi designs developed by WA3FET and NW3Z (**naic.edu/~angel/kp4ao/ham/owa.html**). The OWA Yagi has a feed point impedance of 50 Ω for direct feed and wide bandwidth but as a tradeoff has lower peak gain and F/B. A benefit of the OWA design at VHF and higher frequencies is that the OWA design is less sensitive to small impedance shifts from weather or interaction with surrounding objects such as trees, buildings, and most importantly, other antennas.

The OWL Yagi has a conventional, split-dipole driven element, is designed to have a 12.5 Ω feed point impedance, and can be easily matched to 50 Ω with a λ/4 section of 25 Ω transmission line made from two parallel sections of 50 Ω coax. (See the **Transmission Lines** and **Transmission Line System Techniques** chapters for information on coaxial impedance transformers.) This enables good performance over a wider bandwidth than was previously available.

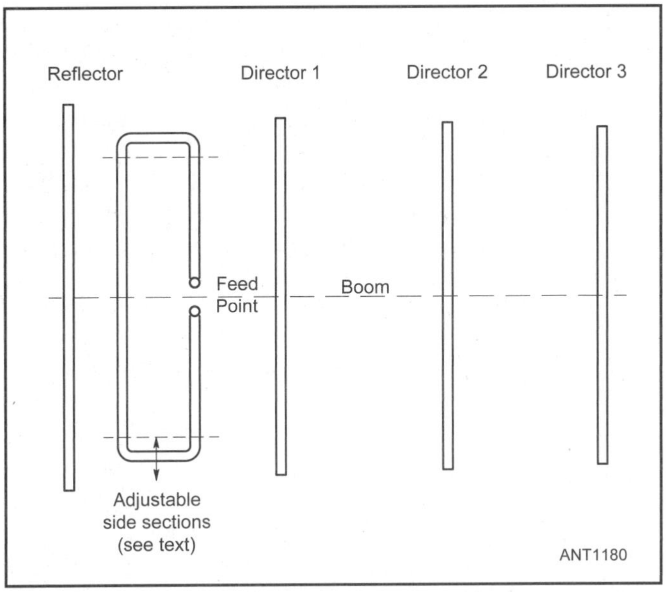

Figure 15.27 — Typical construction for an LFA Yagi with the loop driven element laying along the boom in the same plane as the elements.

An alternate implementation of the OWL is to use a folded dipole for the driven element. This conveys the benefits of closed-loop feed systems, including that the feed point impedance is transformed to 50 Ω for direct connection to feed lines. This is the type of driven element used in the 144 MHz OWL designs later in this chapter.

The OWM (Optimized Wideband Medium Impedance) Yagi is designed for 28 Ω feed point impedance. This impedance can be matched to 50 Ω with a λ/4 section of 37.5 Ω transmission line made from two parallel sections of 75 Ω coax or a matching device can be used. (See the section on 144 MHz and 222 MHz Yagis for more information on building these coaxial cable transformer sections.)

Self-Matched Yagis

"Self-matched" Yagis are those that have the driven element constructed in such a way as to increase the impedance to 50 Ω for direct connection to 50 Ω feed lines. Rearrang-

> **VE7BQH Antenna Performance Tables**
>
> Similar to the Sherwood Engineering receiver performance tables (**sherweng.com/table.html**) that show dynamic range and other performance metrics for popular transceivers, Lionel Edwards, VE7BQH, has compiled the performance data of a large number of antennas for 50, 144, and 432 MHz. (a.k.a. – the VH List) The tables are maintained online at **dxmaps.com/VE7BQH.html** and are also available as downloadable spreadsheet files from **bigskyspaces.com/w7gj/6mTable.htm**.

ing the driven element can include bending the element, using folded dipoles as in the OWL designs in this chapter, or using a loop as for the Loop-Fed Array (LFA).

There are a number of advantages of doing so, not the least of which is that the Yagi can be modeled, optimized and viewed exactly as it will be built with no additional structure (matching device) being added outside the model during the build-phase. This added structure and connections, including the feed line, can and do affect and change performance parameters in the real world. At the same time, direct feed can reduce the susceptibility to man-made noise and drastically increase the power levels of that can fed to the antenna system without problems.

Optimizing and Bandwidth

Figure 15.28 shows a graph of gain versus (F/R – F/B) in a "typical" Yagi with a single point (frequency) of optimization that is focused on maximum gain within the optimization parameter setup. (F/R is the ratio of forward to gain averaged over the entire rear-ward hemisphere — the "rear bubble" — and F/B is the ratio of forward gain to that at the exact opposite direction to the main lobe.) This is not a real plot of any Yagi and is very much exaggerated in order that the point can be illustrated.

The problem with optimizing metrics at a single frequency and to single parameters is the potential impact on real-world performance in changing conditions and from variations in materials used to build these antennas which could result in a shift of performance (and ultimately G/T) away from the specified frequency toward the band edges. For example, as the center of frequency on the VH list (the list of antennas in the VE7BQH Antenna Performance Tables, see sidebar) is 144.1 MHz and the bandwidth of each antenna is measured between 144 MHz and 145 MHz, the potential issue of the antenna's performance shifting within or even outside of its operating range is plain to see in Figure 15.31.

Often, the presented usable bandwidth is simply specified as the frequencies between which SWR is below a certain threshold (1.5:1 for example) rather than an average of all performance parameters over a given range. When correctly optimized, a good Yagi will have characteristics similar to a bandpass filter (BPF) in terms of performance with stable and consistent performance up to several hundred kHz (at VHF) or several MHz (at UHF) on either side of its center frequency. It's not just a nice flat SWR curve over a good range — gain and F/R will remain fairly constant, too.

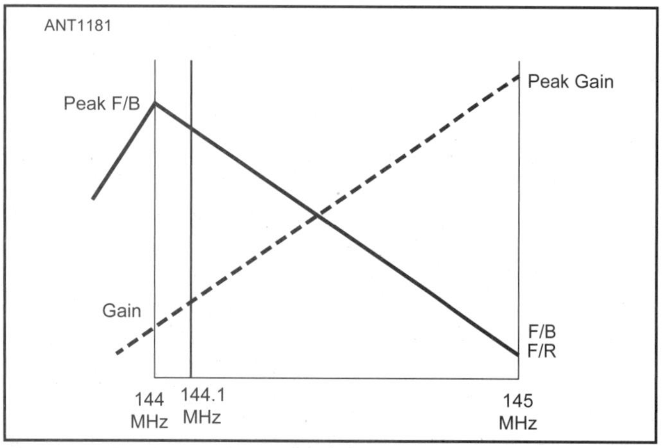

Figure 15.28 — Hypothetical performance of a typical Yagi across the 2 meter weak-signal band.

What stands out clearly in Figure 15.31 is the best F/B (and/or F/R) and best forward gain are typically at opposite ends of the bandwidth of the antenna. Gain is highest at the top of this bandwidth (naturally) because of the increasing boom length (in terms of λ). F/B and F/R drop off very quickly in the same direction, usually because the Yagi is too long for the number of elements the modeler has selected for this given boom length, or the modeler has optimized for an exceedingly long boom length. In that case the Yagi cannot be optimized for a balance of gain and F/B (F/R) across the desired range. This "ski sloping" of performance parameters in opposite directions is very common and often the reason why gain and F/B figures are quoted as being "peak gain, peak F/B."

In Figure 15.31, the vertical line denotes the performance of this hypothetical antenna at 144.1 MHz and the corresponding gain and F/B results. Shifting frequency up and down just 50 kHz or so will show very different gain – F/B combinations which will result in a large variation in antenna temperature and G/T as well. Furthermore, it is important to note how close the center of operation (144.1 MHz) is to the band edge. Taking into account the desired BPF-type characteristics, the center of activity for any 144 MHz Yagi should more likely be focused around 144.300 MHz if modes other than just EME will be practiced by the end user. It would not take too much for narrower-band antennas to move well out of their peak performance characteristic range in real-world conditions (wet weather, ice, other antennas close by, and so on) if they were optimized between 144 and 145 MHz and were being used at 144.100 MHz. While the focus of the VH list is G/T performance at 144.1 MHz for EME applications, the comparison of G/T at three points (perhaps 144.0, 144.1 and 144.2 MHz) may give a much more accurate indication as to what the user might expect for day-to-day or contest use.

Because performance tends to fall off toward the edge of an antenna's design bandwidth, optimizing should be performed with 144.300 MHz, for example, as the true center of operation with a guided bandwidth of 500 kHz either side of that point (143.800 to 144.800 MHz). Doing this ensures very constant performance either side of the center frequency rather than perhaps experiencing the typical tail-off of performance at the band edges as discussed above. This leads to less impressive table values across 144-145 MHz but a more stable design to be used in varying weather conditions. An antenna which yields the most consistent results across a range centered on the most likely frequencies of use is likely to be the most stable for day to day use and/or use in extreme environments and not just for EME applications either!

Optimizing to Minimize Real-World Noise

The collection and pick-up of real world noise is dependent on the lack of side lobes in the elevation (El) plane. If lobes in the El plane are prominent and down-facing, regardless of how quiet a location is believed to be, higher levels of noise will be received in certain directions (direction of the shack and/or house, for example) than if any such lobes were more highly suppressed. When measuring and comparing G/T, rear-facing lobes in back of the 90°-270° line are what are considered for calculation and measurement. (See the sidebar Gain/Noise Temperature (G/T).) However, real-world operation by hams requires us to pay equal consideration to more forward and down facing lobes in this plane. At this point optimization starts to become more complicated — generally speaking, optimizing on one band then scaling to another will not show the same improvements in performance.

Different considerations and attributes must be taken into account during the design phase when switching from designing a Yagi on one band and then looking to repeat the results on another band. Quiet Yagis are very much band-specific — note that what is being discussed here is relevant only when optimizing on 144 MHz.

Take a look at **Figure 15.29** and the design considerations taken in order to not just show a good G/T figure (assume G/T is based on T_a unless noted otherwise), but to also reduce the likelihood of man-made noise pick-up to an absolute minimum from beneath the antenna within its near-field. This particular antenna used a closed-loop driven element to allow direct-feed (50 Ω feed point impedance) and lower noise pickup.

Within Figure 15.32 are two bars marked T1 and T2. T1 shows a sharp taper from the back towards the front. This level of taper right at the back of the antenna and forward is important to ensure good G/T results as tighter suppression from the 90° line backward will yield much better results. However, to continue this level of taper for the first side lobes would be disastrous for near-field noise pick-up. From having very wide side lobes in the azimuth (Az) plane (not much more than 12 dB below the main lobe) additional noise sources could be detected and interfere with signals in the desired capture direction from noise sources either side of center. The ability for this antenna to hear weak signals (real-world) would be greatly reduced by having what in effect would be three forward lobes in both planes, all receiving whatever was beneath or either side of the antenna. It is for this reason that an amount of suppression has been applied to the first lobe to arrive at the best compromise between the overall size of the "rear bubble" and outright forward gain.

The challenge is to achieve the best from the antenna in terms of performance while at the same time, keeping the El pattern as clean as possible. During optimization, GØKSC uses a maximum limit or "marker" for side lobes. Basically, this is a parameter that can be controlled during software optimization that is not so easily achieved when optimizing manually. Some software packages allow the starting point at which F/R is measured (normally 90°) to be moved forward towards the forward lobe. The advantage of so doing is this starting point can be moved forward until it covers the angle from the forward lobe where forward lobes would start to increase in size. While this sounds simple, in practice, getting excellent results take a lot of time and work.

Antennas of typical length up to around six elements tend not to produce side lobes of any consequence, at least not in the Az plane. For weak signal and EME work, the desire is to have much longer antennas than six elements and normally they would have booms of multiple wavelengths. If uncontrolled, the natural course of gain-focused optimization would see very large side lobes at large angles away from the center of the forward lobe upon optimization completion. Simply moving the starting point (within software) further forward than the point of these lobes will result in two side-effects: First, a reduction in forward gain and the second, a "blown" rear bubble with odd small lobes or spikes that cause F/R to be much worse than the starting point.

As the boom gets longer, the forward lobe becomes narrower and in-turn, the side lobes get closer to one another either side of the main forward lobe but exactly how close they sit to the main lobe can be controlled, to a point.

In order to achieve the best overall gain results and to ensure the rear bubble can be minimized, an antenna is best optimized (assuming computer optimization now) with F/B parameters being set just behind the Az side lobe position as in **Figure 15.30**. For example, if the side lobes on a subject antenna are at 50°, the F/B point would be set at 55°. The antenna can then be optimized for bandwidth and gain several times until no further improvements can be made. (At 144 MHz and higher, optimization should be performed in 1° increments.)

At this point, move the optimization point from 55° to 54° and re-optimize then 53° then 52° and so on. Improvements should be seen in terms of gain and bandwidth by doing this method of controlling the elevation lobes in addition to (hopefully) pushing the side lobes closer to the main lobes resulting in less significance or negative consequences. (For best results, computer optimization/controlling of side lobes should only be done in the El plane, so doing will see the Az lobes kept in-check automatically. The same does not happen in reverse should you optimize in the Az plane.)

Each time the optimization results should be saved individually as there will become a point where the gain starts to drop and the rear bubble starts to "blow" (rear lobes growing quickly with further changes). At this point you know you are trying to compress the side lobes too tightly and you should go back to your last improvement optimization for your best usable result. The whole optimization process is much more detailed than the explanation given in these few lines but at least now an understanding of the levels of attention and time taken to optimize this antenna can be perhaps much more appreciated.

OWA YAGIS

This set of long-boom OWA Yagis was designed by Justin Johnson, GØKSC, of Innovantennas (**innovantennas.com**) for the *Antenna Book*. Designs for 7 through 12-element Yagis are provided. These are very high gain antennas with a narrow beamwidth. They are suitable for DXing and EME operation where high gain and low noise are important.

The *EZNEC* model for each antenna is also included in the online material. The elements are specified with metric (mm) measurements, but the diameters are chosen to match the inch-based telescoping tubing sizes available in North America. (See the **Antenna Materials and Construction** chapter.)

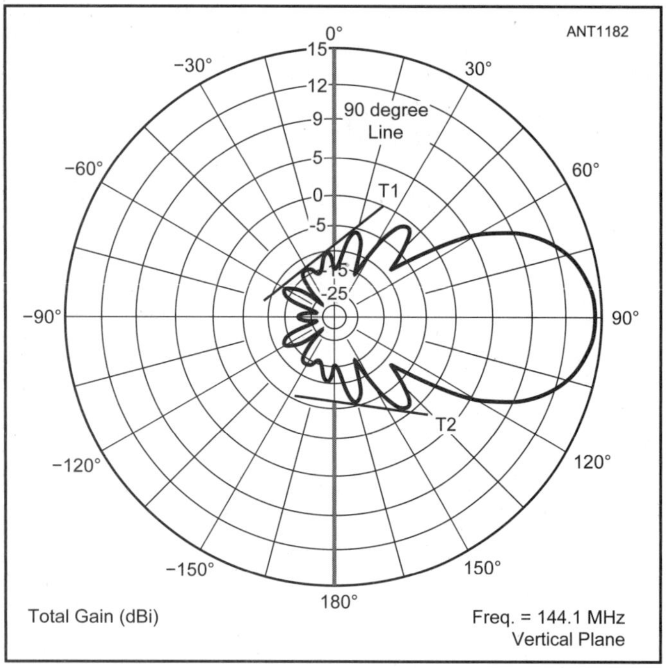

Figure 15.29 — Elevation plot of a 9 element Yagi showing the side lobe taper both in the rear hemisphere (T1) and between the rear hemisphere and the main lobe (T2).

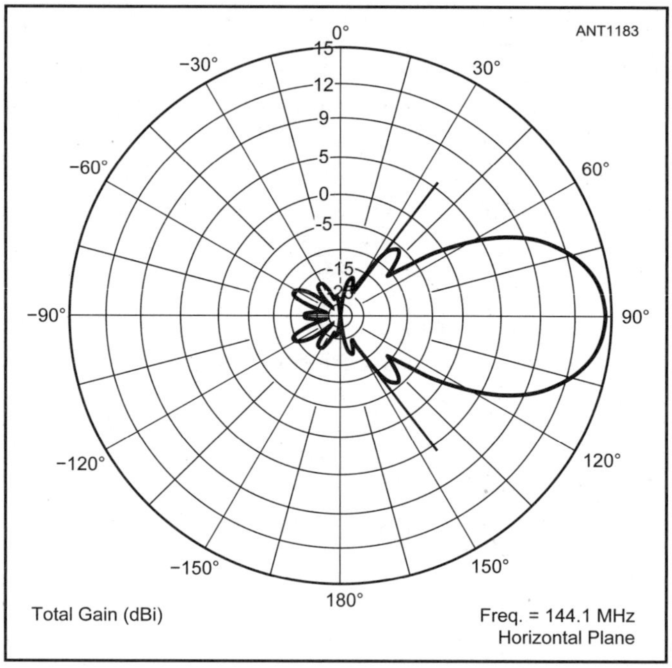

Figure 15.30 — Same elevation plot as in Figure 15.41 showing where optimization limits can be placed to move side lobes closer to the main lobe. This helps minimize pickup of noise from nearby sources and reduces in-band interference.

Use 0.049-inch or 0.058-inch wall thickness tubing as specified in Table 10.3. Lengths are given in the model's Wires table in millimeters (0.001-meter) increments. This represents an excellent compromise between accuracy of the model and specifying available materials for North American readers.

PROJECT: HIGH-PERFORMANCE LFA AND OWL VHF/UHF YAGI DESIGNS

The antenna designs by GØKSC and listed in **Table 15.11** are new designs not previously published or made available as products. Justin is a primary designer of HF, VHF, and UHF antennas for InnovAntennas (**innovantennas.com**). He has published a number of articles featuring innovative and high-performance antennas, including discussions of what makes a design successful, issues for competitive and high-performance antennas, and helpful information on the construction details for these designs. Model files and sample radiation patterns for all of the Yagis are available with this book's online content but require *EZNEC PRO/4* to reproduce the gain and other performance specifications listed.

The Stauff clamps (**us.stauff.com**) recommended for these designs are industrial pipe clamps designed for rugged, outdoor service. The standard series part numbers (DIN 3015, Part 1) in **Table 15.12** are sufficiently rated for these designs. Stauff clamps are easiest to use with booms of square tubing although adapters for round booms are available.

Constructing the Loop Driven Element

The loop driven element may be unfamiliar. GØKSC has created a detailed description of the construction process at **g0ksc.co.uk/intro-lfa/making-the-lfa-loop.html** which is also available as a PDF file included with this book's online content. The following set of instructions are summarized from that document.

Table 15.11
High-Performance LFA and OWL Yagis

Freq (MHz)	*No. Elements*	*Boom Length*	*Peak Gain) (dBi)*	*Peak F/B (dB)*	*E-plane Beamwidth (degrees)*	*H-plane Beamwidth (degrees)*
50	4	12' 8" (3.86 m)	10.6	31.9	42	67
144	9	17' 3" (5.26 m)	14.8	24.7	34	37
144	14	32' 4" (9.86 m)	17.0	33.0	27	29
222	10	11' 5" (3.48 m)	14.5	34.6	37	41
222	19	29' 2" (8.88 m)	18.1	39.7	24	25
432	10	6' 7" (2.01 m)	14.5	25.6	36	40
432	20	17' 0" (5.18 m)	18.6	37.0	23	24

Note: All parameters are free-space

Table 15.12
Stauff Clamps

Standard Series (DIN 3015-1)

¼ in elements:	106,4APP (1 per element)
½ in loop:	212,7PP (3 per loop - 1 for DE1, 2 for DE2)
Angled weld plate	WSP 1A U W1 (2 per loop at DE2)

-PP part numbers are polypropylene material (replace with –AL for aluminum)

Available from **us.stauff.com**

Figure 15.30 shows the orientation of the loop on the boom with the feed point located on the forward side. **Figure 15.31** shows the overall construction and adjustment of the LFA Yagi's loop driven element. LFA driven elements are constructed with straight sections (DE1 and DE2, parallel to the other elements) and side sections of slightly smaller diameter that are adjustable "trombone-style" by sliding in and out of the straight sections. This allows SWR to be adjusted without a separate impedance-matching structure and to compensate for feed point construction variations.

Once the SWR is satisfactory, the sliding sections are secured to the straight sections with a stainless-steel screw (be sure to use anti-corrosion compound), an aluminum rivet, or a hose clamp (the straight section would require a short slot to allow compression by the clamp). The screw and rivet are convenient but have limited contact area. Spot welding the tubing sections together also works very well. If brass tubing is used, the sliding and fixed sections should be soldered together.

The tubing for DE1 and DE2 should be cut 50 mm short of the model's full dipole length in the tables. Measure 30 mm from the end of the remaining straight ½ inch section to the inside of the loop end as in the figure. This additional width provides a correction for the radius at the corners of the loop. The additional 5 mm of width remains fairly constant on all bands since the radius becomes more like a 90° bend at lower frequencies as modeled. (This assumes use of the same bending tool to create all bends.) Absolute accuracy here is not essential; this is a starting point from where the antenna is adjusted for best SWR.

After cutting and deburring the loop's straight sections, cut the side section tubing such that it has approximately 80 mm of extra length beyond the difference between the DE1 and DE2 positions. For example, if the positions of DE1 and DE2 are 0.128 m and 0.235 m, respectively, cut the side section tubing to be (0.235 – 0.128) + 0.080 = 0.107 + 0.080 = 0.187 m long. Use an automotive brake line bending tool (see the PDF instructions for photographs) to bend approximately 40 mm of the section length at a right angle. Insert the bent section into either the DE1 section. Bend the other end of the side section tubing so that the DE2 section is 0.107 m from DE1. Repeat for the remaining side section.

Cut the DE2 section to leave a feed point gap of approximately 10 mm. To support the loop at the feed point (see **Figure 15.32A**), insert a short section of fiberglass, polycarbonate, or Teflon rod approximately 25 mm longer than the gap on each side. Drill through the element and supporting rod. Use stainless steel #8 hardware to hold the element and supporting rod together and create attachment points for the feed line. Use Stauff clamps with angled mounting plates as in Figure 15.35 to support the feed point assembly.

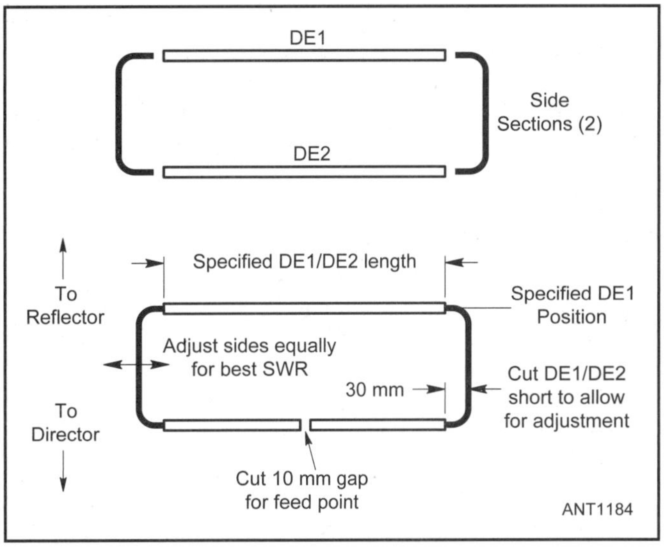

Figure 15.31 — Construction of the LFA loop driven-element showing the sliding end sections and how loop dimensions are measured.

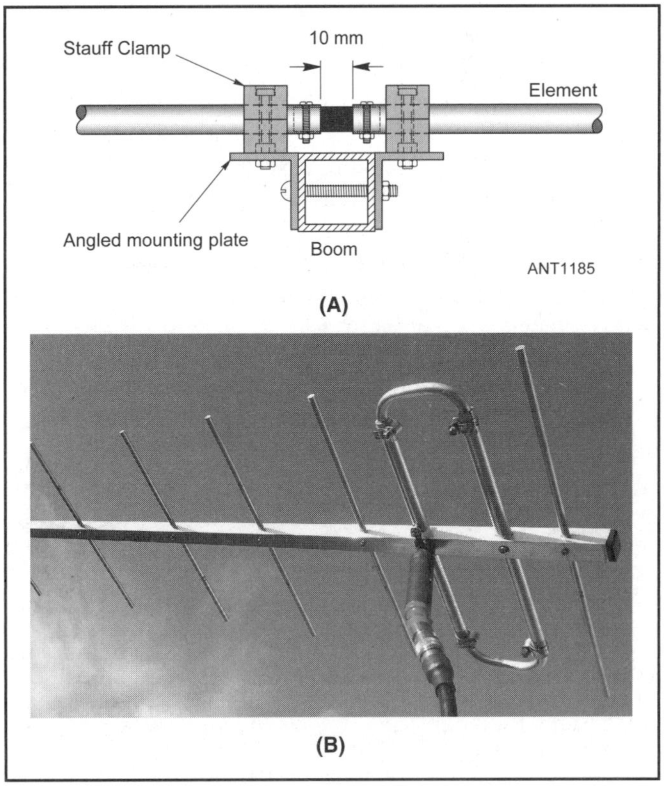

Figure 15.32 — Figure A illustrates mounting the driven element feed point on a square boom using Stauff clamps and angled mounting plate. At B, the driven element loop is mounted using through-the-boom construction.

Note that the exact center of the loop driven element opposite the feed point is at an RF-neutral point and can be connected directly to the boom by using an aluminum clamp. (Substitute –AL for –PP in the Stauff clamp part number or fabricate your own mounting bracket.) Doing so will place the driven element at dc ground for static protection and it will also cause the driven element impedance to increase rapidly away from the design frequency.

In Figure 15.32B, the driven element loop for a 10-element 432 MHz LFA Yagi is shown with a through-the-boom construction option that eliminates the need for extra clamps with the smaller driven element.

Following construction, temporarily mount the beam at least 1 wavelength above ground or pointed at the sky with the reflector at least ½ wavelength above ground, Adjust each of the loop sliding sections in equal increments starting from a symmetrical position until SWR is satisfactory. Following adjustment, secure the sliding sections to the fixed sections as described above.

50 MHZ LFA YAGI

The 4-element design in **Table 15.13** is an illustration of what can be achieved by careful optimization on a fairly short boom (12 feet 8 inches). The design is well suited for stacking and can be handled by small rotators. It is ideal for portable and rover station use as well as at a home station.

The reflector and both directors have three segments of tubing per half-element — one center segment and a pair of segments on each half-element. The driven element loop's DE1 and DE2 section both have two segments per half-element. Element lengths assume a conductive boom with insulated elements.

144 MHZ OWL YAGIS

Common dimensions and notes for the high-performance 144, 222, and 432 MHz Yagis are listed in **Table 15.14**. Two designs are presented in this section — a 9-element in **Table 15.15** and a 14-element antenna in **Table 15.16**. Performance is specified at 144.2 MHz. The E-plane pattern for the 14-element antenna is shown in **Figure 15.33**.

Element lengths assume a conductive 1.25 inch square boom with insulated elements. If a non-conductive boom is used, subtract 1 mm from all element lengths. If a 1.5 inch square conductive boom is used, add 1 mm to all element lengths.

A folded-dipole driven element is used on both antennas. Construction is similar to that of the LFA loop driven-element. Two methods of mounting the driven element are shown in **Figure 15.34**. The feed point's insulating rod is mounted through a short mounting section of boom material which is, in turn, attached to the top of the main boom. The feed point thus straddles the mounting section — be sure to minimize coax-to-feed point leads lengths.

As with the LFA driven element, the point on the folded dipole directly opposite the feed point is a neutral point at RF and can be attached directly to the boom as shown in the figure's front view. The same caution applies regarding rapid impedance change away from the design frequency. An insulating support such as a Stauff clamp can be used, as well.

The boom is assumed to be made from 1.25 inch square tubing. If a ¾ inch square boom is used, an under-boom sup-

Table 15.14
Common Dimensions and Notes for the High-Performance 144, 222, and 432 MHz Yagis

Boom is 1.25" square aluminum unless otherwise specified
Element diameter is ¼" unless otherwise specified
DE1, DE2 diameter ½" (sliding sections are ⅜" diameter)

Note 1– End of boom is zero (0) reference.
Note 2 – DE1 position dimension is the centerline of the rear-most loop tubing
Note 3 – DE1 and DE2 width are the outside edge of the loop.

Table 15.13
4-element 50 MHz LFA Yagi

Peak Gain: 10.6 dBi @ 50.150 MHz
Peak F/B: 31.9 dB @ 50.150 MHz
Beamwidth (E-plane): 42 dB @ 50.150 MHz
Beamwidth (H-plane): 67 dB @ 50.150 MHz
SWR: Below 1.3.1 from 50 MHz to 50.400 MHz
Note: All parameters are free-space

Half-element dimensions and placement (lengths are for half elements)

	Element	*----Section 1 (Middle)----*		*---------Section 2---------*		*--------Section 3--------*	
	Position (m)	*OD (in/mm)*	*Length (m)*	*OD (in/mm)*	*Length (m)*	*OD (in/mm)*	*Length (m)*
Reflector	0.030 (1)	⅝ / 16	0.415	½ / 13	0.315	⅜ / 10	0.788
DE1 (loop)	0.694	⅝ / 16	0.415	½ / 13	0.84 (2)		
DE2 (loop)	1.157	⅝ / 16	0.415	½ / 13	0.84 (2)		
D1	2.213	⅝ / 16	0.415	½ / 13	0.315	⅜ / 10	0.674
D2	3.963	⅝ / 16	0.415	½ / 13	0.84	⅜ / 10	0.610

Note 1— End of boom is zero (0) reference.
Note 2 —The ends of DE1 and DE2 are connected together with ⅜ inch / 10 mm tube.

Table 15.15
9-element 144 MHz OWL Yagi

Gain:	14.8 dBi
SWR:	Less than 1.1:1
F/B:	24.7 dB
Beamwidth (E-plane):	34 degrees
Beamwidth (H-plane):	37 degrees

Performance specified at 144.2 MHz
Note: All parameters are free-space

Element	*Element Position (m)*	*Half-Element Length (m)*	*Element Length (m)*
REF	0.030	0.514	1.028
DE (Note)	0.1625	0.4765	0.953
DIR1	0.453	0.4705	0.941
DIR2	1.009	0.455	0.910
DIR3	1.7275	0.444	0.888
DIR4	2.533	0.437	0.874
DIR5	3.358	0.432	0.864
DIR6	4.222	0.427	0.854
DIR7	4.9685	0.429	0.858

Note: All elements are ½" diameter
Note: DE is 0.953 m wide and 0.026 m high, measured on outside edges

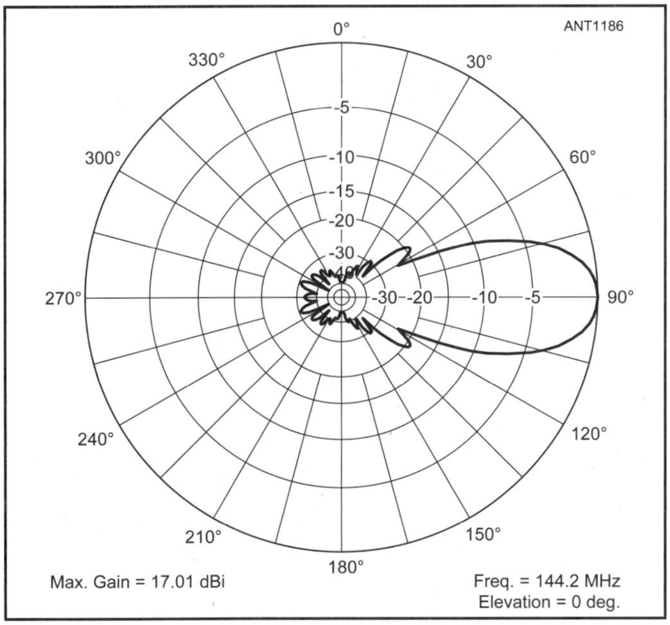

Figure 15.33 — E-plane pattern, 14-element 144 MHz LFA Yagi.

port will be required as in **Figure 15.35**. Alternatively, boom guying could also be used.

222 MHZ LFA YAGIS

Two designs are presented in this section — a 10-element in **Table 15.17** and a 19-element antenna in **Table 15.18**. Performance is specified at 222.1 MHz. The E-plane pattern for the 19-element antenna is shown in **Figure 15.36**.

See the notes on constructing the LFA driven element above. The 19-element antenna will require boom guying or an under-boom as in Figure 15.35.

Table 15.16
14-element 144 MHz OWL Yagi

Gain:	17.0 dBi
SWR:	Less than 1.1:1
F/B:	33.0 dB
Beamwidth (E-plane):	27 degrees
Beamwidth (H-plane):	29 degrees

Performance specified at 144.2 MHz
Note: All parameters are free-space

Element	*Element Position (m)*	*Half-Element Length (m)*	*Element Length (m)*
REF	0.030	0.5115	1.023
DE (Note)	0.253	0.469	0.938
DIR1	0.5785	0.4805	0.961
DIR2	1.156	0.4665	0.933
DIR3	1.8525	0.457	0.914
DIR4	2.686	0.4495	0.899
DIR5	3.526	0.4435	0.887
DIR6	4.4265	0.4395	0.879
DIR7	5.3365	0.436	0.872
DIR8	6.254	0.433	0.866
DIR9	7.1735	0.4295	0.859
DIR10	8.108	0.425	0.850
DIR11	9.060	0.416	0.832
DIR12	9.8625	0.427	0.854

Note: All elements are ½" diameter
Note: DE is 0.948 m wide and 0.026 m high, measured on outside edges

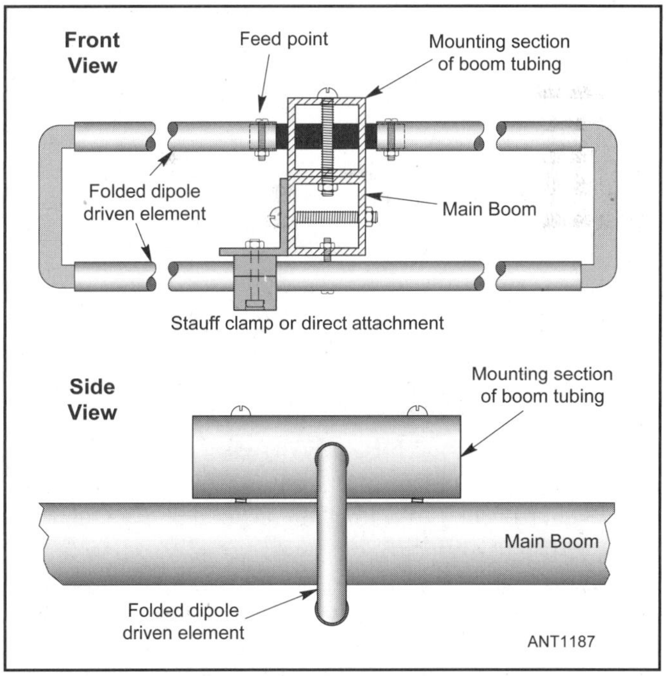

Figure 15.34 — Construction and mounting of an OWL Yagi's loop driven-element. The plane of the loop is perpendicular to the boom.

Table 15.17
10-element 222 MHz LFA Yagi

Gain: 14.5 dBi
SWR: Less than 1.1:1
F/B: 34.6 dB
Beamwidth (E-plane): 37 degrees
Beamwidth (H-plane): 41 degrees
Performance specified at 222.1 MHz
Note: All parameters are free-space

Element	*Element Position (m)*	*Half-Element Length (m)*	*Element Length (m)*
REF	0.030	0.3315	0.6630
DE1 (loop)	0.128	0.233	0.566
DE2 (loop)	0.235	0.233	0.233
DIR1	0.390	0.3075	0.6150
DIR2	0.626	0.292	0.584
DIR4	1.316	0.289	0.578
DIR5	1.819	0.2835	0.567
DIR6	2.358	0.277	0.554
DIR7	2.939	0.2675	0.535
DIR8	3.455	0.2645	0.529

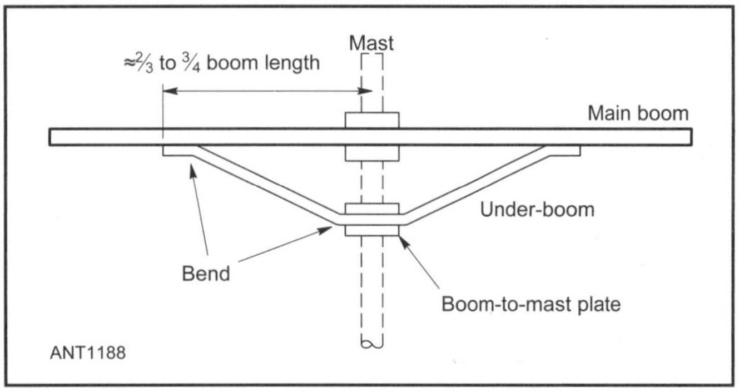

Figure 15.35 — Use of an under-boom to support the long-boom Yagis. The same material is used for both the boom and under-boom. Alternatively, boom guying can be employed.

Element lengths assume a conductive boom with insulated elements. If a non-conductive boom is used, subtract 1 mm from all element lengths.

432 MHZ LFA YAGIS

Two designs are presented in this section — a 10-element broadband LFA in **Table 15.19** and a 20-element antenna in **Table 15.20**. Performance is specified at 432.1 MHz.

The broadband 10-element design provides a flat, low SWR across a 6 MHz bandwidth as shown in **Figure 15.37**. The broad-banded nature of this antenna makes it more accepting of measurement variations in both boom and element lengths.

The 20-element design is optimized for use in stacked arrays, allowing some forward side lobes to appear in exchange for a highly suppressed rear bubble. The forward side lobes are kept close to the main lobe, however, and elevation plane lobes are highly suppressed, as well. As a result, when stacked with the correct separation, no odd "spike-lobes" should appear and the pattern should remain clear. E- and H-plane patterns for the 20-element antenna are shown in **Figures 15.38** and **15.39**.

Table 15.18
19-element 222 MHz LFA Yagi

Peak Gain: 18.1 dBi
SWR: Less than 1.1:1
F/B: 39.7 dB
Beamwidth (E-plane): 24 degrees
Beamwidth (H-plane): 25 degrees
Performance specified at 222.1 MHz
Note: All parameters are free-space

Element	*Element Position (m)*	*Half-Element Length (m)*	*Element Length (m)*
REF	0.030	0.3325	0.665
DE1 (loop)	0.145	0.285	0.570
DE2 (loop)	0.251	0.285	0.285
DIR1	0.411	0.3095	0.619
DIR2	0.676	0.288	0.576
DIR3	0.902	0.2945	0.589
DIR4	1.320	0.2925	0.585
DIR5	1.836	0.2885	0.577
DIR6	2.380	0.285	0.570
DIR7	2.946	0.282	0.564
DIR8	3.536	0.280	0.560
DIR9	4.123	0.2775	0.555
DIR10	4.725	0.2755	0.551
DIR11	5.330	0.273	0.546
DIR12	5.940	0.2715	0.543
DIR13	6.5415	0.2705	0.541
DIR14	7.1385	0.2685	0.537
DIR15	7.7255	0.266	0.532
DIR16	8.3105	0.2545	0.509
DIR17	8.8545	0.2505	0.501

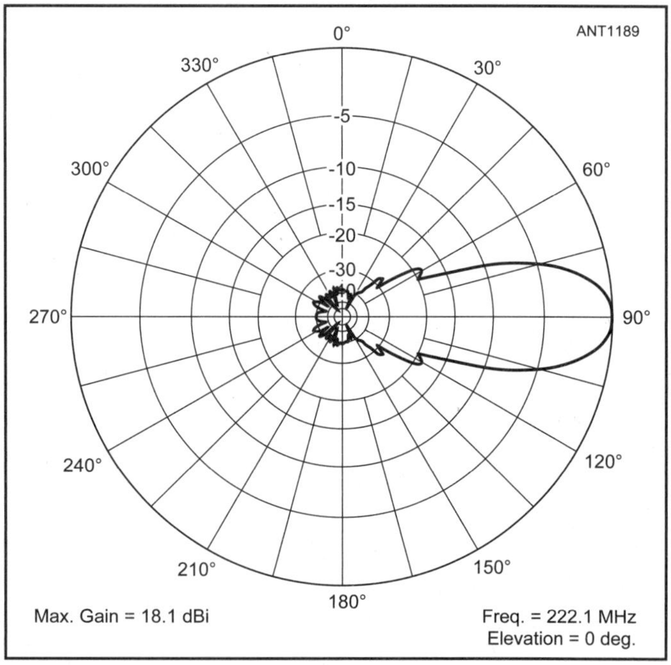

Figure 15.36 — E-plane pattern, 19-element 222 MHz LFA Yagi.

See the notes on constructing the LFA driven element above. All element lengths are based on a metal boom. If a non-conducting boom, such as fiberglass, is used, subtract 1.5 mm from all element lengths.

Table 15.19

10-element 432 MHz LFA Yagi

Peak Gain: 14.5 dBi
SWR: Less than 1.1:1
F/B: 25.6 dB
Beamwidth (E-plane): 36 degrees
Beamwidth (H-plane): 40 degrees
Performance specified at 432.1 MHz
Note: All parameters are free-space

Element	*Element Position (m)*	*Half-Element Length (m)*	*Element Length (m)*
REF	0.030	0.1685	0.337
DE1 (loop)	0.078	0.150	0.300
DE2 (loop)	0.1495	0.150	0.300
DIR1	0.212	0.157	0.314
DIR2	0.3425	0.150	0.300
DIR3	0.494	0.146	0.292
DIR4	0.6845	0.1445	0.289
DIR5	0.9215	0.143	0.286
DIR6	1.1785	0.1405	0.281
DIR7	1.470	0.1365	0.273
DIR8	1.716	0.1355	0.271

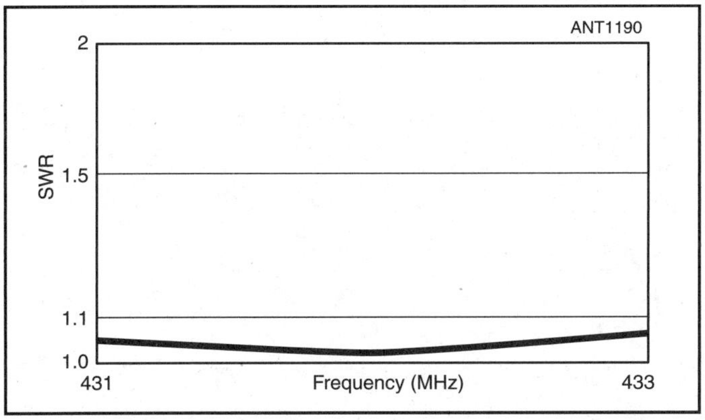

Figure 15.37 — SWR versus frequency, 10-element 432 MHz LFA Yagi.

Both antennas can be constructed using Stauff clamps and a 1.25 inch square boom as for the 144 and 222 MHz Yagis.

For the 10-element antenna, a much lighter version (3 lbs versus 6 lbs) with less wind load can be constructed using a ¾ inch square boom and mounting the elements through the boom, secured by a stainless steel screw. The loop driven element is also mounted through the boom, requiring a wider feed point gap. The non-conductive rod is extended through the boom as shown in Figure 15.33B. The lighter version of the antenna can be mounted to the mast using a single U-bolt through the boom.

For the 20-element antenna, boom guys are required if the 1.25 inch square boom and Stauff clamps are used for construction. If the ¾ inch square boom technique is used, an under-boom is required as in Figure 15.35.

Table 15.20

20-element 432 MHz LFA Yagi

Peak Gain: 18.6 dBi
SWR: Less than 1.1:1
F/B: 37.0 dB
Beamwidth (E-plane): 23 degrees
Beamwidth (H-plane): 24 degrees
Performance specified at 432.1 MHz
Note: All parameters are free-space

Element	*Element Position (m)*	*Half-Element Length (m)*	*Element Length (m)*
REF	0.030	0.167	0.334
DE1 (loop)	0.117	0.153	0.306
DE2 (loop)	0.189	0.153	0.306
DIR1	0.2445	0.15775	0.3155
DIR2	0.4015	0.151	0.302
DIR3	0.556	0.14525	0.2905
DIR4	0.7305	0.14425	0.2885
DIR5	0.959	0.14325	0.2865
DIR6	1.2275	0.14125	0.2825
DIR7	1.5135	0.1395	0.2790
DIR8	1.814	0.138	0.276
DIR9	2.120	0.1365	0.273
DIR10	2.4315	0.13525	0.2705
DIR11	2.750	0.13425	0.2685
DIR12	3.0655	0.13425	0.2685
DIR13	3.378	0.135	0.270
DIR14	3.682	0.13525	0.2705
DIR15	3.982	0.13425	0.2685
DIR16	4.2835	0.13075	0.2615
DIR17	4.598	0.12425	0.2485
DIR18	4.879	0.120	0.240

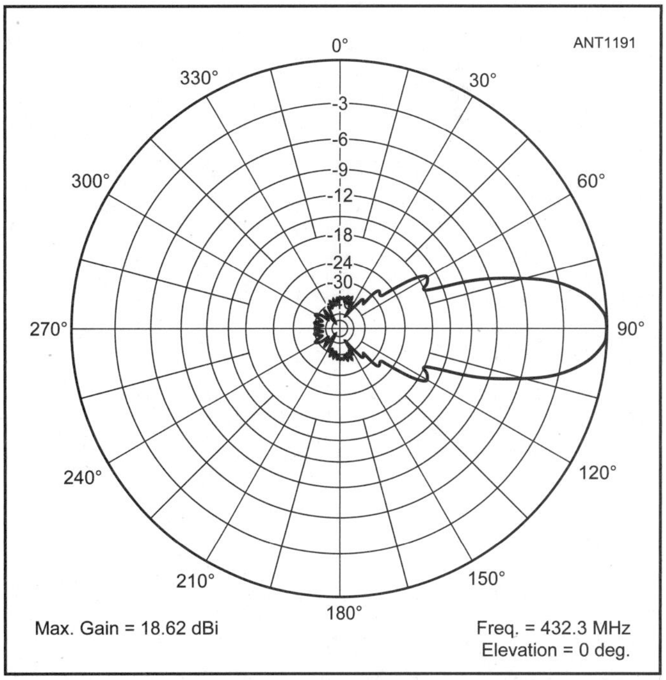

Figure 15.38 — E-plane pattern, 20-element 432 MHz LFA Yagi.

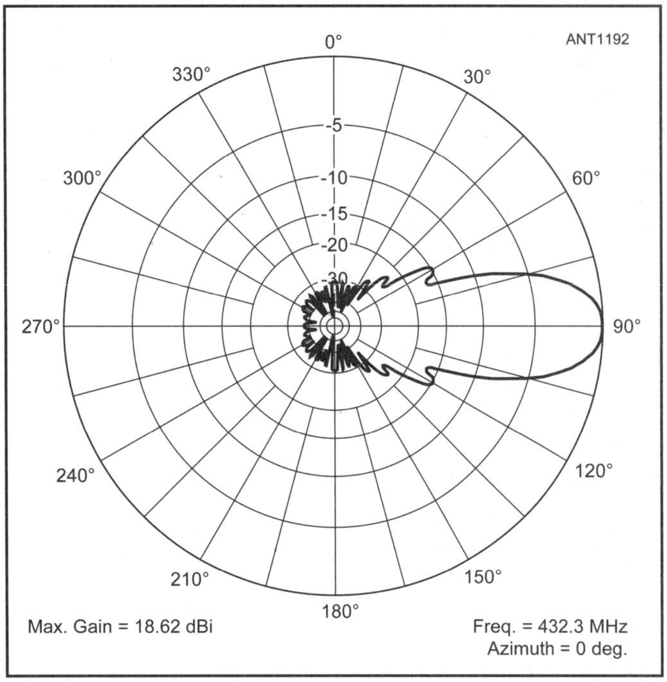

Figure 15.39 — H-plane pattern, 20-element 432 MHz LFA Yagi.

15.3.6 Quads For VHF

The quad antenna can be built with inexpensive materials, yet its performance is comparable to other arrays of its size. Adjustment for resonance and impedance matching can be accomplished readily.

Quads can be stacked horizontally and vertically to provide high gain, without sharply limiting frequency response. Quads can be mounted side by side or one above the other, or both, in the same general way as other beam antennas. Sets of driven elements can also be mounted in front of a screen reflector. The recommended spacing between adjacent element sides is 1⁄2 λ. Phasing and feed methods are similar to those employed with other antennas described in this chapter.

Parasitic elements ahead of the driven element work in a manner similar to those in a Yagi array. Closed loops can be used for directors by making them 5% shorter than the driven element. Spacings are similar to those for conventional Yagis. In an experimental model the reflector was spaced 0.25 λ and the director 0.15 λ. A square array using four 3-element bays worked extremely well.

Because of the small size of the quad at VHF and UHF, many of the mechanical issues associated with HF quads are no longer significant. PVC pipe, fiberglass rod, and wood are all acceptable materials for booms and spreaders.

Quad antennas are best suited for the 6-meter and 2-meter bands. They are very popular for portable and backpacking operation. A quad design for 144 MHz is presented below. See the **Portable Antennas** chapter for a 2-element, 6-meter quad design.

PROJECT: A 144-MHZ 4-ELEMENT QUAD

Element spacing for quad antennas found in the literature ranges from 0.14 λ to 0.25 λ. Factors such as the number of elements in the array and the parameters to be optimized (F/B ratio, forward gain, bandwidth, etc), determine the optimum element spacing within this range. The 4-element quad antenna described here was designed for portable use, so a compromise between these factors was chosen. This antenna, pictured in **Figure 15.40**, was designed and built by Philip D'Agostino, W1KSC.

Based on several experimentally determined correction factors related to the frequency of operation and the wire size, optimum design dimensions were found to be as follows.

Reflector length (ft) = 1046.8/fMHz

Driven element length (ft) = 985.5/fMHz

Directors (ft) = 937.3/fMHz

Cutting the loops for 146 MHz provides satisfactory performance across the entire 144-MHz band.

Figure 15.40 — The 4-element 144-MHz portable quad, assembled and ready for operation. Sections of clothes closet poles joined with pine strips make up the mast. (W1MPO photo)

MATERIALS

The quad was designed for quick and easy assembly and disassembly, as illustrated in **Figure 15.41**. Wood (clear trim pine) was chosen as the principal building material because of its light weight, low cost and ready availability. Pine is used for the boom and element supporting arms. Round wood clothes closet poles comprise the mast material. Strips connecting the mast sections are made of heavier pine trim. (See the previous section on Yagi Construction for more information about wood boom material.) Elements are made of #8 AWG aluminum wire. Plexiglas is used to support the feed point. **Table 15.21** lists the hardware and other parts needed to duplicate the quad.

CONSTRUCTION

The elements of the quad are assembled first. The mounting holes in the boom should be drilled to accommodate 1 1⁄2 inch #8 hardware. Measure and mark the locations where the holes are to be drilled in the element spreaders, **Figure 15.42**. Drill the holes in the spreaders just large enough to accept the #8 AWG wire elements. It is important to drill all the holes straight so the elements line up when the antenna is assembled.

Construction of the wire elements is easiest if the directors are made first. A handy jig for bending the elements can be made from a piece of 2 × 3-inch wood cut to the side length of the directors. It is best to start with about 82 inches of wire for each director. The excess can be cut off when the elements are completed. (The total length of each director is 77 inches.) Two bends should initially be made so the directors can be slipped into the spreaders before the remaining corners are bent. See **Figure 15.43**. Electrician's copper-wire clamps can be used to join the wires after the final bends are made, and they facilitate adjustment of element length. The reflector is made the same way as the directors, but the total length is 86 inches.

The driven element, total length 81 inches, requires special attention, as the feed attachment point needs to be adequately supported. An extra hole is drilled in the driven element spreader to support the feed point strut, as shown in **Figure 15.44**. A Plexiglas plate is used at the feed point to support the feed point hardware and the feed line. The feed point support strut should be epoxied to the spreader, and a wood screw used for extra mechanical strength.

For vertical polarization, locate the feed point in the center of one side of the driven element, as shown in Figure 15.44. Although this arrangement places the spreader supports at voltage maxima points on the four loop conductors, D'Agostino reports no adverse effects during operation. However, if the

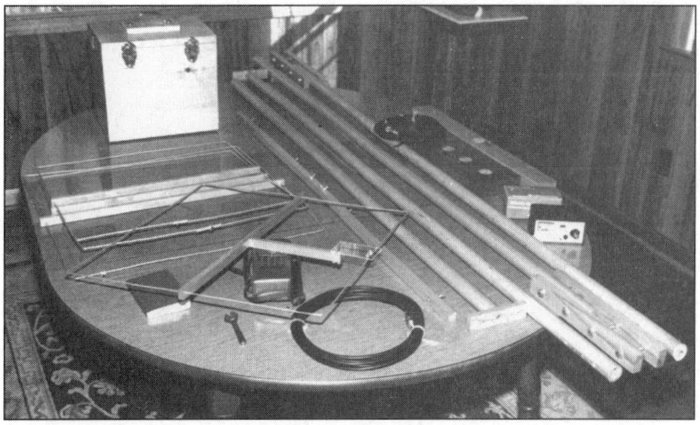

Figure 15.41 — The complete portable quad, broken down for travel. Visible in the foreground is the driven element. The pine box in the background is a carrying case for equipment and accessories. A hole in the lid accepts the mast, so the box doubles as a base for a short mast during portable operation. (W1MPO photo)

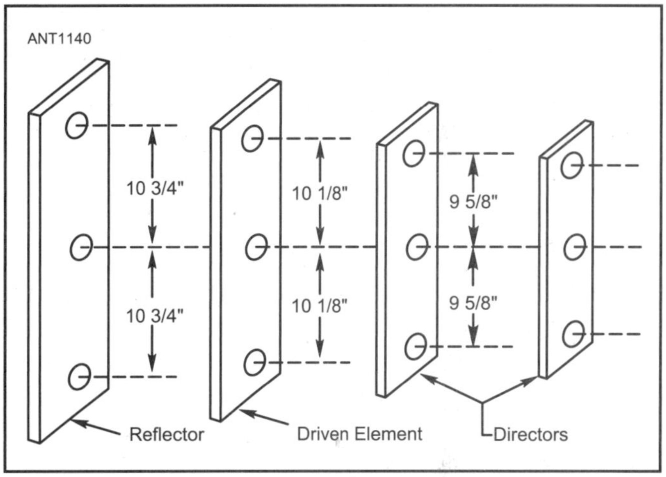

Figure 15.42 — Dimensions for the pine element spreaders for the 144-MHz 4-element quad.

Table 15.21
Parts List for the 144 MHz 4-element Quad

Boom: 3⁄4 × 3⁄4 × 48-inch pine
Driven element support (spreader): 1⁄2 × 3⁄4 × 21 1⁄4 inch pine
Driven element feed point strut: 1⁄2 × 3⁄4 × 7 1⁄2 inch pine
Reflector support (spreader): 1⁄2 × 3⁄4 × 22 1⁄2 inch pine
Director supports (spreaders): 1⁄2 × 3⁄4 × 20 1⁄4 inch pine, 2 req'd
Mast brackets: 3⁄4 × 1 1⁄2 × 12 inch heavy pine trim, 4 req'd
Boom to mast bracket: 1⁄2 × 1 5⁄8 × 5 inch pine
Element wire: Aluminum ground wire (Radio Shack no. 15-035)
Wire clamps: 1⁄4 inch electrician's copper or zinc plated steel clamps, 3 req'd

Boom hardware:
- 6 no. 8-32 × 1 1⁄2 inch stainless steel machine screws
- 6 no. 8-32 stainless steel wing nuts
- 12 no. 8 stainless steel washers

Mast hardware:
- 8 hex bolts, 1⁄4-20 × 3 1⁄2 inch
- 8 hex nuts, 1⁄4-20
- 16 flat washers

Mast material: 1 5⁄16 inch × 6 ft wood clothes closet poles, 3 req'd
Feed point support plate: 3 1⁄2 × 2 1⁄2 inch Plexiglas sheet
Wood preparation materials: Sandpaper, clear polyurethane, wax
Feed line: Low-loss 50 Ω feed line
Feed line terminals: Solder lugs for no. 8 or larger hardware, 2 req'd
Miscellaneous hardware: 4 small machine screws, nuts, washers; 2 flat-head wood screws

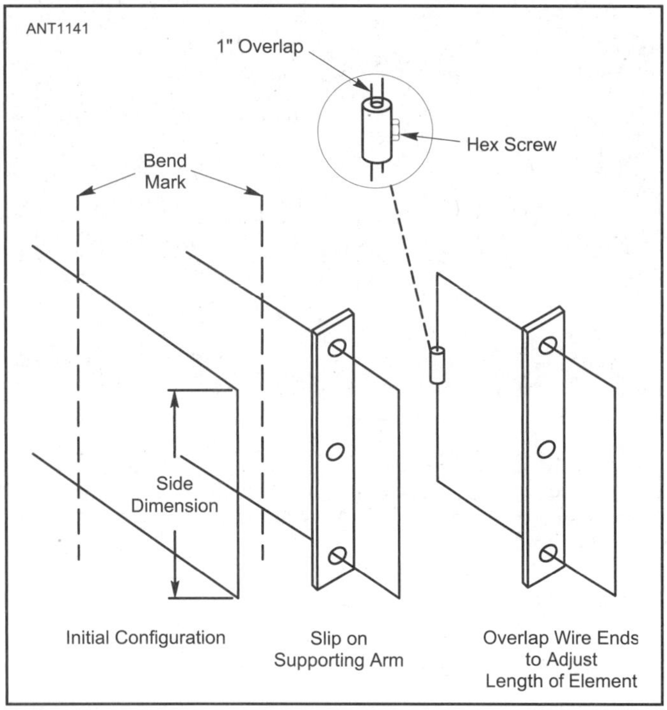

Figure 15.43 — Illustration showing how the aluminum element wires are bent. The adjustment clamp and its location are also shown.

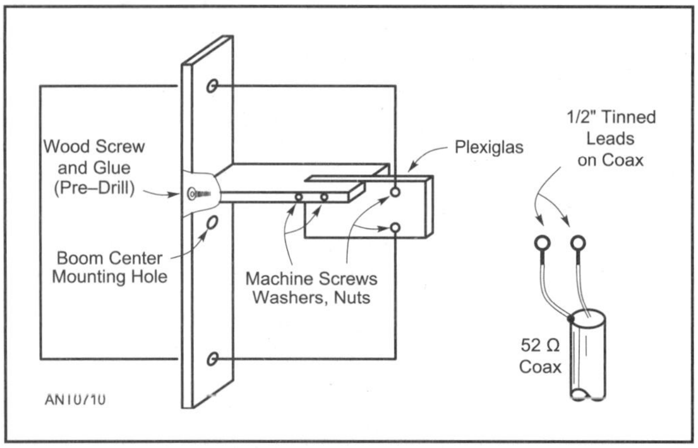

Figure 15.44 — Layout of the driven element of the 144 MHz quad. The leads of the coaxial cable should be stripped to 1⁄2 inch and solder lugs attached for easy connection and disconnection. See text regarding impedance at loop support points.

antenna is to be left exposed to the weather, the builder may wish to modify the design to provide support for the loops at current maxima points, such as shown in Figure 15.44. (The element of Figure 15.44 should be rotated 90° for horizontal polarization.)

Orient the driven element spreader so that it mounts properly on the boom when the antenna is assembled. Bend the driven element the same way as the reflector and directors, but do not leave any overlap at the feed point. The ends of the wires should be 3⁄4 inch apart where they mount on the Plexiglas plate. Leave enough excess that small loops can be bent in the wire for attachment to the coaxial feed line with stainless steel hardware.

Drill the boom as shown in **Figure 15.45**. It is a good idea to use hardware with wing nuts to secure the element spreaders to the boom. After the boom is drilled, clean all the wood parts with denatured alcohol, sand them, and give them two coats of glossy polyurethane. After the polyurethane dries, wax all the wooden parts.

The boom to mast attachment is made next. Square the ends of a 6-foot section of clothes closet pole (a miter box is useful for this). Drill the center holes in both the boom attachment piece and one end of the mast section (**Figure 15.46**). Make certain that the mast hole is smaller than the flat-head screw to be used to ensure a snug fit. Accurately drill the holes for attachment to the boom as shown in Figure 15.46.

Countersink the hole for the flat-head screw to provide a smooth surface for attachment to the boom. Apply epoxy cement to the surfaces and screw the boom attachment piece securely to the mast section. One 6-foot mast is used for attachment to the other mast sections.

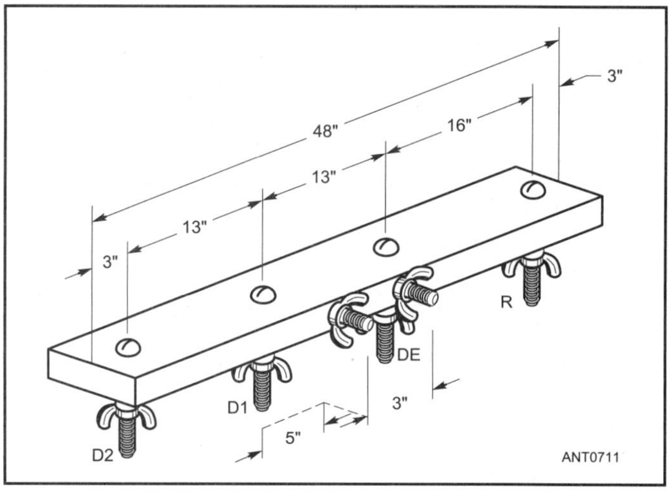

Figure 15.45 — Detail of the boom showing hole center locations and boom to mast connection points.

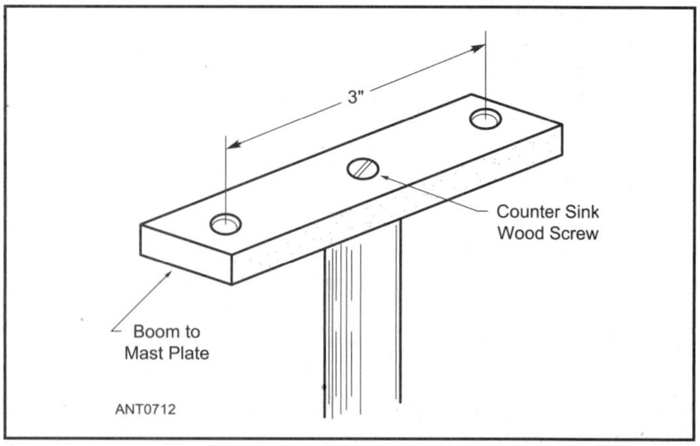

Figure 15.46 — Boom to mast plate for the 144-MHz quad. The screw hole in the center of the plate should be countersunk so the wood screw attaching it to the mast does not interfere with the fit of the boom.

Two additional 6-foot mast sections are prepared next. This brings the total mast height to 18 feet. It is important to square the ends of each pole so the mast stands straight when assembled. Mast-section connectors are made of pine as shown in **Figure 15.47**. Using 3 1⁄2 × 1⁄4-inch hex bolts, washers and nuts, sections may be attached as needed, for a total height of 6, 12, or 18 feet. Drill the holes in two connectors at a time. This ensures good alignment of the holes. A drill press is ideal for this job, but with care a hand drill can be used if necessary.

Line up two mast sections end to end, being careful that they are perfectly straight. Use the predrilled connectors to maintain pole straightness, and drill through the poles, one at a time. If good alignment is maintained, a straight 18-foot mast section can be made. Label the connectors and poles immediately so they are always assembled in the same order.

When assembling the antenna, install all the elements on the boom before attaching the feed line. Connect the coax to the screw connections on the driven element support plate and run the cable along the strut to the boom. From there, the cable should be routed directly to the mast and down. Assemble the mast sections to the desired height. The antenna provides good performance and has a reasonable SWR curve over the entire 144 MHz band (**Figure 15.48**).

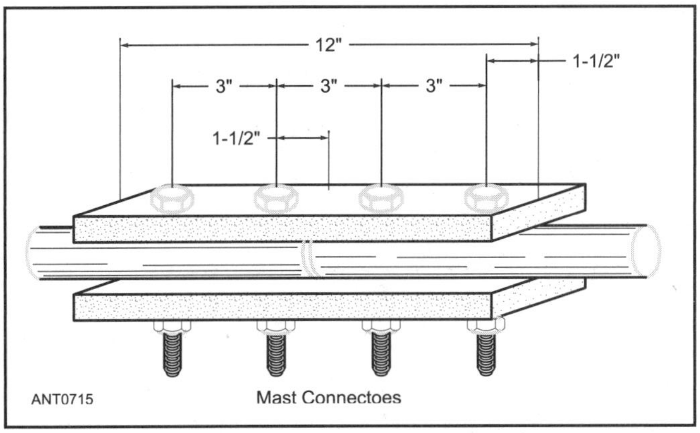

Figure 15.47 — Mast coupling connector details for the portable quad. The plates should be drilled two at a time to ensure the holes line up.

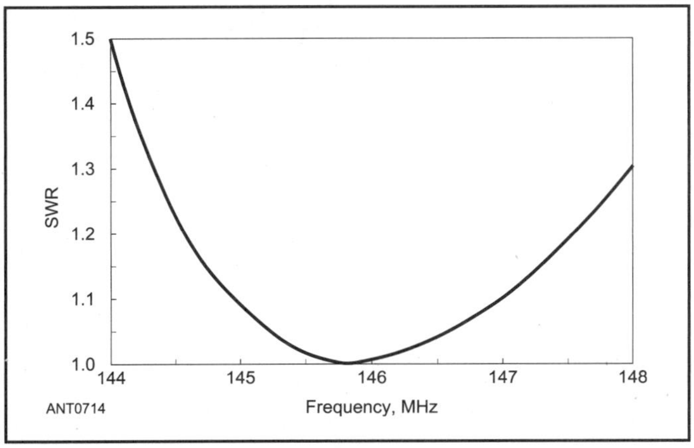

Figure 15.48 — Typical SWR curve for the 144-MHz portable quad. The large wire diameter and the quad design provide excellent bandwidth.

15.3.7 Loop Yagis

The loop Yagi fits into the quad family of antennas, as each element is a closed loop with a length of approximately 1 λ. Several versions are described, so the builder can choose the boom length and frequency coverage desired for the task at hand. Mike Walters, G3JVL, brought the original loop-Yagi design to the amateur community in the 1970s in the out-of-print RSGB *VHF/UHF Manual*. Since then, many versions have been developed with different loop and boom dimensions. G3JVL's *Loopquad* software is available online at **g3jvl.com/programPages/loopQuad.php** to design loop Yagis. Along with the 1296-MHz version described below construction articles for a 902-MHz and 2304-MHz are included with this book's online content.

PROJECT: A LOOP YAGI FOR 1296 MHZ

Described here are loop Yagis for the 1296-MHz band designed by Chip Angle, N6CA. Three sets of dimensions are given. Good performance can be expected if the dimensions are carefully followed. Check all dimensions before cutting or drilling anything. The 1296-MHz version is intended for weak-signal operation, while the 1270-MHz version is optimized for FM and mode L satellite operation. The 1283-MHz antenna provides acceptable performance from 1280 to 1300 MHz.

These antennas have been built on 6- and 12-foot booms. Results of gain tests at VHF conferences and by individuals around the country show the gain of the 6-foot model to be about 18 dBi, while the 12-foot version provides about 20.5 dBi. Swept measurements indicate that gain is about 2 dB down from maximum gain at ±30 MHz from the design frequency. The SWR, however, deteriorates within a few megahertz on the low side of the design center frequency.

THE BOOM

The dimensions given here apply only to a ¾-inch OD boom. If a different boom size is used, the dimensions must be scaled accordingly. Many hardware stores carry aluminum tubing in 6- and 8-foot lengths, and that tubing is suitable for a short Yagi. If a 12-foot antenna is planned, find a piece of more rugged boom material, such as 6061-T6 grade aluminum. Do not use anodized tubing. The 12-foot antenna must have additional boom support to minimize boom sag. The 6-foot version can be rear mounted. For rear mounting, allow 4½ inches of boom behind the last reflector to eliminate SWR effects from the support.

The antenna is attached to the mast with a gusset plate. This plate mounts at the boom center. See **Figure 15.49**. Drill the plate mounting holes perpendicular to the element mounting holes (assuming the antenna polarization is to be horizontal).

Elements are mounted to the boom with no. 4-40 machine screws, so a series of no. 33 (0.113 inch) holes must be drilled along the center of the boom to accommodate this hardware. **Figure 15.50** shows the element spacings for different parts of the band. Dimensions should be followed as closely as possible.

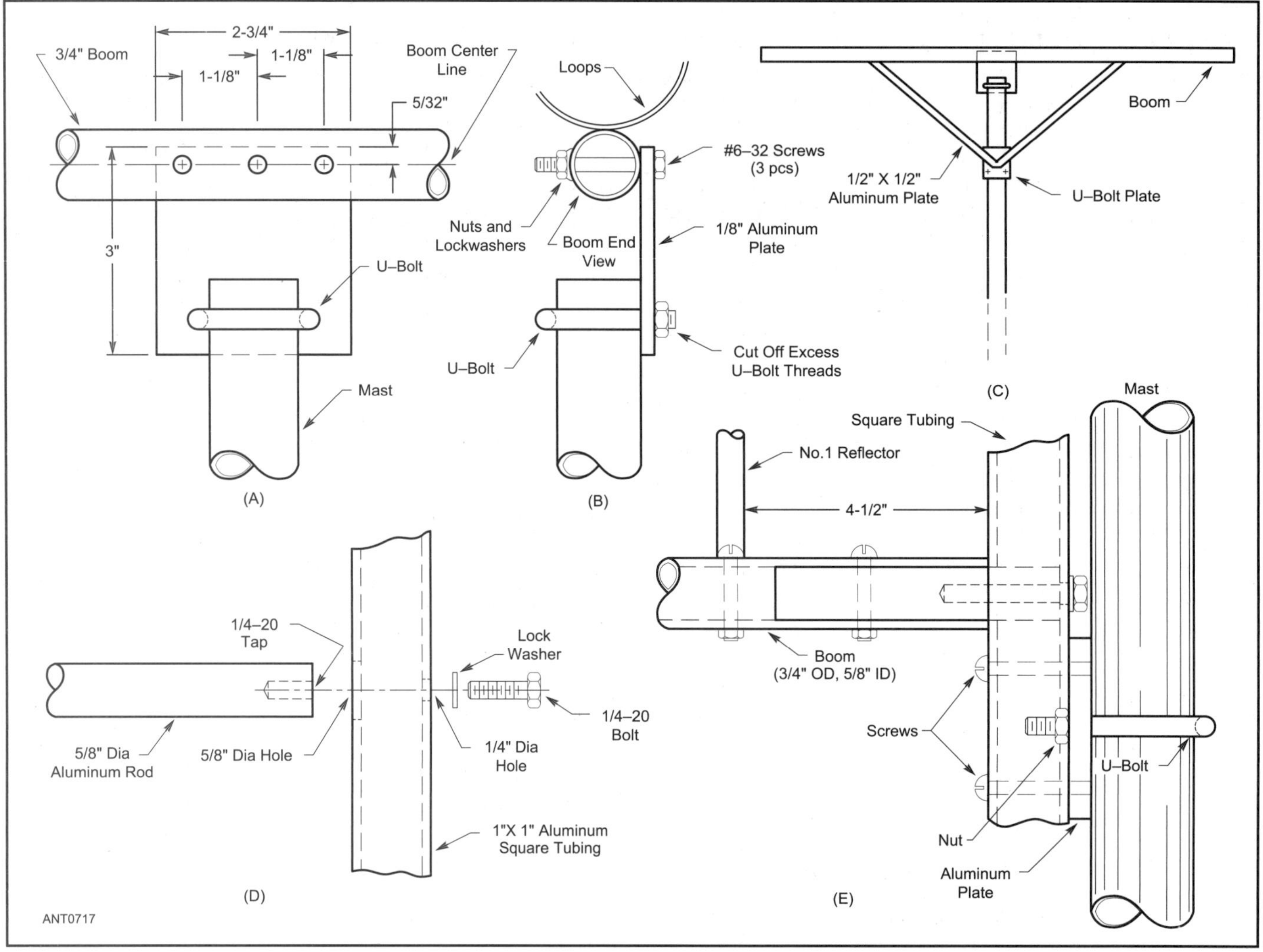

Figure 15.49 — Loop Yagi boom-to-mast plate details are given at A. At B, the mounting of the antenna to the mast is detailed. A boom support for long antennas is shown at C. The arrangement shown in D and E may be used to rear-mount antennas up to 6 or 7 ft long.

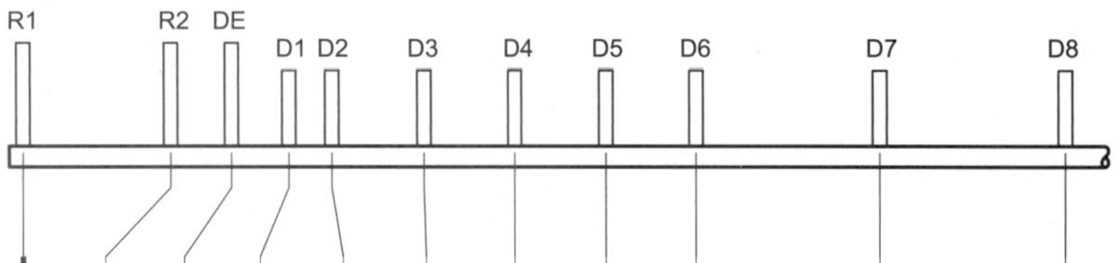

1296	3.050	1.180	1.120	0.830	1.780	1.780	1.780	1.780	3.560	3.560
1283	3.090	1.193	1.135	0.841	1.804	1.804	1.804	1.804	3.607	3.607
1270	3.122	1.202	1.146	0.850	1.822	1.822	1.822	1.822	3.644	3.644

Freq. Element Spacing (inches) | Spacing remains constant for all elements from D6 up →

ANT0718

Figure 15.50 — Boom drilling dimensions. These dimensions must be carefully followed and the same materials used if performance is to be optimum. Element spacings are the same for all directors after D6 — use as many as necessary to fill the boom.

PARASITIC ELEMENTS

The reflectors and directors are cut from 0.032-inch thick aluminum sheet and are ¼ inch wide. **Figure 15.51** indicates the lengths for the various elements. These lengths apply only to elements cut from the specified material. For best results, the element strips should be cut with a shear. If the edges are left sharp, birds won't sit on the elements.

Drill the mounting holes as shown in Figure 15.48 after carefully marking their locations. After the holes are drilled, form each strap into a circle. This is easily done by wrapping the element around a round form. (A small juice can works well.)

Mount the loops to the boom with no. 4-40 × 1-inch machine screws, lock washers and nuts. See **Figure 15.52**. It is best to use only stainless steel or plated-brass hardware. Although the initial cost is higher than for ordinary plated-steel hardware, stainless or brass hardware will not rust and need replacement after a few years. Unless the antenna is painted, the hardware will definitely deteriorate.

DRIVEN ELEMENT

The driven element is cut from 0.032-inch copper sheet and is ¼ inch wide. Drill three holes in the strap as detailed in Figure 15.50. Trim the ends as shown and form the strap into a loop similar to the other elements. This antenna is like a quad; if the loop is fed at the top or bottom, it is horizontally polarized.

Driven element mounting details are shown in **Figure 15.53**. A mounting fixture is made from a ¼-20 × 1¼ inch brass bolt. File the bolt head to a thickness of ⅛ inch. Bore a 0.144-inch (no. 27 drill) hole lengthwise through the center of the bolt. A piece of 0.141 inch semi-rigid hardline (UT-141 or equivalent) mounts through this hole and is soldered to the driven loop feed point. The point at which the UT-141 passes through the copper loop and brass mounting fixture should be left unsoldered at this time to allow for matching adjustments when the antenna is completed, although the range of adjustment is not very large.

The UT-141 can be any convenient length. Attach the connector of your choice (preferably type N). Use a short piece of low-loss RG-8 size cable (or ½-inch Hardline) for the run down the boom and mast to the main feed line. For best results, the main feed line should be the lowest loss 50-Ω cable obtainable. Good ⅞-inch hardline has 1.5 dB of loss per 100 feet and virtually eliminates the need for remote mounting of the transmit converter or amplifier.

TUNING THE DRIVEN ELEMENT

If the antenna is built carefully to the dimensions given, the SWR should be close to 1:1. Just to be sure, check the SWR if you have access to test equipment. Be sure the signal source is clean, however; wattmeters respond to "dirty" signals and can give erroneous readings. If problems are encountered, recheck all dimensions. If they look good, a minor improvement may be realized by changing the shape of the driven element. Slight bending of reflector 2 may also improve the SWR. When the desired match has been obtained, solder the point where the UT-141 jacket passes through the loop and brass bolt.

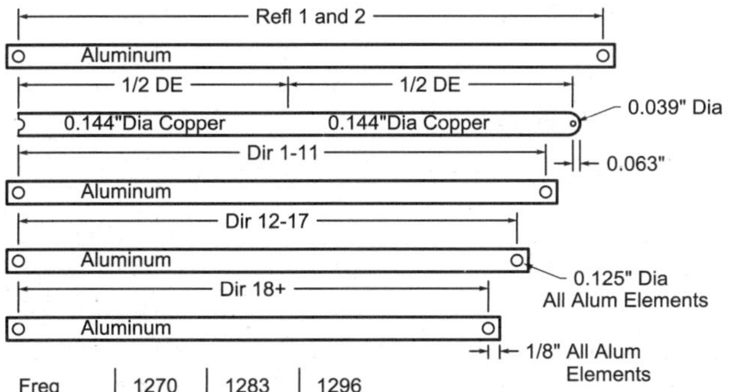

Freq	1270	1283	1296
Refl 1,2	9.929	9.829	9.700
1/2 DE	4.752	4.704	4.643
Dir 1–11	8.445	8.359	8.250
Dir 12–17	8.189	8.106	8.000
Dir 18+	7.882	7.802	7.700

Element Lengths (Inches)
(Hole to Hole)

ANT0719

These Dimensions Apply Only to:
0.250" Element Width
0.0325" Element Thickness
0.750" Diameter Boom

NOTE: All Dimensions are in Inches

Figure 15.51 — Parasitic elements for the loop Yagi are made from aluminum sheet, the driven element from copper sheet. The dimensions given are for ¼-inch wide by 0.0325-inch thick elements only. Lengths specified are hole to hole dist-ances; the holes are located ⅛ inch from each element end.

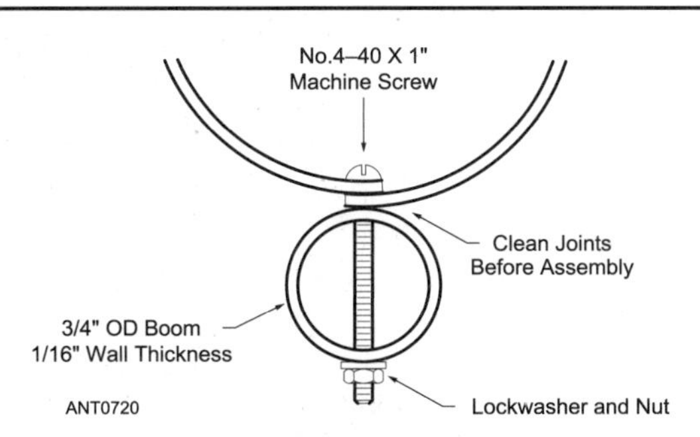

Figure 15.52 — Element-to-boom mounting details.

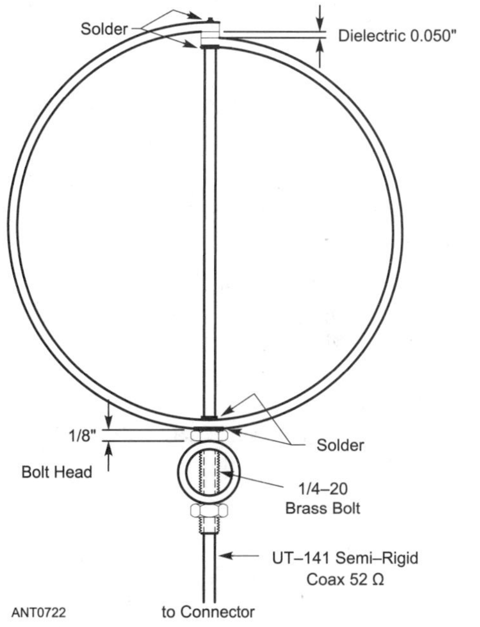

Figure 15.53 — Driven-element details. See Figure 15.57 and the text for additional information.

15.4 Moxon and HB9CV Beams

Along with the basic Yagi, alternate small beam designs are practical and effective in the upper-HF and the VHF/UHF range. The size reduction of these designs is less attractive at higher frequencies since high-performance Yagis with three or more elements are of a practical size. However, in lightweight portable applications such as mountain-topping, a small beam provides useful gain and pattern characteristics. Two such designs are described in this section, the Moxon rectangle and the less-well-known HB9CV beam that is popular in Europe.

15.4.1 Moxon Rectangles

The 2-element Moxon rectangle beam is more completely described in the chapter **HF Beam Antennas,** but its design principles apply at VHF and UHF, as well. The design is popular because it shortens the length of the antenna elements by about 30 percent, has a 50 Ω feed point impedance, provides good gain roughly equal to a 2-element Yagi, and excellent F/B performance. At VHF, Moxons are common on 6 meters, particularly for portable and rover operation. Commercial models of the 2-meter and 6-meter Moxons are available. See the References and Bibliography entries for Cebik for more articles about the Moxon.

PROJECT: MOXON RECTANGLES FOR VHF AND UHF

Moxon designs for the 6-meter, 2-meter, 1.25-meter, and 70-centimeter bands are summarized here with complete construction articles included in the online material. A dual-band Moxon satellite array for 2 meters and 70 cm is included in the **Antennas for Space Communications** chapter and can be used to create separate 2 meter or 70 cm antennas.

Although the Moxon is usually a 2-element design, at VHF and higher frequencies, beams with multiple Moxon rectangles are practical. There are numerous online articles about "Super Moxon" (two Moxon rectangles) and "Super Duper Moxon" (three or four Moxon rectangles) designs.

A critical design parameter of the Moxon is the coupling through a gap between the ends of the elements. At the shorter wavelengths of VHF and higher frequencies, it is important to maintain the exact length of the gap. A non-conductive spacer across the gap is recommended to prevent the element ends from moving and changing the gap distance.

The term *stressed Moxon* refers to a Moxon beam in which the ends of the elements are put in tension which pulls them against each other. This makes it easier to maintain the gap distance since the ends of the elements are less free to move relative to each other. Stressed Moxons for 10 and 6 meters are the most common.

MOXON DESIGN CALCULATOR

Dan Maguire, AC6LA, used an algorithm by LB Cebik, W4RNL, to create a free downloadable tool called *MoxGen* that calculates the antenna's dimensions as a function of frequency and element diameter. The tool also generates both *EZNEC* and *NEC* models. Cebik's algorithm results in antennas with a Z_0 of 50 to 54 Ω, reactance of less than 1 Ω, free-space gain in the range of 5.95 dBi to 6.05 dBi, and a front to back ratio (F/B) greater than 35 dB. The conductor diameters range from 10^{-5} to 10^{-2} λ. The tool is available online at **ac6la.com/moxgen1.html**.

6-METER MOXON

The 6-meter Moxon described here is from the article "A 6 Meter Moxon Antenna" by Allen Baker, KG4JJH in the April 2004 issue of *QST*. (See References and Bibliography, the full article is included in the online material.) Two versions of the design are presented: one is horizontally polarized for operation at the low end of the 6-meter band from 50 – 51 MHz and the second is vertically polarized for FM use at the upper end of the band from 52 – 54 MHz. The Moxon design is particularly useful where a narrow beamwidth is not useful, such as for rover or meteor scatter operation.

The *MoxGen* design calculator was used to generate *EZNEC* models at 50.5 (H-POL in the article) and 53.0 MHz (V-POL), using 5/8-inch OD aluminum tubing. The resulting dimensions for the antennas are presented in **Figure 15.54**. The completed antennas are shown installed in **Figure 15.55**. Both beams sufficiently lightweight to be supported by telescoping fiberglass masts or painter's poles.

2-METER MOXON

The most extensive article describing a Moxon beam for the 2-meter band was written by LB Cebik, W4RNL, "Building a 2 Meter Moxon." It can be found on numerous online websites and discusses both design methods and construction techniques. A design for the vertically polarized antenna in **Figure 15.56** was described in the *QST* article "A Compact Two-Element 2-Meter Beam" that is included in the online material.

220 MHZ MOXON

The antenna in **Figure 15.57** uses dimensions from the MoxGen design calculator. The elements are made from 5 feet of 1⁄4-inch copper tubing, copper elbows, and schedule 40 PVC tubing and plumbing adapters. Only a hack saw, a Dremel tool or file, and a hobbyist butane torch are needed for construction. Sturdy but weighing less than one pound, it is ideal for portable mountain-topping in VHF+ contests or to activate a Summits On the Air (SOTA) peak. The *QST* article "A Moxon Antenna for 220 MHz" is included in the online material.

70 CM MOXON

The 70 cm band is about the highest frequency at which Moxon designs are useful. The antenna in **Figure 15.58** is constructed using solid #12 AWG copper wire on a hand-held PVC tubing boom. Designed using the *MoxGen* software, a similar variation was built for reception of DTV signals near

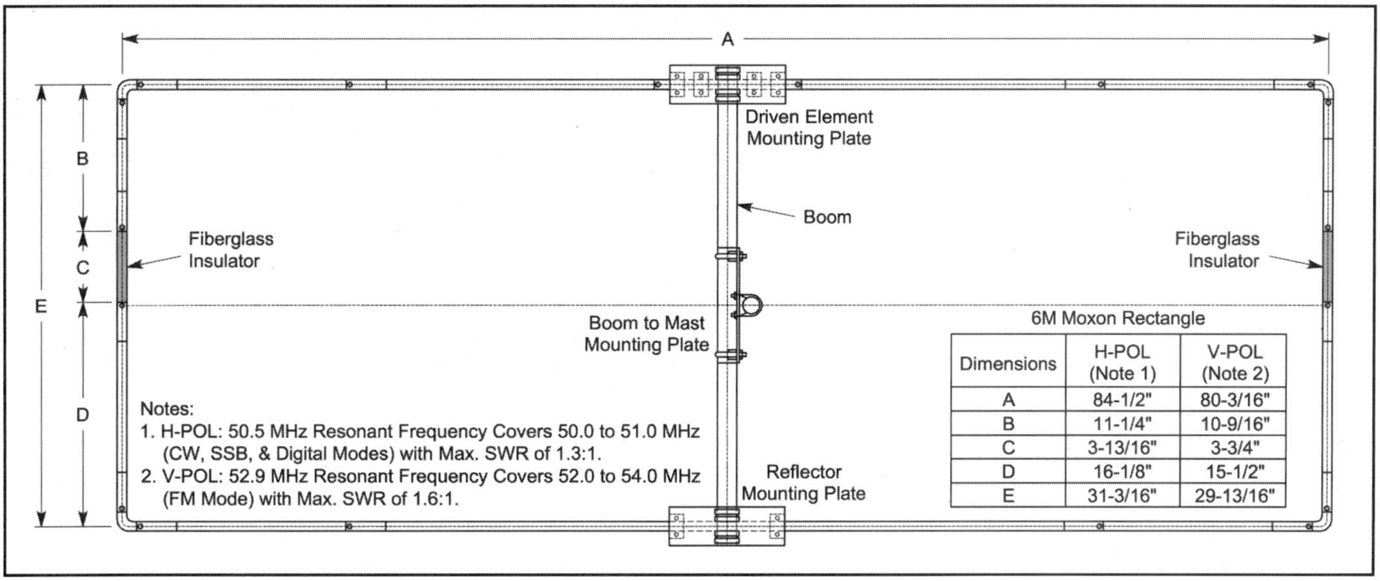

Dimensions	H-POL (Note 1)	V-POL (Note 2)
A	84-1/2"	80-3/16"
B	11-1/4"	10-9/16"
C	3-13/16"	3-3/4"
D	16-1/8"	15-1/2"
E	31-3/16"	29-13/16"

Figure 15.54 — The 6-meter antenna Moxon rectangle with basic dimensions for versions at 50-51 MHz (H-POL) and 52-54 MHz (V-POL).

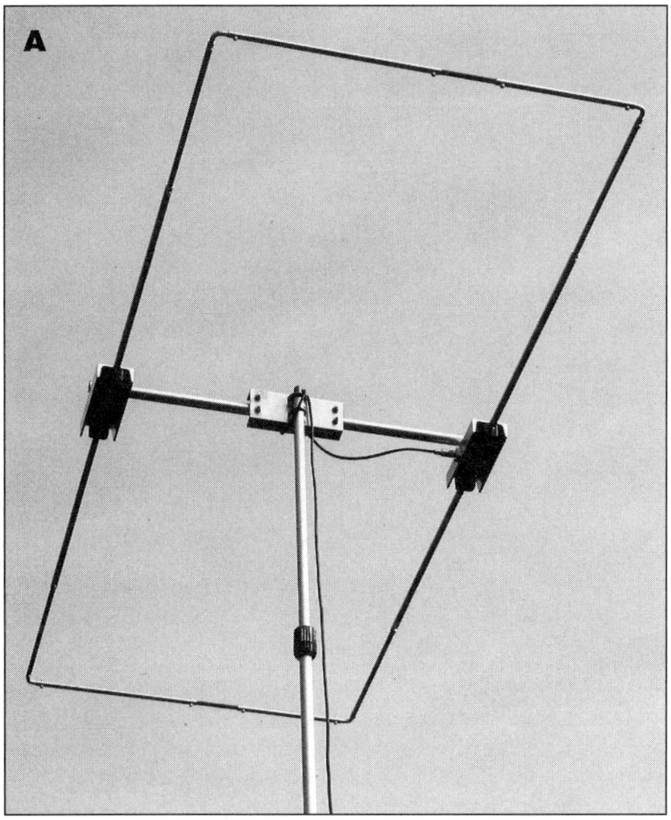

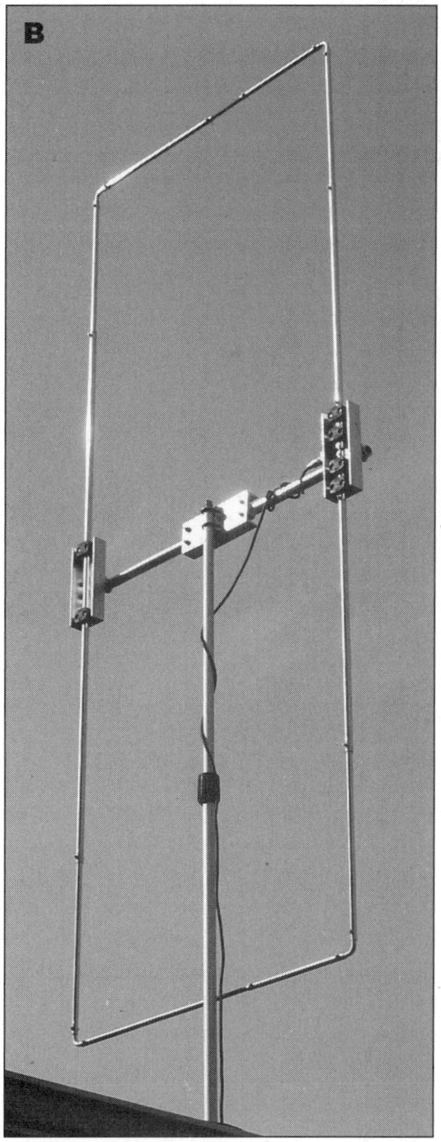

Figure 15.55 —A shows the 6-meter Moxon mounted for horizontal polarization and at B in position for vertical polarization.

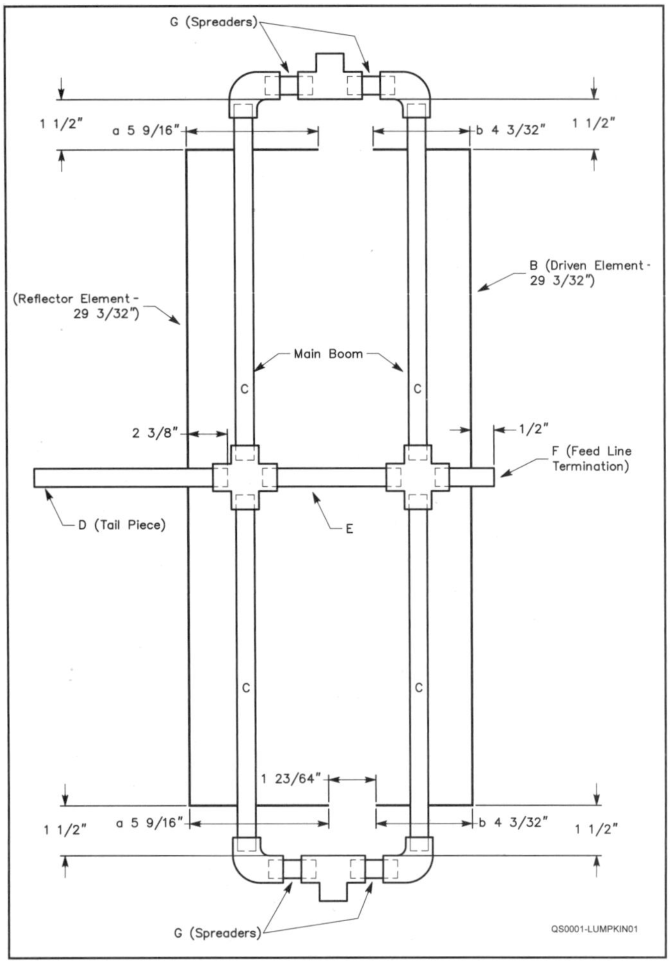

Figure 15.56 — The vertical 2-meter Moxon designed by KB8WEV and WA1FXT.

550 MHz, as well. This antenna would be very useful as a hand-held antenna for locating RFI sources at UHF, as well. The design is described in "Moxon Mighty Mite" which is included in the online material.

15.4.2 HB9CV Beam

The HB9CV Beam has two driven elements and was introduced by HB9CV in the 1950s. It is a coax-fed version of the ZL-Special described in the **Broadside and End-Fire Dipole Array** chapter. The reflector is separated from the forward element by λ/8 or 45 degrees. A 180-degree phasing line connects the elements for a total phase shift of 225 degrees.

Gain is slightly greater than 4 dBd, with good bandwidth and F/B that are relatively insensitive to element length or tubing taper schedule as with a Yagi's parasitic elements. The phasing line requires some attention to detail in construction and a compensating capacitor in series with the feed point is used for impedance matching. **Figure 15.59** sketches the basic design.

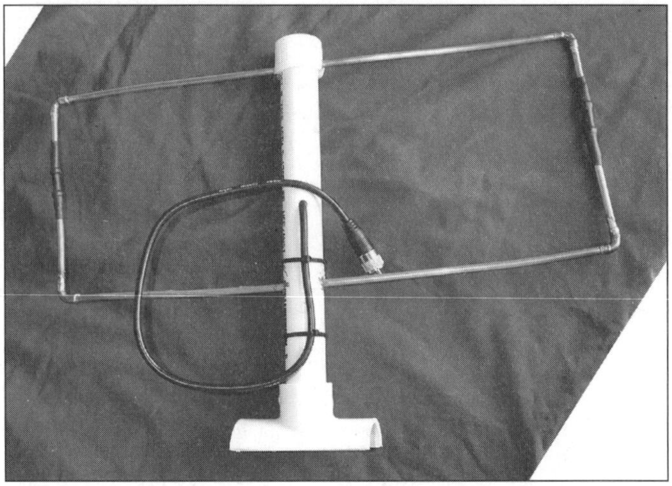

Figure 15.57 — The elements for this Moxon beam for 220 MHz by WB6RLC are copper refrigeration tubing with a PVC boom and handle. Heat-shrink tubing maintains the element tip spacing.

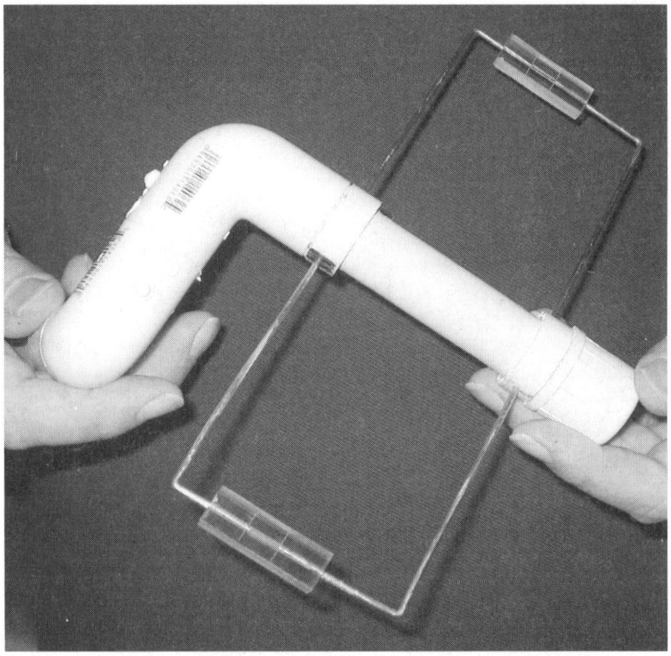

Figure 15.58 — A hand-held UHF Moxon built by W6YE for use in the 70 cm amateur band and for DTV broadcast reception.

PROJECT: HB9CV BEAMS FOR 10, 6 AND 2 METERS

HB9CV designs for 10, 6, and 2 meters are described, including construction details at **dj6ca.de/dj6ca3/hb9cv.pdf**. From that article, dimensions in millimeters are given in **Table 15.22** for a boom of 25 × 25 mm (1-inch) square aluminum and elements of 12 mm OD × 1 mm wall (1/2-inch) tubing. The phasing line is made of 2 mm brass wire held 5 mm from the boom and elements. It should be routed directly above the elements. The phasing line is attached to each element a short distance from the boom.

At the feed point, the body of a coaxial connector such as an SO-239 is attached directly to the boom. From the center conductor of the connector, the compensation capacitor is attached to the point at which the phasing line reaches the forward element. DK7ZB recommends initial adjustment be made with a variable capacitor, then replace it with a fixed-value capacitor.

Table 15.22
HB9CV Beam Dimensions by DK7ZB
All dimensions in mm

Band	L_{FWD}	L_{REFL}	L_{SEP}	Ph_{FWD}	Ph_{REFL}	*C (pF)*
10 m	4900	5300	1330	760	800	56
6 m	2770	3000	750	430	450	30
2 m	945	1020	260	180	190	12

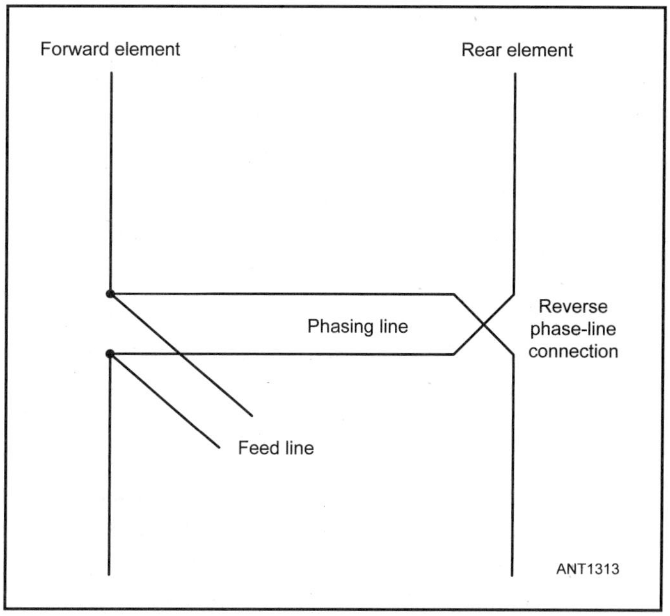

Figure 15.59 — Design dimensions for the HB9CV beam. See text and referenced article for details.

15.5 Reflector Antennas

When a single driven element is used, a reflector screen (as used for collinear arrays bent to form an angle) gives an improvement in the radiation pattern and gain. At 222 and 420 MHz its size assumes practical proportions, and at 902 MHz and higher, practical reflectors can approach ideal dimensions (very large in terms of wavelengths), resulting in more gain and sharper patterns. The corner can be used at 144 MHz, though usually at much less than optimum size. For a given aperture, the reflector does not equal a parabola in gain, but it is simple to construct, broadband, and offers gains from about 9 to 14 dBi, depending on the angle and size. This section was written by Paul M. Wilson, W4HHK. (The original section, including antenna dimensions from 144 through 2304 MHz, is available in the online information as "Corner and Trough Reflector Antennas.") Chapters 17 and 29 of Jasik (see References and Bibliography) provide more background and design information on reflector antennas.

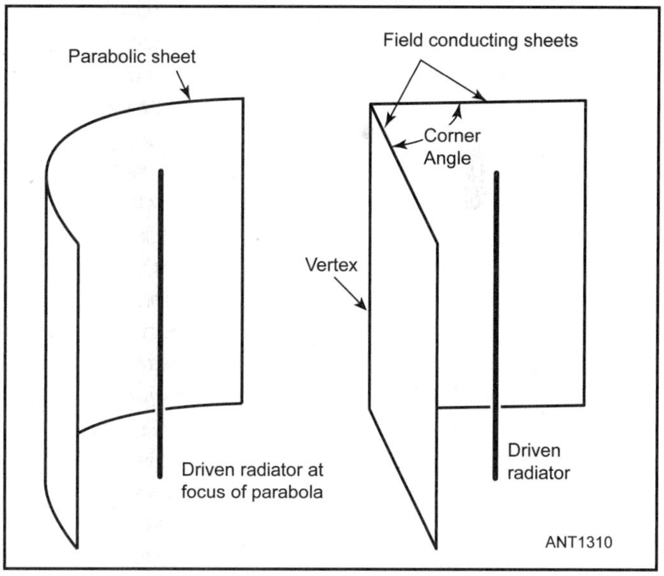

Figure 15.60 — A corner reflector showing the driven radiation, usually a dipole, and the arrangement of the reflecting surfaces.

15.5.1 Corner Reflectors

The basic design and construction of corner reflectors are shown in **Figure 15.60A** and **B**. The driven radiator is a dipole placed on the midline of the antenna. Spacing of the dipole from the reflector, which can be a solid sheet or separate elements, determines feed point impedance, gain, and beamwidth. Typical construction is shown in **Figure 15.61**.

The corner angle can be 90, 60, or 45°, but the side length must be increased as the angle is narrowed. For a 90° corner, the driven element spacing can be anything from 0.25 to 0.7 λ, 0.35 to 0.75 λ for 60°, and 0.5 to 0.8 λ for 45°. In each case the gain variation over the range of spacings given is about 1.5 dB. Because the spacing is not very critical to gain, it may be varied for impedance-matching purposes. Closer spacings yield lower feed point impedances, but a folded dipole radiator could be used to raise this to a more convenient level.

The maximum gain obtained with minimum spacing is the design generally used at 144, 222, and 432 MHz to maintain

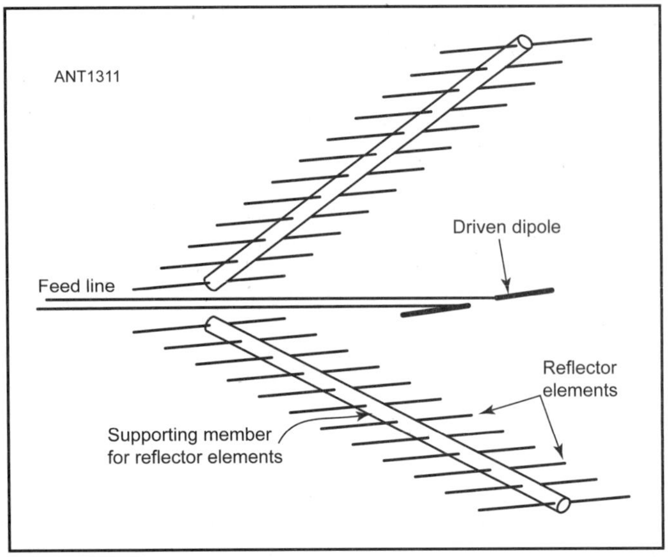

Figure 15.61 — A horizontally polarized square-corner reflector antenna with individual reflector elements forming the reflecting surface.

reasonable side lengths). A 90° corner, for example, should have a minimum side length equal to twice the dipole spacing, or 1 λ long for 0.5 λ spacing. A side length greater than 2 λ is ideal. Gain with a 60° or 90° corner reflector with 1 λ sides is about 10 dB. A 60° corner with 2 λ sides has about 13 dBi gain, and a 45° corner with 3 λ sides has about 14 dBi gain. Reflector length should be a minimum of 0.6 λ. Less than that spacing causes radiation to increase to the sides and rear and decreases gain.

A corner reflector may be used for several bands, or for UHF television reception, as well as amateur UHF operation. For operation on more than one frequency, side length and reflector length should be selected for the lowest frequency, and reflector spacing for the highest frequency.

The reflector and driven element can also be mounted on a ground-plane, which can be used for vertical polarization. The corner reflector and a λ/4 radiator are mounted on the ground plane, permitting direct connection to a coaxial line if the proper spacing is used. A J-pole antenna could be used to maintain the aperture area and provide a match to a coaxial line.

For vertical polarization operation, four 90° corner reflectors built back-to-back (with common reflectors) could be used for scanning 360° of horizon with modest gain. Feed line switching could be used to select the desired sector.

15.5.2 Trough Reflectors

To reduce the overall dimensions of a large corner reflector the vertex can be cut off and replaced with a plane reflector. Such an arrangement is known as a *trough reflector*. See **Figure 15.62**. Performance similar to that of a larger corner reflector can be obtained if the dimensions of S and T as shown in the figure do not exceed the indicated limits. This antenna provides performance very similar to the corner reflector and presents fewer mechanical problems because the plane center portion is relatively easy to mount on a mast or boom. The sides are considerably shorter, as well.

The gain of both corner reflectors and trough reflectors may be increased by stacking two or more and arranging them to radiate in phase, or alternatively by adding further collinear dipoles (fed in phase) within a wider reflector. Not more than two or three radiating units should be used, because the great virtue of the simple feeder arrangement would then be lost.

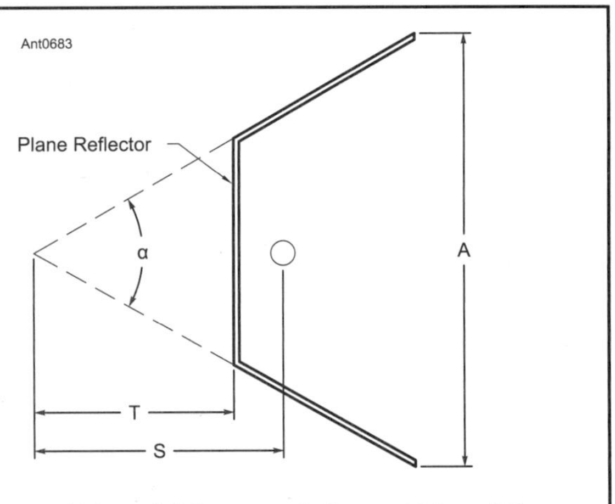

Angle α	*Value of S for maximum gain*	*Gain (dBi)*	*Value of T*
90°	1.5 λ	13.5	1λ - 1.25 λ
60°	1.75 λ	15	1.0 λ
45°	2.0 λ	16	1.9 λ

Figure 15.62 — The trough reflector is a useful modification of the corner reflector. The vertex has been replaced by a simple plane section.

15.6 Helical Antennas

Probably the most common amateur use of the helical antenna is in satellite communications, where the spinning of the satellite antenna system (relative to the Earth) and the effects of *Faraday rotation* cause the polarization of the satellite signal to be unpredictable. Using a linearly polarized antenna in this situation can result in deep fading, but with the helical antenna (which responds equally to linearly polarized signals), fading is essentially eliminated.

This same characteristic makes helical antennas useful in polarization-diversity systems. The advantages of circular polarization have been demonstrated on VHF voice schedules over non-optical paths, in cases where linearly polarized beams did not perform satisfactorily.

Another use for the helical antenna is the transmission of

color ATV signals. Many beam antennas (when adjusted for maximum gain) have far less bandwidth than the required 6 MHz, or lack uniform gain over this frequency range. The result is significant distortion of the transmitted and received signals, affecting color reproduction and other features. This problem becomes more aggravated over non-optical paths.

The helix exhibits maximum gain (within 1 dB) across a range of more than 20 MHz anywhere above 420 MHz. Not only does the helix give high gain over an entire amateur band, but it also allows operation on FM, SSB and CW without the need for separate vertically and horizontally polarized antennas.

HELICAL ANTENNA BASICS

The helical antenna is an unusual specimen in the antenna world, in that its physical configuration gives a hint to its electrical performance. A helix looks like a large air-wound coil with one of its ends fed against a ground plane, as shown in **Figure 15.63**. (Also see the article "The Helical Antenna — Description and Design" by VE3KL in this book's online material.)

The ground plane is a screen of 0.8 to 1.1 λ diameter (or on a side for a square ground plane). The circumference (C_λ) of the coil form must be between 0.75 and 1.33 λ for the antenna to radiate in the axial mode. The coil should have at least three turns to radiate in this mode. The ratio of the spacing between turns (in wavelengths), S_λ to C_λ, should be in the range of 0.2126 to 0.2867. This ratio range results from the requirement that the pitch angle, α, of the helix be between 12° and 16°, where:

$$\alpha = \arctan \frac{S_\lambda}{C_\lambda}$$

These constraints result in a single main lobe along the axis of the coil.

A helix with a C_λ of 1 λ has a wave propagating from one end of the coil (at the ground plane), corresponding to an instantaneous dipole "across" the helix. The electrical rotation of this dipole produces circularly polarized radiation. Because the wave is moving along the helix conductor at nearly the speed of light, the rotation of the electrical dipole is at a very high rate, and true circular polarization results.

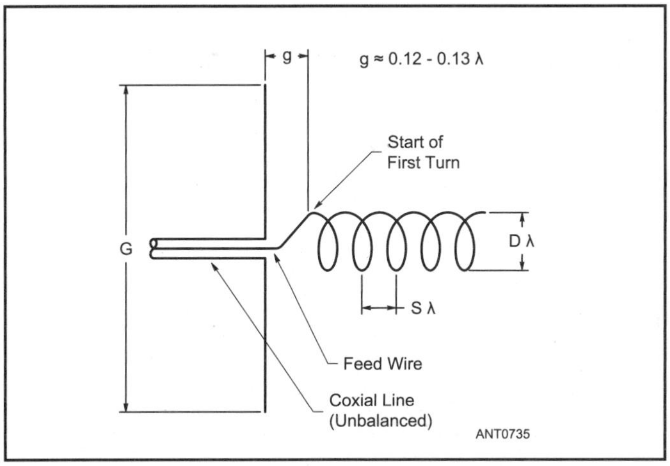

Figure 15.63 — The basic helical antenna and design parameters.

Regarding the type of circular polarization, in simple terms the IEEE definition is that when viewing the antenna from the feed point end, a clockwise winding results in RHCP, and a counterclockwise winding results in LHCP. This is important, because when two stations use helical antennas over a nonreflective path, both must use antennas with the same polarization sense. If antennas of opposite sense are used, a signal loss of at least 20 dB results from the cross-polarization alone.

As mentioned previously, circularly polarized antennas can be used in communication with any linearly polarized antenna (horizontal or vertical), because circularly polarized antennas respond equally to all linearly polarized signals. The gain of a helix appears 3 dB less than the theoretical gain in this case, because the linearly polarized antenna does not respond to linearly polarized signal components orthogonal to it.

The response of a helix to all polarizations is indicated by a term called *axial ratio*, also known as *circularity*. Axial ratio is the ratio of amplitude of the polarization that gives maximum response to the amplitude of the polarization that gives minimum response. An ideal circularly polarized antenna has an axial ratio of 1.0. A well-designed practical helix exhibits an axial ratio of 1.0 to 1.1. The axial ratio of a helix is:

$$AR = \frac{2n + 1}{2n}$$

where
AR = axial ratio
n = the number of turns in the helix

Axial ratio can be measured in two ways. The first is to excite the helix and use a linearly polarized antenna with an amplitude detector to measure the axial ratio directly. This is done by rotating the linearly polarized antenna in a plane perpendicular to the axis of the helix and comparing the maximum and minimum amplitude values. The ratio of maximum to minimum is the axial ratio.

The impedance of the helix is easily predicted. The terminal impedance of a helix is unbalanced, and is defined by:

$$Z = 140 \times C_\lambda$$

where Z is the impedance of the helix in ohms.

The gain of a helical antenna is determined by its physical characteristics. Gain can be calculated from:

$$\text{Gain (dBi)} = 11.8 + 10 \log (C_\lambda{}^2 n\, S_\lambda)$$

In practice, helical antennas do not deliver this amount of gain for antennas with turns count greater than about twelve. This will be discussed further regarding practical antennas.

The beamwidth of the helical antenna (in degrees) at the half-power points is:

$$BW = \frac{52}{C_\lambda \sqrt{nS_\lambda}}$$

The diameter of the helical antenna conductor should be between 0.006 and 0.05 λ but smaller diameters have been used successfully at 144 MHz. The previously noted diameter of the ground plane (0.8 to 1.1 λ) should not be exceeded if you desire a clean radiation pattern. As the ground plane size is increased, the sidelobe levels also increase. The ground plane need not be solid; it can be in the form of a spoked wheel or a frame covered with hardware cloth or screen. Cupped ground planes have also been used according to Kraus (see the References and Bibliography).

50-Ω HELIX FEED

Joe Cadwallader, K6ZMW, presented this feed method in the June 1981 *QST* (see References and Bibliography). Terminate the helix in an N connector mounted on the ground screen at the periphery of the helix. See **Figure 15.64**. Connect the helix conductor to the N connector as close to the ground screen as possible (**Figure 15.65**). Then adjust the first quarter-turn of the helix to a close spacing from the reflector.

This modification goes a long way toward curing a deficiency of the helix — the 140-Ω nominal feed point impedance. The traditional λ/4 matching section has proved difficult to fabricate and maintain. But if the helix is fed at the periphery, the first quarter turn of the helix conductor (leaving the N connector) acts much like a transmission line — a single conductor over a perfectly conducting ground plane. The impedance of such a transmission line is:

$$Z_0 = 138 \log \frac{4h}{d}$$

where

Z_0 = line impedance in ohms

h = height of the center of the conductor above the ground plane

d = conductor diameter (in the same units as h).

The impedance of the helix is 140 Ω a turn or two away from the feed point. But as the helix conductor curves down toward the feed connector (and the ground plane), h gets smaller, so the impedance decreases. The 140-Ω nominal impedance of the helix is transformed to a lower value. For any particular conductor diameter, an optimum height can be found that will produce a feed point impedance equal to 50 Ω. The height should be kept very small, and the diameter should be large. Apply power to the helix and measure the SWR at the operating frequency. Adjust the height for an optimum match.

Typically, the conductor diameter may not be large enough to yield a 50-Ω match at practical (small) values of h. In this case, a strip of thin brass shim stock or flashing copper can be soldered to the first quarter-turn of the helix conductor (**Figure 15.66**). This effectively increases the conductor diameter, causing the impedance to decrease further yet. The edges of this strip can be slit every ½ inch or so, and the strip bent up or down (toward or away from the ground plane) to tune the line for an optimum match.

This approach yields a perfect match to nearly any coax. The usually wide bandwidth of the helix (70% for less than 2:1 SWR) will be reduced slightly (to about 40%) for the same conditions. This reduction is not enough to be of any consequence for most amateur work. The improvements in performance, ease of assembly and adjustment are well worth the effort in making the helix more practical to build and tune.

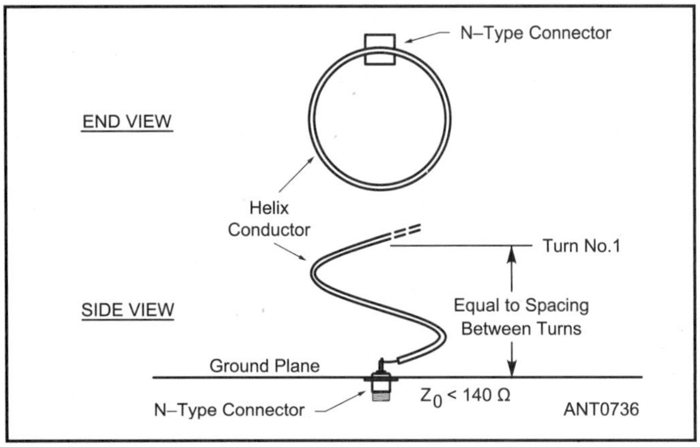

Figure 15.64 — End view and side view of peripherally fed helix.

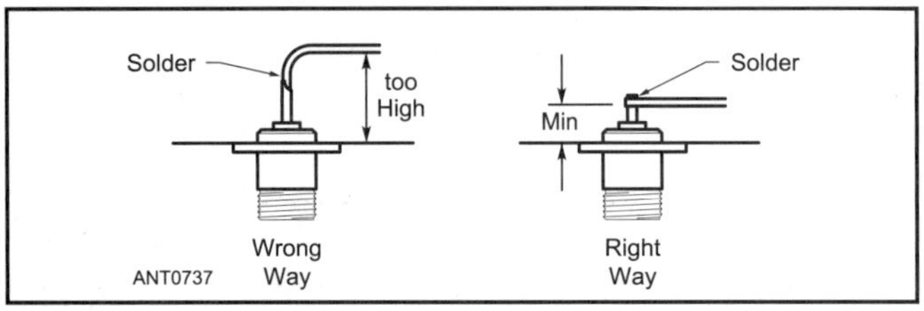

Figure 15.65— Wrong and right ways to attach a helix to a type N connector for 50-Ω feed.

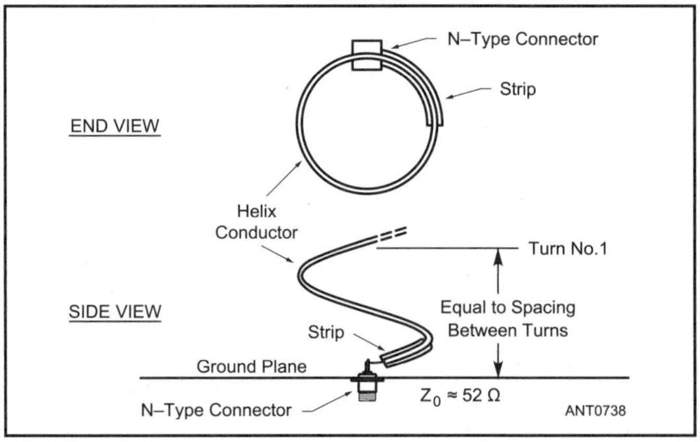

Figure 15.66 — End view and side view of peripherally fed helix with metal strip added to improve transformer action.

15.7 Slot Antennas

(Material in this section is largely taken from Slot Antennas for Ham Radio: The Forgotten Antenna *by John Portune, W6NBC. The book is available in Kindle format from Amazon.)*

The slot antenna is based on a uniform straight narrow rectangular hole cut into a large flat metal plane. This *classic slot* is how most hams picture the slot antenna. By no means is this the only effective configuration, nor does it reveal the many possible uses of the slot antenna in amateur radio.

Following the explanation of how the slot antenna works and a general tuning procedure, several examples of slot antennas are presented. Construction details are available in supplemental articles in the online material.

15.7.1 How the Slot Works

Professional literature usually presents the slot as complementary to the dipole based on Babinet's Principle. (See the reference for Pelosi.) For the slot antenna to be useful to amateurs, however, this level of analysis is unnecessary. A more intuitive explanation is presented here. **Figure 15.67A** shows the relationship of the familiar half-wavelength dipole and slot. While the classic slot looks very much like a folded dipole and even has the same one-wavelength circumference, operation is very different. (See the **Dipoles and Monopoles** chapter for a description of the folded dipole.)

Consider that a dipole is fed by a voltage source (the feed line) in series with the two conductors making up the legs of the antenna. This results in voltages of opposite polarity on each leg of the dipole, creating an *electric dipole*. The voltages drive current back and forth *along* the antenna. The situation is reversed for a slot antenna. Instead of two voltage polarities, the voltage applied *across* the slot results in two current flows *around* the slot, creating a *magnetic dipole*.

As a result, dipoles and slots are said to be *complementary*: a dipole creates a single current from voltage with two polarities while a slot creates two currents from voltage with a single polarity.

Figure 15.67B is a model of the slot made up of a pair of back-to-back shorted ¼-wave transmission lines (i.e., stubs) with voltage applied to both stubs by a feed line. Look carefully at the currents along the stubs and at the end. Everywhere along the slot except at the end of the stub, currents on opposite sides of the slot are in opposite directions so the fields from them cancel. At the end of the slot, however, the currents loop around the slot in the same direction and their radiated fields add together. Figure 15.67C is a schematic representation of the resulting currents.

Remember that an antenna is simply a structure that arranges current flows to create the desired radiation pattern. In the case of a slot antenna, the hole in the conducting plane is the structure that forces current to flow around it. In the simulated current flow shown in Figure 15.67D, notice that the end currents are perpendicular to the axis of the slot just like the applied voltage across the slot's feed point. These high currents at the end are also flowing in the same direction. The ends are

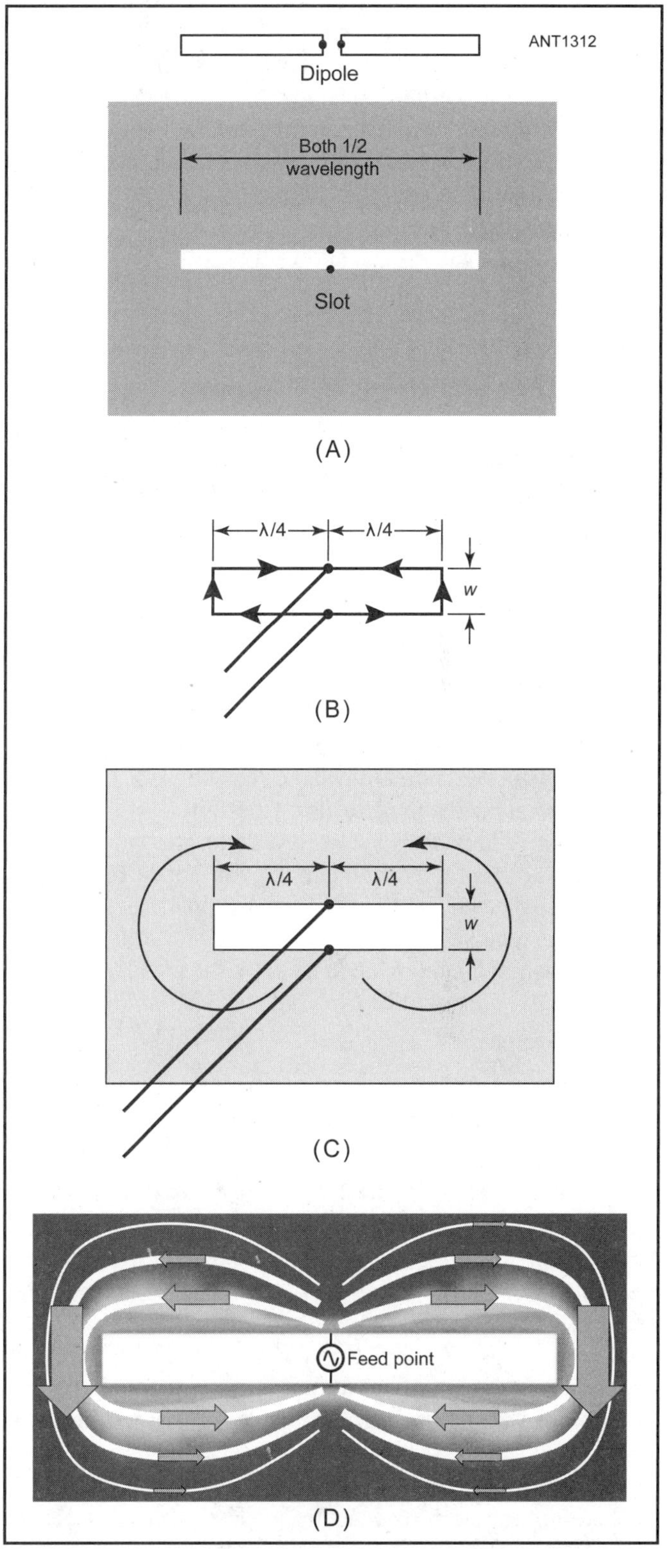

Figure 15.67 — The complementary nature of the slot and the dipole is illustrated in A. B shows an analogy of parallel connected ¼-wave stubs while C is a schematic representation of the current distribution in around the slot. D shows a typical current distribution of the classic slot fed at the center. Current concentrates in phase around the ends of the slot from which the primary radiation occurs. (Graphics at B and C after Figure 13-1a of Kraus – see References and Bibliography)

where the EM field from a slot is radiated — the hole in the plane does not radiate at all.

The radiation patterns of the dipole and the slot antenna have the same orientation — maximum radiation broadside to the antenna axis with minimum strength along the axis. The slot's field is also a minimum along the plane around the slot. The key difference, however, is that the field from a dipole has the same polarization as the axis of the dipole while the field from the slot is polarized perpendicularly to the axis of the slot. i.e., a horizontal slot will radiate a vertically polarized pattern and vice versa. This allows the slot to be used as an omni-directional, horizontally polarized antenna by orienting the slot so that it is vertical.

15.7.2 Slot Matching and Tuning

Recall that the voltage in a dipole is high at the ends and low in the middle and that the current is opposite — high in the middle, low at the ends (see the chapter **Dipoles and Monopoles**). The impedance — voltage divided by the current — is therefore high, often several thousand ohms at the ends, and low in the middle, roughly 72 Ω in free space. This situation is reversed in a slot: the current and the impedance for a narrow straight slot in a large metal plane is very low (nearly a short circuit) at the ends and high in the middle, on the order of 450 – 500 Ω. In practice, slot antennas are fed near the end where the impedance matches 50 or 75 Ω coaxial cable. Fine adjustments in feed point impedance can be made by moving the feed point back and forth along the slot.

Because of the slot's symmetry, there are two matching points along the slot where the feed point impedance (across the slot) will be close to 50 or 75 Ω. These points aren't always at the same relative distance from the ends for different types of slots. Generally, the wider the slot or the plane, the farther the matched points will be from an end. Slot builders should expect to experiment to find the point of lowest SWR. Changes in the slot position in the surrounding metal surface or in the configuration of the metal surface will also affect the position of the matched feed point.

ADJUSTING FEED POINT IMPEDANCE

Begin by attaching the feed line in a "best-guess" location. A moveable magnetic fixture like those in **Figure 15.68** can be used to locate an approximate feed point. For non-magnetic surfaces, magnets on the opposite side of the surface will allow the fixture to stay attached. Brass washers can be used instead of magnets and held to the surface with tape. Move the feed point along the slot until an acceptable SWR is obtained.

ADJUSTING RESONANT FREQUENCY

To adjust the slot's resonant frequency — seen as a change in the frequency of minimum SWR — change slot length, just as with a dipole. The ends of the slot can be easily shortened with the self-adhesive aluminum or copper tape to raise the frequency. (The adhesive on the tape forms a low-reactance capacitance that is transparent at VHF and higher frequencies.) Change both ends by the same amount to preserve the relative position of the slot in the surrounding plane. This is much easier than having to cut the slot longer to lower its frequency. The tape should extend beyond the slot on both sides by at least an inch. As with a dipole, it is useful to start with the slot a bit longer than the expected final length to allow for tuning by shortening the antenna.

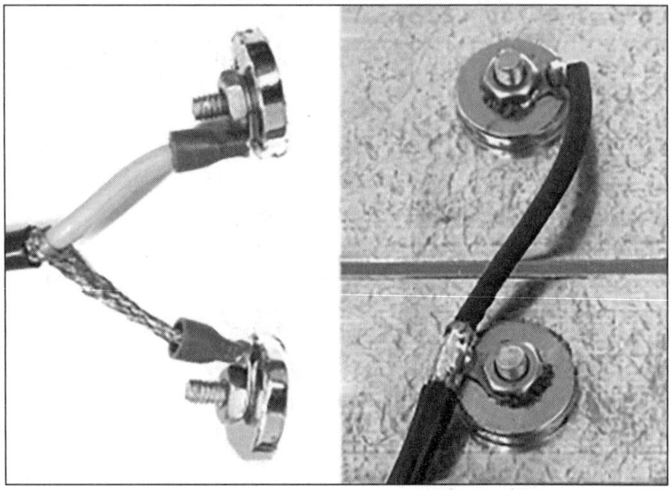

Figure 15.68 — Two movable feed point fixtures using magnets. For non-magnetic surfaces, magnets behind the surface will allow the fixture to stay attached. Brass washers can be used instead of magnets and held to the surface with metallic tape.

TUNING AND CONSTRUCTION NOTES

Using an SWR meter, antenna analyzer, or vector network analyzer, locate an approximate feed point with reasonably low SWR. Then adjust the slot length at both ends with metallic tape. SWR should not change significantly as resonant frequency is adjusted. Repeat the process of adjusting SWR then frequency until the final configuration is reached. It is generally easiest to move the tape at the end closest to the feed point to change the impedance match, and the tape at the other end to change the frequency.

Tune the slot in a location like the intended final location. If, for example, the antenna will be mounted on a wood-framed house with composition roofing tiles, tune it up on a wooden work bench or a wooden ladder several feet off the ground. If the antenna will be mounted over an aluminum patio roof, it may be okay to tune it up over a metal work bench. Adjusting antennas at the working location is more important for slots with narrower bandwidths, such as folded or skeleton slots.

Once the final feed point is located, drill permanent screw holes for screws, nuts, and washers. Alternatively, the feed line shield and center conductor can be soldered directly to the metal surface. For slot antennas made of heavier aluminum, elongated holes for movable screws and nuts can be cut near a feed point.

If the feed line will not be bonded directly to the metal surface around the slot, a feed line choke or choke balun is needed to prevent the shield from carrying common-mode current from the antenna. Ferrite beads can be used as described in the **Transmission Line System Techniques** chapter. Alternately, a wound-coax choke is effective at 2 meters and 220

MHz. 5 or 6 turns of RG-8X or RG-58 in a 2-inch diameter coil is generally sufficient. Above those frequencies, use a ferrite bead choke.

PROJECT: 2 METER SLOT IN A SATELLITE TV DISH

Originally described in March 2016 *QST* magazine, this antenna is shown in **Figure 15.69**. (The full article is included in the online material.) The slot is cut in a common 22 × 32-inch SlimLine DIRECTV® dish.

Because a straight, full-length half-wave slot is too long to fit on the dish, the ends are bent at right angles. The main slot is 24 inches long and the right-angle sections are 7.5 inches each for a total length of 39 inches. Bending the slot only has a modest effect on directivity and gain, filling in the pattern nulls along the slot's main length.

SWR is 1.5:1 or less in the 2 meter band with the feed point being 3.5 to 4.5 inches from one end of the slot. **Figure 15.70** shows the coaxial feed line attached to the dish from the rear. It is not recommended that the dish also be used for TV reception because of the risk of damage to the microwave receiver from the high power 2 meter transmitted signal.

PROJECT: 6 METER "HENTENNA" SKELETON SLOT

The classic slot design is too big for lower VHF and HF operation. A smaller configuration that made HF slots practical for HF is the *skeleton slot*. It was first introduced as the Hentenna for 6 meters by JE1DEU, JH1FCZ, and JH1YST. (The complete description from the *ARRL Antenna Compendium, Vol. 5* is available in the online material.) **Figure 15.71** shows the basic antenna design. Like a classic slot, the antenna is one-half wavelength long. The conductors forming the antenna act as the edges of the slot with the rest of the conducting plane around the slot omitted. Since most of the current flows close to the slot edge (see Figure 15.71D) performance is approximately that of the classic slot although the radiation efficiency is lower.

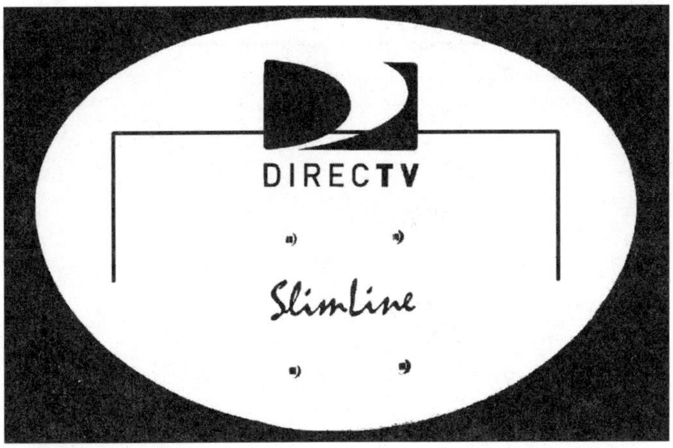

Figure 15.69 — The horizontal slot is cut into the surface of a Dish TV satellite dish.

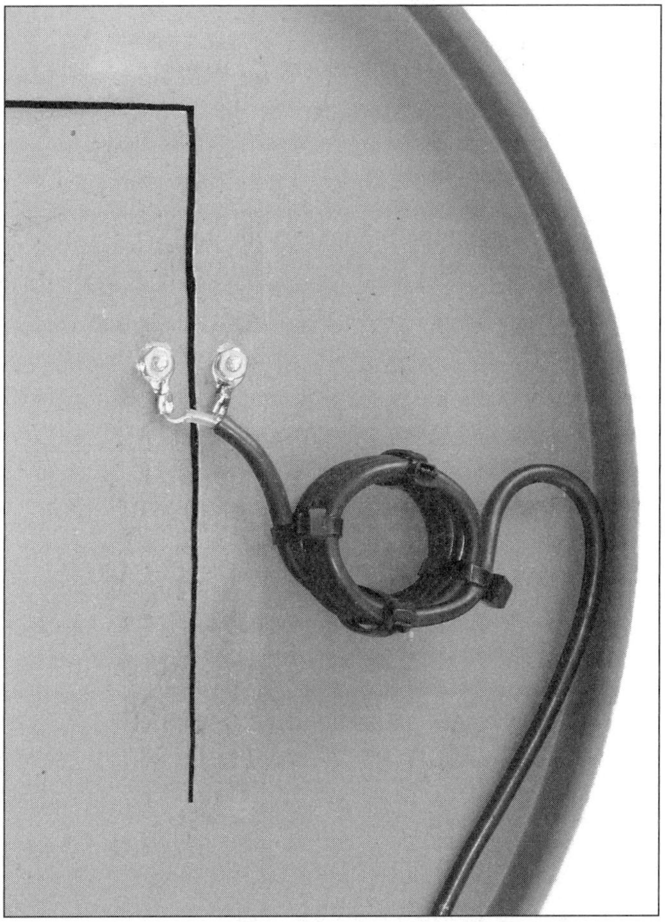

Figure 15.70 — Coaxial feed line is attached to the back of the dish across the slot. Use a feed line choke constructed as a wound-coax coil or with Type 43 ferrite beads.

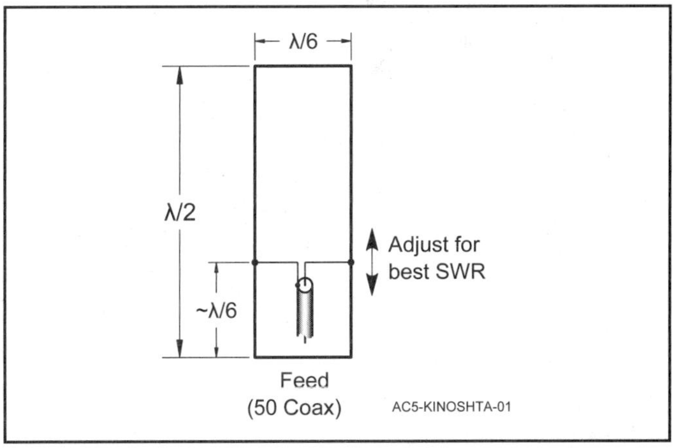

Figure 15.71 — The basic Hentenna is λ/2 high and λ/6 wide and its radiation is horizontally polarized. The antenna is fed with 50 ohm coax, and feed point position is adjusted for the best SWR.

The Hentenna's suggested dimensions are λ/2 long, λ/6 wide, with the feed point at λ/10 from one end. However, any narrow half-wavelength long loop roughly a third as wide as long, has much the same characteristics. The 1:3 ratio of length to width results in a feed point impedance of close to 50 Ω at λ/10 from one end of the slot.

The azimuth pattern in **Figure 15.72** is horizontally polarized and bidirectional perpendicular to the plane of the antenna. Reflectors can be placed behind each of the horizontal elements, creating a beam antenna as described at **qsl.net/dk7zb/Quadlong/Hentenna.htm**. The Hentenna can also be used with the long dimension horizontal, creating a vertically polarized antenna. Hentennas are also practical for the upper HF bands and a version for 75 meters has also been constructed in Japan. Skeleton slots for HF are also described in *ARRL Compendium* articles — see the references for Gordon and Prack.

PROJECT: 2 METER CUBICAL SLOT

If the Hentenna in the previous section is wound around a square form, the result is a *cubical slot* with dimensions significantly smaller than but comparable performance to a full-size half-wavelength antenna. Designed here for 2 meters, the diminutive 10 x 10 x 7 inch "slot cube" antenna in **Figure 15.73** has approximately the same omnidirectional gain as a 2-meter J-pole as shown in **Figure 15.74**. The antenna was described in January 2019 *QST* and the complete article is included in the online material, including construction details. A version for 6 meters was described in December 2019 *QST* and that article is also included.

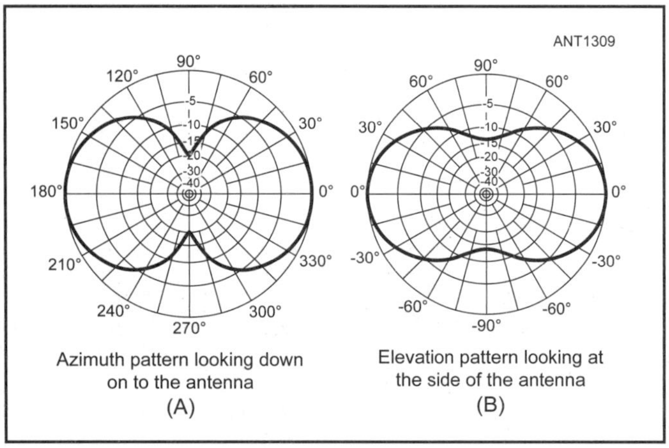

Figure 15.72 — The free-space azimuth (A) and elevation (B) patterns for the Hentenna.

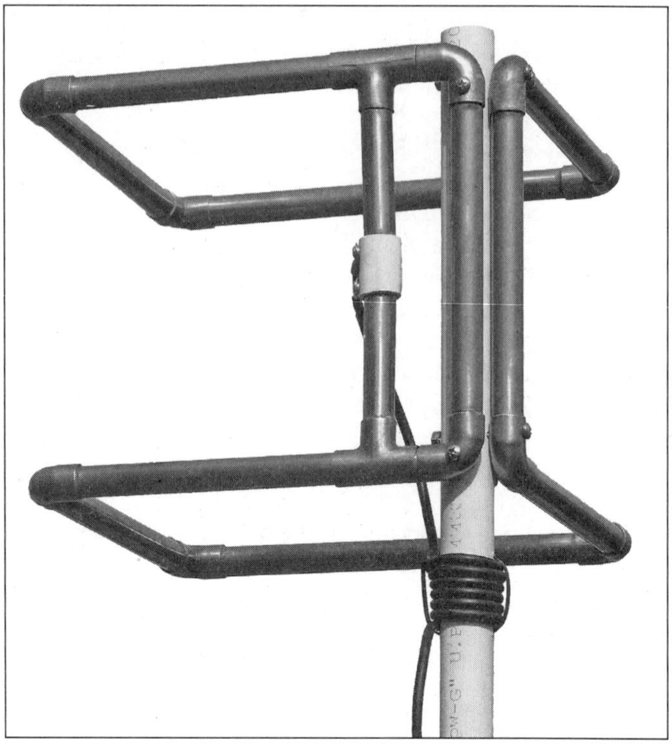

Figure 15.73 — The Slot-Cube antenna for 2 meters is a classic slot folded into a square shape.

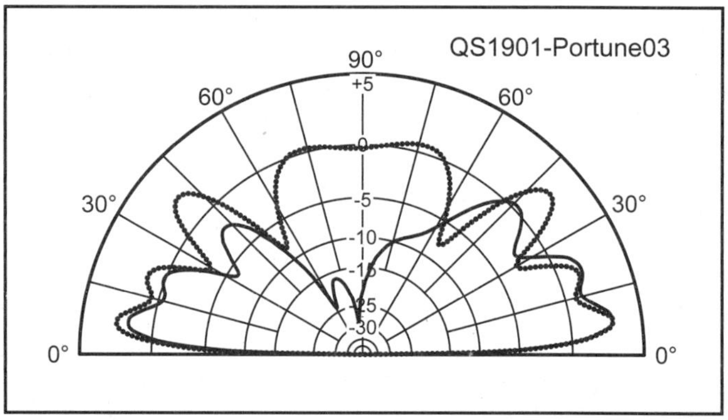

Figure 15.74 — The elevation radiation pattern of the Slot-Cube (dotted line) compared with a J-pole antenna (solid line).

15.8 Microwave Antennas

The domain of amateur microwaves begins at 902 MHz and includes all higher frequency bands. (The 10 GHz and higher bands are also referred to as mm-wave bands.) The short wavelength of microwaves enables a wide range of interesting designs quite different from the antennas based on discrete linear and loop elements popular at lower frequencies. At microwaves, surfaces and shapes are used in ways that are impractical at longer wavelengths.

This section of the book has been extensively updated by Paul Wade, W1GHZ, a prolific designer as well as author of the *QST* column "Microwavelengths." Paul has also published the excellent online *W1GHZ Microwave Antenna Book* and his website, **w1ghz.org**, contains a wealth of information about many facets of microwave operating and building.

The RSGB texts listed in the References and Bibliography provide a more complete treatment of amateur microwave antennas. A number of horn and dish designs, including conversion of surplus offset-feed satellite TV receive dishes are presented in the RSGB publication *Antennas for VHF and Above*.

3D-Printing and CNC Techniques for Microwaves

Amateurs have long been limited to using surplus microwave components or building relatively simple antenna designs because special machining or construction techniques, particularly at 10 GHz and higher frequencies, are beyond most amateur shops. This situation is changing as 3D-printing and CNC machining equipment has become affordable. Amateurs can not only replicate commercial designs but can implement custom designs with subtle and precise aspects. Expect to see more of these techniques in design and construction articles in the amateur literature!

RF Safety for Waveguides, Horns and Dishes

Never look into the open end of a waveguide when power is applied or stand directly in front of a dish while transmitting. Tests and adjustments in these areas should be done while receiving or at extremely low levels of transmitter power (less than 0.1 watt). The FCC has set a limit of 10 mW/cm^2 averaged over a 6-minute period as the safe maximum. Other authorities believe even lower levels should be used. Destructive thermal heating of body tissue results from excessive exposure. This heating effect is especially dangerous to the eyes. The accepted safe level of 10 mW/cm^2 is reached in the near field of a parabolic antenna if the level at $2D^2/\lambda$ is 0.242 mW/cm^2. (D and λ must have the same units.) The equation for power density at the far-field boundary is

$$\text{Power Density} = \frac{137.8P}{D^2}\ \text{mW/cm}^2$$

where

P = average power in kilowatts
D = antenna diameter in feet

For example, a 2-foot dish at 10 GHz has a power density of 0.242 mW/cm^2 at the far field boundary at a power level of 7 watts. Thus, any lower power is within the accepted safe level, but exercise caution.

15.8.1 Microwave Antenna Guidelines

Many antenna construction practices that are common on lower frequencies cannot be used at microwave frequencies. This is the most important reason why all who venture to microwaves are not equally successful. When a proven antenna design is used, copy it exactly; don't change *anything*.

Do not allow the mast to pass through the elements, as is common on antennas for lower frequencies. Avoid any unnecessary metal around the antenna: 1/4 λ at 1296 MHz is only a little over 2 inches. Cut all U-bolts and mounting hardware to the minimum length needed so that no resonant or near-resonant conductors are present to couple to the antenna's field.

After antenna performance, feed line loss is the next most important aspect of antenna system design. Mount the antennas to keep feed line losses to an absolute minimum. Antenna height is less important than keeping the line losses low.

Use the best feed line you can get. As an example of why this is important, here are some realistic measurements of common coaxial cables at 1296 MHz (loss per 100 feet):

- RG-8, 213, 214 coaxial cable: 11 dB
- 1/2-inch foam/copper hardline: 4 dB
- 7/8-inch foam/copper hardline: 1.5 dB

Preamps should be mounted at the antenna wherever practical and only connectors designed for frequency of operation should be used.

15.8.2 Waveguides

Above 2 GHz, coaxial cable is a losing proposition for communications operation. Fortunately, at this frequency the wavelength is short enough to allow practical, efficient energy transfer by an entirely different means. A *waveguide* is a conducting tube through which energy is transmitted in the form of electromagnetic waves. The tube is not considered as carrying a current in the same sense that the wires of a two-conductor line do, but rather as a *boundary* that confines the waves in the enclosed space. Skin effect prevents any electromagnetic effects from being evident outside the guide. The energy is injected at one end, either through capacitive or inductive coupling or by radiation, and is removed from the other end in a like manner. Waveguide merely confines the energy of the fields, which are propagated through it to the receiving end by means of reflections against its inner walls.

EVOLUTION OF WAVEGUIDE

Suppose an open-wire line is used to carry UHF or microwave energy from a generator to a load. Imagine the transmission line is supported with quarter-wave stubs, shorted at the far end. The open end of such a stub presents an infinite impedance to the transmission line, provided that the shorted stub is non-reactive. Thus, the stub acts as an insulating support. Since the stubs act as an open-circuit, an infinite number of them may be connected in parallel without affecting the open-wire line.

Because the shorting link has finite length it also has some inductance. This inductance can be minimized by making the RF current flow on the surface of a plate rather than through a thin wire. If the plate is large enough, it will prevent the magnetic lines of force from encircling the RF current.

The transmission line may be supported from the top as well as the bottom and when infinitely many supports are added, they form the walls of a waveguide at its *cutoff frequency*. **Figure 15.75** illustrates how a rectangular waveguide evolves from a two-wire parallel transmission line.

WAVEGUIDE OPERATION

As a signal propagates along a waveguide, the metal walls contain the electric and magnetic fields. We'll concentrate on the electric field here, because the dominant mode of propagation for waveguide is called TE or *Transverse Electric*. **Figure 15.76** shows how the electric and magnetic fields are oriented for the TE_{10} mode. (See the discussion on waveguide modes below.) The electric field intensity in the rectangular waveguide, which is oriented parallel to the shorter side walls. The electric field is strongest in the center and must be zero at the side walls, since the walls are short circuits. This is the reason for the E-plane and H-plane terminology in Figure 15.74D.

The field strength distribution is half of a sine wave at the operating frequency, and propagates down the waveguide as if it were bouncing off the side walls. For this to work, the width of the waveguide must be at least one-half the wavelength of the propagating signal. At lower frequencies with longer wavelengths, the field cannot be zero at both walls so these signals will not propagate in the waveguide.

WAVEGUIDE DIMENSIONS

Cutoff and Upper Frequencies

The minimum frequency of operation for a waveguide is that at which the waveguide width, a, is 1/2 wavelength. This is called the waveguide's *cutoff frequency*, f_c.

$$f_c = c / 2a$$

where c = the speed of light in free space, 2.9979×10^8 meters per second, and a is the waveguide's larger dimension

A wavelength in the waveguide, λ_g, is longer than a wavelength in free space, λ_0. This implies a velocity faster than the speed of light. But only the *phase velocity* exceeds the speed of light — energy cannot travel faster. The waveguide wavelength varies with frequency as a function of the cutoff frequency:

$$\lambda_g = \frac{\lambda_0}{\sqrt{1 - \left(\frac{\lambda_0}{\lambda_c}\right)^2}}$$

Near the cutoff frequency, λ_g is much longer than the free-space wavelength λ_0, becoming closer to λ_0 as frequency increases.

Waveguide operating frequencies are usually well above the cutoff frequency — near (and below) the cutoff frequency, losses increase and the guide wavelength changes rapidly with frequency causing dispersion of the transmitted waveform. This is why a waveguide makes an excellent high-pass filter.

The height of a rectangular waveguide, between top and bottom walls, determines both the upper frequency limit and the characteristic impedance. The upper limit is the frequency at which the waveguide height is 1/2 λ — above this frequency, the electric field may change orientation and other modes may propagate.

WAVEGUIDE DIMENSIONS

In a rectangular guide the critical dimension is a in Figure 15.76. This dimension must be more than λ/2 at the lowest frequency to be transmitted. In practice, the b dimension usu-

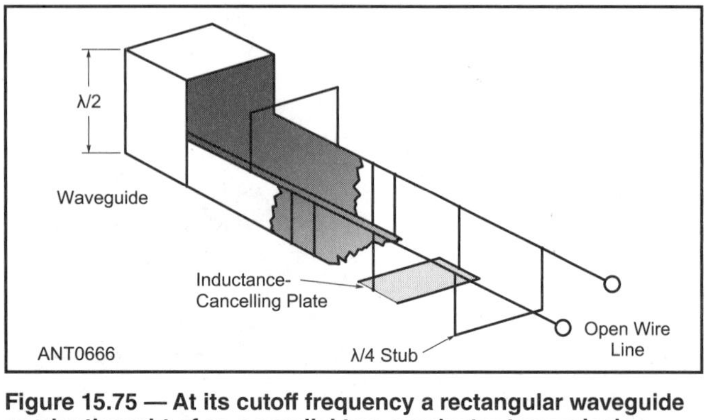

Figure 15.75 — At its cutoff frequency a rectangular waveguide can be thought of as a parallel two-conductor transmission line supported from top and bottom by an infinite number of 1/4-wavelength stubs.

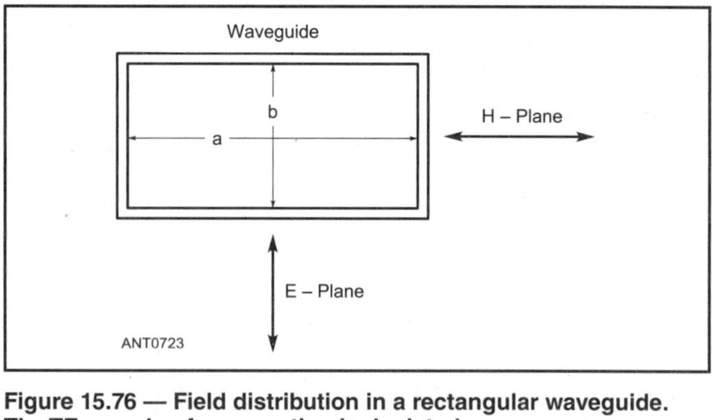

Figure 15.76 — Field distribution in a rectangular waveguide. The TE_{10} mode of propagation is depicted.

ally is made about equal to a/2 to avoid the possibility of operation in other than the dominant mode.

Cross-sectional shapes other than a rectangle can be used, the most important being the circular pipe. Much the same considerations apply as in the rectangular case.

Wavelength dimensions for rectangular and circular guides are given in **Table 15.23**, where X is the width of a rectangular guide and r is the radius of a circular guide. All figures apply to the dominant mode.

Table 15.23
Waveguide Operating Dimensions in Wavelengths

	Rectangular	*Circular*
Cutoff wavelength	*2X*	*3.41r*
Longest wavelength transmitted with little attenuation	1.6X	3.2r
Shortest wavelength before next mode becomes possible	1.1X	2.8r

CHARACTERISTIC IMPEDANCE

The characteristic impedance is usually much higher than 50 Ω and is calculated for TE modes using this formula:

$$Z_0 = 377\left(\frac{\lambda_g}{\lambda_0}\right)\left(\frac{2b}{a}\right)$$

where *a* and *b* are the large and small dimensions, respectively, of the rectangular waveguide. 377 Ω is the approximate impedance of free space.

For example, at 10 GHz, WR90 waveguide is often used. The width is 0.9 inches, or 22.86 mm, and the height is 0.4 inches, or 10.16 mm. The cutoff frequency is 6.56 GHz, but the recommended operating frequency range is 8 to 12.4 GHz. At 10.368 GHz, the free space wavelength is $\lambda_0 = 28.915$ mm, the guide wavelength is $\lambda_g = 37.33$ mm and the characteristic impedance is $Z_0 = 433$ Ω. Several common waveguides are pictured in cross-section in **Figure 15.77**.

For circular waveguide, the cutoff wavelength is $\lambda_c = 1.706 \times$ diameter and the characteristic impedance is

$$Z_0 = 377\left(\frac{\lambda_g}{\lambda_0}\right)$$

WAVEGUIDE MODES

The operating mode described above is for the dominant mode, TE_{10} (or TE_{11} in circular waveguide). This is the lowest frequency mode at which a given waveguide will operate, and is the preferred mode for waveguide transmission.

If there is no upper limit to the frequency to be transmitted, there are an infinite number of ways exist in which the fields can arrange themselves in a guide. Each field configuration is a mode. All modes may be separated into two general groups. One group, designated TM (*Transverse Magnetic*), has the magnetic field entirely crosswise to the direction of propagation, but has a component of electric field in the propagation direction. The other group, designated TE (*Transverse Electric*) has the electric field entirely crosswise to the direction of propagation, but has a component of magnetic field in the direction of propagation. TM waves are sometimes called E-waves in older references and TE waves are sometimes called H-waves. The TM and TE designations are preferred, however. The particular mode of transmission is identified by the group letters followed by subscript numbers; for example TE_{11}, TM_{11} and so on. The number of possible modes increases with frequency for a given size of guide.

Higher-order modes are useful in certain applications, for instance, in multi-mode feed horns, where the additional modes can shape the radiation pattern, special high-power waveguides, and in certain cavity filters.

COAXIAL-WAVEGUIDE TRANSITIONS

Energy may be introduced into or extracted from a waveguide or resonator from a coaxial cable by using adapters called *coaxial transitions.* Energy is coupled via either the electric or magnetic field. A typical transition using the electric field method, shown in **Figure 15.78**, is a probe like a

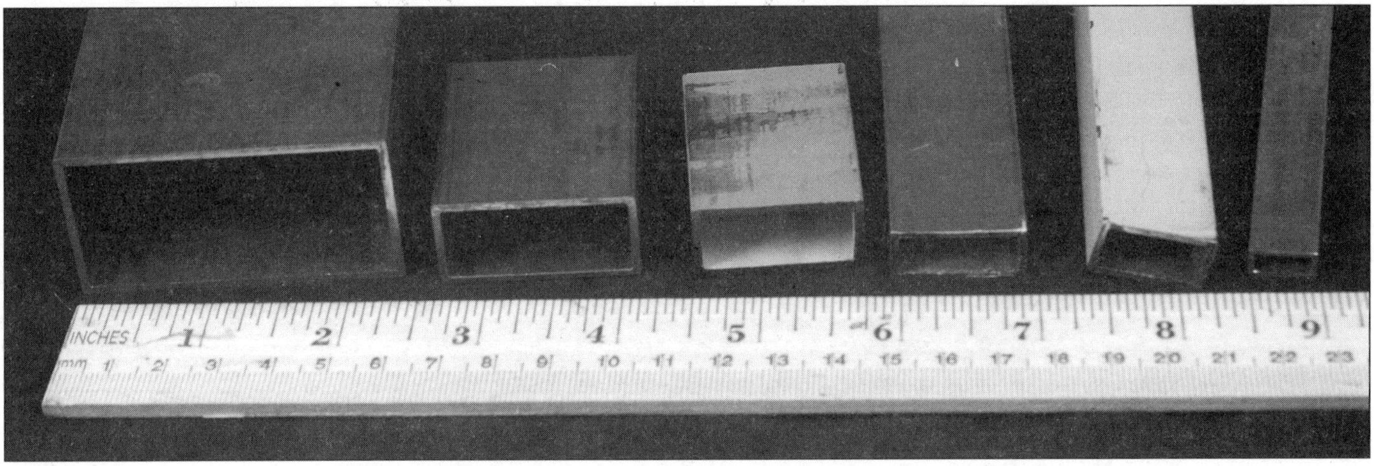

Figure 15.77 — Typical waveguide sizes from WR229 on the left to WR42 on the right.

monopole antenna in the center of a wide wall of the waveguide. The probe in Figure 15.76C is simply a short extension of the inner conductor of the coaxial line, oriented so that it is parallel to the electric lines of force. If the probe were very thin and had no capacitance or inductance, it would be λ/4 long and spaced λ/4 from a short-circuit — the closed end of the waveguide. Actual dimensions, in **Table 15.24**, compensate for the probe inductance and capacitance.

Figures 15.76A and B are methods for weaker coupling, for instance to sample the signal. The loop shown in Figure 15.76B is arranged so that it encloses some of the magnetic lines of force. The point at which maximum coupling is obtained depends upon the mode of propagation in the guide or cavity. Coupling is maximum when the coupling device is in the most intense field.

Coupling can be varied by turning the probe or loop through a 90° angle. When the probe is perpendicular to the electric lines the coupling is minimum. Similarly, when the plane of the loop is parallel to the magnetic lines the coupling is minimum.

Coaxial transitions are widely available as surplus components for most standard waveguide sizes. More explanation of how they work, and the different types can be found on the excellent Microwaves101 website at **microwaves101.com/encyclopedias/waveguide-to-coax-transitions**. In addition, you can learn more about the design of transitions in the *QEX* article, "Rectangular Waveguide to Coax Transition Design" (see reference for Wade).

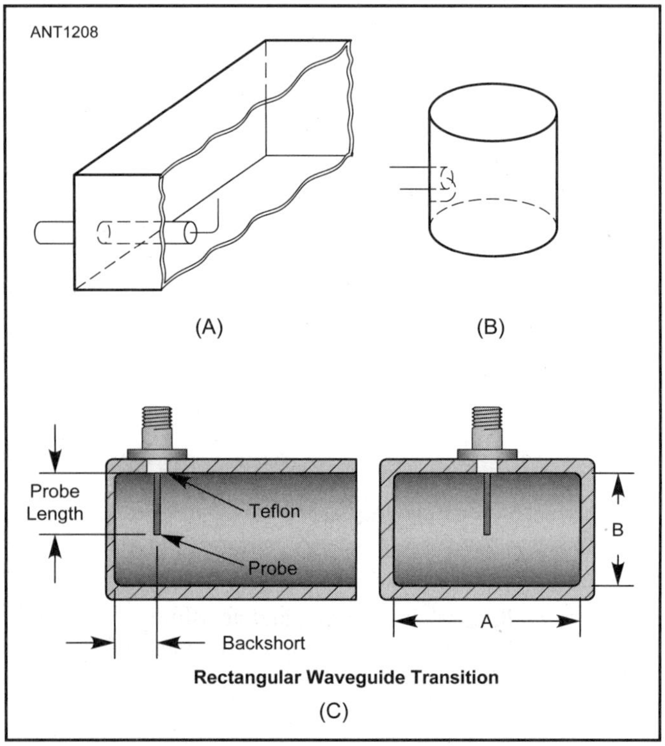

Figure 15.78 — Parts A and B shows methods of coupling coaxial line to waveguide and resonators. At C is a sketch of rectangular waveguide to coax transition, showing dimensions.

WAVEGUIDE TERMINATION

If a waveguide is not terminated in its characteristic impedance, there will be an elevated SWR on the line like any other transmission line. A typical termination is a long horn antenna, which flares out from the end of the waveguide to match the waveguide's characteristic impedance to the impedance of free space, 377 Ω.

Waveguide connections are made by bolting their flanges together firmly. Several flanges are shown in **Figure 15.79**. There are two types of flanges, *flat flanges* and *choke flanges*, which have a groove around the waveguide. The groove acts like a shorted stub that presents a high impedance to the RF energy to prevent leakage. Choke flanges should be mated with flat flanges, but two flat flanges may be mated together.

Waveguides of two different sizes may be mated, but there should be a transition between them since different waveguide

Table 15.24
Waveguide Dimensions and Coax Transitions

Waveguide	*Dimensions (mm)*	*Freq Range (GHz)*	*Freq (GHz)*	*Probe Diam. (mm)*	*Probe Length (mm)*	*Backshort (mm)*	*Bandwidth*
WR42	10.668×4.318	18-26.5	24.192	1.27	2.413	2.489	>17%
WR75	19.05×9.525	10.0-15	10.368	1.27	5.49	5.26	14%
WR90	22.86×10.16	8.2-12.4	10.368	1.27	5.89	5.46	7%
WR112	28.24×12.62	7.05-10	10.368	1.27	6.5	6.6	15%
WR112			5.76	1.27	8.8	9.8	7%
WR137	35.85×15.80	5.85-8.2	5.76	1.27	10.5	8.5	10%
WR159	40.39×20.19	4.9-7.05	5.76	1.27	11.17	10.0	11%
WR187	47.55×22.15	3.95-5.85	5.76	2.36	11.3	11.0	16%
WR187			3.456	2.36	14.5	18.0	5%
WR229	58.17×29.08	3.3-4.9	3.456	1.27	18.2	15.0	8%
WR229			3.456	2.36	17.4	15.06	11%
WR229			3.456	3.175	17	15.6	11%
WR229			3.456	4.76	16.2	16.2	14%
WR229			3.456	6.35	15.5	16.75	17%
WR284	72.14×34.04	2.6-3.95	3.456	6.35	17.5	17.8	27%
WR284			2.304	6.35	20	28	9%
WR340	86.36×43.18	2.2-3.2	2.304	6.35	25	23	11%

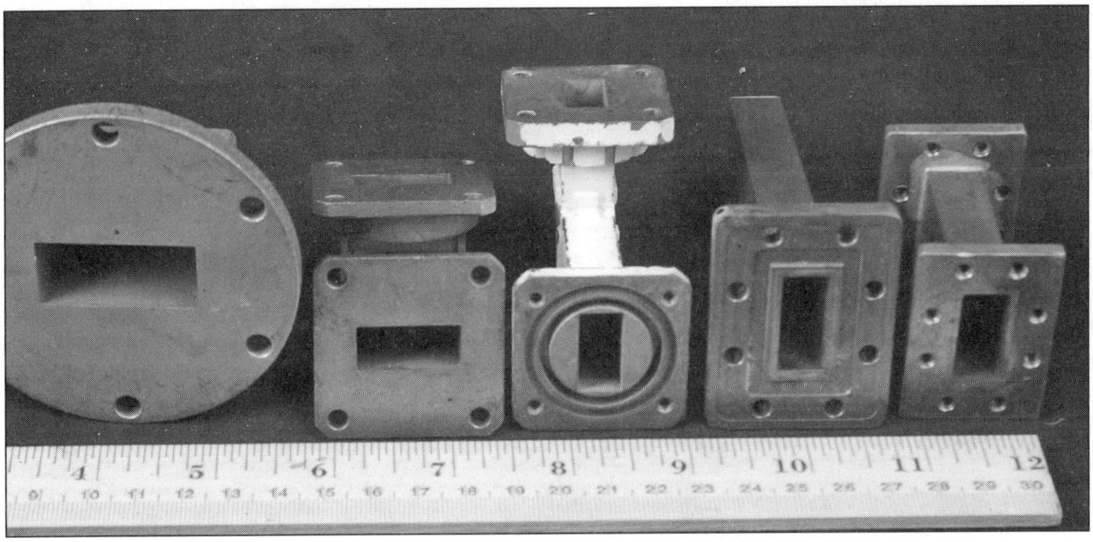

Figure 15.79 — Several typical waveguide flanges used for joining sections of waveguide. The deep grooves in choke flanges (see center flange) place a high impedance in the path of any RF leakage out of the flange.

sizes have different Z_0. Just as in coaxial lines, impedance discontinuities such as at a transition will cause reflections.

PRACTICAL WAVEGUIDES

Standard waveguide sizes dating to World War II are still in use today. The standard designator is WR*xx*, where *xx* is the wide inside dimension in hundredths of an inch; for instance, WR90, often used at 10 GHz, has a wide dimension of 90 hundredths of an inch, or 0.9 inches. There are no standards for circular waveguide, so common copper plumbing is often used — 3/4-inch tubing works well at 10 GHz. Practical dimensions for standard waveguides at amateur microwave calling frequencies are shown in Table 15.27.

Table 15.27 includes dimensions for the waveguide sizes likely to be encountered in microwave work, and probe dimensions for transitions from waveguide to 50 Ω coax. While a waveguide would work very well at lower frequencies, it would be very large — one meter wide for the 2-meter band! The recommended frequency range for each type is also shown in the table. For narrowband amateur work, we can stretch the frequency range a bit to take advantage of available waveguide — some of the waveguide sizes are usable on more than one band. Many smaller size guides are used at mm-wave frequencies.

There are no standard dimensions for circular waveguide, so any available pipe or can may be used as long as the diameter is larger than the cutoff wavelength. Probe dimensions for transitions from circular waveguide to 50 Ω coax are suggested in W1GHZ's Jan/Feb 2001 *QEX* article (see the References) and at **w1ghz.org/QEX/circular_wg.pdf**.

Losses in waveguide are very low, much less than coaxial transmission line, but not negligible at the higher frequencies. For example, WR90 loss is approximately 10 dB per 100 feet at 10 GHz. Power handling is not a problem; even the smallest waveguide is rated at far more than the amateur power limit.

Where the waveguide has to change direction, special fittings called *bends* are used, shown in **Figure 15.80**. These are constructed so that impedance discontinuities from the change in direction are minimized.

Waveguide transmission lines used outdoors will suffer from internal water condensation, like any closed metal container with temperature variations. Even a short length used in a portable station can collect condensation. Commercial installations often pressurize the waveguide with dry air. Otherwise, a drain hole should be provided at the lowest point of a run.

15.8.3 Horn Antennas

Horn antennas are an excellent choice for microwaves — they work well, are easy to build, and are almost foolproof. A horn antenna is the ideal choice for a rover station. It offers moderate gain in a small, rugged package with no adjustments needed, and has a wide enough beam to be easily pointed under adverse conditions. Larger horn antennas can provide higher gain, even enough for EME operation. For horns intended as feed horns for dishes and lenses, beam angle and phase center are more important than horn gain.

HORN DESIGN

An antenna may be considered as a transformer from the impedance of a transmission line to the impedance of free space, 377 Ω. A common microwave transmission line is waveguide, a hollow tube carrying an electromagnetic wave. If one dimension of the tube is greater than one-half wavelength, then the wave can propagate through the waveguide with extremely low loss. If the end of a waveguide is simply left open, the wave will radiate out from the open end.

Practical waveguides have the larger dimension greater than one-half wavelength, to allow wave propagation, but smaller than one wavelength, to suppress higher-order modes which can interfere with low-loss transmission. Thus, the aperture of an open-ended waveguide is less than a wavelength, which does not provide much gain.

For more gain, a larger aperture is desirable, but a larger waveguide is not. However, if the waveguide size is slowly expanded, or tapered, into a larger aperture, then more gain is achieved while preventing undesired modes from reaching

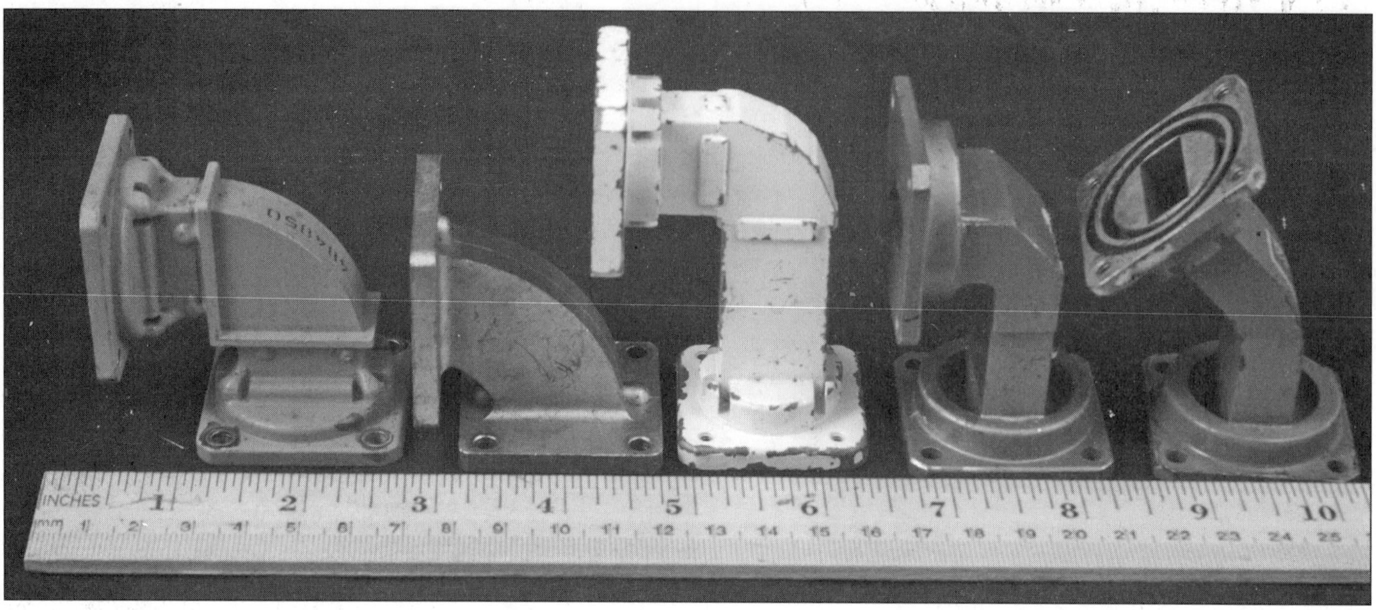

Figure 15.80 — Special sections called bends make right- and 45° angles to avoid introducing impedance discontinuities where the waveguide must change direction.

the waveguide. In common rectangular waveguide, the taper creates a familiar *pyramidal horn*, sketched in **Figure 15.81**. Horns come in many sizes, like those shown in the photograph, **Figure 15.82**. In cylindrical waveguide, a funnel-like taper is called a *conical horn*. The larger conical horn for 2304 MHz shown in Figure 15.82 was made by pop-riveting aluminum flashing to a coffee can. (See the article "How To Build A Tin Can Waveguide WiFi Antenna" by Gregory Rehm at **offgridworld.com/how-to-build-a-tin-can-wifi-antenna-for-5**. The webpage **wikarekare.org/Antenna/WaveguideCan.html** is a calculator for 2.4 GHz band circular horn "cantennas".) based on can diameter along with connector and coupling probe dimensions.)

To achieve maximum gain for a given aperture size, the taper must be long enough so that the phase of the wave is nearly constant across the aperture. An optimum horn is one that provides a specified gain with the least material; several definitions are available. The **Table 15.25** uses approximate dimensions from a set of tables by Cozzens to design pyramidal horn antennas with gains from 10 to 25 dB (see References and Bibliography). Higher gains are possible, but the length of the horn increases much faster than the gain, so very

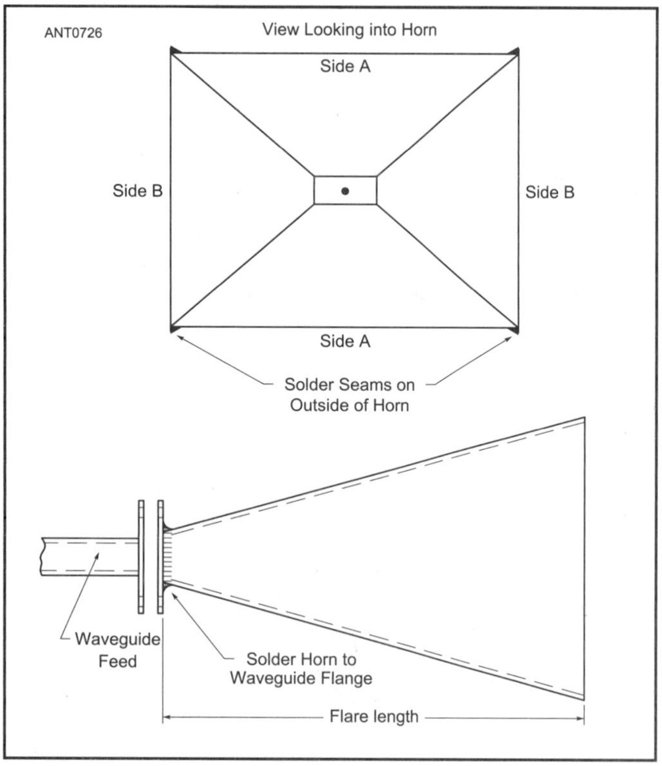

Figure 15.81 — Typical pyramidal horn. These assembly instructions are for the 10 GHz horn project shown in Figure 15.86.

Figure 15.82 — An assortment of horn antennas.

Table 15.25
Pyramidal Horn Dimensions

Gain (dB)	Flare Length (λ)	A (H-plane) (λ)	B (E-plane) (λ)
10	0.08	1.48	1.09
13	0.6	2.09	1.55
16	1.7	2.95	2.18
19	4	4.16	3.08
22	8.7	5.88	4.36
25	18.3	8.31	6.15

high gain horns tend to be unwieldy.

The dimensions in Table 15.28 are in wavelengths, so they are applicable to any frequency. Horns are very forgiving, so the dimensions are not critical — small differences will result in a very small gain difference.

The radiation pattern of a horn antenna can be tailored for special purposes; for instance, a broad azimuth pattern with a narrow vertical pattern might be useful to cover a broad sector without needing rotation, useful for a beacon or mesh network. In *Antennas* (see Bibliography) Kraus gives the following approximations for beamwidth in degrees and dBd gain (with respect to a dipole):

$$E_{plane} = \frac{56}{A_e} \text{degrees}$$

$$H_{plane} = \frac{67}{A_e} \text{degrees}$$

and for gain

$$G \cong 10 \log_{10} (4.5\, A_{e\lambda}\, A_{h\lambda}) \text{ dB over dipole}$$

where $A_{e\lambda}$ is the aperture dimension in wavelengths in the E-plane and $A_{h\lambda}$ is the aperture in wavelengths dimension in the H-plane. Horns shorter than the optimum horns will have less gain than this equation.

There are many varieties of horn antennas. If the waveguide is flared out only in the H-plane, the horn is called an H-plane *sectoral horn*. Similarly, if the flare is only in the E-plane, an E-plane sectoral horn results. Sectoral horns for 10 GHz and that cover 24 and 47 GHz are shown in **Figure 15.83**. If the flare is in both planes, the antenna is called a pyramidal horn.

For a horn of any given aperture, directivity (gain along the axis) is maximum when the field distribution across the aperture is uniform in magnitude and phase. When the fields are not uniform, sidelobes that reduce the directivity of the antenna are formed. To obtain a uniform distribution, the horn should be as long as possible with minimum flare angle. From a practical point of view, however, the horn should be as short as possible, so there is an obvious conflict between performance and convenience.

Figure 15.84 illustrates this problem. For a given flare angle and a given side length, there is a path-length difference from the apex of the horn to the center of the aperture (L), and from the apex of the horn to the edge of the aperture (L′). This causes a phase difference in the field across the aperture, which in turn causes formation of sidelobes, degrading directivity (gain along the axis) of the antenna. If L is large this difference is small, and the field is almost uniform. As L decreases however, the phase difference increases, and directivity suffers. An optimum (shortest possible) horn is constructed so that this phase difference is the maximum allowable before sidelobes become excessive and axial gain markedly decreases.

The magnitude of this permissible phase difference is different for E-plane and H-plane horns. For the E-plane horn, the field intensity is quite constant across the aperture. For the H-plane horn, the field tapers to zero at the edge. Consequently, the phase difference at the edge of the aperture in the E-plane horn is more critical and should be held to less than 90° (1/4 λ). In an H-plane horn, the allowable phase difference is 144° (0.4 λ). If the aperture of a pyramidal horn exceeds one wavelength in both planes, the E-plane and H-plane patterns are essentially independent and can be analyzed separately.

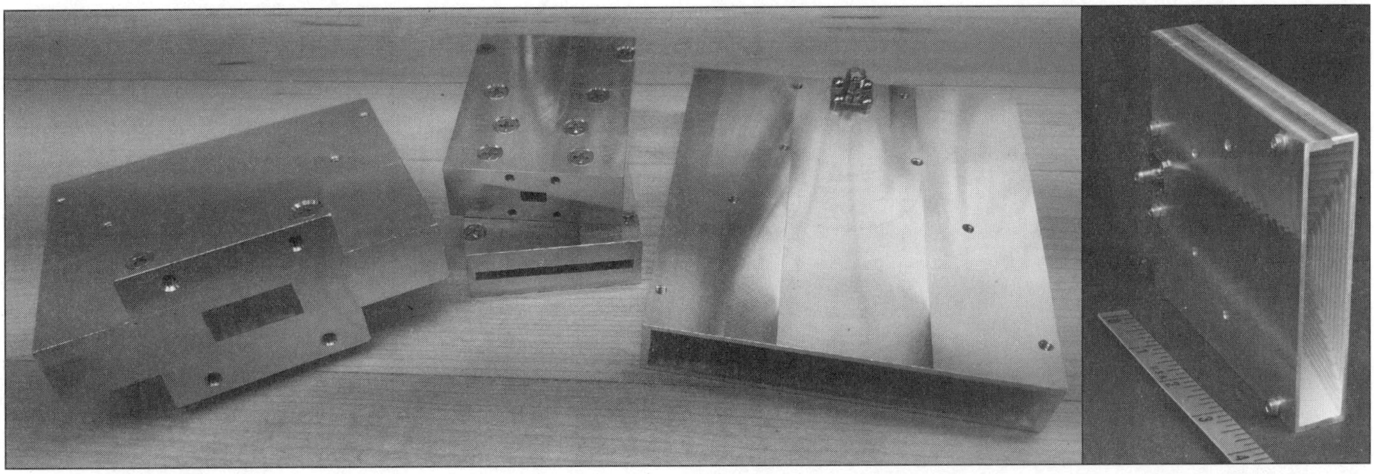

Figure 15.83 — Sectoral horns. Left to right in A: 10 GHz horn with WR-90 waveguide input, front and back of 24 and 47 GHz horn with WR-28 waveguide input, and a 10 GHz horn with an SMA coaxial input. The photo at B shows typical mounting of the H-plane horn for horizontal polarization. (Photos by Paul Wade, W1GHZ)

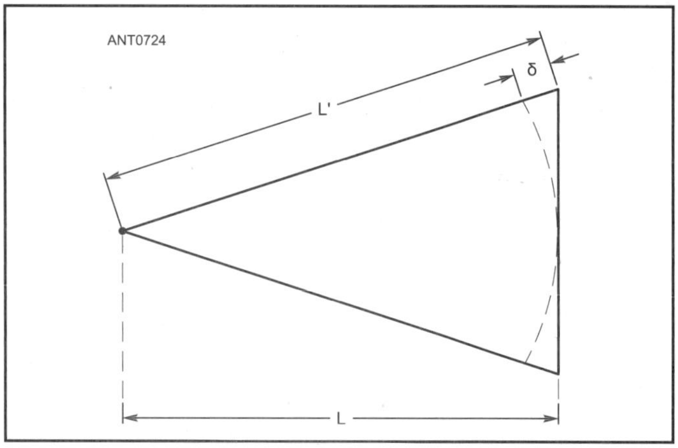

Figure 15.84 —The path-length (phase) difference between the center and edge of a horn antenna is δ.

The usual direction for orienting the waveguide feed is with the broad face horizontal, giving vertical polarization. If this is the case, the H-plane sectoral horn has a narrow horizontal beamwidth and a very wide vertical beamwidth. This is not a very useful beam pattern for most amateur applications. The E-plane sectoral horn has a narrow vertical beamwidth and a wide horizontal beamwidth. Such a radiation pattern could be useful in a beacon system where wide coverage is desired.

The most useful form of the horn for general applications is the optimum pyramidal horn. In this configuration the two beamwidths are almost the same. The E-plane (vertical) beamwidth is slightly less than the H-plane (horizontal), and also has greater sidelobe intensity.

Small horns may be constructed from sheet metal, from raw PC board material, or even machined from solid metal for extremely high microwave frequencies. Larger horns have been made from mesh screening and from foil-coated Styrofoam insulation. Templates and construction instructions are provided in the document "Horn Construction and Templates" in the online material.

Figure 15.85 — 3D-printed horns before and after metalization.

A recent construction technique is 3D-printed horns. The printed plastic is transparent to RF, so the horn must be metalized. Glenn Robb, KS4VA, and Michelle Thompson, W5NYV, have worked to perfect the techniques. Some of Glenn's horn antennas are shown in **Figure 15.85**. See the "Microwavelengths" column in the January 2019 issue of *QST* for details.

Surplus horns may be found in many shapes and sizes, for instance, on satellite TV antennas and various WiFi devices. The key is the input waveguide size — if the diameter or large rectangular dimension is greater than 0.6 λ and less than 1 λ, the horn will work as an antenna, so it is worth a try.

15.8.4 Parabolic Dish Antennas

Parabolic dish antennas can provide extremely high gains at microwave frequencies. A 2-foot dish at 10 GHz can provide more than 30 dB of gain. The gain is only limited by the size of the parabolic reflector; a number of hams have dishes larger than 20 feet, and occasionally a much larger commercial dish is made available for amateur operation. For example, the former 1000-foot dish Arecibo dish in Puerto Rico was operational on 432 MHz EME on a few occasions. All dish antennas have high directivity (sharp patterns); high gains are only achievable if the antennas are properly implemented, and dishes have more critical dimensions than horns and lenses. The fundamental parameters are explained here using pictures and graphics as an aid to understanding the critical areas and how to deal with them.

New commercial dishes are expensive, but surplus ones can often be purchased at low cost. Some amateurs build theirs, while others modify satellite TV dishes or even circular metal snow sleds for the amateur bands. **Figure 15.86** shows a dish using a homemade coffee-can feed described below.

Figure 15.86 — Coffee-can 2304 MHz feed described in text mounted on a 4-foot dish.

ALTERNATIVES

Bear in mind that the narrow beamwidth of a dish may make contacts more difficult, particularly in windy conditions. It is often easier to complete a contact for all but the longest paths with smaller, easier to point antennas, such as horns and flat panel antennas. As an extreme example, Rex Moncur, VK7MO, has made 10 GHz EME contacts with a horn antenna — DX doesn't get any farther than that.

For a rover station, a reasonable size horn might be a good compromise with adequate gain and moderate beamwidth for easy aiming. I often use the 17.5 dBi Gunnplexer horn, with a 12-inch lens ready to place in front of it when signals are marginal.

AIMING

A quality compass and a way of accurately aligning a dish antenna to it are essential for successful operation. Narrow beamwidth and frequency uncertainty can make searching for weak signals frustrating and time-consuming. A heavy tripod with setting circles is a good start; hang a heavy object like a portable station operating battery from the center of the tripod and it will be more stable, especially in the wind. Calibrate your headings by locating a station with a known beam heading rather than by eyeballing the dish heading; small mechanical tolerances can easily shift the beam a few degrees from the apparent *boresight* (the line along which the dish is aimed).

DISH ANTENNA DESIGN

A dish antenna works the same way as a reflecting optical telescope. Electromagnetic waves, either light or radio, arrive as parallel rays (or planar wavefronts) from a distant source and are reflected by a parabolic mirror to a common point, called the *focus*. When a ray of light reflects from a mirror or flat surface, the angle of the path leaving (angle of reflection) is the same as the angle of the path arriving (angle of incidence). If the mirror is a flat surface, then two rays of light leave in parallel paths; however, if the mirror is curved, two parallel incident rays leave at different angles. If the curve is parabolic ($y = ax^2$) then all the reflected rays meet at one point, as shown in **Figure 15.87**. A dish is a *parabola of rotation*, a parabolic curve rotated around an axis which passes through the focus and the center of the curve.

A transmitting antenna reverses the path: The light or radio wave originates from a point source at the focus and is reflected into a beam of rays parallel to the axis of the parabola, as shown in Figure 15.87.

There are two basic types of parabolic dishes: *prime-focus* dishes, the classic shape, and *offset-fed* dishes, like the popular small satellite TV dishes. While almost all offset-fed dishes that you are likely to find have the same basic geometry, prime-focus dishes come in various configurations, from very deep dishes to shallow ones. They are characterized by the *f/D ratio*, the ratio of focal length of the parabola to its diameter. Deep dishes (such as a soup bowl) have a small f/D, less than about 0.35, while shallow dishes (such as a dinner plate) have larger f/D and thus a larger focal length for a given diameter. All dishes with the same f/D have the same geometry, regardless of size, which simplifies antenna system design.

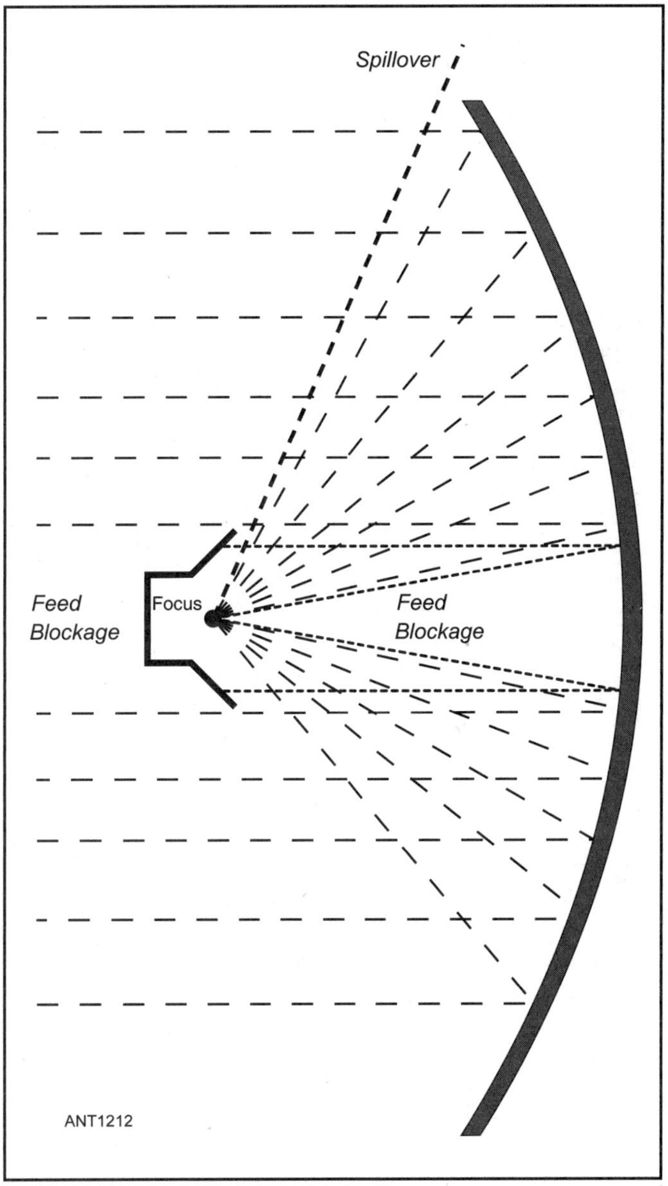

Figure 15.87 — Geometry of parabolic dish antenna.

ILLUMINATING THE DISH

Some of the difficulties found in real antennas are easier to understand when considering a transmitting antenna but are also present in receiving antennas, since antennas are reciprocal. One difficulty is finding a point source, since any antenna, even a half-wave dipole at 10 GHz, is much bigger than a point. (A point source is equivalent to the *isotropic radiator* used as a reference for specifying gain.) Even if we were able to find a point source, it would radiate equally in all directions, so the energy that was not radiated toward the reflector would be wasted. The energy radiated from the focus toward the reflector illuminates the reflector, just as a light bulb would. What we are looking for is a point source that illuminates only the reflector, without any spillover missing the reflector or aimed away from the dish entirely.

APERTURE, GAIN, AND EFFICIENCY

The aperture, A, of a dish antenna is the area of the reflector as seen by a passing radio wave:

$$A = \pi r^2$$

where r is the radius, half of the dish diameter.

If the dish antenna is replaced with a much larger one, the greater aperture of the larger dish captures much more of the passing radio wave, so larger dish has more gain than the smaller one. From a little geometry, we find that the gain is proportional to the aperture area.

The gain of a dish with reference to an isotropic radiator is calculated as:

$$G_{dB} = 10\log_{10}\left(\eta\frac{4\pi}{\lambda^2}A\right)$$

where η is the efficiency of the antenna.

How much efficiency should be expected? References suggest that 55% is reasonable and 70 to 80% is possible with very good feeds. These values are possible with large dishes, > 25 λ in diameter, but many amateur dishes are relatively small. Realizing an efficiency greater than 50% is difficult for small dishes, and efficiency decreases further for diameters less than 10 λ.

See **Table 15.26** for parabolic antenna gain for the bands 420 MHz through 10 GHz and diameters of 2 to 30 feet. The 55% efficiency assumed in the table is rather optimistic for small dishes.

A close approximation of beamwidth may be found from

$$\psi = \frac{70\lambda}{D}$$

where

ψ = beamwidth in degrees at half-power points (3 dB down)

D = dish diameter in feet

λ = wavelength in feet

Table 15.26
Gain, Parabolic Antennas*

	Dish Diameter (Feet)						
Frequency	*2*	*4*	*6*	*10*	*15*	*20*	*30*
420 MHz	6.0	12.0	15.5	20.0	23.5	26.0	29.5
902	12.5	18.5	22.0	26.5	30.0	32.5	36.0
1215	15.0	21.0	24.5	29.0	32.5	35.0	38.5
2300	20.5	26.5	30.0	34.5	38.0	40.5	44.0
3300	24.0	30.0	33.5	37.5	41.5	43.5	47.5
5650	28.5	34.5	38.0	42.5	46.0	48.5	52.0
10 GHz	33.5	39.5	43.0	47.5	51.0	53.5	57.0

*Gain over an isotropic antenna (subtract 2.1 dB for gain over a dipole antenna). Reflector efficiency of 55% assumed.

PRACTICAL DISH ANTENNAS

Feed Patterns

The parabolic dish antenna was first described with a point source at the focus so that energy would radiate with uniform magnitude and phase in all directions. The problem is that energy not radiated toward the reflector is wasted. What is desired is a feed antenna that only radiates toward the reflector and has a phase pattern that appears to radiate from a single point.

We have already seen that efficiency is a measure of how well the aperture is used. If the whole reflector is illuminated, then we should be using the whole aperture. Perhaps the feed pattern should be as shown in **Figure 15.88**, with uniform feed illumination across the reflector. Looking more closely at the parabolic surface, the focus is farther from the edge of the reflector than from the center. Since radiated power diminishes with the square of the distance (inverse-square law), less energy is arriving at the edge of the reflector than at the center; this is commonly called *space attenuation* or *space taper*. In order to compensate, more power must be provided to the edge of the dish than in the center. This is done by adjusting the feed pattern as shown in **Figure 15.89** to have constant illumination over the surface of the reflector.

Simple feed antennas, like a circular horn (coffee-can feed) used by many hams, have a $\cos^n(\theta)$ pattern like the idealized pattern shown in **Figure 15.90**. **Figure 15.91** superimposes the ideal pattern on our desired pattern; there is too much energy in the center, not enough at the edges, and some misses the reflector entirely. The missing energy at the edges is called *illumination loss* and the energy that misses the reflector is called *spillover loss*. The more energy we have at the edge, the more spillover we have, but if we reduce spillover, then the outer part of the dish is not well illuminated and is not contributing to the gain. Therefore, simple horn feeds are not ideal for dish feeds (although they are useful). In order to have very efficient dish illumination we need to increase energy near the edge of the dish and have the energy drop off very quickly beyond the edge.

Edge Taper

Almost all feed horns will provide less energy at the edge of dish than at the center, as in Figure 15.92. The difference in power at the edge is referred to as the *edge taper*. With different feed horns, edge taper can be varied. Different edge tapers produce different amounts of illumination loss and spillover loss, as shown in **Figure 15.92**: a small edge taper results in larger spillover loss, while a large edge taper reduces the spillover loss at the expense of increased illumination loss.

Plotting these losses versus the energy at the edge of the dish in **Figure 15.93**, we find that the total efficiency of a dish antenna peaks with an illumination taper, like Figure 15.91, so that the

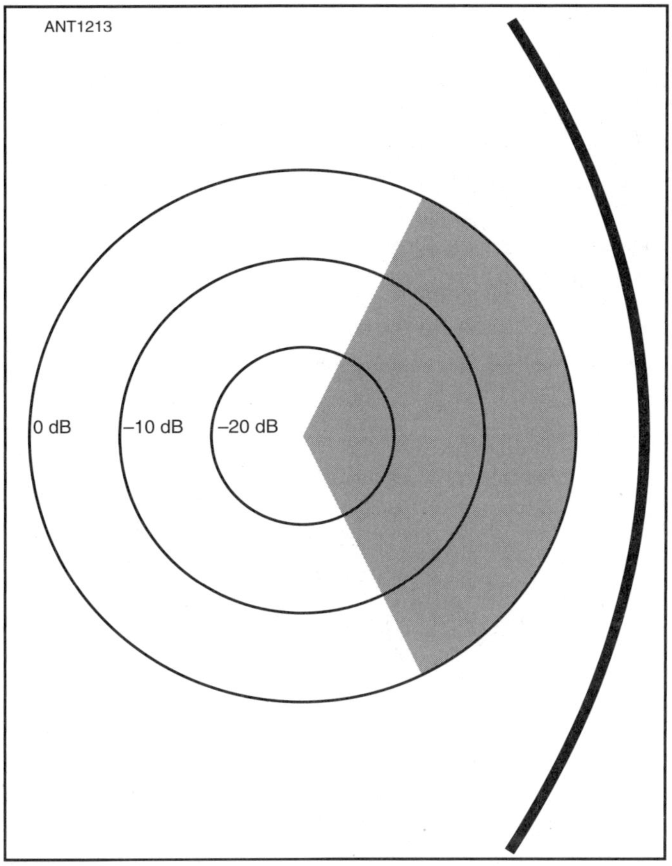

Figure 15.88 — Parabolic dish antenna with uniform feed illumination.

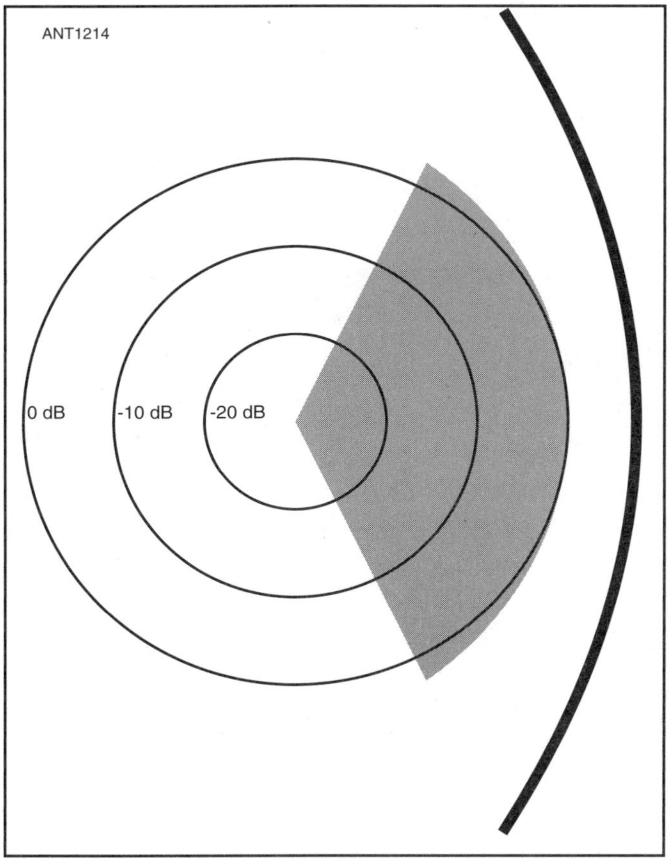

Figure 15.89 — Desired dish illumination - uniform reflector illumination.

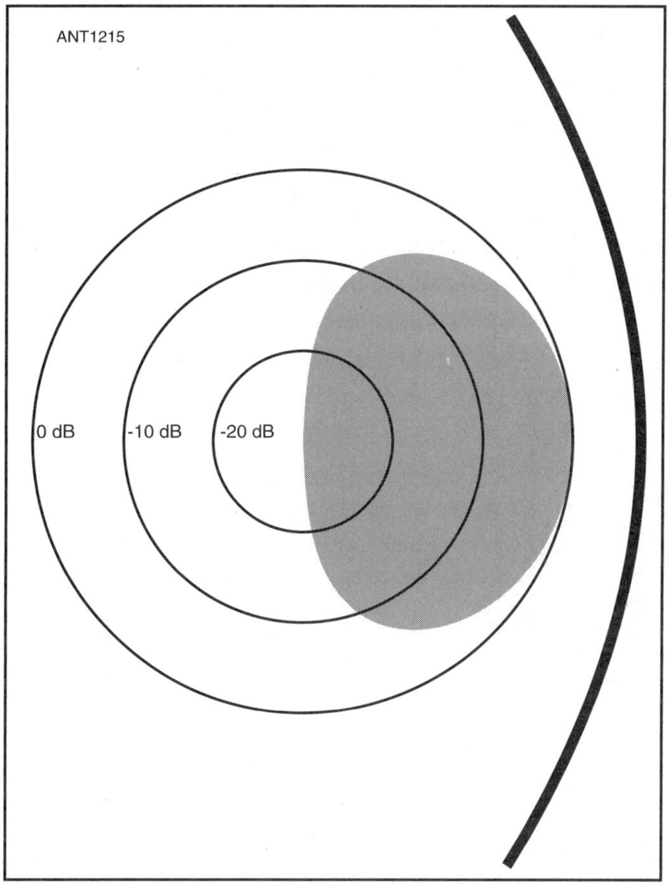

Figure 15.90 — Parabolic dish antenna with typical feed horn illumination.

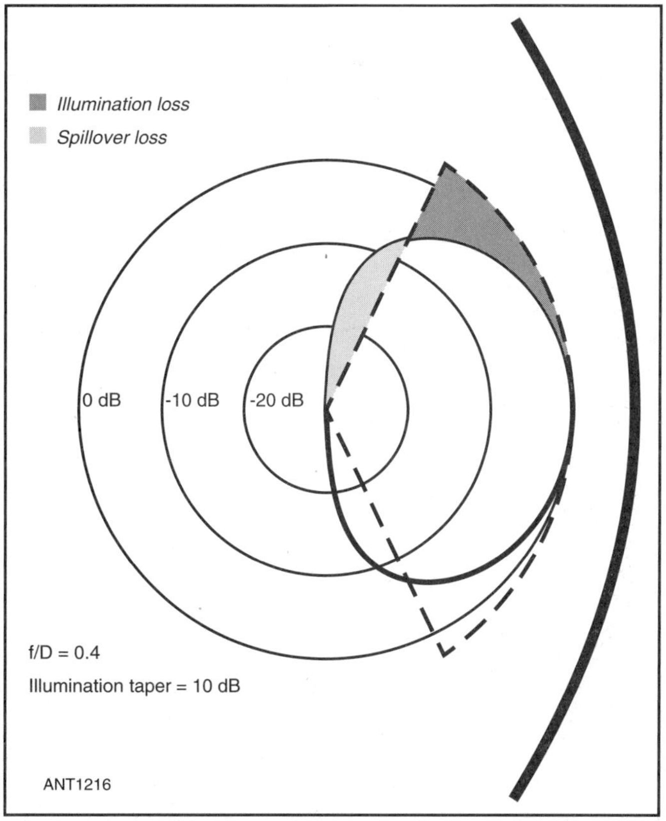

Figure 15.91 — Typical vs. desired dish illumination.

energy at the edge is about10 dB lower than the energy at the center. This is often referred to as 10 dB edge taper or edge illumination — often recommended but not explained. However, some high-efficiency feeds shape the radiation pattern for maximum dish performance. For these feeds, the best edge taper may not be 10 dB.

Gain/Temperature (G/T)

When an antenna is receiving a signal from space, like a satellite or EME signal, there is very little background noise emanating from the sky compared to the noise generated by the warm (300° K) earth during terrestrial communications. Most of the noise received by an antenna pointed at the sky is *earth noise* arriving through feed spillover. As we saw in Figure 15.91, the spillover can be reduced by increasing the edge taper, while Figure 15.92 shows the efficiency, and thus the gain, decreasing slowly as edge taper is increased. The best compromise is reached when *G/T*, the ratio of gain to

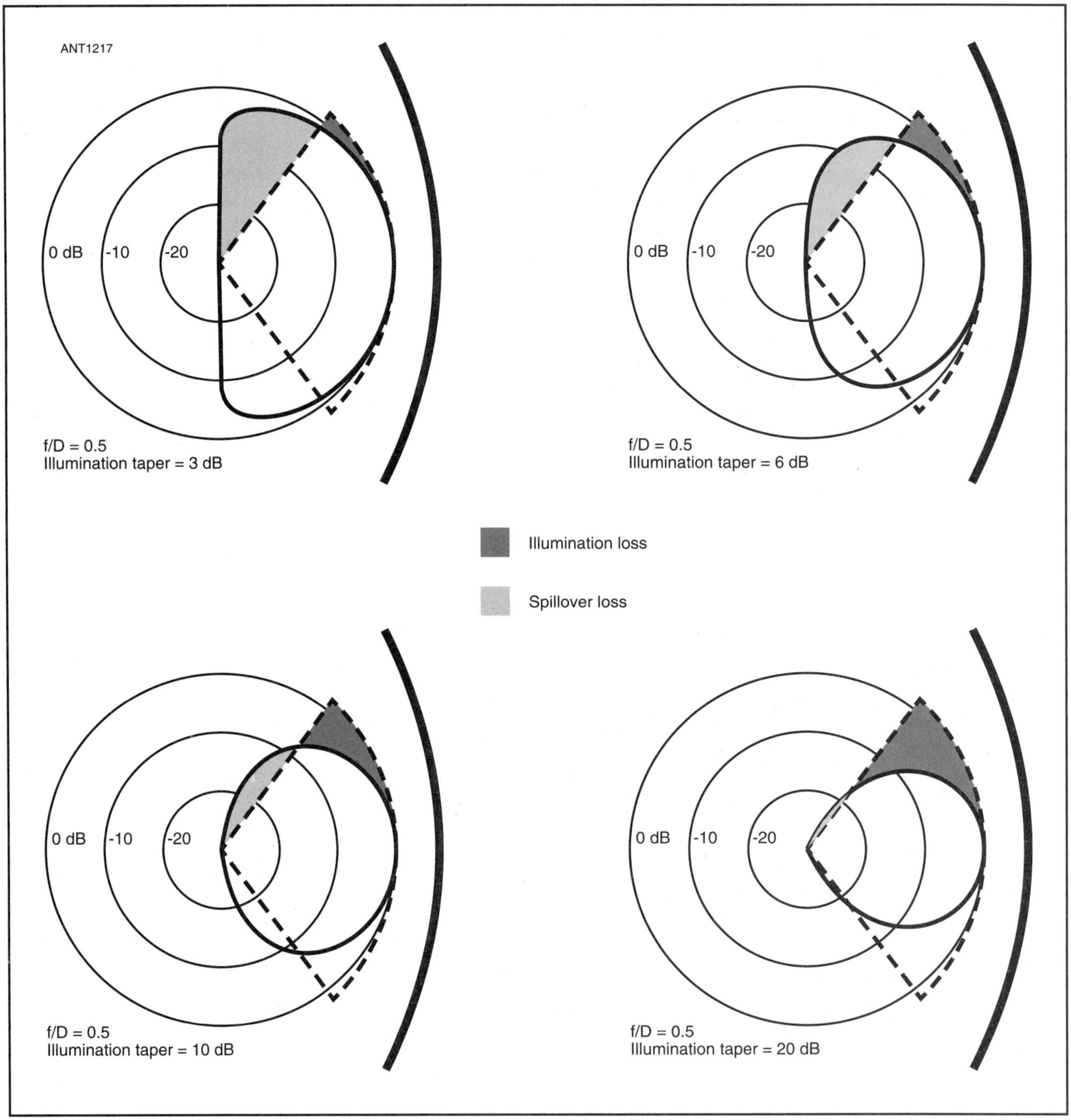

Figure 15.92 — Dish illumination with various illumination tapers.

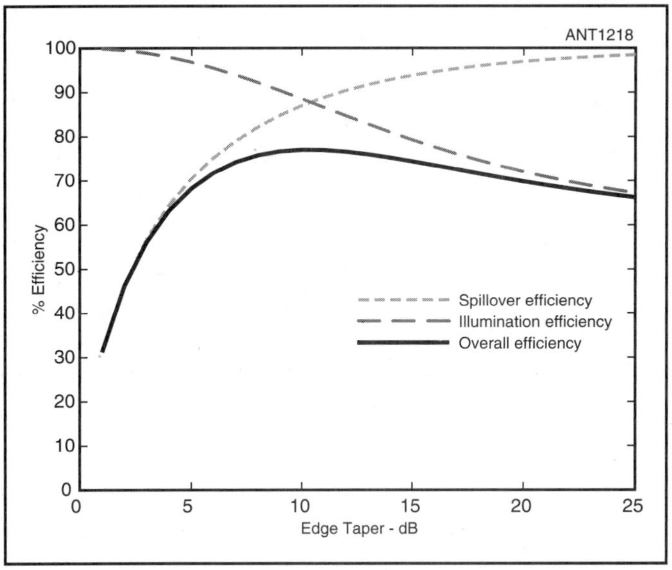

Figure 15.93 — Efficiency vs. edge taper for a dish.

antenna noise temperature, is maximized. This typically occurs with a larger edge taper than for maximum gain. The optimum edge taper for G/T is a function of receiver noise temperature and sky noise temperature at any given frequency.

Focal Length and f/D Ratio

All parabolic dishes have the same parabolic curvature, but some are shallow dishes while others are much deeper, more like a bowl. They are just different parts of a parabola which extends to infinity. A convenient way to describe how much of the parabola is used is the *f*/D ratio, the ratio of the *focal length*, f, to the diameter, D, of the dish. All dishes with the same f/D ratio require the same feed geometry, in proportion to the diameter of the dish. The figures so far have depicted one arbitrary f/D: **Figure 15.94** shows the relative geometries for commonly used f/D ratios, typically from 0.25 to 0.65, with the desired and idealized feed patterns for each.

To calculate the focal length and f/D ratio of a dish, measure the diameter of the dish and the depth, d, in the center of the dish. This may need to be an approximation for some dishes, due to holes or flat areas in the center. The focal length is calculated as:

$$f = \frac{D^2}{16d}$$

Notice the feed horn patterns for the various f/D ratios in Figure 15.96. As f/D becomes smaller, the feed pattern to illuminate it becomes broader, so different feed horns are needed to properly illuminate dishes with different f/D ratios. The feed horn pattern must be matched to the reflector's f/D. Dishes with larger f/D ratios need a feed horn with a moderate beamwidth, while a dish with an f/D of 0.25 has its focus level with the edge of the dish and the subtended angle that must be illuminated is 180 degrees. Also, the edge of the dish is twice as far from the focus as the center of the dish, so the desired pattern would have to be 6 dB stronger (according to the inverse-square law) at the edge as in the center. This is an extremely difficult feed pattern to generate, and consequently, it is almost impossible to efficiently illuminate a dish this deep.

Given a choice, a reflector with a large f/D (0.5 to 0.6) would be preferable. As described earlier, dishes with small f/D are hard to illuminate efficiently and are more sensitive to focal length errors. On the other hand, a dish that is available for the right price is always a good starting point!

Phase Center

A well-designed feed for a dish or lens has a single *phase center*, so illuminating radiation appears to emanate from a single point source, at least in the feed's main beam which is the part of the pattern that illuminates the dish or lens. Away from the main beam, the phase center may move around and appear at multiple points because stray reflections and surface currents affect the radiation pattern. Also, the phase center will move with frequency, adding difficulty to broadband feed design. Fortunately, amateur microwave operation only uses narrow frequency ranges.

Symmetry of E-plane and H-Plane

On paper, we can only depict radiation in one plane. For a simple antenna with linear polarization, like a dipole, this is all we really care about. A dish, however, is three-dimensional, so it must be fed uniformly in all planes. The usual plane for linear polarization is the E-plane, while the plane perpendicular to it is the H-plane. Unfortunately, most antennas not only have different radiation patterns in the E- and H- planes but also have different phase centers in each plane, so both phase centers cannot be at the focus. A good feed antenna has the same phase center in both E- and H- planes and all other planes.

Focal Length Error

The most critical dimension in a dish antenna is the focal length — the axial distance from the feed to the center of the dish. **Figure 15.95** shows the loss as the feed horn is moved closer and farther from the focus for various f/D dishes with uniform illumination; the tapered illumination used in practice will not have nulls as deep as these curves. It is clear that dishes with small f/D are much more sensitive to focal length error. Remember that a wavelength at 10 GHz is just over an inch! Lateral errors in feed horn position are far less serious; small errors have little effect on gain but do result in shifting the beam slightly off boresight.

Notice that the focal length error in Figure 15.94 is in *wavelengths*, independent of the dish size. A 1/4-wavelength error in focal length produces the same loss for a 150-foot dish as for a 2-foot dish, and a 1/4-wavelength at 10 GHz is just over 1/4 inch. Another implication is that multiband feeds should be optimized for the highest band, since they will be less critical at lower bands with longer wavelengths.

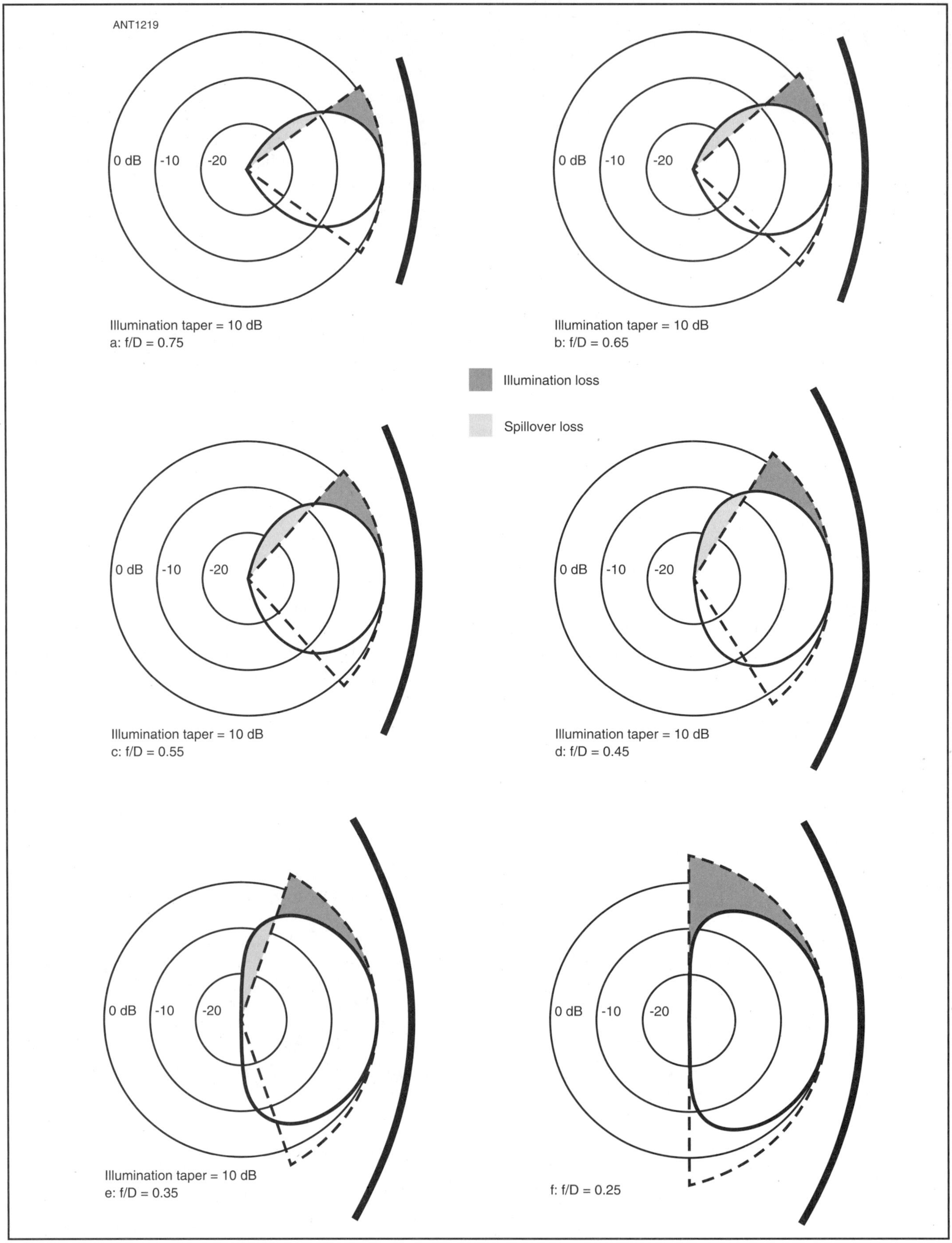

Figure 15.94 — Dish illumination for various f/D ratios.

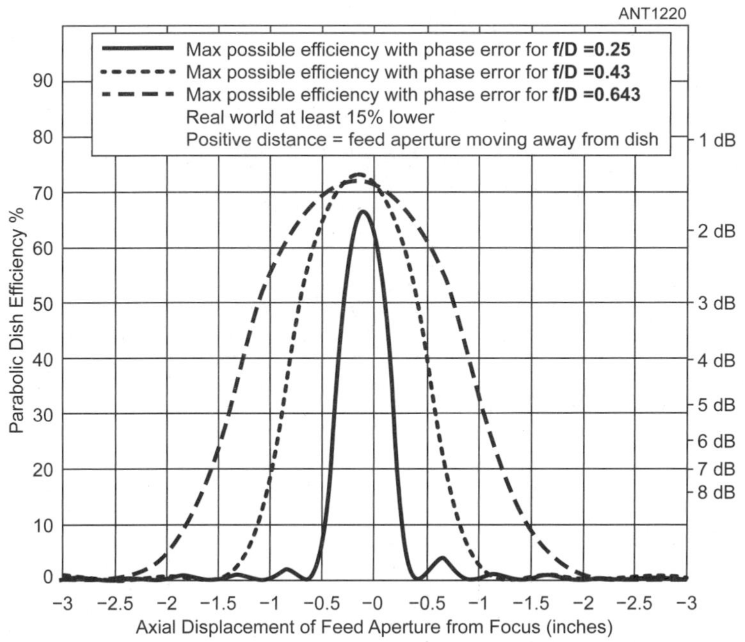

Figure 15.95 — Maximum efficiency versus phase error.

Total Efficiency

We want high efficiency because a dish has the same size, wind loading, and narrow beamwidth regardless of efficiency — we should get as much performance as possible for these operational difficulties.

The major factors affecting aperture efficiency are illumination taper and spillover, but there are several other factors that can significantly reduce efficiency. Because the feed horn and its supporting structures are in the beam of the dish, part of the radiation is blocked or deflected. A real feed horn also has sidelobes, so part of its radiation is in undesired directions and thus wasted. Finally, no reflector is a perfect parabola, so the focusing of the beam is not perfect. The result is quite a list of contributions to total efficiency:

- Illumination taper
- Spillover loss
- Asymmetries in E- and H-Planes
- Focal point error
- Feed horn sidelobes
- Blockage by the feed horn
- Blockage by supporting structures
- Imperfections in parabolic surface.
- Feed line loss

The most critical are:

Focal point error — the phase center of the feed must be at the focal point of the parabolic reflector. Errors here can add up to many dB.

Feed illumination — the feed must efficiently illuminate the reflector. The difference between a good feed and a poor one can be a few dB.

Everything else is a matter of good engineering practice. Shortcuts might only cost a few tenths of a dB, but a few of them can add up.

PRACTICAL FEED SYSTEMS

An optimum feed would approximate the desired feed pattern for the f/D of the parabolic reflector in both planes and have the same phase center in both planes.

The feed aperture is located at the focal point of the dish and aimed at the center of the reflector. The feed mounts should permit adjustment of the aperture either side of the focal point and should present a minimum of blockage to the reflector. Correct distance to the dish center places the focal point about 1 inch inside the feed aperture. The use of a nonmetallic support minimizes blockage. PVC pipe, fiberglass and Plexiglas are commonly used materials. A simple test by placing a material in a microwave oven reveals if it is satisfactory up to 2450 MHz. PVC pipe has tested satisfactorily and appears to work well at 2300 MHz. A simple, clean looking mount for a 4-foot dish with 18 inches focal length, for example, can be made by mounting a length of 4-inch PVC pipe using a PVC flange at the center of the dish. At 2304 MHz the circular feed is approximately 4 inches ID, making a snug fit with the PVC pipe. Precautions should be taken to keep rain and small birds from entering the feed.

Circular Feed

One of the simplest feed horns for a prime-focus dish is a plain cylindrical waveguide. It provides moderately good performance which can be improved by the addition of choke rings, described below. (Rectangular waveguide feeds can also be used, but dish illumination is not as uniform as with round guide feeds.) A circular feed can be made of copper, brass, aluminum, or even tin cans. The circular feed must be within a proper diameter range for the frequency being used. This feed operates in the circular waveguide's dominant TE mode. The guide must be large enough to pass the mode with no attenuation, but smaller than the diameter that permits the next higher mode to propagate. To support the desirable mode in circular waveguide, the cutoff frequency, F_c, is given by

$$F_C\,(TE_{11}) = \frac{6917.26}{d\text{ (inches)}}$$

where

f_c = cutoff frequency in MHz for mode
d = waveguide inner diameter

Circular waveguide will support the mode having a cutoff frequency

$$F_C\,(TM_{01}) = \frac{9034.85}{d\text{ (inches)}}$$

The wavelength in a waveguide always exceeds the free-space wavelength and is called guide wavelength, λ_g. It is related to the cutoff frequency and operating frequency by the equation

$$\lambda_g = \frac{11802.85}{\sqrt{f_0^2 - f_C^2}}$$

where

λ_g = guide wavelength, inches
f_0 = operating frequency, MHz
f_C = waveguide cutoff frequency, MHz

An inside diameter range of about 0.66 to 0.76 λ is suggested. The lower frequency limit (longer dimension) is dictated by proximity to the cutoff frequency. The higher frequency limit (shorter dimension) is dictated by higher order waves. See **Table 15.27** for recommended inside diameter dimensions for the 902 MHz to 10 GHz amateur bands.

The probe that excites the waveguide and makes the transition from coaxial cable to waveguide is approximately λ/4 λ long and spaced from the closed end of the guide by 1/4 guide wavelength, but adjustments will be needed for good VSWR. The length of the feed should be 2 to 3 guide wavelengths. The latter is preferred if a second probe is to be mounted for polarization change or for *polaplexer* operation where duplex communication (simultaneous transmission and reception) is possible because of the isolation between two properly located and oriented probes. The second probe for polarization switching or polaplexer operation should be spaced 3/4 guide wavelength from the closed end and mounted at right angles to the first probe. (A polaplexer is a polarization-based diplexer antenna, or antenna feed, which supports two simultaneous inputs or outputs that are independent and isolated from each other by use of orthogonal (at right angles) linear polarization. (See the article by Munn listed in the References and Bibliography.)

Table 15.28 gives the subtended angle at focus for dish f/D ratios from 0.2 to 1.0. A dish, for example, with a typical f/D of 0.4 requires a 10-dB beamwidth of 130 degrees. A circular waveguide feed with a diameter of approximately 0.7 λ provides nearly optimum illumination but does not uniformly illuminate the reflector in both the magnetic (TM) and electric (TE) planes. At 1296 and 2304 MHz, coffee cans are roughly the right diameter, roughly 0.71 λ, and have been frequently used as a feed horn.

Open waveguide feeds are simple and work reasonably well, but performance can be significantly improved by adding a choke ring which shapes the feed radiation pattern for better dish illumination. A sketch is shown in **Figure 15.96.**

A version of the choke ring popularized by Barry Malowanchuk, VE4MA, has a choke depth, C, of 1/2 λ and choke diameter, B, of one λ greater than the horn diameter, A. However, the dimensions which offer best performance are a choke depth of 0.45 λ and a choke width of 1.2 λ greater than the horn diameter. The choke position may be adjusted to optimize the horn projection for different f/D — the horn projection should be larger for small f/D. The phase center of these feeds is very close to the center of the aperture of the central horn. Patch antennas have also been used as feeds for dishes. (See examples in the **Antennas for Space Communication** chapter.)

Table 15.27
Circular Waveguide Dish Feeds

Freq. (MHz)	*Inside Diameter Circular Waveguide Range (inches)*
915	8.52-9.84
1296	6.02-6.94
2304	3.39-3.91
3400	2.29-2.65
5800	1.34-1.55
10,250	0.76-0.88

MECHANICAL SUPPORT

There are two critical mechanical problems: mounting the feed horn to the dish and mounting the dish to a tripod. Most small dishes have no backing structure, so the thin aluminum surface is easily deformed. Larry Filby, K1LPS, discovered that some cast-aluminum frying pans have a rolled edge that sits nicely on the back of a dish. This is a good use for an old

Table 15.28
f/D Versus Subtended Angle at Focus of a Parabolic Reflector Antenna

f/D	*Subtended Angle (Deg.)*	*f/D*	*Subtended Angle (Deg.)*
0.20	203	0.65	80
0.25	181	0.70	75
0.30	161	0.75	69
0.35	145	0.80	64
0.40	130	0.85	60
0.45	117	0.90	57
0.50	106	0.95	55
0.55	97	1.00	52
0.60	88		

Taken from graph "f/D vs Subtended Angle at Focus," page 170 of the 1966 *Microwave Engineers' Handbook and Buyers Guide*. Graph courtesy of K. S. Kelleher, Aero Geo Astro Corp, Alexandria, Virginia

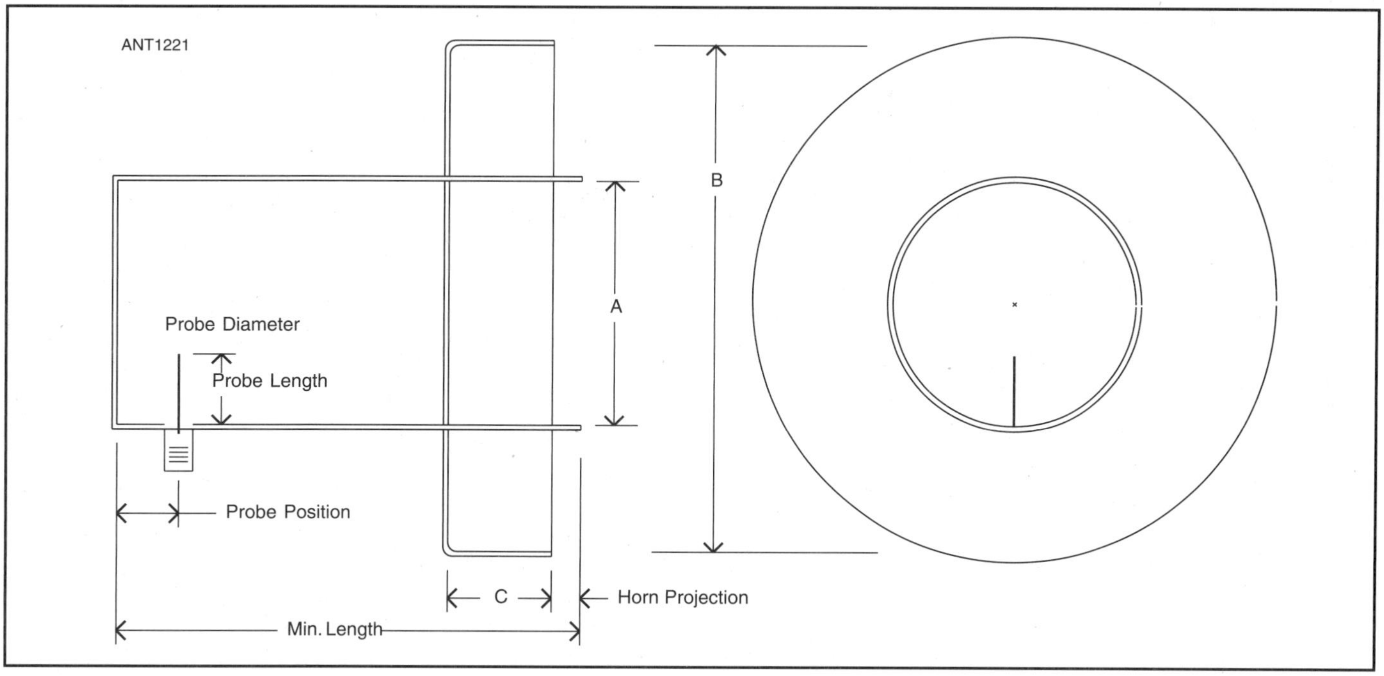

Figure 15.96 — A choke ring mounted on a circular feed to improve dish illumination.

frying pan with worn-out non-stick coating. Drill and tap a few holes in the edge of the old pan, screw the dish to it, and you have a solid backing. A solid piece of angle iron or aluminum attaches the bottom of the frying pan to the top of a tripod.

The mounting structure for the feed horn is in the RF field of view, so we must minimize its blockage. We do this by using non-conductive materials and by mounting the support struts diagonally, so they aren't in the plane of the polarization. Fiberglass is a good material; plant stakes or bicycle flags are good sources. Using four rather than three struts is recommended — if they are all the same length, then the feed will be centered. The base of the struts should be attached to the backing structure or edge of the frying pan; the thin dish surface is not mechanically strong.

The feed horn is in the center of the beam, also blocking part of the beam and reducing gain and efficiency. If the electronics are placed near the feed horn, they may add additional blockage, while placing the electronics behind the dish requires lossy feed line. A good compromise is to place an LNA at the feed horn for best G/T, while the transmit signal suffers feed line loss.

There is also a mechanical problem. Prime-focus dishes are mounted and supported from the rear, resulting in an unbalanced structure with all the weight on one side. Small dishes may be balanced by the weight of the electronics on the back. Larger dishes may require a counterweight.

OFFSET PARABOLIC DISHES

An offset-fed dish has some advantages. The major advantage is that the feed horn is not in the beam of the antenna, so that the whole reflector is utilized, and efficiency is higher. Equipment may also be placed out of the beam but close to the feed horn for minimum feed line loss. But setting up an offset-fed dish is much less obvious: where is the focus, where to point the feed horn, and how to aim the antenna?

Almost all offset dishes, especially the ubiquitous small satellite-TV dishes, use a geometry shown in **Figure 15.97** where the oval reflector projects as a circle looking along the beam from the front, so the effective diameter, D, equals the width of the oval. The bottom of the offset dish is the vertex of a full parabola, so that the vertex, focus and the beam are still in line. This simplifies the required calculations. (For a more complete treatment, see "Microwavelengths" in the April 2018 issue of *QST*.)

Focal length, f, is calculated from the height and width of the reflector using Legon's equation:

$$f = \frac{\text{width}^3}{16 \times \text{depth} \times \text{height}}$$

The resulting f/D is about 0.6 for most common offset dishes.

The feed horn is placed with its phase center at the focus and aimed so that the reflector is evenly illuminated. Note in Figure 15.100 that the focus is closer to the bottom of the dish than to the top — the feed must be aimed slightly higher than the center of the dish to compensate. The feed is aimed up toward the dish by the feed angle:

$$\varphi_f = 2\tan^{-1}\left(\frac{1}{4 \times f/d}\right)$$

about 40 degrees for common offset dishes.

The offset reflector is then tilted forward by the tilt angle φ_c to aim the beam on the horizon:

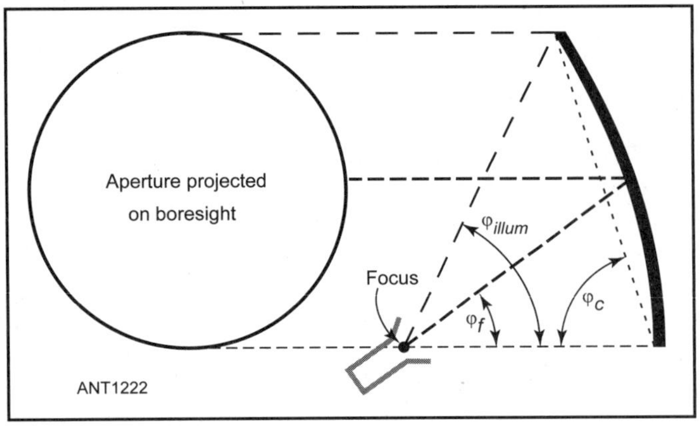

Figure 15.97 — Common offset parabolic dish antenna.

$$\varphi_c = \tan^{-1}\left(\frac{4f}{D}\right)$$

about 67 degrees for common offset dishes.

Then the feed horn must illuminate the whole reflector, a subtended angle of:

$$\varphi_o = 2\tan^{-1}\left(\frac{1}{2 \times f/d}\right)$$

about 80 degrees for common offset dishes.

The focal point of an offset dish is the most important dimension, but the location is not obvious. If you find one with the original feed assembly, it should be close to your calculations. Otherwise, the focal point is separated from the bottom edge of the dish by the focal length, and from the top edge by a distance = D/sin j_o.

The feed horn should be chosen to properly illuminate the f/D of the reflector, about 0.6 for common offset dishes. The aiming angle for the feed is less critical — aiming a little above the center will work fine.

PROJECT: Feed Horns for Offset Dish

The subtended angle that the feed horn must illuminate is narrower for offset dishes, which suggests that a higher gain antenna is required. A simple rectangular horn may be designed to provide equal beamwidths in the E- and H- planes with a common center.

Figure 15.98 is a template for a 10 GHz feed horn using WR-90 waveguide, with dimensions chosen to illuminate a common satellite TV dish and to have the same phase center in both planes. The phase center is about 6 mm inside the horn aperture, centered in the horn. **Figure 15.99** is a template for a 5.76 GHz horn using WR-137 waveguide, with phase center about 6mm inside the horn aperture. Both are suitable for the ubiquitous small satellite TV dishes.

A higher performance feed horn is the dual-mode horn, invented and patented by Dick Turrin, W2IMU. In the sketch of **Figure 15.100**, the conical section of the horn generates a second waveguide mode which cancels currents in the rim of the horn and thus reduces unwanted sidelobes. The dimensions shown in Table 15.32 are fairly critical.

Practical Considerations for Offset Dishes

Small errors in an offset-fed dish result in a beam which is tilted slightly up or down, are easily compensated for by tilting the antenna elevation. The final elevation angle should be found by peaking on a distant signal. A bubble level on the dishset at the approximate angle for a horizontal beam angle assists with aiming.

Offset dishes also have mechanical problems. Ideally, the electronics are placed under the feed horn, with short feed line and out of the beam. However, this puts all the weight at the end of the feed support, as shown in **Figure 15.101A**. If the reflector is mounted from the rear, as most are, a sturdy tripod is required even for a small dish. Another choice is to mount the offset dish on top of the electronics, as in Figure 15.101B. A wooden wedge holds the dish at the required tilt angle.

With any dish, it is desirable to have some elevation adjustment since microwave signals can bend due to atmospheric effects. Distant (beyond line-of-sight) signals often peak at a few degrees of elevation, and occasionally below the horizon.

For portable operation, always calibrate azimuth and elevation on a signal at each setup. Bouncing around in a vehicle tends to shift adjustments and even distort parabolic reflectors

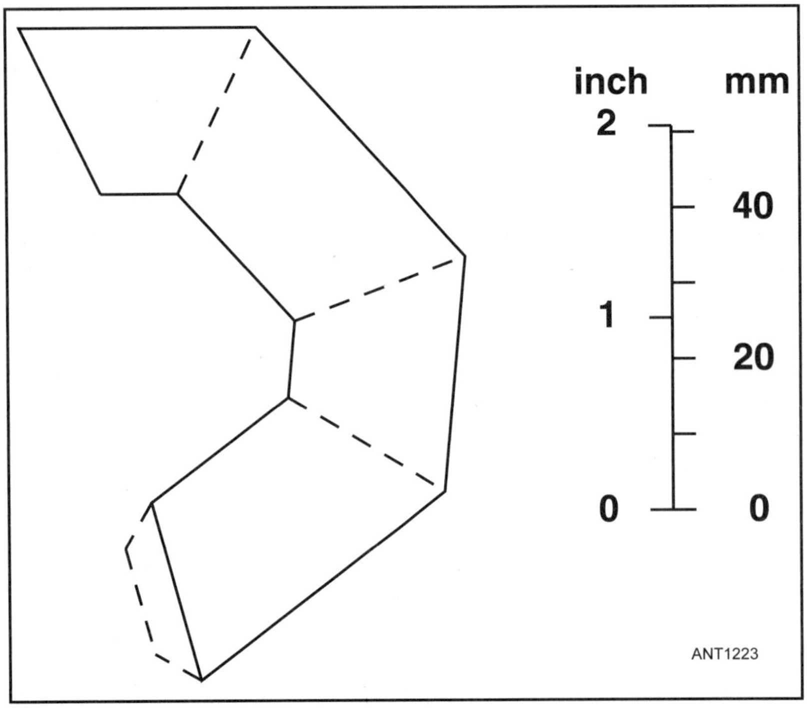

Figure 15.98 — Feed horn template for RCA DSS offset dish and WR-90 waveguide at 10.368 GHz.

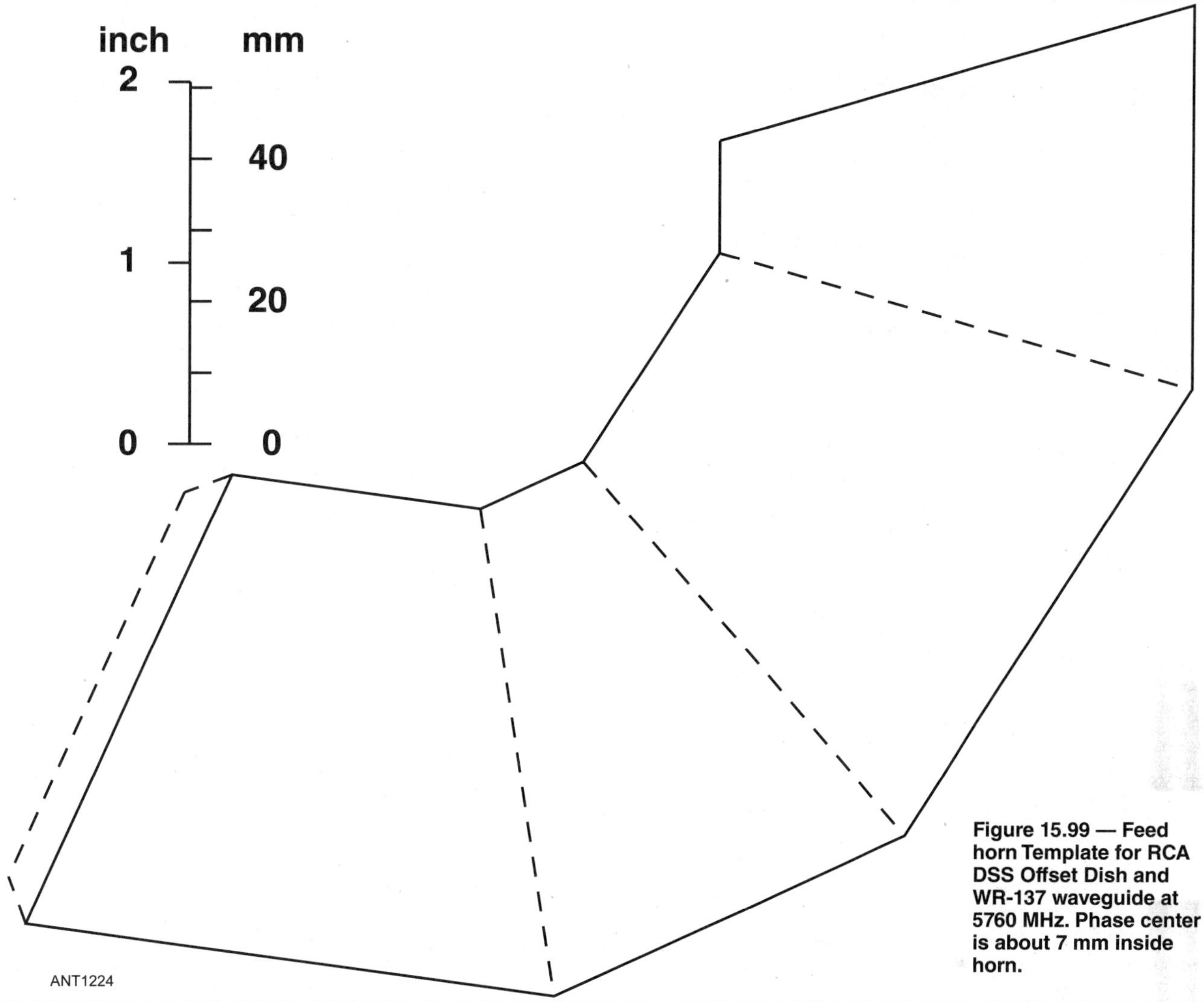

Figure 15.99 — Feed horn Template for RCA DSS Offset Dish and WR-137 waveguide at 5760 MHz. Phase center is about 7 mm inside horn.

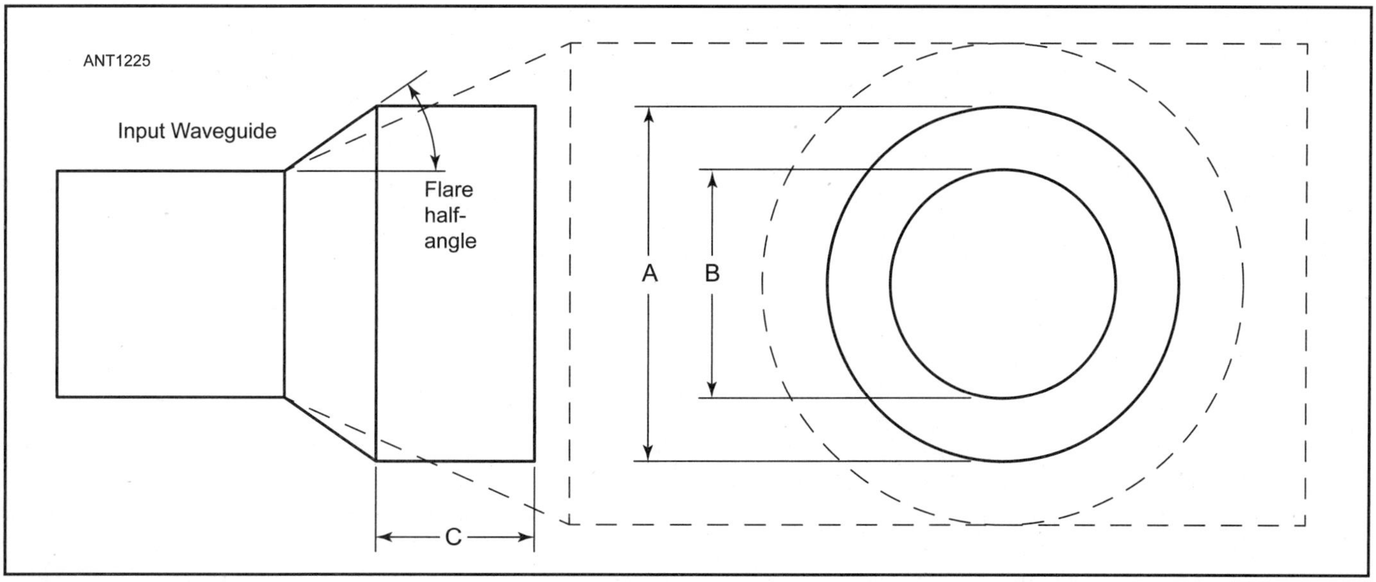

Figure 15.100 — The W2IMU dual-mode feed horn. See Table 15.32 for dimensions.

(A)

Figure 15.101 — Mounting the electronics under the feed horn (A) places most of the assembly weight to the rear, requiring a heavy-duty tripod. Mounting the dish over the electronics (B) requires more feed line but is more balanced.

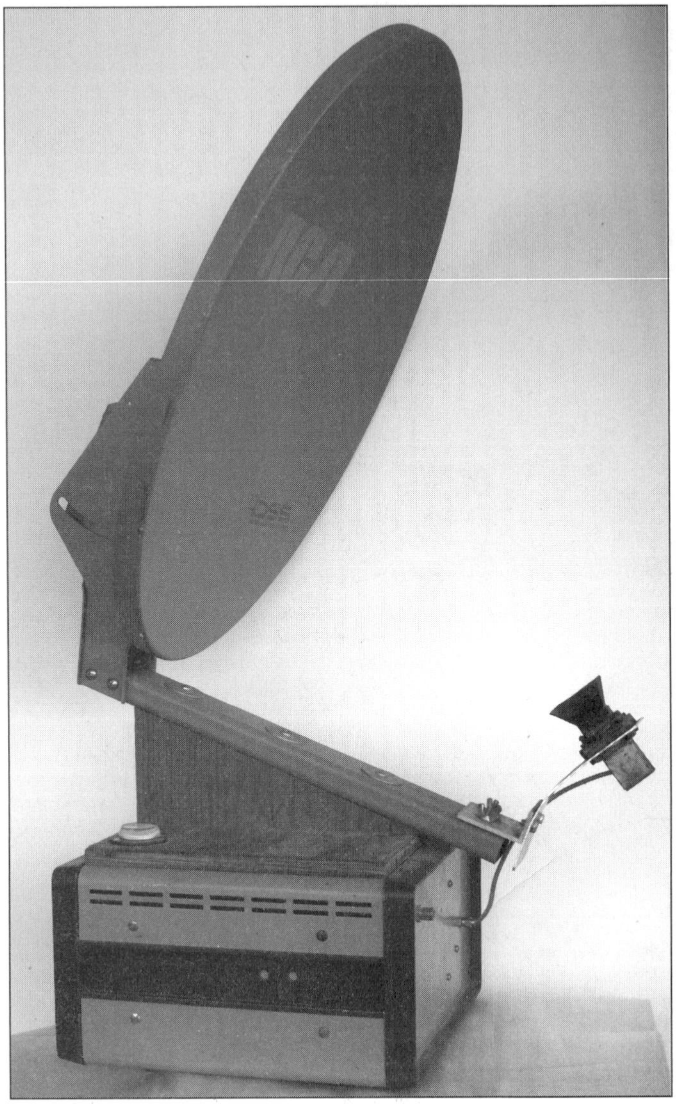

(B)

slightly, so aiming by eye might be off. If you are lucky enough to have a beacon available, calibration is easier and more accurate.

15.8.5 PROJECT: Vivaldi Antennas

The following material is reprinted from the RSGB publication *Microwave Know-How* (see References and Bibliography). The Vivaldi antenna in **Figure 15.102** is an exponential antenna from the same family as V-beams and rhombics (see the **Long-Wire and Traveling-Wave Antennas** chapter). They have exceptionally wide bandwidth. The lowest frequency is determined by the width of the opening.

The higher frequency of operation is determined by how accurately the slot is formed. As an example, the 75 mm PCB version has an excellent return loss from 5 GHz to 18 GHz and is usable from 2 GHz. (See **wa5vjb.com/pcb-pdfs/10-25GHzSweep.pdf** for additional construction information.)

All versions start with the template shown in Figure 15.105. Place the template on a photocopy machine and enlarge or reduce to the desired frequency range as shown in **Table 15.29** Cut out the template and mark your material as shown in **Figure 15.103**. Thin brass, tin plate, or PC board material

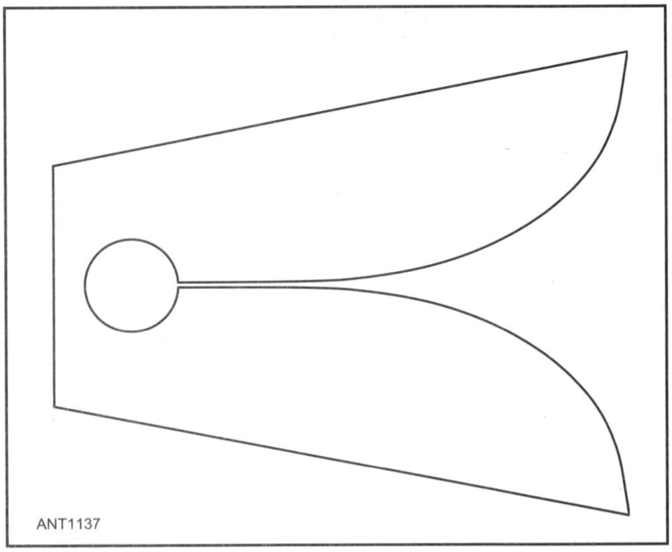

Figure 15.102 — The template for a Vivaldi antenna. Scale as shown in Table 15.33.

have all been used.

Cut out the antenna using sharp scissors or a band saw. The feed line shield should be soldered to one side of the slot and the center conductor to the other side as close to the circle as possible. (See **Figure 15.104**.) Both semi-rigid and Teflon braided coax types can be used.

Vivaldi antennas make excellent test antennas for use with test instruments or can be used as dish feeds over several bands. The phase center of the Vivaldi does move back and forth in the narrow region of the slot, but when the dish is at the highest frequency of planned use, the lower bands will be focused very close. Mount the narrow area of the slot at the focus of the dish.

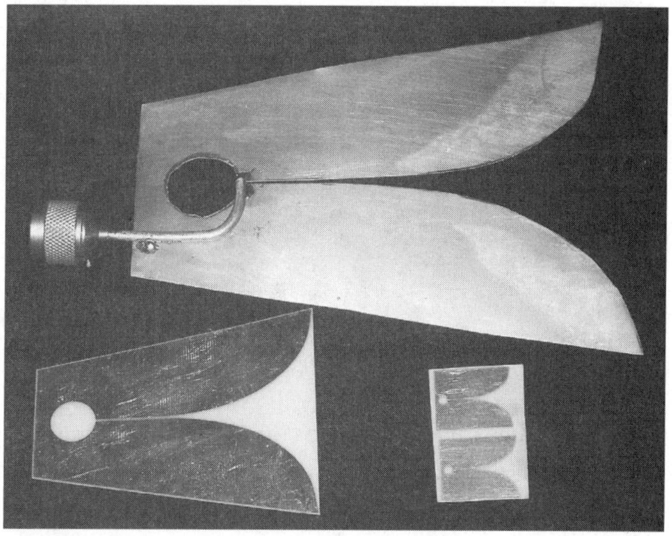

Figure 15.104 — A complete Vivaldi antenna.

15.8.6 Patch Antennas

The following material is adapted from the RSGB publication *Microwave Know-How.* (See References and Bibliography for additional articles by Kraus and Krug.) Patch antennas (also called *microstrip antennas*) are a good example of how an antenna's shape is used at microwave frequencies in ways not possible at 70 cm and longer wavelengths. Patch antennas become practical at and above the 902 MHz band and are very common in commercial microwave applications such as GPS reception, wireless telephony, and wireless data links. As more amateurs investigate operation at microwave frequencies, the patch antenna should receive more attention. A comprehensive tutorial on microstrip antennas is available from *Microwaves & RF* magazine. (See the References and Bibliography entry for Puglia.)

The patch, an example of which is shown in **Figure 15.105**, consists of a radiating surface mounted over a ground plane although there are many variations of the basic design. The patch is approximately λ/2 on a side for a square patch. Patch antenna gain is on the order of 7 to 9 dBi.

Some patches are constructed of double-sided PCB material with the patch etched on one side and the unetched side acting as the ground plane. The shape of the patch is such that when excited by a signal, the resulting currents form patterns that create a useful radiation pattern. It works the same as an arrangement of discrete elements. The closest electrical analogy is that the square patch acts similarly to a pair of slot antennas fed in phase and approximately λ/2 apart.

Since the impedance of the patch is high at the edges where current is low (just as in a linear element), the feed point is usually close to the center of the patch. Placement of the feed point determines the feed point impedance and influences the

Table 15.29
Dimensions of Two Dual-Mode Feeds and the Original W2IMU Feed

Dimensions shown in wavelengths may be scaled to any frequency

f/D	*Flare Angle*	*B = Aperture Diam.*	*C = Output Length*
0.55	30°	1.31 λ	1.31 λ
0.7	27.4°	1.63 λ	2.8 λ
0.8	24.9°	1.79 λ	3.52 λ

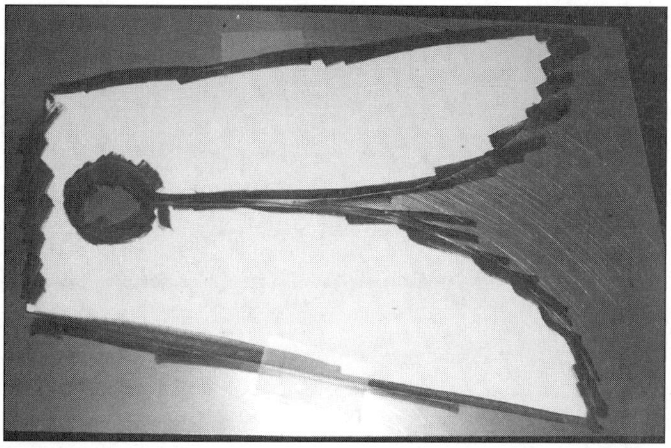

Figure 15.103 — Marking out a Vivaldi antenna using the template placed on your chosen material.

Figure 15.105 — Two patch antennas for the 23 cm band. The patch on the left is constructed from sheet metal and the one on the right from PCB material.

pattern of current on the surface of the patch. An alternate method of feeding the patch is to create a 50-Ω microstrip or stripline transmission line from a location with a 50-Ω impedance to the edge of the structure where a feed line can be attached.

It is not necessary for the patch to be rectangular in shape and could conveniently be round or polygon shaped. A rectangular patch with its opposite corners cut off will produce circular polarization.

FLAT-PANEL PATCH ARRAY ANTENNAS

Flat panel antennas are arrays of printed antennas which can provide good gain in a compact package. A version for 24 GHz is shown in **Figure 15.106**, with 256 printed patch antennas. Compare this with the collinear dipole arrays discussed earlier in this chapter — the printed array is groups of four patches combined with a tree of printed transmission lines. An array like this can provide very good gain, which we can estimate from the aperture area of the array.

A printed antenna like this can be economically produced in large quantities but would be very expensive to make only a single antenna. A significant amount of engineering is required. A dense array like this has significant mutual coupling between adjacent antenna elements, which must be compensated -- notice that the combining lines are not all identical. And for low loss, the array is printed on an expensive Teflon-based dielectric.

Fortunately, flat panel antennas have been mass-produced for a number of applications and can often be found at reasonable prices on online auction sites. These are usually intended for outdoor use, so they are packaged with a weatherproof cover. Look for versions that are close to or include the desired microwave ham band. Just be wary of the advertised gains — a better estimate can be made from the aperture area of the array.

PROJECT: A PATCH ANTENNA FOR 23 CM

This simple patch antenna for the middle range of the 23 cm band was designed by Kent Britain, WA5VJB. The antenna works for use as a dish feed as well as for point-to-point communication such as for D-STAR, ATV, or satellite contacts.

The antenna can be made from almost any sheet metal. The base can be made from sheet aluminum, brass, copper, or PCB material. It is probably easier to assemble if the patch is made from something that can be soldered. Figure 15.95 shows two patches. The one on the right is made from PCB material and the one on the left from galvanized sheet steel. **Figure 15.107** shows the dimensions for the 23 cm band patch.

Since the very center of the patch is electrically neutral, similar to the center of a dipole, you can use a metal screw to support the patch over the conductive plate or ground plane. This provides a dc ground for the antenna and dissipates any static charge. A #4 or #6 brass or similar screw can be used. The diameter of the screw is not important but the height at

Figure 15.106 — An array of printed patch antennas for 24 GHz.

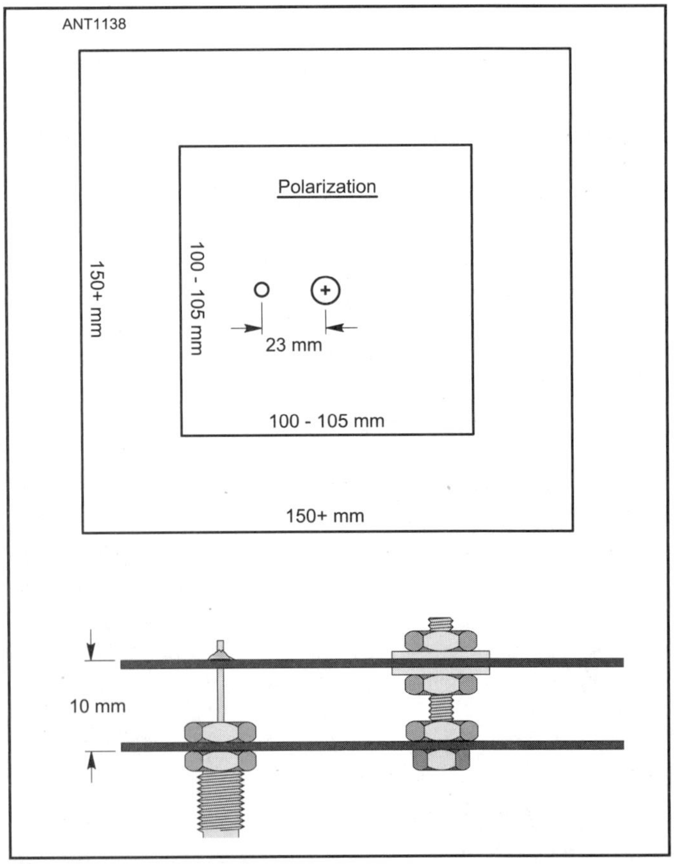

Figure 15.107 — Dimensions for the 23 cm patch antenna. The size of the patch determines the frequency range of the antenna (see text). The orientation of the feed point determines the antenna's polarization.

Figure 15.108 — An illustration showing how the patch is mounted above the ground plane using the center screw and, in this case, the SMA connector.

which it holds the patch above the ground plane is. Adjust the height of the patch above the ground plane for the best impedance match. If swept frequency measurements are not possible, adjustment at a single frequency is acceptable.

Coaxial feed line is attached to the patch 23 mm from the mounting screw as shown in Figure 15.107 and **Figure 15.108**. The orientation of the line from the feed point to the center of the patch determines the antenna's polarization. If the antenna is placed with the feed point below the center, the antenna will be vertically polarized.

An SMA connector is used for this design, but coax can be soldered directly to the patch. The center conductor attaches to the patch and the shield to the ground plane. Ground plane size is not critical and 150 mm × 150 mm or larger will work well.

The typical patch will have a bandwidth of 50 MHz at this frequency. To use the 1240-1280 MHz portion of the band, increase the patch to 105 mm × 105 mm. For 1280-1325 MHz reduce the patch size to 100 mm × 100 mm.

15.8.7 Periscope Antenna Systems

One problem common to all who use microwaves is that of mounting an antenna at the maximum possible height while trying to minimize feed line losses. The higher the frequency, the more severe this problem becomes, as feeder losses increase with frequency. Because parabolic dish reflectors are most often used on the higher bands, there is also the difficulty of waterproofing feeds (particularly waveguide feeds). Inaccessibility of the dish is also a problem when changing bands. Unless the tower is climbed every time and the feed changed, there must be a feed for each band mounted on the dish. One way around these problems is to use a periscope antenna system (sometimes called a "flyswatter antenna").

The material in this section was prepared by Bob Atkins, KA1GT, and appeared in *QST* for January and February 1984. **Figure 15.109** shows a schematic representation of a periscope antenna system. A plane reflector is mounted at the top of a rotating tower at an angle of 45°. This reflector can be elliptical with a major to minor axis ratio of 1.41, or rectangular. At the base of the tower is mounted a dish or other type of antenna such as a Yagi, pointing straight up. The advantage of such a system is that the feed antenna can be changed and worked on easily. Additionally, with a correct choice of reflector size, dish size, and dish to reflector spacing, feed losses can be made small, increasing the effective system gain. In fact, for some system configurations, the gain of the overall system can be greater than that of the feed antenna alone.

GAIN OF A PERISCOPE SYSTEM

Figure 15.110 shows the relationship between the effective gain of the antenna system and the distance between the reflector and feed antenna for an elliptical reflector. At first sight, it is not at all obvious how the antenna system can have a higher gain than the feed alone. The reason lies in the fact that, depending on the feed to reflector spacing, the reflector may be in the near field (Fresnel) region of the antenna, the far field (Fraunhofer) region, or the transition region between the two.

In the far field region, the gain is proportional to the reflector area and inversely proportional to the distance between the feed and reflector. In the near field region, seemingly strange things can happen, such as decreasing gain with decreasing feed to reflector separation. The reason for this gain decrease is that, although the reflector is intercepting more of the energy radiated by the feed, it does not all con-

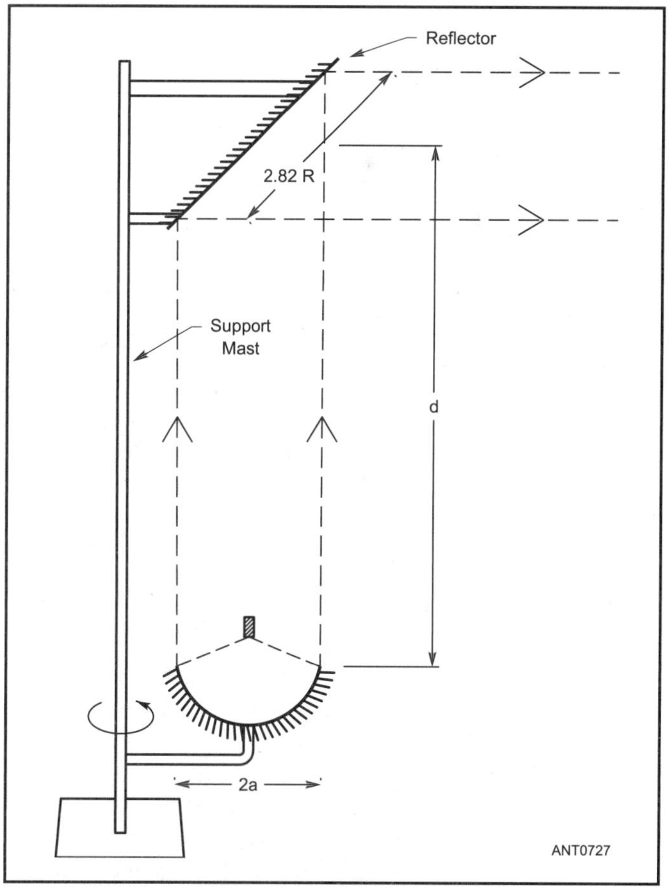

Figure 15.109 — The basic periscope antenna. This design makes it easy to adjust the feed antenna.

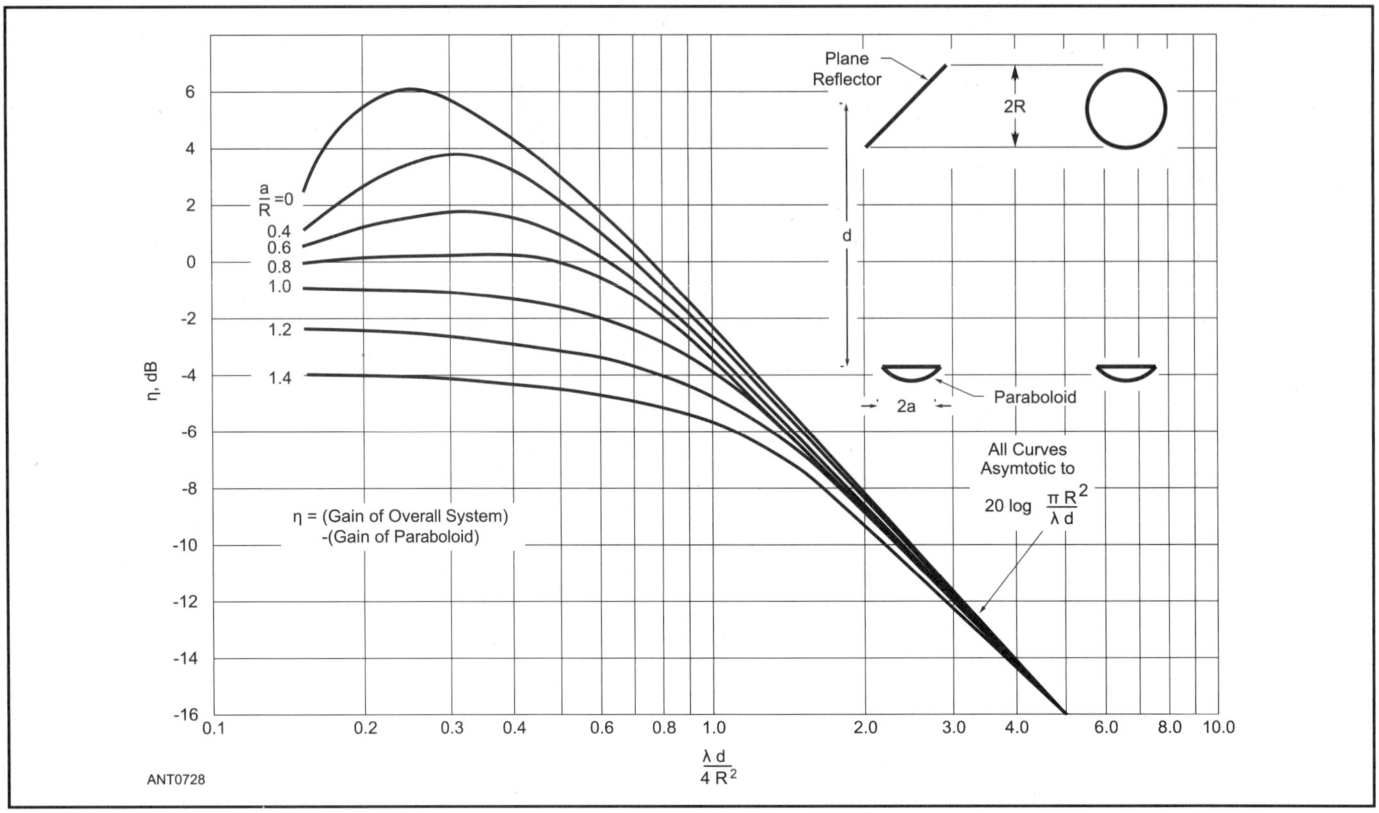

Figure 15.110 — Gain of a periscope antenna using a plane elliptical reflector (after Jasik — see References and Bibliography).

Table 15.30
Scaling for the Vivaldi Antenna Template

Opening	*Low End Frequency Response*
40 mm	10 GHz
75 mm	5 GHz
150 mm	2 GHz
200 mm	1 GHz

tribute in phase at a distant point, and so the gain decreases.

In practice, rectangular reflectors are more common than elliptical. A rectangular reflector with sides equal in length to the major and minor axes of the ellipse will, in fact, normally give a slight gain increase. In the far field region, the gain will be proportional to the area of the reflector. To use Figure 15.109 with a rectangular reflector, R^2 may be replaced by A / π, where A is the projected area of the reflector. The antenna pattern depends in a complicated way on the system parameters (spacing and size of the elements), but **Table 15.30** gives an approximation of what to expect. R is the radius of the projected circular area of the elliptical reflector (equal to the minor axis radius), and b is the length of the side of the projected square area of the rectangular reflector (equal to the length of the short side of the rectangle).

For those wishing a rigorous mathematical analysis of this type of antenna system, several references are given in the References and Bibliography at the end of this chapter.

MECHANICAL CONSIDERATIONS

There are some problems with the physical construction of a periscope antenna system. Since the antenna gain of a microwave system is high and, hence, its beamwidth narrow, the reflector must be accurately aligned. If the reflector does not produce a beam that is horizontal, the useful gain of the system will be reduced. From the geometry of the system, an angular misalignment of the reflector of X degrees in the vertical plane will result in an angular misalignment of 2X degrees in the vertical alignment of the antenna system pattern. Thus, for a dish pointing straight up (the usual case), the reflector must be at an angle of 45° to the vertical and should not fluctuate from factors such as wind loading. A mechanism for small adjustments in the tilt angle is useful for alignment and for variations in propagation as described above.

The system in Figure 15.108 shows a rotating mast or tower, which is fine if you have one. The entire periscope system may also be mounted on the side of a tower, which works well except for some loss going through the tower in one direction. The polarization also varies with direction, so polarization compensation may be required (though this seems less important for rain scatter contacts).

The reflector itself should be flat to better than 1/10 λ for the frequency in use. It may be made of mesh, provided that the holes in the mesh are also less than 1/10 λ in diameter. A second problem is getting the support mast to rotate about a truly vertical axis. If the mast is not vertical, the resulting beam will swing up and down from the horizontal as the system is rotated, and the effective gain at the horizon will fluctuate. Despite these problems, amateurs have used periscope antennas successfully on the bands through 78 GHz. A recent test (see "Microwavelengths" in July 2022 *QST*) verified that a periscope system has gain commensurate with reflector size. Periscope antennas were used in commercial service for point-to-point transmission but recent regulations on sidelobe limits discourage their use.

Circular polarization is not often used for terrestrial operation, but if it is used with a periscope system there is an important point to remember. The circularity sense changes when the signal is reflected. Thus, for right hand circularity with a periscope antenna system, the feed arrangement on the ground should produce left hand circularity. It should also be mentioned that it is possible (though more difficult for amateurs) to construct a periscope antenna system using a parabolically curved reflector. The antenna system can then be regarded as an offset fed parabola. More gain is available from such a system at the added complexity of constructing a parabolically curved reflector, accurate to 1/10 λ.

15.8.8 Omnidirectional Microwave Antennas

Omnidirectional antennas are ideal for microwave beacons and handy for test antennas. If you are lucky enough to have enough local microwave stations, then an omni might be good for a mobile or station antenna or even for a microwave repeater.

A real omnidirectional antenna would radiate in all directions in a sphere, but hams use the term loosely for an antenna that radiates in all azimuth directions — there is little point in radiating into the sky. Coincidentally, it is easier to make this sort of antenna than a true omnidirectional one.

A complication for microwaves is that horizontal polarization is normally used on the air. The vertical whips used by VHF mobiles have 360-degree azimuth coverage by their nature but with vertical polarization. To achieve the same coverage with horizontal polarization takes a bit more work.

WAVEGUIDE SLOT ANTENNA

One type of antenna that can radiate horizontal polarization with a broad azimuth pattern is a *slot antenna*. A slot in an infinite metal plane is the dual of a dipole — a vertical slot has a radiation pattern identical to a horizontal dipole of the same size in free space. Infinite planes are as hard to find as free space, but we can make a working antenna with slots in a metal sheet. (Theory and design information on waveguide slot antennas is available in chapters 8 and 9 of Jasik and chapter 13 of Kraus — see References and Bibliography.)

A waveguide slot antenna, pictured in **Figure 15.111**, has an array of λ/2 slots cut in the broad wall of a waveguide which acts as the transmission line feeding them. A vertical slot behaves like a horizontal dipole. Thus, the slots act like a vertical array of dipoles and the array provides more gain.

If the slots are spaced an electrical half-wavelength apart along the transmission line, their impedances all appear in parallel. The impedance of a slot is controlled by the distance each slot is displaced from the center line of the waveguide. If we add identical slots on the other face of the waveguide, the result is a broad radiation pattern in both directions, a cloverleaf pattern with a few dB variation, resulting in an approximately omnidirectional antenna with horizontal polarization and gain. To make the radiation pattern more uniform, some implementations have added metal wings to the narrow sides of the waveguide.

The electrical wavelength in a waveguide is longer than a wavelength in free space, so the slot spacing must be more than one-half wavelength in free space, complicating the calculations. Choosing the right combination of slot length, spacing, and displacement results in a well-matched antenna with an omnidirectional radiation pattern; a spreadsheet at **w1ghz.org/software/slotantenna.xls** calculates these dimensions. (The author acknowledges the help of Dan Welch, W6DFW in validating the calculations by making some very accurate slot antennas on a CNC machine to fine-tune the dimensions.) Figure 15.107 is a 10 GHz version made by Dan — the tuning screws aren't needed when the dimensions are right.

For those who do not have access to a manual or CNC milling machine, microwave slot antennas can also be made by hand. Donn Baker, WA2VOI, makes slot antennas for 10 GHz by scribing the slot pattern on the waveguide, drilling a row of holes, and filing out to the scribe lines. Hams have made these antennas for microwave bands from 1296 MHz to 24 GHz — Rene Barbeau, VE2UG, made the 1296 MHz waveguide slot antenna shown in **Figure 15.112**. He used ordinary rectangular aluminum tubing with dimensions not too different than commercial waveguide dimensions and made the slots with drills and files.

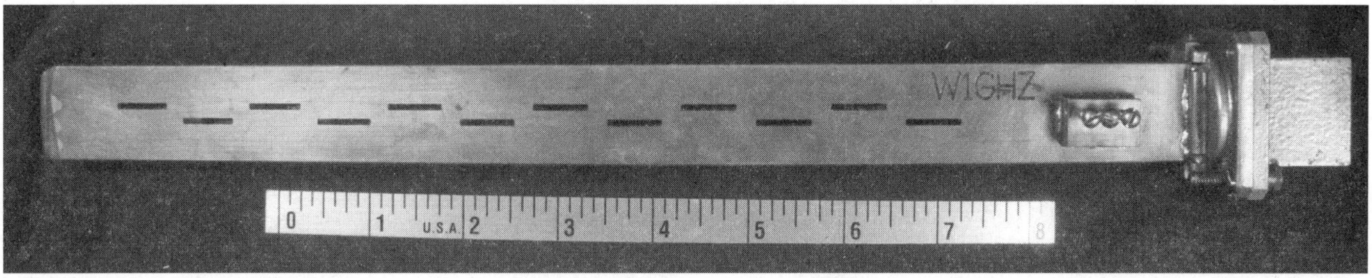

Figure 15.111 — 24-slot waveguide slot antenna for 10 GHz made by Dan Welch, W6DFW.

Figure 15.112 — A waveguide slot for 1296 MHz and its maker, Rene Barbeau, VE2UG.

Figure 15.113 — An Alford slot antenna for 2.4 GHz made by Rob Swinbank, MØDTS.

Figure 15.114 — An omnidirectional discone antenna for frequencies above 3 GHz made by Don Twombly, W1FKF.

ALFORD SLOT ANTENNA

The Alford Slot is frequently confused with the waveguide slot antenna but is a much different antenna. It is a single long slot cut lengthwise in a round tube. It is based on a 1947 paper, "Long Slot Antennas," by Andrew Alford (available from **w1ghz.org/antbook/Long_Slot_Antennas_Alford.pdf**). Rob Swinbank, MØDTS, made the 2.4 GHz version shown in **Figure 15.113**.

A long slot has more gain than a simple λ/2 antenna. The electrical wavelength in the slot, like the waveguide, is longer than a wavelength in free space, so that currents in the long slot do not have the phase reversals that create many lobes in a long dipole. The slot wavelength is controlled mainly by the inner diameter of the tube. Alford suggests a slot 2 λ long in a tube with an inner diameter of 0.14 λ. This is approximately 32 mm at 1296 MHz, about the size of a mast, so a thin-wall mast could also be a sturdy antenna.

The slot is fed in the center by a balanced transmission line connected to the sides of the slot, with the transmission line travelling inside the tube along the wall opposite the slot. According to Alford, a typical impedance is 250 Ω. A half-wave balun of semi-rigid coax could make a reasonable match to 50 Ω coax.

Like the waveguide slot antenna, wings may be added along the slot to make the radiation pattern more uniform. These also affect the slot impedance, so they can also improve matching. Both types of slot antenna may be stacked for higher gain.

DISCONE ANTENNA

All the omnidirectional antennas discussed so far are fairly narrowband, so a separate antenna is needed for each band. If vertical polarization is acceptable, the discone antenna is extremely broadband with up to a 10:1 frequency range. **Figure 15.114** shows one made by Don Twombly, W1FKF, for frequencies above 3 GHz. The antenna is made up of a disc, connected at the center to the center conductor of the coax feed line and a cone, connected to the end of the coax outer conductor and surrounding it. The cone length is λ/4 at the lowest frequency and the disc diameter is 0.7 times the cone length; the cone angle is roughly 30 degrees but not critical. Building one on semi-rigid coax, as Don did, makes a good support for a small microwave version.

15.9 References and Bibliography

Source material and more extended discussion of topics covered in this chapter can be found in the references given below and in the textbooks listed at the end of the **Antenna Fundamentals** chapter.

REFERENCES FOR SLOT ANTENNAS

J. Kraus, *Antennas, Second Edition*, Chapter 13

L. Gordon, K4VX, "The Double Magnetic Slot Antenna for 80 Meters," *ARRL Antenna Compendium, Vol. 4*.

R. Prack, ""Magnetic Radiators--Low Profile Paired Verticals for HF," *ARRL Antenna Compendium, Vol. 2.1*

G. Pelosi and S. Selieri, "Historical Corner: Babinet's Principle in Electromagnetics: Why Does a Slot Radiate Like a Dipole?" IEEE Antennas & Propagation Magazine, April 2017, pp 144-148.

RSGB BOOKS

Antennas for VHF and Above (Potters Bar: RSGB, 2008).

International Microwave Handbook (Potters Bar: RSGB, 2008).

Microwave Know-How for the Radio Amateur (Potters Bar: RSGB, 2010).

Radio Communication Handbook, 10th ed. (Potters Bar: RSGB, 2009).

MICROWAVE ANTENNAS

S. Silver, *Microwave Antenna Theory and Design*, McGraw-Hill, 1949. (Volume 12 of Radiation Laboratory Series, reprinted 1984)

A.W. Love, *Electromagnetic Horn Antennas*, IEEE Press, 1976.

T. Milligan, *Modern Antenna Design*, 2nd edition, Wiley, 2005.

T. Bird, *Fundamentals of Aperture Antennas and Arrays*, Wiley, 2016.

P. Wade, *W1GHZ Microwave Antenna Book*, **w1ghz.org/antbook/contents.htm**

OTHER PUBLICATIONS

B. Atkins, "Periscope Antenna Systems," The New Frontier, *QST*, Jan 1984, p 70 and Feb 1984, p 68.

B. Atkins, "Horn Antennas for 10 GHz," The New Frontier, *QST*, Apr 1987, p 80 and May 1987, p 63.

B. Atkins, "The New Frontier: Loop Yagi for 2304 MHz," *QST*, Sep 1981, p 76.

A. Baker, "A 6 Meter Moxon Antenna," *QST*, Apr 2004, pp 64-69.

R. Bancroft, *Microstrip and Printed Antenna Design (2nd Edition)* (Raleigh, NC: SciTech Publishing, 2009)

J. Belrose, "Technical Correspondence: Gain of Vertical Collinear Antennas," *QST*, Oct 1982, pp 40-41.

J. Belrose, "Gain of Vertical Collinear Antennas," *QST*, Oct 1982, pp 40-41.

J. Cadwallader, "Easy 50-Ohm Feed For A Helix," *QST*, June 1981, pp 28-29.

L.B. Cebik, "A Short Boom, Wideband 3 Element Yagi for 6 Meters," *QST*, Aug 2007, pp 41-45.

L.B. Cebik, "2X3=6," *QST*, Feb 2000, p 34-36.

L.B. Cebik, "Building a Medium-Gain, Wide-Band, 2 Meter Yagi," *QST*, Dec 2004, pp 33-37.

L.B. Cebik, "Notes on the OWA Yagi," *QEX*, Jul/Aug 2002, pp 22-34.

L.B. Cebik, "An LPDA for 2 Meters Plus," *QST*, Oct 2001, pp 42-46.

L.B. Cebik, "VK2ABQ Squares and Moxon Rectangles," *Modeling and Understanding Small Beams*, various online sources.

L.B. Cebik, "The Moxon Rectangle: A Review," various online sources.

M. Collis, "Omni-Gain Vertical Collinear for VHF and UHF," *73*, Aug 1990.

D. Conn, "The Helical Antenna — Description and Design," *TCA*, Jan/Feb 2006.

D. Cozzens, "Tables Ease Horn Design," *Microwaves*, March 1966, pp. 37-39.

J. Drexler, "An Experimental Study of a Microwave Periscope," *Proc. IRE*, Correspondence, Vol 42, Jun 1954, p 1022.

D. Evans and G. Jessop, *VHF-UHF Manual*, 3rd ed. (London: RSGB), 1976.

N. Foot, "WA9HUV 12 foot Dish for 432 and 1296 MHz," The World Above 50 Mc., *QST*, Jun 1971, pp 98-101, 107.

N. Foot, "Cylindrical Feed Horn for Parabolic Reflectors," *Ham Radio*, May 1976, pp 16-20.

G. Gobau, "Single-Conductor Surface-Wave Transmission Lines," *Proc. IRE*, Vol 39, Jun 1951, pp 619-624; also see *Journal of Applied Physics*, Vol 21 (1950), pp 1119-1128.

R. E. Greenquist and A. J. Orlando, "An Analysis of Passive Reflector Antenna Systems," *Proc. IRE*, Vol 42, Jul 1954, pp 1173-1178.

G. A. Hatherell, "Putting the G Line to Work," *QST*, Jun 1974, pp 11-15, 152, 154, 156.

R. Heslin, "Three-Band Log Periodic Antenna," *QST*, Jun 1963, pp 50-52.

D. L. Hilliard, "A 902 MHz Loop Yagi Antenna," *QST*, Nov 1985, pp 30-32.

G. Hoch, "Extremely Long Yagi antennas," *VHF Communications Magazine*, Mar 1982, pp 131-138.

G. Hoch, "More Gain from Yagi Antennas," *VHF Communications Magazine*, Apr 1997, pp 204-211.

W. C. Jakes, Jr., "A Theoretical Study of an Antenna-Reflector Problem," *Proc. IRE*, Vol 41, Feb 1953, pp 272-274.

H. Jasik, *Antenna Engineering Handbook*, 2nd ed. (New York: McGraw-Hill, 1984).

J. Johnson, "An intro to OWL yagis," **g0ksc.co.uk**

J. Johnson, "Making the OWL Match," **g0ksc.co.uk**

J. Johnson, "The OWL Folded Dipole," **g0ksc.co.uk**

R. T. Knadle, "UHF Antenna Ratiometry," *QST*, Feb 1976, pp 22-25.

J. Kraus, *Antennas, Second Edition*, McGraw Hill, 1988.

G. Kraus, "Modern Patch Antenna Design," *VHF Communications Magazine*, Jan 2001, pp 49-63.

F. Krug, "Micro-Stripline Antennas," *VHF Communications Magazine,* Apr 1985, pp 194-207.

Z. Lau, "RF: A Small 70-cm Yagi," *QEX*, Jul 2001, p 55.

T. Moreno, *Microwave Transmission Design Data* (New York: McGraw-Hill, 1948).

E. Munn, "The Polaplexer Revisited," **ham-radio.com/sbms/sd/ppxrdsgn.htm**.

W. Overbeck, "The VHF Quagi," *QST*, Apr 1977, pp 11-14.

W. Overbeck, "The Long-Boom Quagi," *QST*, Feb 1978, pp 20-21.

W. Overbeck, "Reproducible Quagi Antennas for 1296 MHz," *QST*, Aug 1981, pp 11-15.

J. Post, "The Copper Cactus," *73*, Feb 1992, p 9.

K. Puglia, "A Brief Tutorial on Microstrip Antennas, Parts 1 through 4," *Microwaves & RF*, Nov and Dec 2018, Jan and Feb 2019.

S. Powlishen, "An Optimum Design for 432 MHz Yagis — Parts 1 and 2," *QST*, Dec 1987, pp 20-24, and Jan 1988, pp 24-30.

J. Reisert, "VHF/UHF World: Designing and Building Loop Yagis," *Ham Radio*, Sep 1985, pp 56-62.

G. Southworth, *Principles and Applications of Waveguide Transmission* (New York: D. Van Nostrand Co, 1950).

P. P. Viezbicke, "Yagi Antenna Design," *NBS Technical Note 688* (U. S. Dept. of Commerce/National Bureau of Standards, Boulder, CO), Dec 1976.

D. Vilardi, "Easily Constructed Antennas for 1296 MHz," *QST*, Jun 1969, pp 47-49.

D. Vilardi, "Simple and Efficient Feed for Parabolic Antennas," *QST*, Mar 1973, pp 42-44.

P. Wade, "Parabolic Antennas," *QST*, Apr 2018, pp 57-58.

P. Wade, "From a Parabolic Dish to an Antenna," *QST*, Oct 2018, pp 60-61.

P. Wade, "Omnidirectional Microwave Antennas," *QST*, Oct 2016, pp 56-57.

P. Wade, "Periscope Antenna Systems", Chapter 8, *W1GHZ Microwave Antenna Book*,**w1ghz.org/antbook/chap8.pdf**

P. Wade, "Understanding Circular Waveguide Experimentally", *QEX*, Jan/Feb 2001. Also **w1ghz.org/QEX/circular_wg.pdf**)

P. Wade, "Rectangular Waveguide to Coax Transition Design," *QEX*, Nov/Dec 2006, pp 10-17.

B. Walker, *Magic Band Antennas for Ham Radio*, (Newington: ARRL, 2018).

Williams, "Understanding Microwave Radiolink Antennas," *Mobile Radio Technology*, Apr 1990, pp 36-58.

TABLE OF CONTENTS

Chapter 16 — Online Material

Article

- 5/8-Wavelength Whips for 2 Meters and 222 MHz
- "6-Meter Halo Antenna for DXing" by Jerry Clement, VE6AB
- "A 6m Hex Beam for the Rover" by Darryl Holman, WW7D
- "A 6 Meter Halo" by Paul Danzer, N1II
- "A New Spin on the Big Wheel" by L.B. Cebik, W4RNL and Bob Cerreto, WA1FXT
- "A Simple 2 Meter Bicycle-Motorcycle Mobile Antenna" by John Allen, AA1EP
- "A Two-Band Halo for V.H.F. Mobile" by Ed Tilton, W1HDQ
- "A VHF-UHF 3-Band Mobile Antenna" by J.L. Harris, WD4KGD
- "Bicycle-Mobile Antennas" by Steve Cerwin, WA5FRF and Eric Juhre, KOKJ
- "Introduction to Roving" by Ward Silver, NOAX
- "Omnidirectional 6 Meter Loop" by Bruce Walker, N3JO
- "Six Meters from Your Easy Chair" by Dick Stroud, W9SR
- "The DBJ-2: A Portable VHF-UHF Roll-up J-pole Antenna for Public Service" by Edison Fong, WB6IQN
- "The VHF-UHF Contest Rover Experience — Parts 1 and 2" by Greg Jurrens, K5GJ

Chapter 16

VHF and UHF Mobile and Rover Antennas

Mobile antennas used by amateurs on the VHF and UHF bands usually support one of two applications; FM repeaters for local communication and weak-signal "roving" for competitions and activation of rare locations. The first half of the chapter, updated previously by Alan Applegate, KØBG, presents popular types of mobile antennas for VHF and UHF and discusses issues regarding mounting style and installation technique. The second half discusses the antennas and antenna systems used by rovers, including installation. This material is based on contributions from several experienced rover station builders who are identified in the text.

16.1 Antennas For VHF-UHF FM

16.1.1 Antennas For Handheld Transceivers

For frequencies above 30 MHz, most mobile installations permit the use of a full-size antenna but for handheld radios smaller, loaded antennas are used. Antennas designed for use with VHF/UHF handheld FM transceivers can also be considered mobile antennas, even flexible "rubber duck" antennas consisting of a spiral winding of flexible wire in a flexible enclosure.

Pictured in **Figure 16.1** is a telescoping full-size quarter-wave antenna for 2 meters and beside it a flexible antenna for the same band. The flexible antenna is a helically wound radiator made of stiff copper wire enclosed in a protective covering. The inductance of the helical windings provides electrical loading for the antenna. This avoids the problems of a lengthier, cumbersome antenna attached to a handheld radio while sacrificing some efficiency and bandwidth compared to the full-size antenna. The compact flexible antenna withstands the normal rigors of portable use much better than would a full-size antenna. For these antennas, survivability over long use outweighs electrical efficiency.

The use of a full-size antenna will greatly improve the performance of handheld transceivers. By using a coaxial adapter, the transceiver can be connected directly to the feed line of mobile antennas such as those described in the following sections. This allows much more effective use of a handheld transceiver in a vehicle. A mobile antenna can also be installed on top of a metal appliance at home for improved operation. For example, a mag (magnet) mount antenna on top of a refrigerator or file cabinet is a popular way of improving local coverage of a handheld radio.

SMA connectors have become quite popular on handheld

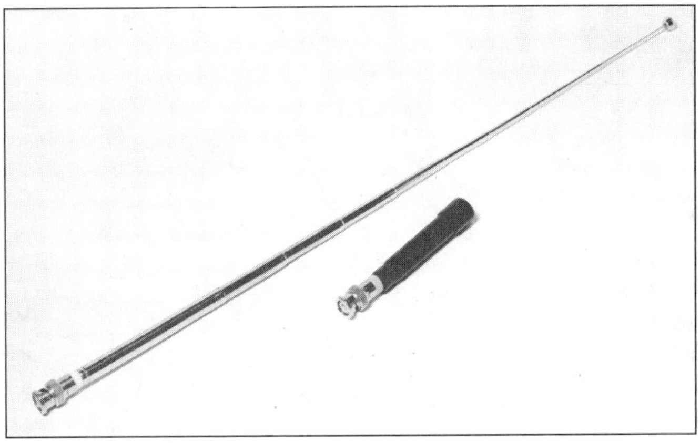

Figure 16.1 — A telescoping ¼-wavelength antenna and a flexible "rubber duck" antenna, both designed for use on 2 meters. The telescoping antenna is approximately 19 inches long when extended, while the flexible antenna is only 3½ inches long. The flexible antenna is a helically wound radiator used because of its mechanical strength.

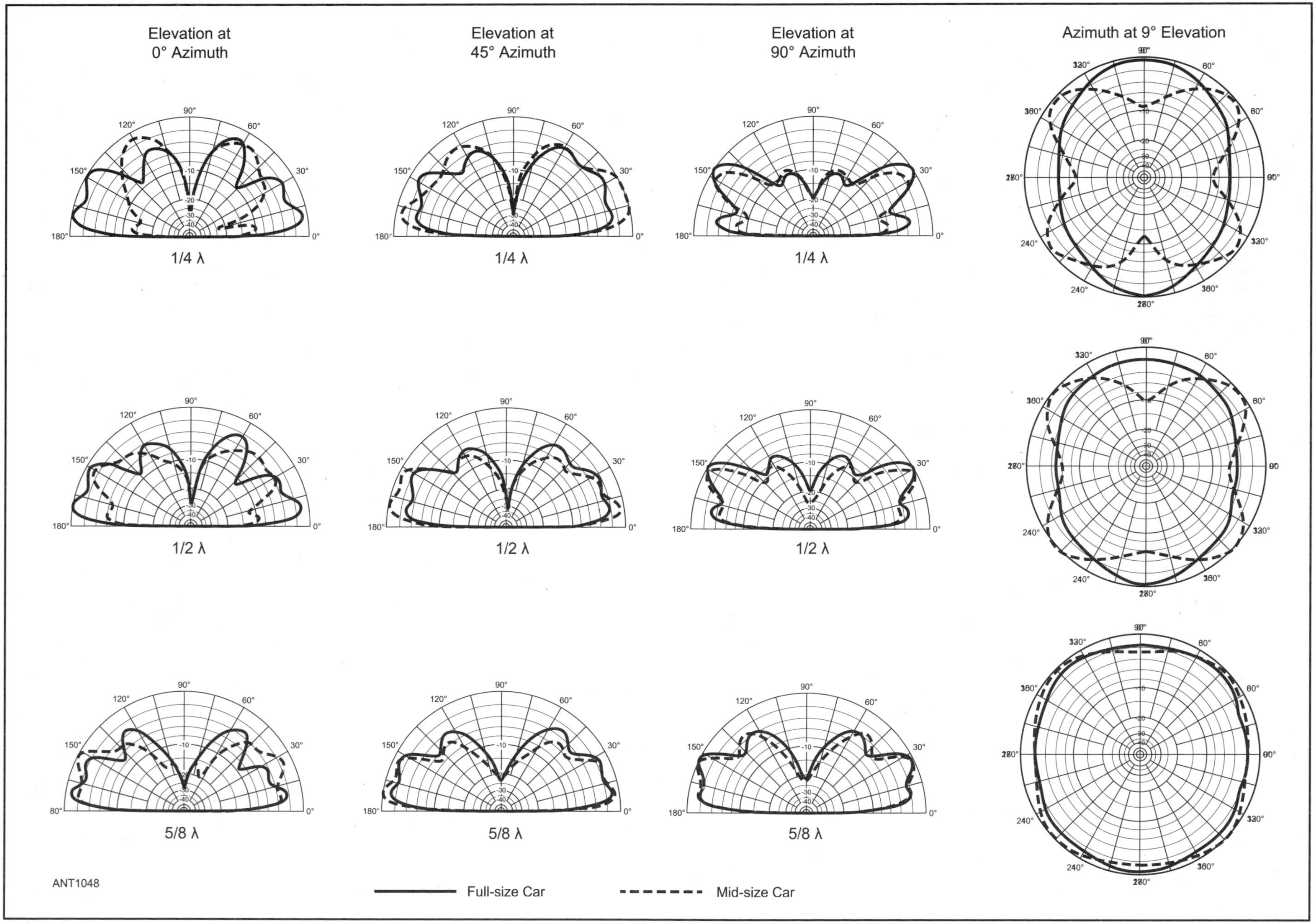

Figure 16.2 — Elevation and azimuth patterns showing the comparison for full and mid-sized cars for the three most popular VHF mobile antennas. (From "VHF Mobile Antenna Performance — The Other Half of the Story" by Dan Richardson, K6MHE.)

radios, particularly the "reverse SMA." (See the section "Other RF Connectors" in the **Transmission Lines** chapter.) Adapters from SMA to larger connector families such as UHF can put a lot of stress on the smaller SMA. This can damage the SMA connector's attachments to the transceiver's internal circuit board. To avoid this stress, use a flexible cable with an SMA connector on one end and the desired RF connector on the other.

16.1.2 Mobile Whips

At VHF and UHF, mobile antennas are often full-size whips (meaning ¼- to ⅝-wavelength long) and simple collinear arrays that provide extra gain on the higher frequency bands. There is always great debate about the best antenna for urban and suburban FM use. Which antenna to select depends on many factors — mounting style, mechanical characteristics, local terrain — and can't be based solely on advertised gain. Mobile antennas come in ¼-, ½-, ⅝-λ, and even in collinear styles where several elements are stacked atop one another.

It has been established that in general, ¼-λ vertical antennas for mobile repeater work are not as effective as ⅝-λ verticals. With a ⅝-λ antenna, more of the transmitted signal is directed at a low vertical angle, toward the horizon, offering a gain of about 1 dB over the ¼-λ vertical. However, in areas where the repeater is located nearby on a very high hill or a mountain top, the ¼-λ antenna will usually offer more reliable performance because it radiates more power at higher vertical angles.

Dan Richardson, K6MHE, has done extensive work on mobile VHF antennas, including modeling the various types, and how mounting location affects their radiation patterns. **Figure 16.2** shows representative azimuth patterns for roof mounted antennas. (The complete article is posted on his website **k6mhe.com/files/mobile_vhf_ant.pdf**.) The radiation patterns of antennas mounted on a trunk lid would be different from those depicted in the chart. Where — and how — the antenna is mounted would determine the actual pattern. Radiation pattern distortion aside, proper trunk lid mounting is a good alternative to roof mounting, especially when garage door clearance is an issue.

As can be seen from the patterns, there really isn't much difference between the radiation patterns of a ¼-, ½-, or ⅝-λ antenna. In fact, the vehicle in question and the antenna's mounting location affect the pattern more than the style! Since most mobile VHF and UHF operation is via FM repeaters, where the difference in height between the mobile and the repeater can be a major consideration, a ¼-λ antenna with more radiation at higher vertical angles can be a better choice.

Single-band whips are inexpensive and give excellent performance with proper mounting. If more gain and multiband use is required, the dual-band collinear that operates on both 2 meters and 70 cm is very popular. The Larsen NMO2/70BK shown in **Figure 16.3** is a typical example. Electrically it is a center-loaded ½-λ on 2 meters with gain identical to a ¼-λ ground-plane. On 70 cm it is a 2-element collinear with a few dB gain over a ¼-λ ground-plane. Other models are available which operate on three and even four bands. Antennas covering three or four bands are heavier and require sturdier mounting.

Antenna Types for SSB and CW on VHF/UHF

Operating SSB and CW on 6 and 2 meters and 70 cm offers some exciting prospects for all license classes. While communications on the VHF bands are often considered line-of-site, propagation *beyond* line-of-site is common as discussed in the **Propagation of Radio Waves** chapter. This is especially true when using a "weak signal" mode such as SSB or CW, but there's a catch.

FM communications utilize vertically polarized antennas. Vertical polarization can be used for SSB but depending on the propagation path, signal strength from a vertically-polarized mobile antenna can have up to a 20 dB disadvantage compared to a horizontally-polarized antenna.

Fortunately, horizontally-polarized antennas are of manageable size on the VHF bands, although they are not as simple to construct as vertically polarized whips. Dipoles and small beams present too much wind resistance to withstand the normal mobile environment. The usual solution is a loop antenna.

Figure 16.A shows an M² Antenna Systems (**m2inc.com**) horizontally polarized 6 meter loop called a *halo* (for circular versions) or *squalo* (if square as shown). Equivalent antennas for 2 meters and 70 cm are common. Although this particular design is square, they're still called loops and have a roughly omnidirectional pattern. The "Big Wheel" design is another option. Projects for both types of antennas are provided later in this chapter.

Modern mobile SSB/CW transceivers usually output 100 W PEP on 6 meters and at least 50 W PEP on 2 meters and 70 cm. Under good band conditions, using horizontally-polarized antennas, *beyond* line-of-sight distances can exceed 200 miles even without any sky-wave or tropospheric scatter present!

Figure 16.A — A squalo (square halo) is a popular horizontally polarized VHF/UHF mobile antenna.

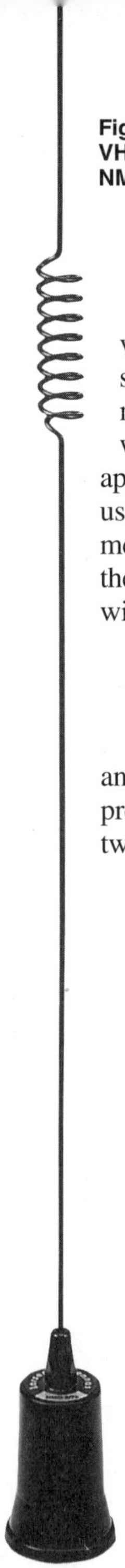

Figure 16.3 — A common style of dual-band VHF/UHF mobile whip antenna. (Larsen model NMO2/70BK)

SIX METER MOBILE WHIPS

Antennas for 6 meter FM operation are larger versions of those for 2 meters and often use the same mounts. However, their ground plane requirements are more significant because of the longer wavelength. If radials are used, they should be approximately $\lambda/4$ in length — about 53 inches. If used on a vehicle, center the antenna on the largest metal surface available, such as the roof or middle of the trunk. As a bonus, a 2 meter 5/8-λ whip antenna will also perform well as a $\lambda/4$ whip on 6 meters.

1/4-WAVELENGTH WHIPS FOR VHF AND UHF

The 1/4-wavelength vertical whip is simple to make and can be made for nearly any type of mount. The preferred stainless-steel wire or rod is available from two-way radio shops and CB antenna dealers. Cut the whip to length using a grinding wheel or score it with a file and break it — use eye protection! Any type of wire can be used in a pinch. Coat hangers, copper wire from home wiring cable, galvanized fence wire — all have been successfully used to replace broken or missing whips. Being able to repair or substitute for a broken antenna is a skill any amateur can learn for flexibility and resiliency during emergency situations.

Table 16.1 shows the approximate lengths for $\lambda/4$ whips in the VHF and UHF amateur bands based on a 3/32-inch diameter whip. Thinner whips will be slightly longer and thicker whips slightly shorter. Be sure to include the antenna base in the total length of the antenna. If the base holds the whip with a set screw, cut the whip approximately 5% long and adjust for best SWR before making a final trim to length.

Table 16.1
1/4-Wavelength Whip Lengths

Frequency (MHz)	*Length (inches)*
53	53
146	19 3/16
222	12 5/8
440	6
902	2 7/16

To Drill Or Not To Drill?

The decision to drill holes in sheet metal to mount antennas can be hotly debated. While no-hole mounts can be used satisfactorily, it is best to look at both sides of the issue.

One common reason given not to drill is if the vehicle in question is leased, but that doesn't preclude a drilled hole. If it did, there wouldn't be any leased commercial vehicles. What lease agreements specify is body damage such as from an accident or mistreatment. Properly installed NMO mounts, for example, are often acceptable.

Drilled holes and waterproof mounts also minimize common-mode current on the coaxial feed line that could interfere with or receive RFI from on-board computers and electrical devices. Aside from the hole itself, a permanent mount also minimizes damage to the finish.

16.2 Mounts for Whip Antennas

VHF and UHF antennas are much smaller and lighter than HF antennas, making mounting quite a bit easier. Some permanent mounts require drilling holes in the vehicle, while others use a hood or trunk lid seam so screw holes don't show. Still others clamp around the outside of a trunk or door edge. For temporary installations, magnetic base mounts are available. For best performance, VHF and UHF antennas should be permanently affixed to the vehicle.

The roof of a vehicle is an inviting place to mount a VHF or UHF antenna as this maximizes performance, but a few precautions need to be followed. First, it is not uncommon for side air bags to be mounted within the headliner area with control wiring running through the roof support pillars. Further, the roof is supported by cross bracing to meet rollover standards. These braces must be avoided. A repair manual for the vehicle in question is a good resource in avoiding installation problems and finding the manufacturer's preferred routes for coaxial and control cables.

The type of mount is also a concern when roof mounting, as the mount must be securely waterproof. If you're unsure about drilling holes in your vehicle (see the sidebar "To Drill Or Not to Drill?"), use the services of a local two-way radio service or vehicle entertainment system installation company.

The center of the trunk lid is a second-best location but care must be taken to assure the antenna doesn't interfere with the opening of the trunk. With the trunk fully open, place the antenna at the desired mounting location to check clearance. Don't forget to include the height of the mount itself and account for vibration of the antenna and trunk lid. Whatever mount is used, care must be taken to assure clearance of the coax cable and control leads if present.

If the antenna's overall length is too great, overhead clearance becomes a problem. While lightly touching the garage door or carport top may be acceptable, if the antenna is long enough to drag the inner surface of the door or roof, you run the chance of catching the antenna between garage door panels or getting it stuck in a rafter. This will damage the antenna and often the vehicle. In these cases, you're much better off with a shorter $\frac{1}{4}$-λ antenna.

NMO — NEW MOTOROLA MOUNT

The recommended antenna mount for VHF and UHF antennas is the NMO (from "New Motorola") as it is waterproof even when the antenna is removed. A permanent NMO mount (see **Figure 16.4**) usually requires a $\frac{3}{4}$-inch hole. Antennas with an NMO base have an integral O-ring or washer to seal the internal surfaces against water.

SO-239 MOUNT

Some VHF antennas mounts have a modified SO-239 chassis coax connector with the mating PL-259 forming the base of the antenna. The standard connector type allows you to connect a coaxial cable to the antenna mount, if desired. Most SO-239 mounts *are not* waterproof, especially when the antenna is removed, and shouldn't be used for through-hole body mounting and should be capped when not in use.

STUD MOUNT

While popular at HF, the stud mount is less common at VHF and UHF. Larsen and other manufacturers offer mounts with a male $\frac{5}{16}$-24 stud. Detachable whips are then available for all VHF and UHF bands.

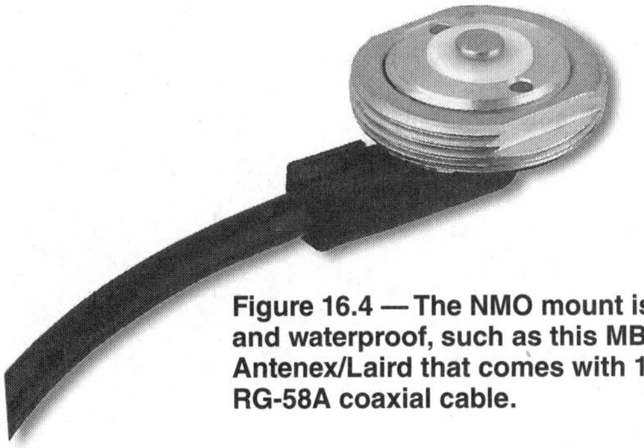

Figure 16.4 — The NMO mount is popular and waterproof, such as this MB8 from Antenex/Laird that comes with 17 feet of RG-58A coaxial cable.

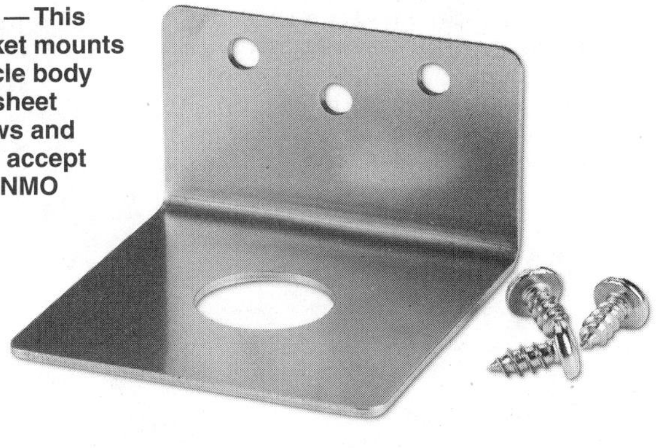

Figure 16.5 — This angle bracket mounts to the vehicle body with three sheet metal screws and is drilled to accept a standard NMO mount.

ANGLE BRACKETS

Angle brackets are generally attached by three or more sheet metal screws. Properly secured, they work well for lightweight antennas but routing coax through weather seals can be troublesome.

Angle brackets come in about a dozen different styles. The one shown in **Figure 16.5** is pre-drilled for an NMO mount. The brackets are often well-suited for installation along the hood and trunk seams.

Modern vehicles have very little clearance between the body structure and the various doors and hatches. Be sure to check clearance before you actually attach the bracket. Some vehicles may require specially bent or extended brackets as well.

CLIP OR LIP MOUNTS

There are a variety of mounts designed to clamp on the edge or "lip" of a trunk, hood, or hatch. Set screws are used to secure the mount to the lip and provide the requisite grounding of the mount. The set screws both secure the mount and make a connection to the sheet metal through the body paint. **Figure 16.6A** shows a typical "hatchback" style adjustable mount with an NMO base and **Figure 16.6B** is a close-up showing the set screws holding the mount to the vehicle body.

All modern vehicles are dipped in a zinc compound before final assembly and painting. When exposed to air, zinc rapidly oxidizes but in this case the oxidation is a good thing! When a piece of road debris nicks the paint down to the zinc layer, it quickly oxidizes, and protects the base metal underneath. Do not remove this zinc coating to bare metal! This removes the protective coating, allowing the underlying steel to rust and creates an intermittent connection.

The coax must often make sharp bends around the lip of the trunk or hood. Because clearance is minimal many lip mounts come preassembled with about 10 feet of miniature, low-loss coax with a connector. While feed line loss isn't much of a concern for HF mobile antennas, it can be significant at UHF where loss is much higher. Low-loss cable such as RG-400 can be used, if necessary.

All lip mounts bring the coax cable into the trunk or passenger cabin through the weather seal, potentially allowing water to enter. Running the cable under the seal as in Figure 16.6 is often an option. Take care to dress the cables and seals to direct water toward a drain hole or other exit.

(A)

(B)

Figure 16.6 — (A) shows an adjustable lip mount made by Diamond. (B) is a close-up of the mount showing the set screws that hold the mount to the vehicle and make an electrical connection to the vehicle.

GLASS MOUNTS

"Through-glass" or "on-glass" mounts such as the Larsen KG2/70CXPL use adhesive to hold the base of the antenna and cable fitting to opposite sides of a window, relying on metal foil surfaces to create a capacitor and pass VHF/UHF signals. The mount must be clear of window heating strips and cannot be used on tinted (passivated) glass that contains colloidal-sized metallic particles to provide protection from harmful UVA and UVB rays. Antenna performance is somewhat of a compromise because of the lack of a ground-plane but allows a permanent mount without holes, clamps, or magnets.

The outside surface of the coaxial feed line also becomes part of an on-glass antenna because there is no ground-plane, creating a path for common mode current. This allows the coax to both radiate and pick up noise in the vehicle interior.

LUGGAGE RACK MOUNTS

The biggest issue with using luggage racks as an antenna mount is excessive ground loss. Most luggage racks consist of plastics, composites, and insulated metal beams electrically isolated from the vehicle's metal body. As such, they rarely provide a good ground-plane for the antenna and routing the feed line through door or window weather seals can create leaks. Like on-glass antenna mounts, luggage rack mounting is a compromise for when a permanent mount is not possible

MAGNET MOUNTS

Mag (magnet) mounts are very popular for VHF and UHF operation. They rely on capacitance to make their electrical connection to the vehicle ground plane, so common-mode current on the feed line shield can become a problem. Nevertheless, mag mounts do deliver acceptable performance at VHF and UHF.

Mag mounts are available with the antenna and feed line attached as in **Figure 16.7** or as the mount by itself. There are mag mounts for any of the popular antenna bases — NMO, stud mount, and SO-239. A spare dual-band mag mount, a set of VHF and UHF whips, and several coax connector adapters are a valuable addition to your emergency response capabilities.

Be wary of the fine grit that can work its way under the magnet and scratch the paint. If you do use a mag mount for long periods of time, remove it and clean the magnet surface occasionally. For temporary installations, a plastic sandwich bag around the magnet protects the finish against grit while still maintaining a solid attachment.

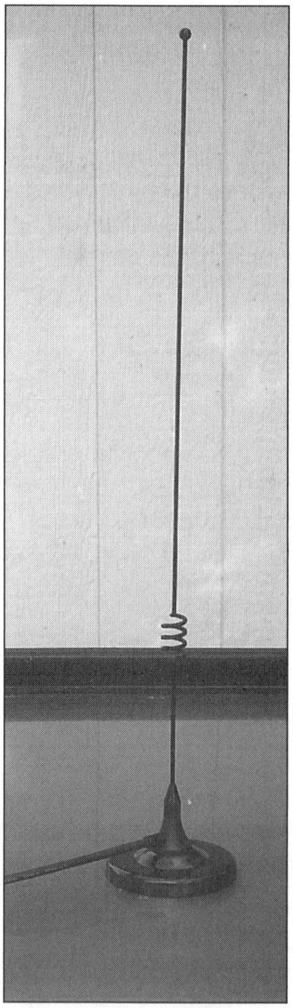

Figure 16.7 — A typical dual-band VHF/UHF mag mount with an integral antenna and feed line.

SPECIALTY BRACKETS AND ADAPTERS

Because there are so many variations in vehicles there are many different types of brackets for mounting antennas. One of the most common is the three-way mirror mount in **Figure 16.8** that is sold by many companies. This particular version is drilled to pass the shoulder insulator of the SO-239 to ⅜-24 threaded stud-mount adapter shown in the foreground. You can find a wide variety of brackets at hamfest flea markets, from vendors of antenna accessories, online from manufacturers and distributors, and at truck stops and CB shops.

The performance of the antenna depends on the size of what the bracket is attached to.

Figure 16.8 — The mirror-mount style of clamp-on bracket. This particular bracket is drilled for an SO-239 to ⅜-24 stud mount. The bracket can be mounted on vertical or horizontal struts.

Most mirror mounts are just barely big enough to act as a counterpoise at UHF but if they are securely mounted to a metal vehicle body, performance will be acceptable. The radiation pattern of the antenna will rarely be omnidirectional due to the off-center antenna placement.

Adapters are also available that convert mounts such as the NMO to other types of bases and connectors, such as the various stud mounts and SO-239 connector. This allows your antenna mount to accommodate other types of antennas but generally increases the length of the antenna by an inch or so, lowering the antenna's resonant frequency. A few mount adapters should be included in your mobile equipment kit.

16.3 PROJECT: Bicycle Mobile Antennas For VHF And UHF

Operating while mobile from a bicycle is increasingly popular for recreation or during commuting to work. (The Bicycle Mobile Hams of America website, **bmha-hams.org**, has a lot of information about operating from your bike.) Being able to radiate an effective signal is straightforward but requires a slightly different approach to conventional mobile operation. For starters, most bicycles and accessories are not made of steel, so mag-mount antennas cannot be used. The frame of the bicycle is mostly oriented vertically so the conventional horizontal ground plane is not available. And of course, personal safety is of paramount importance on a bicycle. This project and the articles included in this book's online material provide some examples of effective antennas and mounting techniques you can use on your bike.

Unlike the conventional $\lambda/4$ ground-plane, the vertical dipole or J-pole do not use the bicycle frame as part of the antenna. While simple to construct, the main challenge is to support the antennas on the bicycle without adding a lot of weight. A common

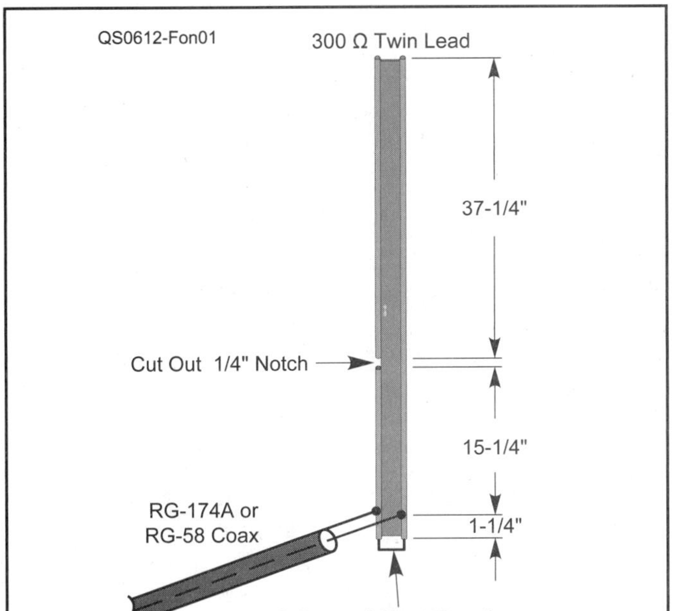

Figure 16.9 — A 2 meter flexible J-pole antenna. Any 50 Ω coaxial cable can be used. RG-58 or RG-8X is recommended for bicycle or other mobile use.

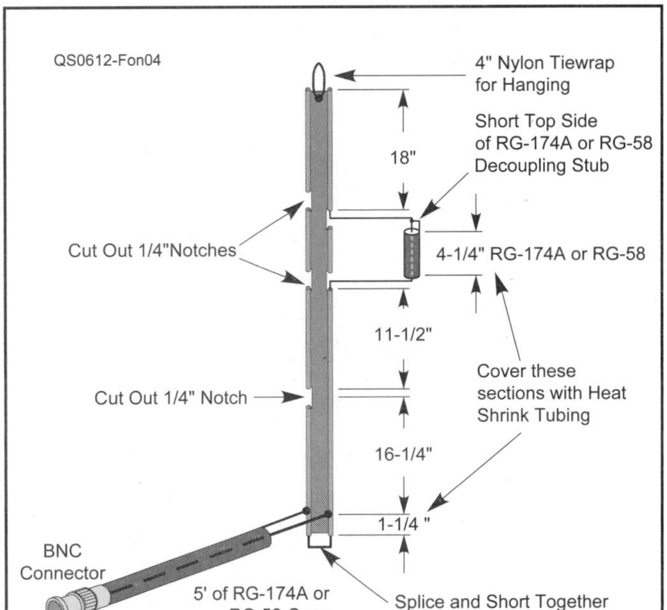

Figure 16.10 — The 2 meter/70 cm J-pole version. See the construction article included with this book's online material for information about tuning the antenna and attaching the feed line.

accessory provides the solution — a bicycle safety flag. Safety flags lift a high-visibility pennant on a slim fiberglass tube that mounts to the bike using a pressed-steel axle mount. Lightweight antennas can be attached to the fiberglass tube and a feed line run along the frame to the transceiver.

The J-pole shown here is a flexible "roll-up" design by Edison Fong, WB6IQN, originally published in March 2007 *QST* as the DBJ-2. **Figure 16.9** shows the initial 2 meter antenna design. RG-174A coax can be used as in the original design which was optimized for weight. Less lossy RG-58 or RG-8X coax would be a better choice if more weight is not a problem. The antenna in **Figure 16.10** works on both 2 meters and 70 cm. Both antennas are discussed in detail, including more construction and tuning details, in the article provided with this book's online material.

An alternate antenna shown in **Figure 16.11** is a vertical dipole based on the design by Charles Lofgren, W6JJZ, "The Bike 'n Hike Special" described in *QST*'s "Hints and Kinks" column. The antenna consists of a 39-inch radiating λ/2 whip of #14 or #16 AWG wire and an RG-58 coaxial tuning stub attached to the feed line ¼ λ below the radiating whip. The shorted stub adds some inductive reactance at a low impedance point in the feed line to raise the impedance to 50 Ω. From that point, any length of 50 Ω feed line to the transceiver can be used. (See the section "Matching Stubs" in the **Transmission Line System Techniques** chapter for information about how the shorted stub tunes the antenna system.)

The length of the stub depends on the velocity factor (VF) of the coaxial cable being used. Solid polyethylene dielectric coax has a VF of 0.66 (66%), while foam dielectric cable is typically 0.80 (80%). Check the velocity factor of your cable using an antenna analyzer or consult the table of coax characteristics in the chapter on **Transmission Lines**.

The stub should be 1.6 inches long for VF 66% cable and 2.0 inches long for VF 80% cable. Begin with the stub about ⅜ inch too long so that it can be trimmed to length after installation. Note that the length of the stub includes the short piece of center conductor that connects to the main feed line center conductor. Approximately ¼ inch is enough center conductor and braid to attach the stub to the main feed line. Leave

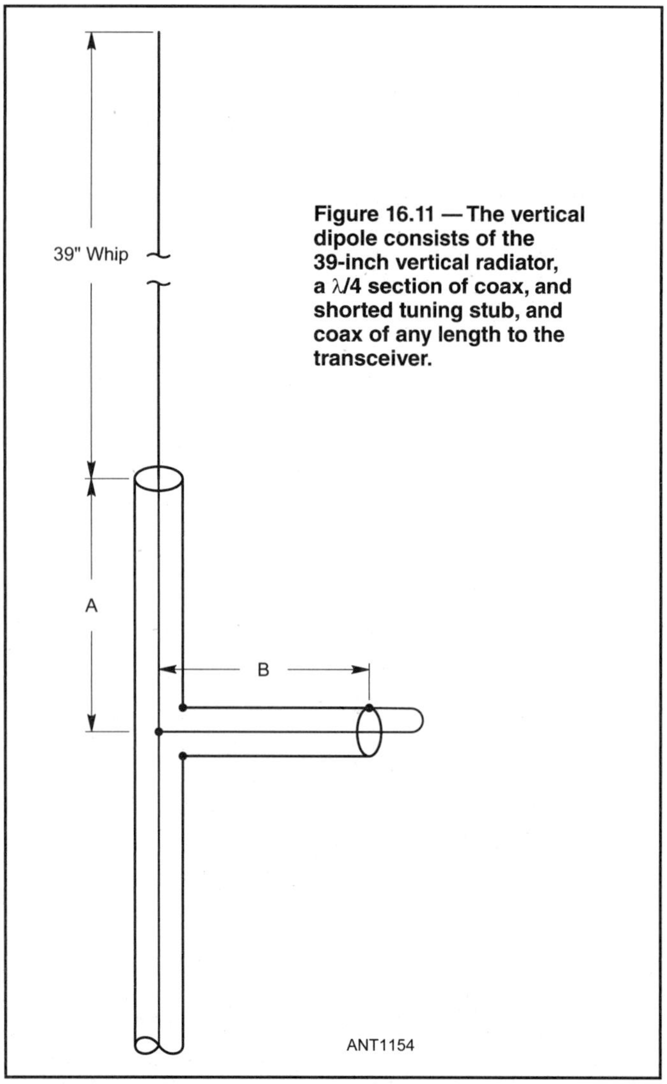

Figure 16.11 — The vertical dipole consists of the 39-inch vertical radiator, a λ/4 section of coax, and shorted tuning stub, and coax of any length to the transceiver.

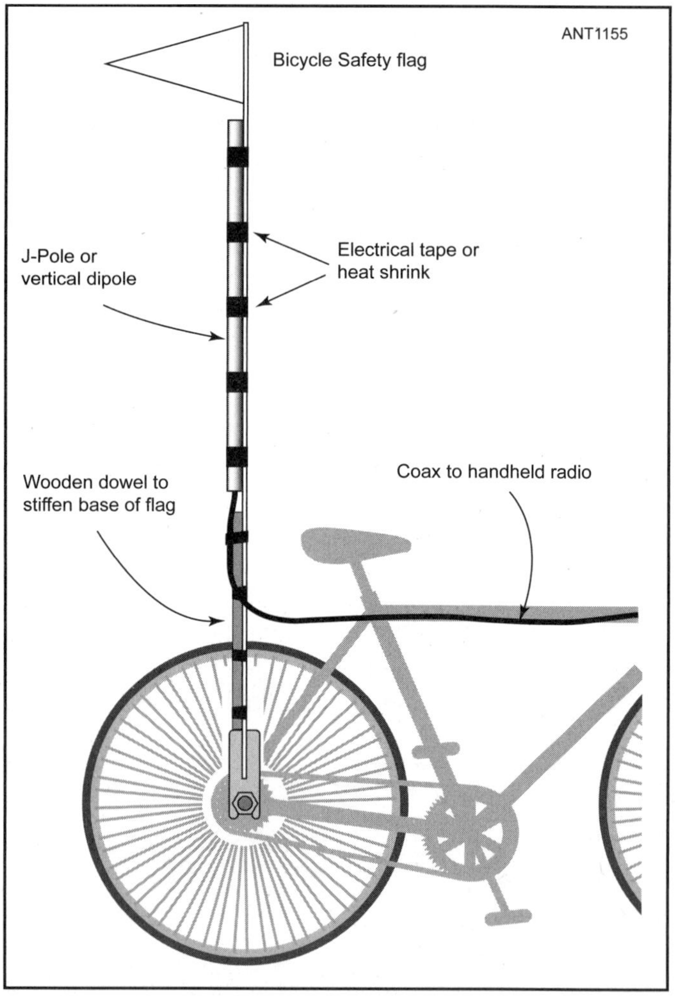

Figure 16.12 — Either the J-pole or vertical dipole can be attached to the fiberglass tube supporting a rear-axle mounted bicycle safety flag. Use tape or heat-shrink tubing to secure the antenna to the fiberglass. A wooden dowel can be used to stiffen the tube if necessary.

approximately ½ inch of dielectric and a small bit of center conductor exposed on the other end to adjust the stub length.

To attach the stub to the coax feed line, remove about 1 inch of jacket from the main feed line. Using sharp wire cutters, cut through the braid without damaging the dielectric and push it toward the jacket. Use a sharp knife to expose a short section of the center conductor. Solder the stub's center conductor to the main feed line center conductor and insulate it with liquid electrical tape or heat-resistant glue. Slide the main feed line's braid back toward the stub attachment point. Solder the braid of the main feed line and stub. Weatherproof the stub attachment point with more liquid electrical tape and a wrap of good-quality electrical tape.

At the other end of the stub, twist the braid and center conductor of the stub together but don't solder them. Mount the antenna in the clear (at least several feet above the ground and away from any metallic objects). Use an SWR meter or antenna analyzer to adjust the length of the stub to give minimum SWR at the desired frequency. Since the stub is intentionally too long, adjustment consists of untwisting the braid and center conductor, removing a small amount of dielectric, twisting the braid and center conductor together again, and re-measuring. When the stub is at the desired length, solder the braid and center conductor together and seal the stub with heat shrink or tape.

Secure the completed antenna to the safety flag's fiberglass tube with heat shrink tubing or wraps of tape as shown in **Figure 16.12**. If the assembly needs additional support, a length of wooden dowel can be taped to the fiberglass for additional rigidity. If the assembly vibrates or rubs against the frame or a rack, a length of plastic hose can be used to protect the antenna.

16.4 PROJECT: Big Wheel for Two Meters

The following section is an overview of the construction project, "A New Spin on the Big Wheel" by L. B. Cebik, W4RNL, and Bob Cerreto, WA1FXT, in the March 2008 issue of *QST*. The complete article detailing the design's history, evolution, and critical elements is included with this book's online material with all construction details and drawings.

Most attempts to develop a horizontally polarized omnidirectional (HPOD) 2 meter antenna have sought to minimize the antenna's size. Shapes such as circles (halos), squares and rectangles usually result in the need for either hypercritical dimensions or difficult matching conditions — or both. By turning to more conventional full size structures using three dipoles, we can reduce the number of critical parameters and ease the process of replicating the antennas in a home workshop. In fact, we shall describe two versions of the same basic antenna. One is a triangle of three dipoles that folds into a flat package, suitable for easy transport to a hilltop. The other is a circle of three dipoles suitable for mobile operation that requires somewhat less space but needs greater precision in construction. Both antennas share a common feed system and display broadband characteristics that ease the builder's task.

THE THREE DIPOLE DESIGN

The center and right outlines in **Figure 16.13** show the basic triangular and circular forms that emerged from the original design at left. Note that the current magnitude curves place the feed points of the dipoles at high current, relatively low impedance positions.

Both forms are very broadband in virtually every operating parameter once the builder gets the dimensions correct. The triangle, with a wider separation between the dipole end tips, is less critical with respect to dimensions, but requires more space. The circular version, with tighter coupling between dipole tips, requires more careful construction, but results in a more compact structure. In fact, for the same performance, the circular three-dipole antenna is smaller than the original big wheel.

The far-field performance of the three-dipole HPODs and the big wheel are virtually identical. Therefore, the data in **Figure 16.14** applies equally to all three designs. At a height of 20 feet above average ground, the three elements in all of the designs provide an average gain in the lowest lobe of about 7.2 dBi. The azimuth pattern is as close to circular as is possible with fewer than four elements. The gain variation for the worst

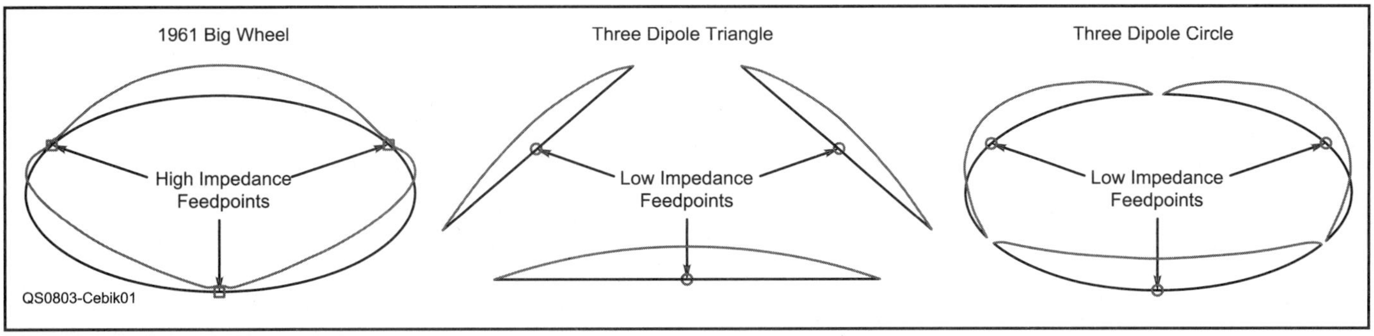

Figure 16.13 — Relative current magnitudes on three different three element HPOD antennas.

case was less than 0.3 dB.

The modeled SWR curve applies to both of the three-dipole models. Because the dipoles of the final designs present feed point impedance close to 50 Ω, we may use standard coaxial cable of virtually any length to reach the hub without changing the impedance significantly. Matched to a 50-Ω main feed point at the hub junction, the SWR curve is very flat and in the model shown in the graph, the SWR is acceptable (well under 2:1) for at least 8 MHz in the 2 meter range. Moreover, the circularity of the pattern and the gain are virtually constant across the entire 2 meter band. Even though the antenna is likely to see service only in the first MHz of the band, the broadband characteristics ease the difficulty of successfully building a version at home.

To obtain a 50-Ω main feed point impedance, the three-dipole arrays use a somewhat nonstandard arrangement at the hub. Both of our three-dipole designs use a series connection of the lines with the source. The resulting hub impedance is close to 150 Ω, and any stray reactances become very small portions of the impedance magnitude. Therefore, a simple λ/4 matching section can handle the impedance transformation to the 50-Ω region.

THE THREE-DIPOLE TRIANGLE

Each dipole is broadside to a direction 120° from the adjacent dipoles. The goal is to find dimensions that will achieve this goal plus provide a workable feed point impe-dance at each dipole. The prototype constructed to test the basic model of this arrangement used ½-inch diameter aluminum tubing as a light but sturdy material. Each dipole used a 2-inch length of 0.375-inch diameter fiberglass rod as a center insulator. The dipole halves are held in place with #6 stainless steel sheet metal screws. The gap should be as small as is feasible, ⅛ to ¼ inch. These same screws fasten the ends of the coax cable to the element with a stainless steel

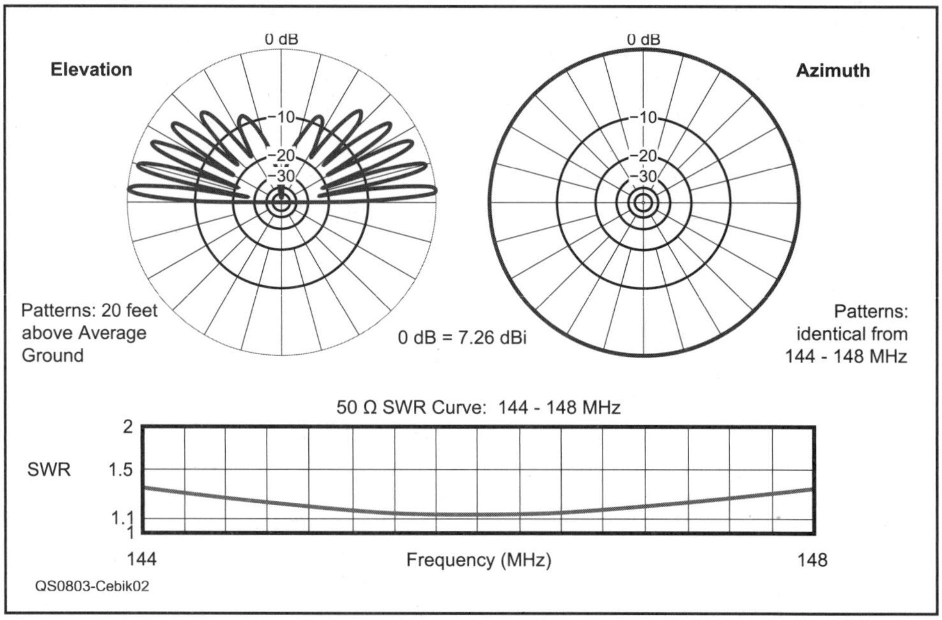

Figure 16.14 — Representative elevation and azimuth patterns and 50-Ω SWR curve for a three-dipole HPOD antenna using either a triangular or a circular shape at 20 feet above average ground. The patterns of the original big wheel are virtually identical in shape and strength.

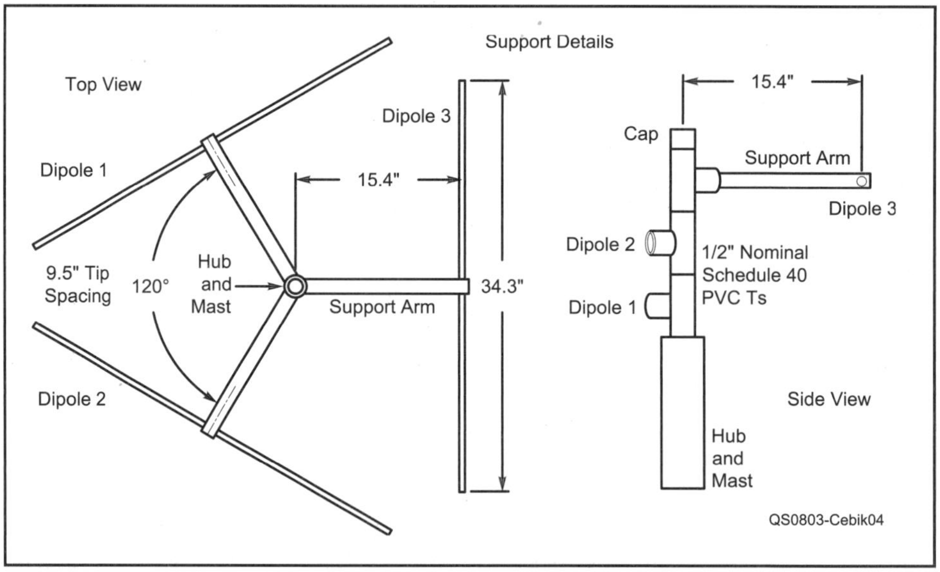

Figure 16.15 — Some details of the support structure used for the three-dipole 2 meter triangle.

Table 16.2
Dimensions for a Three-Dipole 2 Meter Triangle

Design Frequency (MHz)	*Element Diameter (inches)*	*Radius to Feed Point (inches)*	*Dipole Length (inches)*	*Tip-to-tip Spacing (inches)*
146	0.5	15.4	34.3	9.5
146	0.375	15.3	34.7	9.15
144.5	0.5	15.6	34.7	9.6
144.5	0.375	15.5	35.1	9.25

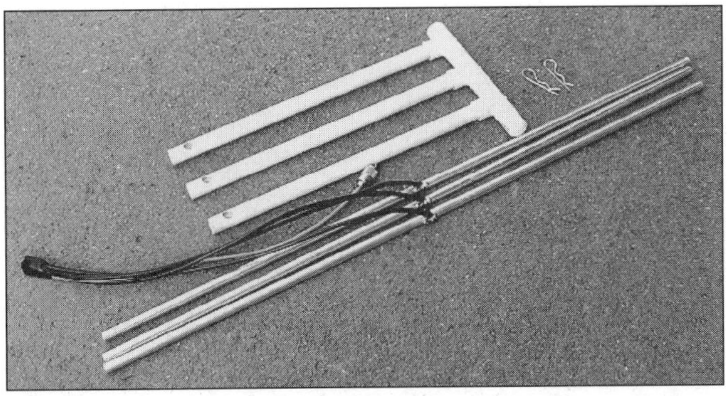

Figure 16.16 — The triangle HPOD disassembled for transport.

Figure 16.17 — The circular HPOD suitable for mobile use.

washer to prevent electrolysis between the aluminum element and the copper wires. For ease of disassembly in portable operation, the prototype used lugs under the screws.

Table 16.2 lists some dimensions for both 0.5- and 0.375-inch aluminum tubing, perhaps the two most likely materials for this project. For the triangle, 146 MHz was used as the design frequency because the performance and the SWR do not significantly change across the band. This center-design frequency also provided a good view of the antenna's broadband properties. However, the table also lists dimensions that are usable if the builder wishes to place the performance center of the antenna at 144.5 MHz. The prototype used the half-inch-diameter material and the 146 MHz dimensions for that material.

Note the length of the dipole. It is about 3.3 inches shorter than an independent dipole composed of the same material. The resonant impedance (50 Ω) is lower than the usual value for a standard dipole of about 70 Ω. The three dipoles in the triangle do interact by virtue of both the proximity of their feed points and the closeness of their tips. The dimensions of the triangle are therefore quite critical to successful operation of the array as designed. However, in the triangular form, they are not finicky, and cutting errors of ⅛ to ¼ inch will not materially affect performance.

In fact, the relatively relaxed conditions for the triangle prompted the particular design that emerged. The prototype may be useful for field or hilltop service, since the support structure and the elements and their cable come apart and store in a flat package for transport. **Figure 16.15** provides a few of the support structure details and **Figure 16.16** shows the antenna disassembled for transport.

For a permanent installation or for mobile use, you may prefer a circle of three dipoles as shown in **Figure 16.17**. The circle has no loose dipole ends and is more compact than the triangle. Indeed, it is aesthetically more pleasing. However, such pleasure comes at a cost. The construction and adjustment of the elements are somewhat more critical, although completely manageable.

16.5 PROJECT: Halo For Six Meters

The following section is based on the construction project "Omnidirectional 6-Meter Loop" from the book *Magic Band Antennas for Ham Radio* by Bruce Walker, N3JO (see References and Bibliography). The full article is included in this book's online material as are two other articles, "A 6 Meter Halo" by Paul Danzer, N1II and "6-Meter Halo Antenna for DXing" by Jerry Clement, VE6AB. One of these versions will be a good addition to your mobile station, depending on your resources. VE6AB's halo is shown mounted on a mobile mast in **Figure 16.18**.

You may also enjoy reading two additional construction articles also included in the online material; "Six Meters from your Easy Chair," by Dick Stroud, W9SR in the January 2002 issue of *QST* and one of the original halo articles, "A Two-Band Halo for V.H.F. Mobile," by Ed Tilton, W1HDQ, in the September 1958 issue of *QST*.

The halo (or "squalo" if the loop is square rather than round — see **Figure 16.19**) satisfies several key elements for an inexpensive 6 meter antenna: omnidirectional, horizontal polarization, no exotic components or materials, easy to adjust. With care, the construction should be robust enough for mobile use. Use an anti-oxidation compound such as Noalox or Penetrox for all unsoldered metal-to-metal connections to avoid corrosion.

The halo is basically a half-wave dipole bent into a circle and fed with a gamma match. **Figure 16.20** shows the basic design and typical dimensions for the Omnidirectional 6 Meter Loop by Bruce Walker, N3JO. **Figure 16.21** shows the dimensions of the plate holding the ends of the main antenna together, the feed point connector, and the mast mounting

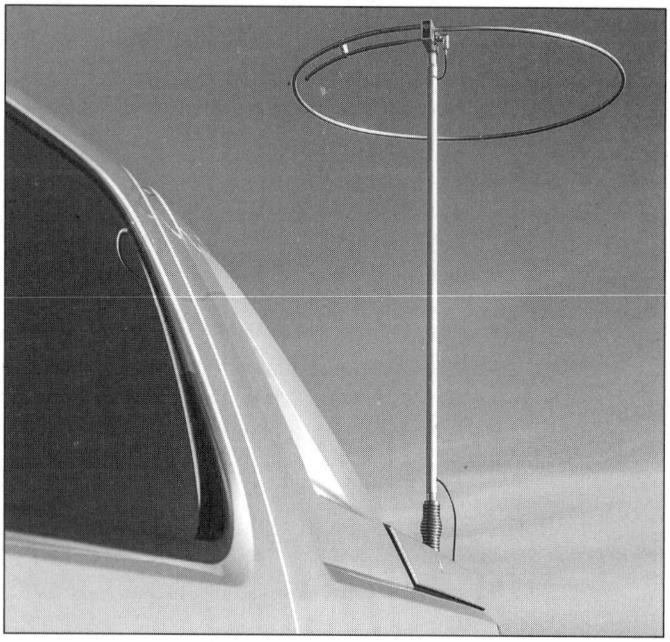

Figure 16.18 — A 6 meter halo antenna can be used as a mobile antenna if carefully constructed. The antenna shown here was designed and built by Jerry Clement, VE6AB.

Figure 16.19 — The "squalo" is the square version of the halo antenna. This one is available from Cushcraft.

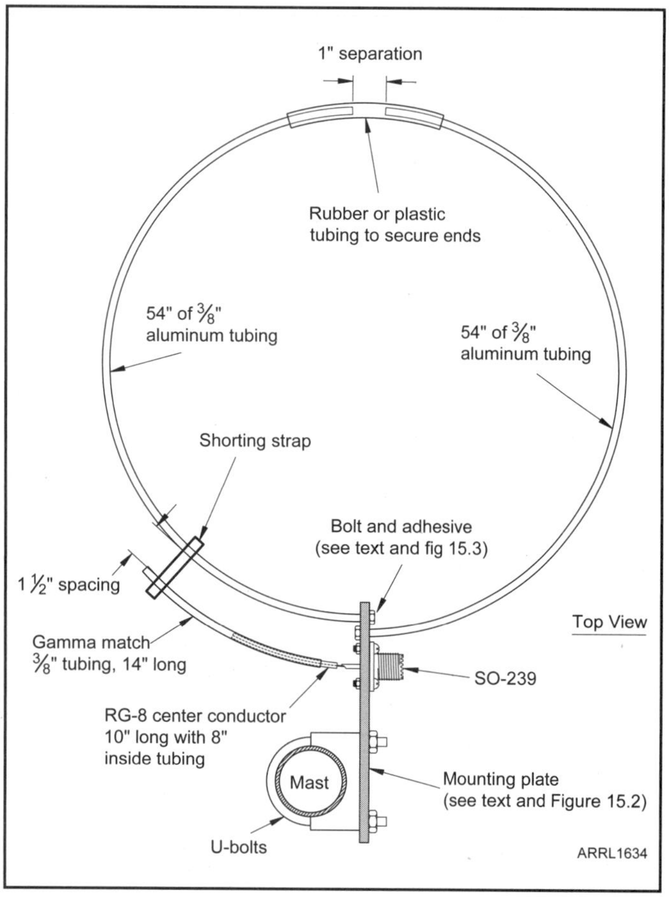

Figure 16.20 — Dimensions of N3JO's omnidirectional 6 meter loop. The loop is mounted so that it is horizontal.

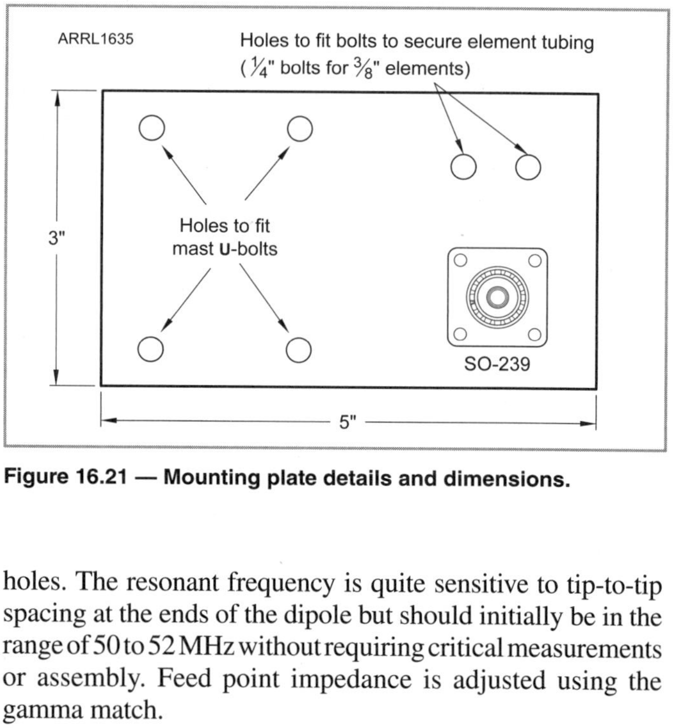

Figure 16.21 — Mounting plate details and dimensions.

holes. The resonant frequency is quite sensitive to tip-to-tip spacing at the ends of the dipole but should initially be in the range of 50 to 52 MHz without requiring critical measurements or assembly. Feed point impedance is adjusted using the gamma match.

Similar to the gamma match design in the **VHF, UHF, and Microwave Antennas** chapter, the assembly shown in **Figure 16.22** is made from a 14-inch piece of the ⅜-inch tubing used for the main antenna. The gamma match tube should be curved to follow the main halo ring. Spacing between the main antenna and the gamma match tube is 1½ inch. The gamma match is adjusted by moving the strap back and forth. This should be done with the antenna well off the ground and away from any other conductive surfaces.

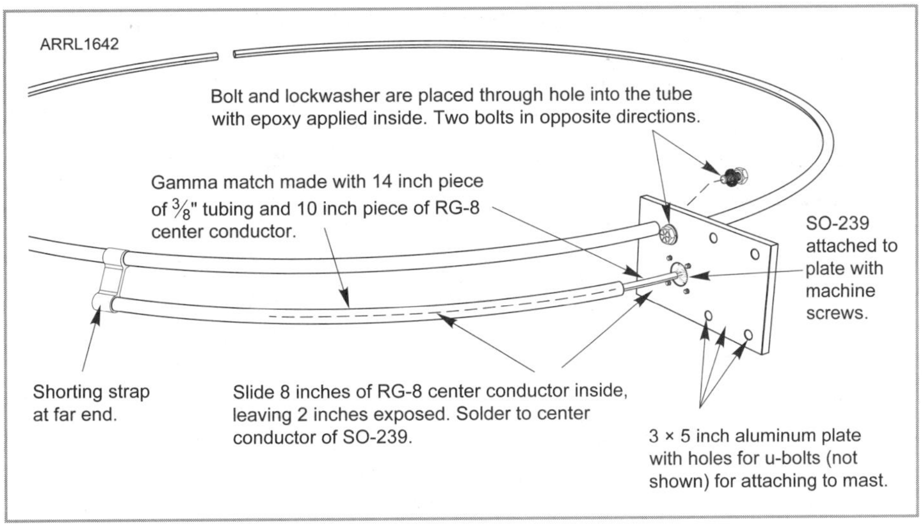

Figure 16.22 — The N3JO halo matching section details.

16.6 Rover Antenna Systems

Roving is a big part of VHF+ contesting and getting more popular all the time. The basic idea is to activate grid squares that are the contest multipliers. Rover stations can either operate in nearly continuous motion or can drive to and operate from a few advantageous locations. Rover antennas are of the same type used at fixed stations but mounted on masts or racks attached to or carried by vehicles.

Because the stations move, often operating at highway speeds, roving places extra requirements on antennas and mounting hardware. A top-tier rover station may also have antennas for as many bands as a fixed station. This creates many challenges for station design and building.

This section discusses some of those challenges and how different rover stations approach the problem. Thanks to contributors Andrea Slack, K2EZ; Wyatt Dirks, ACØRA; Steve Kostro, N2CEI; Rich Rosen, K1DS; Jim Duffey, KK6MC; Darryl Holman, WW7D; Ron Ochu, KOØZ; Pete Kobak, KØBAK; and Jon Kirkland, KM4FMU who shared some of their tips. You can also get a lot of good ideas from looking at the ARRL Soapbox web pages for after-contest reports. (**arrl.org/soapbox**) Two articles on roving are included in the online material, as well.

Before discussing technical details, the choice of operating style should drive the choice of antennas and their mounting, rotation, cabling, etc. A mismatch between expectations and equipment will result in on-air frustration, rework, and wasted time and money. Before committing to a significant antenna system, it is important to consider how it is to be used. This is also true for fixed stations but roving places a premium on all aspects of the antenna system. Knowing what questions to ask is the most important part of any type of station design!

Beginners are encouraged to start with modest antennas to get a feel for a particular operating style. There are lots of VHF+ contest opportunities so a few "practice runs", even with simple vertical antennas, can pay big benefits. See the sidebar "Resources for Rovers" to find sources of good information, including a video about how to get started.

SAFETY IN MOTION

Operating while in motion can present significant safety hazards, both to other drivers and the rover operator. First, the antenna system, including cables, must be secure at the expected driving speeds. A "shakedown" drive with another driver following closely and to the side to look for vibration or loose hardware may spot trouble before it happens.

Many states restrict operating "two-way radio equipment" while in motion. They may require hands-free operation or place other constraints on what you can do while driving. Not many public safety officers will recognize amateur radio equipment as different from a mobile phone, so be sure you drive carefully and in compliance with any local laws. Carrying a printed copy of regulations with you can be helpful. One solution to the operate-while-driving problem is to have two people in the vehicle with one driving and one operating.

16.6.1 Rover Antenna Selection

As you can see in **Table 16.3**, there are two primary antenna designs on the VHF/UHF "low bands" of 6 meters through 70 cm: omnidirectional antennas and Yagis. The Moxon rectangle is also popular on 6 meters. For these bands, the antennas are large enough to be limited by vehicle size laws. On higher frequency bands, straight-element and loop-element Yagis dominate. Beginning at 5.6 GHz, dishes become practical for a mobile station.

Antenna stacking distances for a rover station can be smaller than normally accepted practice. The degradation in pattern is worth the tradeoff of a manageable antenna package. How-

Table 16.3
Examples of Antennas on Active Rover Stations

Band	*Antenna*	*Notes*
6 meters/50 MHz	3-element Yagi	6-foot boom to meet size limits
	Halo	
	Stressed Moxon	
	Hex beam	Rotatable in motion
	Dipole	Broad pattern, easy to lift
2 meters/144 MHz	7-element Yagi	Below 6m Yagi on mast
	Stacked halos or Big Wheels	
	8-element "Cheap Yagi"	
	4-element "Cheap Yagi"	Rotatable in motion
1-1/4 meters/222 MHz	10-element Yagi	With 70cm Yagi on cross-boom
	Stacked halos or Big Wheels	
	8-foot Yagi	
	10-element "Cheap Yagi"	
	6-element "Cheap Yagi"	Rotatable in motion
70 cm/432 MHz	15-element Yagi	With 1¼ m Yagi on cross-boom
	Stacked halos or Big Wheels	
	8-foot Yagi	
	12-element LFA Yagi	Passive elements mounted with single screw for easy replacement
	8-element "Cheap Yagi"	Rotatable in motion
	11-element "Cheap Yagi"	
33 cm/902 MHz	6-foot loop Yagi	Single or on H-frame
	8-foot Yagi	
	33-element loop Yagi	12-foot boom
	10-element "Cheap Yagi"	Rotatable in motion, use on vert pol for FM
23 cm/1.2 GHz	6-foot loop Yagi	Single or on H-frame
	8-foot Yagi	
	24-element loop Yagi	6-foot boom
	10-element "Cheap Yagi"	Rotatable in motion, use on vert pol for FM
13 cm/2.3 GHz	6-foot loop Yagi	Single or on H-frame
	45-element loop Yagi	7-foot boom
	18-element Yagi	Rotatable in motion, commercial WiFi Yagi
3.4 GHz	6-foot loop Yagi	On H-frame
	45-element loop Yagi	4.5-foot boom
5.6 GHz	Up to 2-foot dish	
	0.9-m dish	Dual-band with 10 GHz
10 GHz	Up to 2-foot dish	
	0.9-m dish	Dual-band with 5.6 GHz

"Cheap Yagi" refers to designs by WA5VJB at **wa5vjb.com/yagi-pdf/cheapyagi.pdf.**
Note that some of the longer-boom Yagis above 50 MHz may be too long for use while in motion.
Consider beamwidth on the higher-gain antennas with respect to pointing accuracy.
Quad designs with equivalent number of elements to the Yagis are also popular.

ever, adjacent antennas on 3rd harmonics should be avoided. Place 6-meter antennas at the top for the best elevation pattern, which can be very important for taking advantage of Es propagation.

SIX METERS

Ideally, a 6-meter antenna should be at least one wavelength (about 20 feet) above the ground. If the band is open, height is less critical. Three-element Yagis are popular but may have to be stowed when the vehicle is moving due to mechanical concerns or size limits. For 2-element Yagis, the Moxon rectangle is becoming popular, particularly the SM-50 "stressed

6-Meter Hex Beam by WW7D

A 6-meter antenna that takes well to the open road is the 2-element hex beam. With no free element ends to oscillate in the wind, similar to a stressed Moxon, there is less mechanical vibration. The overall footprint is smaller than a Yagi, as well. Darryl Holman, WW7D, provides construction details of his 6-meter hex beam in the article "A 6m Hex Beam for the Rover" that is included in the online material. The article also includes several good photos of his vehicle-mounted antenna mast.

Moxon" design in **Figure 16.23** manufactured by PAR Electronics which is only 84 × 31 inches (see **parelectronics.com/stress-moxon.php**).

6-meter beams designed before *WSJT-X* modes became important may not have good performance at the FT8 and FT4 frequencies around 50.313 MHz. Most Yagis have a low-pass response and gain can drop quickly with frequency, so an antenna with good gain at 50.125 MHz can be mediocre on 50.313 MHz. Consider retuning the antenna somewhat higher in the band or use a design with wider bandwidth.

Halos, including stacks of multiple halos, are popular on 6 meters, as well. A number of stations use one or two halos in motion, then switch to higher-gain beams when at a stationary operating location.

Figure 16.23 — The stressed Moxon SM-50 by PAR Electronics is a Moxon rectangle designed with the forward element under tension. The resulting lightweight construction is robust under rover conditions.

2 METERS THROUGH 70 CM

For contacts within populated areas, 2 meters can be the most popular band. For all three of these bands, a modest-size horizontally polarized beam with a fairly wide pattern is best. This allows a rover to make contacts quickly across a wide area. If the route will not be in a populated area, a longer beam works better although its beamwidth is smaller. Halos and Big Wheels for local/regional coverage and a longer-boom Yagi is a good combination.

902-1296-2304-3400 MHZ

Loop Yagis are the usual antennas used by rovers on these bands. The antennas should be mounted with the loops facing downward to limit damage when passing under tree limbs. It's easy to straighten out damaged loops by removing them from the boom and using a rolling pin to roll them back into shape. Repair one loop at a time to maintain their proper order on the boom. Versions with 6-foot booms are usually adequate, especially if the rover is in an advantageous location. "Loopers" can be mounted on a single cross boom or in an H-frame array. The long boom models may need additional stabilization to keep them aligned with the other antennas and each other.

5-10-24 GHZ

Small dishes are best on these bands, although some rovers have used horns over shorter distances. A 2-foot diameter dish with a dual feed for 5 and 10 GHz is popular. Dual-feed designs by W1GHZ are available for 10 GHz and 24 GHz. These bands usually require transverters which should be mounted in a waterproof box behind the dish to minimize feed line losses. The rover should be able to carefully aim the dish in

Resources for Roving

While this book has a lot of good information about antenna systems for rovers, there is a lot to learn. The best resource for learning about effective roving is other rovers, and the best place to find other rovers is a contest club. There are many contest clubs such as the Society of Midwest Contesters (**w9smc.com**), and some specialize in VHF+ contesting, such as the Packrats (**packratvhf.com**) in Pennsylvania and New Jersey and the Pacific Northwest VHF Society (**pnwvhfs.org**). You can join most clubs even if you don't live in their neighborhood and many post their newsletters and other articles online. You will be sure to find useful information about roving and rover stations there. You can find contest clubs by using the ARRL's Find-A-Club service (**arrl.org/find-a-club**) and entering "contest" in the search window.

VHF roving beginners might enjoy a video by Scott Farrell, KE4WMF, entitled, "VHF Contest Rover – A Beginner's Journey," showing his VHF contest rover setup. The 27-minute video is indexed, which makes it easy to move to a part you're interested in. The rover is also featured on Page18 of October 2022 *QST*.

FM Antennas

Making FM QSOs is an important part of rover strategy in areas with a lot of amateurs. Consider including vertically polarized antennas in your rover antenna system. If you are close to an urban or suburban area, whips will do fine. (Remember that a ⅝-wave 2-meter whip will work on 6 meters, too.) Farther out, a small beam oriented for vertical polarization is more productive. Another option is to tilt a beam approximately 45 degrees from horizontal, giving up some horizontally polarized gain to gain the stronger vertically polarized signal and use the same antenna on SSB and FM..

Digital Roving and Antennas

Much of the activity on 6 meters and 2 meters in VHF+ contests has moved to the *WSJT-X* digital modes like FT8, FT4, and Q65. While this sounds complicated, simple digital roving doesn't require high-power transmissions or high-gain antennas. Adding an onboard computer and digital interface may be as effective as increasing antenna size and power output. Because of the reduced need for high-gain antennas on 6 and 2 meters, available space might be better used for antennas for more bands or more antenna gain for higher bands where *WSJT-X* modes are less popular or impractical due to frequency drift.

both azimuth and elevation because the beamwidth of these dishes can be as little as 2–3 degrees. Offset-feed dishes are less sensitive to elevation (see the section on Rotating Rover Antennas).

LOG PERIODICS

A log periodic is an easy way for a rover to get on 5 or 6 bands. There can be a big mechanical advantage in simplifying to a single rotatable antenna. Although they sacrifice gain for frequency coverage, a "log" can be very practical, especially if it's more important to activate many bands than it is to work a few more-distant grids. A six-band log periodic (50-1300 MHz, for example) plus a 5-band transverter gets the station on six bands. Receive-only logs can often be used at 100 W or less, as well. Log periodics are available from Tennadyne, Create, and other manufacturers. A project to convert a TV log periodic to amateur bands is included in the **Frequency-Independent Antennas** chapter.

16.6.2 Omnidirectional Rover Antennas

The lack of directionality of halos and Big Wheels is sometimes an advantage and sometimes a disadvantage. It is an advantage when moving because there is no aiming required. Omnidirectional patterns also make it easier to find stations on the band. This is important in populated areas when operators are moving to different frequencies and the rover must find them quickly.

A disadvantage (along with lower signal strength in the main lobe) is that in lower-activity areas it is common to stay on or near the calling frequency and rely on antenna directivity to provide isolation from other stations. A rover operating with omnidirectional antennas in those areas is at a disadvantage because multiple stations would be received at the same time while they could use the beams to reduce interference.

Stacking halos or Big Wheels with $\lambda/2$ separation increases gain by 3 dB from narrowing the vertical beamwidth. While the required height is not very practical on 6 meters, on 2 meters through 70 cm and higher bands a stack can be used even in motion. In practice the narrower vertical beamwidth aims the peak radiation closer to the horizon so the perceived improvement is a bit higher. Two 6 meter halos can be stacked on an extendable mast, so that when the mast is collapsed, both halos are close together and function like a single halo. A stationary operating location, the mast can be extended to yield the extra gain.

Finally, halos and Big Wheels are simple, easy to tune antennas and, if well-built, robust. Should damage occur, they can often be bent back into shape. When every on-the-road or at-the-site minute counts, survivability and simplicity of tuning are key attributes.

HALOS ON THIRD HARMONICS

Some 2 meter halos will also operate on 70 cm, the third harmonic, with gain broadside to the plane of the halo. (This is straight up if the halo is horizontal.) Oriented vertically with the feed point at the bottom, this type of halo has a bidirectional pattern broadside to the antenna at low angles and nulls in the plane of the halo. Beamwidth is around 120 degrees. Mounting two halos separately on a single mast at right-angles to each other creates a switchable forward-rearward or side-to-side pattern. This is a handy compromise between omnidirectional and small beam antennas. Not all halos will operate with acceptable SWR on the 3rd harmonic and some experimenting is required.

16.6.3 Rover Feed Lines

Keep coax runs short to minimize weight and loss. Use good low-loss, flexible coax, recognizing that the lower loss of short runs gives you more choices from available cable.

We often forget that minimizing common-mode current can be even more important in roving than in fixed stations. After all, the antennas are only a few feet from electronics in most rover stations. Use ferrite core chokes to block the unwanted current (see the **Transmission Line Systems Techniques** chapter).

Rover stations take more mechanical abuse in vibration, wind loading, and being assembled and disassembled multiple times — sometimes during the same contest! Make it part of your standard routine to test all cables each time before hitting the road as center pins can wander and cables can break. In the winter, keep coax in the vehicle until you install it. Cold coax is stiff!

Getting your feed lines into the car needn't require any holes. KK6MC uses a "pool noodle" slit down one side on a window and around the vehicle frame (see **Figure 16.24**). Run the cables inside and raise the window until the foam compresses around them. See the **Receiving Antennas** chapter section on mobile direction-finding for additional ideas.

Each make and model of vehicle has different ways to get cables in and out of the passenger and cargo areas. By reading contest results and the after-contest reports on **3830scores.com** you may find a rover station using a similar vehicle — ask the operator how they solved the problem. Vehicle service bulletins for installing radio equipment will show how the manufacturer planned for antennas on the vehicle, although probably not to the degree of a rover station! (See the chapter on **Mobile and Marine HF Antennas**, as well.)

Figure 16.24 — An inexpensive "pool noodle" makes a coax-friendly window seal for getting feed lines into and out of KK6MC's vehicle. Slit the foam along one side, slide it over the window, and raise the window until the foam seats around the cables.

16.6.4 Rover Antenna Supports

For the best performance, get your antennas at least λ/2 above the ground or top of the car. That's 10 feet for a 6 meter antenna, so a ground-mounted mast should be at least 16 feet high. On 2 meters, 40 inches is sufficient and it gets easier as the frequency increases.

There are many ways to get your antennas in the air. The easiest is a telescoping mast like a painter's pole or fiberglass mast with locking-sections. A drive-on base can be simple — a piece of lumber with a pipe flange having a short, threaded pipe stub attached. The mount in **Figure 16.25** used by Jim Wilson, K5ND, is all-wood design. Roll a tire onto the mount, add the mast, secure it to the vehicle's body or roof rack, and up go the antennas. If you have a trailer hitch, U-bolts can clamp a telescoping mast or painter's pole to a hitch-mount bike rack as in **Figure 16.26**.

Trailer-hitch mounted masts as in **Figure 16.27** are practical and sturdy. Tripods mounted in the bed of a pickup truck can support large arrays (**Figure 16.28**) as can custom racks that mount on vehicle roof racks (**Figure 16.29**). The exact design will depend on your vehicle and whether you want to operate in motion or "shoot and scoot" style, stopping at a series of operating sites. If the mast will be exposed while driving, a "bend-over" capability on the mount is a good idea to avoid mast damage if there is a collision with something overhead.

Many rovers have found that a simple system of raising the antennas once an operation spot has been reached is the most efficient. Some rovers have been fortunate enough to acquire vans or trucks with powered telescoping masts. Others have

Figure 16.25 — A simple "drive-on" mount for a painter's pole or other inexpensive mast. A strut attached to K5ND's vehicle roof rack secures the mast at about head height.

Figure 16.26 — A trailer-hitch bike rack can serve as a sturdy mount for an extendable mast such as this aluminum telescoping pole on NØAX's car. The mast can be attached to the bike rack with U-bolts or brackets.

Figure 16.27 — Heavier trailer-hitch masts can support several antennas. This mast for KK6MC's rover is supported by a strut attached to the roof rack.

Figure 16.28 — A roof-top tripod for TV antennas is mounted in WØZF's pickup truck on a wooden frame bolted to the bed. This also makes installing a rotator easy and even large arrays can be supported at highway speeds.

used manual telescoping masts, military surplus mechanical crank elevated masts, or cantilevered masts that can be laid down for travel and raised when on site. Additional roof racks or custom frames are usually required for large masts and antenna arrays. Having all the antennas attached to the mast and the coaxial cables connected makes for a quick set-up on site. The easier and quicker it is to set up and tear down, the more effective on-site time will be.

Driving with beams mounted on a mast may not be practical, particularly long Yagis. The antennas could easily be damaged (or cause damage) at highway speeds. Installing and removing beams at each stop is time-consuming so being able to quick-disconnect the antenna and mast is very helpful. **Figure 16.30** shows the Quick Disconnect Antenna Mount from Down East Microwave (**downeastmicrowave.com/product-p/qdam.htm**) that consists of two parts: one plate that stays attached to the mast and the other to the antenna boom. The boom plate is placed against the mast plate and rotated to lock into place, held with a removable pin. Since the antennas are typically lightweight, heavy-duty bolts and nuts aren't needed. Similar homebrew solutions are easily imagined.

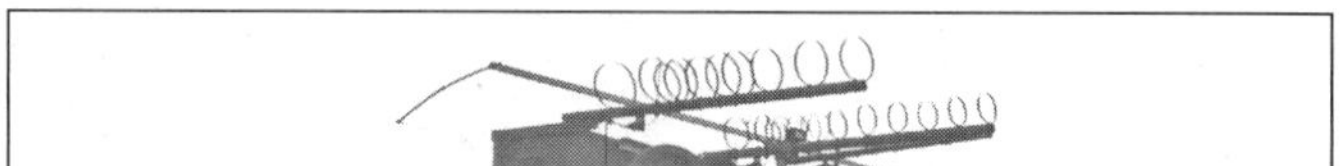

Figure 16.29 — N6NB's 11-band (6 meters through 24 GHz) mobile antenna farm is mounted on a frame attached to the vehicle's roof rack.

Figure 16.30 — The Down East Microwave QDAM (Quick Disconnect Antenna Mount) is designed for beam antennas. Matching plates on the mast and antenna boom are placed together and twisted into a locking position. A locking pin holds the assembly in place without threaded hardware. (Photo courtesy Down East Microwave)

(A)

(B)

(C)

Figure 16.31 — Several examples of heavy-duty tripods used to hold a microwave dish and receive electronics by WAØCNS, AF4JF (B), and W8MQW (C).

For microwave rovers, dish antennas and the associated receive electronics, are usually connected together in a single package. This requires a sturdy tripod to support the weight and hold the antenna steady, particularly in windy locations. **Figure 16.31** shows several examples of heavy-duty tripods used for microwave stations. Tripods are also useful for smaller arrays as shown by K1DS's stack of WA5VJB "Cheap Yagis" on 222 MHz, 432 MHz, and 902 MHz in **Figure 16.32**. Speaker mounts for portable PA systems can also hold a substantial load in place on an extendable mast.

ROTATING ROVER ANTENNAS

Using a regular fixed-station antenna rotator requires the use of an inverter to supply the 120 V ac from a vehicle's dc power system. Inverters are not expensive but if you prefer all-dc operation, the Yaesu G-800SA rotator operates from 13.8 V dc. To speed up rotation, some operators use a 12 V to 24 V converter to power the rotator, with much faster rotation as a result. RF noise from inverters and converters can be a problem so test them on-the-air before operating.

Turning the antenna by hand, known as an "Armstrong rotator", is an option as well, but it is hard for a single operator to peak up a weak signal when trying to rotate an antenna. Some operators use the vehicle itself as the rotator, driving slowly in a circle with the antennas fixed on their mounts. Another option is to have large, high-gain antennas for use with the vehicle stopped and a low-gain set for use while in motion.

To aim the antennas, use a good-quality compass and many GPS apps, including in vehicles, will provide a fairly accurate

Figure 16.32 — A tripod also makes an effective short mast for portable operation by a rover. K1DS uses a tripod to hold this short stack of 222 MHz, 432 MHz, and 902 MHz Yagis. (Photo courtesy of Rick Rosen, K1DS)

Figure 16.33 — An engineering compass provides better resolution, magnifying optics, and a crosshair to make aiming a high-gain antenna easier. (Photo by Ron Ochu, KO0Z)

direction. A grid square target bearing can be provided by apps such as *HamGPS* or *Easy QTH Locator*.

For the demanding aiming requirements of a high-gain microwave dish, use an engineering compass with its magnifying optic and crosshair for high resolution (see **Figure 16.33**). This is very important when trying to aim a dish with a beamwidth of 3 degrees!

Find an object on the horizon as a landmark to aim at coinciding with the predicted beam heading. Once the signal is detected by slowly panning the dish a few degrees left and right, adjust the elevation. For the most part, elevation, once set, stays the same except for rain-scatter contacts. An offset dish's pattern is not as sensitive to elevation as a center-fed dish.

Antenna Height and Width Limits

Know the laws for vehicle size and clearance where you will be traveling. Federal law restricts commercial vehicle width to 2.6 meters (102.4 inches) on the interstate highway system and most states have similar rules. Exceptions to this limit are made for required safety equipment, such as mirrors, but this does not include amateur radio equipment.

There are a few different maximum heights that tractor-trailers may have, but the most common limit is 13 feet 6 inches. There are no federal height restrictions, which are set by the states. Open road height limits range from 4.11 meters (13 feet, 6 inches) to 4.27 meters (14 feet). Apps are available that will tell you about low clearances along a specific route — see **freeappsforme.com/apps-for-low-clearance**.

Antennas are not as rigid as truck bodies, and many places don't actively trim smaller branches because the trucks simply push them aside without damage. Roving with antennas at the maximum height limit is likely to result in antenna damage. Heights under 12 feet are more reasonable.

Yagis should be limited to boom lengths of approximately 6 feet. Mounting points for such an antenna must be in the center of the boom instead of at a wind or weight balance point. Remember to account for turning radius which can be quite a bit longer than boom length for lower-frequency antennas. Fixed-mounted Yagis, or those rotated only when stopped, can be much longer.

16.6.5 Miscellaneous Rover Notes

For what it is worth, I have 4 to 5 mpg worth of antenna. I used to get 19 to 20 mpg highway but now get 15 mpg on the highway. — *K2EZ*

I prefer wood booms to aluminum booms. Wood doesn't fatigue like metal does and this can become important when driving at highway speeds, where the antennas may be oscillating for hours in the air stream. I also drive down many Forest Service roads with low-hanging foliage, so the antennas do get rather beat up. The wooden antennas booms don't bend, but occasionally break. Wood booms are much easier to replace than metal booms. — *WW7D*

Heading or Bearing?

Heading is the direction the vehicle or antenna is pointing. Bearing is the direction to the station being contacted. Directions start at 0 degrees for North and increases clockwise through East (90 degrees), South (180 degrees), and West (270 degrees).

Use quality hardware, preferably with only one or two wrench sizes required, and good lock washers. Make a checklist to test all connections at each stop. Carry spare hardware. Use colored vinyl tape to mark antennas, feed lines, and radio antenna connections to avoid confusion. — *KK6MC*

On-the-road repairs can be made a lot easier if element lengths are written on the boom so that they can be replaced if broken. This is particularly important with wooden booms and the "Cheap Yagi" designs in Table 16.3. Element spacings written on the boom help if the boom is broken. Also, quick and dirty repairs can be made with duct tape or Gorilla Tape™ to reattach elements. — *KK6MC*

Remember that the rover is usually the little station being sought by the bigger fixed stations, so having an adequate signal is usually OK and that bigger antennas can be unwieldy and less productive. — *K1DS*

16.7 References and Bibliography

J. Allen, "Simple 2 Meter Bicycle-Motorcycle Mobile Antennas," *QST*, Aug. 1995, pp. 69-70.

S. Cerwin and E. Juhre, "Bicycle-Mobile Antennas," *QST*, Mar. 1993, pp. 52-53.

J. Clement, "6-Meter Halo Antenna for DXing," *QST*, Feb. 2017, pp. 30-33.

P. Danzer, "A 6 Meter Halo," *QST*, Sep. 2004, pp. 37-39.

E. Fong, "The DBJ-2: A Portable VHF-UHF Roll-up J-pole Antenna for Public Service," *ARRL Antenna Compendium*, Vol. 8, pp. 155-157.

B. Walker, *Magic Band Antennas for Amateur Radio* (Newington: ARRL 2019)

TABLE OF CONTENTS

Chapter 17 — Online Material

Articles

- “A 12-Foot Stressed Parabolic Dish” by Richard Knadle, K2RIW
- “A Parasitic Lindenblad Antenna for 70 cm” by Anthony Monteiro, AA2TX
- “A Portable Helix for 435 MHz” by Jim McKim, WØCY
- “A Simple Fixed Antenna for VHF/UHF Satellite Work” by L.B. Cebik, W4RNL
- “An EZ-Lindenblad Antenna for 2 Meters” by Anthony Monteiro, AA2TX
- “Build a 2-Meter Quadrifilar Helix Antenna” by David Finell, N7LRY
- Converted C-Band TVRO Dishes PDF
- “Double-Cross Antenna – A NOAA Satellite Downlink Antenna” by Gerald Martes, KD6JDJ
- “EME with Adaptive Polarization at 432 MHz” by Joe Taylor, K1JT, and Justin Johnson, GØKSC
- “Inexpensive Broadband Preamp for Satellite Work” by Mark Spencer, WA8SME
- “L Band Helix Antenna Array” by Clare Fowler, VE3NPC
- “Quadrifilar Helix As a 2 Meter Base Station Antenna” by John Portune, W6NBC
- “Simple Dual-Band Dish Feed for Es’hail-2 QO-100” by Mike Willis, GØMJW; Remco den Besten, PA3FYM; and Paul Marsh, MØEYT
- “The W3KH Quadrifilar Helix” by Eugene Ruperto, W3KH (plus two Feedback items)
- “The Two Meter EZ Lindenblad Revisited,” by Tom Planer, KJ9P and Grant Zehr, AA9LC
- “Two-Meter Eggbeater” by Les Kramer, WA2PTS and Dave Thornburg, WA2KZV
- “WRAPS: A Portable Satellite Antenna Positioning System” by Mark Spencer, WA8SME
- “WRAPS Rotator Enhancements Add a Second Beam and Circular Polarization” by Mark Spencer, WA8SME
- “QO-100: Working the First Ham Satellite in Geostationary Orbit” by Bill Dzruilla, NZ5N
- “Stress Offset Dish for 1296 MHz” by Al Katz, K2UYH

Chapter 17

Antennas for Space Communications

When we consider amateur space communications, we usually think about two basic modes: satellite and Earth-Moon-Earth (EME — also referred to as *moonbounce*). Both modes communicate using one of the Earth's satellites — our natural satellite (the Moon) or one of a variety of man-made satellites. The distances involved and the motion of the targets place special requirements on antennas for both types of communications as discussed in this chapter. (Antennas for meteor scatter modes are covered in the **VHF, UHF, and Microwave Antenna Systems** chapter.)

Because of technological advances, particularly regarding new digital modes that allow communications with extremely weak signals, the traditional distinction between antenna systems for satellite communications and for EME communications has become blurred. Thus, this chapter has been rearranged by antenna type and then specific requirements for each type of operation are discussed.

Material in this chapter, originally by KD1K, K2DH, and K1JT, has been updated by Doug Grant, K1DG (EME sections); Sean Kutzko, KX9X (Portable Satellite Antennas); and reviewed by Patrick Stoddard, WD9EWK. Wherever possible, designs referenced or illustrated in the text are also listed in the Bibliography. For additional information on constructing antennas, feeds, and equipment techniques for use at microwave frequencies, see the AMSAT website (**amsat.org**) and the ARRL and RSGB books listed in the References and Bibliography. These resources provide a wealth of information for the experimenter.

17.1 Space Communication Antenna Systems

There are two main differences between the Moon and man-made satellites in orbits closer to the Earth. The first is one of distance. The Moon is about 250,000 miles from Earth, while man-made satellites in highly elliptical orbits can be as far as 52,000 miles away. This 5:1 difference in distance makes a huge difference in the signals that arrive at the satellite, since transmission loss varies as the square of the distance. In other words, the signal arriving at the Moon is 20 dB weaker than that arriving at a geosynchronous satellite 25,000 miles high, due to distance alone.

The second difference between the Moon and a man-made satellite is that the Moon is a *passive reflector* — and not a very good one at that, since it has a craggy and rather irregular surface, at least when compared to a flat mirror-like surface that would make an ideal reflector. Signals scattered by the Moon's irregular surface are thus weaker than those for better reflecting surfaces. By comparison, a man-made satellite is an *active* system, where the satellite receives the signal coming from Earth, amplifies it and then retransmits the signal (usually at a different frequency) using a high-gain antenna. Think of a satellite as an ideal reflector, with gain.

The net result of these differences between a man-made satellite and the Earth's natural satellite is that moonbounce (EME) operation challenges the station builder considerably more than satellite operation, particularly in the area of antennas. Successful EME requires higher transmitting power and receiver sensitivity, along with sophisticated computer software for digital modes or an excellent operator capable of pulling weak analog signals out of the noise.

There are areas of commonality between satellite and EME antenna requirements, of course. Both require consideration of the effects of polarization and elevation angle, along with the azimuth directions of transmitted and received signals. High-performance Yagi arrays or helical antenna systems designed for satellite operation will likely suffice to make EME contacts using digital modes such as those of the *WSJT* software suite (**sourceforge.net/projects/wsjt**). Dish antennas, such as those converted from commercial C-band (4 to

8 GHz range) TVRO (television, receive only) service will certainly suffice for both types of communication.

This chapter will first explore antennas suitable for satellite operations and then describe the antennas needed for EME work.

17.1.1 Antenna Systems For Satellites

Amateur satellites provide links from 2 meters and up and these provide opportunities to use antennas of many types — from the very simple to the pretty complex. Antenna design and construction requirements for use with amateur satellites vary from low-gain antennas for low-Earth-orbit (LEO) satellites to higher-gain antennas for the high-altitude elliptical-orbit satellites (HEO) and geosynchronous satellites such as QO-100. The AMSAT website (**amsat.org**) is a good general resource for antenna and transceiver design, operating information and satellite parameters. See the AMSAT website's Station and Operating Hints page for antenna designs for satellite operations and other useful accessories and station components.

Contacts can be made via FM LEO satellites with a basic dual-band VHF/UHF FM transceiver. Some amateurs manage to work the FM birds with hand-held radios and a multielement directional antenna such as the popular Arrow Antenna shown in **Figure 17.1A**. Of course, this means they must aim their antennas at the satellites, even as they cross overhead. It is best to hold the antenna and manually aim it instead of using a tripod. This allows you to rotate the antenna to compensate for polarization shift in the ionosphere and from satellite tumbling. This reduces fading and improves contact quality and speed. A diplexer, shown in Figure 17.1B allows a single radio to use different antennas on each band, such as on 2 meters and 70 cm.

Omnidirectional fixed antennas that do not track a satellite are a home station option for starting out of if using rotators is not possible or practical. The M2 Antenna Systems EB-144 and EB-432 Eggbeater antennas shown in **Figure 17.2** are a commercial option. The turnstile-over-reflector antenna has been around for a long time, as shown in **Figure 17.3**. L.B.

Receiving NOAA Satellite Signals

US National Oceanographic and Atmospheric Administration (NOAA) polar orbiting weather satellites (POES) transmit data for production of gray-scale images of the ground below them. Data is transmitted at 137 MHz frequency used by the NOAA satellites and can be received twice a day. There are many free programs available to decode the data and produce images. The article "Double-Cross — A NOAA Satellite Downlink Antenna" included with the online material describes a fixed antenna shown in the photo designed for the 137 MHz frequency and can receive signals from any other satellite in that band. The SatNOGS system described in this chapter's section on Antenna Position Control can also be used to receive weather satellite data automatically.

Figure 17.A — The Double Cross antenna is made from four dipoles. [Gerald Martes, KD6DJ]

(A)

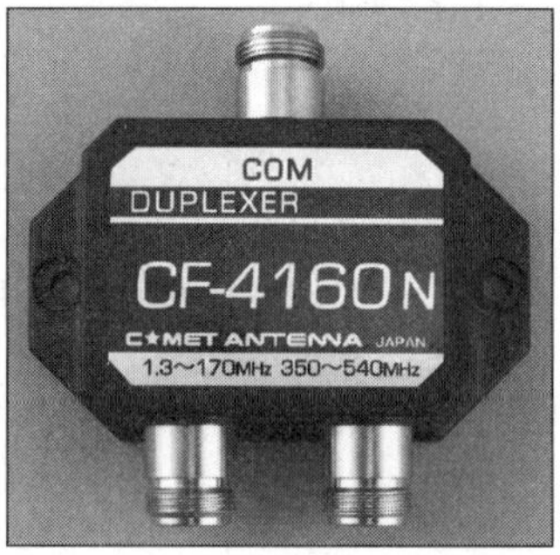

(B)

Figure 17.1 — A dual-band handheld and a lightweight Arrow Antenna (A) can be used to make contacts through FM repeater satellites such as SO-50, AO-91, AO-91 and others. When used in an open location free of foliage, the antenna provides enough gain to work the satellites, even close to the horizon. A diplexer (B) allows a single dual-band radio to use the 2 meter and 70 cm sections separately. These units are available from manufacturers of dual-band handheld and mobile radios. [Photo (A) courtesy Keith Baker, KB1SF]

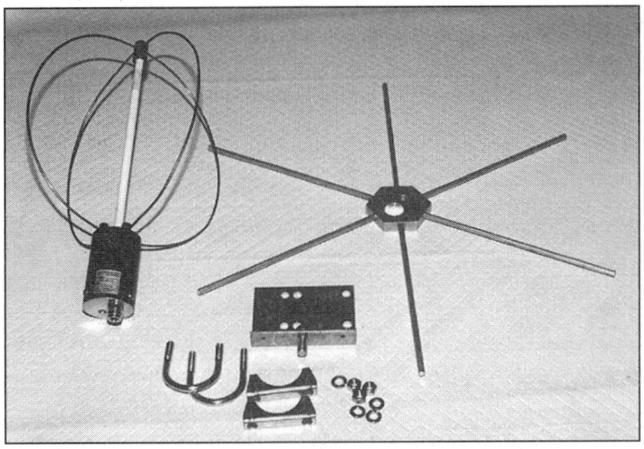

Figure 17.2 — Eggbeater antennas are popular for base station LEO satellite operations. This M² EB-432 eggbeater antenna for 70 cm is small enough to put in an attic. Antenna gain pattern is helped with the radials placed below the antenna.

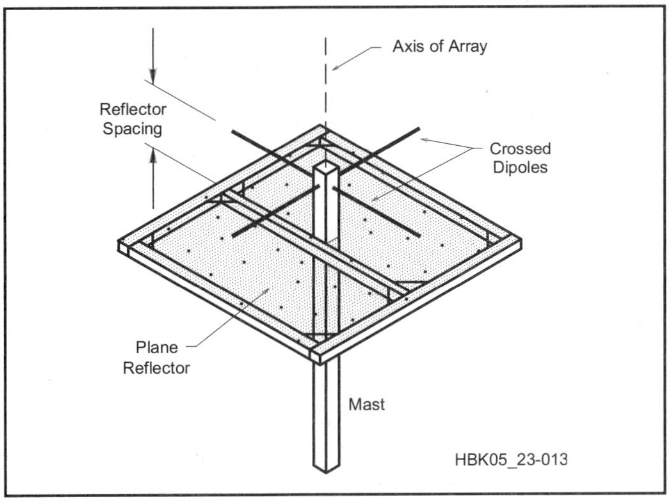

Figure 17.3 — The Turnstile Over Reflector antenna has served well for LEO satellite service for a number of years.

Cebik, W4RNL, described a fixed satellite antenna system that uses crossed-Moxon antennas to produce a circularly polarized, hemispherical pattern. This system is described in the article "A Simple Fixed Antenna for VHF/UHF Satellite Work" included with the online material and is shown in **Figure 17.4**.

For even better performance, at the modest cost of a single, simple TV antenna rotator, check out the fixed-elevation *Texas Potato Masher* antenna by Gerald Brown, K5OE, shown in **Figure 17.5.** This antenna provides a dual-band solution for medium-gain directional antennas for LEO satellites. This is a considerable improvement over omnidirectional antennas and does not require an elevation rotator for good performance. If an az-el rotator is available (see the Antenna Position Control section) reflecting screens can be added to the Moxon-pair antennas of W4RNL for even better performance.

A step up from a rotatable fixed-elevation antenna is a pair of short Yagi antennas similar to the handheld Arrow in Figure 17.1, or an Elk Antennas 2-meter/70-centimeter log periodic (**Figure 17.6**). A 3-element Yagi on 2 meters and a 4 – 7 element Yagi on 70 cm will work quite well with a broad enough pattern that elevation control is not required. A fixed elevation of 15 degrees will work reasonably well. Inexpensive Yagi designs by WA5VJB for satellite operation are online at **wa5vjb.com**.

Figure 17.4 — This Moxon pair, with lower but smoother gain across the sky, offers the fixed-antenna user the chance to build a successful beginning satellite antenna. Reflecting screens can be added if a small az-el rotator is available.

There was still one early LEO satellite operating on the 10 meter band as of early 2023. The 1974 AO-7 spontaneously recovered from a battery failure and can be used whenever its solar panels are illuminated. Its 10-meter downlink covers 29.3 to 29.5 MHz. Low-gain antennas for 10 meters, such as dipoles, are used to receive the signal from this satellite.

High Earth Orbit (HEO) satellites such as the Phase 3 platforms launched in the 1980s are no longer operational. AMSAT's GOLF (Greater Orbit, Larger Footprint: **amsat.org/greater-orbit-larger-footprint-an-introduction-to-the-amsat-golf-program**) program will place satellites into 500 to 600 km orbits that require somewhat higher gain antennas and transmit/receive ability. (Launches of the GOLF satellites have been delayed as of early 2023 but new launch dates are being scheduled.) For these satellites, a set of higher-

Figure 17.5 — Jerry Brown, K5OE, uses his Texas Potato Masher antennas to work LEO satellites.

Figure 17.6— The Elk Antenna 2M/440L5 log periodic beam covers both the 2-meter and 70-centimeter bands.

gain Yagi antennas will be required for VHF and UHF links (See the Yagi Arrays section of this chapter.) Satellites also use S-band (2.4 GHz) and X-band (10 GHz) frequencies (see **Table 17.1**), such as the QO-100, the Es'hail-2/P4-A geosynchronous platform serving most of ITU Region 1. (See **amsat-dl.org/en/p4-a-wb-transponder-bandplan-and-operating-guidelines**.) Similar platforms are under development, such as the "five-and-dime" architectures using C-band (5 GHz) and X-band. The GOLF series of satellites referenced in the previous paragraph may include some microwave capabilities, as well. Advantages of microwave systems include:

- Good performance with physically small downlink antennas.
- Availability of good quality receive converters and transmitting modules.
- Availability of preamps at reasonable prices.

PREAMPLIFIERS AND FEED LINES

Preamplifiers are available from Advanced Receiver Research, High Sierra Microwave, SSB Electronic, and other vendors. The WA5VJB preamp design "cookbook" (**wa5vjb.com/references/preamp-Cookbook.pdf**) has a number of tips and circuits for building your own preamp. An inexpensive broadband preamp suitable for receiving telemetry by WA8SME is described in the article "Inexpensive Broadband Preamp for Satellite Work" included in the online material.

Preamps will need to be mounted at the antennas and their manufacturers will have the appropriate mounting hardware and enclosures available. Preamps are generally not needed for hand-held antennas since the feed line length is very short.

When installing a fixed station satellite antenna, pay attention to feed line quality and loss. LMR-240 is a good choice for satellite antennas, especially on 70 cm. For long feed lines, consider using hardline between the station and the antenna support with a flexible line making the connection to rotating antennas.

Table 17.1
Amateur Satellite Band Designations

10 meters (29 MHz): H
2 meters (145 MHz): V
70 cm (435 MHz): U
23 cm (1260 MHz): L
13 cm (2.4 GHz): S
5 cm (5.6 GHz): C
3 cm (10 GHz): X

17.1.2 Antenna Systems for Earth-Moon-Earth (EME)

The antenna is arguably the most important element in determining an EME station's capability. It is not accidental that the baseline station requirements outlined in **Table 17.2** use Yagi arrays on the VHF bands and parabolic dishes at 1296 MHz and above. One of these two antenna types is almost always the best choice for EME.

The gains of some nominal antennas of each type are illustrated graphically in **Figure 17.7**, which helps to show why Yagis are nearly always the best choice for EME on the VHF bands. They are light, easy to build and have relatively low wind resistance. Stacks of four Yagis are small enough that they can be mounted on towers for sky coverage free of nearby obstructions. Larger arrays of 8, 16 or even more Yagis are possible, although the complexity and losses in phasing lines and power dividers then become important considerations, especially at higher frequencies. Long Yagis are narrowband antennas, usable on just a single band.

We usually think of the linear polarization of a transmitted signal as being "horizontal" or "vertical." Of course, on the spherical Earth these concepts have meaning only locally. As seen from the Moon, widely separated horizontal antennas may have very different orientations (see **Figure 17.8**). Therefore, in the absence of Faraday rotation an EME signal trans-

Table 17.2
Typical Antenna and Power Requirements for CW EME

For use with JT65 or other encoded digital modes, subtract approximately 10 dB of gain or power.

Freq (MHz)	*Ant Type*[1]	*G (dBi)*	*HPBW (deg)*	*TxPwr (W)*
50	4×12 m	19.7	18.8	1200
144	4×6 m	21.0	15.4	500
432	4×6 m	25.0	10.5	250
1296	3 m	29.5	5.5	160
2304	3 m	34.5	3.1	60
3456	2 m	34.8	3.0	120
5760	2 m	39.2	1.8	60
10368	2 m	44.3	1.0	25

[1]Example antennas for 50, 144 and 432 MHz are Yagi arrays with stated lengths; those for 1296 MHz and higher are parabolic dishes of specified diameter.

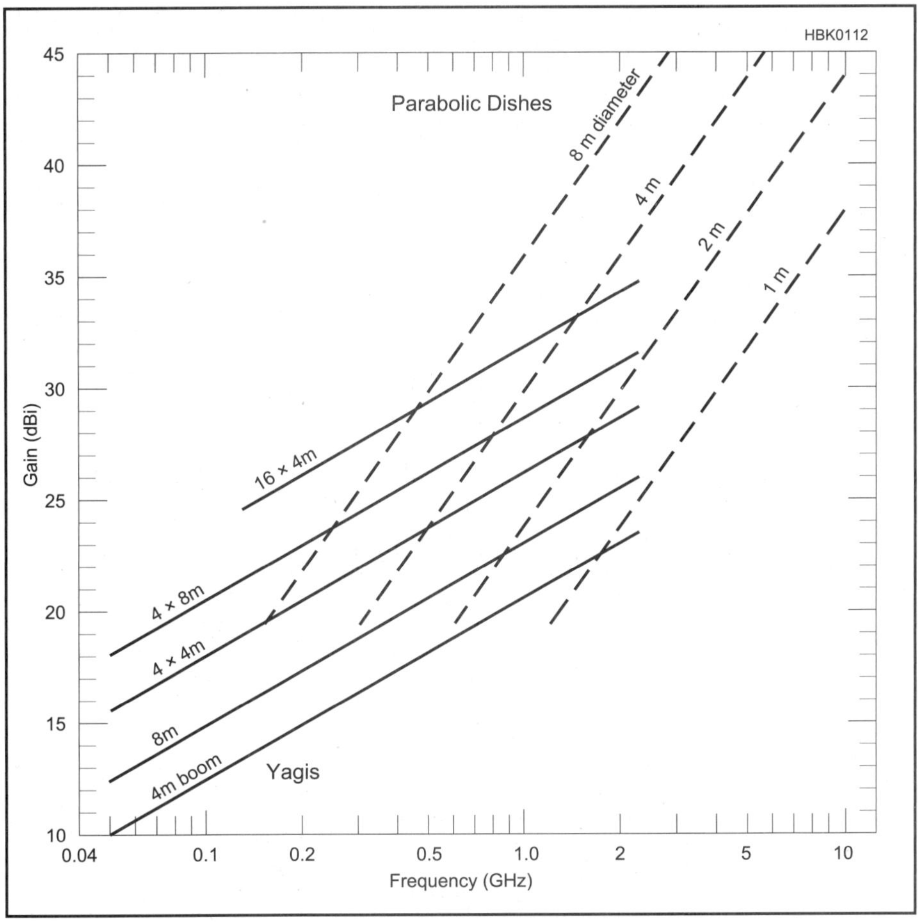

Figure 17.7 — Representative gains of practical Yagi antennas, arrays of Yagis and parabolic dishes as a function of frequency. Yagi arrays make the most cost-effective and convenient antennas for EME on the VHF bands, while parabolic dishes are generally the best choice above 1 GHz.

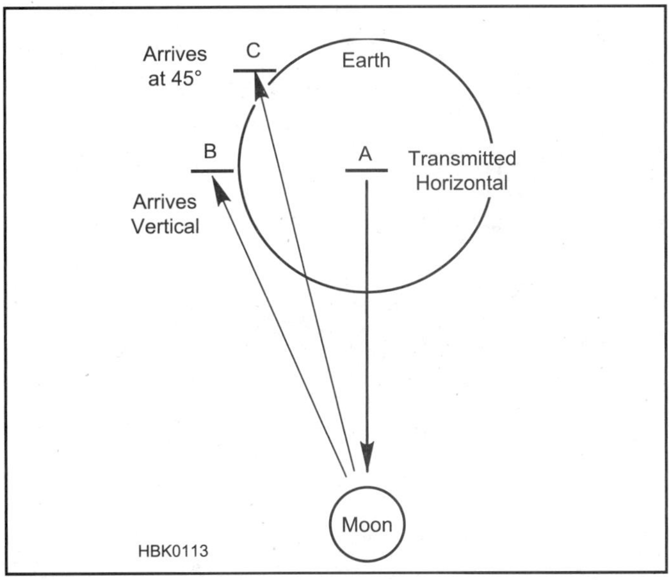

Figure 17.8 — The spherical Earth creates spatial polarization offsets for well-separated stations with horizon-oriented linear polarization. Here, a signal transmitted horizontally at A arrived with vertical polarization at B and midway between horizontal and vertical at C. When combined with Faraday rotation, offsets close to 45° can lead to apparent one-way propagation. See text for details.

mitted with horizontal polarization by station A will have its linear polarization misaligned at stations B and C by angles known as the spatial polarization offset. (*Faraday rotation* is a rotation of the polarization of radio waves when the waves travel through the ionosphere, in the presence of the Earth's magnetic field.) In Figure 17.8 the signal from A arrives with vertical polarization at B and at 45° to the horizon at C. Suppose C is trying to work A and $q_s = 45°$ is the spatial polarization offset from A to C. The return signal from C to A will be offset in the opposite direction, that is, by an amount $-q_s = -45°$. The Faraday rotation angle θ_F, on the other hand, has the same sign for transmission in both directions. Thus, the net polarization shift from A to C is $\theta_F + q_s$, while that from C to A is $\theta_F - q_s$. If θ_F is close to any of the values ±45°, ±135°, ±225°, …, then one of the net polarization shifts is nearly 90° while the other is close to 0°. The result for stations with fixed linear polarization will be apparent one-way propagation: for example, A can copy C, but C cannot copy A.

Obviously no two-way contact can be made under these conditions, so the operators must wait for more favorable circumstances or else implement some form of polarization control or polarization diversity. One cost-effective solution is to mount two full sets of Yagi elements at right angles on the same boom. Arrays of such *cross-polarized* or "Xpol" Yagis make especially attractive EME antennas on the VHF and lower UHF bands because they offer a flexible solution to the linear polarization misalignment problem.

At 1296 MHz and above, gains of 30 dBi and more can be achieved with parabolic dishes of modest size. As a result, these antennas are almost always the best choice on these bands. Their structure does not depend on any radio frequency resonances, so in many ways dishes are less critical to build than Yagis. Element lengths in high-gain Yagis must be accurate to better than 0.005 λ, while the reflecting surface of a dish need be accurate only to about 0.1 λ.

A parabolic antenna has a single feed point, so there are no losses in phasing lines or power splitters. You can use a dish on several bands by swapping feeds, and with suitable feed designs you can produce either linear or circular polarization, including dual polarizations. A very attractive and convenient option is to transmit in one sense of circular polarization and receive in the opposite sense. Transmitting in right-hand circular and receiving in left-hand circular has become the standard for EME at 1296 and 2304 MHz and will probably become the standard on higher bands as well.

More information about circular polarization is presented later in this chapter.

As made clear in Figure 17.7, the 432 MHz band lies in a transition region where both Yagis and parabolic dishes have attractive features. Either four long Yagis or a 6-meter (approximately 20 foot) dish can produce enough gain (about 25 dBi) to let you work many other EME stations on this band. Many linear-polarization systems are already in use — for good reason, since most amateur use of this band is for terrestrial communication — so converting everyone to circular polarization is impractical.

Therefore, schemes have been devised to physically rotate dish feeds and even whole Yagi arrays to cope with the resulting polarization alignment problems. Another scheme is to use a dual-polarization dish feed or dual-polarization Yagis, as described above and increasingly used on 144 MHz.

One of the biggest amateur EME stations in the world is HB9Q. This station includes excellent antennas for all VHF, UHF, and microwave EME bands. The 144/432MHz antenna shown in **Figure 17.9A** is of particular interest. It is a parabolic dish approximately 15 meters (50 feet) in diameter. Besides its impressive size, the feed system is innovative.

Instead of a dipole feed, the dish is illuminated by cross-polarized Yagis on both bands as shown in Figure 17.9B; two pairs of 4-element Yagis for 144 (one pair is vertically polarized, one pair is horizontally polarized) and a single 7-element cross-polarized Yagi for 432. The antennas are configured for circular polarization on transmit and used together for adaptive polarization on receive.

As mentioned earlier, another option for dealing with changing polarization is to physically rotate an entire linear-polarized array. This approach has been used by NC1I for his 432 MHz system as shown in **Figure 17.10A**. The array consists of (48) 15-element K1FO rear-mount Yagis for a total of 720-elements arranged in 12 bays of 4 Yagis each. Each Yagi's driven element is fed with 200-Ω open-wire line made of #8 wire and homebrew Teflon insulators. Connecting 4 of these in parallel gives a 50-Ω impedance for each bay of 4 Yagis. The twelve bays are connected to a pair of 6-way power dividers, which are then connected to a single 2-way divider.

The entire array can be rotated between horizontal and vertical polarization. The polarization rotator mechanism consists of a prop-pitch motor and heavy duty mast mounted in a 12" × 12" × 20" rectangular steel tube with a pair of heavy-duty 3.5" bearings. Elevation control is achieved by use of a heavy-duty 36" linear actuator and azimuth rotation is done by a large prop-pitch rotator. The system is balanced by several large counterweights (see Figure 17.10B).

Most amateurs believe that EME antenna systems are gargantuan monsters and certainly many "big-gun" EME stations have extraordinary antenna systems. However, excellent results are possible with modest antennas and stations. For example, EME rover KA6U has traveled the country activating many rare states and grid squares on EME using a station optimized for rapid deployment. Deployable in less than an hour, his EME antenna system, shown in **Figure 17.11** consists of:

144 MHz: 2 × 10-element H/V Yagis
222 MHz: 2 × 16-element Yagis
432 MHz: 4 × 25-element Yagis
1296 MHz: 2.4M folding dish

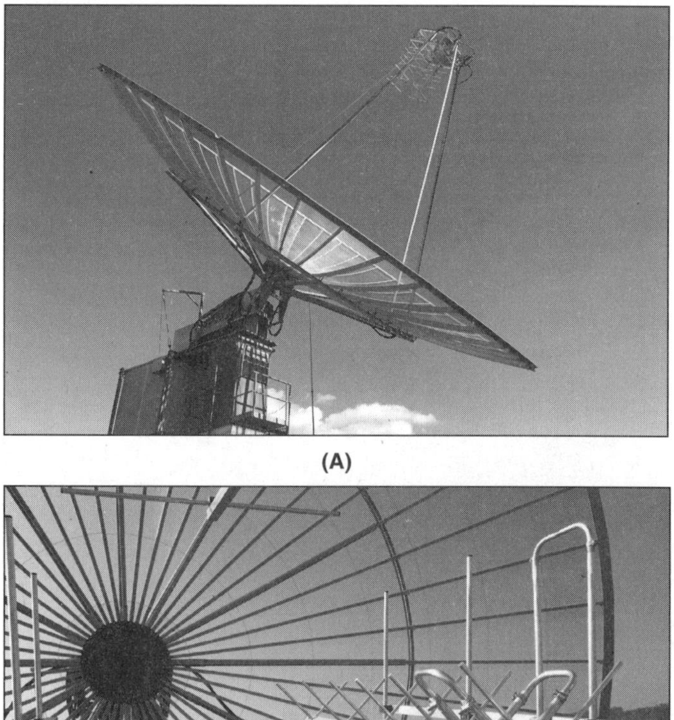

(A)

(B)

Figure 17.9 — The 50-foot dish used at HB9Q for EME on 144 and 432 MHz (A) and the feed system (B). (Photo courtesy of HB9Q)

(A)

Figure 17.10 — NC1I uses the array in A of (48) 15-element Yagis for EME on 432 MHz and rotates the entire array from horizontal to vertical polarization with the impressive mechanism shown at B. (Photos courtesy of Frank Potts, NC1I)

(B)

Figure 17.11 — KA6U can set up his portable EME station antenna system (144 MHz system shown) in less than an hour. (Photo courtesy of Peter Van Horne, KA6U)

ANTENNA PATTERN

A clean pattern with good suppression of side and rear lobes is important for all EME antennas — especially at 432 MHz and above, where excessive noise pickup through sidelobes can significantly increase the system noise temperature, T_S. For Yagi arrays you should use modern, computer optimized designs that maximize G/T_S, the ratio of forward gain to system noise temperature. Be sure to pay attention to maintaining a clean pattern when stacking multiple antennas. First sidelobes within 10-15° of the main beam may not be a major problem, because their solid angle is small and they will look mostly at cold sky when EME conditions are favorable. Side and rear lobes farther from the main beam should be suppressed as much as possible, however. Remember that even close-in sidelobes will degrade your receiving performance at low elevations.

For parabolic dishes, G/T_S is optimized by using a feed with somewhat larger taper in illumination at the edge of the dish than would yield the highest forward gain. Best forward gain is generally obtained with edge taper around −10 dB, while best G/T_S occurs around −15 dB. Edge taper of −12 dB is usually a good compromise. Some good reproducible designs for dish feeds are described or referenced later in this chapter.

17.1.3 Portable Satellite Antenna Systems

Portable satellite operating is becoming increasingly popular in support of programs such as VHF/UHF Century Club (VUCC). Operating from a infrequently-activated or even rare grid square can attract a lot of attention and some operators are even making "grid-peditions" to activate several such squares in one trip. Operating from the field places a premium on effective, robust equipment that can be transported to the field and deployed quickly.

RESOURCES FOR PORTABLE OPERATING

As this material was prepared in early 2023, there were approximately 15 active linear satellites and 7 active FM satellites, with more being scheduled for launch. AMSAT announcements (**amsat.org**) and the website's table of active satellites will keep you up to date on what satellites are available and their current status, frequencies, modes, and operational notes. Be aware that satellite modes can be changed by their control stations and power status can vary seasonally as sunlight to solar panels changes.

Sean Kutzko, KX9X, produced a series of videos aimed at satellite beginners for DX Engineering. You can find them on the DX Engineering YouTube channel at **youtube.com/@DXEngineering**. The Mercer County ARC (MCARC) also hosts an extended program by KX9X on satellite operating that includes portable operating.

FREQUENCIES

Most amateur radio satellites operate on a combination of 2 meters and 70 centimeters. There are a handful of satellites that use 10 or 15 meters. The AMSAT website maintains pages for uplink and downlink frequencies of currently active satellites; search for "AMSAT linear summary" and "AMSAT FM Summary."

Paul Overn, KEØPBR, has created the GridMaster Satellite Cheat Sheet on his satellite blog at **ke0pbr.wordpress.com**, which shows the relationship between the uplink and downlink frequencies as a pass progresses, another key element of success in the field.

OPERATING REQUIREMENTS

Antenna needs vary between portable and home operating. Home stations will benefit from larger antennas and a rotator that can be interfaced with satellite tracking software, such as *SatPC32* or *MacDoppler*. Portable operations, such as grid expeditions, can certainly use these tools if the operator is willing to construct such a station for portable use. Several satellite tracking apps exist for both Android and Apple IOS platforms to facilitate the proper tracking of satellites with handheld antennas.

Smaller, hand-held beam antennas offer good performance in a small package, balancing weight and size against signal strength. Regardless of approach, all satellite antennas should have as clear a view of the horizon as possible. Trees can function as attenuators, especially on 70 centimeters. Buildings that get in the way of the direct signal path between operator and satellite should be avoided. The ideal satellite operating site is on a hill with an unobstructed 360-degree view of the horizon. If that can't be obtained, a site with a clear view of the horizon is preferable over a high-elevation site with an obstructed view. If you're in an urban area, think outside the box: rooftops, public scenic views, or the tops of parking garages have proven to be excellent operating sites for many satellite operators. Careful analysis of a satellite's trajectory over your horizon may turn up a location with a clear view of the sky in that particular direction. If you live in an antenna-restricted neighborhood, operating portable with a handheld Yagi or log periodic will almost always be preferable to operating from home with a compromise antenna.

Because of the close proximity of transmit and receive radios and antennas, diplexers or low pass/high pass filters should be employed to avoid desensitization of the receive radio during transmit. Isolating the receiver from the transmit signal will resolve most desensitization issues.

COMMON ANTENNA TYPES

Mobile Whips

Mobile whips are the ultimate compromise antenna for satellite use. While some skilled satellite operators have used them with modest success, they will simply not perform well even under ideal circumstances and should be avoided by beginning or intermediate satellite operators.

Omnidirectional

Several omnidirectional antennas are shown in Figures 17.2 through 17.5 and discussed later in this chapter. Eggbeaters are generally two vertical loops 90 degrees out of phase. The turnstile is a crossed pair of dipoles at right angles fed 90 degrees out of phase. A quadrifilar helix (QFH) is another omnidirectional satellite favorite, although somewhat large on 2 meters for portable operating. These antennas are designed to illuminate most of the visible hemisphere overhead. They are often used with a ground plane beneath them acting as a reflector to reinforce overhead radiation.

While omnidirectional antennas are a compromise antenna for satellite use, they do have their place: they offer an acceptable satellite solution without needing a rotator, and will perform reasonably well for most passes if mounted above local obstacles. Keep in mind, however, that if you have the ability to put up directional antennas with gain, they will provide better performance.

Beams

As with all other VHF/UHF weak-signal pursuits, directional antennas are the gold standard for satellite operating to maximize signal strength. Portable operators should consider hand-held, dual-band directional Yagis or log periodics as their main antenna. These have multiple elements for 2 meters and 70 centimeters on a common boom and offer as much as 8 dBd gain with a 20–30 dB front-to-back ratio. Most are lightweight (under 2 pounds) and have booms less than 40 inches long.

The two most common commercially-available handheld Yagis for satellite work are the Arrow dual-band beam antenna (see Figure 17.1) and the Elk 2M/440L5 log periodic (Figure 17.6). Both are quite effective for satellite operating. To build antennas yourself, design and construction plans from Kent Brittain, WA5VJB, offer several inexpensive satellite Yagi designs; see the **VHF, UHF, and Microwave Antennas** chapter or search online for "WA5VJB Cheap Yagis." Three to five elements on 2 meters and five to seven elements on 70 centimeters provide sufficient gain without tightening the pattern excessively.

A phenomenon called *polarization fading,* which produces deep fading, occurs when the operator's receive antenna elements are no longer aligned with the tumbling satellite's transmit antenna. If linearly polarized VHF/UHF Yagis are used, a deep fade will occur during every satellite pass until the satellite's antenna returns to the same alignment as the operator's antenna. Circularly polarized Yagis help minimize fading by responding to all polarizations of the signal.

Unlike EME or event terrestrial weak-signal communications, you can have "too much antenna" on the satellites. A high-gain antenna is more difficult to keep aimed at the satellite. 5 watts of transmit power is more than enough to be heard through nearly every satellite, as well. Care should be taken to keep effective radiated power (ERP) low, so as not to overload a satellite's transponder. Overly strong signals will reduce the capabilities of the satellite's receiver, making it difficult for other users to get in and hear themselves on the downlink. This is especially noticeable on the AO-7 linear satellite, which has been in orbit since 1974 and is quite fragile.

A lightweight camera tripod is sufficient to support and stabilize a beam antenna. Even a monopod can help support a small beam. Tripod mounts generally don't allow easy rotation of the antenna and will restrict your ability to rotate the beam along its axis to adjust for polarization fading during tracking. (A special cradle could be used that allows the boom to be rotated.) The most flexible choice is to hold beam antennas in your hand; this permits the operator to quickly adjust for polarization fading and keep the satellite's receive signal as strong as possible during a pass.

HIGH-GAIN ANTENNAS

Dishes and horns offer great gain and directivity on the microwave bands; however, their use in the amateur satellite world is somewhat limited. Only the QO-100 satellite which covers most of Europe, Africa, and the Middle East is active on microwave frequencies as of early 2023.

SYSTEM COMPONENTS

Feed Line and Connectors

Choosing a feed line involves three tradeoffs: weight, loss, and flexibility. Use the highest quality feed line possible and to avoid loss, use the minimum length needed. Feed line losses on 2 meters and 70 centimeters can be significant with long feed lines. While home stations often use 0.4-inch thick LMR-400; for portable or rover operation using a hand-held directional antenna, LMR-240 Superflex provides a good balance between the tradeoffs and will be effective in lengths under 10 feet. Avoid RG-8, RG-58, and RG-59 cables for satellite use because their losses on 70 centimeters, even a short length, will reduce your satellite station's capabilities.

BNCs are often found on portable/handheld antenna systems, while PL-259 and N connectors will be utilized on larger/home station antennas. BNCs have the advantage of quick connect/disconnect and low loss at UHF.

Diplexers

A *diplexer* (often incorrectly called a *duplexer*) acts as a filter, isolating your transmitted signal from the front end of your receiver. This becomes important in a full-duplex operating mode, where you need to receive your own transmitted signal in real time. A a satellite station's receiver is usually close to the transmitter (often in the same radio) and antennas tend to be on the same boom, mast or tower, as well. This proximity of transmit and receive antennas, coupled with the proximity of the receiver to the transmitter, can cause a phenomenon known as desensitization, or *desense*. Diplexers reduce this phenomenon quite effectively and help make full-duplex operation possible by isolating the 2 meter band from the 70 centimeter band. The diplexer is generally mounted on a dual-band antenna at the end of the main feed line. Both the MFJ 916 and the Comet CF4160 (see Figure 17.1) are reasonably priced. Both come in several models with different types of antenna connectors; be sure to order the correct model number for your application.

MiniCircuits.com also offers low-pass and high-pass receive-only filters that are extremely compact with BNC male and female connectors; they can be added to a feed line very simply with minimal increase in weight. BLP-200+ is a low pass filter for your 2 meter feedline and it is very effective but can only handle 0.5 W. Be sure the filter is adequately rated before installing it in a transmit feed line.

At communication sites where high-power transmitters are in operation, you may need a band-pass or notch filter to prevent receiver overload. Again, make sure the filter is adequately rated.

Preamplifiers

A good low-noise amplifier (LNA) preamp can make a world of difference for satellite operation, especially for weak 70 cm downlink signals. Typical used in weak-signal VHF/UHF operating, a preamp will work best mounted at the antenna to minimize signal loss on a long coax run. Be sure your preamp is waterproof and has RF sensing that will turn the preamp off when RF is detected. Many portable operators do not bother with preamps to handheld antennas, as they typically use short runs (less than 5 feet) of high-quality low-loss feedline, such as LMR-240 Superflex.

17.2 Circularly Polarized Antennas

Linearly polarized antennas are horizontal or vertical in terms of the antenna's position relative to the surface of the Earth, a reference that loses its meaning in space. (See the **Antenna Fundamentals** chapter for a discussion on polarization.) If spacecraft antennas used linear polarization, ground stations would not be able to maintain polarization alignment with the spacecraft because of its changing orientation. Thus, the ideal antenna for random satellite signal polarization is one with *circular polarization* or *CP*.

Circular polarization is simply linear polarization with a direction that continually rotates as it travels through space as in **Figure 17.12**. The direction of polarization can be imagined as the second hand of a watch that is moving forward with the wave such that the second hand makes one complete revolution per wavelength traveled. The second hand represents the *instantaneous polarization* of the signal.

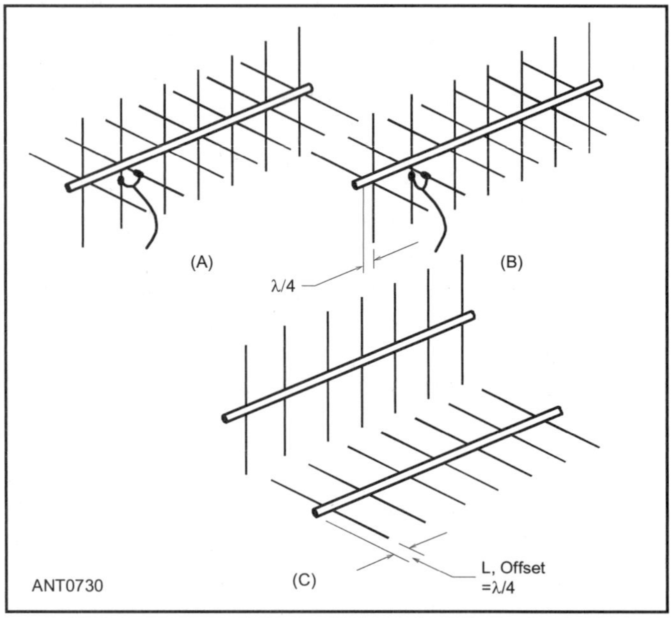

Figure 17.13 — Evolution of the circularly polarized Yagi. The simplest form of crossed Yagi, A, is made to radiate circularly by feeding the two driven elements 90° out of phase. Antenna B has the driven elements fed in phase but has the elements of one bay mounted ¼ λ forward from those of the other. Antenna C offers elliptical (circular) polarization using separate booms. The elements in one set are perpendicular to those of the other and are ¼ λ forward from those of the other.

POLARIZATION SENSE

Polarization *sense* is a critical factor, especially in EME and satellite work. The IEEE standard uses the term "clockwise circular polarization" for a *receding* wave (one traveling away from the observer). Amateur technology follows the IEEE standard, calling clockwise polarization for a receding wave as *right-hand circular polarization* or *RHCP*. This means that the second hand of the watch traveling with the receding wave is revolving clockwise. A wave for which polarization rotates in the opposition direction is *left-hand circular polarization* or *LHCP*.

When making satellite contacts using a circularly polarized antenna, it is often convenient to have the capability of switching polarization sense. This is because the sense of the received signal from some of the LEO satellites reverses when the satellite passes its nearest point to you. If the received signal has right-hand circular polarization as the satellite approaches, it may have left-hand circular polarization as the satellite recedes. A sense reversal occurs in EME communications as well, because of the phase reversal of the signal as it is reflected from the lunar surface. A signal transmitted with RHCP will be returned to the Earth with LHCP. Similarly, the polarization is reversed as it is reflected from a dish antenna so that to transmit an RHCP signal, the feed antenna for the dish needs to be LHCP.

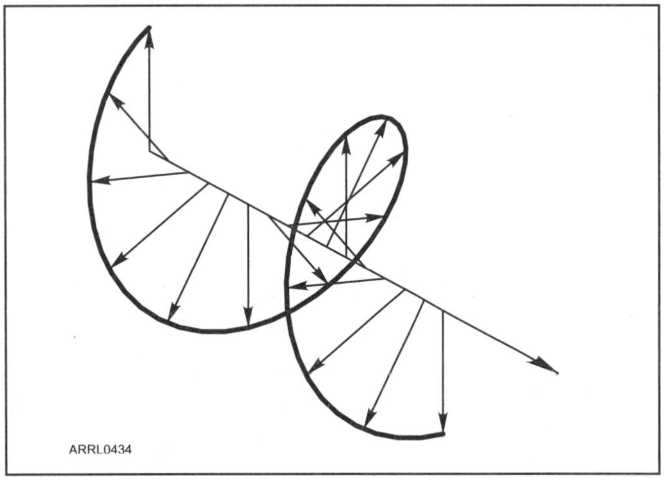

Figure 17.12 — The polarization of a circularly polarized wavefront rotates around its central axis, either clockwise (right-hand or RHCP) or counterclockwise (left-hand or LHCP).

17.2.1 Crossed Linear Elements

Dipoles radiate linearly polarized signals and the polarization direction depends on the orientation of the antenna. If two dipoles are arranged as horizontal and vertical dipoles, and the two outputs are combined with the correct phase difference (90°), a circularly polarized wave results. Because the electric fields are identical in magnitude, the power from the transmitter will be divided equally between the two fields. Another way of looking at this is to consider the power as being divided between the two antennas — hence the gain of each is decreased by 3 dB when taken alone in the plane of its orientation.

A 90° phase shift must exist between the two antennas and the simplest way to obtain this shift is to use two feed lines to a *coplanar pair* of crossed-Yagi antennas in which the elements lie approximately in the same plane, as shown in **Figure 17.13A**. One feed line section is 1/4 λ longer than the other.

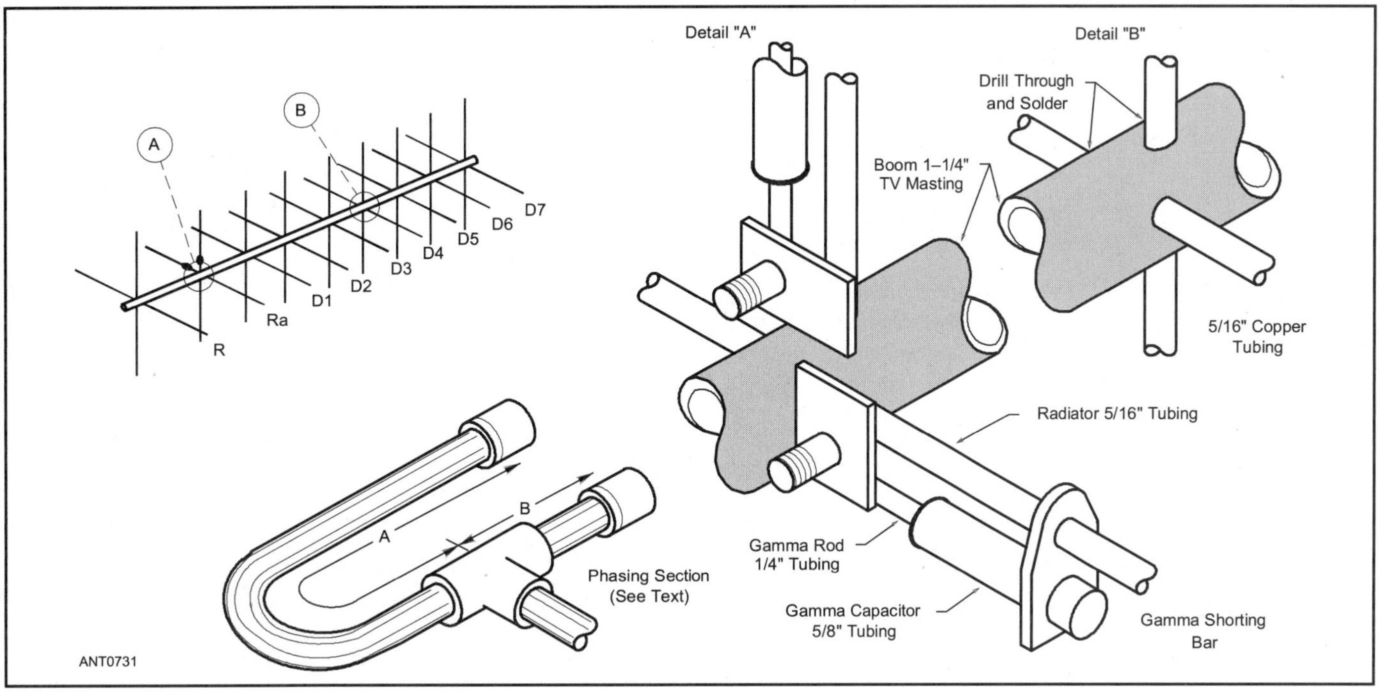

Figure 17.14 — Construction details of a co-planar crossed-Yagi antenna.

These separate feed lines are then connected in parallel with a common transmission line to the transmitter or receiver. An example is shown in **Figure 17.14**. Assuming negligible coupling between the crossed antennas, the impedance presented to the common transmission line by the parallel combination is one half that of either section alone. (This is not true when there is mutual coupling between the antennas, as in phased arrays.)

This creates some difficulties for the antenna builder. With this phasing-line method, any mismatch at one antenna will be magnified by the extra 1/4 λ of transmission line. This upsets the current balance between the two antennas, resulting in a loss of polarization circularity. Another factor to consider is the attenuation of the cables used in the harness, along with the connectors. Good low-loss coaxial line should be used with Type N or BNC connectors. A practical construction method for implementing a RHCP/LHCP coplanar switched system is shown in **Figure 17.15**.

Another method to obtain circular polarization is to use equal-length feed lines and place one antenna 1/4 λ ahead of the other. This offset pair of Yagi-crossed antennas is shown in Figure 17.13B. The advantage of equal-length feed lines is that identical load impedances will be presented to the common feeder, as shown in **Figure 17.16**, which shows a fixed circularity-sense feed. To obtain a switchable-sense feed with the offset Yagi pair, you can use a configuration as in **Figure 17.17**, although you must compensate for the extra phase shift added by the relay and connectors.

Figure 17.13C diagrams a popular method of mounting two separate off-the-shelf Yagis at right angles to each other. The two Yagis may be physically offset by 1/4 λ and fed in parallel, as shown in Figure 17.10C, or they may be mounted with no offset and fed 90° out of phase. Neither of these

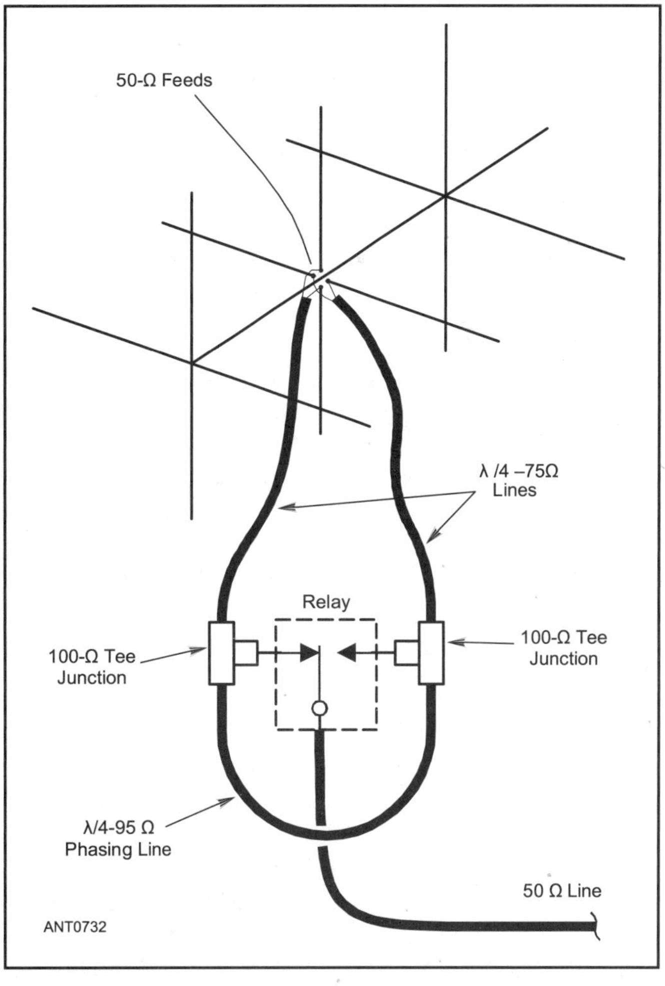

Figure 17.15 — Co-planar crossed Yagi, circularly polarized antenna with switchable polarization phasing harness.

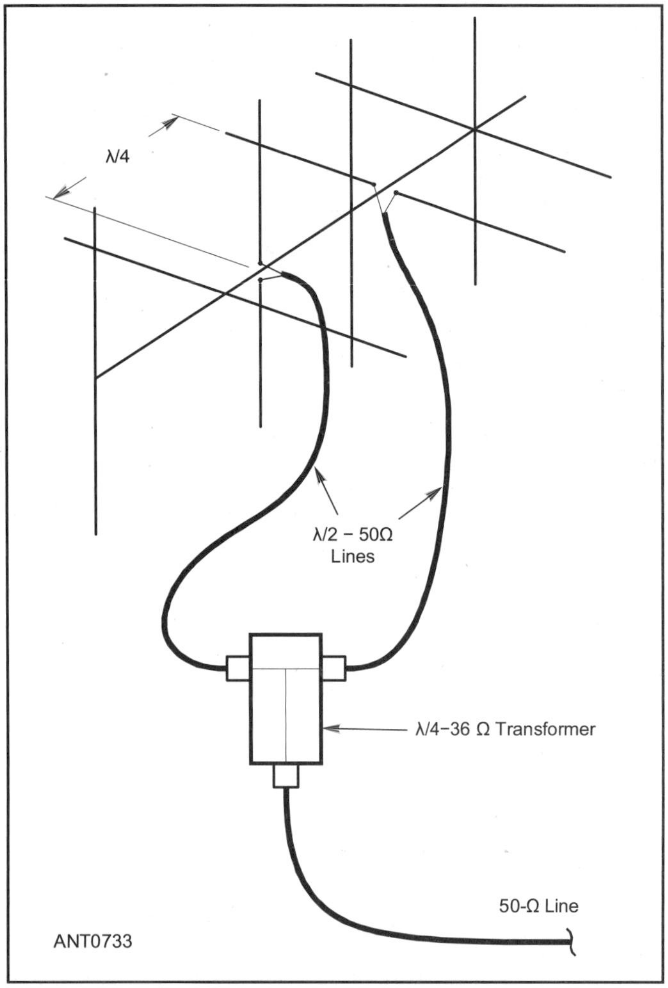

Figure 17.16 — Offset crossed-Yagi circularly polarized antenna-phasing harness with fixed polarization.

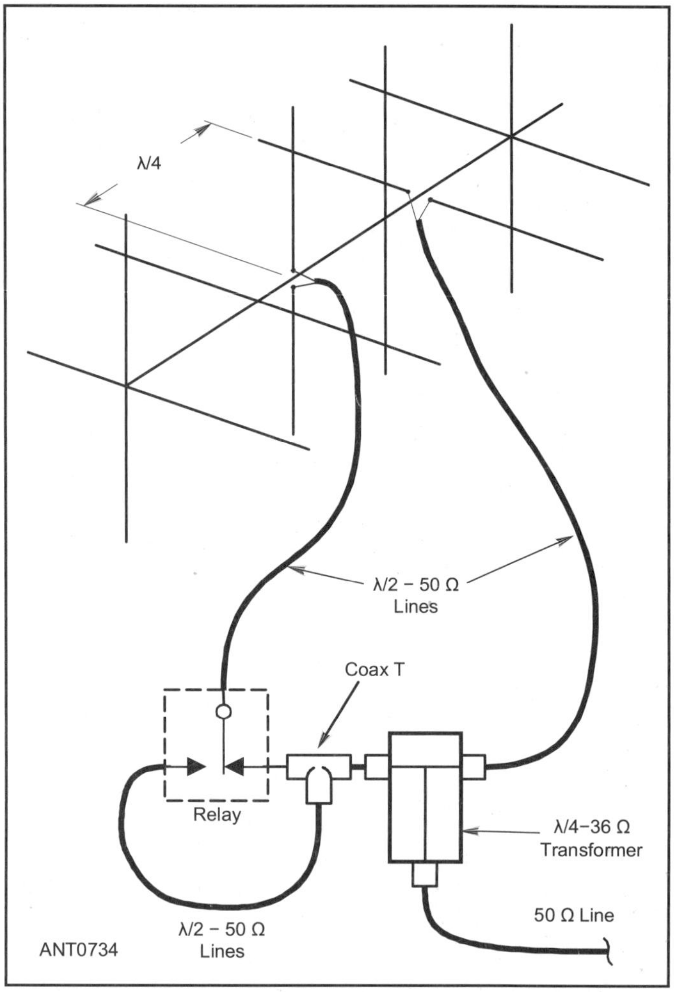

Figure 17.17 — Offset crossed-Yagi circularly polarized antenna-phasing harness with switchable polarization.

arrangements on two separate booms produces true circular polarization. Instead, *elliptical polarization* results from such a system, an example of which is shown in **Figure 17.18**.

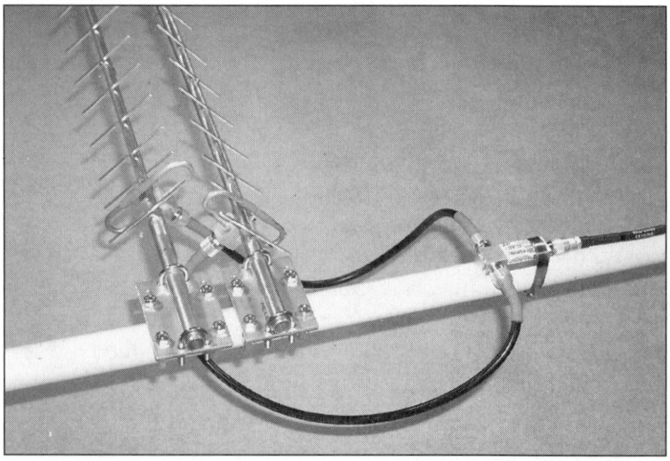
Figure 17.18 — An example of offset crossed-Yagi circularly polarized antennas with fixed polarization. This example is a pair of M2 23CMM22EZA antennas for 1296 MHz, mounted on an elevation boom.

17.2.2 The Eggbeater Antenna

The eggbeater antenna shown in Figure 17.2 is a popular design named after the old-fashioned kitchen utensil it resembles. The antenna is composed of two full-wave loops of rigid wire or metal tubing. Each of the two loops has an impedance of 100 Ω, and when coupled in parallel they offer an ideal 50-Ω impedance for coaxial feed lines. The loops are fed 90° out of phase with each other and this creates a circularly polarized pattern.

An eggbeater may also use one or more parasitic reflector elements beneath the loops to focus more of the radiation pattern upward. This effect makes it a "gain" antenna, but that gain is at the expense of low-elevation reception. Toward the horizon an eggbeater is actually horizontally polarized. As the pattern rises in elevation, it becomes more and more right-hand circularly polarized. Experience has shown that eggbeaters seem to perform best when reflector elements are installed just below the loops.

Eggbeaters can be built relatively easily, but commercial models such as the one shown in Figure 17.2 are available. The spherical shape of the eggbeater creates a fairly compact antenna when space is an issue, which is another reason why it is an attractive design. (See the online material.)

17.2.3 The Turnstile Antenna

The basic turnstile antenna in Figure 17.3 consists of two horizontal half-wave dipoles mounted at right angles to each other (arranged like the letter "X") in the same horizontal plane with a reflector screen beneath. When these two antennas are excited with equal currents 90° out of phase, their typical figure-eight patterns merge to produce a nearly circular pattern. (See the online material.)

To get the radiation pattern in the upward direction for space communications, the turnstile antenna needs a reflector underneath. For a broad pattern it is best to maintain a distance of 3/8 λ at the operating frequency between the reflector and the turnstile. Homemade turnstile reflectors often use metal window-screen material that you can pick up at many hardware stores. (Make sure it is a metal, not plastic, screen material.)

Like their cousins the eggbeaters, turnstiles are relatively easy to build. In fact, building one may be your only choice since turnstiles are rarely available off the shelf.

17.2.4 The Lindenblad Antenna

The Lindenblad antenna shown in **Figure 17.19A** is constructed from linear elements, is circularly polarized, and has an omnidirectional radiation pattern. With most of its gain at low elevation angles as shown in Figure 17.19B, it is ideal for accessing Low-Earth-Orbit (LEO) satellites. Because it is omnidirectional, it does not need to be pointed at a satellite, eliminating the need for an azimuth/elevation (az/el) rotator system. This makes the Lindenblad especially useful for portable or temporary satellite operations. It is also a good general purpose antenna for a home station because its circular polarization is compatible with the linearly polarized antennas used for FM/repeater and SSB/CW operation. Two complete construction articles for Lindenblad antennas are included with the online material. An improved version of the AA2TX design, "The Two Meter EZ Lindenblad Revisited," by KJ9P and AA9LC is included in the online material and is listed in the References and Bibliography for Planer and Zehr.

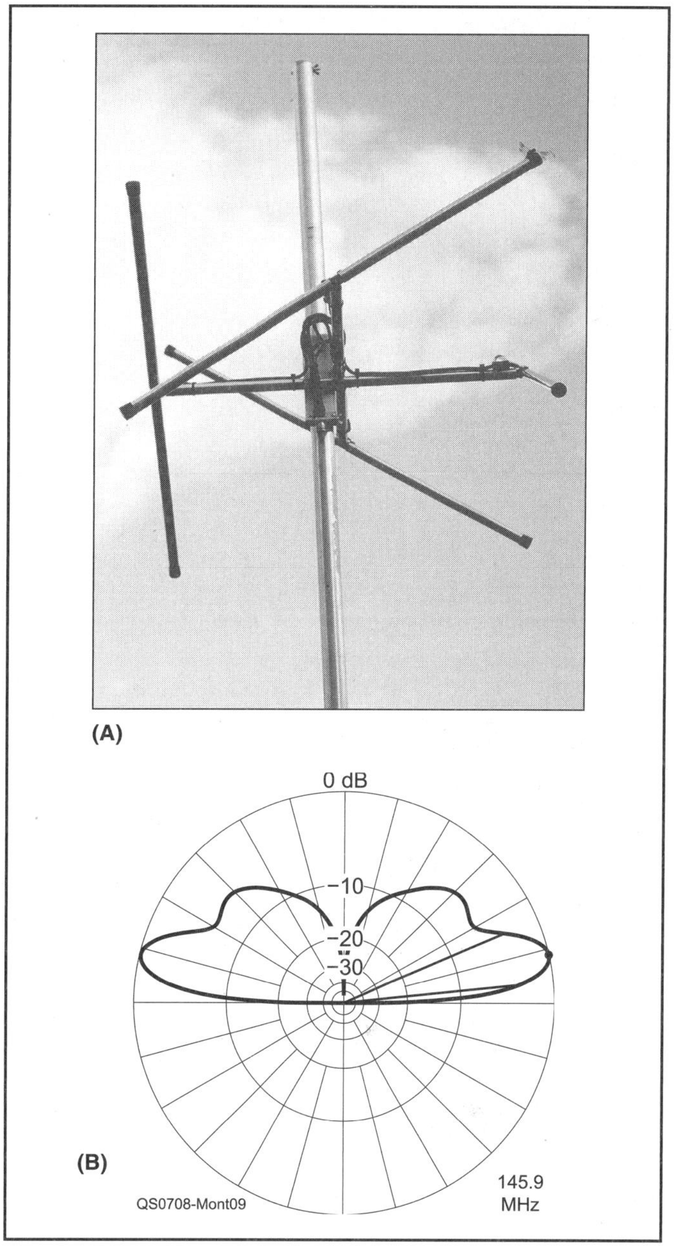

Figure 17.19 — The Lindenblad antenna in A has circular polarization and an omnidirectional azimuthal pattern as shown in B. [Anthony Montero, AA2TX, photo]

17.2.5 The Quadrifilar Helix (QFH)

Designed for spacecraft use in the early days of space exploration, the *quadrifilar helix* (QFH) antenna (also called the quadrifilar helicoidal antenna) has not gained much popularity on the ham bands. Yet, as a general-purpose base-station antenna, such as the 2 meter version in **Figure 17.20**, it's hard to beat. The pattern is almost omnidirectional in both planes, like the mythical isotropic radiator, receiving nearly to the horizon. No matter what direction signals come from, or whether the polarization is vertical or horizontal, the QFH receives them. It's good for overhead satellites, such as the International Space Station, for horizontally polarized 2-meter SSB simplex stations on the horizon, and also for vertically polarized mobile and repeater stations. It isn't a gain antenna — no true omni can be. The primary benefit of a QFH is the coverage afforded by its pattern.

The QFH is often used by hams for receiving weather satellite pictures from the 137 MHz NOAA automatic picture transmitting (APT) satellites in low polar orbit. Its omnidirectional and circular polarization characteristics accommodate the constantly changing direction and polarization of the APT satellite signals. Several have been built for this service. Three of these weather birds still fly by every day — NOAA 15, 17, 18 and 19.

The QFH can be envisioned as follows: Take two vertical

Figure 17.20 — W6NBC's Quadrifilar Helix base station antenna [John Portune, W6NBC, photo]

full wavelength rectangular loops with open feed points *at the top*. Now place them on the same vertical axis, but with one loop rotated 90° horizontally so that they are in quadrature. Also, you need to make one loop slightly larger than the other. This creates a phase shift at the feed point to compensate for the physical rotation of the loops. Next, twist both loops horizontally a quarter turn into helices. Finally connect the feed points in parallel to create a quadrifilar helix antenna.

The curious eggbeater-like configuration of the QFH has useful characteristics — an almost perfectly spherical radiation pattern as well as circular polarization throughout the pattern. This version is right-handed. For left, twist the loops in the opposite direction. For the general purpose 2 meter base station antenna, the twist direction does not matter. And yes, there is a small loss working linear polarized signals (vertical or horizontal) with a circularly polarized antenna, but it is quite acceptable. Commercial broadcast antennas often use this very technique to accommodate both mobile (vertical) as well as home antennas (horizontal).

After experimenting ham style with square loops and tall versus thin rectangular ones, and the small size difference between the two loops as well as the amount of twist, it has been concluded that the QFH is a dimensionally tolerant design. The performance changed little with all these variations.

The antenna shown in Figure 17.18 is described in the complete construction article by John Portune, W6NBC, included with the online material along with another QFH construction article by Eugene Ruperto, W3KH.

17.2.6 Helical Antennas

The axial-mode helical antenna was introduced by Dr John Kraus, W8JK, in the 1940s. **Figures 17.21** and **17.22** show examples of S-band (2400 MHz), V-band (145 MHz), and

Figure 17.21 — A 16-turn S-band helical antenna. This is about the maximum length of any practical helix. Note the SSB UEK2000 downconverter mounted behind the reflector of the antenna. [Dick Jansson, KD1K, photo]

Figure 17.22 — A pair of helical antennas for service on 2 meters and 70 cm. The 2-meter helical antenna is not small! [Dick Jansson, KD1K, photo]

U-band (435 MHz) helical antennas, all constructed by KD1K for satellite service. (See the **VHF, UHF, and Microwave Antennas** chapter for design and construction information on the helix antenna.)

This antenna has two characteristics that make it especially interesting and useful in many applications. First, the helix is circularly polarized with a fixed polarization sense determined by its configuration. The polarization rotates about the axis of the antenna.

The second interesting property of the helical antenna is its predictable pattern, gain and impedance characteristics over a wide frequency range. This is one of the few antennas with both broad bandwidth and high gain. The benefit of this

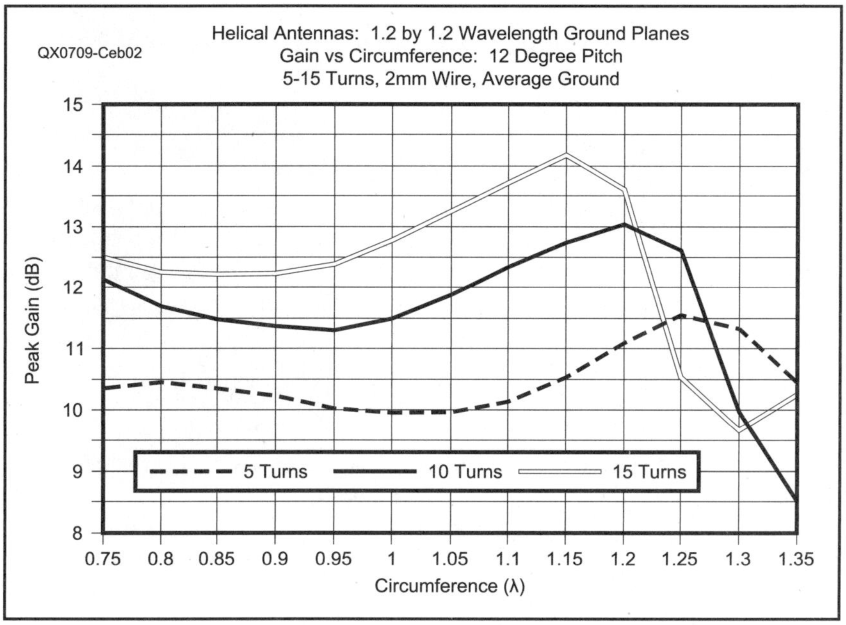

Figure 17.23 — Modeled gain of 5-, 10-, and 15-turn helices over ground planes 1.2 λ per side.

plane is a wire grid, 1.2 λ on a side and 1 λ above average ground. The wire used for the helix is 2 mm in diameter.

The peak gain of the helices is about 11.7, 13.0, and 14.2 dBi for the 5, 10 and 15-turn antennas, respectively. Note that the gain increases almost linearly with the increase in the number of turns. This is an important fact to keep in mind when comparing axial-mode helices with alternatives to them as circularly (or nearly circularly) polarized antennas.

An axial-mode helical antenna rarely yields perfect circular polarization. Instead, it yields *elliptical polarization*, with a major and a minor axis and a tilt angle. The antennas approach perfect circularity most closely along the axis of the helix. The modeled antennas here improve their circularity with increased length. More pertinent to amateur use is the fact that an axial-mode helix does not produce a perfect single-lobe pattern. **Figure 17.24** shows the total field patterns of the 5, 10 and 15 turn helices over an elevated ground screen. In each case, we can see a considerable collection of side lobes. Each model uses the circumference that produces the best gain, but that circumference does not yield the lowest level of side lobes. Reducing the circumference produces lower gain (from 1 to 2 dB, depending upon the length of the helix), but results in a cleaner pattern. Circumferences below about 0.85 λ rarely have any sidelobes at all through the 15-turn design shown here.

As well, there are remnants of opposite direction polarization within the total field of the axial-mode helix. **Figure 17.25** shows the dominant right-hand polarized component of a 15-turn helix over a ground-screen elevated above average ground. The left-hand component is down by 25 dB, with some of the lower lobes being composed mainly of left-hand

property is that, when used for narrowband applications, the helical antenna is very forgiving of mechanical inaccuracies.

Figure 17.23 shows the modeled gain of 5-, 10-, and 15-turn helix antennas with varying circumferences in terms of wavelength. (See the Bibliography entry for Cebik.) The ground

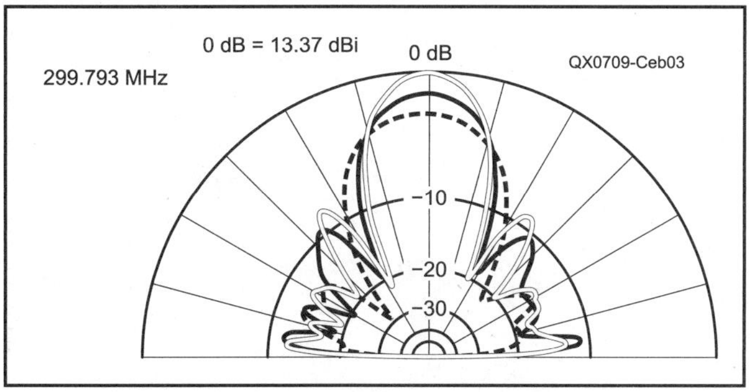

Figure 17.24 — Comparative elevation patterns of 5-, 10-, and 15-turn helices over ground planes 1.2 λ per side.

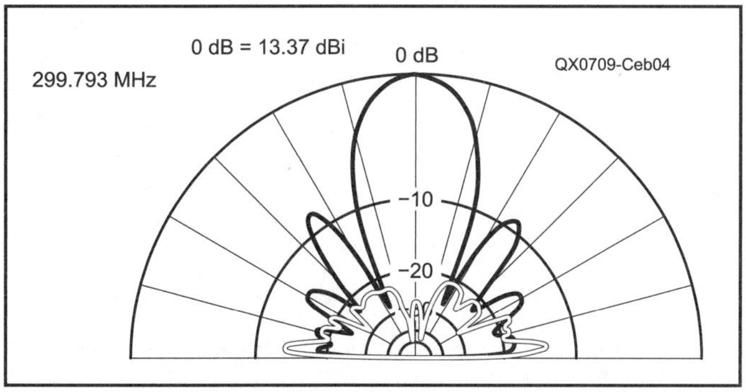

Figure 17.25 — Right-hand and left-hand polarized components of the elevation pattern of a 15-turn helix over a ground plane 1.2 λ per side.

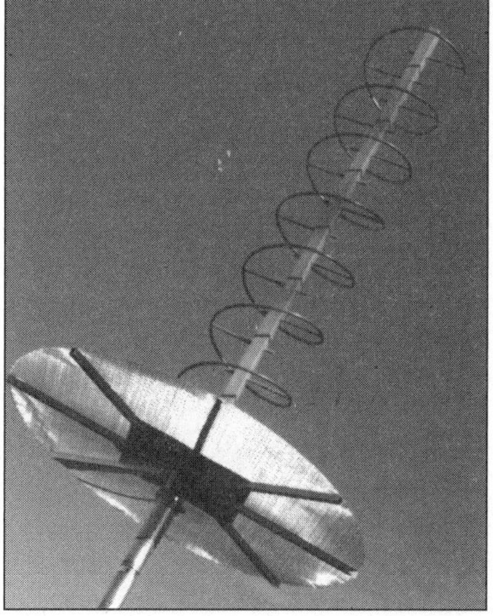

Figure 17.26 — The portable 435-MHz helix assembled and ready for operation.

components. All of these facets of axial-mode helix performance have a bearing on the sensitivity of such antennas to off-axis signals, whether at high or low angles relative to the axis that marks the centerline of the helix. How much side lobe and oppositely polarized lobe suppression is enough, of course, you must determine based on your application and your local circumstances. Given the low signal levels associated with space communication, reducing off-axis noise is an important consideration in selecting and designing antennas.

PORTABLE HELIX FOR 435 MHZ

Helical antennas for 435 MHz are excellent uplinks for U-band satellite communications. The true circular polarization afforded by the helix minimizes signal *spin fading* that is so common in these applications. The antenna shown in **Figure 17.26** fills the need for an effective portable uplink antenna for OSCAR operation. Speedy assembly and disassembly and light weight are among the benefits of this array. This antenna was originally designed by WØCY.

Although the helix is about the most tolerant of any antenna in terms of dimensions, the dimensions given here should be followed as closely as possible. Most of the materials specified are available in any well supplied do-it-yourself hardware or building supply store.

The portable helix consists of eight turns of ¼-inch soft-copper tubing spaced around a 1-inch fiberglass tube or maple dowel rod 4 feet, 7 inches long. Surplus solid aluminum shield hardline can be used instead of the copper tubing if necessary. The turns of the helix are supported by 5-inch lengths of ¼-inch maple dowel mounted through the 1-inch rod in the center of the antenna. For further details, a complete parts list, and construction information see the online material.

HELIX ARRAY FOR L BAND (23 CM)

A four-element array of 27-turn helixes is described in the presentation "L Band Helix Antenna Array" by Clare Fowler, VE3NPC, provided with the online material. While originally designed for use with HEO satellites, the array is also suitable for EME operation, particularly using digital modes. Each antenna has a calculated gain of 19 dBi and the array has an estimated actual gain of 23 dB.

17.3 Yagi Arrays

The Yagis in this section are typical of the high-performance designs used for terrestrial communications. For satellite or EME operation, they are often combined into arrays of 2, 4, 8 or even more antennas with both azimuth and elevation position control. Designs of such Yagis can be found in the **VHF and UHF Antenna Systems** chapter or commercial models are available.

17.3.1 Arrays For Satellites

It is not necessary to use a high-gain Yagi array to access an LEO satellite except possibly when it is very near the horizon. Reliable operation via future HEO satellites, however, will require more gain and Yagi arrays are very popular from VHF through 1.2 and 2.4 GHz.

Figure 17.27 shows the satellite antennas at KD1K. The Yagi antennas are used for the U- and L-band uplinks and the V-band downlink, while the S-band dish antenna is for downlink. These satellite antennas are tower mounted at 63 feet (19 meters) to avoid pointing into the many nearby trees and suffering from the resulting "green attenuation." Of course, satellite antennas do not always need to be mounted high on a tower if dense foliage is not a problem. If satellite antennas are mounted lower, feed line length and losses can be reduced.

Another benefit, however, to tower mounting of satellite antennas is that they can be used for terrestrial ham communications and contests. The fact that the antennas are set up for circular polarization (CP) does not really degrade these other operating activities.

Figure 17.27 — Details of KD1K's tower cluster of satellite antennas including a home-brew elevation rotator. Top to bottom: M2 436-CP30, a CP U-band antenna; two M2 23CM22EZA antennas in a CP array for L band; "FABStar" dish antenna with helix feed for S band; M2 2M-CP22, a CP V-band antenna (only partially shown.) To left of the dish antenna is a NEMA 4 weatherproof equipment box with an internal 40-W L-band amplifier and hosts externally mounted preamplifiers. (KD1K photo)

Experience has clearly shown the advantages of using RHCP antennas for both the uplink and downlink communications. The antennas shown in Figure 17.27 are a single-boom RHCP Yagi antenna for U band, a pair of closely spaced Yagi antennas phased for RHCP for L band (see Figure 17.18), and a helix-fed offset dish antenna for S band described below. The antenna gain requirements for U band can easily be met with the gain of a 30-element crossed Yagi. Antennas of this size have boom lengths of 4 to 4.5 wavelengths.

It is possible to build suitable Yagis for these bands from material that appears elsewhere in this book, but the dimensional tolerances may be challenging for most amateurs' workshops. Most satellite operators choose instead to purchase antennas from commercial suppliers. M2 Antenna Systems (**m2inc.com**) for example, offers a broad line of high-performance CP Yagis for these bands.

U-band uplink requirements have clearly demonstrated the need for gain of 16 to 17 dBic RHCP, with an RF power of less than 50 W PEP at the antenna (≈ 2500 W PEP EIRP with a RHCP antenna) depending upon the *squint angle*. The squint angle is the angle at which the main axis of the satellite is pointed away from your antenna on the ground. If the squint angle is less than half of the half-power beamwidth, the ground station will be within the spacecraft antenna's nominal beamwidth. dBic means the gain of a circularly polarized antenna with respect to that of an isotropic antenna with the same polarization characteristic.

A gain of 16 to 17 (dB isotropic-circular) RHCP can be obtained from a 30-element crossed Yagi — good news, considering that the satellite may be over 60,000 km (37,000 miles) from your station. Success on U-band uplinks is easier than those for L band at squint angles wider than 20°. At squint angles less than 10°, U-band uplink operation can even be done with 1-5 W power outputs to a RHCP antenna (≈ 200 W PEP EIRP with RHCP). These lower levels mean that smaller antennas can be used. In practice, these uplinks will produce downlink signals that are 10 to 15 dB above the noise floor, or S7 signals over an S3 noise floor. The beacon will give a downlink S9 signal for these same conditions.

Experience with L-band uplinks has demonstrated that 40 W PEP delivered to an antenna with a gain of ≈ 19 dBic (3000 W PEP EIRP with RHCP) is needed for operations at the highest altitudes and with squint angles ≈ 15°. The compact L-band antenna arrangement with two 22-element antennas in a RHCP array shown in Figure 17.18 is an example of such an antenna system.

Using an L-band uplink for HEO operations instead of the U-band uplink will allow the use of Yagi antennas that are more manageable since their size for a given gain is only one third of those for U-band. With L band there is a narrower difference between using a dish antenna and a Yagi, since a 21- to 22-dBic dish antenna would be only about 1.2 meters (4 feet) in diameter. However, some of us may not have such "real estate" available on our towers and may seek the lower wind-loading solution offered by Yagis. Long-boom rod-element Yagi, or loop-Yagi antennas are commercially offered by M2 Antenna Systems (**m2inc.com**) and Directive Systems

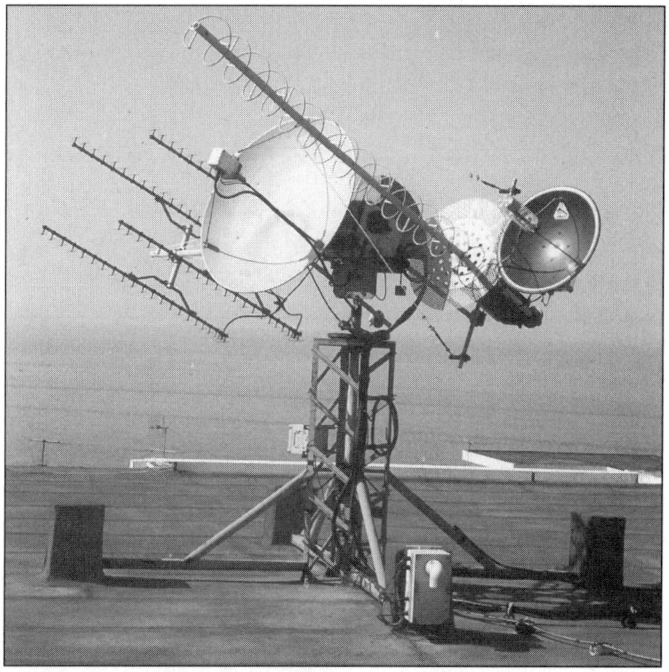

Figure 17.28 —Left to right: array of 4 × 23-element Yagi horizontally polarized for L band; 1.2-meter dish with 3-turn helix feed for S band; 15-turn RHCP helical antenna for U band; 60-centimeter dish for X band. All microwave preamplifiers and power amplifiers are homebrew and are mounted on this antenna cluster.

(**directivesystems.com**) although this band is about the highest for practical Yagis. The example shown in Figure 17.18 is a pair of rod-element Yagi antennas from M2 in a CP arrangement with a gain of 18 to 19 dBic.

Other amateurs have successful HEO experience with different arrangements. **Figure 17.28** shows a 4 × 23 element linear array for a 1270 MHz, a 1.2 meter solid dish for 2400 MHz, a 15 turn helical antenna for 435 MHz, and a 60 cm dish for 10,451 MHz This arrangement clearly shows the advantage and accessibility of having a roof-mounted antenna.

17.3.2 Arrays For EME

Several types of antennas for 2 meters and 70 cm are popular among EME enthusiasts. Perhaps the most popular antenna for 144-MHz operation is an array of either 4 or 8 long-boom (14 to 15 dBi gain) Yagis. The 4-Yagi array provides approximately 20 dB gain, and an 8-Yagi array gives an approximate 3 dB increase over the 4-antenna array. **Figure 17.29** shows the computed response at a 30° tilt above the horizon for a stack of four 14-element 2-meter Yagis, each with a boom length of 3.1 λ (22 feet). At 432 MHz, EME enthusiasts often use 8 or 16 long-boom Yagis in an array as seen in Figure 17.8 previously. However, recent advances in Yagi design as described in the **VHF and UHF Antenna Systems** chapter make smaller arrays of high-performance antennas a satisfactory alternative.

Arrays of stacked Yagis are sensitive to conductors in the same plane as the antenna elements. For example, stacking a pair of horizontally-polarized Yagis can be one over the other

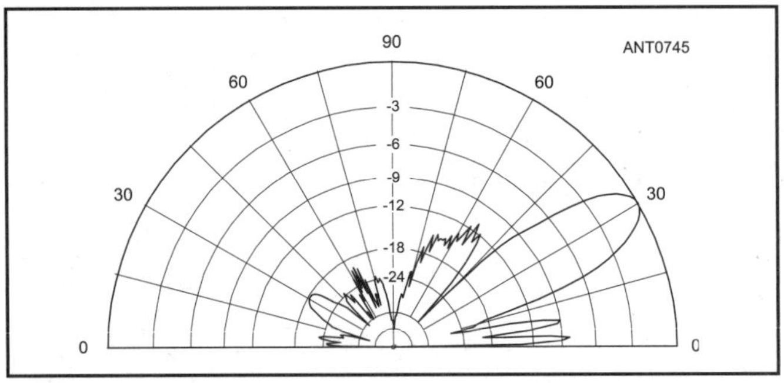

Figure 17.29 — *EZNEC Pro* elevation pattern for four 14-element 2-meter Yagis (3.6 λ boom lengths) at an elevation angle of 30° above the horizon. The computed system gain is 21.5 dBi, suitable for 2-meter EME. This assumes that the phasing system is made of open-wire transmission lines so that feed line losses can be kept below 0.25 dB.

or side-by-side. In the case of vertical stacking (which yields a narrow vertical pattern) as shown in **Figure 17.30A**, the mast can be metal and will have minimal impact on the stack performance. However, if the antennas are stacked horizontally (to create a narrower horizontal pattern) as shown in Figure 17.30B, a conductive crossboom will seriously degrade the array performance since the crossboom is in the same plane as the elements. A non-conductive crossboom strong enough to support the weight of the Yagis and the bending moment is acceptable but may be costly. One solution is to use a conductive metal crossboom and hang the antennas below the boom on short non-conductive masts, at least a half-wavelength long at the frequency of interest, as shown in Figure 17.30C.

If the Yagis are mounted vertically, obviously the situation changes. Vertical stacking on a conductive metal mast will degrade performance, while mounting at the ends of a horizontal crossboom will work fine.

An array of four horizontally-polarized Yagis in an "H-frame" configuration as shown in **Figure 17.31** can use metal construction for the crossboom and vertical risers since the crossboom is generally far enough away from the antenna elements as to minimize interaction and the vertical masts have no effect. The second crossboom shown as a dashed line may be needed as a strengthening element to prevent the lower crossboom from sagging.

There are several choices for mounting cross-polarized Yagis in an H-frame configuration as shown in **Figure 17.32**. If the antennas are mounted with the elements in the vertical and horizontal directions ("+" configuration) the parts of the vertical masts closest to the antennas should be non-conductive. The remainder of the H-frame can be metal. If the Yagis are mounted with the elements tilted 45 degrees from horizontal/vertical ("X" configuration), the H-frame can be all-metal. The feed lines should be routed either off the back of each antenna and/or dressed away from the plane of the antenna elements at a 45-degree angle to minimize interaction – remember, the feed lines are made of conductive material!

The main disadvantage of Yagi arrays is that the polarization plane of the individual Yagis cannot be conveniently changed. One way around this is to use cross-polarized Yagis and a relay switching system to select the desired polarization, as described in the previous section. This represents a considerable increase in system complexity to select the desired polarization. Some amateurs have gone so far as to build complicated mechanical systems to allow constant polarization adjustment of all the Yagis in a large array.

Polarization shift of EME signals at 144 MHz is fairly rapid, and the added complexity of a relay-controlled cross-polarized antenna system or a mechanical polarization adjustment scheme is probably not worth the effort. At 432 MHz, however, where the polarization shifts at a much slower rate,

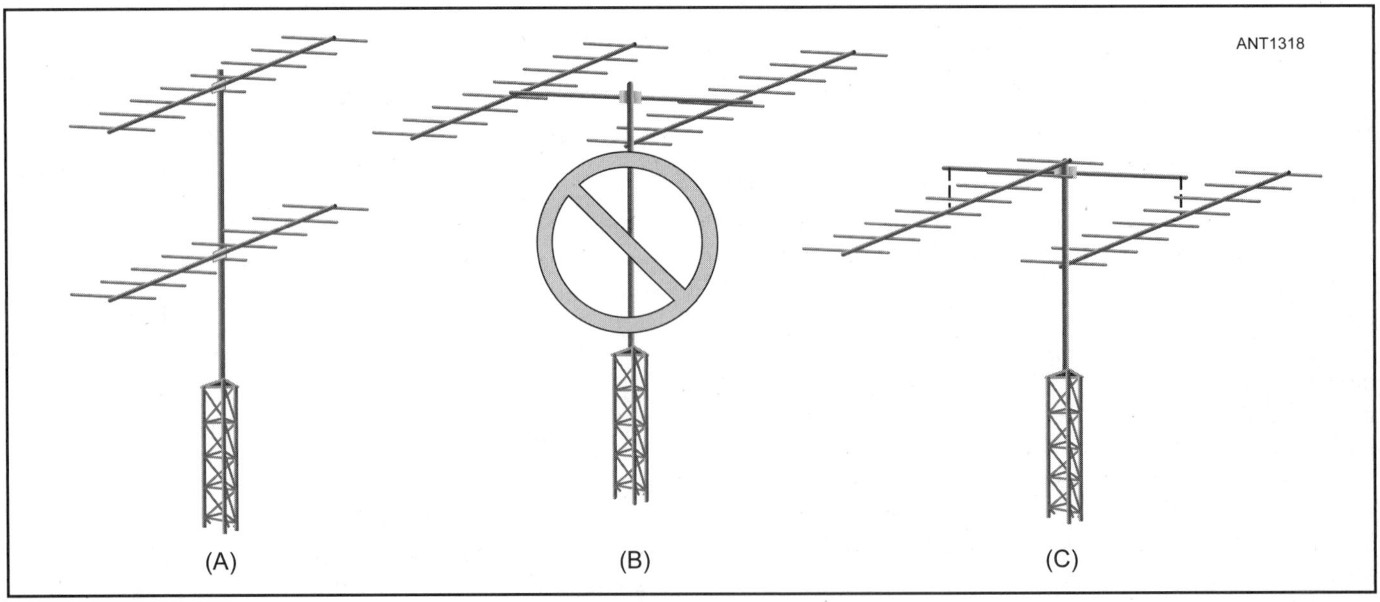

Figure 17.30 — Options for stacking horizontally-polarized Yagis; (A) and (C) are acceptable; (B) will perform poorly due to interaction of a conductive horizontal cross-boom and the Yagi elements.

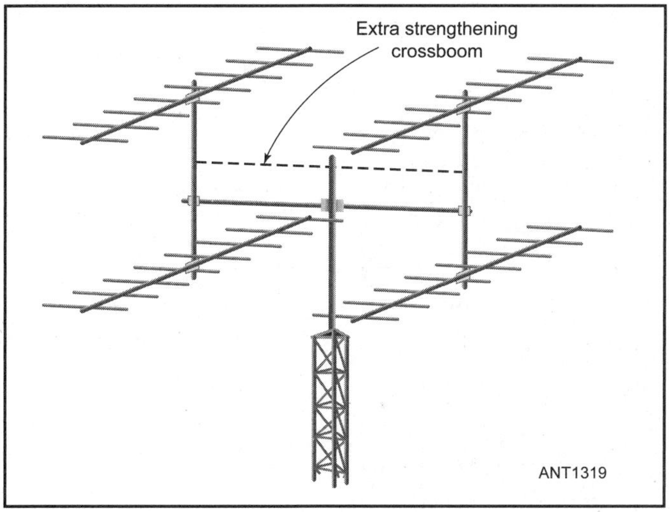

Figure 17.31 — A four-Yagi H-frame stack. The dashed line shows an additional strengthening cross-boom that prevents sagging of the cross-booms.

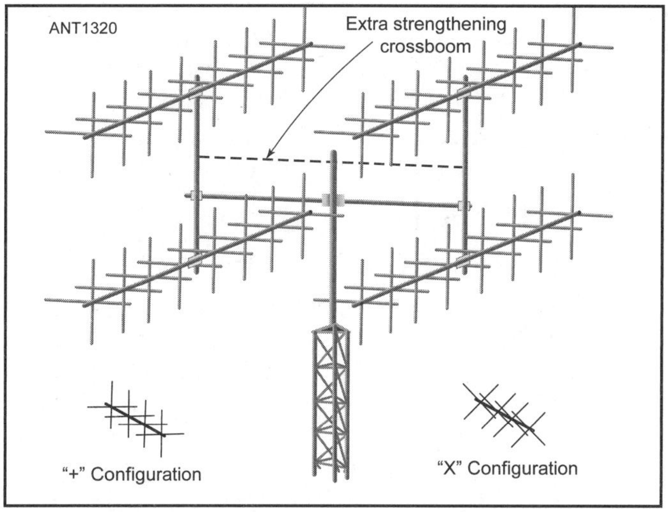

Figure 17.32 — Stacking four Yagis improves pattern in both horizontal and vertical planes; Yagis can be mounted H/V ("+" configuration) or tilted 45 degrees ("X" configuration).

an adjustable polarization system does offer a definite advantage over a fixed one. An example of a 70 cm Yagi array with switchable-polarization is shown in **Figure 17.33** and described in the article "EME with Adaptive Polarization at 432 MHz" by Joe Taylor, K1JT, and Justin Johnson, GØKSC (available with the online material).

Figure 17.34A shows another option for switching antenna polarization. This arrangement maintains both polarizations for receiving but connects the two antennas together through λ/4 sections of 75-Ω coax when transmitting to create circular polarization to overcome fading due to Faraday rotation. The λ/4 sections transform the antenna impedances to 100 Ω, and when connected in parallel, back to 50 Ω. This arrangement assumes that the H and V antennas have a λ/4 delay either in the feed lines or in the mechanical construction of the array. The box shown in Figure 17.34B, built by DK5YA, uses relays with high enough isolation to eliminate the need for switching the LNA inputs to resistors as is sometimes done.

An extreme example of a stacked Yagi array for EME work was built by DL7APV. It consists of 128 11-element Yagis for 432 MHz, stacked 8 high and 16 wide. Each Yagi driven element is a folded dipole fed with home-brew 200-Ω open wire line. Pairs of Yagis are connected in parallel for a 100-Ω impedance, then stepped up to 400 Ω with a 3λ/4 section of 200-Ω line. Each pair is connected in parallel with another pair of Yagis to yield an array of 4 Yagis with a 200-Ω impedance. This process repeats again and again, and the final step down to the 50-Ω coaxial feed line is accomplished with a 4:1 balun. The construction of the array, including the mount and positioning system, took 10 years.

The array delivers over 33 dB of gain with a horizontal –3 dB beamwidth of 1.8 degrees and vertical beamwidth of 3.8 degrees. This performance allows stations as small as 50 W and a dipole antenna to contact DL7APV on 70-centimeter EME using digital modes.

Figure 17.33 — Four-Yagi dual-polarization 432 MHz array at the Princeton University station, W2PU. The Yagis are rear-mounted; boom length is 3.5 meters, and stacking distance is 1.2 meters in each direction. (Photo courtesy Joe Taylor, K1JT)

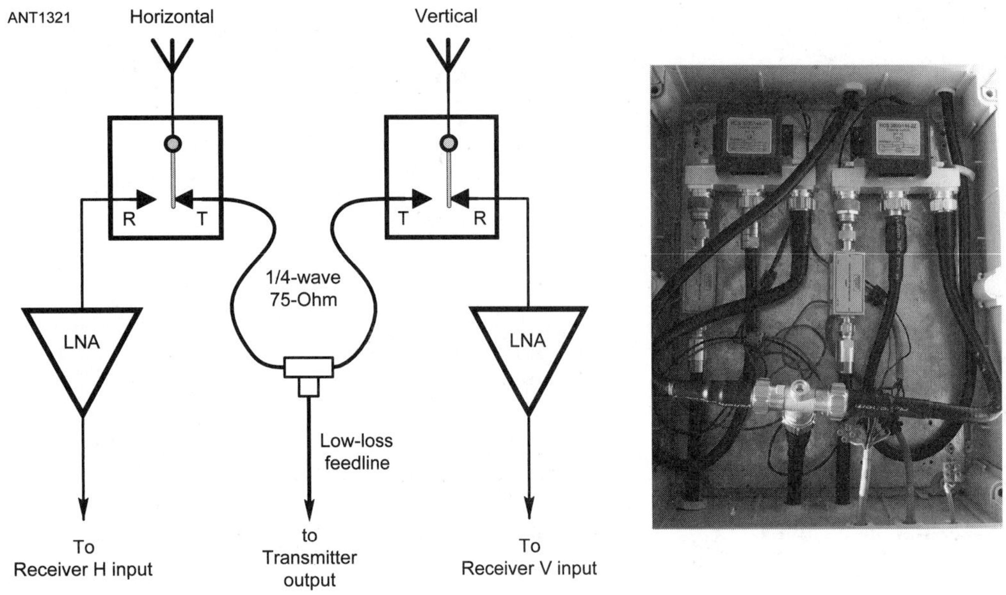

Figure 17.34 — Polarization switching box built by DK5YA uses separate feed lines for H and V receivers and a single feed line for circular polarization on transmit. (Photo courtesy Udo Langenohl, DK5YA)

17.4 Parabolic Reflector (Dish) Antennas

Very few antennas evoke as much interest among UHF amateurs as the parabolic dish, and for good reason. First, the parabola and its cousins — Cassegrain, hog horn and Gregorian — are probably the ultimate in high-gain antennas. One of the highest-gain antennas in the world (148 dB) is a parabola. This is the 200-inch Mt. Palomar telescope. (The very short wavelength of light rays causes such a high gain to be realizable.)

Second, the efficiency of the parabola does not change as size increases. With Yagis and collinear arrays, the losses in the phasing harness increase as the array size increases. The corresponding component of the parabola is lossless air between the feed horn and the reflecting surface. If there are a few surface errors, the efficiency of the system stays constant regardless of antenna size. (See the **VHF, UHF, and Microwave Antennas** chapter for design and construction information on dish antennas.)

The major problems associated with parabolic dish antennas are mechanical ones. For example, a dish of about 16 feet in diameter is the minimum size required for successful analog EME operation on 432 MHz. With wind and ice loading, structures of this size place a real strain on the mounting and positioning system. Extremely rugged mounts are required for large dish antennas, especially when used in windy locations. **Figure 17.35** shows the impressive 7-meter diameter dish built by David Wardley, ZL1BJQ. A smaller dish used for 1296 MHz operation is shown in **Figure 17.36**.

For portable use, such as for DXpeditions and rare grids, Al Katz, K2UYH, designed the lightweight offset dish shown in **Figure 17.37** for use on 1296 MHz. Its maximum dimension is 7.5 feet, and it breaks down into easily transported components. An article by K2UYH describing the design and construction of the dish is available in the online material

Figure 17.35 — ZL1BJQ's homemade 7-meter (23-foot) parabolic dish, just prior to adding 1/2-inch wire mesh. (Photo courtesy ZL1BJQ)

Several aspects of parabolic dish antennas make the extra mechanical problems worth the trouble, however. For example, the dish antenna is inherently broadband, and may be used on several different amateur bands by simply changing the feed. An antenna that is suitable for 432 MHz work will most likely be usable on several of the higher amateur bands too. Increased gain is available as the frequency of operation is increased.

Another advantage of a dish is the flexibility of the feed system. The polarization of the feed, and therefore the polarization of the antenna, can be changed with little difficulty. It is a relatively easy matter to devise a system to rotate the feed remotely from the station to change polarization. Because polarization changes can account for as much as 30 dB of signal attenuation, the rotatable feed can make the difference between consistent communications and no communications at all.

Figure 17.36 — This 3-meter TVRO dish with aluminum frame and mesh surface was outfitted for 1296 MHz EME as a joint effort by VA7MM and VE7CNF. The dual circular polarization feed is a VE4MA/W2IMU design.

Figure 17.37 — A 7.5-foot stress offset dish for 1296 MHz. The dish was designed by K2UYH for portable operation and EME DXpeditions. [Photo courtesy of Al Katz, K2UYH)

17.4.1 SHF EME Challenges For Dishes

The challenges met when successfully building a station for EME at 900 MHz to 5.7 GHz only become more significant on the SHF bands at 10 GHz and above. Absolute attention to detail is the primary requirement, and this extends to every aspect of the EME antenna system. The dish surface is probably the most difficult problem to solve. As was discussed earlier, shape and accuracy of the reflector contribute directly to the overall gain of the antenna.

But where slight errors in construction can be tolerated at the lower frequencies, the same cannot be said at millimeter wavelengths. Those who have attempted EME on 10 and 24 GHz have discovered that the weight of the dish reflector itself will distort its shape enough to lower the gain to the point where echoes are degraded. Stiffening structures at the back of such dishes are often found necessary.

Pointing accuracy is also paramount. A 16-foot dish at 10 GHz has a beamwidth about equal to the diameter of the Moon — 0.5 degrees. This means that the echo degradation due to the Moon's movement away from where the dish is pointed is almost immediate, and auto-tracking systems become more of a necessity than a luxury. At these frequencies, most amateurs actually peak their antennas on moon noise — the black-body radiation from the Moon that becomes the dominant source of noise in space.

At these frequencies, the elevation of the Moon above the horizon also plays a role in the ability to communicate since tropospheric absorption due to water vapor is greatest at low elevation angles (the signal must pass through a greater portion of the troposphere than when the Moon is highly elevated). It is beyond the abilities of most amateurs to construct their own dishes for these frequencies, so surplus dishes for Ku-band (12 GHz) satellite TV (typically 3 meters in diameter) are usually employed, as are high-performance dishes designed for millimeter-wave radar and point-to-point communications at 23 and 38 GHz.

17.4.2 Dish Antennas For Satellites

Dish antennas are not required for satellite operation except in the case of HEO or geosynchronous satellites operating with microwave up or down-links. At lower frequencies, Yagi arrays are the more practical choice.

A 1.2-meter L-band dish antenna and 40 W of RF power (6100 W PEP EIRP with RHCP) can also provide a superb uplink for squint angles even up to 25 degrees. A dish antenna can have a practical gain of about 21 to 22 dBic. These uplinks will provide the user a downlink that is 10 to 18 dB above the transponder noise floor. In more practical terms, these are S7 to 8 signals over an S3 transponder noise floor, making for very comfortable "armchair" copy.

KD1K shows in **Figure 17.38** what can be done with a 1.2 meter dish antenna kit for HEO operations. **Figure 17.39** shows a WØLMD 8-foot TVRO dish with patch feed, az/el mount, a U-band Yagi, and an L-band helical antenna.

Other hams have also taken advantage of surplus dishes. **Figure 17.40** shows modified MMDS dishes, by K5GNA, and **Figure 17.41**, by K5OE, both using helix feeds.

A spun-aluminum dish antenna works well for HEO satellites. The G3RUH-ON6UG 60 cm unit with its S-band patch feed is shown in **Figure 17.42**. With a gain of 21 dBi it provides a 2.5 dB sun noise signal.

Parabolic dish antennas are usually considered as suitable only for fixed locations. The lightweight dish and circular polarity feed shown in **Figure 17.43** was designed and built by W2HRO and **Sub-Lunar.com**. (See also the portable dish for 1296 MHz by K2UYH in Figure 17.37.) The dish uses flexible fiberglass ribs and a conductive fabric reflector. This dish is available in 6-foot (1.8 meter) and 8-foot (2.4 meter) versions, weighs less than 12 pounds, and folds up into a

Figure 17.38 — KD1K's completed antenna system mounted to the tower and ready to go. The 40 W, 23 cm amplifier is in the box below the KG6IAL 1.2-meter dish. This system would be suitable for HEO or geosynchronous satellites. [Dick Jansson, KD1K, photo]

Figure 17.39—WØMLD created this 8-foot dish with patch feed for S band for working HEO satellites. On the left is a helical antenna for L band and on the right is a 2 × 9-element offset-feed Yagi for U band. A homebrew az/el mount is provided.

Figure 17.40 — K5GNA's "circularized" mesh modification of an MMDS dish antenna with a helix-CP feed and preamp. The dish modification reduces the spillover loss by making the antenna fully circular. [Gerald Brown, K5OE, photo]

Figure 17.41 — Mesh modification of an MMDS dish antenna by K5OE, with a helix-CP feed and preamplifier by Down-East Microwave mounted directly to the helix feed point. [Gerald Brown, K5OE, photo]

small 8 × 8 × 52 inch (approximately 20 cm × 20 cm × 132 cm) package. It is suitable for EME work on the 1296 MHz and the feed can be configured for RCHP transmit and LHCP receive.

Figure 17.42 — G3RUH's 60 cm spun-aluminum dish with CP-patch feed is available as a kit.

Figure 17.43 — Sub-Lunar Systems Folding Fabric EME Parabolic dish (photo courtesy Paul Andrews, W2HRO)

First Amateur Geosynchronous Satellite - QO-100

(This sidebar contains material from a May 2000 QEX article about QO-100 by Bill Dzruilla, NZ5N. The article explains and illustrates numerous other details of the complete system used to operate through QO-100. While the footprint of this satellite does not include North America, other geosynchronous satellites are being considered. Using them will require similar equipment. An additional article by GØMJW, PA3FYM, and MØEYT describes a dual-band dish feed. Both are included in the online material. – Ed.)

Qatar OSCAR 100, also called Es'hail-2, or just QO-100 for short, is the first ham satellite in geostationary orbit. The footprint includes all of Europe, Africa, and the Middle East and extends as far as Brazil, China, and Antarctica, but unfortunately does not include any part of the USA. QO-100 provides service to a third of the globe using a small, inexpensive station and antenna. QO-100 has both a narrow band transponder for SSB, CW, and digital modes and a wide band transponder for DATV.

The narrow band uplink is on 2.4 GHz and the downlink is from 10.4895 to 10.4900 GHz. All that is needed for those within the footprint to make SSB, CW, and digital QSOs via this transponder is 1) a 25 to 80 cm TV satellite dish with a low-noise block downconverter (LNB), and 2) to receive, a USB-dongle software defined receiver (SDR) plugged into a laptop or tablet, and 3) to transmit, a 2.4 GHz upconverter that provides 1 to 5 W output at the antenna.

Satellite dish antennas designed to receive TV broadcast channels in the 10 to 12 GHz band will receive QO-100. Since the satellite is in geostationary orbit, a rotator is not needed, as the dish stays pointed at the same spot at all times. We can also use the same TV LNB (Low Noise Block downconverter) that is mounted at the focal point of the dish. See **Figure 17.A** for a photograph of the dish, LNB, and homemade patch feed antenna.

For greater stability, the LNB's stock local oscillator can be replaced with a temperature compensated crystal oscillator (TCXO) or an oven controlled crystal oscillator (OCXO), but this may not be really necessary, since the SDR software can provide adequate frequency drift correction. The LNB typically has a local oscillator frequency of 9.75 GHz. Thus, to receive the QO-100 lower beacon at 10.4895 GHz, we need to connect the LNB to a receiver that is tuned to 739.5 MHz.

A dual-band satellite like QO-100 presents special challenges to the single-dish station. A traditional double feed would be bulky and reduce gain due to its size, blocking some of the signals. Mike Willis GØMJW, Remco den Besten, PA3FYM, and Paul Marsh, MØEYT, responded by designing a dual-band antenna feed that combines a patch antenna on 2.4 GHz and a waveguide feed on 10 GHz. Their article, "Simple dual band dish feed for Es'hail-2 / QO-100," is included in the online material for this book.

17.5 Antenna Position Control

EME and satellite antennas have high gain and narrow main beams that must be properly aimed in two coordinates. Although polar mounts (one axis parallel to the Earth's axis) have sometimes been used, by far the most popular mounting scheme today is the elevation-over-azimuth or az/el mount. Readily available computer software can provide azimuth and elevation coordinates for the Moon, and a small computer can also control antenna positioning motors to automate the whole pointing system.

For mechanical reasons it is desirable to place the antenna's center of gravity close to the intersection of the vertical (azimuth) and horizontal (elevation) axes. On the other hand, the mounting structure must not interfere with critical active regions of the antenna. Stacked Yagis are generally mounted so that metallic supporting members are perpendicular to the radiating elements or located at midpoints where the effective apertures of separate Yagis meet. Feed lines and conducting support members must not lie in the active planes containing Yagi elements, unless they run wholly along the boom. For dual-polarization Yagis, feed lines should be routed toward the rear of each Yagi and any mid-boom support members must be nonconducting. For space communications there is nothing magical about using horizontal and vertical for the two orthogonal polarizations, and there are some advantages to mounting cross-Yagis with elements in the "X" rather than "+" orientation.

Parabolic dishes are usually mounted from behind, with counterweights extending rearward to relieve torque imbalance on the elevation axis. Jack-screw actuators designed for positioning TVRO dishes can be readily adapted for elevation control. Standard heavy-duty antenna rotators can be used for azimuth positioning of dishes up to about 3 meters in size. Larger dishes may require heavier, one-of-a-kind designs for pointing control.

17.5.1 Position Controllers

Operators through the years have employed many methods for the control of their antenna positions, ranging from true *Armstrong* manual positioning, to manual operation of the powered antenna azimuth and elevation rotators, to fully automated computer control of the rotators. While computer control of the rotators is not essential, operation is greatly eased with their use. (See also the section on Rotators in the chapter **Building Antenna Systems and Towers**.)

A standalone controller translates computer antenna-position information into controller commands with an understanding of antenna-position limits. Yaesu (**yaesu.com**) produces the GS-232 computer control interface that can be used for tracking with their G-5500 az/el rotator system. The ARS-USB controller in **Figure 17.44** by EA4TX (**ea4tx.com/en/tienda/antenna-rotator-system/ars**) emulates a GS-232 control interface for use with az/el rotators compatible with the Yaesu protocols. A number of individual amateurs are using inexpensive microcontrollers to perform az/el position control and

Figure 17.44 — AMSAT-NA LVB Tracker Box assembly.

an online search for "satellite azimuth elevation control" will result in several useful links.

Other options include the SPX-01 controller from the RF Ham Store (**rfhamdesign.com/products/spx-antenna-rotators/spx-01-az--el/index.php)** which includes both the rotators and aiming controller in both a low- and high-resolution version. Also see the section on the SatNOGS system later in this chapter.

Azimuth position control and readout for satellite and EME antennas is no different than what is needed for terrestrial operation. Feedback from the rotator to the controller/readout is usually provided by either a potentiometer or a magnet-operated reed switch inside the rotator. A newer option is the use of a magnetic azimuth sensor, such as the RGMS Magnetic Azimuth Sensor from 4O3A unit from 4O3A Signature. (**4o3a.com/azimuth-magnetic-sensor**) This device can be used with a variety of controller/readout options including the company's Rotator Genius product and provides a direct readout of azimuth with no calibration required.

17.5.2 Elevation Control

Satellite antennas need to have elevation control to point up to the sky. This is the "el" part of az/el control of satellite antennas. Generally, elevation booms for CP satellite antennas need to be nonconducting so that the boom does not affect the radiation pattern of the antenna. One possibility that provides extra mounting strength is to make the center section a piece of heavy pipe (for greater strength) with fiberglass extensions for the antennas. For smaller installations, a continuous piece of fiberglass-epoxy boom can be placed directly through the elevation rotator.

Elevation boom motion needs to be powered and one solution by KD1K, shown in **Figure 17.45**, uses a surplus jack-screw drive mechanism. Note the method used to provide bearings for the elevation mechanism. The elevation axis is a piece of heavy-duty 1-1/2-inch pipe, (1-15/16-inch OD) and large 2-inch journal bearings are used for the motion. Jack-screw mechanisms usually operate on 24 V and usually include a magnet-reed-switch arrangement for position feedback.

Another option for position feedback is an inclinometer. Various products intended for industrial applications are available and can be adapted to amateur antenna control by operators with some design skill. The Green Heron "GHE_Incli-

Figure 17.45 — KD1K's homebrew elevation rotator drive using a surplus-store drive screw mechanism. Note also the large journal bearing supporting the elevation axis pipe shaft. [Dick Jansson, KD1K, photo]

nometer" produces an analog voltage proportional to the elevation angle. This output is compatible with the Green Heron series of controllers and others. (**greenheronengineering.com/product/model-ghe_inclinometer-inclinometer**)

Robust commercial solutions for az/el rotators have given operators good service over the years. See **Figure 17.46**. Manufacturers such as Yaesu and M2 (**m2inc.com**) and AlfaSpid (**alfaradio.ca**) are among these suppliers.

EME operators have begun using powerful and accurate dual axis slew drives (see **Figure 17.47**) to point their dishes and arrays. These slew drives are being manufactured in high volume for the solar power industry and prices have been declining. These slew drives move very slowly since they are designed to track the Sun and maximize efficiency of a solar panel, but 0.1 degree resolution pointing is achieved. These units can be easily controlled by devices such as the Green Heron RT-21.

Don't forget to provide a rotator loop of coax to allow your antenna to rotate properly in both planes and to allow water to drip off. Also, make sure you position the loop so that it doesn't snag on anything as the antenna rotates throughout its range of motion.

17.5.3 PROJECT: Wraps — A Portable Satellite Antenna Positioning System

This design was originally published as an article of the same name by Mark Spencer, WA8SME, in the January 2014 issue of QST. The full article is included with the online material and shows all construction details and references.

DESIGN

WRAPS is a portable, battery operated satellite antenna rotator system using commercial, off-the-shelf (COTS) parts. It can be built using simple hand tools with a minimum of machine work. This rotator system should be an affordable alternative to the industry standard — the Yaesu G-5500 system — which is an excellent and proven rotator for base station operations. It is a limited-duty rotator intended for small handheld Arrow and Elk class satellite antennas,

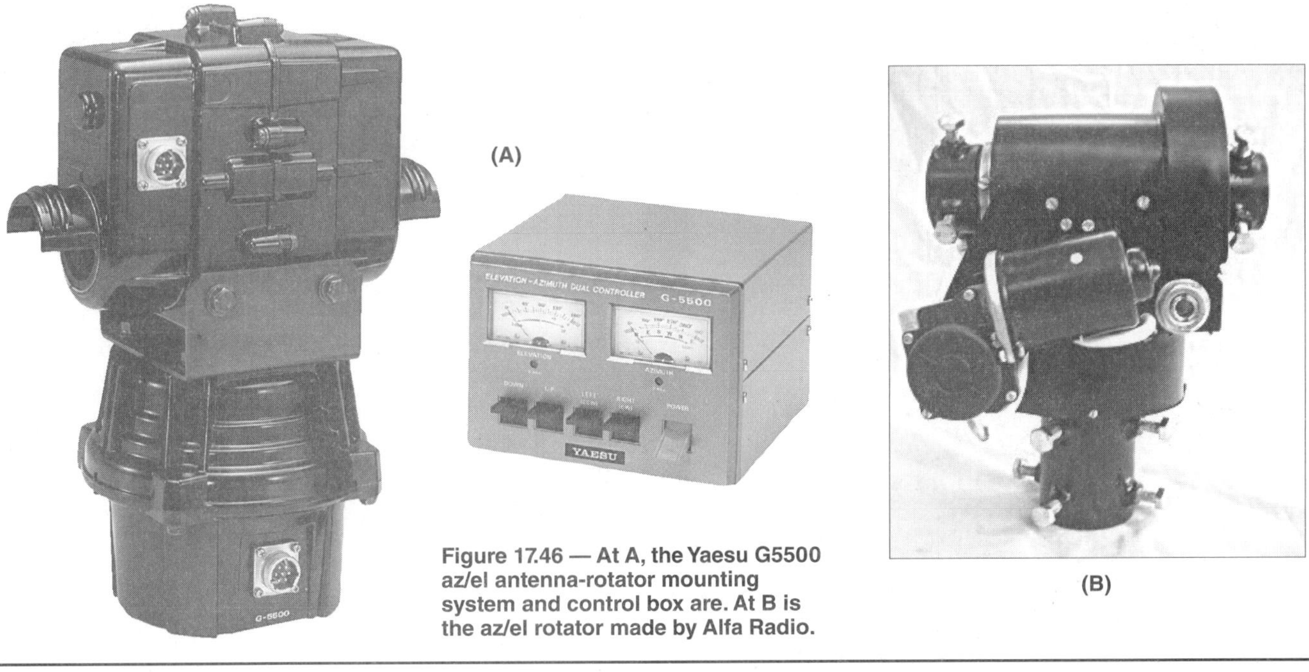

Figure 17.46 — At A, the Yaesu G5500 az/el antenna-rotator mounting system and control box are. At B is the az/el rotator made by Alfa Radio.

Figure 17.47 — A slew drive developed for solar panel positioning can be used as an az-el rotator for EME dishes and Yagi arrays. (Picture courtesy of Paul Andrews, W2HRO and Sub-Lunar)

and can be used to receive Fox satellite signals.

The positioning system is powered by a 12 V battery such as a small sealed UPS battery. The cost of parts, including all the associated cabling and computer interfaces, is approximately one-quarter of that for the G-5500 system. This design includes a USB interface that works with *SatPC32* and other satellite tracking software packages running the EASYCOM protocol. WRAPS is designed for lightweight antennas only, and is not intended to handle large antenna arrays. It is not weatherproof, nor designed for continuous unattended operation.

Figure 17.48 shows a block diagram of the WRAPS circuitry. The heart of the WRAPS circuit is a PIC microcontroller that:

- Receives positioning commands from the satellite tracking program which runs on the personal computer (PC)
- Translates those commands into rotator positions (analog to digital converter values).
- Reads the current rotator positions and determines if a position change is required, and if so, in which direction.
- Commands the motors ("MOT" in the figure) to turn in the proper direction.
- Monitors the motors as they move.
- Stops the motors when they reach the commanded position.
- Waits for the next position update.

The motors are controlled through the individual H-bridge circuits using a pulse width modulation (PWM) produced by the PIC microcontroller to set the motor speed.

WRAPS makes use of precision parts manufactured for the robotics community. **Figure 17.49** illustrates the elevation (el) part of the rotator. The el rotator uses a geared 0.5 rpm dc motor that provides excellent torque at an affordable price. Construction is similar to an "erector set" project. There are a couple of cutouts required in the aluminum channel chassis of the el rotator. These cuts are easy to make with a hand hacksaw, and the rough edges can be cleaned up with a metal file. Eleven holes must be drilled in the rotator chassis box along with some hacksaw, drill, and tap work on two metal brackets made from home improvement store aluminum stock supplies. Finally, a few PVC pipe fitting parts require some drilling. The az rotator is a 1 rpm motor mounted inside the rotator body enclosure along with the associated position potentiometer as seen in **Figure 17.50**.

The azimuth and elevation rotator positions are determined by the wiper positions of wire-wound potentiometers that are connected to the motors by a pair of 36:50 ratio gears. Make the brackets for accurately mounting the potentiometers from circuit board material.

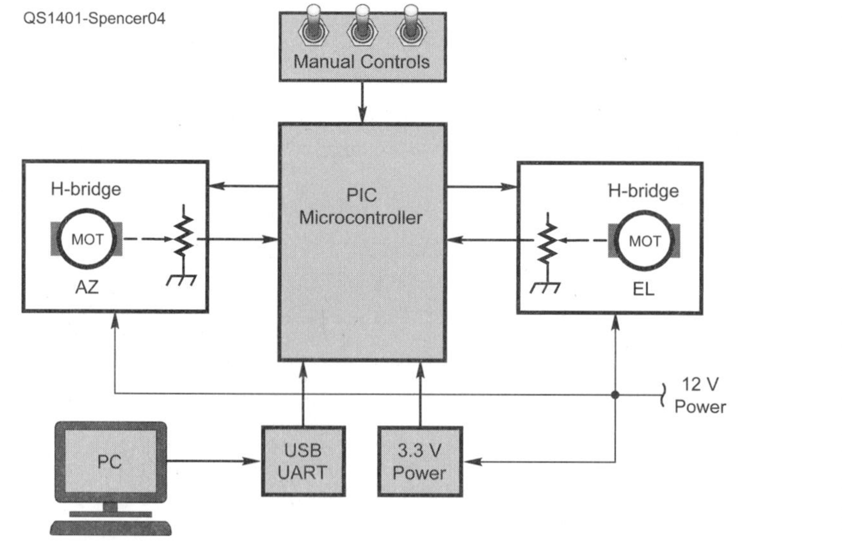

Figure 17.48 — The WRAPS antenna positioning system block diagram.

Figure 17.49 — The elevation (el) positioning assembly. [Mark Spencer, WA8SME]

Figure 17.50 — The azimuth (az) positioning assembly. [Mark Spencer, WA8SME]

The microcontroller program is written in the C programming language. Position switches allow you to manually position the rotator motors. A calibration (**CAL**) button switch allows adjustments in the firmware if the system gets out of calibration. The rotator is set to 0 degrees az and 0 degrees el, press the **CAL** button, and that location is stored in the PIC microcontroller program. Then, set the rotator to 359 degrees az and 90 degrees el, press the **CAL** button to store the other stop position in the PIC program.

17.5.4 SatNOGS

SatNOGS stands for Satellite Network Of Ground Stations (**satnogs.org** and **wiki.satnogs.org**) and is a project associated with the Libre Space Foundation (**libre.space**). SatNOGS stations are used to build an open-source global network of automated satellite ground stations to automate the process of collecting satellite telemetry data. All the information you need to build a SatNOGS system is available on the project website, including an online community of users for support and assistance with building and operating the station.

As part of the project, an azimuth-elevation position control system (i.e. – an az-el rotator) was developed that could be made of 3D-printed parts. (3D-printing design files are available on the SatNOGS website.) The control hardware is sufficiently strong to manage a circularly-polarized Yagi or helix antennas on the uplink and downlink band. The control software also supports commercial az-el rotators, such as the Yaesu G-5500.

The SatNOGS antenna system of Corey Shields, KB9JHU is shown in **Figure 17.51A**. Figure 17.51A shows the az-el rotator mounted on a small tripod designed for TV antennas. The antenna booms and element-to-boom clamps are also 3D-printed. Figure 17.51B shows the inside of the az-el rotator with the 3D-printed gears and other mechanical parts, along with the microprocessor controllers for the motors. A complete set of instructions for assembling the rotator showing all of the parts is available at **satnogs.dozuki.com/Guide/SatNOGS+Rotator+v3+Mechanical+Assembly/7?lang=en**.

The SatNOGS ground station was primarily designed for receive-only telemetry collection but the system can also be used for two-way communication. If the satellite orbital elements are available, the SatNOGS system will automatically track the satellite while you operate. Building and maintaining a telemetry collection system would be an excellent club project, particularly at the secondary or university level.

(A)

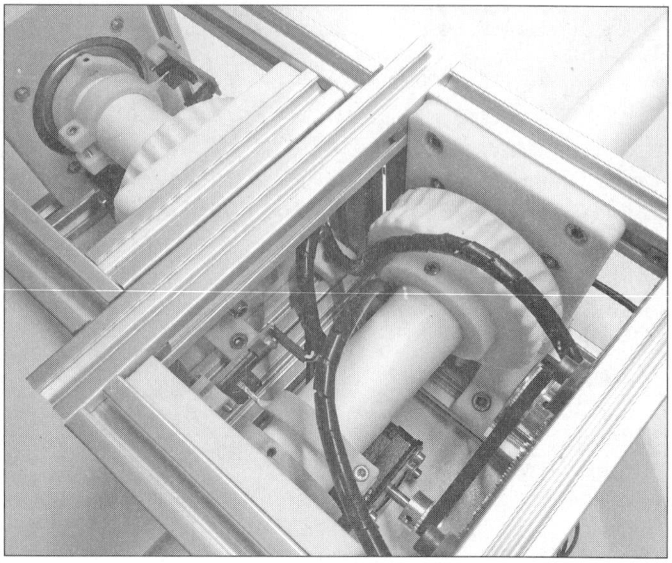

(B)

Figure 17.51 — The SatNOGS antenna system of Corey Shields, KB9JHU, is shown in photo A. The internal construction of the az-el rotator including the 3D-printed gears and other components is shown in photo B. [Photo B courtesy of Comzeradd and the SatNOGS wiki]

17.6 References and Bibliography

ARRL AND RSGB BOOKS

ARRL UHF/Microwave Projects (CD or book), ARRL (out of print).

ARRL UHF/Microwave Experimenter's Manual, ARRL (out of print).

International Microwave Handbook — 2nd Edition, RSGB.

Microwave Know How, RSGB.

Microwave Projects, Vol. 1 and Vol. 2, RSGB.

OTHER PUBLICATIONS

Brown, G., "A Helix Feed for Surplus MMDS, Antennas," *Proceedings of the 2001AMSAT-NA Symposium*, Oct. 2001, pp. 89 – 94.

Brown, G., "A K-Band Receiver for AO-40," *Proceedings of the 2002 AMSAT-NA Space Symposium*, Oct. 2002.

Brown, G., "Build This No-Tune Dual-Band Feed for Mode L/S," *The AMSAT Journal*, Vol. 26, No. 1, Jan./Feb. 2003.

Brown, G., "Dual-Band Dish Feeds for 13/23 cm," *Proceedings of the 2002AMSAT-NA Symposium*, Oct. 2002, pp. 123 – 131.

Brown, G., "The Texas Potato Masher: A Medium-Gain Directional Satellite Antenna For LEOs," *The AMSAT Journal*, Vol. 22, No. 1, Jan./Feb. 1999.

Cebik, L., "The Axial Mode Helical Antenna," *QEX*, Sep./Oct. 2007, pp. 51 – 56.

DeMaw, D., "The Basic Helical Beam," *QST*, Nov. 1965, pp. 20 – 25, 170.

Foot, N., "Cylindrical Feed horn for Parabolic Reflectors," *Ham Radio*, May 1976, pp. 16 – 20.

Hallidy, D., "Microwave EME Using a Ten-Foot TVRO Antenna," *The ARRL UHF/Microwave Projects Manual, Vol. 2* (ARRL, 1997) pp. 10-9 to 10-13. (out of print).

Jansson, D., "Product Review: M^2 23CM22EZA 1.2 GHz Antenna," *QST*, Sep. 2002, pp. 59 – 61.

Jasik, H., *Antenna Engineering Handbook*, 1st ed. (McGraw-Hill, 1961).

Knadle, R., "A Twelve-Foot Stressed Parabolic Dish," *QST*, Aug. 1972, pp. 16 – 22.

Koehler, J., "An Inexpensive Az-El Rotator System", *QST*, Dec. 1998, pp. 42 – 46.

Kraus, J., *Antennas* (McGraw-Hill, 1988). See "The Helical Antenna," Chapter 7 and "Patch or Microstrip Antennas," pp. 745 – 749.

Kraus, J., "A 50-Ohm Input Impedance for Helical Beam Antenna," *IEEE Transactions on Antennas and Propagation*, Nov. 1977, p. 913.

Krome, E., "Development of a Portable Mode S Ground Station." *The AMSAT Journal*, Vol. 16, No. 6, Nov./Dec. 1993, pp. 25 – 28.

Krome, E., "S band Reception: Building the DEM Converter and Preamp Kits," *The AMSAT Journal*, Vol. 16, No. 2, Mar./Apr. 1993, pp. 4 – 6.

Krome, E., *Mode S: The Book*, pp. 96, 109.

Krome, E., "Mode S: Plug and Play!," *The AMSAT Journal*, Vol. 14, No. 1, Jan. 1991, pp. 21 – 23, 25.

Malowanchuk, B., "Use of Small TVRO Dishes for EME," *Proceedings of the 21st Conference of The Central States VHF Society, 1987*, pp. 68 – 77.

Malowanchuk, B., "Selection of An Optimum Dish Feed," *Proceedings of the 23rd Conference of The Central States VHF Society, 1989*, pp. 35 – 43.

Miller, J., "Mode S — Tomorrow's Downlink?" *The AMSAT Journal*, Vol. 15, No. 4, Sep./Oct. 1992, pp. 14 – 15.

Miller, J., "'Patch' Feed For S-Band Dish Antennas" (see **jrmiller.demon.co.uk/products/patch.html**).

Miller, J., "A 60-cm S-Band Dish Antenna," *The AMSAT Journal*, Vol. 16 No. 2, Mar./Apr. 1993, pp. 7 – 9.

Miller, J., "Small is Best," *The AMSAT Journal*, Vol. 16, No. 4, July/Aug. 1993, p. 12.

Monteiro, A., "An EZ-Lindenblad Antenna for 2 Meters," *QST*, Aug. 2007, pp. 37 – 40.

Monteiro, A., "A Parasitic Lindenblad Antenna for 70 cm," *QST*, Feb. 2010, p. 46.

Orban Microwave, "The Basics of Patch Antennas," (see **orbanmicrowave.com/technical-articles**).

Planer T., and Zehr, G., "The Two Meter EZ Lindenblad Revisited," *AMSAT Journal*, Nov./Dec. 2018, pp. 22 – 28.

Portune, J., "The Quadrifilar Helix as a 2 Meter Base Station Antenna," *QST*, Oct. 2009, pp. 30 – 32.

Ruperto, E., "The W3KH Quadrifilar Helix Antenna," *QST*, Aug. 1996, pp. 30 – 34. See also "Feedback", June 1999 *QST*, p. 78 and Sep. 1999 *QST*, p. 80.

Seydler, R., "Modifications of the AIDC 3731 Downconverters."

Thiel D., and Smith, S., *Switched Parasitic Antennas for Cellular Communications*, (Artech House, 2002). See Chapter 3, "Patch Antennas," pp. 79 – 96.

Tillitson, G., "The Polarization Diplexer — A Polaplexer," *Ham Radio*, Mar. 1977, pp. 40 – 43.

Thornburg D., and Kramer, L., "The Two-Meter Eggbeater," *QST*, Apr. 1971, pp. 44 – 46.

Vilardi, D., "Simple and Efficient Feed for Parabolic Antennas," *QST*, Mar. 1973, pp 42-44.

Wade, P., *Online Microwave Antenna Handbook*, 1998 – 2004. See "Chapter 4, Parabolic Dish Antennas," **w1ghz.org/antbook/contents.htm**.

Zibrat, T., "2.4 GHz Patch Design," (see **qsl.net/k3tz**).

TABLE OF CONTENTS

Chapter 18 — Online Material

Articles

- "A 70-cm Power Divider" by Zack Lau, W1VT
- "Feeding Open-Wire Line at VHF and UHF" by Zack Lau, W1VT
- "Rewinding Relays for 12 V Operation," by Paul Wade, W1GHZ
- "Increasing Side Suppression by Using Loop-Fed Directional Antennas" by Justin Johnson, GØKSC

Chapter 18

VHF, UHF, and Microwave Antenna Systems

As for HF antenna systems, there are many items at VHF, UHF, and microwave frequencies that affect how the overall antenna system works. Techniques and devices or design elements that apply to operating at VHF and above are dealt with in greater detail here.

It is recommended that you begin by reading the System Design Basics section of the **HF Antenna System Design** chapter since many of the issues discussed there apply equally at higher frequencies. Contest clubs, particularly VHF+ contest clubs, are another source of excellent information on antenna system design. You can find these clubs by using the ARRL's Find-A-Club service at **arrl.org/find-a-club**.

The material has been collected from various ARRL publications, including other chapters of this book's earlier editions. The *QST* column "Microwavelengths," by Paul Wade, W1GHZ (**w1ghz.org**), is another source, covering many important microwave topics. Justin Johnson, GØKSC, updated the material on stacked antenna systems along with David Olean, K1WHS. Frank Donovan, W3LPL, contributed material on 6-meter beams.

18.1 Transmission Lines and Devices

Transmission line principles are covered in detail in the **Transmission Lines** chapter. As at HF, RF is carried principally via coaxial cables at VHF/UHF although parallel-wire transmission lines (window line or twin-lead) are used on the VHF and low UHF bands. Microstrip and other PC board transmission lines are increasingly common at UHF and above. At 10 GHz and higher frequencies, waveguide becomes feasible for amateur use. At VHF and higher frequencies, the primary consideration for transmission lines is loss, which increases dramatically with frequency.

While not in widespread use at VHF/UHF today, properly built parallel-wire line can operate with very low loss in VHF and UHF installations. A total line loss under 2 dB per 100 feet at 432 MHz can easily be obtained. A line made of #12 AWG wire, spaced ¾ inch or more with Teflon spreaders and run essentially straight from antenna to station, can be better than anything but the most expensive coax. Such line can be home-made or purchased at a fraction of the cost of coaxial cables, with comparable loss characteristics. Careful attention must be paid to efficient impedance matching if the benefits of this system are to be realized. A similar system for 144 MHz can easily provide a line loss under 1 dB. (See the article "Feeding Open-Wire Line at VHF and UHF" in the online material.

Small coax such as RG-58 or RG-59 should never be used in VHF operation if the length of the run is more than a few feet. Lines of ½-inch diameter (RG-213 or RG-11) work fairly well at 50 MHz, and are acceptable for 144-MHz runs of 50 feet or less. These lines are somewhat better if they employ foam instead of solid dielectric material but still very lossy. Updated designs for low-loss flexible coax, such as Belden 9913 and the LMR-series and various equivalents, are better choices for longer run. Although designed for use in receive-only cable and satellite TV systems, RG-6 in its various shielding configurations is also useable at VHF and above but only at low power (100 W and lower) because of the lightweight conductors and use of F connectors.

Aluminum-jacket *hardline* coaxial cables with large inner conductors and foam insulation (dielectric) are well worth their cost. Another form of hardline known by its trade name of Heliax has a corrugated outer jacket. Some types of Heliax use foam dielectric, while others are air-insulated with the center conductor supported by a helical plastic strip.

Hardline can sometimes be obtained for free from local cable TV operators as "end runs" — pieces at the end of a roll. A common CATV cable is ½-inch OD 75-Ω hardline. Matched-line loss for this cable is about 1.0 dB/100 feet at 146 MHz and 2.0 dB/100 feet at 432 MHz. Also available from CATV companies is the ¾-inch 75-Ω hardline, sometimes with a black self-healing hard plastic covering. This line has 0.8 dB of loss per 100 feet at 146 MHz, and 1.6 dB loss per 100 feet at 432 MHz. There will be small additional losses for either line if 75-to-50-Ω transformers are used at each end. The **Transmission Line System Techniques** chapter describes synchronous transmission line transformers for converting between 50- and 75-Ω lines on a single band. Hardline must not be bent too sharply, because it will kink.

Commercial connectors for hardline are more expensive than for flexible cable but provide reliable connections with full waterproofing. They are often available at very reasonable prices via online sites including adapters to UHF and other connector types. Enterprising amateurs have homebrewed low-cost connectors. If they are properly waterproofed, connectors and hardline can last almost indefinitely. See the **Transmission Lines** chapter for details on hardline connectors.

Beware of any "bargains" in coax for VHF or UHF use. Feed line loss can be compensated to some extent by increasing transmitter power, but once lost, a weak signal can never be recovered in the receiver.

Effects of weather on transmission lines should not be ignored. Well-constructed open-wire line works optimally in nearly any weather, and it stands up well. The best grades of coax are completely impervious to weather — they can be run underground, fastened to metal towers without insulation and bent into any convenient position with no adverse effects on performance.

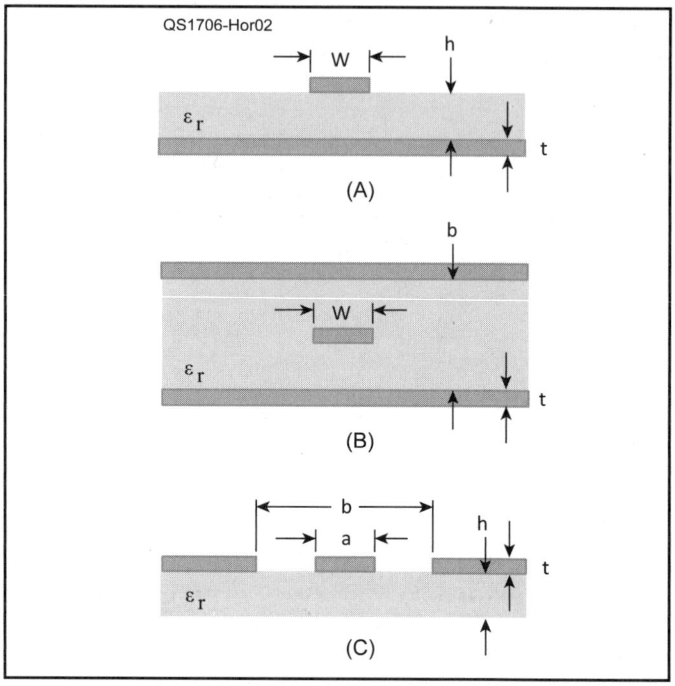

Figure 18.1 — Types of PC transmission line: microstrip (A), stripline (B), and coplanar waveguide (C). Dimensions shown are used by online calculators to determine the line's characteristic impedance. The PCB material's relative permittivity is ε_r.

18.1.1 PC Transmission Lines

PC board material can be used to create a transmission line. There are several variations in which the PC trace forms one of the conductors and ground plane layers form the other. These are summarized in **Figure 18.1,** where ε_r is the dielectric constant of the PC board material. (FR4 fire retardant glass-epoxy is the most common material at and above VHF.)

Microstrip (Figure 18.1A) is the most common of the PC transmission lines, consisting of an isolated trace above a ground plane.

Stripline (Figure 18.1B) is also common in multilayer boards with the PC trace embedded in the PC board material and centered between two ground plane layers.

Offset stripline (not shown) is a variation of stripline in which the PC trace is not centered between the ground plane layers.

Coplanar waveguide (Figure 18.1C) is feasible at microwave frequencies.

In microstrip and stripline the RF energy is mostly (but not completely) confined to the region between the large surface of the PC trace and the ground plane. Current is spread across the surface of the PC trace at a depth determined by the *skin effect*. (See the *ARRL Handbook* for more information on skin effect.)

In contrast, the RF energy in coplanar waveguide is contained between the edges of the PC trace and the edges of the adjacent ground plane. The middle surfaces of the PC trace carry little, if any, current. This increases resistive losses because the current is concentrated in a smaller region but the waves travel mostly in air and so have lower losses. This becomes an important tradeoff at microwave frequencies.

Since most designs work with 50-Ω impedances, combinations of common copper foil thicknesses, trace widths, and board layer thicknesses have been calculated to produce 50 Ω. Several are shown in **Table 18.1**. For the interested reader, see Wadell's book that is listed in the Reference section of this chapter. The free program *AppCAD* (**hp.woodshot.com**) can handle many PC transmission line design calculations, along with S parameters and balun calculations.

With high-volume commercial and consumer electronics operating at microwave frequencies, connectors for PC transmission lines have become widely available. See the **Transmission Line** chapter's table of connector styles for possible candidates. These small connectors cannot handle a lot of power but are adequate for receiving and low-power transmitting applications. Adaptors and adaptor cables are available to convert these connectors to the more common SMA, UHF, BNC, N, and other styles used by amateurs.

18.1.2 Microwave Switches and Relays

Unless a transmitter's power is very low, we must protect the receiver from the transmitter. If we can keep the leakage power reaching the receiver front end to a maximum of perhaps 1 mW (0 dBm), it should be safe as long as the receiver amplifier is not powered. Otherwise, the preamplifier could be damaged or could amplify the leakage enough to damage the next stage or mixer.

Table 18.1
50-Ω Transmission Line Dimensions

Type of Line	*Dielectric (ε_r)*	*Layer Thickness in mils (mm)*	*Center Conductor in mils (mm)*	*Gap (mm)*	*Characteristic Impedance (Ω)*
Microstrip	Prepreg (3.8)	6 (0.152)	11.5 (0.292)	N/A	50.3
		10 (0.254)	20 (0.508)		50.0
Stripline	FR4 (4.5)	12 (0.305)	3.7 (0.094)	N/A	50.0
Coplanar WG	Prepreg (3.8)	6 (0.152)	14 (0.35)	20 (0.50)	49.7

Information from Maxim Integrated, Tutorial 5100 (**maximintegrated.com/en/app-notes/index.mvp/id/5100**)

One way to protect the receiver front end from the transmitted signal is to use separate antennas, far enough apart to attenuate the transmit signal. This could also enable full-duplex operation if so desired, perhaps for a data or repeater link. We must also take care that the antennas are never pointed directly at each other — a precaution we must also take when multiple operators converge on a portable location, or when we operate on multiple bands with separate antennas for different bands.

For higher-performance stations, an RF switch is needed. At HF and VHF, ordinary relays are often adequate for modest powers levels, but they are unsatisfactory for microwaves. Coaxial relays for microwave operation are designed to have low VSWR and good isolation, often shorting out the unconnected terminal to improve isolation. As frequency increases, isolation usually decreases and VSWR gets worse, so each relay has a maximum useful frequency.

Good microwave switches and relays are expensive, but common as surplus items. **Figure 18.2** shows a good selection of surplus coaxial relays; generally, the larger ones are suitable for higher power levels while the smaller ones often work up to 10 GHz. A few coaxial relays will work up to 24 GHz.

An unused relay is preferred, since some used ones are less reliable — one contact may not make a consistent low-resistance connection. If a relay is used or specifications cannot be located, some testing with a power meter will show whether it makes reliable contact and has adequate isolation.

Many surplus relays operate with a coil voltage in the 24 to 28 V range. If only 12 V is applied to the coil, some will exhibit an audible "click" but only operate partway, not completing the switching operation to make contact. Higher voltage is needed to operate reliably. Circuits and kits are available to enable relay operation from a 12 V battery for portable operation. An alternative is to rewind the relay coil to operate from 12 V directly. (The article "Rewinding Relays for 12 V Operation" is available in the online material.)

For a 1 W transmitter (+30 dBm), at least 30 dB of isolation is needed to keep the leakage under 0 dBm; for 10 W (+40 dBm), 40 dB isolation is required. At 10 GHz, few stations run much higher power and small SMA relays can't handle much higher power. The alternative is a waveguide switch.

WAVEGUIDE SWITCHES

Waveguide switches contain curved sections of waveguide that are moved to connect different ports; most are symmetrical with four ports — the fourth terminates the disconnected transmitter or receiver. Isolation is usually very good, but not perfect, especially at high powers. Waveguide switches like those in **Figure 18.3** are used at 10 GHz and higher bands. The largest one is for WR-187, covering 3.95 to 5.85 GHz with cutoff at 3.16 GHz, so it might work at 3456 as well as 5760 MHz. These lower frequency switches are large, heavy and probably unnecessary except at very high power levels.

A caution about power handling: The coaxial relays have delicate gold contacts, which are easily damaged by "hot-switching" — switching while RF power is present. Even

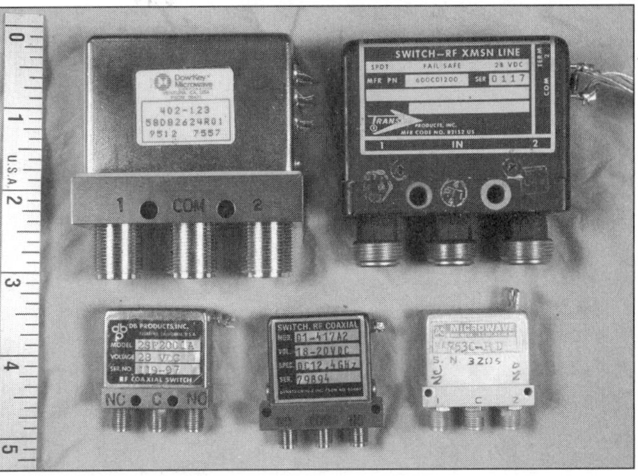

Figure 18.2 — Microwave coaxial relays with Type-N and SMA connectors.

Figure 18.3 — Waveguide switches for WR-75 (10 GHz), WR-42 (24 GHz) and WR-189 (5760 MHz).

1 W can quickly damage the small relays. Waveguide switches can also be damaged by hot-switching. Use a sequencer to make sure that the relay or switch operates and the preamp power is off before transmit power output is enabled.

TRANSFER SWITCHES

The transfer switch in **Figures 18.4** and **18.5** allow you to connect a load a termination to both transmitter and receiver so that neither is left open or shorted, except during the instant of switching. The action can be visualized by thinking of the switch as a bridge rectifier. Actuation of the blade pairs forms conducting paths in similar manner to the conduction states of a bridge during alternate half-cycles of ac. Figure 18.4 shows the Dow-Key 412-series as an example of this switch.

The isolation in a transfer switch is, by necessity, 6 dB less than in the corresponding 402-series switch (both types of switches are common as surplus and used equipment), since there are two leakage paths rather than one. But you would have to use solid-shield cable for the leak to be noticeable. Figure 18.5 shows some typical applications of a transfer switch. Transfer switches are also useful for inserting phasing line delay cables in a system as a means of controlling the pattern of multiple-Yagi systems. Such techniques are useable on 50 MHz and even higher frequencies for added versatility to eliminate ground noise problems and raise the elevation

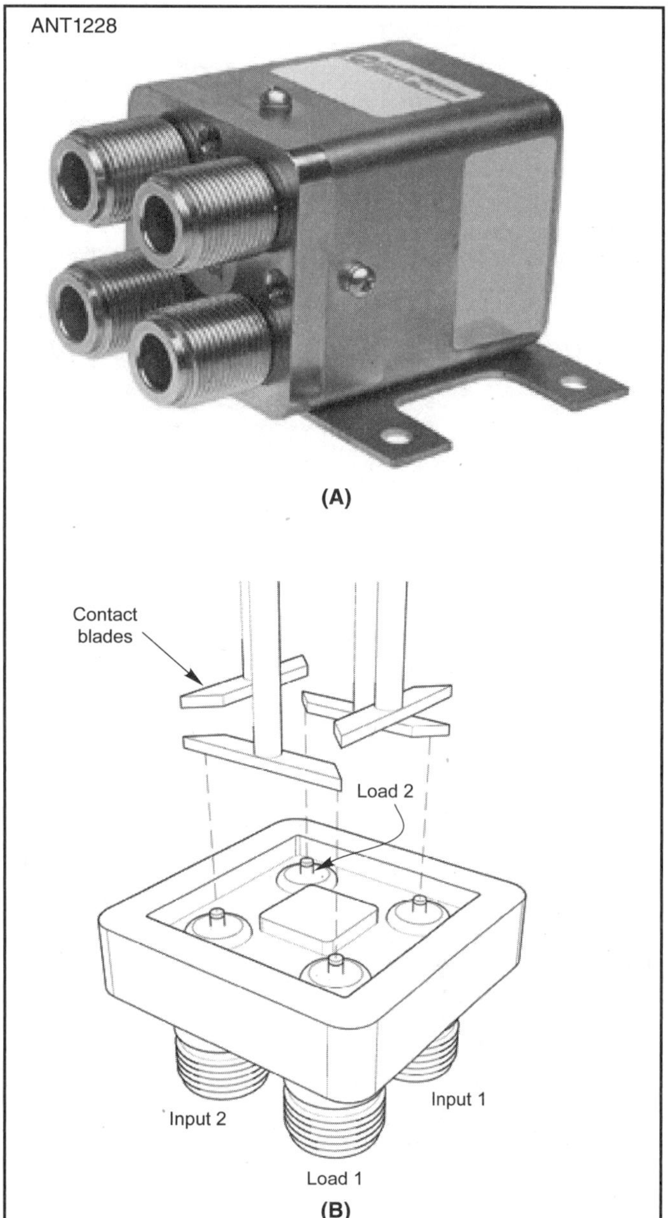

Figure 18.4 — A Dow-Key 412-series microwave transfer switch (A), with an interior view (B). The parallel blade pairs move up or down simultaneously (see text).

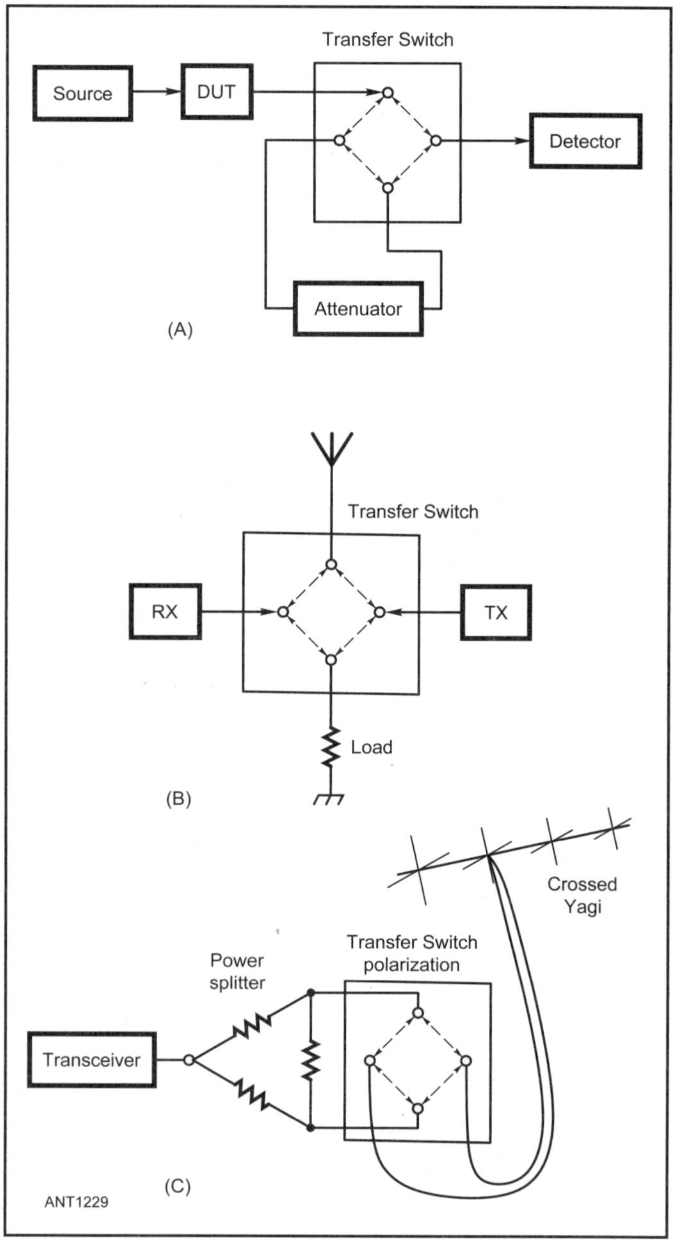

Figure 18.5 — Three circuits for application of 412-series switches: Circuit A inserts or bypasses an attenuator. Circuit B grounds the receiver input during transmission and the transmitter output during reception for weak-signal work. In circuit C, the switch selects the sense of a circularly polarized antenna. One of the transmission lines from the power splitter to the transfer switch should be $\lambda/4$ longer than the other.

pattern for close-in forward scatter work or pattern steering for horizon EME work.

18.1.3 Circulators and Isolators

The RF switch protects the receiver, but what protects the transmitter? Microwave power amplifier devices are less forgiving than the tubes in an HF amplifier, and more expensive. High VSWR is the usual culprit for failures. There might be a problem with the feed line, or forgetting to connect the antenna at a portable setup.

One solution is a microwave device called a *circulator*, which can prevent reflected power from getting back to the transmitter. A typical circulator, like the round one on the left in **Figure 18.6**, has three ports and a circular arrow on the side; power only flows in the direction of the arrow. Power from the transmitter goes in to Port "T" and comes out Port "A," going to the antenna. Reflected power comes back into Port "A" and comes out Port "R." If Port "R" is terminated in a 50 Ω load, then all the reflected power is absorbed and none flows back to Port "T," so the transmitter is always happy. More commonly, the ports are numbered 1, 2, 3, with power flowing in that order. An isolator is a circulator with an integral load on the third port, so only two connectors are available, input (1) and output (2).

A circulator contains disks of a special ferrite material with strong magnets on each side, so that the ferrite is in a strong magnetic field. Figure 18.6 shows an open unit on the right; a stripline transmission line between the disks connects the three ports. According to Pozar (see the References and Bibliography), the ferrite disks form a resonant cavity. The magnetic field creates two resonant modes, which add at the adjacent port in one direction and cancel in the other direction. Also described are waveguide *isolators*, which operate somewhat differently.

Although a circulator is resonant, most are fairly broadband, with usable performance over a frequency range of an octave or more. Some isolators and circulators are shown in **Figure 18.7**; smaller ones are for higher frequencies, as one would expect if they are resonant devices. Typical performance would be greater than 20 dB of isolation with less than 1 dB of insertion loss and VSWR less than 1.3 over the operating range. Some amateurs have experimented with additional small magnets to adjust performance; the operating frequency range does not change, but isolation and loss can be optimized for an amateur band within the operating range. Since they are magnetic devices, they should be kept away from other magnets and from iron or steel — use brass or stainless screws for mounting.

The power-handling capability of an isolator is usually limited by the size of the internal load, while a circulator may have a larger external load. If the isolator is protecting an amplifier, a temperature sensor attached to the load could be used to warn of excessive reflected power and shut down the transmitter before anything is damaged.

Isolators and circulators have other important uses. Since they provide a good termination not only at the operating frequency but also at low frequencies where amplifying devices may have excessive potential gain, they help to maintain stability if placed between stages, or ahead of potentially unstable preamps. Circulators may also be used to separate signals going in different directions, for instance, using a common mixer for both transmit and receive.

These devices can also be fairly expensive, but are common as surplus. Units with unknown specifications can be very cheap — comparing sizes with known units can help to guess the frequency range. Many surplus assemblies contain isolators that can be salvaged — good isolators have been found in otherwise useless and unwanted microwave assemblies.

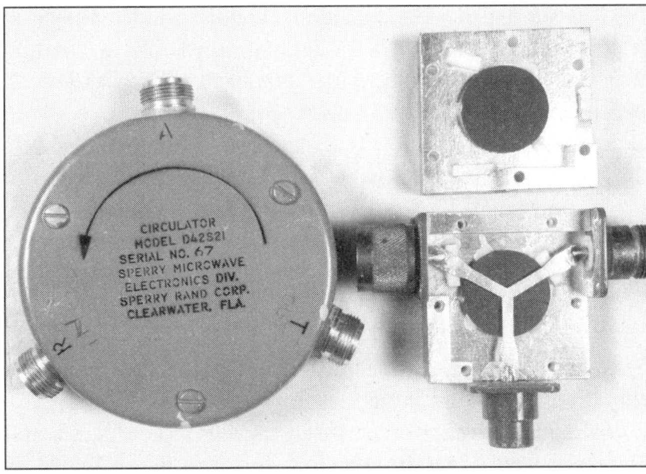

Figure 18.6 — Circulator on left has arrow showing one-way RF transmission. Isolator on right opened to show the internal construction.

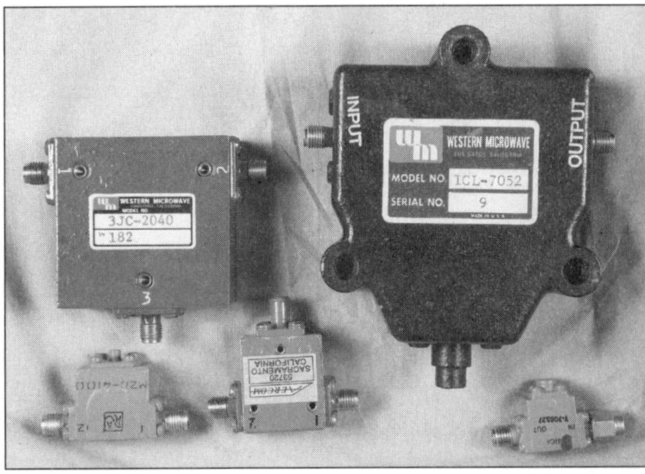

Figure 18.7 — Typical isolators and circulators. Largest is for 1296 MHz. Circulator marked "3JC-2040" indicates that it covers 2.0 to 4.0 GHz. Small isolators all work at 10 GHz.

18.1.4 Power Dividers

Power dividers are used on the VHF bands in place of coaxial synchronous transmission line transformers whenever high performance and low loss are required. (See the **Transmission Line Systems Techniques** chapter.)

The advantage of using power dividers becomes evident on the higher VHF and UHF bands since all of the impedance transformation is done within the power divider and not along the entire length of a coaxial matching transformer. The high VSWR within a coaxial feed line matching section will result in increased loss.

A power divider performs the transformation over a single quarter wavelength in a low-loss, air dielectric structure. The rest of the system thus remains matched at 50 Ω and losses remain low. This technique lowers system losses when compared to coaxial cable matching systems and provides a wider bandwidth compared to multiple quarter wavelengths of conventional coaxial cable techniques. The power dividers shown here use the same principles in a more compact package that is suitable to VHF and microwave use alike.

Power dividers are most often used in place of coaxial synchronous transmission line transformers on the 432 MHz and higher frequency bands. (See the **Transmission Line System Techniques** chapter.) The power dividers shown here use the same principles but in a compact package more suitable to UHF and microwave use.

PROJECT: COAXIAL POWER DIVIDERS

These dividers are built from 1-inch OD square tubing. Type-N receptacles fit on the outside perfectly. Brass or aluminum are good for the sleeve, but copper should be used for the center conductor. Silver coating the center conductor isn't necessary, perhaps saving 0.1 dB on 23 cm. Plastic plugs can be used for the open ends of the divider, but a ventilation hole should be provided to keep water from condensation from accumulating.

The characteristic impedance of a coaxial line with square outer conductor is

$$Z_0 = 138\log\left(1.08\frac{D}{d}\right)$$

where

D = inner width of the outer sleeve

d = the OD of the inner conductor

Assuming D is ⅞ inch, a 35.4-Ω section transforming 50 Ω to 25 Ω would have a ½-inch-OD inner conductor.

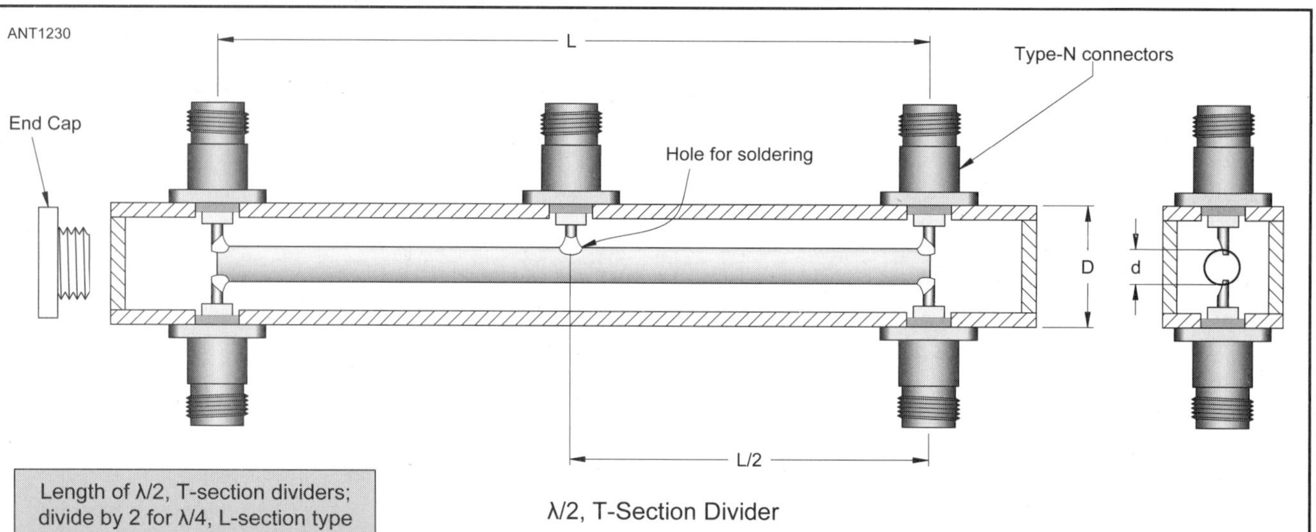

Length of λ/2, T-section dividers; divide by 2 for λ/4, L-section type		
f (MHz)	L (mm)	L (inches)
432	347	13-13/16
1296	116	4-9/16
2304	65	2-9/16

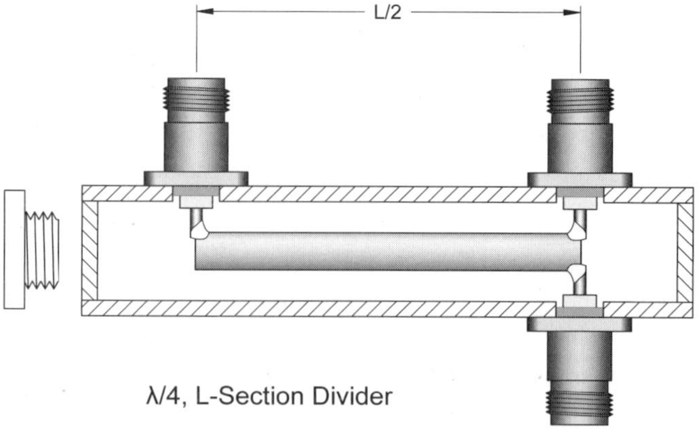

Division Ratio	λ/4 L Section		λ/2 L Section	
	Z	D/d	Z	D/d
2 : 1	35.4 Ω	1.67	70.7 Ω	2.98
3 : 1	28.9 Ω	1.50		
4 : 1	25.0 Ω	1.40	50.0 Ω	2.13
6: 1			40.8 Ω	1.83
8 : 1			35.4 Ω	1.67
Table is only valid for 50-Ω systems				

Figure 18.8 — Construction details of coaxial power dividers (see text).

For higher transformation ratios (4, 6 and 8-way dividers), λ/2 T sections should be used because of the greater bandwidth (and because one cannot put six connectors around a four-side coaxial line). The six-way transformer uses a 40.8-Ω line to match three 50-Ω ports in parallel to 100 Ω on either side of the center connector. If D is again ⅞ inch, the center conductor for the six-way unit is 7⁄16-inch OD.

For other configurations, see **Figure 18.8**. The length of the inner conductor must be exactly λ/4 or λ/2 end-to-end; the same goes for the center-to-center spacing of the connectors. Make the sleeve long enough to receive the end plugs. It should be noted that if wideband performance is not a must, dividers can be used in the third-harmonic mode. A 70-cm T divider, suspended in the radiator plane of four or six 23-cm Yagis will make an excellent feed with very short coaxial lines.

Designs for 144, 220, and 903 MHz are available at **home.teleport.com/~oldaker/power_dividers.htm**. A 50 Ω quarter-wave, four-port power splitter design is also available on the web page. A coaxial power splitter design for 50 MHz is shown in **Figure 18.9**. A complete depiction of how to build it is given by G3WOS at **gare.co.uk/6m_antenna**.

WILKINSON DIVIDERS

Three forms of the Wilkinson combiner/divider are shown in Figure **18.10**. These circuits work as dividers or combiners. The combiner form (signal flow left to right) is shown here. The circuits in Figure 18.10A and B include a transformer as part of the network. This has the advantage that, so long as there is a good, low-SWR match on the output port, there is excellent isolation between the two input ports. The insertion loss is nominally 3 dB.

The traditional Wilkinson combiner has a 2:1 ratio of input to output impedance. The variation in Figure 18.10B uses a transformer with a turns ratio (2:1 impedance ratio) to obtain 50 Ω on all ports.

The transmission line version in Figure 18.10C replaces the transformer with a pair of λ/4 transmission line transformers to divide the input signal between the pair of output ports. All three ports must have the same impedance, Z_0. A resistor between the output ports with a value of $2Z_0$ reduces loss and increases isolation. The λ/4 sections must have a characteristic impedance of

$$Z_0 \times \frac{\sqrt{2}}{2} = 0.707\ Z_0$$

Since most amateur equipment and loads have an input of 50 Ω, using RG-59 or RG-11 with an impedance of 75 Ω will result in acceptable performance. If isolation between the output ports is not required and a 35-Ω transmission line can be constructed, the divider in Figure 18.10D can be used. Two sections of 75 Ω RG-11 or hardline can be used if a slight mismatch is acceptable.

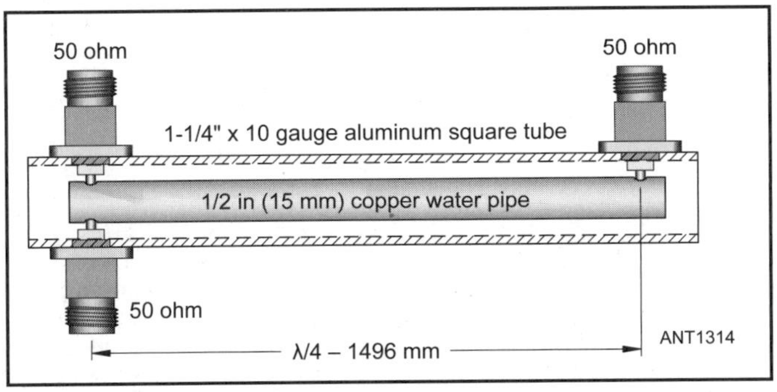

Figure 18.9 — Dimensions of a coaxial power splitter for 50 MHz.

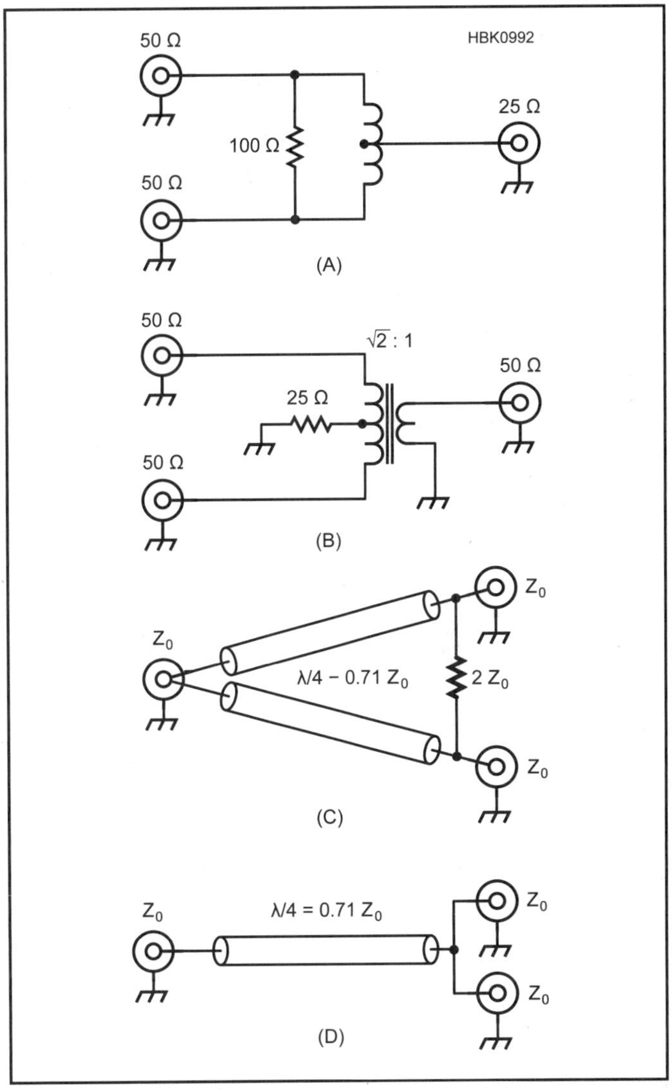

Figure 18.10 — Four forms of the Wilkinson power combiner/divider. A and B show a lumped-element implementation. The version at C uses a pair of λ/4 transmission lines acting as synchronous transformers. If all three ports are terminated in Z_0, then ports A and B are isolated from each other. If isolation between the output ports is not required, the divider at D can be used.

18.2 Impedance Matching and Baluns

Impedance matching is covered in detail in the **Transmission Line System Techniques** chapter. While advances in modeling have resulted in more designs featuring 50-Ω feed point impedances for direct connection of coaxial feed lines, impedance matching is still an important technique in antenna system design. The various technical aspects of impedance matching are similar at HF and above 50 MHz but the electrical size of the various components can be a primary factor in the choice of methods. Only the matching devices used in practical construction examples later in this chapter are discussed in detail here. This should not rule out consideration of other methods, however.

Impedance matching at the antenna takes on more importance at VHF and UHF because of feed line loss. At HF, the moderate additional feed line loss caused by an impedance mismatch at the antenna can be tolerated and the impedance matched to 50 Ω at the transmitter with an antenna tuner. At VHF and above, with feed line loss much higher, even moderate SWR can result in unacceptable additional losses. Thus, impedance matching is usually done at the antenna so that the minimum matched-line loss is obtained. For that reason, antenna tuners are not usually employed on the bands above 50 MHz.

18.2.1 Universal Stub

As its name *universal stub* implies, the double-adjustment stub of **Figure 18.11A** is useful for many matching purposes. The stub length is varied to resonate the system and the transmission line attachment point is varied until the transmission line and stub impedances are equal. In practice this involves moving both the sliding short and the point of line connection for zero reflected power, as indicated on an SWR bridge connected in the line.

The universal stub allows for tuning out any small reactance present in the driven part of the system. It permits matching the antenna to the line without knowledge of the actual impedances involved. The position of the short yielding the best match gives some indication of the amount of reactance present. With little or no reactive component to be tuned out, the stub must be approximately λ/2 from the load toward the short.

The stub should be made of stiff bare wire or rod, spaced no more than 1/20 λ apart. Preferably it should be mounted rigidly, on insulators. Once the position of the short is determined, the center of the short can be grounded, if desired, and the portion of the stub no longer needed can be removed.

It is not necessary that the stub be connected directly to the driven element. It can be made part of a parallel-wire line as a device to match coaxial cable to the line. The stub can be connected to the lower end of a delta match or placed at the feed point of a phased array. Examples of these uses are given later.

18.2.2 Delta Match

Probably the most basic impedance matching device is the *delta match*, fanned ends of a parallel-wire line tapped onto a λ/2 antenna at the point of the best impedance match. This is shown in Figure 18.11B. Both the side length and the points of connection either side of the center of the element must be adjusted for minimum reflected power on the line, but as with the universal stub, you needn't know the impedances. The delta match makes no provision for tuning out reactance, so the universal stub is often used as a termination for it.

At one time, the delta match was thought to be inferior for VHF applications because of its tendency to radiate if improperly adjusted. The delta has come back into favor now that accurate methods are available for measuring the effects of matching. It is very handy for phasing multiple-bay arrays with open-wire lines, and its dimensions in this use are not particularly critical. It should be checked out carefully in applications like that of Figure 18.11C, where no tuning device is used.

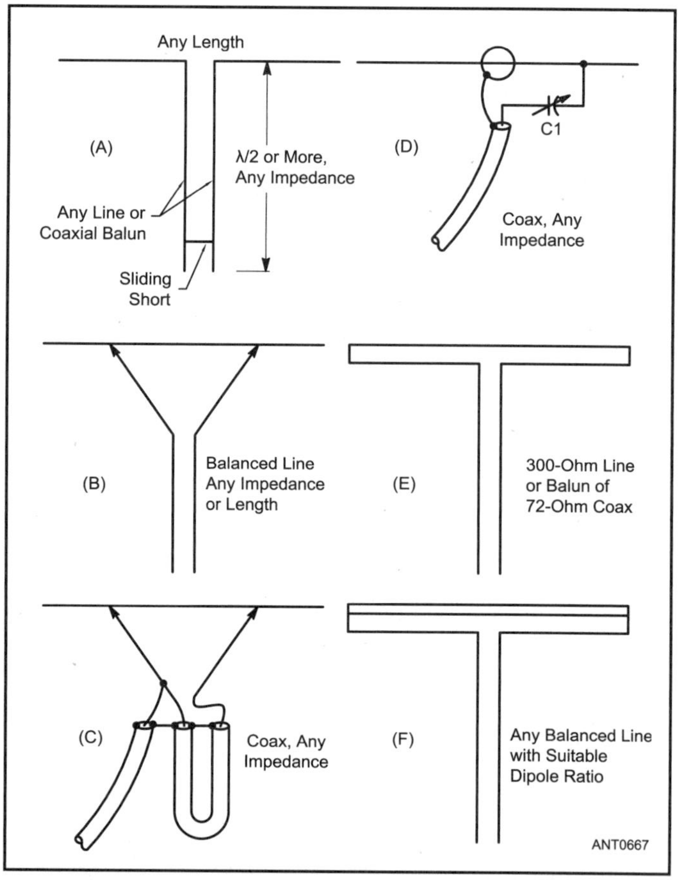

Figure 18.11— Matching methods commonly used at VHF. The universal stub, A, combines tuning and matching. The adjustable short on the stub and the points of connection of the transmission line are adjusted for minimum reflected power on the line. In the delta match, B and C, the line is fanned out and connected to the dipole at the point of optimum impedance match. Impedances need not be known in A, B or C. The gamma match, D, is for direct connection of coax. C1 tunes out inductance in the arm. A folded dipole of uniform conductor size, E, steps up antenna impedance by a factor of four. Using a larger conductor in the unbroken portion of the folded dipole, F, gives higher orders of impedance transformation.

18.2.3 Gamma and T Matches

An application of the same principle allowing direct connection of coax is the *gamma match*, Figure 18.11D. Because center of a λ/2 dipole is at an RF voltage neutral point, the outer conductor of the coax is connected to the element at this point. This may also be the junction with a metallic or wooden boom. The inner conductor, carrying the RF current, is tapped out on the element at the matching point. Inductance of the arm is tuned out by means of C1, resulting in electrical balance. Both the point of contact with the element and the setting of the capacitor are adjusted for zero reflected power, with a bridge connected in the coaxial line.

The capacitance can be varied until the required value is found, and the variable capacitor replaced with a fixed unit of that value. C1 can be mounted in a waterproof box. The maximum required value should be about 100 pF for 50 MHz and 35 to 50 pF for 144 MHz.

The capacitor and arm can be combined in one coaxial assembly, with the arm connected to the driven element by means of a sliding clamp and the inner end of the arm sliding inside a sleeve connected to the center conductor of the coax. An assembly of this type can be constructed from concentric pieces of tubing, insulated by a plastic or heat-shrink sleeve. RF voltage across the capacitor is low when the match is adjusted properly, so with a good dielectric, insulation presents no great problem. The initial adjustment should be made with low power. A clean, permanent high-conductivity bond between arm and element is important, since the RF current is high at this point.

Because it is inherently somewhat unbalanced, the gamma match can sometimes introduce pattern distortion particularly on long-boom highly directive Yagi arrays. This effect is more noticeable on higher frequencies and can be minimized by reducing the size of the gamma match hardware as much as possible. At 50 MHz, pattern distortion is typically negligible, whereas a 70 cm Yagi will show significant pattern distortion.

The *T Match*, essentially two back-to-back gamma matches, one driving each side of the driven element, create a balanced feed system and has become popular for this reason. A coaxial balun (see the following section on baluns) is used to convert the 200 Ω balanced T-match to the unbalanced 50 Ω coaxial feed line. The K1FO Yagi designs (included in the online material) all utilize T match feed systems as examples of practical applications.

18.2.4 Folded Dipole

As described in the **Dipoles and Monopoles** chapter, if a single conductor of uniform size is folded to make a λ/2 dipole as shown in Figure 18.11E, the impedance is stepped up four times. Such a folded dipole can be fed directly with 300-Ω line with no appreciable mismatch. If a 4:1 balun is used, the antenna can be fed with 75-Ω coaxial cable. Higher step-up impedance transformation can be obtained if the unbroken portion is made larger in cross-section than the fed portion, as shown in Figure 18.11F.

18.2.5 Beta or Hairpin Match

The feed point resistance of most multielement Yagi arrays is less than 50 Ω. If the driven element is split and fed at the center, it may be shortened from its resonant length to add capacitive reactance at the feed point. Then, shunting the feed point with a wire loop resembling a *hairpin* causes a step-up of the feed point resistance. The beta or hairpin match is described in the **VHF, UHF, and Microwave Antennas**.

18.2.6 Baluns at and Above VHF

Baluns, circuits, and transmission line structures that transfer power while isolating balanced and unbalanced systems are discussed in the Transmission Line Baluns and Matching Devices section of the **Transmission Line System Techniques** chapter. Because of the high importance of pattern control to minimize unwanted noise pickup on the feed line, chokes and choke baluns are used to decouple the outer surface of the feed line. At VHF, both coaxial and ferrite baluns and chokes are used. Coiled-coax chokes are effective at 50 and 144 MHz. At UHF and higher frequencies, coaxial sleeve-type baluns are preferred.

Ferrite bead choke or current baluns become less attractive at VHF and higher frequencies due to the properties of the ferrite material. However, bead-type choke baluns using type #43 and #61 material can be effective at 50 MHz and even 144 MHz.

Examples of 1:1 coaxial choke baluns with no impedance transformation are shown in **Figure 18.12**. The coaxial sleeve balun, open at the top and connected to the outer conductor of the line at the lower end (A) is the preferred type. At B, a conductor of approximately the same size as the line is used with the outer conductor to form a λ/4 stub. Another piece of coax, using only the outer conductor, will serve this purpose. This is known as a *Pawsey stub* or *Pawsey balun* and is widely used at UHF and higher frequencies. At microwave frequen-

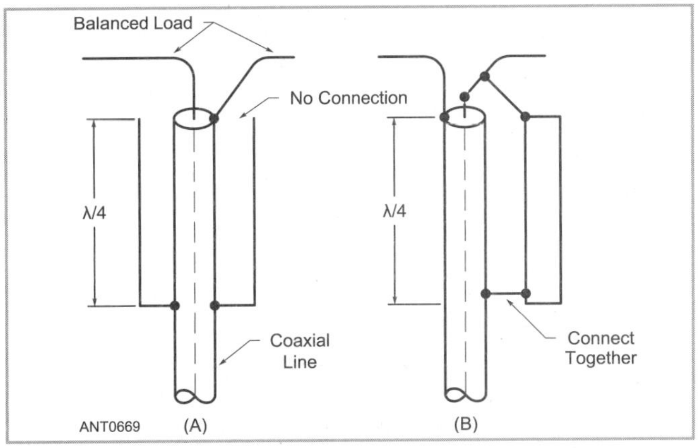

Figure 18.12 — The balun conversion function, with no impedance transformation, can be accomplished with ¼ λ lines, open at the top and connected to the coax outer conductor at the bottom. The coaxial sleeve at A and related designs are preferred at VHF and higher frequencies.

cies, sleeve and Pawsey baluns can be implemented on printed-circuit boards.

An example of a balun made from coaxial cable is shown in **Figure 18.13**. This type of balun gives an impedance step-up of 4:1 (typically 50 to 200 Ω or 75 to 300 Ω). The looped portion must be an electrical λ/2 so this is a single-band device. Since the physical length depends on the velocity factor of the line, it is important to check the line's electrical length using an analyzer (see the **Antenna and Transmission Line Measurement** chapter).

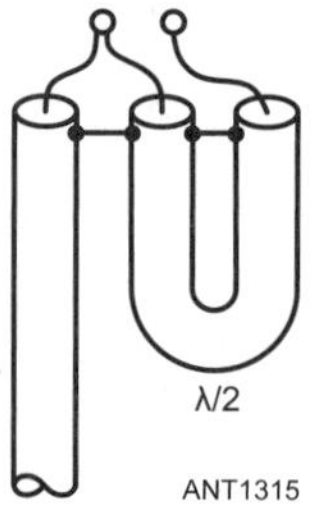

Figure 18.13 — The λ/2 balun provides a 4:1 transformation ratio, stepping up the feed line 50 Ω impedance to the 200 Ω at the T-match.

18.3 6-Meter Yagi Height Selection

In a 2022 Dayton Hamvention Antenna Forum presentation discussing high-performance 6-meter Yagis, Frank Donovan, W3LPL, stresses the need to consider the expected types of propagation and local terrain when deciding on the height at which to install the antennas. The adage of "higher is better" does not always apply and can actually hurt station performance if the resulting elevation pattern misses angles at which the desired signals are likely to be received. (See the **Radio Wave Propagation** chapter for more information.) The presentation, "Selecting, Constructing, Operating and Maintaining High Performance 6 Meter Yagis" is available as a PDF at **pvrc.org** (an online search for the title will return the location of both the video and slides).

Single-hop sporadic E (Es) is by far the most common Es propagation mode. Distances covered are typically about 1,400 to 2,000 km (800 to 1,200 miles) and occasionally 800 to 2,400 km (500 to 1,500 miles). Double-hop Es propagation in which the signal makes two successive reflections from Es clouds typically covers 2,800 to 4,000 km (1,600 to 2,400 miles) and occasionally as little as 2,000 km (1,200 miles). Finally, above-the-MUF partial reflections called "chordal hops" directly between Es clouds before returning to the ground cover from 2000 km (1,200 miles) to 10,000+ km (6,000+ miles). **Table 18.2** from data provided by K9LA summarizes these types of Es propagation.

The preferred type of 6-meter beams for these modes of propagation are a 3- to 6- (or more) element horizontal Yagis. **Figures 18.14A – D** show elevation patterns for 5-element 6-meter Yagis at heights from 25 through 100 feet. Each has advantages and disadvantages:

25 feet: A few dB poorer than 50 feet at lower angles but better at higher angles, more degraded by housing within 1000 feet, adequate height if higher is not possible

50 feet: An excellent height for almost all Es, subject to degradation by dense housing within 1000 feet

70 feet: 1 to 2 dB better for Es than at 50 feet, minor degradation by dense housing within 1000 feet, degraded by a deep null at 6 to 10 degrees

100 feet: too high for most Es propagation, unwanted deep null at 4 to 7 degrees, first lobe is very low-angle which is good for multi- and chordal-hop Es below 5 degrees

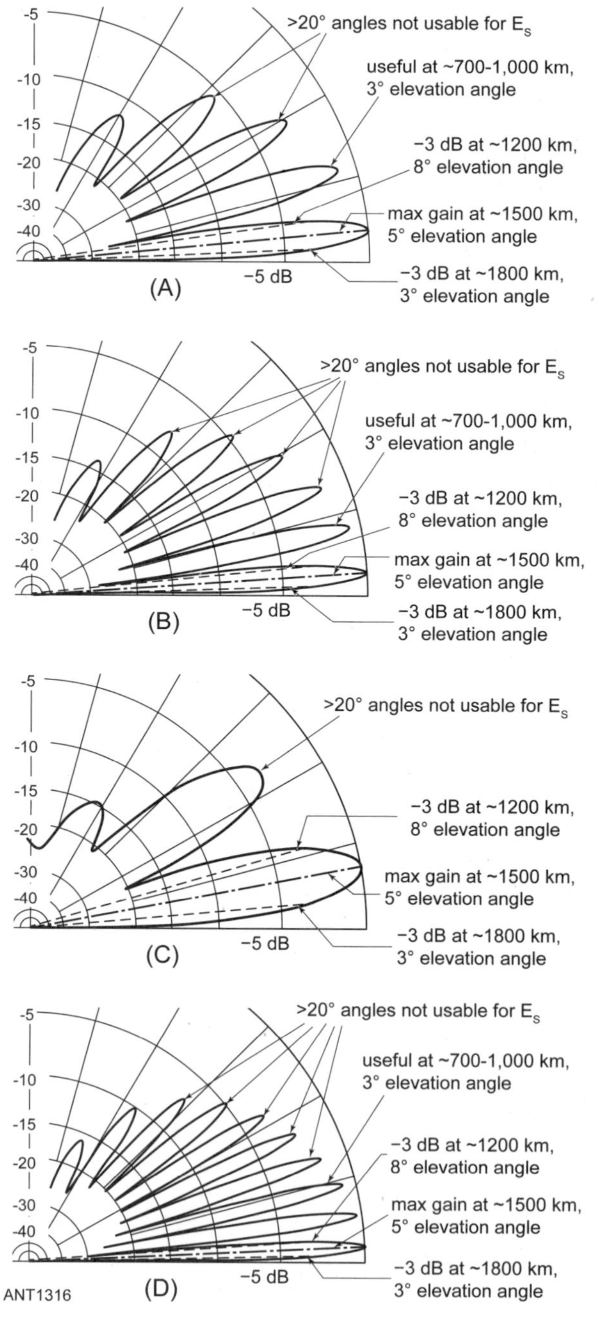

Figure 18.14 — Elevation patterns for 5-element 6-meter Yagis at heights from 25 through 100 feet. (See text.)

Table 18.2
Antenna Heights and Elevation Angles for 6-Meter Es Propagation

Elevation Angles	*Single-Hop Distance (km)*	*Optimum Height*	*Occurrence*
Below 5°	1400-2300 km	70 feet	Frequent
5° to 8°	1200-1400 km	50 feet	Very Frequent
8° to 12°	800-1200 km	25 feet	Not Frequent
12° to 15°	700-800 km	17 feet	Rare

A height of 40 to 50 feet (2 to 2½ λ) is a good choice for consistent performance. Higher antennas at 70 feet or more are appropriate for the instances of extremely low angle "DX" propagation. This height will be more useful as true F_2 propagation occurs at the peak of a solar cycle. Heights below 70 feet are also subject to increasing degradation of the elevation pattern by small buildings and dense forest within 1,000 feet. (See the discussion of Fresnel Zones in the **HF Antenna Design** chapter.)

It is important to remember that angle of arrival is determined primarily by the "last" reflection for multi-hop propagation and may vary above or below the ranges shown here. Different locations, proximity of water or mountains, and local terrain will all affect what is "best." In addition, other modes such as TEP, hybrid Es-TEP, aurora, and tropo will have their own characteristics. Be prepared to experiment to see what works best. If practical, a pair of beams — one low and one high — with patterns that complement each other would make a good system. The antennas would not have to be stacked in the usual sense, just independently selectable for the best signal at the time.

Meteor scatter or MS is another popular 6-meter mode which occurs in the E region at similar heights to Es. It displays propagation at angles like those encountered in regular Es. Because of the short-term nature of MS, a narrow azimuth pattern may not be desirable because off-axis meteors may be missed. See the sidebar "Meteor Scatter: How Much Antenna is Too Much" in the **VHF, UHF, and Microwave Antennas** chapter.

18.4 Stacking Yagis

Where suitable provision can be made for supporting them, two Yagis mounted one above the other and fed in phase can provide better performance than one long Yagi with the same theoretical or measured gain and their wider azimuth (Az) coverage can provide excellent results. The pair occupies a much smaller turning space for the same gain, and their wider elevation (El) coverage can provide excellent results.

The additional gain produced by the stack results from compression of the elevation plane lobes. Very high-angle and down-facing lobes (that could otherwise pick up unwanted man-made noise) are reduced or removed which can be an advantage where noise sources below the antennas are present. Another advantage is the retention and sometimes slight extension of a single antenna's Az beamwidth. Achieving up to 3 dB extra gain over the same or slightly wider beamwidth is why many serious DXers and contesters stack Yagis this way.

The wide Az coverage for a vertical stack often results in contacts that might be missed with a single narrow-beam long-boom Yagi pointed in a different direction. On long ionospheric paths, a stacked pair occasionally may show an *apparent* gain much greater than the measured 2 to 3 dB of stacking gain. Some of this apparent increase is due to reduced fading effects from multiple Yagis. (See also the extensive section on stacking Yagis in the **HF Antenna System Design** chapter.)

It should be reinforced that vertical stacking of horizontally polarized Yagis (H-plane stacking) does not narrow the Az beamwidth, only the El beamwidth. Horizontal stacking of the same antennas (E-plane stacking) narrows the Az beamwidth but not the El beamwidth. To narrow both beamwidths, stacking is required in both the E- and H-planes, usually implemented as a four-antenna "H-frame" array.

OPTIMUM STACKING DISTANCE

The fundamentals of Yagi stacking are laid out by Ian White, GM3SEK, in the VHF/UHF Long Yagi Workshop section of his website (**ifwtech.co.uk/g3sek/index.htm**). The goal is to separate the antennas just enough that their capture areas (or *effective aperture*) do not overlap. This allows each antenna to fully contribute to the overall performance without creating additional sidelobes. The capture area of the Yagi can be thought of as an ellipse centered on the elements of the antenna.

Assuming horizontally polarized Yagis, as stacking distance increases beyond optimum, the El pattern sidelobes will increase. This narrows the main lobe and more noise to be received from outside the main beam of the antenna. Stacking distances narrower than optimum ("under-stacking") allow a tradeoff between less gain and smaller vertical sidelobes. The tradeoff of a small amount of gain in order to gain improvements in reduced noise may be worthwhile.

Optimum vertical spacing for Yagis with booms longer than 1 λ or more is about 1 λ (984/50.1 = 19.64 feet), but this may be too much for many builders of 50-MHz antennas to handle. Worthwhile results for 50-MHz stacks can be obtained with separation as small as ½ λ (10 feet), but ⅝ λ (12 feet) is markedly better. The difference between 12 and 20 feet, however, may not be worth the added structural problems involved in the wider spacing, at least at 50 MHz. The closer spacings give lower measured gain, but the antenna patterns are cleaner in both azimuth and elevation than with 1 λ spacing. Extra gain with wider spacings is usually the objective on 144 MHz and higher-frequency bands, where the structural problems are not as severe.

Yagis can also be stacked in the same plane (collinear elements) for sharper Az directivity. A spacing of 5/8 λ between the ends of the inner elements yields approximately the maximum gain within the main lobe of the array.

Modern, low noise Yagis exhibit different characteristics from more traditional designs. (The pattern of a low-noise Yagi minimizes minor lobes that would pick up local noise.) This can result in over-stacking at much smaller distances than would otherwise be expected. The result is a very clean main lobe with secondary lobes tight against the main lobe although less than 20 dB down. For this reason, while there are stacking formulas such as that developed by DL6WU below, it is good practice to model any proposed stack in software to ensure such lobes are not present.

DL6WU STACKING FORMULA

For antennas on the same band and assuming "long-boom" antennas, a formula developed by DL6WU gives excellent results that are close to optimum for traditional Yagi designs.

$$D = \lambda / (2 \times \sin(B/2))$$

where

D = the stacking distance

λ = the wavelength (D and λ will be in the same units)

B = the –3 dB beamwidth of the antenna.

For vertical stacking distance use the antenna's El beamwidth and for horizontal stacking distance, use the Az beamwidth. (A calculator for the DL6WU formula is available online at **dg7ybn.de/Stacking/6WU_online_calc.htm**.)

The formula is approximate. For E-plane stacking (in the plane of the elements) the antennas should have a boom length greater than 0.7 λ and for H-plane stacking, a boom length greater than 2 λ. It is safest to restrict the formula's use to Yagis of at least 2 λ boom length.

FEEDING A STACK

If individual antennas of a stacked array are properly designed, they look like non-inductive resistors to the phasing system that connects them. The impedances involved can thus be treated the same as resistances in parallel.

The most popular method of feeding stacked Yagis is to use a power divider/splitter and 50 Ω coaxial lines of the same length. A power divider provides 50 Ω outputs (2, 3, 4, 6, 8, etc.) for one 50 Ω input. The advantage being that equal lengths of cable can be used to feed each antenna from the power divider. Thus, each cable is cut exactly to the required size which in turn reduces potential loss. This method of feeding is ideal when each Yagi has a direct 50 Ω feed point impedance. However, some older Yagi designs with folded dipoles and much higher impedances such as 300 Ω can be fed with parallel tuned feed lines.

Three sets of stacked dipoles are shown in **Figure 18.15**. Whether these are merely dipoles or the driven elements of Yagi arrays makes no difference for the purpose of these examples. Two 300 Ω antennas at A are 1 λ apart, resulting in a paralleled feed point impedance of 150 Ω at the center. (The actual impedance is slightly less than 150 Ω because of coupling between bays, but this can be neglected for illustrative purposes.) This value remains the same regardless of the impedance of the phasing line. Thus, any convenient line can be used for phasing, as long as the *electrical* length of each line is the same.

The velocity factor of the line must be taken into account as well. As with coax, this is subject to so much variation that it is important to make a resonance check on the actual line used. A ½ λ line is resonant both open and shorted, but the shorted condition (both ends) is usually the more convenient test condition. (See the **Transmission Line System Tech-**

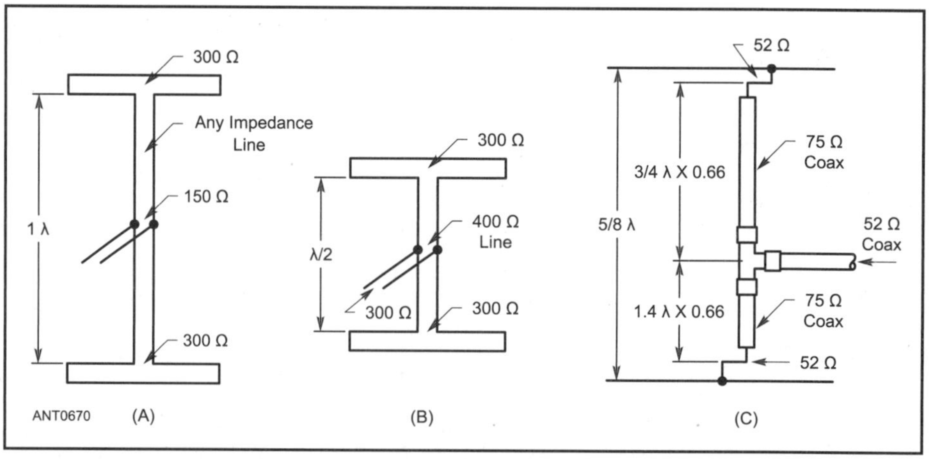

Figure 18.15 — Three methods of feeding stacked VHF arrays. A and B are for bays having balanced driven elements, where a balanced phasing line is desired. Array C has an all-coaxial matching and phasing system. If the lower section is also ¾ λ no transposition of line connections is needed. Note that Array C has gamma matches shown schematically at the 52 Ω points. They are connected to opposite sides of the driven element to add 180 degrees of phase shift between the elements and bring them back into phase.

niques chapter for more about resonant sections of feed line and synchronous transformers or Q-sections.)

The impedance transforming property of a ¼-λ line section can be used in combination matching and phasing lines, as shown in Figure 18.15B and C. At B, two bays spaced ½ λ apart are phased and matched by a 400-Ω line, acting as a double-Q section, so that a 300-Ω main transmission line is matched to two 300-Ω bays. The two halves of this phasing line could also be ¾-λ or 5/4-λ long, if such lengths serve a useful mechanical purpose. (An example is the stacking of two Yagis where the desirable spacing is more than ½ λ.)

A double-Q section of coaxial line is illustrated in Figure 18.15C. This is useful for feeding stacked bays that were designed for 50-Ω feed. A spacing of ⅝ λ is useful for small Yagis, and this is the equivalent of a full electrical wavelength of solid-dielectric coax such as RG-11.

If one phasing line is electrically ¼ λ and ¾ λ on the other, the connection to one driven element should be reversed with respect to the other to keep the RF currents in the elements in phase — the gamma match is located on opposite sides of the driven elements in Figure 18.15C. If the number of ¼ λ lengths is the same on either side of the feed point, the two connections should be in the same position, and not reversed. Practically speaking however, you can ensure proper phasing by using exactly equal lengths of line from the same roll of coax. This ensures that the velocity factor for each line is identical.

One marked advantage of coaxial phasing lines is that they can be wrapped around the vertical support, taped or grounded to it, or arranged in any way that is mechanically convenient. The spacing between bays can be set at the most desirable value, and the phasing lines placed anywhere necessary.

18.4.1 Stacking Yagis For Different Frequencies

In stacking horizontal Yagis one above the other on a single rotating support, certain considerations apply when the bays are for different bands. As a very general rule of thumb, the minimum desirable spacing is half the boom length of the higher frequency Yagi although computer modeling or manufacturer recommendations for equivalent antennas give better results.

For example, assume the stacked two-band array of **Figure 18.16A** is for 50 and 144 MHz. This vertical arrangement is commonly referred to as a "Christmas tree" because one of its shape. The 50 MHz Yagi has 5 elements on a 12-foot boom. It acts like a ground plane to the 8-element 144 MHz Yagi on a 12-foot boom directly above it.

The exact Yagi designs for the examples used in this section are in this book's online material. They may be evaluated as monoband Yagis using the *YW* (*Yagi for Windows*) program also supplied. In each case the bottom Yagi in the stack (at the top of the tower) is assumed to be 20 feet high.

Ideally, distances between antennas for 2 meters and 70 centimeters or 6 meters and 2 meters should be greater. In the two examples of Figure 18.16, the elements of the lower band antennas will conduct when the higher band is in use and this will distort pattern (best case) or create common-mode RF on the feed lines (worst case). Where 2-meter, 70-centimeter and 6-meter antennas are being stacked on the same mast, it is difficult to suggest a good combination and there is likely to be some trial and error for particular installation helped by careful modeling. One recommendation is to place 6 meters lowest, then 70 centimeters (which will not 'see' the 6-meter

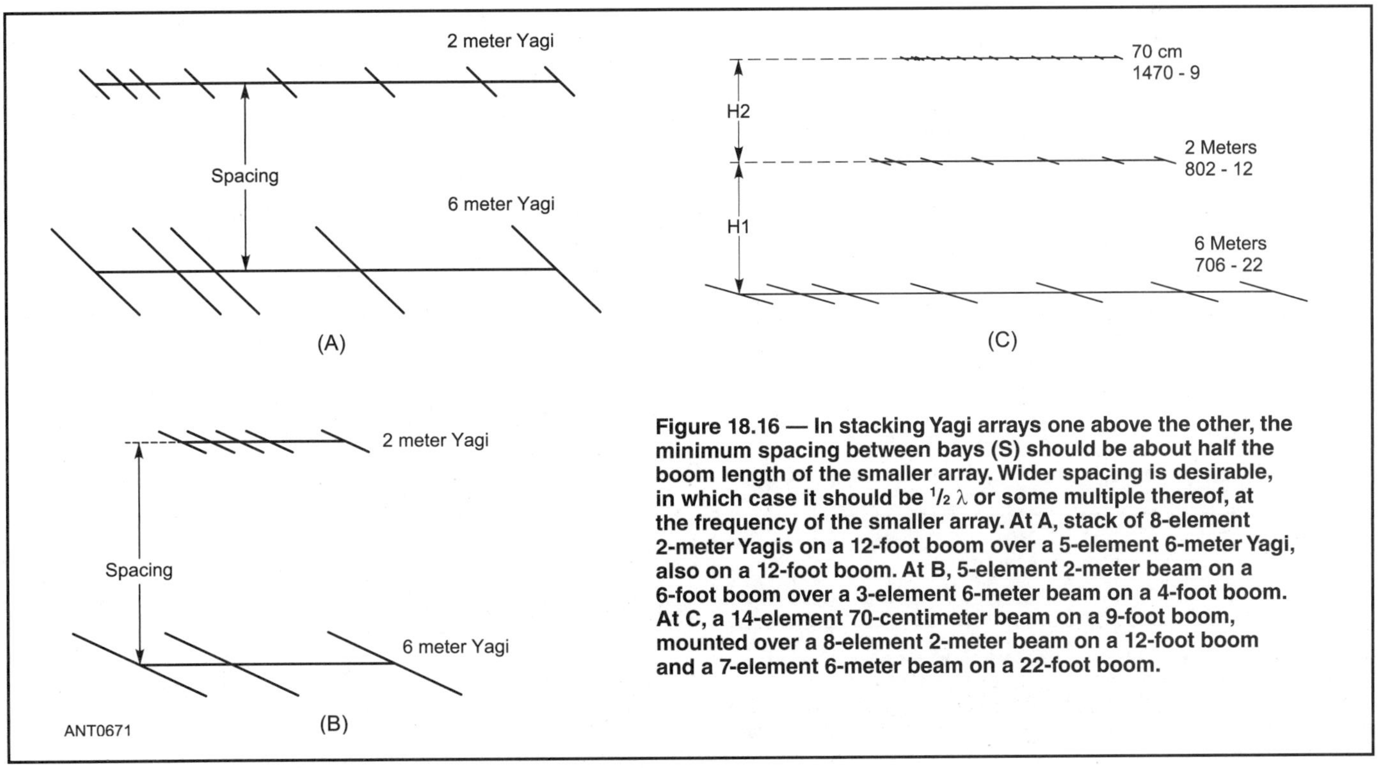

Figure 18.16 — In stacking Yagi arrays one above the other, the minimum spacing between bays (S) should be about half the boom length of the smaller array. Wider spacing is desirable, in which case it should be ½ λ or some multiple thereof, at the frequency of the smaller array. At A, stack of 8-element 2-meter Yagis on a 12-foot boom over a 5-element 6-meter Yagi, also on a 12-foot boom. At B, 5-element 2-meter beam on a 6-foot boom over a 3-element 6-meter beam on a 4-foot boom. At C, a 14-element 70-centimeter beam on a 9-foot boom, mounted over a 8-element 2-meter beam on a 12-foot boom and a 7-element 6-meter beam on a 22-foot boom.

antenna in the same way as a 2-meter antenna), then separate 70 centimeters and 2 meters by the maximum distance possible with the 2-meter antenna on top to help minimize this issue.

The tables of antenna performance by VE7BQH (see the **VHF, UHF, and Microwave Antennas** chapter) also include recommend stacking distances. Comparable antennas can be used as approximations for a homebuilt or unlisted antenna. For antennas on different bands, separate the antennas by at least one-half the recommended stacking distance for the higher-frequency antenna.

VE7BQH Antenna Performance Tables

Similar to the Sherwood Engineering receiver performance tables (**sherweng.com/table.html**) that show dynamic range and other performance metrics for popular transceivers, Lionel Edwards, VE7BQH, has compiled the performance data of a large number of antennas for 50, 144, and 432 MHz. (a.k.a. – the VH List) The tables are maintained online at **dxmaps.com/VE7BQH.html** and are also available as downloadable spreadsheet files from **bigskyspaces.com/w7gj/6mTable.htm**.

SWR CHANGE IN A MULTI-FREQUENCY STACK

Modern computer modeling programs reveal that while the feed point SWR can indeed be affected from nearby lower-frequency antennas, by far the greatest degradation is in the forward gain and rearward pattern of the higher-frequency Yagi when the booms are closely spaced. In fact, the SWR curve is usually not affected enough to make it a good diagnostic indicator of interaction between the two Yagis.

Figure 18.17 shows an overlay of the SWR curves across the 2-meter band for four configurations: an 8-element 2-meter Yagi (802-12) by itself, and then over a 5-element 6-meter Yagi (506-12) with spacings between the booms of 1, 2, 4 and 6 feet. The SWR curves are similar — it would be difficult to see any difference between these configurations using typical amateur SWR indicators for anything but the very closest (1-foot) spacing. For example, the SWR curve for the 2-foot spacing case is virtually indistinguishable from that of the Yagi by itself, while the forward gain has dropped more than 0.6 dB because of interactions with the 6-meter Yagi below it.

In fact, SWR curves are usually not affected enough to make a good diagnostic indicator of interaction between Yagis. As a Yagi antenna is affected by other obstructions within its aperture, the first evidence of degradation is seen in the low-level lobe structure typically around 90 degrees off of the boresight heading. As the obstruction or interaction increases, then larger sidelobes are affected and you may start to see a slight drop off in forward gain, as more power gets concentrated in sidelobes. The typical SWR curves will not change to any great degree while this is going on.

GAIN AND PATTERN DEGRADATION DUE TO STACKING

Figure 18.18 shows four overlaid rectangular plots of the azimuth response from 0 to 180 degrees for the 8-element 2-meter Yagi described above, spaced 1, 2, 4, and 6 feet over a 5-element 6-meter beam. The rectangular presentation gives more detail than a polar plot. The most closely spaced configuration (with 1-foot spacing between the booms) shows the

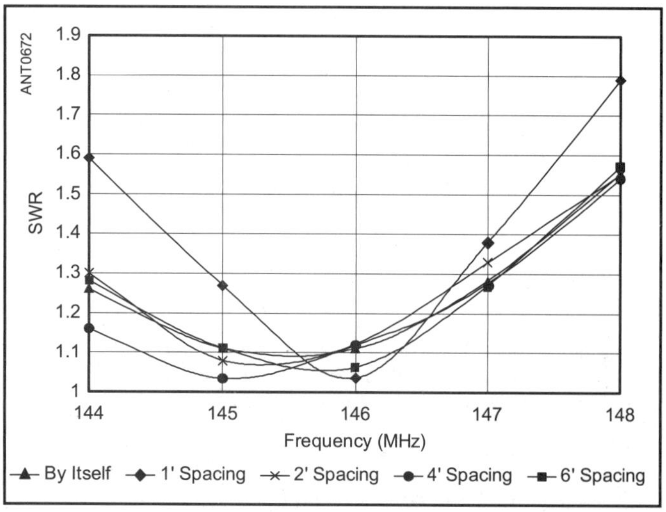

Figure 18.17 — SWR curves for different boom spacing between 8-element 2-meter Yagi on 12-foot boom, over a 5-element 6-meter Yagi on a 12-foot boom. For spacings greater than 1 foot between the booms, differences between the SWR curves are difficult to discern.

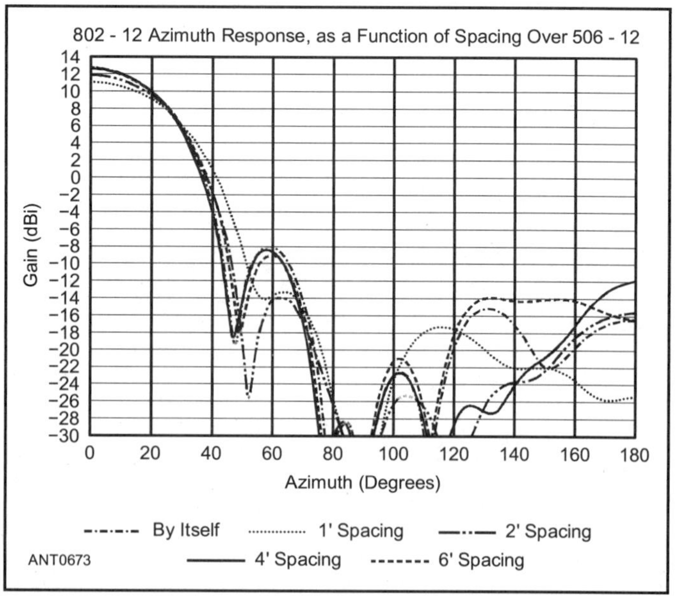

Figure 18.18 — Plots of the 8-element 2-meter Yagi's azimuth response from 0° to 180° for spacing distances from 1 to 6 feet. The sidelobe at about 60° varies about 6 dB over the range of boom spacings, while the shape of worst-case F/R curve varies considerably due to interactions with the lower 6-meter beam. The gain for the 1-foot spacing is degraded by more than 3 dB compared to the 2-meter antenna by itself.

largest degradation in the forward gain, a drop of 1.7 dB. The worst-case front-to-rear ratio for the 6-foot spacing is 29.0 dB, while it is 36.4 dB for the 1-foot spacing — actually better than the F/R for the 8-element 2-meter Yagi by itself. Performance change due to the nearby presence of other Yagis can be enormously complicated (and sometimes unintuitive).

What happens when a different kind of 6-meter Yagi is mounted below the 8-element 2-meter Yagi? **Figure 18.19** compares the change in forward gain and the worst-case F/R performance as a function of spacing between the booms for two varieties of 6-meter Yagis: the 5-element design on a 12-foot boom (506-12) and a 7-element Yagi on a 22-foot boom (706-22). The spacing of "0 feet" represents the 8-element 2-meter Yagi when it is used alone, with no other antenna nearby. This sets the reference expectations for gain and F/R.

The most severe degradation occurs for the 1-foot spacing, as you might imagine, for both the 12 and 22-foot boom lengths. Over the 5-element 6-meter Yagi, the 2-meter gain doesn't recover to the reference level of the 8-element 2-meter beam by itself until the spacing is greater than 9 feet. However, the gain is within 0.25 dB of the reference level for spacings of 3 feet or more. Interestingly, the F/R is higher than that of the 2-meter antenna by itself for the 1, 2 and 5-foot spacings and for spacings greater than 11 feet. The 2-meter F/R in the presence of the 12-foot 5-element 6-meter Yagi remains above 20 dB for spacings beyond 1 feet.

Overall, the 2-meter beam performs reasonably well for spacings of 3 feet or more over the 5-element 6-meter Yagi. Put another way, the 2-meter beam's performance is degraded only slightly for boom spacings greater than 3 feet. A spacing of 3 feet is less than the old rule of thumb that the minimum spacing between booms be greater than one-half the boom length of the higher-frequency Yagi, which in this case is 6 feet long.

For the 7-element 6-meter Yagi, the 2-meter gain recovers to the reference level for spacings beyond 7 feet, but the F/R is degraded below the reference level for all spacings shown in Figure 18.19. If we use a gain reduction criterion of less than 0.25 dB and a 20-dB F/R level as the minimum acceptable level, then the spacing must be 5 feet or more over the larger 6-meter Yagi. Again, this is less than the rule of thumb that the minimum spacing between booms be greater than one-half the boom length of the higher-frequency Yagi.

Now, let's try a smaller setup of 2- and 6-meter Yagis stacked vertically in a Christmas-tree configuration to see if the rule of thumb for spacing the booms still holds. **Figure 18.20** shows the performance curves versus boom spacing for a 5-element 2-meter Yagi (502-4) on a 4-foot boom stacked over a 3-element 6-meter Yagi on a 6-foot boom (306-6). Again, the 1-foot spacing produces a substantial gain reduction of about 1.3 dB compared to the reference gain when the 2-meter Yagi is used by itself. Beyond a boom spacing of 3 feet the 2-meter gain drops less than 0.25 dB from the reference level of the 2-meter Yagi by itself and the F/R remains above about 20 dB. In this example, the simple rule of thumb that the minimum spacing between booms be greater than half the boom length (half of 4 feet) of the higher-frequency Yagi does not hold up. However, the same minimum spacing of 3 feet we found for the larger 2-meter Yagi remains true. Three feet spacing is almost 0.5 λ between the booms at the higher frequency.

ADDING A 70-CENTIMETER YAGI TO THE CHRISTMAS TREE

Let's get more ambitious and set up a larger VHF/UHF Christmas tree, with a 14-element 70-centimeter Yagi on a 9-foot boom (1470-9) at the top, mounted 5 feet over an 8-element 2-meter Yagi on a 12-foot boom (802-12). At the bottom of the stack (at the top of the tower) is either the 5-element 6-meter beam on a 12-foot boom (506-12), or a 7-element 6-meter beam on a 22-foot boom (706-22). See Figure 18.15C. As before, we will vary the spacing between the 70-centimeter Yagi and the 2-meter Yagi below it to assess the interactions that degrade the 70-centimeter performance.

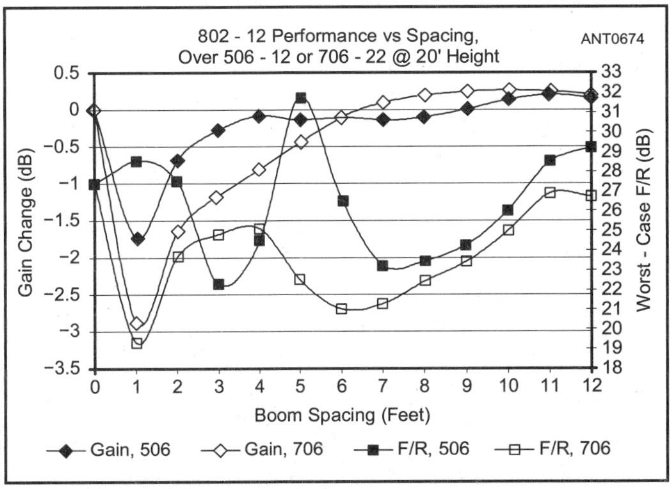

Figure 18.19 — Plot of 8-element 2-meter Yagi's gain and worst-case F/R as a function of distance over two types of 6-meter beams, one on a 12-foot boom and the other on a 22-foot boom. Beyond a spacing of about 5 feet the performance is degraded a minimal amount.

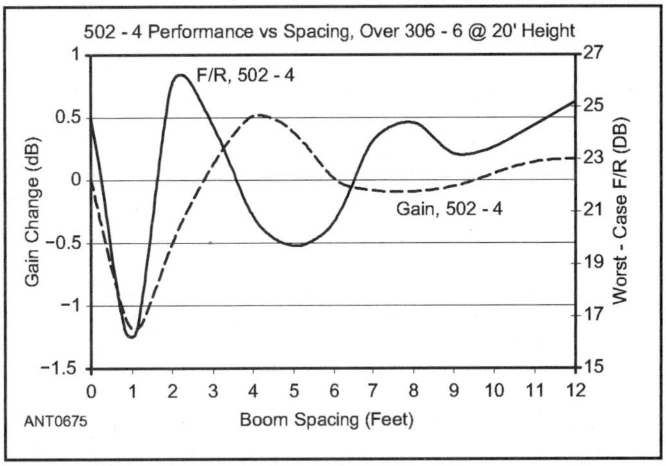

Figure 18.20 — Plot of gain and worst-case F/R of a 5-element 2-meter Yagi on a 4-foot boom as a function of distance over a 3-element 6-meter beam on a 6-foot boom. Beyond a spacing of about 3 feet the performance is degraded a minimal amount.

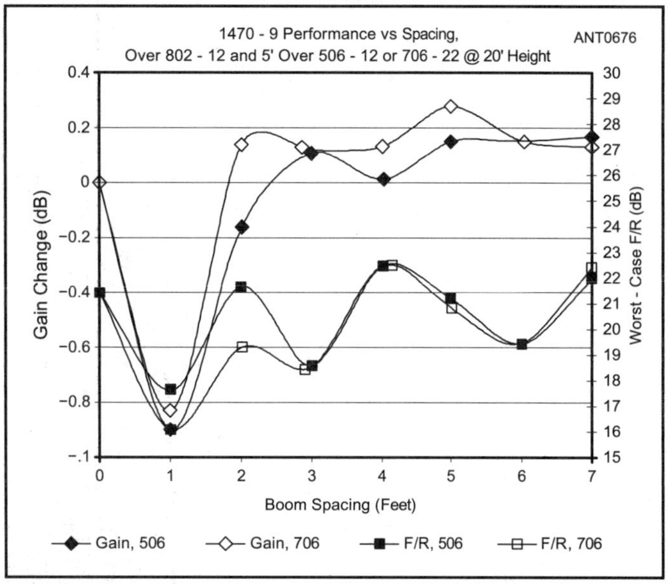

Figure 18.21 — Performance of a 14-element 70-centimeter Yagi on a 9-foot boom, mounted a variable distance over an 8-element 2-meter Yagi on a 12-foot boom, which is mounted 5 feet above either a 5-element 6-meter Yagi on a 12-foot boom or a 7-element 6-meter Yagi on a 22-foot boom. Beyond a spacing of about 4 feet, the performance of the 70-centimeter beam is degraded a minimal amount.

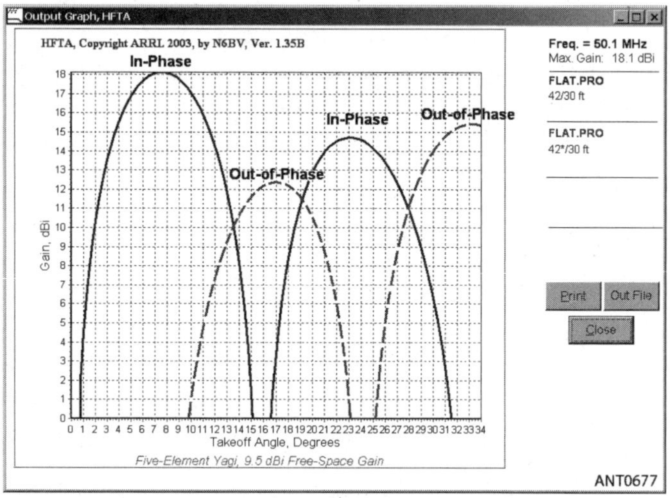

Figure 18.22 — *HFTA* comparison plots of the elevation responses for two 5-element 6-meter Yagis mounted at 42 and 30 feet above flat ground, when they are fed in-phase and out-of-phase. By switching the phasing (adding a half-wavelength of coax to one of the antennas), the elevation angle can be controlled to enhance performance when a sporadic-E cloud is nearly overhead.

Figure 18.21 compares the change in gain and F/R curves as a function of boom spacings between the 70-centimeter and 2-meter Yagis for the two different 6-meter Yagis (with a fixed distance of 5 feet between the 2-meter and 6-meter Yagis). In this example, the 70-centimeter Yagi was designed to be an intrinsic 50 Ω feed, where the F/R has been compromised to some extent. Still, the F/R is greater than 20 dB when the 70-centimeter Yagi is used by itself.

For spacings greater than 4 feet between the 70-centimeter and 2-meter booms, the 70-centimeter gain is equal to or even slightly greater than that of the 70-centimeter antenna by itself. The increase of gain indicates that the elevation pattern of the 70-centimeter antenna is slightly compressed by the presence of the other Yagis below it. The F/R stays above at 19.5 dB for spacings greater than or equal to 4 feet. This falls just below our desired lower limit of 20 dB, but it is highly doubtful that anyone would notice this 0.5 dB drop in actual operation. A spacing of 4 feet between booms falls under the rule of thumb that the minimum spacing be at least half the boom length of the higher-frequency Yagi, which in this case is 9 feet.

What should be obvious in this discussion is that you should model the exact configuration you plan to build to avoid unnecessary performance degradation.

18.4.2 Stacking Same-Frequency Yagis

This subject has been examined in some detail in the **HF Antenna System Design** chapter. The same basic principles hold at VHF and UHF as they do on HF. That is, the gain increases gradually with increasing spacing between the booms, and then falls off gradually past a certain spacing distance.

At HF, it is important to avoid nulls in the antenna's elevation response, covering all the angles needed for geographic areas of interest. At VHF/UHF, propagation is usually at low elevation angles for most propagation modes, and signals are often extremely weak. Thus, achieving maximum gain is a common design objective for a VHF/UHF stack.

However, if the antennas are installed in an environment with high noise levels, giving up some forward gain to reduce noise may also be effective. For example, it is possible for each 0.1 dB of gain reduction to result in 1.5 dB of noise reduction to the rear of the antenna. Thus, giving up 0.4 dB of gain could result in a full S-unit (4 × 1.5 = 6 dB) of noise reduction. This discriminates against interference and noise sources.

Six meter sporadic-E can sometimes occur at high elevation angles, especially if the E_s cloud is overhead, or nearly overhead. Since sporadic-E is exactly that, sporadic, it's not a good design practice to try to cover a wide range of elevation angles, as you must often do at HF to cover large geographic areas. On 6 meters, you can change to high-angle coverage when necessary. For example, you might switch to a separate Yagi mounted at a low height, or you might provide means to feed stacked antennas out-of-phase. **Figure 18.22** shows an *HFTA* (*HF Terrain Assessment*) plot of two 5-element 6-meter Yagis, fed either in-phase or out-of-phase to cover a much wider range of elevation angles than the in-phase stack alone.

Figure 18.23A shows the change in gain for four 2-meter stacked designs, as a function of the spacing in wavelengths between the booms. The 3-element Yagi is mounted on a 2-foot boom (occupying 0.28 λ of that boom). The 5-element Yagi is on a 4-foot boom (0.51 λ of the boom), while the 8-element Yagi is on a 12-foot boom (1.72 λ of boom). The biggest antenna in the group has 16 elements, on a 27-foot boom (4.0

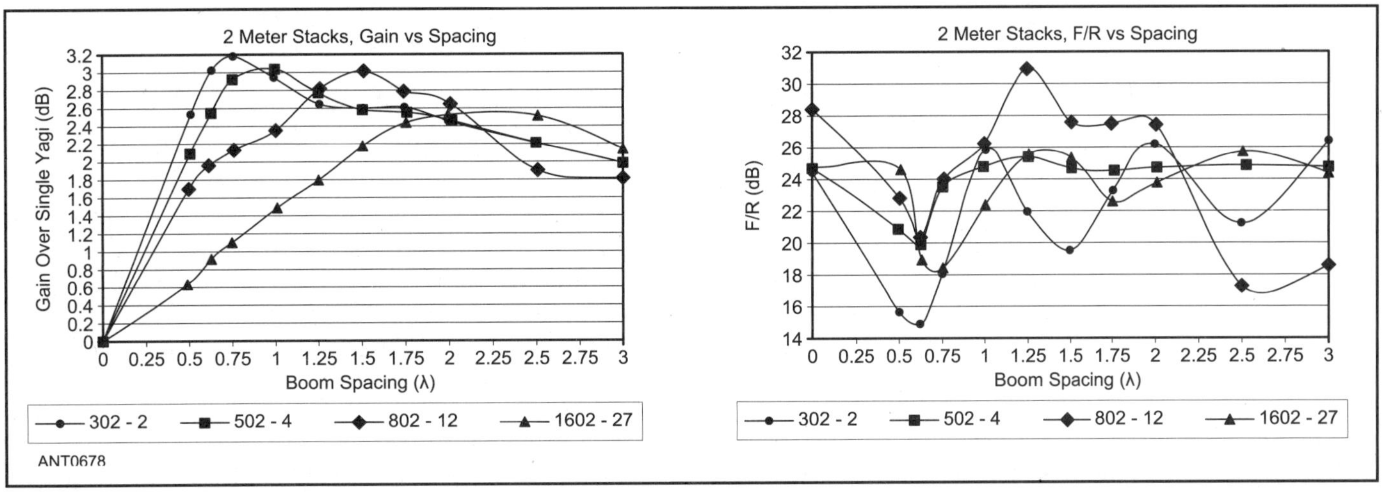

Figure 18.23 — The change in gain for four 2-meter stack designs as a function of the spacing in wavelengths between the booms. The exact spacing between booms is not overly critical with gain relatively stable around the peaks. F/R is more sensitive to spacing. (See text for detailed discussion.)

λ of boom). This range of boom lengths pretty much covers the practical range of antennas used by hams.

The stack of two 3-element Yagis peaks at 3.2 dB of additional gain over a single Yagi for 0.75 λ spacing between the booms. Further increases in spacing see the gain change gradually drop off. Figure 18.23B shows the worst-case F/R of the four stacks, again as a function of boom length. The F/R of a single 3-element Yagi is just over 24 dB, but in the presence of the second 3-element Yagi in the stack, the F/R of the pair oscillates between 15 to 26 dB, finally remaining consistently over the desired 20-dB level for spacings greater than about 1.7 λ, where the gain has fallen about 0.6 dB from the peak possible gain. A boom spacing of 1.7 λ at 146 MHz is 11.5 feet. Thus, you must compromise in choosing the boom spacing between achieving maximum gain and the best pattern.

The increase in gain of the stack of two 5-element Yagis peaks at a spacing of about 1 λ (6.7 feet), where the F/R is an excellent 25 dB. Having more elements on a particular length of boom aids in holding a more consistent F/R in the presence of the second antenna.

The gain increase for the bigger stack of 8-element Yagis peaks at a spacing of about 1.5 λ (10.1 feet), where the F/R is more than 27 dB. The 16-element Yagi's gain increase is 2.6 dB for a spacing of about 2.25 λ (15.2 feet), where the F/R remains close to 25 dB. The stacking distance of 15.2 feet for an antenna with a 27-foot-long boom may be a real challenge physically, requiring a very sturdy rotating mast to withstand wind pressures without bending.

These examples show that the exact spacing between booms is not overly critical since the gain varies relatively slowly around the peak. Figure 18.23A shows that the boom spacing needed to achieve peak gain from a stack increase when higher-gain (longer-boom) individual antennas are used in that stack. It also shows that the increase in maximum gain from stacking decreases for long-boom antennas. Figure 18.23B shows that beyond boom spacings of about 1 λ, the F/R pattern holds well for Yagi designs with booms longer than about 0.5 λ, which is about 4 feet at 146 MHz.

The plots in Figure 18.23 are representative of typical modern Yagis. You could simply implement these designs as is, and you'll achieve good results. However, it is recommended that you model any specific stack you design, just to make sure. Since the boom spacings are displayed in terms of wavelength, you can extend the results for 2-meters to other bands, provided that you use properly scaled Yagi designs to the other bands too.

You can even tweak the element dimensions and spacings of each Yagi used in a stack to optimize the rearward pattern for a particular stacking distance. This strategy can work out well at VHF/UHF, where stacks are often configured for best gain (and pattern) and are "hard-wired" with fixed lengths of feed lines permanently joined together at the junctions.

This contrasts with the situation at HF (and even on 6 meters). The HF operator usually wants flexibility to select individual Yagis (or combinations of Yagis) from the stack, to match the array's takeoff angle with ionospheric propagation conditions. The designer of a flexible HF stack thus usually doesn't try to redo the element lengths and spacings of the Yagis to optimize a particular stack.

OPTIMIZING YAGI STACKS AT VHF AND ABOVE

Starting with the DL6WU stacking formula discussed at the beginning of this section, further optimization of stacking distances is required in order to achieve the cleanest, tightest symmetrical patterns, maximizing front to rear (F/R) and front to back (F/B), and eliminating any "spike" lobes appearing in the elevation or azimuth patterns.

For a detailed discussion of the issues involved at this level of optimization, see the article "Development and Real World Replication of Modern Yagi Antennas (III) — Manual Optimisation of Multiple Yagi Arrays" by Justin Johnson, GØKSC, available in the online material. It is important to note that the optimization described in the article is not being carried out for absolute best sky temperature and/or G/T although the results prove not to be too far away from optimum in these areas.

UPTILT OF STACK PATTERN

Repeater system builders with antennas on very tall towers often design the antenna elevation pattern to have some downtilt of a few degrees. (**repeater-builder.com/antenna/downtilt.html**) This balances coverage at long distances with coverage in areas nearer the tower that may be below the antenna's main lobe. Similarly, high-gain 50 MHz antenna systems with narrow elevation patterns focused at the horizon may miss signals arriving at a few degrees above the horizon. In this case, uptilt in the antenna radiation pattern is needed.

Tropospheric signals arrive at some small vertical angle at VHF and UHF, not at zero degrees. F_2 or Es propagation on 50 MHz will also produce signals with a small vertical angle above the horizon. Local signals and noise will arrive at much lower elevation angles, being mostly line of sight. Providing a slight amount of uptilt to an antenna pattern on 50 MHz can improve SNR for Es or over-the-horizon signals during periods of intense local interference (as during a VHF contest) or when the station is receiving local power line or other man-made noise. (See **directivesystems.com/information/tech-notes/50-mhz-4-yagi-contesting-array-2** for a more complete discussion.)

Uptilt is created in an elevation pattern of two or more vertically stacked beam antennas by adding feed line to the higher antennas, delaying the signals for higher antennas as if they were moved backward horizontally in a tilted array. The diagram of **Figure 18.24** shows how to calculate the necessary delay for the uptilt angle, θ:

$$\text{Tan}(\theta) = \frac{\textit{Free space delay}}{\textit{Stack separation}} \text{ or}$$

$$\textit{Free space delay} = \textit{Stack separation} \times \tan(\theta)$$

Free space delay is calculated as a length and must be in the same units of length as stack separation, such as feet or meters.

For example, assume that a 5 degree uptilt is needed with a stack separation of 24 feet. Using the formula, the free space delay is 24 feet × tan (5 degrees) = 24 × 0.0875 = 2.1 feet. To determine the physical length of feed line that must be added to the higher antenna, multiply free space delay length by the feed line's VF since the signals move slower in the feed line. Assuming LMR-400 with a VF of 0.85 is used, the physical length of cable required is 2.1 feet × 0.85 = 1.79 ft or 1 ft 9.4 inches. Add this amount of feed line to the second-lowest antenna, twice this amount to the third antenna, three times this amount to the fourth antenna, and so on.

18.4.3 Short-Yagi Vertical Stacks

VHF arrival angles are typically quite low and do not vary anywhere near as much as seen at HF frequencies. At 144 MHz and above, the arrival angles are between 0 and 3 degrees typically and depend on tropospheric scatter arrival angles. With enhanced tropo events such as inversion layer formation and ducting, the arrival angle varies over only a very few degrees very close to the horizon. To achieve higher gain at those low elevation angles, a long Yagi will concentrate energy across a very narrow horizontal angle. This can cause all sorts of operational problems.

At the same time, the elevation lobes of a single Yagi contain wasted energy at angles above 5 degrees that will not contribute to a stronger signal at the other end of the path. In addition, a concentrated main lobe will not illuminate much geographical area. This combination can make contacts with other stations outside of the main lobe that much more difficult. Mechanically, very long Yagis can stress rotating systems and stress towers due to their added lengths.

A vertical array of very short Yagis can be used to eliminate many of the problems mentioned for much longer antennas. If a short Yagi is optimized for a clean pattern, the net effect is a broadening of the main lobe as the sidelobes are reduced. Reducing any lobes in the H plane will increase the vertical pattern beamwidth and importantly, will allow a wider stacking distance over that of a less clean design. The wider stacking distances allow a greater improvement in array gain over that of the single antenna recovering gain lost compared to the long Yagis.

The desirable wide horizontal beamwidth remains with a vertical stack of Yagis, while the vertical lobes are constricted in the H plane due to the stacking effects. Generally, a vertical array of four or more short Yagis will eliminate much wasted energy in all of the vertical sidelobes. Having a wider horizontal beamwidth from such action can minimize wear and tear on rotator systems as antenna peaking becomes less important. As an example, a well-designed 5-antenna stack of short Yagis can have a –3 dB beamwidth of over 52 degrees and a –10 dB beamwidth approaching 90 degrees. A drawback of the wider beamwidth can be seen when there is external noise present. Noise will be picked up over a wider beamwidth with a vertical array of short Yagis as opposed to the very narrow pattern of a long Yagi.

Vertical arrays of wide beamwidth Yagis that are fixed toward areas of high activity can be very beneficial. Fixed arrays of short Yagis can also be end-mounted on a single tower leg to simplify installation and provide excellent performance with few mechanical problems. Two fixed arrays are shown in **Figure 18.25**.

Another positive feature of side-mounted antennas involves rain static effects. The side-mounted array will be located below the tower top. Static charges will be dissipated by antennas on the top of the tower, leaving the side-mounted array relatively immune to static buildup.

To achieve the benefits of such an array, it is very important to design a proper feed system that keeps losses to a minimum. Larger low-loss coax may be easily accommodated along the tower. All long runs of coaxial cable should be matched at 50 Ω and any matching sections should be quarter-wave power dividers to minimize loss in the matching system. Very wide bandwidths and low losses can be maintained with large arrays when power dividers and larger coaxial cables are employed.

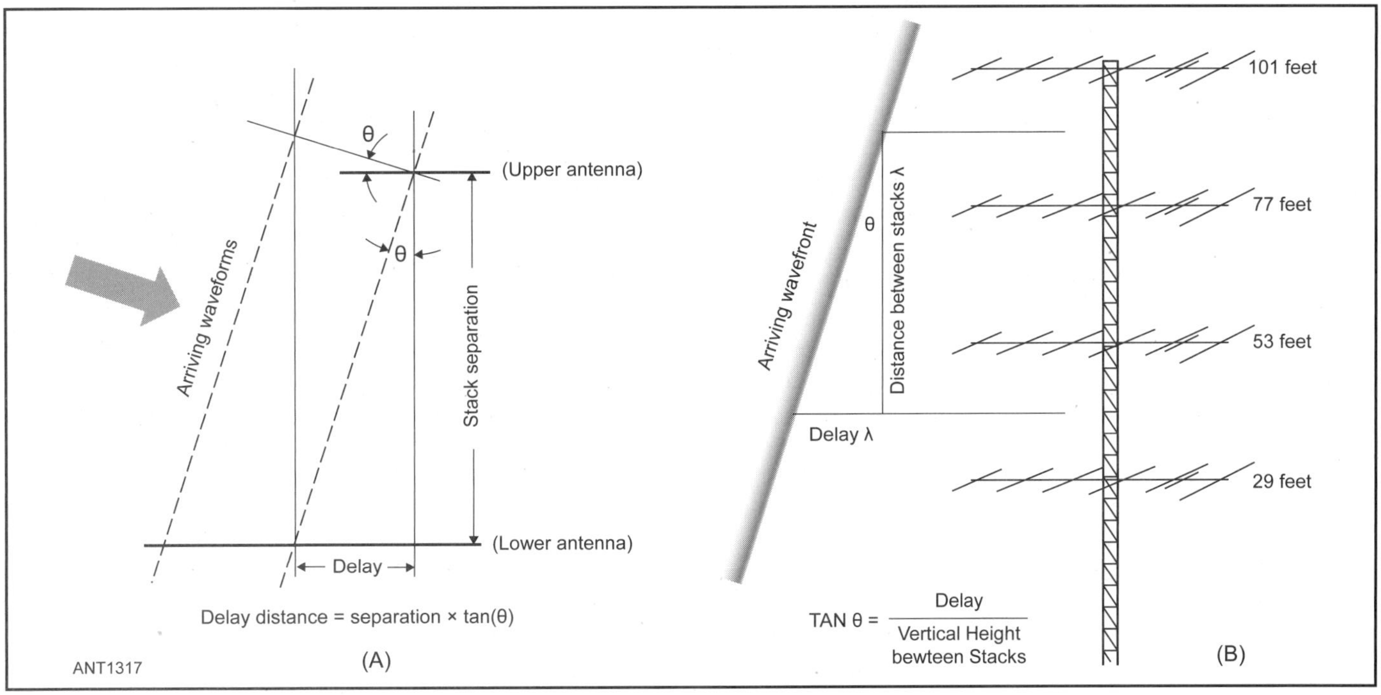

Figure 18.24 — Adding progressive amounts of delay to higher antennas in a stack creates uptilt in the stack's elevation pattern focus.

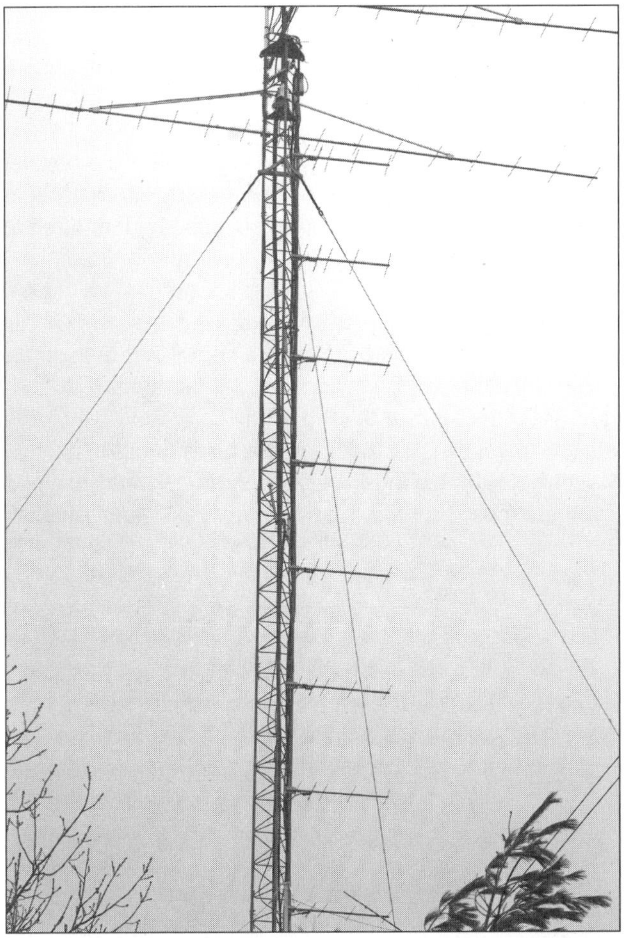

Figure 18.25 — An eight-high vertical array (above) of short five-element 222 MHz Yagis. Boom length is 48 inches and vertical beamwidth is approximately 7 degrees. A four-high vertical array for 432 MHz is shown at right. (Photos courtesy of Dave Olean, K1WHS)

18.4.4 Stacking Stacks of Different-Frequency Yagis

The investment in a tower is usually substantial, and most hams want to put as many antennas as possible on a tower, if interaction between the antennas can be held to a reasonable level. Really ambitious weak-signal VHF/UHF enthusiasts may want "stacked stacks" — sets of stacked Yagis that cover different bands. For example, a VHF contester might want a stack of two 8-element 2-meter Yagis mounted on the same rotating mast as a stack of two 5-element 6-meter Yagis. Let's assume that the boom length of the 8-element 2-meter Yagis is 12 feet (1.78 λ). We'll assume a boom length of 12 feet (0.61 λ) for the 5-element 6-meter Yagis.

From Figure 18.23, we find the stacking distance between the 8-element 2-meter beams for peak gain and good pattern is 1.5 λ, or 10 feet, but adequate performance can be had for a boom spacing of 0.75 λ, which is 5 feet on 2 meters.

The boom spacing for two 5-element 6-meter beams is 1 λ for peak stacking gain, but a compromise of 0.625 λ (12 feet) still yields an acceptable gain increase of 2 dB over a single Yagi. The overall height of the rotating mast sticking out of the top of the tower is thus set by the 0.625 λ stacking distance on 6 meters, at 12 feet. In-between the 6-meter Yagis at the bottom and top of the rotating mast we will mount the 2-meter Yagi stack. With only 12 feet available on the mast, the spacing for symmetric placement of the two 2-meter Yagis in-between the 6-meter Yagis dictates a distance of only 4 feet between the 2-meter beams. This is less than optimal.

The performance of the 2-meter stack in this "stack within a stack" is affected by the close spacing, but the interactions are not disastrous. The stacking gain is 1.62 dB more than the gain for a single 8-element 2-meter Yagi and the F/R remains above 20 dB across the 2-meter band.

On 6 meters, the stacking gain for two 5-element 6-meter Yagis spaced 12 feet apart is 2.2 dB more than the gain of a single Yagi, while the F/R pattern remains about 20 dB over the weak-signal portion of the 6-meter band. As described in the **HF Antenna System Design** chapter, stacking gives more advantages than merely a gain increase, and 6-meter propagation does require coverage of a range of elevation angles because much of the time ionospheric modes are involved.

Noise Rejection Using Stacked Quads

ARRL Antenna Book contributor Justin Johnson, GØKSC, has written a short article describing his experimental results as to how very high front-to-side ratios can be achieved with a pair of stacked quads. By changing the feed points of the quads from the traditionally symmetric arrangement, useful improvements in the radiation pattern were achieved. The article is available in this chapter's online material.

Increasing the length of the rotating mast to 18 feet sticking out of the top of the tower will increase performance, particularly on 2 meters. The stacking gain on 6 meters will increase to 2.3 dB while the F/R decreases to 18.5 dB, modest changes both. The 18-foot mast allows the 2-meter Yagis to be spaced 6 feet from each other and 6 feet away from both top and bottom 6-meter antennas. The stacking gain goes to 2.14 dB and the F/R approaches 27 dB in the weak-signal portion of the 2-meter band.

It should be noted that it is possible for a VHF/UHF stack to be too high above ground. Pattern break-up can then occur, resulting in multiple lobes with deep nulls between them. On receive, this would result in fast 'chopping' or fading. This can be managed through boom length selection and the use of identical Yagis but will not completely cure the problem. Careful modeling should be done to ensure this does not occur. As a rule, a VHF or UHF stack needs to be high enough that there is a clear horizon in each direction but no higher.

Whether the modest increase in stacking gain is worth the cost and mechanical complexity of stacking two 2-meter Yagis between a stack of 6-meter Yagis is a choice left to the operator. Certainly, the cost and weight of a rotating mast that is 20 feet long (18 feet out of the top of the tower and 2 feet down inside the tower), a mast that must be sturdy enough to support the antennas in high winds without bending, should give pause to even the most enthusiastic 6-meter weak-signal operator.

18.5 References and Bibliography

A. Barnes, *International Microwave Handbook*, 2nd Ed., RSGB, 2008.

H. Jasik, *Antenna Engineering Handbook*, 2nd Ed. (New York: McGraw-Hill, 1984).

H.W. Johnson and M. Graham, *High Speed Digital Design* (Prentice Hall, 1993).

Microwaves 101, **microvaves101.com**.

M. Pozar, *Microwave Engineering*, 2nd Ed., Wiley, 1998, pp, 537-543.

J. Reisert, "VHF/UHF World," *Ham Radio* column.

P. Wade, "Microwavelengths," *QST* column.

B. Wadell, *Transmission Line Design Handbook*, ISBN: 0-89006-436-9.

Z. Lau, "RF: A 70-cm Power Divider," *QEX*, July/Aug. 1999, pp. 56-58.

Z. Lau, "RF: Feeding Open-Wire Line at VHF and UHF," *QEX*, Jan./Feb. 2000, pp. 59-63.

The ARRL UHF/Microwave Experimenter's Manual (Newington: ARRL, 2006). (This book is out of print.)

TABLE OF CONTENTS

Chapter 19 — Online Material

Articles

- "6 Meter 4 Element Portable Yagi" by Zack Lau, W1VT (plus separate element design drawing)
- "A 6-Meter Portable Yagi Antenna" by Scott McCann, W3MEO
- "A One Person, Safe, Portable and Easy to Erect Antenna Mast" by Bob Dixon, W8ERD
- "A Portable 2-Element Triband Yagi" by Markus Hansen, VE7CA
- "A Portable End-Fed Half-Wave Antenna for 80 Meters" by Rick Littlefield, K1BQT
- "A Portable Inverted V Antenna" by Joseph Littlepage, WE5Y
- "A Simple and Portable HF Vertical Travel Antenna" by Phil Salas, AD5X
- "A Simple HF-Portable Antenna" by Phil Salas, AD5X
- "A Small, Portable Dipole for Field Use" by Ron Herring, W7HD
- "A Super Duper Five Band Portable Antenna" by Clarke Cooper, K8BP
- "A Two-Element Yagi for 18 MHz" by Martin Hedman, SMØDTK
- "An Off Center End Fed Dipole for Portable Operation on 40 to 6 Meters" by Kai Siwiak, KE4PT
- "Compact 40 Meter HF Loop for Your Recreational Vehicle" by John Portune, W6NBC
- "Fishing for DX with a Five Band Portable Antenna" by Barry Strickland, AB4QL
- "Getting the Antenna Aloft" by Stuart Thomas, KB1HQS
- Ladder Mast and PVRC Mount
- "The Black Widow — A Portable 15 Meter Beam" by Allen Baker, KG4JJH
- "The Ultimate Portable HF Vertical Antenna" by Phil Salas, AD5X
- "The W4SSY Spudgun" by Byron Black, W4SSY
- "Two Portable 6-Meter Antennas" by Markus Hansen, VE7CA
- "Tuning Electrically Short Antennas for Field Operation" by Ulrich Rohde, N1UL, and Kai Siwiak, KE4PT
- "Zip Cord Antennas and Feed Lines for Portable Applications" by William Parmley, KR8L
- "A Skyhook for the 90s"
- "Dual Band Wire Beam for 17 and 12 Meters" by Allen Baker, KG4JJH
- "The Black Widow - A Portable 15 Meter Beam" by Allen Baker, KG4JJH

Chapter 19

Portable Antenna Systems

As with any radio operation, the antenna is the single most important piece of equipment in a portable setup. Portable operation is usually taken to mean a temporary operating site but "temporary" can be applied to anything from a 30-minute visit to a several-day installation. The station might be used to activate a park or summit, for "hilltopping" during a VHF+ contest, for public service or emergency communications, or during Field Day. Transportation to and from the site can be by vehicle, allowing substantial amounts of equipment, or by human power which demands lightweight gear. (See the *ARRL Handbook* for more information about portable stations.)

Several basic questions need to be answered when preparing for portable operation and selecting antennas:

• Where will you operate? What footprint limitations does this imply? Remember that you will represent every ham operator to the public. Plan accordingly.

• How will you transport your gear and what constraints does that impose?

• How much time do you have to setup and tear down at the portable location?

• What bands do you want to use? Is an antenna tuner part of the equipment?

• What is your budget? Can you build antennas to reduce the budget?

The complete antenna system must be considered, including supports, feed line, and accessories. The effective antenna system must be easily packed and stored, transported, unpacked, and erected — usually by a single person. The antenna should be able to radiate and receive effectively in a variety of installation environments. The system should be robust enough to be used again and again. With such a wide range of operating needs, it should not be a surprise that antenna systems designated as "portable" come in a wide variety of sizes and shapes for use on any amateur frequency. This book contains many antenna designs that can be adapted for portable operating. The examples here illustrate how their designers addressed the challenges. For even more ideas, use the ARRL website's Periodicals and Search tools to look for "portable antenna" and "portable beam."

Antennas optimized for portability can also be used in more permanent installations, particularly where a "low profile" antenna is needed as discussed in the **Stealth and Limited Space Antennas** chapter. The antennas in the **Mobile and Marine HF Antennas** chapter can often be employed as portable antennas, too, so there is overlap between the three appli-

Basic Safety for Portable Operation

As with all portable antennas, RF exposure can be an issue as RF power begins to exceed QRP levels. For typical portable operating, antennas are closer to the ground than for permanent stations and the antenna is relatively close to the operating position. This results in higher RF field strengths at ground level, particularly for the uncontrolled areas near the antenna. Take the necessary steps to keep people away from the antenna, particularly any high-voltage points, and consider your transmitted power level, as well.

Physical safety is important, too. Keeping people away from the base or feed point of the antenna will help prevent them from tripping over radials or guys! The edge of the radial field is a good point at which to establish a "safety perimeter" with yellow safety tape to establish both electrical and mechanical security.

Don't use rocks or other inappropriate weights when trying to get a line over a support. It is too easy to end up with an object caught in a tree or structure where you can't get it down or it even causes damage. The correct tool for that job is an arborist's throw bag and line. Give the public a good impression of amateur radio by doing the job right.

In a public site, there are likely to be additional safety rules and constraints on putting up antennas. For example, driving anything like a guy stake or ground rod into the ground, even temporarily, is often not permitted. Putting a line over a tree branch may also be prohibited.

Finally, if you are setting up in a public area, using anything that looks like a weapon to launch a line into or over a support is likely to attract the attention of the staff or security personnel. This especially includes slingshots, archery equipment, "spud guns," and similar items that are banned from parks and recreational areas for good reason. Use of drones may also be prohibited. Know the rules before you start setting up!

cations. Often, the only meaningful difference is the mounting of the antenna or how it is supported. The goal of this chapter is not necessarily for you to reproduce a design exactly but to give you examples of how other amateurs have satisfied their operating needs in ways you might find useful as well.

This section includes material originally contributed by Matt Heere, N3NWV, to the ARRL Handbook's Station Construction chapter. The ARRL also publishes *Portable Operating for Amateur Radio* by Stuart Thomas, KB1HQS, along with the more general *Portable Antenna Classics, HF Dipoles for Amateur Radio*, and the latest in the series, *Even More Wire Antenna Classics, Vol. 3* (see the References and Bibliography). You'll find many designs and ideas you can use or adapt for the type of operating you prefer.

19.1 Wire Antennas

The most common horizontal wire antennas used for portable operation are the end-fed half-wave (EFHW), inverted-V, and λ/2 dipoles. These typically require some kind of support 10 feet or more high — such as a tree or one of the portable masts described later in this chapter. If trees are used, some means of getting the support lines over a branch is also required. These antennas are described in more detail in the **General Purpose MF and HF Antennas** and **Multiband HF Antennas** chapters.

19.1.1 End-Fed Half-Wave

Figure 19.1 shows the EFHW antenna, a half-wavelength dipole fed at one end. See the EFHW description in the **Multiband HF Antennas** chapter for more information on how to build the antenna and its feed point impedance transformer.

The EFHW can be used on any band for which it is an integer number of half-wavelengths long. It may also present an acceptable impedance on nonresonant bands. For example, an EFHW for 80 meters will also be useable on 40, 20, 15, and 10 meters, as well as 30, 17, and 12 meters with a somewhat higher SWR. The 80 – 10-meter and 40 – 10-meter versions are the most popular for portable operation.

The free end is supported by a tree, mast, or other convenient attachment point and the feed point can be close to the ground or elevated. The EFHW is popular for portable and temporary operation in the sloping configuration shown. It can also be installed horizontally with the feed point elevated. Both ends of the antenna will be high voltage points and should be kept clear of tree branches and leaves, and away from where they can be touched accidentally.

An impedance transformer is used to change the feed point's high impedance to a lower value so that coaxial feed line can be used. Placing the feed point a few feet from one end will also lower the impedance somewhat. A ground rod is not required.

The EFHW requires a counterpoise to stabilize the feed point impedance. The outer surface of the coaxial feed line often serves as the counterpoise, so do not use a feed point choke balun without a counterpoise wire.

If it is necessary to reduce common-mode RF current on the feed line, a choke balun or "line isolator" can be added 10 feet or more from the feed point, or where the feed line reaches ground level if the feed point is elevated.

High voltage is present at the ends of any resonant wire antenna. Because the EFHW is often installed with its feed point (one end of the antenna) near ground, the high-voltage point should be made inaccessible to curious people and pets. Limiting power to 100 W or less is also prudent when using an EFHW in a portable or temporary station.

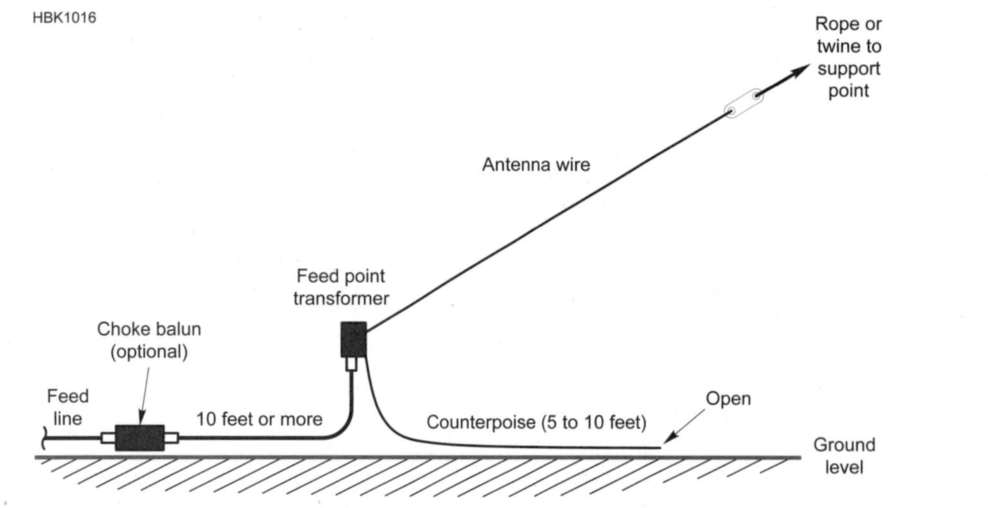

Figure 19.1 — For portable or temporary use, it is common to keep the feed point near ground level and support the other end with a multi-section fiberglass mast or with a rope over a tree branch.

END-FED RANDOM WIRE

A wire antenna can also be connected directly to a tuner which eliminates the weight of a feed line and connectors in a lightweight station. This configuration — sometimes referred to as a "random-wire," also connects the tuner and radio directly to the antenna and any ground system so RFI from common-mode current can be a problem above QRP power levels.

Although the name "random wire" implies any length will work, that is not the case. One-quarter and one-half-wavelength will present the extreme values of impedance of around 35 and 2,500 Ω so they are avoided. The most common configuration is approximately 84 feet of antenna wire and an un-un 9:1 impedance transformer for use on 80 – 6 meters.

An un-un impedance transformer (see the **Transmission Line System Techniques** chapter) with separate windings (no common connection) can reduce common-mode RF on the equipment. Because of the likelihood of significant RF voltage at the tuner and other equipment, having a good bonding scheme is helpful in avoiding RFI and similar problems.

PROJECT: 80/75 METER EFHW

On the 80/75-meter band, an EFHW antenna typically has a bandwidth of 100 kHz for SWR that is in range of most tuners, especially the internal tuners common to transceivers. To use different parts of the band requires tuning the antenna. This could be done by adding or removing wire at the free end of the antenna, but it is more convenient to tune the antenna at the impedance transformer.

The EFHW configuration developed by K1BQT addresses this need and is intended for use as a portable antenna for regional communication using NVIS propagation with a transmitter power around 100 W. (See the article "A Portable End-Fed Half-Wave Antenna for 80 Meters" in the online material.) The transformer has a tuned secondary winding so that the frequency of minimum SWR can be adjusted to cover the entire 3.5–4 MHz band.

19.1.2 Inverted-V Antenna

The inverted-V antenna is a strong, lightweight portable antenna. More information on it can be found in the **General Purpose MF and HF Antennas** chapter. The antenna can be fed directly with 50 or 75 Ω coaxial cable. Bandwidth is approximately the same as a dipole.

The apex of the antenna can be raised or lowered to any convenient height depending on available supports. The antenna can be made light enough for limited backpacking and is useful for emergency communications and Field Day. Since it is easy to raise and lower from a single support, it might also be a good choice for a stealth antenna where permanent antennas may not be used. (A self-supporting, rotatable inverted-V antenna design for 20 – 10 meters is included in the online material. See the References and Bibliography entry for Joe Littlepage, WE5Y.)

Lengths for the legs on the 40- through 10-meter bands are given in **Table 19.1**. The minimum height given in the table places the ends of the legs at ground level. Raising the center of the antenna will improve performance and will also cause the antenna's resonant frequency and feed point impedance to increase a few percent as will changing the angle between the legs. Be prepared to make final measurements and adjustments with an antenna analyzer or SWR meter.

19.1.3 PROJECT: Multi-Band Linked HF Dipole

The linked dipole is a variation on the trap dipole design presented in the **Multiband HF Antennas** chapter. This antenna is a dipole with insulators separating each leg into multiple sections instead of traps. At each insulator, a jumper with an alligator can short out the insulator to extend the antenna. This design by Phil Salas, AD5X, covers 20 – 10 meters but the design can be reworked for any combination of bands. (The original article, "A Simple HF-Portable Antenna" is included in this book's online material.) This video by N3NWV shows how to construct the antenna, including using 3D printing for the insulators: **youtube.com/watch?v=a4YoO0Am4Tg**.

The basic antenna in the article is a full-size 20 meter dipole with a conventional center insulator. Insulators are inserted to make the individual sections that can be added to the center-most element. **Figure 19.2** shows a typical insulator with the alligator clip attached. Since this antenna is intended for low power operating, the insulators can be easily made from nylon rod or PVC pipe, but any insulating material will work.

Table 19.1
Dimensions for Inverted V Antenna
Center angle of 120 degrees is assumed
Minimum center height is with ends of antenna at ground level

Band (Meters)	*Design Frequency (MHz)*	*Leg Length*	*Min. Center Height*	*Overall Length*
40	7.15	31 feet, 9 inches	16 feet	55 feet
60	5.37	42 feet, 3 inches	21 feet	73 feet
20	14.175	16 feet, ½ inches	8 feet	28 feet
17	18.1	12 feet, 6½ inches	6½ feet	22 feet
15	21.175	10 feet, 9 inches	5½ feet	19 feet
12	24.94	9 feet, 1 inches	4½ feet	16 feet
10	28.4	7 feet, 12 inches	4 feet	14 feet

Compact Antennas

"Loading" is the process of using some combination of inductance and capacitance to make a radiating element resonant at a frequency lower than the natural resonant point of the radiator alone. The best-known example of this technique is a coil (inductor) loaded vertical antenna, where the loading coil is placed at or near the bottom of the vertical radiator. This design allows for the vertical radiator to be shorter, in many cases quite a lot shorter, than a full quarter of a wavelength. Coil loading is also possible with horizontal antennas. Dipoles with traps to allow multi-band operation are shorter than their monoband counterparts for the same frequencies because the inductance in the traps electrically elongates the radiating element.

For portable use the advantages of having a physically smaller antenna are obvious. It is the operator's footprint at the remote location which benefits the most, and given that our locations are often shared public spaces, a reduced footprint can be a big improvement. While a loaded antenna design may not ultimately be any lighter, smaller components are easier to pack which makes them easier to transport.

Loaded antennas tend to have a narrow bandwidth. For an operator who wants to setup and operate on one frequency this is a non-issue. However, if you intend to change bands, or even to move significantly within one band, be prepared to visit the antenna and make physical adjustments to the whip, coil, or both. A good antenna tuner can solve this problem within a band, or at least most of a band, but band changing will require a trip to the antenna. Marking of the coil/whip/tuning capacitor can make these adjustments quick and easy, but they still need to happen.

Smaller antennas also need less in the way of support. Guy ropes and heavy bases can be replaced with modest tripod legs or small single ground spikes. Hanging from trees becomes practical from far lower branches. In addition to these footprint advantages, deployment times are reduced when the deployment is simplified. Footprint and deployment time are the two characteristics that make antennas practical or not. A small tripod with a nearly invisible steel whip placed directly on the ground is very unlikely to draw attention from the non-hams with whom we share our public spaces.

Physically compact antennas trade performance for size and, depending on one's perspective, operational convenience as well. Performance will vary from design to design, but no matter the arrangement a compact antenna is turning more of the amplifier power into heat than would a naturally resonant antenna. The more loading used, the lower the efficiency gets.

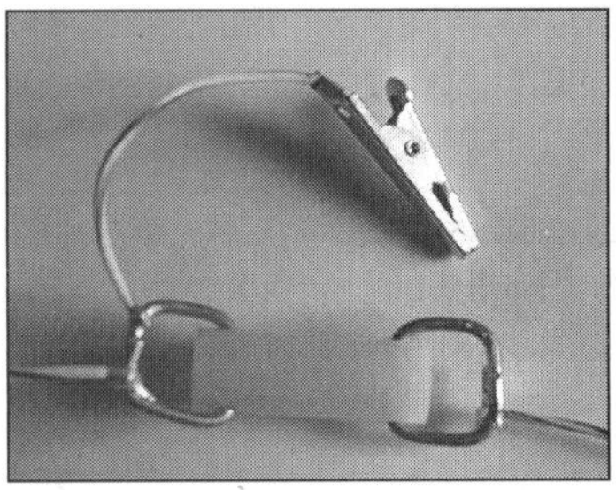

Figure 19.2 — For the multi-band dipole, antenna length and resonant frequency are changed by using alligator clips to short out insulators.

Start by building the section for the highest frequency band you want to use. Then add a section of wire and another insulator on each side for the next lowest band. Use the clip to short circuit the insulator and connect the new section. Adjust the new section's length to present a minimum SWR at the desired frequency. Add additional sections until the lowest frequency configuration is reached.

The original design for 20 through 10 meters is as follows with the lengths referring to the sections added on each side:

10 meters:	8 feet 3 inches
12 – 10 meters:	10 inches
15 – 12 meters:	1 foot 4 inches
17 – 15 meters:	1 foot 8 inches
20 – 17 meters:	3 feet 9 inches

Each side thus has a total length of 15 feet, 10 inches and the full antenna is 31 feet 8 inches long. The design can be extended to 6 meters by starting with the 6-meter section in the middle. On the lower frequency end, the dipole can be extended as far as is practical for your circumstances.

19.2 Whips and Ground-Plane Antennas

Many variations of the monopole antenna are used for portable operating, including loaded and unloaded whips, full-size and trap antennas. Since monopoles are usually mounted vertically, the term "vertical antenna" is used.

Vertical antennas can be ground-mounted, if they are self-supporting, or hung from a tree or other suitable support. The tradeoff for that simplicity is a greater dependence on the quality of ground system making up the "missing half" of a ground-plane antenna. (See the **Effects of Ground** chapter for more information.) Providing a reasonable ground system reduces losses and improves the performance of the portable antenna system.

19.2.1 Vertical and Sloping Dipoles

Vertical dipoles are also good performers in a portable setup if a sufficiently tall support is available. These antennas are discussed in the **General Purpose MF and HF Antennas** chapter. If a typical dipole is mounted vertically, it is a chal-

Pedestrian Mobile

Have you ever considered operating while hiking? Some amateurs are operating "pedestrian mobile" using PRC-type backpack military surplus radios with standard vertical whips and less than 50 W transmit power. One or two "drag wire" radials are often used to improve transmit efficiency. (See **groups.io/g/hfpack** for more information.) Most QRP transceivers are suitable for this type of operation.

The article "Tuning Electrically Short Antennas for Field Operation" by Ulrich Rohde, N1UL, and Kai Siwiak, KE4PT, discusses matching the impedance of "man-pack" style whip antennas at HF. It is included in the online material and in the References and Bibliography.

Figure 19.3 (Figure 15, page 53, July 2017) – A base-loaded whip antenna mounted on a Wolf River Coil with a sliding contact and support tripod. Radials are attached to the tripod legs.

lenge to extend the feed line at right angles to the dipole. This creates an asymmetric configuration that increases coupling between the dipole and the feed line, increasing common-mode RF current on the coax shield's outer surface. This may not be a problem, but to block the current a choke balun at the feed point is a popular solution. (See the **Transmission Line System Techniques** chapter.)

Designs that use the coax shield as one leg of the dipole are also presented in the material on vertical dipoles. A high impedance choke on the coax acts as the end insulator for the antenna. This simplifies attaching the feed line since it is at the bottom of the antenna which also locates the feed line away from the strongest radiated fields.

A sloping dipole is often a good compromise. It does not require a support as high as for a completely vertical dipole and is also an effective radiator. It is easier to run the feed line at right angles to the antenna, minimizing coupling, and a balanced feed line can also be used, making the antenna a multi-band system if an antenna tuner is used.

19.2.2 Whip Antennas

Whip antennas are most often used for mobile operation and are discussed extensively in the chapters on **VHF and UHF Mobile and Rover Antennas** and **Mobile and Marine HF Antennas**. They are easily adapted to portable operation not mounted on a vehicle or boat.

There are three basic types of whip antennas used for portable operation: unloaded, base-or-center loaded, and helically wound. Unloaded whips resonant on 10 or 6 meters as ¼-wave antennas are very efficient if used with a good ground plane of radials or mounted on a metal surface.

Base or center loaded whips are very common for HF portable operation. A popular configuration that can be quickly set up and on the air is shown in **Figure 19.3**. A multi-turn coil with a sliding contact is mounted on a tripod that sits on the ground. Radials are attached to the mounting tripod. A whip with a 3/8-24 base is attached to the top of the coil and the sliding contact positioned for the lowest SWR by using an antenna analyzer or some other SWR measuring device. Adjustable screwdriver-style antennas can also be used if 12 V is available to power the drive motor.

Both the manual-adjust coil and screwdriver antennas can be mounted on a section of aluminum mast to create a center-loaded whip. This increases antenna efficiency as discussed in the **Dipoles and Monopoles** chapter. An example is shown in **Figure 19.4** and a construction article about the antenna by AD5X is included in the online material. For the center-loaded antenna, guying is required in a strong breeze. Three lengths of light nylon cord or fishing line are sufficient to stabilize the antenna.

Whether base- or center-loaded, a ground-mounted whip is most effective when used with a dozen or more radials as discussed in the chapter **Effects of Ground** discussion on Real Wire Radial Systems. Transmitted signal strength can be improved by several dB just by adding a few more radials. More radials will also reduce the amount of common-mode RF current on the coax feed line. Placing a roll or two of wire mesh (hardware cloth or chicken wire) under the antenna as part of the ground-plane will also reduce ground losses.

Helically wound, single-band mobile whips can also be used with a set of ground radials replacing a vehicle's metal body. The same directions for radials apply as for the base- and center-loaded whips. Most of these antennas have a ⅜-24 base and can be attached directly to commercial loading coils.

Adjusting the helically wound antennas requires sliding the top stinger in and out of the top of the coil. To avoid this time-consuming process, adjust the stinger for the highest frequency in the band you intend to use. To operate on lower

Figure 19.4 — The complete antenna set up in AD5X's front yard. Total height is about 16 feet. The loading coil (white) is directly in front of the background vehicle.

frequencies, attach a short piece of wire with an alligator clip on one end to the whip at the top of the wound section. By having a set of clips with different wire lengths, the antenna's operating frequency can be quickly changed without having to move the stinger.

19.2.3 Whip Dipoles

A pair of loaded mobile whips can also be configured as a dipole. These antennas can be mounted on a short mast and tripod. Setting up and taking down these antennas is quick and is completely independent of any other support. Brackets for mounting mobile whips in a dipole configuration are available from commercial vendors, such as those shown in **Figure 19.5**. This style of antenna can be adapted to any band for which mobile whips are available. Any whip antenna that uses ⅜-24 threads can be used. A pair of wire elements can also be attached making the system quite versatile.

The mast for the antenna needs only be strong enough to hold the antenna securely above head height, 8 to 10 feet. Wooden poles, push-up fiberglass masts, painter poles, or TV mast sections would also work well.

The low height of the dipole makes this antenna useful for NVIS operation in support of emergency communications, as described in the January 2005 *QST* article by Robert Hollister, N7INK. Another design was published in the May 2003 issue of *QST* by Ron Herring, W7HD, including instructions for making the mounting bracket. (Both articles are included with this book's online material.)

19.2.4 PROJECT: Tree-Mounted HF Ground-Plane Antenna

A tree-mounted, vertically polarized antenna does not cost much, is inconspicuous, and it works. This antenna was described by Chuck Hutchinson, K8CH in *QST* for September 1984 (see Bibliography). In addition, losses in the ground are reduced by raising the radials off the ground.

The antenna itself is simple, as shown in **Figure 19.6**. A piece of RG-58 coax runs to the feed point of the antenna and is attached to a center insulator used as the feed point at the base of the vertical element. Two radials are soldered to the coax braid at this point. Another piece of wire forms the vertical element. The top of the vertical section is suspended from a tree limb or other convenient support, and in turn supports the rest of the antenna. The radials are stretched out to either side of the vertical element and may be sloping or straight.

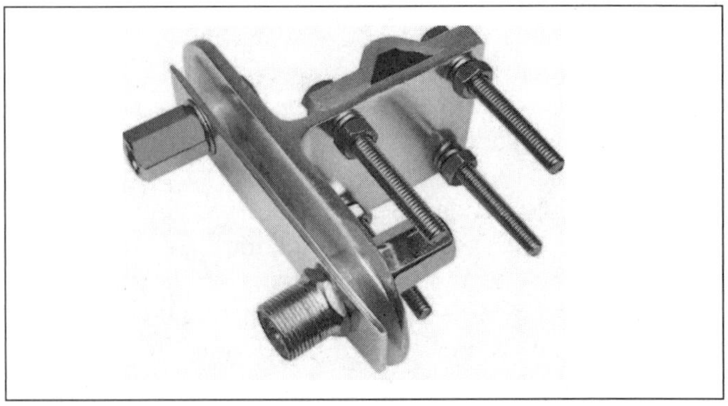

Figure 19.5 — A commercial mast-mountable insulator from Buddipole (buddipole.com) that accommodates whips and wire elements in a variety of configurations. Brackets to create a dipole from a pair of mobile whips are available from several vendors, such as the MFJ-347 shown here.

All three wires of the antenna are λ/4 long as discussed in the **Dipoles and Monopoles** chapter. This generally limits the usefulness of the antenna for portable operation to 7 MHz and higher bands, as temporary supports higher than 35 or 40 feet are difficult to come by.

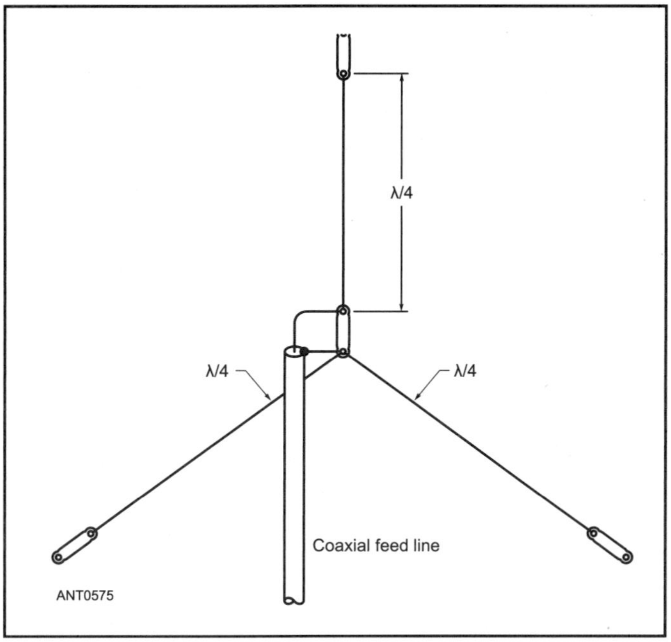

Figure 19.6 — Dimensions and construction of the tree-mounted ground-plane antenna from K8CH. The outside ends of the two radial wires are tied off to stakes or other convenient points.

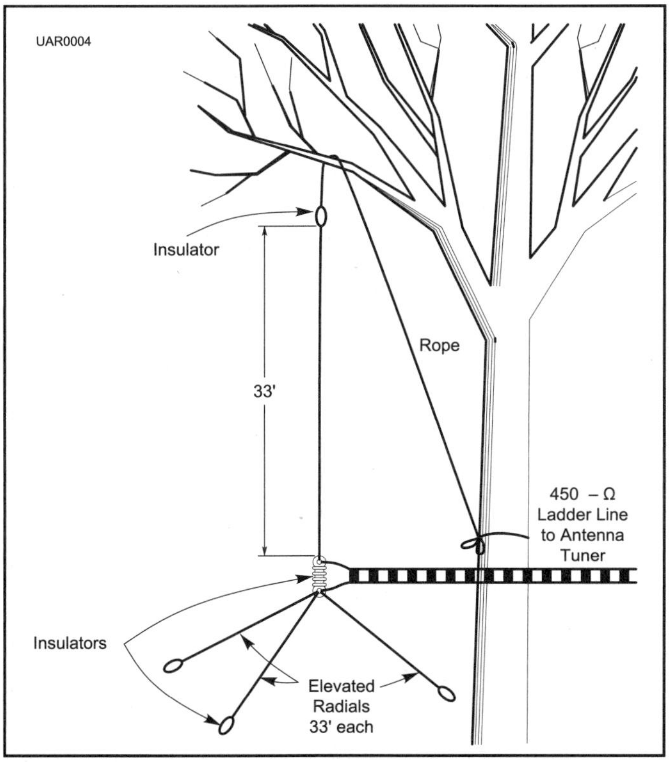

Figure 19.7 — A tree-mounted ground-plane antenna that is resonant on 40 meters but can be used on all HF bands with a tuner.

The outside surface of the coaxial cable shield will couple to the antenna and may carry substantial common-mode current. This re-radiates a signal just as the antenna does and is generally not a problem unless the current disrupts operation of the transmitter. To reduce common-mode currents on the feed line, use a choke balun as described in the chapter **Transmission Line System Techniques**.

The tree-suspended vertical can also be used for fixed station installations to make an invisible antenna. A shallow slit in the ground is sufficient for burying the coax feeder. The radiator and radials are difficult to see unless you are standing right next to the tree, especially if a dark color of insulation is used.

A similar antenna in **Figure 19.7** by Al Brogdon, W1AB, is cut for resonance on the 40 meter band but is fed with 450 Ω window line (see References and Bibliography). With a tuner, this antenna can be used on all HF bands, including 160 meters according to the author. Like the single-band version, there will be significant common-mode current on the feed line due to the unbalanced configuration. This may require chokes on coax from the tuner or a λ/4 counterpoise wire to manage RF hot spots or RFI in a portable station.

19.2.5 PROJECT: Five-Band Portable Vertical Antenna

This multi-band vertical antenna project uses five quarter-wave vertical monopoles in parallel, using a common ground screen of 16 radials. This allows multi-band operation without requiring an antenna tuner. (The entire article is included with this book's online material and at least one similar commercial design is available.)

The antenna, shown schematically in **Figure 19.8A**, consists of four quarter-wave elements attached to spreader rods and the longest, 20 meter element wrapped around the central support. Each antenna is terminated in a banana plug that is attached to a feed point ring on the mast. Each of the 16 radials is 17 feet long and attached to a similar ring at the bottom of the antenna. Radial length is not critical — add more radials close to the base of the antenna to improve efficiency. Remember that the length of the connection from the radial attachment ring to the feed point RF connector also counts as

Small Transmitting "Magnetic" Loops

A fairly popular choice for portable operation, the small transmitting "magnetic" loops are very portable and can be set up quickly. A short mast and a lightweight tripod are sufficient to support the loops and no ground radials or systems are required. The theory behind small transmitting loops is covered in the **Loop Antennas** chapter. If you plan on using a small loop, be sure to review the RF Exposure safe distances tables in that chapter. Examples of the loops and a construction project is included in the **Stealth and Limited-Space Antennas** chapter.

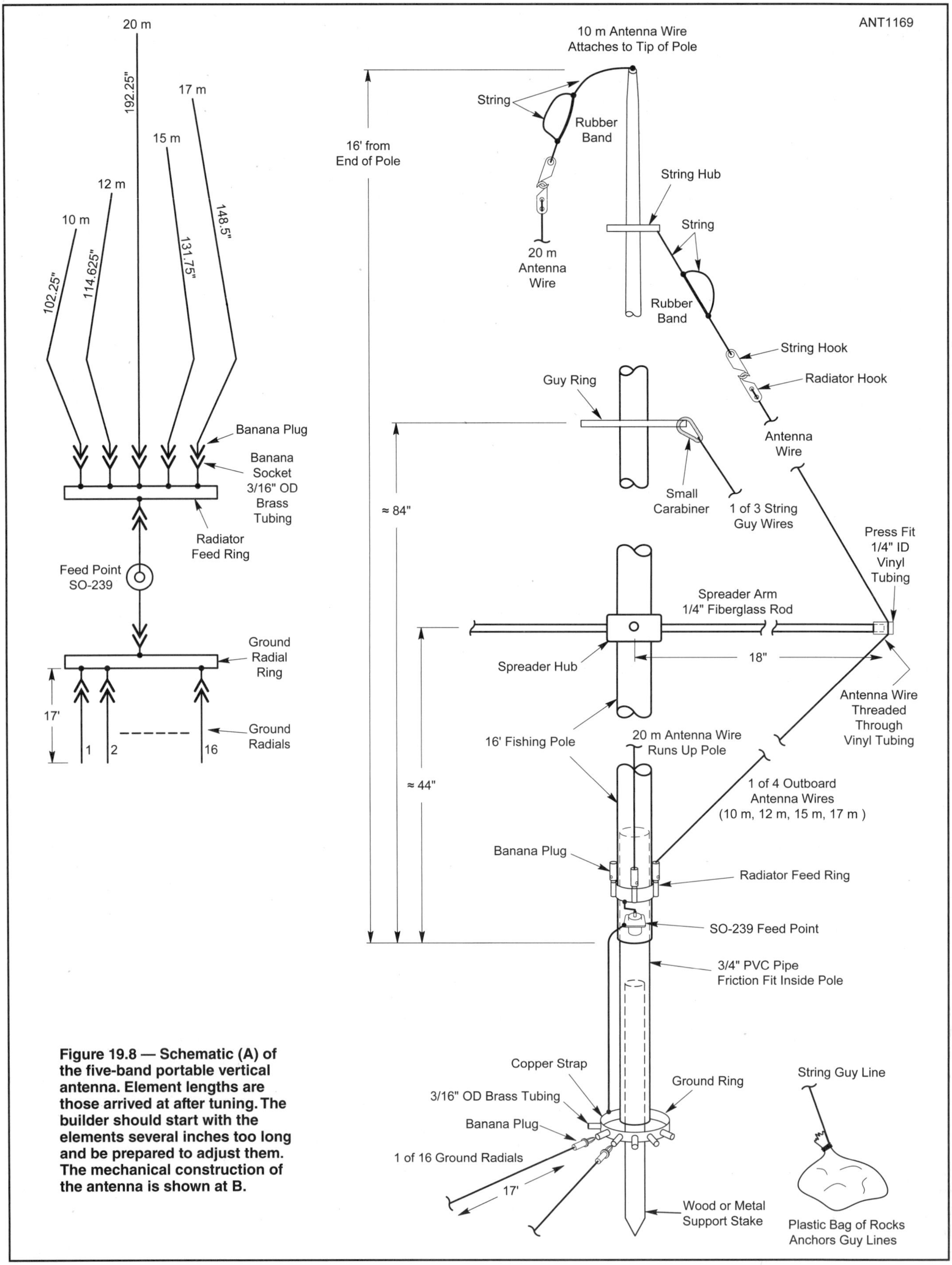

Figure 19.8 — Schematic (A) of the five-band portable vertical antenna. Element lengths are those arrived at after tuning. The builder should start with the elements several inches too long and be prepared to adjust them. The mechanical construction of the antenna is shown at B.

part of the antenna and should not be changed after tuning.

Tuning consists of beginning with the 10-meter element. Trim about 1/2 of the total length needed to bring the element to resonance. This is in recognition of the interactive tuning process. Move to the 12-meter element and repeat, then the 15 meter element and so forth. Continue to tune each element in sequence until the SWR is acceptable on all bands.

Mechanically, the antenna is assembled on a portable fiberglass fishing rod, 16-feet long. A ground stake and PVC pipe provide the base support. A triangular guy attachment point slides down over the top of the pole until it rests on the top of a middle section. Guying may not be required if the base support stake and pipe are sufficiently sturdy.

19.3 Beam Antennas

Simple horizontal and vertical antennas are light and easy to use for portable operating but having some gain and directivity in the field is very nice. While a full-size HF triband Yagi is probably out of the question for most portable operations, smaller antennas can still provide good performance at low cost and with relative simplicity of installation. This is particularly true on the higher frequency HF bands. For portable VHF/UHF/microwave operation, full-size beams with modest boom lengths are well-suited for portable operation.

On the lower HF bands, consider a rotatable dipole. Several vendors offer lightweight, multiband models covering the HF bands starting at 40 meters. While not strictly a beam antenna, the dipole's pattern has directivity and it has a wide bandwidth.

More options for directive antennas are presented in the **Phased Arrays** chapter and the **Broadside and End-Fire Dipole Arrays** chapter and not duplicated here. Phased arrays of verticals are practical for all of the HF bands, although 80 meter designs take some experience to put up and stay up. Driven arrays have a long history in amateur radio — the Bobtail curtain, Half-square, Bi-square, Lazy-H, and many others are well-suited for temporary stations.

19.3.1 PROJECT: Portable 6 Meter Beam

A 6 meter wavelength is short enough that full-size antenna elements aren't heavy and don't require special mechanical assemblies. At the same time, long distance propagation from sporadic-E and other modes is common, particularly in the peak summer months for portable operation. As a result there are quite a few 6 meter antenna designs to choose from! The quad design presented here has a short turning radius with useful gain and light weight.

The References and Bibliography and online material contain plenty of additional designs. The recent ARRL publication *Magic Band Antennas for Ham Radio* contains numerous designs as does the website of Martin Steyer, DK7ZB (**qsl.net/dk7zb**).

TWO-ELEMENT QUAD

The quad antenna in **Figure 19.9** was originally described by Markus Hansen, VE7CA, in *The ARRL Antenna Compendium, Vol 5*. After years of HF operation, he became enthusiastic about VHF/UHF operation when he got on 6 meters and discovered the joys of driving to high mountain peaks to operate. Not only does an antenna have to be portable for this kind of operation, but it must also be easily assembled and disassembled. Articles describing the 2-element quad and 3-element Yagi for 6 meters are provided with this book's online material.

19.3.2 PROJECT: 10-Meter Moxon Beam

The Moxon rectangle design is explained in the **HF Beam Antennas** chapter. It looks like a 2-element Yagi but with the tips of both elements bent back towards each other. As with similar 6 meter designs, the 10 meter dimensions in **Figure 19.10** are suited to both mobile and portable operation.

This design constructs the antenna as a wire loop in three sections: the two halves of the driven element and the reflector. The #14 AWG insulated wires are mounted on a pair of crossed fiberglass spreaders. A choke balun is recommended at the feed point. A pair of snap-on Type 31 or 43 cores is sufficient to reduce coupling between the feed line and the antenna.

The antenna weight is quite modest, depending on the materials used for construction but not more than several pounds. It can be mounted on a lightweight mast and ½ wavelength above ground (16 feet) should be sufficient to produce enough low-angle radiation for DX contacts.

Figure 19.9 — The 2-element 6 meter quad by VE7CA is easy to assemble and does not require a tall support to be effective. (Photo by Markus Hansen, VE7CA)

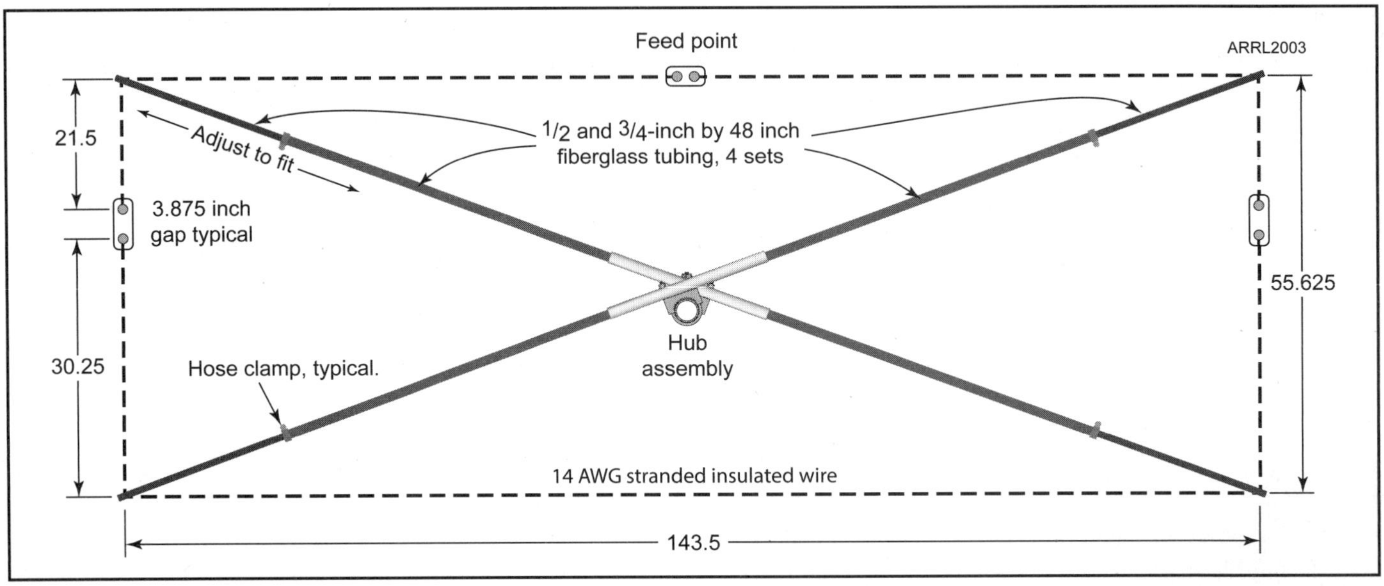

Figure 19.10 — Dimensions for the 10-meter Moxon. Fiberglass spreaders are used to hold the wire loop forming the driven element and reflector.

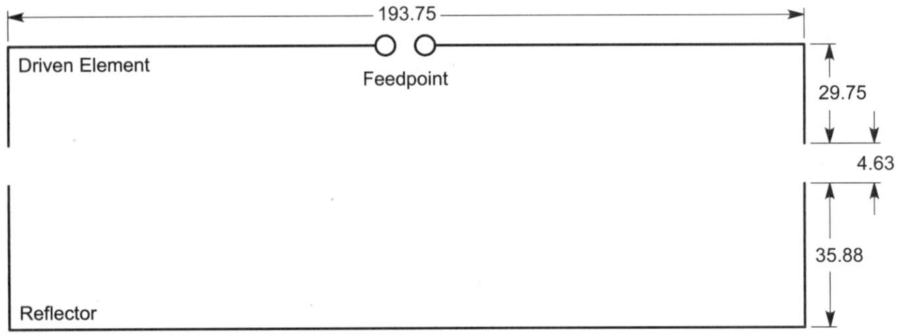

Figure 19.11 — The basic dimensions of the Moxon rectangle for 15 meters.

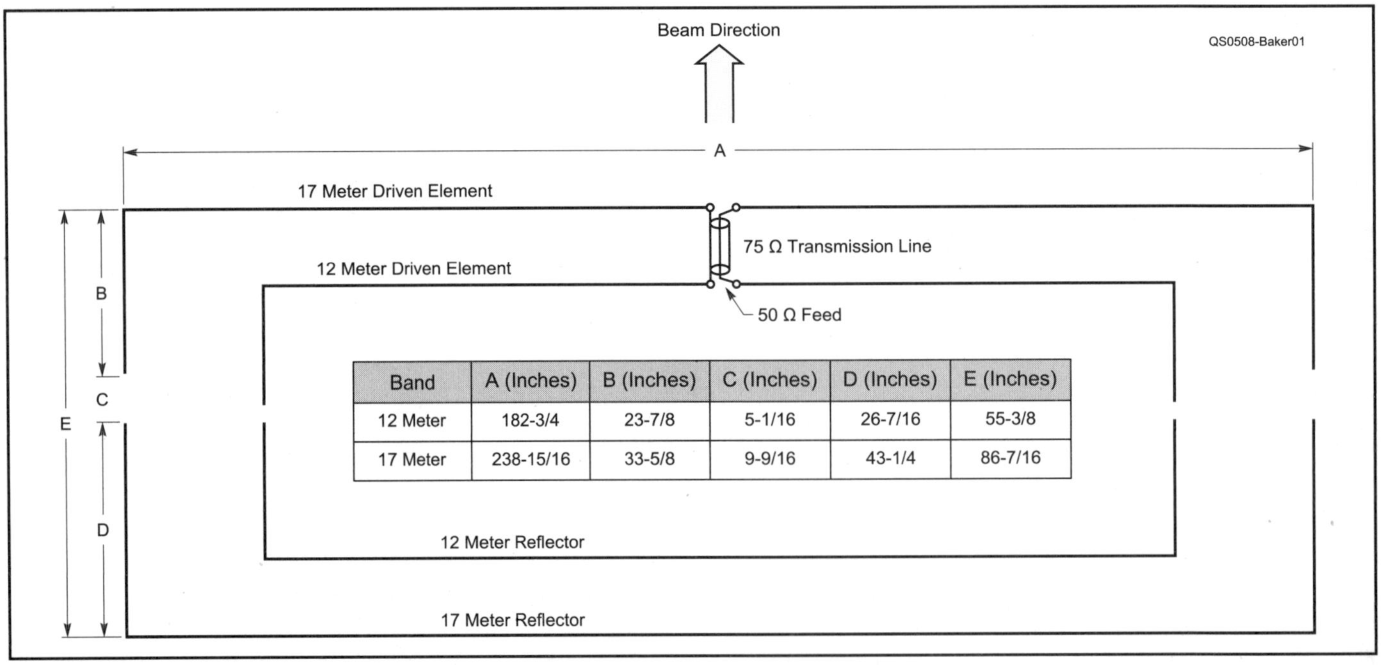

Band	A (Inches)	B (Inches)	C (Inches)	D (Inches)	E (Inches)
12 Meter	182-3/4	23-7/8	5-1/16	26-7/16	55-3/8
17 Meter	238-15/16	33-5/8	9-9/16	43-1/4	86-7/16

Figure 19.12 — The dual-band Moxon for 17 and 12 meters with basic element dimensions.

Figure 19.13 — The completed "Black Widow" 15 meter beam mounted on a painter's pole mast.

19.3.3 PROJECT: 12-, 15-, and 17- Meter Moxon Beams

Moxon rectangle designs for three of the upper HF bands were created by Allen Baker, KG4JJH. The first is a single-band design for 15 meters (see **Figure 19.11**) The second is a dual-band design for 17 and 12 meters (see **Figure 19.12**).

Both designs use fishing poles mounted on a central hub with the antenna wire elements stretched between their tips under tension. The figures present a mechanical drawing of the antenna showing the antenna's basic construction. **Figure 19.13** shows the completed 15 meter antenna mounted on a short mast. Construction articles for these antennas are included in the online material.

19.3.4 PROJECT: 20 and 40 Meter Beams

Below 18 MHz (17 meters), rotatable beam antennas with full-size elements start to become rather unwieldy for most portable operation. Smaller commercial two- or three-element tri-band Yagis for 20–10 meters with boom lengths of 12 to 18 feet are widely available. Several vendors offer beams with wire elements stretched between fiberglass spreaders, as well. Rotatable beams for 40 meters are not usually considered portable except, perhaps, for Field Day and special temporary contest-style operation.

Focusing instead on lighter-weight designs that can be suspended with ropes from a pair of supports at modest height, the following two wire beams are presented for 20 and 40 meters. Designed by Bob Rose, KC1DSQ, and Bob Glorioso, W1IS, the antennas have 10-foot spreaders that can be easily carried on or in a regular minivan-size vehicle. (Complete construction articles for both antennas are included in the online material.)

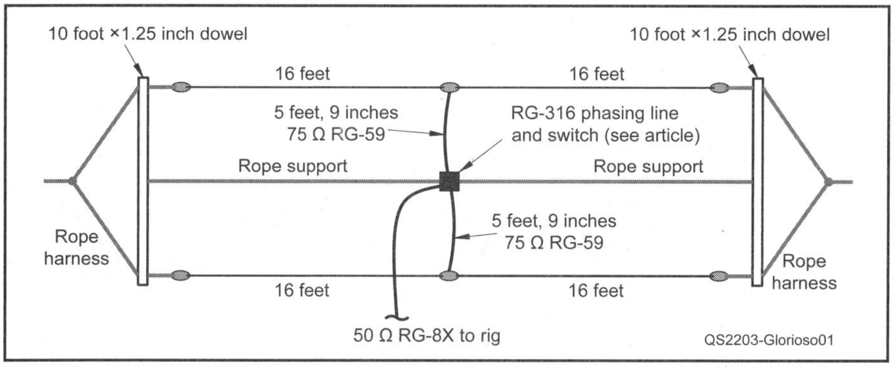

Figure 19.14 — Top view of the 20-meter phased dipole beam. A relay at the junction of the phasing lines allows the beam direction to be reversed.

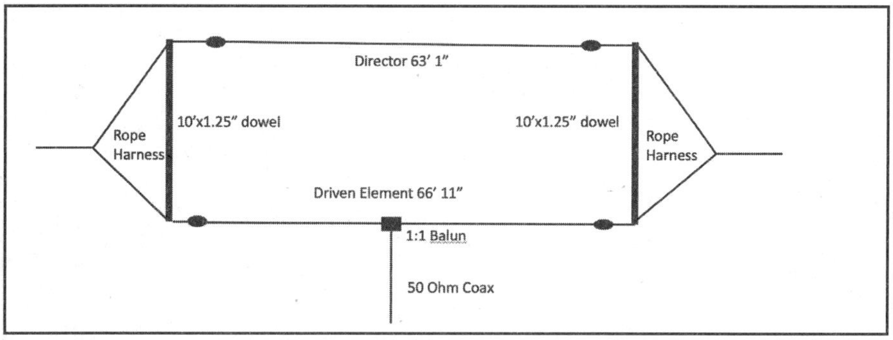

Figure 19.15 — The 40-meter wire beam layout and dimensions. Beam direction is reversed by flipping the antenna over.

The 20 meter antenna in **Figure 19.14** is a pair of dipoles 10 feet apart and driven so that they radiate signals 90 degrees out of phase. Because the 10-foot spacing is less than ¼-wavelength (17.4 feet), the total length of the 75 Ω phasing line between the dipoles is 128.1 degrees. (The complete theory for the antenna design is available in the online material.) The result is a forward gain of 11.3 dBi at a height of 40 feet for an elevation angle of 25 degrees. A relay box at the junction of the feed lines allows the direction of the beam's pattern to be reversed by switching the phasing lines.

The 40 meter antenna is a standard Yagi design with a unidirectional pattern from a driven element and a director (see **Figure 19.15**). This configuration was chosen for portability and a 50 Ω feed point impedance, instead of using a reflector and with wider spacing. At 40 feet in height, the antenna's calculated gain is 8.4 dB at 7.2 MHz for an elevation angle of 40 degrees. The antenna's beam direction can be reversed by flipping the antenna over, using the coaxial feed line from the ground.

19.4 Ultralight Antenna Systems

The following section was contributed by frequent Summits On The Air (SOTA: ***sota.org.uk****) activator, Fred Maas, KT5X. More information about Ultra-Light stations and operating are available at* ***ke6mt.us/2018/12/ultra-lyte-summits-on-the-air-by-fred-kt5x*** *and* ***ke6mt.us/wp-content/uploads/2018/12/KT5X-WS0TA-SOTA-UltraLyte.pdf****.*

WHAT IS AN ULTRA-LIGHT STATION?

A lightweight portable HF station once meant a 50-pound backpack carrying a tube radio, a relatively ineffective whip antenna, and a lead-acid battery. Today's technology provides a proliferation of surprisingly capable tiny transceivers. Use a lithium-chemistry battery and one is on the way to an ultra-light station that excels for portable applications where it must be carried some distance. A hike or a backpacking expedition to activate a SOTA peak makes an ultra-light approach as in **Figures 19.16** and **19.17** almost essential.

There are many small and light 5 W HF transceivers that are as light as a few ounces without a case. They are sensitive, stable, and have respectable filtering. Some draw as little as 30 mA in receive mode, so that a very small lithium battery may be all that is needed for power. ("Lithium" includes to all varieties of the lithium-ion chemistries.) Add an antenna, a device for matching impedance, line to support the antenna, a feed line, and a method of logging to complete an ultra-lite system. Some locations may not offer natural supports (trees) for an antenna therefore a lightweight supporting pole may also be needed.

TYPICAL ULTRA-LIGHT ANTENNA SYSTEM COMPONENTS

Wire Antennas: A lightweight pole won't support heavy wire but #26 or even #28 gauge can be used at low power levels. Teflon-insulated stranded wire adds strength without adding much weight. Teflon-insulated wire doesn't tend to kink and it pulls easily over a tree branch without shorting to it.

Such wire can easily be supported by heavy thread or non-stretch braided fishing line. It is extremely strong, essentially weightless, and presents no wind resistance. At QRP power levels, it can be tied directly to the end of the wire using fishing knots or a small piece of perf board.

Antenna wire can be taped to the pole leaving four or feet of wire dangling. (See the Special Consideration section comment on conductive poles) The wire may then be connected directly to the transceiver or matching units, eliminating the feed line altogether. Banana plugs, a binding post, or a terminal strip can be used.

If a tree or other support is available, wire antennas can be supported at either end or anywhere along the wire. The usual method of getting lightweight cord over a branch is to attach a modest weight and throw it. An empty arborist's bag can be filled with rock or dirt at the site. A flexible pole can also be used to get the line over a low branch — see the section on Half-Squares below.

Random-Length Antennas: A random-length wire usually requires a manual or auto-tuner which adds weight and an additional failure point. Usually fed at ground level or directly at the transceiver, it can develop a relatively high current point near the ground which is usually lossy. It frequently requires a counterpoise or radial wire (see the **Effects**

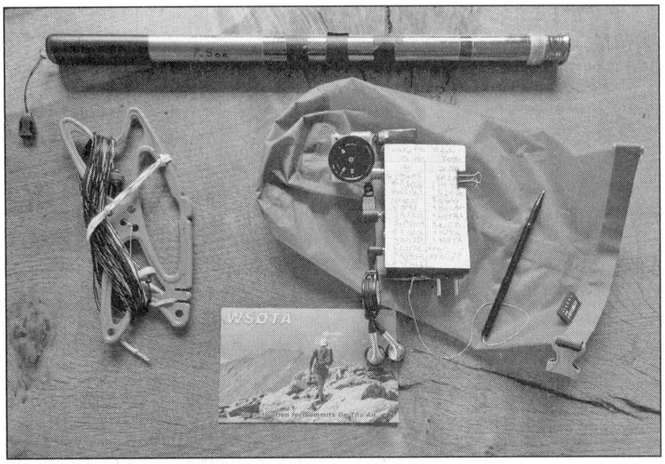

Figure 19.16 — A one-pound portable HF station consisting of a radio with a paper log clipped to the back, a touch paddle, LiPo battery, impedance transformer plugged directly into the radio, 18-foot fishing pole that collapses to 18 inches, and a #28 AWG Teflon wire 20/30/40 (trapped) end fed halfwave on a figure-8 winder.

Figure 19.17 — A typical ultra-light station in use.

of Ground chapter for a discussion of counterpoise systems.) which is a part of the antenna that is also laying on the lossy ground.

End-Fed Half-Wave (EFHW) Antennas: The best end-fed antenna choice may be a half-wave wire. (See the chapter on **Multiband HF Antennas** for a more complete discussion of the EFHW.) At higher power levels, an EFHW often generates enough common-mode RF current on the feed line or equipment to cause problems, but not at the low power levels generally used for SOTA activations. It will radiate exactly as the same wire would if fed at the center. Expect to adjust the wire length for the particular pole being used and deploy the pole the same way each time for consistent results.

The impedance at the end of an EFHW is high so there is very low RF current. The RF voltage is high and will couple to the ground which will affect the impedance and possible ground losses. Nevertheless, this eliminates the need for a set of ground radials. The operator, radio, and headphones, or a short piece of wire connected to the radio or tuner enclosure are usually sufficient to serve as a type of counterpoise.

There are advantages to deploying the EFHW antenna wire as an inverted-L. Low-angle radiation for DX will come from the vertical leg and high-angle radiation for regional coverage will come from the horizontal leg. This reduces the amount of wire that must be supported by the length of the vertical leg.

Multiband EFHW Antenna: A 40-meter EFHW is about 67 feet long which is two half-waves on 20 meters, three on 15 meters, and four on 10 meters. It will not be perfectly resonant on all four bands, but close enough to be used if a tuner is available.

A way to use the 40 meter EFHW on higher bands without a tuner is to place a miniature SPST switch in the wire at the half-wave resonant point for each additional desired band. The switches will be easy to reach and take only a minute to change for each band.

Another approach is to create a resonant half-wave antenna on 20 meters by connecting a stub of wire that acts as a parallel antenna. After trimming the EFHW for resonance on 7 MHz, connect the wire in the exact center of the EFHW. Make this stub about 30 inches long to start. Trim it for minimum SWR on the 20 meter frequency of intended use. **Figure 19.18** shows how to install it and protect it from breaking off during use.

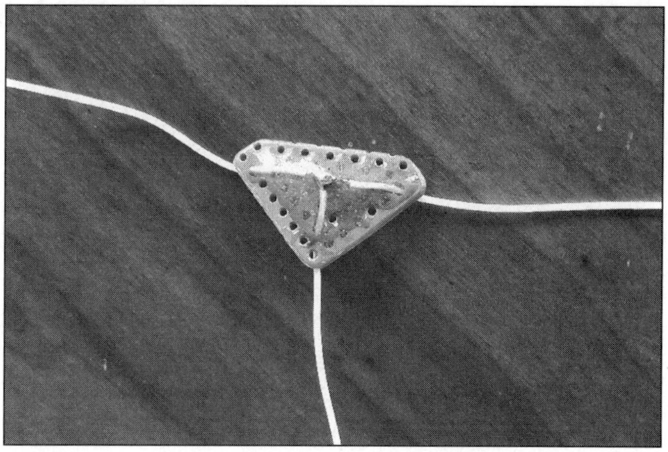

Figure 19.18 — Wire stub creates a resonant length on 20 meters (see text).

PROJECT: EFHW As Half-Square: (See the **Broadside and End-Fire Dipole Arrays** chapter) A directional HF antenna for portable use, a 40-meter EFHW can be deployed as the 20-meter Half-Square array in **Figure 19.19**. This antenna is bi-directional and radiates well at very low elevation angles. It will continue to function as a 40-meter EFHW even with the ends dangling down. Both 20 and 40 meters are popular bands at any point of the solar cycle.

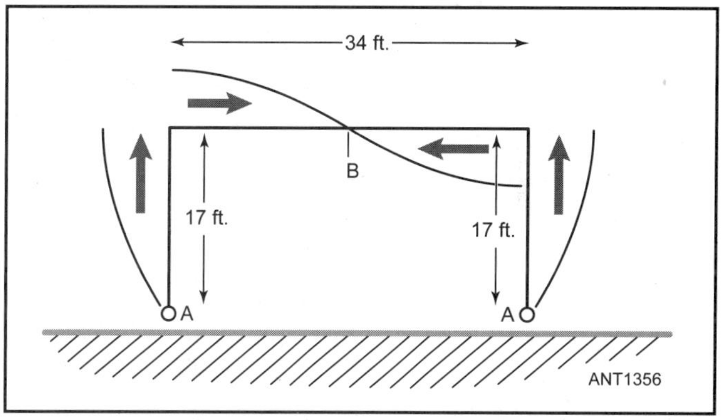

Figure 19.19 — A 40 meter EFHW configured as a 20 meter Half-Square array acts as a directional portable antenna. The arrows indicate current direction and the distance from the wire indicates magnitude. Feed the antenna at A with an impedance transformer. Adjust the 20 meter resonant frequency with a short tuning stub at B. (See text)

Find a tree limb that is at least 20 feet high. Use the pole to reach up and drape the antenna wire over the limb. Now pull the wire using the pole over and away from the limb until about 17 feet of wire is still hanging down from the limb. Anchor the pole such that about 34 feet of wire is horizontal, the remaining 17 feet is hanging down the pole, and this inverted-U is broadside to the most desirable direction.

Next, bring the other end of the antenna wire through the top of the extended pole and down to about five feet high on the pole. Tape it to the pole at that point with about four more feet of the wire dangling below where it is taped to the pole. This will be the antenna's feed point at A.

In Figure 19.19, at B is the 20-meter resonating stub, if needed. Radiation from the two current segments shown pointing at each other along the horizontal wire cancels out. Radiation from the currents along the two vertical wires are in-phase and add in the far field providing about 4.2 dBi gain and at low elevation angles broadside to the antenna.

Inverted-Vee Dipole: An EFHW can be put up in an inverted-vee shape and it will work fine. If you prefer a center-fed antenna, the inverted-vee dipole may be a good choice. Assuming you have a 15 – 20 foot or higher support, the antenna feed point should be at the highest point. The inverted-vee is usually fed with lightweight coaxial cable (see the section below on Transmission Line and Connectors). If you want to use the antenna on its even harmonics, however, the high SWR will increase feed line loss dramatically.

Supporting Pole: Select a lightweight, telescoping pole. There are inexpensive 15 – 20-foot fiberglass and carbon-fiber poles that telescope to less than 30 inches, some to as little as 18 inches, and weigh ten ounces or less. Such poles are sometimes called Tenkara poles after a common manufacturer. Used properly, these can support an antenna suitable for QRP operation.

An antenna attachment point may need to be added to the tip. A short string glued to the tip is provided. A small clip can be tied to it or the string can be replaced by gluing a typical fishing pole ferrule, called a "tip-top" to the end of the pole.

The thinnest (top) section of these poles is too flimsy to support an antenna but can be permanently telescoped into the next section, creating a double-wall section, leaving just the tip or string protruding. Hot glue can be used for this purpose as it remains flexible.

Impedance Matching: End-fed antennas present a very high impedance that is beyond the capabilities of most auto-tuners. Here are two simple matching devices suitable for ultra-light operating. Either can be built into a dental floss case and weigh less than an ounce. If a feed line is not used, the antenna can be connected directly to the tuner.

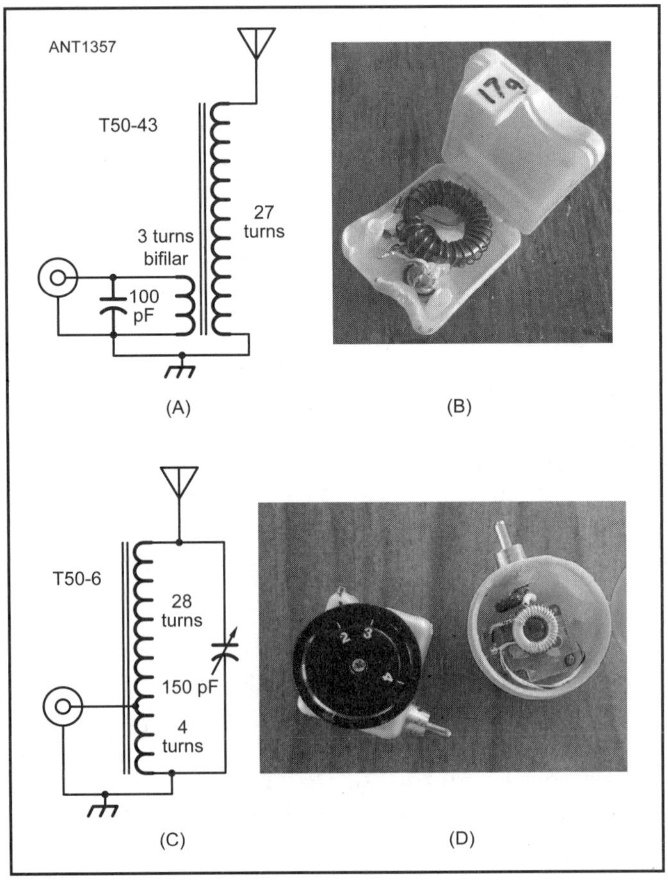

Figure 19. 20 — A broadband impedance transformer for use with low-power HF (A and B). A version tunable from 7–21 MHz is shown at C and D. B and D show the transformers mounted in light-weight plastic enclosures.

The broad band high impedance transformer in **Figure 19.20A** weighs less than an ounce and can be built into a dental floss case as shown in Figure 19.20B. It can be plugged directly into the transceiver with the antenna wire connected directly to it, eliminating any need for feed line. Wound on a T50-43 ferrite toroid, the primary is 3 bifilar turns with a 27-turn secondary. The compensating capacitor across the primary may be 100 to 140 pF and should be an NPO type, rated at 500 V or more. The 9:1 turns ratio creates an 81:1 impedance ratio. Turns ratios from 3:1 to 9:1 are popular. See the End-Fed Half-Wave discussion in **Multiband HF Antennas** for more information about impedance matching transformer design and construction.

The impedance transformer in Figure 19.20C and 19.20D is tunable from 7-21 MHz. The transformer is made using a T50-6 powdered-iron toroid with 28 turns of #28 AWG magnet wire tapped at the fourth turn. This creates a 7:1 turns ratio and a 49:1 impedance ratio. A miniature two gang 15 – 140 pF broadcast-band variable capacitor can be used at QRP levels.

Transmission Line and Connectors: The lightest and least-lossy feed line is no feed line — connect an EFHW or random-length wire directly to the tuner (if used) and the tuner directly to the transceiver. This requires the operator and transceiver to be at the feed point of the antenna which is not always practical. A feed point can be up in the air if you have a support for it and is required for antennas such as a center-fed inverted-vee. Let's assume you're within 50 feet of the feed point, what are your ultra-light feed line options?

There are basically two choices: 300 Ω TV twin lead and 50-Ω RG-174 coax. RG-174 is the lightest at 0.4 pounds/50 feet but it is lossy: 1 dB/50 feet at 10 MHz. Twin lead is a little heavier at up to 1.25 pounds/50 foot but has less loss: 0.1 dB/50 feet at 10 MHz. (Twin lead varies widely in weight and loss.) If you are primarily weight-sensitive and can accept some loss, use the coax but keep it as short as possible. 300-Ω twin lead will also require an impedance transformer or tuner which adds more weight but may already be a part of your kit.

Coaxial connectors add weight and are constantly being taken on and off, becoming another possible point of failure, and are best eliminated. RCA plugs and jacks are lighter and may be easier to use and less prone to failure. At HF, you can also avoid connectors altogether in favor of lightweight terminal strips like the Wago lever nuts (**wago.com/us/wire-splicing-connectors/compact-splicing-connector/p/221-412**) that accommodate wire sizes as small as #24 AWG.

SPECIAL CONSIDERATIONS

- It is best not to try to guy a lightweight pole. Guying adds set up time, complexity, weight, and lines that may become tangled. An antenna held to one side allows the pole to be secured by wedging it between rocks, stuck into a bush or shrub, lashed to a stump or other object, or leaned against a tree limb. The pole can also be used as a tool to lift insulated wire antenna over a tree limb.
- When extending or collapsing a lightweight fiber pole,

NEVER TWIST IT! The material bends, but it is not elastic. The fibers will separate and will never recover. Instead, push or pull sections firmly in a straight line.

• Always lean the pole away from the wind to reduce the stress on the pole. A pole bent to one side is also unlikely to accidentally telescope the sections back together.

• Do not allow antenna wire to wrap around a conductive carbon fiber or metal pole. The additional capacitance to ground will detune the antenna.

• Winding wire and support lines on a figure-8 winder (see Figure 19.16) used for kite lines will prevent the kinks and tangles that form if the wire is simply coiled up.

• Solder will wick along stranded wire inside the insulation and that area of wire will become brittle and likely to break. Use minimum heat for a minimum amount of time when soldering #26 and #28 Teflon antenna wire to connections. Don't flex wire into which solder may have wicked.

19.5 Antenna Supports

19.5.1 Masts

Lightweight masts such as the popular extendable fiberglass and aluminum models that reach up to 80 feet in height are widely available. These can hold up lightweight wire antennas and an inverted V can also serve as two of the guying lines. It is common practice to leave two or three of the top sections nested to provide enough strength for heavier antennas. If your mast sections tend to slip back into each other, a small hose clamp around the smaller diameter section will prevent sliding. Another option is to cut heavy rubber bands and tie them around the smaller section.

Supporting tubular masts is usually done with guys of nylon cord or fishing line. This is fairly straightforward but requires at least three guy points. (See the **Building Antenna Systems and Towers** chapter for more information on guying.) One person can put up a light- or medium-weight mast with a little planning. Start by anchoring two of the guy lines. Place the pole's base at the desired location and walk it up until the two guys are tight, then keep tension on the third guy as you walk to where it will be anchored. It is important that the base not be able to slip during the operation.

If you are not able to drive guy stakes into the ground (see the sidebar on Portable Operating Safety), other possibilities include using concrete- or sand-filled buckets as shown in **Figure 19.21**. SOTABEAMS has produced an excellent YouTube video, "Erecting a SOTABEAMS HF Dipole" (**youtube.com/watch?v=RI6IRgQLokk**) showing how to safely put up and guy a telescoping pole holding an inverted V.

Figure 19.21 — A five-gallon plastic bucket filled with sand and rocks weighs from 40 to 60 pounds and makes a solid base for a fiberglass mast.

Two of the more popular designs for vehicle-based portable operating are the "drive-on mount" and the trailer hitch mount. **Figure 19.22A** illustrates the basic drive-on concept. A flange, wood block, or pipe stub is attached to a sturdy board or plank. The board is placed on the ground and the vehicle is driven on to it, securing the base of the mount. The mast can be secured to a vehicle roof rack for extra support. A welded metal version is shown in Figure 19.24B. **Figure 19.23** shows a trailer hitch mount in which the mast is held upright by a vertical tube welded to a conventional trailer hitch bar. Commercial versions are available from several vendors and the FGHM64 from M2 Antenna Systems (**m2inc.com**) includes a telescoping 24-foot mast. Masts constructed of separate aluminum or fiberglass sections are also widely available new or as military surplus. The June 2011 *QST* article by

Bob Dixon, W8ERD, shows how to use a mast tripod to construct a sturdy mast rising to 40 feet. **Figure 19.24** is a drawing of how the various pieces go together, including guying lines. Since the mast is assembled from the bottom, piece by piece, it is much easier to erect than a mast which must be pulled up from horizontal or lifted and placed in a base.

As with many types of accessories, the problem of temporarily holding modest loads aloft without guying has been addressed for many other situations. In addition, you can take advantage of the lower costs that come with high-volume sales. One such solution is aluminum or fiberglass telescoping flag poles for RVs. These come with trailer hitch and drive-on mounts and heights of 20 feet or more.

An aluminum extension ladder, properly guyed, can serve as a mast as described in the article included in the online material. A trip to the hardware store will also turn up several other candidates, such as painter's poles and extendable handles.

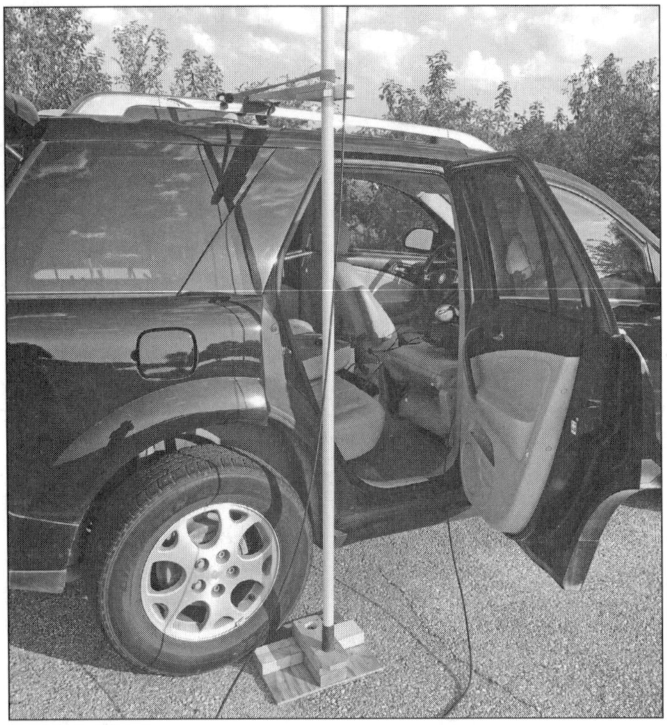

(A)

(B)

Figure 19.22 — Two examples of drive-on mounts for portable masts. At A, a fiberglass mast base is secured by the mount and additional support is provided by a strut attached to the roof rack of K5ND's vehicle. B shows a heavy-duty welded metal mount made by W3ATB that holds a mast upright on its own. [Photos courtesy Jim Wilson, K5ND, and Tim Carter, W3ATB]

Figure 19.23 — K5ACL's welded mast mount attaches to a conventional trailer hitch receiver. [Courtesy Johnny Twist, K5ACL]

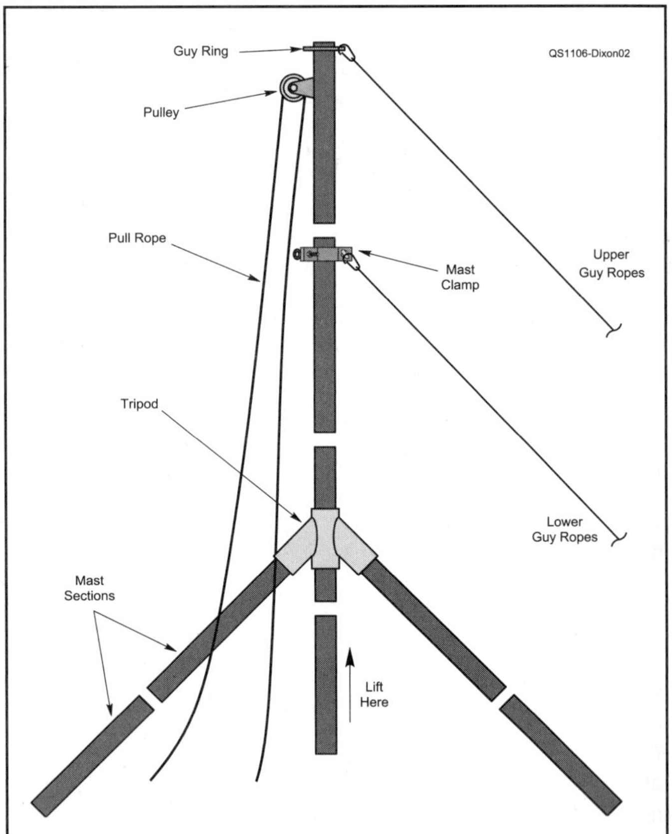

Figure 19.24 — Aluminum mast sections can be combined with a tripod center section to create a mast up to 40 feet high.

19.5.2 Trees

Finally, there is the issue of getting the antenna over a supporting structure or tree. Assuming it's not safe to climb to the support point, you'll have to throw or launch a light line over it and pull up the heavier support rope. (An excerpt from *Portable Operating for Amateur Radio* by Stuart Thomas, KB1HQS, discusses this problem — you can find it in the online material.)

You have several choices, starting with using whatever is at hand that is heavy enough to pull the light line back down to the ground but not so heavy as to not be able to throw sufficiently high. All kinds of things have been used to get antennas into trees — water bottles, rocks, tools (and some are still in there). Professional arborists face this issue all the time and use *throw bags* to get their lines into trees.

If throwing is not an option, the next step is usually a tennis ball launcher for exercising dogs (available at pet stores) or a slingshot and fishing reel, such as the EZ-Hang (**ezhang.com**). These work up to heights of about 100 feet. If more height is needed, "spud guns" that use compressed air or hair spray as a propellant can put lines tied to tennis balls over really tall trees. (See the article "The W4SSY Spudgun" in the References and Bibliography and the online material.)

As noted in this chapter's sidebar on safety, if you are setting up in a public area, using anything that looks like a weapon to launch a line into or over a support is likely to attract the attention of the staff or security personnel. This especially includes slingshots, archery equipment, "spud guns", and similar items that are banned from parks and recreational areas for good reason.

With any launching device, *think before you shoot.* If a line attached to a projectile snags or doesn't pay out freely, the projectile can snap back with full force. The projectile might not go where you intend, so be sure no innocent bystanders are down-range or near the launching device. Be aware of any power lines in the area, such as behind or even in a tree. If you overshoot, what might the projectile hit or travel over? If the wind is blowing, what happens if the projectile drifts off-line? Think things through and avoid hazards.

Some have begun using remote control (RC) drones to carry lines over trees, as well. There are two basic techniques:

• Fly over and land on the other side. In this technique, the drone carries a very light line such as fishing monofilament all the way over the tree. It then clears the tree and lands on the other side, still tethered to the line. The light line is then attached to a heavier line that is pulled back over the tree and attached to the antenna. Adequate space for the drone to land on the other side of the tree is required and the line can tangle in a propellor when it extends up from drone on the way down. The drone only has to lift the light line and does not have to have a drop attachment.

• Drop a line from above the tree. A *payload drone* with a lift-and-drop capability carries a weight heavy enough to fall completely through the tree while attached to the light line. The arborist's bag (up to 1 pound) or fishing weights are often used to pull the light line down through the tree. Drones that can lift these heavier loads are more expensive.

Kite and Balloon-Supported Antennas

Effective operating on the lower HF bands requires large antennas. If long-distance contacts are the goal, then a low radiation angle is needed. A horizontal antenna needs to be around ½ wavelength above ground to bring the radiation pattern's main lobe down to where it's needed. That's 120 feet on 80 meters and 240 feet on 160 meters. These heights are usually out of reach for portable stations not around big trees. A ¼-wave vertical ground plane antenna is still 66 feet high at 80 meters and 132 feet high on 160 meters.

Faced with the need to hold a wire sufficiently vertical, the idea of using a balloon often seems attractive. These have been used to hold up light wires as high as ½-wavelength on 160 meters (about 250 feet). If you are going to try a balloon, you should review some of the basics, which might not be obvious at the outset, before you head for the operating site. Lee Jennings, ZL2AL, discusses these techniques in "Kite and Balloon Antennas" (**zl2al.com/2619/kite-and-balloon-antennas**) or search for the title and his call sign. Another article is Don Daso, K4ZA's, "A Skyhook for the 90s" in May 1997 *QST* (included in the online material).

Kites are another popular technique of lifting antennas. In fact, Marconi used kites to lift antennas in his early wireless experiments. They are better suited for ultra-light portable operating since all that's needed to use them are the kite, a tether, and the wind! There are several good online websites for using kites as antenna supports. SOTABeams maintains an online FAQ at **sotabeams.co.uk/kites-faq**. Bob Marshall-Read, YB5AQB (ex-G4VGO), has used kite-lifted antennas on Top Band for many years and describes many of them at (**qsl.net/g4vgo**).

Before you decide to use such an antenna on "all bands," remember that the longer a straight-wire antenna, the more it becomes a long-wire antenna that radiates more and more in the direction of the antenna. That ½-wave vertical on 160 meters with such a good low-angle signal becomes a cloud-burner on the higher HF bands!

19.6 Feed Lines and Impedance Matching

19.6.1 Feed Line Considerations

A feed line for portable station operation will be used and managed differently than at a fixed station. Portable use implies:

• Feed line will be coiled and uncoiled many, many times. It must survive this without degradation or damage. See the sidebar "The Over-Under Method of Coiling" for tips on how to keep feed line neat without tangling.

• Weight is a consideration. Feed line will be carried regularly, perhaps in backpacking or other highly weight-constrained scenarios.

• Size is a consideration. There is only so much room to pack a portable station and the feed line can easily become the single largest item with which you much contend.

• Not all types of connectors are suited for repeated attachment and disconnect cycles. SMA connectors are generally rated for a low number of mating cycles. Both UHF and BNC connectors can withstand many mating cycles if properly cared for.

• Feed lines encounter more stress during portable operation than at fixed stations. Cables can pull out of connectors, shields and center pins can work loose, and so forth. Crimped connections are generally more reliable than solder, particularly in an application where frequent movement of the connection will occur. Provide stress relief to the cable wherever practical.

• Having multiple, shorter, lengths of coax and appropriate splice adapters is a convenient and reasonable choice for temporary use with varying distances between the radio and antenna.

SELECTING FEED LINES

Balanced conductor feed lines are usually impractical for portable use with some exceptions for certain types of equipment and antennas. They cannot be run along the ground and offer few options for durable mechanical connections to equipment: binding posts are usually used. For the cable lengths typical of a portable station, the low loss of balanced feed lines isn't worth the complications.

While many types of coaxial cable are available, just a few are practical for portable use. The two most popular choices are RG-8X and RG-58. Larger cables such as RG-213 are too heavy and stress connectors through repeated bending. Smaller cable such as RG-174 is used by operators with extreme weight or size requirements (see the section on Ultralight Operating) but have significantly higher loss per foot.

At HF and for the lengths generally encountered for portable setups, either RG-8X or RG-58 are roughly equivalent. **Table 19.2** is based on 50 feet of cable with a 2:1 SWR antenna system being operated on the 10-meter band. This combination represents a typical limit for a portable station. Lower SWR or lower frequencies will reduce these losses.

These losses are quite modest. Even RG-174 with 30% more signal loss than RG-213 results in less than 1 S-unit lower signal strength at the receiving station. Choosing a cable is thus more often based on price and availability. RG-8X is also generally more durable than RG58, which is worth the extra size and weight to some operators. Finally, some antenna systems which rely on the feed line to act as a counterpoise benefit from the larger surface area of RG-8X cable shield. (Counterpoises are discussed in the **Effects of Ground** chapter.)

Cable rated "direct bury" has a heavy and stiff jacket compared to general purpose cable making it harder to deal with. Even if coax does encounter some water temporarily, it can be thoroughly dried on returning home. It is important, however, to keep water out of the RF connectors. Be prepared to do some light waterproofing in the field that can be easily removed for transport home. A roll of quality vinyl electrical tape such as Scotch 33+ will do the job, and is an important part of a field station repair kit.

The Over-Under Method of Coiling

It is quite frustrating to encounter a coil of wire or cable that unwinds itself into an unending snarl of tangled loops and twists. It's better to learn the skill of coiling cable and wire so that it is not twisted as it is coiled. Once "trained," a cable wound to avoid continuous twists will be easily wound that way again. The best method, used by audio and RF engineers and techs, is known as the "over-under" method.

There are many online videos demonstrating this method. A short and simple demonstration can be seen by searching YouTube (**youtube.com**) for "Over-Under Cable Wrapping". Start by laying the cable out straight and removing kinks and twists. Then, holding the cable's end in one hand, pick up the cable a foot or two away and make one twist of the cable away from you so that the cable forms a loop. Pass that loop to the hand holding the cable end. Repeat, but twist the other way, creating an opposite-coiling loop and pass it to the holding hand as well. This is much easier seen than described in words so watch the video and practice the skill. You won't regret it!

Once coiled, don't use tape to hold the coil together. Hook-and-loop fasteners for cable are widely available and worth the small expense to keep your cables in good order so they can be used over and over again.

Table 19.2 Feed Line Loss

50 feet of cable, 2:1 SWR, 28 MHz

Type	*Loss (%)*	*Loss (dB)*
RG-213	14%	0.65
RG-8X	20%	0.97
RG-58	25%	1.2
RG-174	44%	2.5

19.6.2 Impedance Matching

Amateur transceivers are designed to operate with a 50 Ω resistive load. Significant time is generally spent tuning and tweaking antennas which are installed permanently to get them as close as possible to being this idea load.

Portable scenarios do not provide the luxury of time for extensive tweaking and adjusting. A portable antenna system generally includes compromises for size and weight or available supports. Even antennas resonant by design are often not resonant at exactly the same frequencies depending on how and where they are deployed. The EFHW that tuned perfectly at home might have a SWR shifted away from the desired frequency when deployed "zig-zag" through a tree at the park or at a different angle or height.

Adjustable impedance matching circuits, aka "antenna tuners," are the simplest solutions to these problems. An antenna tuner will compensate for some level of mismatch between the antenna and the radio, without having to adjust either. The degree of mismatch a given tuner can compensate for varies, so having some knowledge of the behavior of your antenna is still required.

Tuners can be either automatic or manual. An automatic tuner is very convenient in that it will work with a low power input and quickly find an impedance match to 50 Ω on its own. The manual tuner may have a similar range of impedances it can match but depends on the operator's skill to find the right settings. See the **Transmission Line System Techniques** chapter for a discussion of tuner circuits and operation.

Automatic tuners built into HF radios are typically limited to an SWR of 3:1 or less. This is enough range to handle an antenna for which resonance has shifted due to how it is deployed. It is also enough capability to extend the workable range of narrow bandwidth (high Q) antenna designs somewhat.

If you require a larger matching range, or if your radio does not include a tuner, then you should consider a dedicated external antenna tuner. A manual tuner offers several not-so-obvious benefits over an automatic tuner in portable situations:

• No electrical power is required to run a manual tuner, conserving precious battery capacity in a portable station.

• Manual tuners have fewer moving parts. While automatic tuners are not necessarily delicate, most manual tuners are sufficiently rugged for portable use.

• Manual tuners generally offer the largest range of impedance matching.

• Manual tuners behave predictably. They only change the impedance when the operator adjusts them. This is sometimes convenient when you have an antenna that is changing on its own such as blowing in the wind or being actively rained upon, and you don't want an automatic tuner trying to compensate, known as "chasing the antenna around."

• Manual tuners work equally well and the same way with any radio

• All else being equal, a manual tuner will generally be less expensive than an automated model.

19.7 References and Bibliography

Baker, A., "The Black Widow — A Portable 15 Meter Beam," *QST*, May 2003, pp 35 – 39.

Brogdon, A., *Low Profile Amateur Radio*, (ARRL, 2006).

Black, B., "The W4SSY Spudgun," *QST*, Mar. 2009, pp. 67 – 69.

Cebik, L., "Two Hilltoppers for 10 Meters," *ARRL Antenna Compendium, Vol 6* (ARRL, 1999).

Cooper, C., "Super Duper Five Band Portable Antenna," *QST*, May 2007, pp. 34 – 36.

Daso, D., "A Skyhook for the 90s," *QST*, May 1997, pp. 31 – 33.

Decesari, R., "A Portable Quad for 2 Meters," *QST*, Oct. 1980, pp. 26-28 and "Portable Quad for 2 Meters, Part 2," Technical Correspondence, *QST*, June 1981, pp. 39 – 40.

DeMaw, D., "A Traveling Ham's Trap Vertical," *QST*, Oct. 1980, pp. 28 – 31.

Dixon, R., "A One Person, Safe, Portable and Easy to Erect Antenna Mast," *QST*, June 2011, pp. 30 – 32.

Even More Wire Antenna Classics, Vol 3 (ARRL, 2014).

Fisher, D., "Supporting Portable Antennas Without Guy Wires," *QST*, May 2011, pp. 30 – 31.

Hall, J., "Zip-Cord Antennas — Do They Work?," *QST*, Mar. 1979, pp. 31 – 32.

Hansen, M., "A Portable 2-Element Triband Yagi," *QST*, Nov. 2001, pp. 35 – 37.

Hansen, M., "Some More VE7CA 2-Element Portable Yagis," *The ARRL Antenna Compendium, Vol 7,* (ARRL, 2002), p. 183.

Hedman, M., "A Two-Element Yagi for 18 MHz," *QST*, Aug. 2018, pp. 38 – 40.

Herring, R., "A Small, Portable Dipole for Field Use," *QST*, May 2003, pp. 33 – 34.

HF Dipole Antennas for Amateur Radio (ARRL, 2019)

Hollister, R., "A Portable NVIS Antenna," *QST*, Jan. 2005, pp. 56 – 58.

Hutchinson, C., "A Tree-Mounted 30-Meter Ground-Plane Antenna," *QST*, Sep. 1984, pp. 16 – 18.

Johns, R., "A Ground-Coupled Portable Antenna," *QST*, Jan. 2001, pp. 28 – 32.

Littlepage, J., "A Portable Inverted V Antenna," *QST*, June 2005, pp. 36 – 39.

McCoy, L., "A Windowsill Semivertical," *QST*, June 1967, pp. 42 – 44.

More Wire Antenna Classics, Vol. 2 (ARRL, 2014).
Parmley, W., "Zip Cord Antennas and Feed Lines for Portable Applications," *QST*, Mar. 2009, pp. 34 – 36.
Portable Antenna Classics (ARRL, 2015).
Portune, J., "Compact 40 Meter HF Loop for Your Recreational Vehicle," *QST*, Mar. 2007, pp. 41 – 43.
Rohde U., and. Siwiak, K., "Tuning Electrically Short Antennas for Field Operation" *Microwave Journal*, May 2019, pp. 104 – 124.
Salas, P., "A Simple and Portable HF Vertical Travel Antenna," *QST*, July 2002, pp. 28 – 31.
Salas, P., "The Ultimate Portable HF Vertical Antenna," *QST*, July 2005, pp. 28 – 34.
Schecter, C., "A Deluxe RV 5-Band Antenna," *QST*, Oct. 1980, pp. 38 – 40.
Siwiak, K., "An Off Center End Fed Dipole for Portable Operation on 40 to 6 Meters," *QST*, Mar. 2015, pp. 44 – 46.
Strickland, B., "Fishing for DX with a Five Band Portable Antenna," *QST*, May 2014, pp. 36 – 41.
Thomas, S., KB1HQS, *Portable Operating for Amateur Radio* (ARRL, 2018).
Victor, R., "The Miracle Whip: A Multiband QRP Antenna," *QST*, July 2001, pp. 32 – 35.
Voorhees, P., "A Portable Antenna Mast and Support for Your RV," *QST*, Sep. 2010, pp. 34 – 35.
Wire Antenna Classics (ARRL, 1998).

TABLE OF CONTENTS

Chapter 20 — Online Material

Articles

- "A Compact Loop Antenna for 30 through 12 Meters" by Robert Capon, WA3ULH
- "A Disguised Flagpole Antenna" by Albert Parker, N4AQ
- "A 6-Meter Moxon Antenna" by Allen Baker, KG4JJH
- "An All-Band Attic Antenna" by Kai Siwiak, KE4PT
- "An Antenna Idea for Restricted Communities" by Cristian Paun, WV6N
- "Apartment Dweller Slinky Jr Antenna" by Arthur Peterson, W7CZB
- "Better Results with Indoor Antennas" by Fred Brown, W6HPH
- "Honey, I Shrunk the Antenna!" by Rod Newkirk, W9BRD
- "Small High-Efficiency Loop Antennas" by Ted Hart, W5QJR
- "Short Antennas for the Lower Frequencies — Parts 1 and 2" by Yardley Beers, WØJF
- "Stealth 6-Meter Wire Beam" by Bruce Walker, N3JO
- Tuning Capacitors for Transmitting Loops
- "Using LPDA TV Antennas for the VHF Ham Bands" by John Stanley, K4ERO
- "A High-Power 160- and 80-Meter Transmitting Loop Antenna" by Steve Adler, VK5SFA
- "K1FM's HF Magnetic Loop" by Alain De Carolis, K1FM
- "HF Magnetic Loop for 80 Through 20 Meters" by John Chappell, W3HX

Chapter 20

Stealth and Limited-Space Antennas

The biggest challenge facing many hams today is putting up an effective antenna. Many homes come with severe restrictions or even prohibitions on external antennas of any sort. Apartment and condominium dwellers have even more limiting circumstances. The traveling ham faces a new set of challenges at every stop. Yet many persevere and have rewarding experiences in Amateur Radio without big towers and high wires. The secret? According to Steve Ford, WB8IMY, author of ARRL's *Small Antennas for Small Spaces*, it's "using the best antenna possible for a given circumstance." That may be a wire in an attic or dangling from a high-rise window but you can get on the air and make lots of contacts. Enjoyable hamming — even DXing — is very achievable without the traditional "aluminum farm" and that is the focus of this chapter.

Much of the material in this chapter is collected from WB8IMY's book mentioned above, Al Brogdon, W1AB's *Low Profile Amateur Radio*, and Steve Nichols, GØKYA's RSGB book *Stealth Antennas*. In addition, several projects from the pages of *QST* and other sources are provided. It is not expected that you will be able to exactly duplicate these designs. Use them as a starting point, adapting to your circumstances, and learn to adjust and work with the resources available. You may also find the **Portable Antennas** chapter interesting reading. The Villages Radio Club, K4VRC (**k4vrc.com**) in one of the largest Florida housing developments has lots of information about limited-space and low-profile antennas on its website under "Resources."

The goal of presenting this collection of antenna designs is to inspire imagination and innovation on the part of the reader. As you review these antennas, think about how you might apply the same styles and approaches to your station. Most antennas for small spaces are just variations of full-size antennas described in other chapters. Antennas can be folded or bent and then adjusted to compensate. Loading coils or wires can be added to make an antenna look larger electrically. An antenna inside a structure may need some retuning but can often be made to work. Perhaps these antennas will answer the question, "Would antenna X work in my situation?" Give your imagination free reign!

Once you have selected a design, be prepared to experiment and adjust. The *antenna analyzer* described in the **Antenna and Transmission Line Measurement** chapter is an invaluable tool for this type of antenna building.

20.1 Installation Safety

Why start with a discussion of safety? Because your antennas will likely be a lot closer to power wiring and power lines than the traditional dipole in the trees. In addition, you and your family and possibly your neighbors will be a lot closer to the antenna than if it is installed outside and well above the ground. The *ARRL Handbook* contains additional information on electrical and RF safety and grounding.

20.1.1 Electrical Safety

Before installing or even designing an antenna, check the area around your home and property for power lines, including the household voltage "service drops" to your house. Don't mistake a power line for a cable TV or telephone line. Working on building roofs or lowering wires and cables over the edge of a building or out a window can place you or a wire or cable in contact with hazardous, even lethal, voltages. Here are some rules to live by:

• Keep all objects — including masts, poles, ladders, tools, and antennas far away from power lines at all times. If in doubt — stop. You can be electrocuted if you are touching anything even a little bit conductive that comes in contact with a power line. High voltage electricity does not need much conductivity to create hazardous currents.

• Antennas and masts should never be closer than 10 feet to a power line or your electrical service wiring.

• If you are moving an antenna or taking one down, look for new power lines that may have been installed or rerouted since the antenna was first put in place.

• Never assume that any power line is insulated — any contact may be lethal.

• Don't rely on fiberglass or wooden poles to act as insulators.

• Know first aid for electrical shock and don't work alone if possible.

Installing indoor and otherwise stealthy antennas invariably means drilling holes through and driving fasteners into walls and ceilings. Before drilling or hammering or driving, be sure that you are not about to come in contact with an electrical wire or a water or gas pipe. If you are in doubt, stop and get professional help. The cost and small delay are minor compared to that of a fire or leak. Remember that detectors designed to find metal piping or conduits will not find plastic pipe.

20.1.2 Personal Safety

You may have seen comedy sketches where someone puts a foot through the ceiling but it isn't very funny when it's your or your friend's ceiling! Take steps to be sure that you are working safely and not placing yourself in a risky position. When working in unusual spaces in, around, or on top of your home, someone else should be at home in case you become stuck or fall.

When working in an attic or crawl space, make sure you have adequate lighting. If you plan on working in these areas frequently, consider installing permanent lighting. At any rate, an ac or battery operated "trouble light" with an LED bulb will provide plenty of light. Carry a strong flashlight with fresh batteries since it is inevitable that you'll be working in the shadows at some point. A head-mounted LED lamp works well.

Do not attempt to walk on attic joists as they make poor footing, leading to the aforementioned ceiling damage and possible injury. Use boards placed across the joists to support your weight. Again, if you expect to be working in the attic regularly, permanently install boards or plywood sheets.

Glass wool insulation is an irritant as the fibers break off and can stick in skin or be inhaled. Wear gloves, long-sleeve shirts and pants when working around insulation. If the insulation is loose (not in batts or rolls) wear a face mask. A face mask is also a good idea in crawl spaces to avoid inhaling rodent or insect droppings, dust or mold spores.

If you are working on a pitched roof, consider using a safety harness sturdily anchored to a tie point or chimney. Review basic climbing safety techniques and equipment in the chapter **Building Antenna Systems and Towers**.

Evaluate whether the antenna, its supports, and any guys or tethers present a safety hazard to someone who isn't looking for the antenna. You may be trying to install the antenna so it *can't* be seen! That makes it easy for someone to walk into a guy line or trip over a feed line, for example. Try to locate or orient the antenna and its various accessory pieces to avoid these accidents. A plastic ball on the end of a whip or rod will cushion any inadvertent contact, as well.

20.1.3 RF Safety

It is a good assumption that the antennas in this chapter will be installed fairly close to people. As such, you should consider the potential effects of your transmitted signal and are required to evaluate your station for RF exposure.

The evaluation procedure — required of all FCC-licensed amateurs — isn't as involved as you might think. No test equipment is required and no paperwork must be submitted to the FCC although you need to log your evaluation results and keep them at your station. An RF safety evaluation amounts to entering some values into an online calculator to determine whether your station is in compliance — it's that simple. (Note that the FCC updated its rules on RF exposure in 2021. See the article "Understanding the Changes to the FCC RF Exposure Rules" at **arrl.org/files/file/Technology/QST20210901.pdf** that explains the changes and what you must do to be in compliance with the rules.)

Figure 20.1 shows the output from the ARRL's RF Exposure calculator at **arrl.org/rf-exposure-calculator**. The antenna was a dipole (2.2 dBi gain) being used on 10 meters (28.3 MHz) for conversational SSB at 100 W PEP. You can include the effects of ground reflections or not.

The calculator mentions *controlled* and *uncontrolled* environments. These terms refer to whether people know RF is present and can take steps to control their exposure. (The **Safe Practices** chapter defines these terms and includes a large section on RF exposure and RF safety. Another resource is the ARRL RF Exposure web page at **arrl.org/rf-exposure**.) Assuming other people live in your home and nearby, values for the uncontrolled environment should be used. Even so, you will probably find that in most cases your station

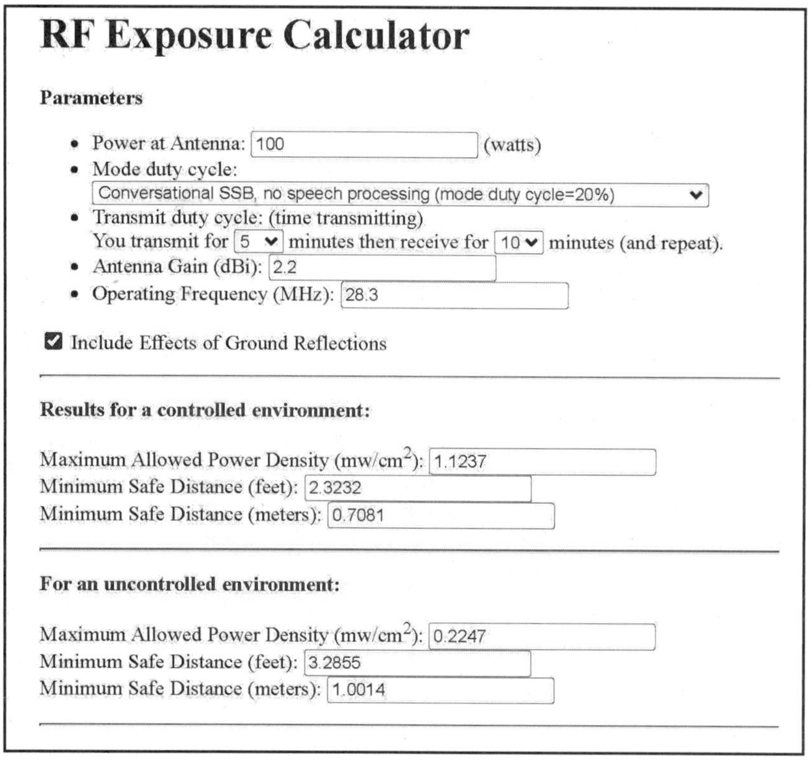

Figure 20.1 — The ARRL's RF Exposure calculator provides a simple report based on frequency, antenna gain, power applied, and operating mode.

is in full compliance when transmitting with 100 W or less and for separations of approximately 10 feet. You will find that you must be running a fair amount of power at VHF or UHF and be fairly close to the antenna to exceed the RF level for compliance. As you use the calculator, print or store the individual reports to create your evaluation record.

Amateurs using small transmitting loops should also be cautious about RF exposure from high field strengths near the antenna. The antenna's high Q means that a lot of energy is present near the antenna, even at low power. A table of safe distances is provided in the Small Transmitting Loops section of this chapter.

20.2 Locations for Antennas

If you live in an apartment or condominium, do you have an attic space overhead? If so, find the access door. It is often hidden away in a closet or utility room. With a ladder or step-stool, grab a flashlight, open the hatch and take a look around. If you can easily (and safely) climb into the attic, go ahead and take some measurements. How much height is available? How much horizontal length? What does the insulation look like? Is it blown-in material or paper-backed batts or do you see sections of insulation with reflective metallic backing? Metallic-backed insulation acts as a shield and rules out such spaces for antennas. The same concern applies to metal buildings or buildings with metal siding or roofing.

As a test, take a portable radio into the space and try to receive signals. If you have a "world-band" shortwave radio, this is a great use for it. Start outside the space by tuning in a signal near a frequency at which you will want to operate. Then enter the space with the radio operating. If the signals stay the same level or get louder, an antenna will probably work well in the space. If the signal levels drop, the space will probably not work well for whatever reason. For VHF/UHF operation, a hand-held radio can be used in the same way.

If you don't have an attic, check out the inside of the apartment. Are there any rooms that might accommodate an antenna secured to the ceiling? If so, how much space is available? If you are considering VHF/UHF antennas, don't neglect the windows, especially if you live above the ground floor or have multiple floor levels. If the windows have metal screens, can they be removed? It is quite possible to be successful in pointing directional VHF/UHF antennas through windows.

Even apartment and condominium dwellers should examine the property for nearby trees. Depending on how restrictive the landlord or condo association might be, trees provide excellent opportunities for discreet long-wire antennas.

If you live in a house, your antenna location options expand considerably. Take a walk around the yard and make some measurements. Look for convenient supports such as trees and note their distances from each other and your house. Make a simple map from your measurements for planning.

Don't neglect the roof of your home. A chimney can support small VHF antennas but is not designed to handle the stresses of larger antennas. You may wish to consider a roof tripod such as are available for large TV antennas. (See the **Building Antenna Systems and Towers** chapter for examples.)

It cannot be over-emphasized that you will likely need to be inventive more than the traditional outdoor antenna builder. Browse websites, read magazine articles and books, and ask other club members about their experiences. The more information you have, the more likely it is that you'll be able to find an acceptable solution for your particular situation with a little experimentation.

20.3 RF Interference

Because your antenna is likely to be close to your living quarters, it will also be close to the many electronic devices in use today, including appliances and security systems. Realistically, you should expect some interference when operating at (or above) the 100-W level. You will probably also experience interference *from* these devices and systems. *The ARRL RFI Book* is an excellent resource to help you deal with interference as is the *ARRL Handbook*.

Nevertheless, many interference issues are quite manageable. Perhaps you can operate with low power. Keep the antennas as far as possible from your electronics and those of your neighbors. Learn how the radiation patterns of your antennas might be used to direct your strongest signal away from them. Study how to apply ferrite chokes to keep your signal out of electronics and vice versa — Jim Brown, K9YC has written an on-line tutorial (see References and Bibliography) about the use of ferrites to fight RFI.

Be especially aware that indoor antennas often couple very strongly to nearby or adjacent power wiring, telephone and network cables, security system wiring, etc. The best solution is to avoid placing antennas in close proximity to other wiring. If that is not possible, be prepared to mitigate interference with chokes and other measures such as the "Resonant Breaker" described in "Better Results with Indoor Antennas" by Fred Brown, W6HPH, included with this book's online material. Archives of the RFI email reflector (**contesting.com/FAQ/rfi**) have a lot of examples of how to deal with a variety of situations. Be sure to follow good reflector etiquette — to avoid asking a question that has already been answered, search the archives first!

Another option is to use modes that concentrate your power into narrow bandwidths, allowing you to communicate with a minimum amount of power. For example, CW, PSK31 or PSK63, and the various *WJST* modes such as FT8 pack the entire signal into a bandwidth of less than 100 Hz. In addition, PSK and *WJST* modes are *constant-power* modes and do not cause clicks and thumps and garbled voices in equipment receiving the signal unintentionally. In fact, PSK and *WSJT* modes are used by many hams with antenna restrictions to make contacts around the world at powers of just a few watts.

20.4 Indoor Antennas

20.4.1 Indoor HF Wire Antennas

The basic antennas presented in the chapters **Loop Antennas** and **General Purpose MF and HF Antennas** can be adapted to many styles of installation. Most of them are quite forgiving of being bent and folded although you will have to make adjustments from the full-size antenna to achieve resonance at the frequency you want. Remember that the more an antenna is folded or coiled, the less efficient it becomes because the radiation from the different parts of the antenna tend to cancel out. Keep as much of the antenna in a straight line as you can.

The common $\lambda/2$ dipole in **Figure 20.2** is a very tolerant antenna. At 14 MHz, it is approximately 33 feet long and can be bent to fit many different rooms, under a roof line or eaves, in a hallway, etc. Very thin wire can be used at low power such as #28 AWG stranded hook-up wire that comes in a number of colors to blend in with the surrounding material. You can use adhesive tape or hooks to hold it against the wall or ceiling. **Figure 20.3** shows a multiband antenna fed with ladder line. You can also use the clear 300-Ω twinlead sold for use with FM radio antennas.

Loop antennas can also be used as long as they are not too much smaller than one wavelength. (Very small transmitting loops are covered later in this chapter.) **Figure 20.4** shows how a loop extended around a ceiling can be fed with low-loss ladder line or twin-lead on multiple bands. Making the loop as large as possible allows it to be effective on the lowest possible frequencies. A loop can also be installed in an attic as described in the section below. Another option is to install a loop around the edges of a roof line as described in the article "160 to 6 Meter Hidden Antenna" by Bruce Walker, N3JO, in his book *Magic Band Antennas for Ham Radio* (see the References and Bibliography).

Attics and upper-story bedrooms under peaked roofs can make a good home for inverted-V style antennas. Support the feed point at or near the peak of the roof and run the legs down the roof joists or to the floor joists. A dual-band inverted-V can be installed with the pairs of legs connected in parallel and run at right angles to each other. Inverted-V wire Yagi antennas for 20 meters and higher frequency bands can also be made if the attic has a desirable orientation.

If you are working in an attic-type space, the simplest way to hold wire against wooden trusses and joists is a plastic coaxial cable clip of the sort used for cable TV wiring. Avoid attaching bare or enameled wire directly against wood. PVC-insulated wire can be carefully stapled directly to wood supports.

To get the feed line from the attic to your transmitter, you may be able to find the cap for an internal wall and drill a hole

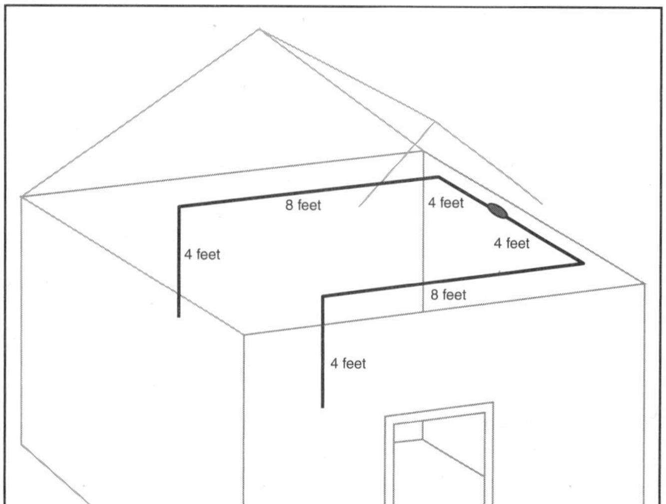

Figure 20.2 — A dipole antenna for the 20-meter band can fit into a small room with a bit of folding.

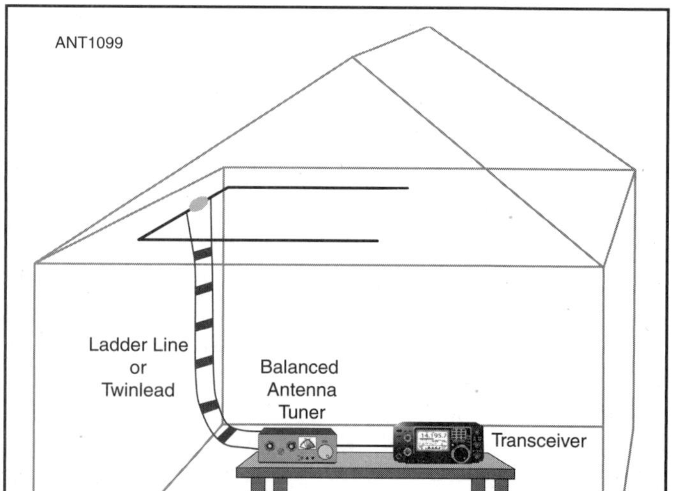

Figure 20.3 — A multiband ceiling dipole fed with ladder line or twinlead. Unlike a tuned dipole, the length isn't critical. As a rule of thumb, make each leg of the dipole as long as the space allows and make sure both legs are of equal length.

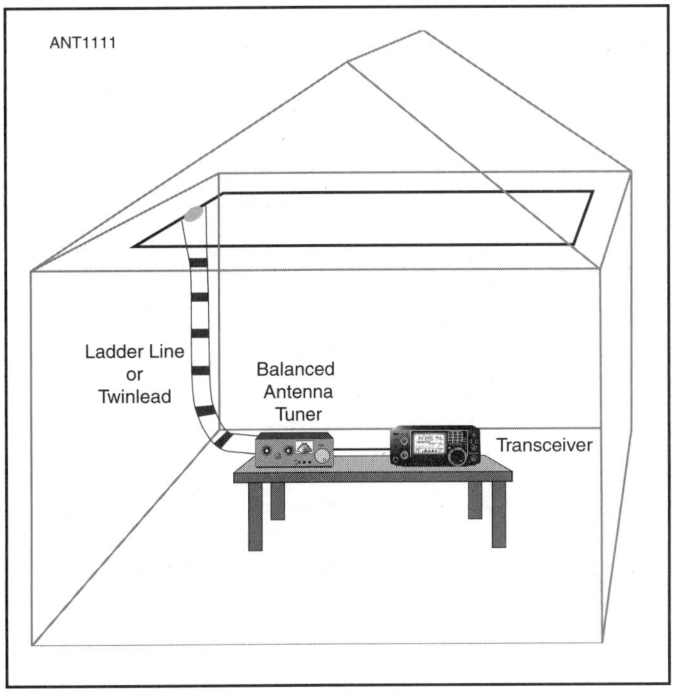

Figure 20.4 — A loop installed around the ceiling of a room can be fed with balanced feed line and a tuner for multiband operation.

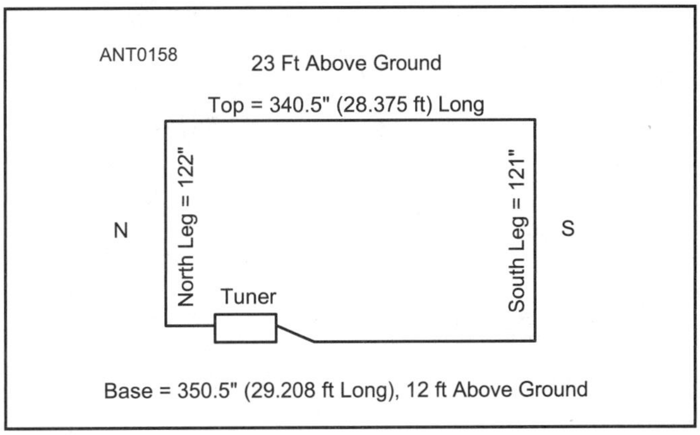

Figure 20.5 — Diagram showing layout of W8TP's indoor hidden loop antenna.

The Slinky Antenna

If folding an antenna reduces its effectiveness, what about coiling it? This is just what happens when a Slinky™ toy is used as the antenna element! The Slinky Antenna was first described in an Oct. 1974 *QST* article by W7ZCB (see the References and Bibliography and this book's online material). As you might imagine, the antenna is nothing more than a dipole made out of two metal Slinky toys and stretched out until resonance is reached. W7ZCB was able to use his version on 80, 40, and 20 meters. It has been reported that the standard Slinky's quarter-wave resonance occurs on 40 meters when stretched to about 7.5 feet, so a full half-wave dipole would be about 15 feet long. This is well within the space available in a good-sized room. If you try this antenna, be sure to get a metal version as there are plastic models, as well.

in it for the feed line to drop down between wall studs. You can then install an "old work" electrical box and an appropriate plastic cover plate for a professional-quality installation. Do not run feed line through the same hole as ac wiring or in conduit carrying ac wiring as that is an unsafe practice as well as increasing the probability of RF interference.

PROJECT: AN INDOOR STEALTH LOOP

Ted Phelps, W8TP, wrote an article in *The ARRL Antenna Compendium Vol 7* describing his attic-mounted wire loop antenna, fed with an automatic antenna tuner. The full article is included with this book's online material.

Figure 20.5 shows the final dimensions of the loop hidden the attic of his condo. The antenna is a single-turn rectangular loop, erected in a north-south vertical plane and made from nearly 78 feet of heavy #6 AWG stranded, aircraft primary wire in a PVC jacket, held taut at the lower corners and supported by a pulley and guy rope at each upper corner. The antenna will provide a mix of vertical and horizontal polarization on the different bands, covering many directions at a wide range of vertical angles.

PROJECT: COMPACT HF LOOP

Rod Newkirk, W9BRD, contributed several designs for multi-turn and tuned loops that can be used on the HF bands. His *QST* article, "Honey, I Shrunk the Antenna!" presented several variations that are suitable for installing in an attic or garage and can also be used for portable operation. (This article is included with this book's online material.)

Figure 20.6 shows a single-turn tuned W9BRD loop that is designed for 40 meters (see the referenced entry for Brogdon, *Low Profile Amateur Radio*). The circumference L should be

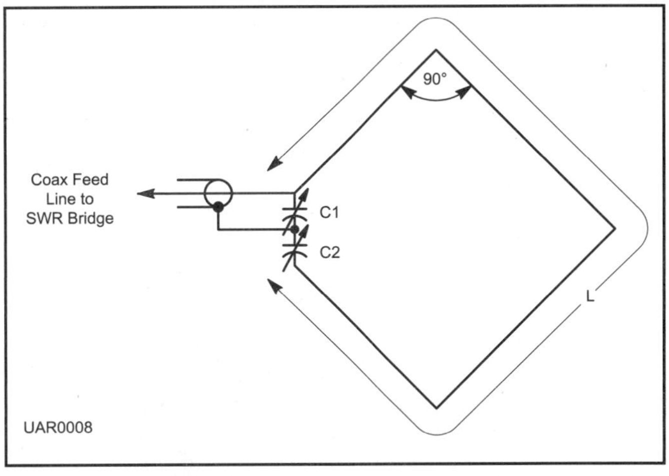

Figure 20.6 — W9BRD's compact loop antenna. L is somewhat shorter than $\lambda/4$ (25 feet for 7 MHz). C1 and C2 are both 300 pF broadcast receiving variable capacitors. The loop can be any shape with a large cross-section.

somewhat shorter than λ/4, about 25 feet for 7 MHz. C1 and C2 are 300 pF must be frequently re-turned since the bandwidth of the loop is about 50 kHz. At power levels of up to 100 W, broadcast-style 365 pF variable capacitors can be used.

To use the loop on the next highest frequency band of 30 meters, insert a third capacitor in series with the loop, opposite the feed point. To use the loop at 14 MHz or higher-frequency bands, you'll have to re-scale the length of the loop accordingly. Smaller-value variable capacitors will make the tuning adjustments less sensitive at higher frequencies, as well.

PROJECT: ALL-BAND ATTIC ANTENNA

This design by Kai Siwiak, KE4PT, describes an inverted L antenna installed in the attic of his home. The system uses an automatic antenna tuner, similarly to the antennas shown in Figures 20.3 and 20.4. The full article is included with this book's online material.

The L is horizontal and laid out as shown in **Figure 20.7**. It comprises two parallel lengths of #9 AWG aluminum wire connected together at the far end, and spaced about 38 inches apart. The horizontal portion is about 48 feet long and a bit more than 14 feet above the ground, under the roof of the house. The horizontal length is approximately one wavelength at 21 MHz so the antenna pattern is very nearly omnidirectional from 20 meters down to 80 meters.

The parallel wires are brought together and emerge from the ceiling on a far wall of the house in a storage closet. Both of the parallel wires are joined together and connected to the antenna post of the AH-4 tuner. Connecting the wires together in this way creates a "thick" radiating element for which the feed point impedance varies more smoothly with frequency and eases the job of the antenna tuner.

A copper ground wire runs from the tuner ground connection to an outside 8-foot ground rod. The antenna shares this ground rod with a conductive mast supporting a 2-meter J-pole that tops out at 21.7 feet. This mast also functions as part of the HF radiating system.

A length of 50-Ω coaxial cable connects the tuner through an eight-turn, 5-inch diameter choke balun to the transceiver at the operating position in the ham station on the other side of the wall of the storage closet.

Indoor antennas should be very carefully considered from the RF exposure point of view, especially for those within the dwelling. A spot check of near fields of the antenna both near the vertical and near the horizontal parts of the wires shows that for this antenna, the 3.3-foot result from the 6-meter 4*nec*2 model gives sufficient compliance distance safety margin on all lower frequency bands. Evaluate unusual antennas very carefully, especially if a ground or ground post is part of the system!

Cool That Hot-Spot with Quarter-Wave Wires

Using indoor, portable, and temporary antennas often results in an RF "hot spot" on the station equipment. The antennas are usually quite close to the station equipment and in the case of a random-wire antenna, may actually use the station equipment as part of the radiating system. If the hot spot is causing RF burns or otherwise upsetting the operator or equipment, the trick of attaching a λ/4 piece of wire to the equipment at the hot spot is often employed. If one end of the wire is left unconnected (open) the other end will present a low impedance at the λ/4 frequency. This can reduce the RF voltage substantially but the other end of the wire will be at a high RF voltage. Be sure to keep the other end of the wire clear of anything conductive, flammable, or where a person can touch it. The hot spot isn't gone, it just got moved to the unconnected end of the wire! Having a set of wires cut for different bands with an alligator clip on one end can be a very handy problem-solving addition to your tool kit.

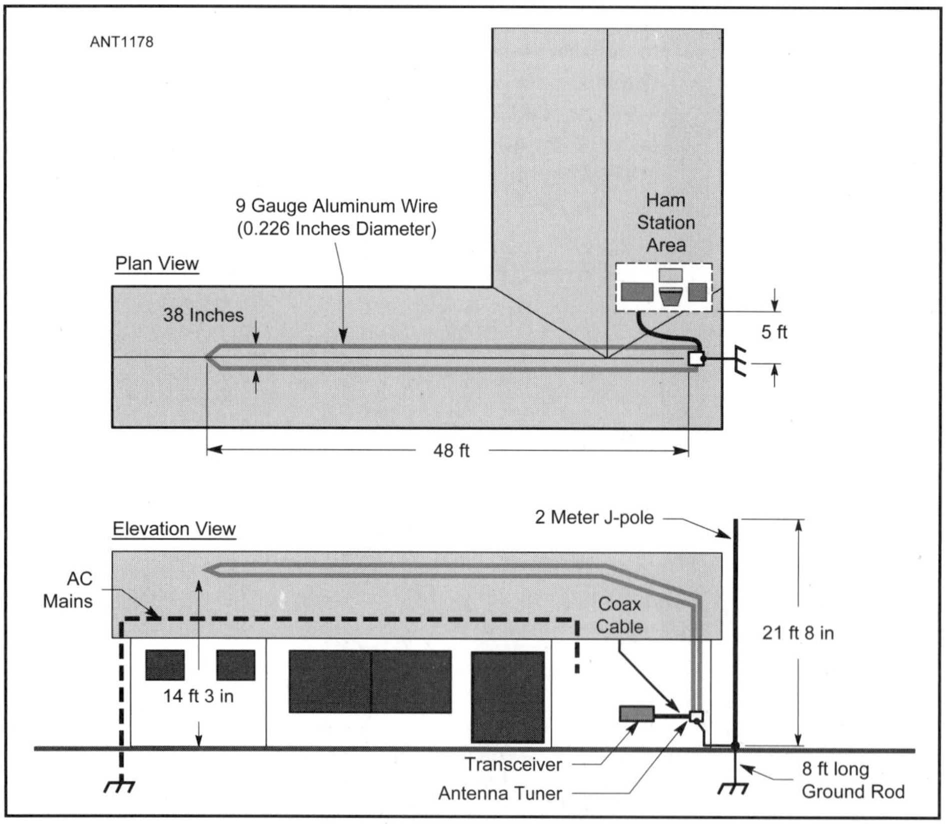

Figure 20.7 — Plan and elevation views of the attic inverted L antenna.

20.4.2 Mobile HF Antennas Indoors

Another popular option for indoor HF use is antennas intended for mobile operation. After all, mobiling is certainly another example of a limited-space application! (See the chapter **Mobile and Marine HF Antennas** for more information about the mobile antennas described in this section.)

The same general concerns for mobile antennas mounted on vehicles apply to mobile antennas used indoors regarding the importance of how the antennas are mounted and having a large conductive surface to act as a ground plane. A mobile whip can be used quite effectively when mounted on a sufficiently large metal surface. For example, a windowsill (see **Figure 20.8**) or balcony railing will suffice. If those metal structures are also tied into a building's steel frame, the antenna will be very effective.

When using a mobile antenna in this way, if the metal item to which the antenna is clamped is not sufficiently large, a counterpoise wire should be added to the system. The counterpoise should be approximately $\lambda/4$ long at the frequency of operation and acts as the "missing half" of the antenna in lieu of a full ground plane. The counterpoise in this case is actually a radiating element and should be kept away from the operator and any electronics. If above the ground floor, the counterpoise can be allowed to hang down alongside the building. There may be significant RF voltage present at the end of the counterpoise so place it where it cannot be touched or arc to another surface.

The popular "screwdriver" mobile antenna (see the **Mobile and Marine HF Antennas** chapter) can also make an effective and tunable HF antenna in an attic or unused room. **Figure 20.9** shows the screwdriver mounted on a ground plane that in turn rests on the ceiling joists. Shorter models are small enough to fit comfortably under a peaked roof. Along with sheet metal any mesh will do for the ground plane, such as hardware cloth or chicken wire. Even aluminum foil could be used, such as on insulation panels. The more extensive the ground plane, the more effective the antenna will be. Screwdriver antennas also have the advantage of being tunable with a remote controller for use on all HF bands.

To lower the frequency range of a screwdriver antenna, the whip can be extended with horizontal wires, either as an Inverted L or as a T antenna. A capacitance hat can be added at the top of a sturdy whip or at the top of the adjustable coil. (See the **Multiband HF Antennas** chapter) The adjustable coil is then used to bring the entire antenna to resonance. Adding whip length (either physically or electrically) may lower the operating range such that a reasonable match on the upper HF bands and 6 meters is no longer attainable. In this case, an auto-tuner at the antenna feed point may be used.

It is also possible to use mobile whips configured to form a

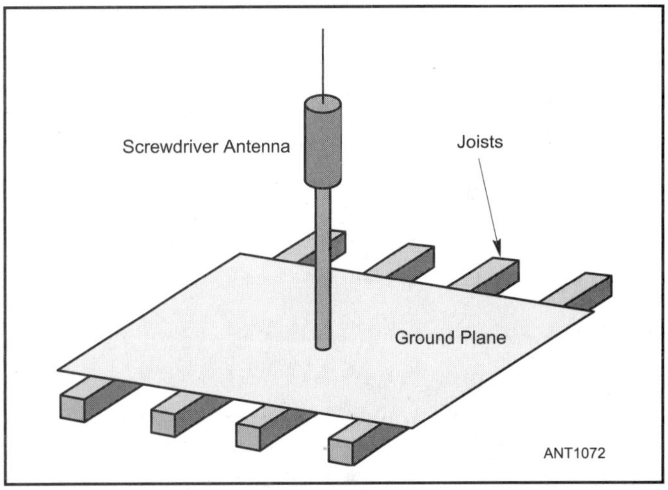

Figure 20.9 — A screwdriver antenna can be mounted on a ground plane for an effective, tunable attic antenna.

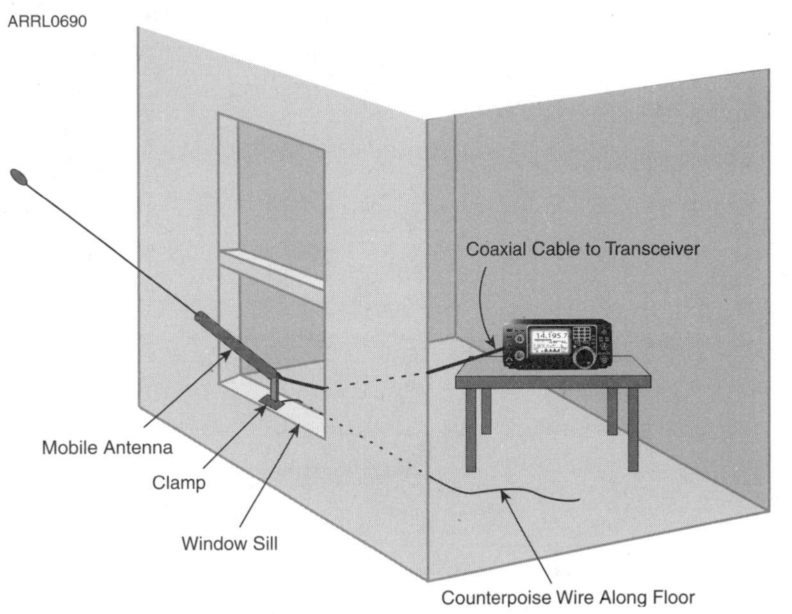

Figure 20.8 — A mobile antenna can be clamped to a windowsill or balcony railing. A counterpoise wire approximately $\lambda/4$ long at the operating frequency provides an additional radiating element to complete the antenna. For multiband operation, a counterpoise cut for each band should be used. If the frame or railing is tied into the building's metal structure, the counterpoise may not be necessary.

Figure 20.10 — This pair of CB mobile antennas were trimmed slightly to resonate on 10 meters then attached to a mounting bracket. This created an effective apartment-sized antenna.

dipole as in **Figure 20.10**. Many antenna parts dealers sell brackets with an SO-239 coax connector and tapped fittings for the popular 3/8-24 threaded antenna base. A pair of mobile whips can be attached as in the figure and supported on a camera tripod or other suitable base. This makes an excellent portable antenna, too.

20.4.3 Indoor VHF And UHF Antennas

Operating with indoor antennas for VHF and UHF operation is much less difficult than creating an effective HF antenna indoors. For example, placing a simple mag mount whip on top of a refrigerator or filing cabinet makes a reasonable base station antenna for local 2-meter or 70-cm FM contacts. Any of the designs for ground-plane antennas in the **VHF, UHF, and Microwave Antenna Systems** chapter is easily adapted to indoor use. The "roll up" J pole designs are particularly good for portable and travel antennas.

An excellent "make do" antenna for 2 meters can be as simple as two pieces of wire. **Figure 20.11** shows the idea. The antenna can be installed permanently, for example on an apartment window, or as a portable antenna that can be taken along when traveling or as part of a "go kit." The wires need not be stiff — small-gauge stranded wire also works quite well. In an emergency situation, this is an easy antenna to construct from almost any source of wire and dimensions are not critical. A short (less than 10 feet) feed line of RG-174 miniature coax is sufficient and keeps the entire package small.

Creating an effective installation for SSB and CW operation — the so-called *weak signal* modes — is more challenging. Horizontal polarization is required for sustained success but it is not always necessary to have multi-element beams. 6 meters provides a lot of opportunities for long-distance contacts to amateurs who can't put up outdoor antennas. Relatively omnidirectional antennas such as a horizontal "halo" (**Figure 20.12**) or dipole can make many contacts, including with distant stations when sporadic E propagation is occurring. (See the **Radio Wave Propagation** chapter.)

Nevertheless, if you can manage an antenna with some directivity, it will help. The 2-element Moxon design for 6 meters described by Allen Baker, KG4JJH, measures 84 ×

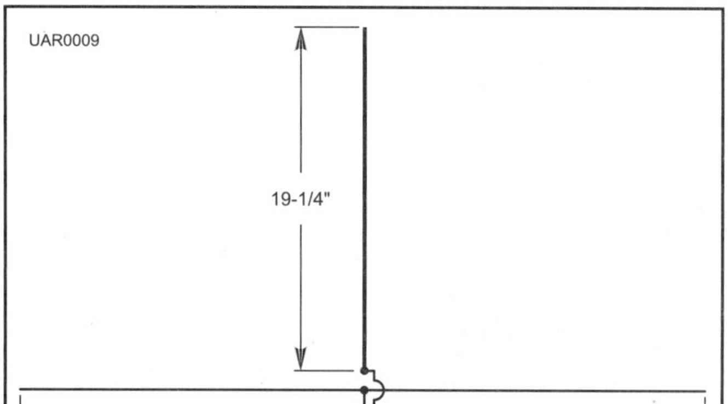

Figure 20.11 — This simple ground plane for 2-meter FM can be made from solid or stranded wire and taped to the inside of a window.

Figure 20.12 — A typical 6-meter horizontal full-wave loop antenna can be used either indoors or outdoors. The radiation pattern is omnidirectional with horizontal polarization.

Figure 20.13 — The 2-meter PortaQuad by National RF isn't intended for permanent outdoor use, but it would be a fine directional antenna inside a room or attic.

31 inches and being flat, is a natural candidate for ceiling mounting. The 3-element wire "stealth" Yagi for 6 meters designed by Bruce Walker, N3JO, is about 10 feet by 5 feet is another good ceiling mount antenna. Both of these articles are included in this book's online material and the book *Magic Band Antennas for Ham Radio* is full of useful antenna designs for limited-space stations.

Quad beams for VHF and UHF are also fairly small antennas, even on 6 meters where quad elements are only 5 feet on a side. A 2-element quad for 6 meters can fit many attic spaces or be suspended from a ceiling mount.

Quads and small beams for 2 meters and higher frequencies are even smaller. **Figure 20.13** shows an example for 2 meters. A light-duty TV rotator can turn any of these antennas. A note of caution — the higher the frequency of operation, the higher the attenuation from building materials as well as rain and snow on roofs, especially at UHF and microwaves.

Don't discount dipoles! These simple antennas give a bit of extra gain over a $\lambda/4$ ground plane and are easy to make and tune. A J-pole, which is really a dipole that is end-fed through a tuning stub, does not have to be vertical and is attic-sized as low as 28 and 50 MHz. If you are really adventurous, try one of the curtain antennas in the **Broadside and End-Fire Dipole Arrays** chapter.

20.5 Outdoor Antennas

This book contains plenty of candidates for outdoor antenna designs in spaces of limited size. The antennas in the chapter **Portable Antennas** address similar limited-space needs as the amateur with a limited fixed space. The builder should start with a good idea of the available supports or ground area, decide on a horizontal or vertical antenna, and begin reviewing the antenna books and articles. Jim Brown, K9YC, has contributed a short paper on antennas suitable for small residential lots — look for Antennas for Limited Spaces at **k9yc.com/publish.htm**.

The main challenge addressed in this chapter, however, is how to put up such an antenna in the face of restrictions against them or when esthetics just don't permit the usual construction techniques. There are two basic approaches to putting up such a stealth antenna; invisibility and disguise.

20.5.1 Invisible and Camouflaged Antennas

An invisible antenna is one that is constructed so as to be difficult to see. Many amateurs have been able to operate for long periods using invisible antennas without being detected. The secret to making an antenna invisible is to think small and thin. Thin wire, small coax, placing the antenna in trees or other foliage — all of these are time-tested techniques for making an antenna "disappear."

Thin wire can be used up to surprisingly high power before its resistance becomes an issue. Assuming you'll be using power levels of 100 W or less, you can use wire as small as #30 AWG. For sizes below #24 AWG, however, the challenge of keeping it up due to breakage becomes the bigger issue. Use stranded wire for better flexibility and be careful not to tension the wire too heavily — it will stretch, then break.

Think "small," too. Insulators, feed points, supporting lines, and coaxial feed line all need to be small so as not to attract the eye. Insulators and feed points can be homebrewed from scrap plastic or fishing supplies. Woven fishing line is usually tough, UV-resistant, and very hard to see against the sky or foliage (just ask the fish!). If possible, use colors that blend in to the surroundings.

Small diameter coax such as RG-174 can be dismayingly lossy (see the table of coaxial cable parameters in the **Transmission Lines** chapter) and should only be used for very short runs. RG-58, RG-59, and RG-6 can be used for longer runs and have the added benefit of looking very much like the cable TV service drop. Parallel-wire lines have much lower loss and are lighter than coax but are much harder to conceal. If you get a good deal on a long length of subminiature Teflon-insulated cable such as RG-393 or similar, it makes a very good miniature feed line.

Camouflage can make the antenna blend in to its environment so it is difficult to see or at least less noticeable. If you are considering an attic loop (see the section on Indoor Antennas) perhaps you could put the same loop outside around the edge of a roof as in **Figure 20.14**. Under the eaves or deck railing can also work. Choose a wire color similar to the background and small, insulating supports to hold the wire.

Look for ways to make your antenna look like or integrate

Making Radials Disappear

How do you create an effective ground screen of radial wires without an unsightly mess covering your lawn? The answer is to let the lawn do the work for you!

Get a large pizza cutter — it will be ruined for kitchen use so don't use the family's prize pie divider. You'll also need a spool of thin stiff iron wire — rebar tie wire will do fine as will the lawn staples available from gardening and landscaping shops. Cut at least a half-dozen 6-inch lengths of wire for each radial you plan on installing and bend them in half to form a narrow U — these are radial pins. Your radial wire can be any convenient type although a dark insulation or enamel coating will help with the disappearing act. Bare wire is fine, too.

Start by mowing the grass as short as you reasonably can. Attach a radial to the base of the antenna and cut a narrow slot in the grass into which you lay your radial wire. As you move away from the antenna, hold the radial down with the radial pins every few feet. The cost of each pin is quite low so use as many as you need.

Once all of the radials are in, water the grass well. A little fertilizer won't hurt. In a matter of days, the grass will have grown high enough to completely hide the radial wires — you won't be able to see them even if you know they are there! Over time, the grass (and the worms) will conspire to pull the wires deeper toward and even below the surface of the ground. The radial pins will also quickly rust away and disappear if you used iron wire. The only thing sticking up out of the yard in a couple of weeks will be the ends of the radials at the antenna.

them into accepted objects. For example, if you have a garden, trampoline, or volleyball net in your back yard, a wire dipole can be woven into the netting very easily. Clothesline can be made out of insulated wire, although hanging wet laundry on it may change the tuning!

20.5.2 Disguised Antennas

A disguised antenna is an antenna that is easy to see but the viewer doesn't recognize it as an antenna! The classic example of the disguised antenna is a flagpole antenna such as that described by Geoff Haines, N1GY in the December 2010 issue of *QST*. To the non-ham, it's a basic flagpole. To the ham, it's a 23-foot ground-plane vertical with an automatic tuner at the base. Albert Parker, N4AQ took a different tack by hiding a Hustler 4-BTV 4-band trap vertical inside a flagpole made of PVC pipe (see References and Bibliography). A windsock can be held up by a fiberglass pole holding a vertical wire as can a bird house or feeder or area lighting. Another long-time favorite method is hiding the antenna near an approved structure such as a drain pipe or gutter. Hams have even used metal gutters and downspouts as antennas with a variety of results but it can be difficult to maintain good connections at joints. With plastic guttering so common, why not put a wire antenna directly into the gutter? With horizontal gutters, pooling water can be a problem but most vertical gutters are immune. Put your antenna in the gutter itself! The challenge will be to get the feed line to the antenna and keep water out of the feed line.

If your gutters or downspouts are metallic, try loading them up as described by Craig LaBarge, WB3GCK at **qsl.net/wb3gck/spout.htm**. Craig's example is just one way of using an automatic antenna tuner and counterpoise wires to create a surprisingly effective, yet completely invisible antenna.

Take a look around and see what metal objects are outside in your yard or around your home. Almost anything can be made into an antenna as the photo in **Figure 20.15** shows. Martin Ehrenfried, G8JNJ (**g8jnj.webs.com**) converted an outdoor drying rack into a vertical dipole with end loading. Lawn chairs, garden tools, sports equipment — any metal object can be made to radiate. The Ventenna (**ventenna.com**) is a roof-mounted antenna for VHF or UHF that looks just like an ordinary drain pipe.

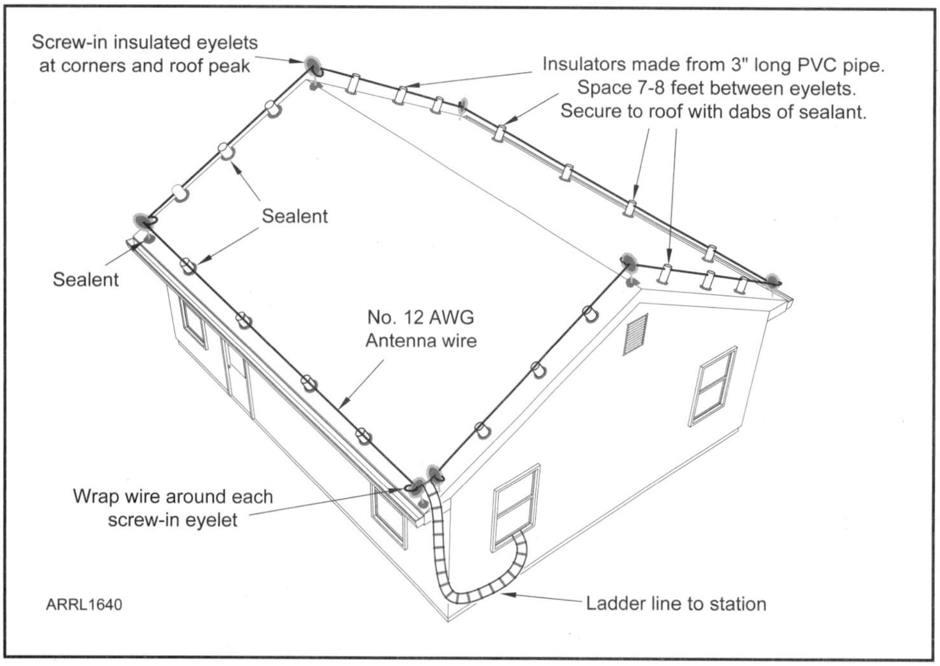

Figure 20.14 — Loops and other wire antennas can be installed around the edges of a roof using small standoff insulators. The feed point can be located near a place where it is convenient for the feed line to enter the building, such as a window frame, next to a downspout, or through a vent pipe.

Figure 20.15 — Martin, G8JNJ, converted a scrap laundry drying rack into a stealthy HF vertical. At A is the complete antenna showing the top and bottom counterpoise and capacity hat, respectively. B shows the upper capacity hat. [Photos courtesy of the RSGB and Martin Ehrenfried, G8JNJ]

Figure 20.16 — A rooftop 2-meter antenna made from PVC pipe and heavy-duty 2-inch wide foil tape. A coax pigtail is attached inside of the pipe. The antenna is adjusted using the TUNE and MATCH tape segments.

For 2-meter use, take a look at the W6NBC slot antennas made from a satellite dish and a piece of PVC vent pipe. The satellite dish antenna is described in the **VHF, UHF, and Microwave Antennas** chapter. The antenna in **Figure 20.16** is a slot antenna constructed by attaching aluminum foil to a plastic sleeve that fits over a rooftop drain pipe. If you don't want to run the feed line across the roof, a hole in the vent pipe will allow it to be lowered into the building. At a convenient spot, drill a hole in the wall and pipe for the feed line to exit.

20.5.3 Modified TV Antennas

That's not a typo, TV antennas can really be modified for use on the amateur bands! With over-the-air broadcast DTV having established a sizeable presence, TV antennas are once again popping up on rooftops and chimneys. The most familiar TV antennas are an LPDA with V-shaped elements for the lower frequency channels. (See the **Frequency-Independent Antennas** chapter.) The lower TV bands, VHF Channels 2 – 6 (54 – 88 MHz) are received with the four largest elements, while Channels 7 – 13 (175 – 216 MHz) use the same elements operating in the third harmonic mode. A corner reflector with a dipole at its focal point is often used to receive the lower UHF channels while multiple parasitic directors at the front of the antenna are used for the higher UHF channels.

John Stanley, K4ERO, has contributed an article about converting one of these antennas to cover the 50, 144, and 222 MHz bands. It is included with the online material for this book. The procedure involves lengthening some of the elements and removing the higher UHF elements. The 300 Ω feed system impedance was retained and the antenna used with 300 Ω twin-lead which is very light and has the additional benefit of maintaining the disguise of the antenna as a TV receive antenna. A 6:1 impedance transformer could be used to convert 300 Ω to 50 Ω or a 4:1 transformer could be used with low-loss RG-6 cable. A tuner at the transceiver could then take care of any resulting mismatch.

It is a very effective disguise to look like something familiar. In this case, people are used to TV receive antennas, various covenants and restrictions usually allow them, and they are often available for free. In fact, K4ERO used pieces from a second TV antenna to lengthen the lower-channel elements for use on 6 meters.

Painting for Minimum Visibility

It is possible to paint an antenna to make it less noticeable for your neighbors. The color will depend on the background colors, of course. If the antenna will be viewed against trees, a dark color like green, black, or brown will blend in well. Against the sky, painting the antenna light gray or a greenish-blue will help it blend in like a water tower. The US Air Force and US Navy know that a mid-range "primer gray" color has the least visibility in a wide variety of settings.

Getting the paint to stay on the antenna will take some careful preparation of the surface. Talk with someone in the paint store about what you are painting — they may have some guidance about how to clean and prime the surface. Follow the instructions on any preparation compounds carefully to be sure your paint job is a success. Peeling paint is quite visible in any color! Be sure the paint is specified for outside/external use so that solar ultraviolet and temperature swings don't cause it to break down.

Finally, you can usually get paint in several finish styles. From the most to least reflective: gloss and high-gloss, satin, matte or flat. The most reflective are also the easiest to clean and might collect the least dirt or algae. Satin is somewhat reflective. Matte and flat are almost the same with plenty of pigment but their rougher finish may get dirtier faster.

20.6 Small Transmitting Loops

Small transmitting loops such as the one shown in **Figure 20.17** have become very popular for portable and temporary operation. They are small enough to fit on an apartment balcony or patio, in a garage, or in an attic, as well. The section on these antennas in the **Loop Antennas** chapter covers them in detail.

As noted earlier in this chapter's section on RF Safety, amateurs using small transmitting loops should be cautious about RF exposure from high field strengths near the antenna. It is common to see photos of the operator and radio on a picnic table with the loop antenna just a few feet away. **Table 20.1** provides a list of safe distances based on frequency and power. Because these popular loop antennas are often used in portable operation, careful attention should be paid to insuring RF exposure limits are not exceeded and that people cannot inadvertently get too close to the antenna.

When building or assembling these loops, take extra care to avoid loose or corroded connections. Radiation resistance of small loops is very, very low and any resistance in a connection or component will reduce efficiency dramatically. Connectors should be tight and adjustable joints clean and snug. Avoid placing the loop near conductive surfaces or structures where the antenna's field can couple to lossy elements. Ferrite chokes (see the **Transmission Line System Techniques**) should be used to decouple the feed line from the antenna, as well.

If you use the loop inside a building constructed with large amounts of iron or other conductive materials, you will simply have to live with the loss if the loop cannot otherwise be relocated. For that reason, avoid placing loops in attics with metal roofs or where metal siding is nearby.

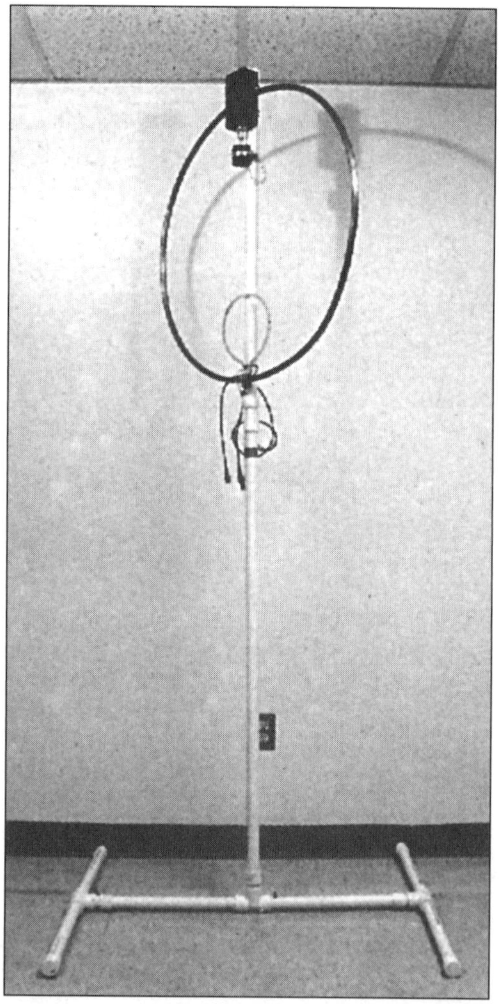

Figure 20.17 — Photo of compact transmitting loop designed by Robert Capon, WA3ULH. This uses a 1-inch PVC H-frame to support the loop made of flexible ⅝-inch copper tubing. The small coupling loop made of RG-8 couples the loop to the coax feed line. The tuning capacitor and drive motor are at the top of the loop, shown here in the ARRL Laboratory during testing.

20.6.1 Constructing Small Transmitting Loops

This section is based on material contributed by Rich Quick, W4RQ. There is an optimum balance between the size of the HF loop, the thickness of the conductor and the relative size of the feeding loop that results in an antenna that has the widest tuning range with close to 50 Ω feeding impedance. Small HF loops are typically between 0.08 and 0.4 λ in circumference over the operating range. That works out to approximately 3 meters in circumference for an HF loop the covers 7 to 30 MHz. All else equal, a larger loop will be more efficient than a smaller loop.

It is important to note that the usual construction techniques for antennas can create excessive losses in small loops. Loop radiation resistance is on the

Table 20.1
Minimum Compliance Distances from Small (1.0 m diameter) Transmitting Loops

Freq (MHz)	*Controlled Distance (m)*	*Uncontrolled Distance (m)*
Power = 10 watts		
7	2.1	2.9
14	2.1	2.9
18	1.9	2.7
21	1.8	2.5
28	1.5	2.1
Power = 100 watts		
7	3.3	4.3
14	3.4	4.7
18	3.1	4.4
21	2.9	4.2
28	2.5	3.9*
Power = 400 watts		
7	4.2	5.7
14	4.5	6.5
18	4.2	6.9*
21	4.0	7.1*
28	3.7*	7.3*

** - Electric field limit*

UK ICNIRP compliance distances from "Safety distances for small HF loop antennas," AE7PD, Radcom, June 2017, pages 46 and 47.

Figure 20.18 — This high-power loop by VK5FSA uses very heavy conductors to reduce losses. All connections are welded or very low resistance to minimize losses.

order of fraction of an ohm. To minimize resistive losses, solder or weld all connections that carry antenna current. Sliding contacts, clamped joints and connections, and undersized conductors can hurt performance significantly. Bolted connections should be avoided because at RF these joints generally have high resistance, especially after being subjected to weathering. Do not use crimp or clamp joints for the same reason.

For portable and temporary use, try to permanently assemble as much of the antenna as possible with soldered or welded connections. Where sections of tubing are joined, use a long concentric sleeve with lots of contact area and large sheet metal screws with tight threads in both pieces of tubing. Straps or leads should be of very heavy wire with soldered terminals that have a lot of contact area. Clean all contact surfaces before assembling.

A circular shape provides the best radiation resistance to conductor loss resistance ratios, hence is most efficient. Loop conductor diameter should be between 1 and 5 cm. Heavy conductors help reduce losses. For a given cross-section, tubular conductors will be less lossy than flat conductors because of current bunching at flat conductor edges. Using a continuous piece of tubing will minimize conductor losses.

The lowest loss material practical for HF antennas is pure electrical grade copper. T60 aluminum alloys have 66% the conductivity of electrical grade copper. Avoid the high loss of construction grade aluminum and soft copper tubing. Flexible tubing made with a lead-copper alloy should be avoided due to increased resistivity. Rigid copper tubing, refrigeration tubing or large copper wire should be used. Often it is convenient to fashion loops from RG-213, LMR-400, LMR-500, or LMR-600 coax cable. These work well, especially for portable loop antennas. Using hardline cable with a solid copper shield is both low-resistance and mechanically sturdy.

Components in a resonant transmitting loop are subject to both high currents and voltages as a result of the large circulating currents found in the high-Q tuned circuit formed by the antenna. Loop circulating current can range from about 8 A at 10 W to more than 25 A at 100 W RF input power. This makes it important that any fixed capacitors have a high RF current rating, such as transmitting micas or the Centralab 850 series.

Be aware that even a 100-W transmitter can develop currents in the tens of amperes, and peak voltages across the tuning capacitor in excess of 5000 V. This consideration also applies to any conductors used to connect the loop to the capacitors. A piece of #14 AWG used as a jumper and carrying a high current may create more loss than the rest of the loop conductor! It is therefore best to use copper strips or large diameter wire to make any connections. Make the best electrical connection possible, using soldered or welded joints.

The tuning capacitor should be very high Q — greater than 1000 to 4000. For example, a very high-quality tuning capacitor with no mechanical wiping contacts, such as a vacuum-variable or a transmitting butterfly capacitor, might have an unloaded Q of about 5000. This implies a series loss resistance of less than about 0.02 Ω for a capacitive reactance of 100 Ω. This relatively tiny loss resistance can become significant, however, when the radiation resistance of the loop is only on the order of 0.1 Ω!

The highest Q capacitors are vacuum variables, followed by butterfly air dielectric capacitors. Both are hard to find and can be expensive. Often an inexpensive but lower-Q dual-stator capacitor is used. The key is to find a variable range that can resonate with the loop inductance over the desired tuning range. Avoid capacitors that have mechanical 'wiper' connections in the circuit path. They are lossy. Ensure that the capacitor peak voltage rating is sufficient for the loop transmitter power. Use heavy gauge wire to connect the capacitor to the loop.

Because of the sensitivity to loss in the tuning capacitor, there is a lot of interest in designs that avoid sliding or wiping contacts. For example, a "trombone" tuning capacitor design (see "Tuning Capacitors for Transmitting Loops" in the online material) uses concentric copper tubing to construct the linear version of a butterfly capacitor, controlled by a dc motor similarly to a screwdriver mobile antenna.

An enclosure surrounding the capacitor can affect the Q, and therefore losses, dramatically. Use a polymer enclosure that does not absorb RF energy. Wooden enclosures might be inexpensive and look good, but some types of wood can absorb RF energy, especially after absorbing moisture.

If you are not sure about an enclosure's effect on RF, place a piece of the material in a microwave oven together with a glass of water. (The material must *not* have any metal fasteners or fittings.) The water provides a load for the oven in the case of a low-loss material. Run the oven on high for about 1 minute. If the material heats up, it absorbs RF, don't use it. Be careful, a piece of lossy material can become hot enough to burn you!

For portable loops that use coax and coaxial connectors for portable assembly, use gold plated connectors since gold will not corrode or oxidize. Make sure the connectors are well-tightened during assembly as a loose connector is very lossy in these antennas.

A secondary feeding loop circumference should be about 20% of the main loop circumference and located opposite the capacitor resonated gap. A gamma-type feeding arrangement is also possible for single band operation, but the gamma match can distort the radiation pattern of the loop. A toroidal transformer match might also be suitable for single-band operation.

SMALL LOOP PROJECTS

There are many buildable designs in the literature and online using all sorts of loop conductors, tuning components, and methods of assembly. Several are listed here and need to be evaluated carefully for your circumstances. (Three design articles from *QST* are included in the online material.) For example, a permanently installed indoor loop does not need waterproof enclosures or connections. A loop that is used temporarily and then disassembled needs easily disconnected parts, even if that adds loss resistance to the antenna. Wherever you can, take steps to improve efficiency by lowering losses and the antenna will perform better!

A high-power design by Steve Adler, VK5SFA illustrates the careful attention that must be paid to the high voltages and currents in the typical loop. In this case, to use high power, a vacuum-variable capacitor and all-welded and soldered connections are shown in **Figure 20.18**. This is not a lightweight antenna! The photo illustrates low-loss components and connections.

Loops for lower power use are described in the articles "K1FM's HF Magnetic Loop" by Alain, De Carolis, K1FM, and "HF Magnetic Loop for 80 Through 20 Meters" by John Chappell, W3HX. The first article is aimed at portable loop operation from a backyard or away from home. This loop can be easily disassembled for transport or storage. The second has a more robust construction that is designed for permanent installation. Finally, a very well-designed loop is presented by Jerry Clement, VE6AB, at **jerryclement.ca/MachineShop/Antenna-Werks/i-WHQvdc5**.

20.7 References and Bibliography

A. Baker, "A 6-Meter Moxon Antenna," *QST*, Apr. 2004, pp 65-69.

A. Brogdon, *Low Profile Amateur Radio*, 2nd edition (Newington: ARRL, 2006). (out of print but available used)

F. Brown, "Better Results with Indoor Antennas," *QST*, Oct. 1979, pp. 18-21.

J. Brown, "RFI, Ferrites, and Common Mode Chokes For Hams," **audiosystemsgroup.com/publish.htm**.

S. Ford, *Small Antennas for Small Spaces* (Newington: ARRL, 2011).

M. Gruber, Ed., *The ARRL RFI Book*, 3rd Edition (Newington: ARRL, 2010).

G. Haines, "Constructing a Flagpole Antenna," *QST*, Dec. 2010, pp. 30-32.

E. Hare, *RF Exposure and You* (Newington: ARRL, 1998). (Out of print, but available for download from **arrl.org/rf-exposure**.)

I. Grigorov, *Urban Antennas*, *Vol. 1*, *Antennex* Online Magazine, 2001.

J. Malone, "Can a 7 foot 40m Antenna Work?." *73*, Mar. 1975, pp. 33-38.

R. Marris, "An In-Room 80-Meter Transmitting Multiturn Loop Antenna," *QST*, Feb. 1996, pp. 43-45. Also see Feedback, *QST*, May 1996, p. 48.

S. Nichols, *Stealth Antennas,* 2nd edition (Potters Bar: RSGB, 2014).

A. Parker, "A Disguised Flagpole Antenna," *QST*, May 1993, p. 65.

A. Peterson, "Apartment Dwellers' Slinky Jr Antenna," *QST*, Oct. 1974, pp. 22-23.

T. Phelps, "A Hidden Loop Antenna," *The ARRL Antenna Compendium, Vol 7* (Newington: ARRL, 2002), pp. 160-162.

B. Walker, *Magic Band Antennas for Ham Radio* (Newington: ARRL, 2018).

TABLE OF CONTENTS

Chapter 21 — Online Material

Articles

- "How To Build A Capacity Hat" by Ken Muggli, KØHL
- "Screwdriver Mobile Antenna" by Max Bloodworth, KO4TV
- "Table of Mobile Antenna Manufacturers" by Alan Applegate, KØBG
- "Optimum Design of Short Coil Loaded High-Frequency Mobile Antennas" by Bruce Brown, W6TWW

Support Files

- MOBILE.EXE - Mobile whip design software by Leon Braskamp, AA6GL

Chapter 21

Mobile and Marine HF Antennas

Mobile antennas are designed for use while in motion. At the mention of mobile antennas, most amateurs think of a whip antenna mounted on an automobile or other vehicle. While it is true that most mobile antennas are vertical whips, mobile antennas can also be found in other places. For example, antennas intended for use aboard a boat or ship are usually called *marine* or *marine antennas*. Whip antennas are common in marine service, but wire antennas attached to masts are also common.

Few amateurs construct their own antennas for HF mobile and marine use, since safety requirements dictate very sound mechanical construction. (A short directory table of mobile antenna manufacturers is included with this book's online material.) Even if commercially made antennas are installed, most require some adjustment to optimize the particular installation and type of operation desired. The information in this chapter will provide a better understanding of the requirements for designing and choosing HF mobile antennas and using them effectively.

The chapter begins with a discussion of mobile antenna fundamentals at HF, updated from previous editions by Alan Applegate, KØBG. The following sections explain the more important attributes of the most popular designs and how to get the best from them. This will include mounting, impedance matching, and other important issues to all types of mobile antennas. Several examples of mobile antenna installation are provided. Information on constructing a capacitive hat-loaded whip and an adjustable "screwdriver" HF mobile antenna is included with this book's online material.

The second half of the chapter covers marine HF antennas for sail and power boats. The material was contributed by Rudy Severns, N6LF, and John Thompson, K3MD. The text discusses important issues regarding placement and safety of the marine HF system. Several examples of common installation practices are given, based on antenna designs presented elsewhere in this book.

21.1 HF Mobile Antennas

21.1.1 HF Mobile Antenna Overview

High frequency mobile antennas come in every imaginable configuration of efficiency, overall length, quality, design, sturdiness, ease of mounting, and selling price. The design, mounting method employed, and most importantly where the antenna is mounted, all affect maximum efficiency — the most important aspect of HF mobile and portable operation. The right combination of strengths and weaknesses depends on how you expect to use the antenna. **Figure 21.1** shows a typical mobile whip installation for HF operation.

Propagation conditions and ignition noise are usually the limiting factors for mobile operation on 10 through 28 MHz. Antenna size restrictions affect operation somewhat on 7 MHz and much more on 3.5 and 1.8 MHz. From this perspective, perhaps the optimum band for HF-mobile operation is 7 MHz.

If you intend to chase DX, 20 meters and above are perhaps the best choices as antennas for those bands offer the best efficiency for a given physical size. For local communication, 28 MHz is also useful since a full-size whip is not too large for convenient use and is easy to build. In fact, a slightly shortened CB whip works very well.

On the HF bands, full-size antennas are impractical, and

Figure 21.1 — A simple HF mobile whip can be mounted on almost any vehicle. (Ward Silver, NØAX, photo)

some form of electrical loading is employed to shorten the antenna. Commonly used loading techniques consist of placing a coil at the base of the whip (base loading), or at the center of the whip (center loading). These and other techniques for reducing the physical size of antennas are discussed in this section.

For typical antenna lengths used in mobile operation, the difficulty in constructing suitable loading coils increases as the frequency of operation is lowered. Radiation resistance of the antenna decreases as the antenna becomes electrically shorter. In addition, the required inductance to resonate the antenna gets larger. The result is that the fraction of the applied power lost as heating in ohmic losses increases and the antenna becomes less efficient.

References to "ground" in this section are to the total system consisting of the vehicle's metal surfaces that conduct return current to the antenna feed point as well as the Earth around the vehicle that couples capacitively to the vehicle and antenna.

Designing short HF mobile antennas requires a careful balance of loading coil Q, loading coil position in the antenna, ground loss resistance, and length-to-diameter ratio of the antenna. The optimum balance of these parameters can be realized only through a thorough understanding of how they interact. The information in this section is practical suggestions based on that understanding.

An extensive discussion of loading techniques for short vertical antennas is included in the **Dipoles and Monopoles** chapter. A complete mathematical approach to designing coil-loaded whip antennas was first published by W6TWW in the *ARRL Antenna Compendium, Vol 1* (see the References and Bibliography section) and is available in this book's online material. Finally, the program *MOBILE.EXE*.also performs several key calculations and may be downloaded from the online information.

21.1.2 Inductive Loading

Mobile antennas shorter than λ/4 wavelength operate below their resonant frequency and have a feed point impedance that is highly capacitive. For the average 102-inch whip, the capacitive reactance may range from about –150 Ω at 21 MHz to as high as –8,000 Ω at 1.8 MHz, while the radiation resistance R_r, varies from about 15 Ω at 21 MHz to as low as 0.1 Ω at 1.8 MHz. The equivalent series-RC circuit is shown in **Figure 21.2**.

Figure 21.3 shows the approximate capacitance of whip antennas of various average diameters and lengths. For 1.8, 4 and 7 MHz, the loading coil inductance required (when the loading coil is at the base) would be approximately the inductance required to resonate in the desired band (with the whip capacitance taken from the graph). For 10 through 21 MHz, this rough calculation will give more than the required inductance, but it will serve as a starting point for the final experimental adjustment that must always be made.

For an antenna less than 0.1 λ long, the approximate radiation resistance is:

$$R_r = 273 \times (\ell\, f)^2 \times 10^{-8}\,\Omega$$

where ℓ is the length of the whip in inches and f is the frequency in MHz.

Since the radiation resistance is low, to dissipate power as radiation, considerable current must flow in R_r. However, little current can be made to flow in the circuit with a comparatively high series reactance. To cancel out the capacitive reactance and tune the antenna to resonance, we add a loading coil (inductance) of equal, but opposite reactance in series with the antenna as shown in **Figure 21.4**.

BASE LOADING

Placing the loading coil at the bottom of the antenna is referred to as *base-loading*, and many practical mobile antenna systems have been built using this scheme which is convenient mechanically.

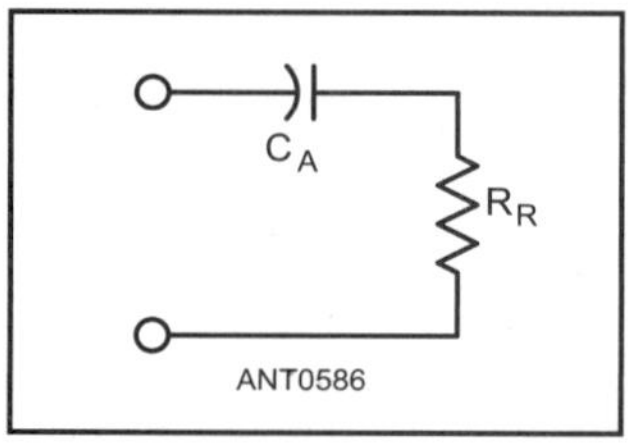

Figure 21.2 — At frequencies below resonance, the whip antenna will show capacitive reactance as well as resistance. R_R is the radiation resistance, and C_A represents the antenna capacitance.

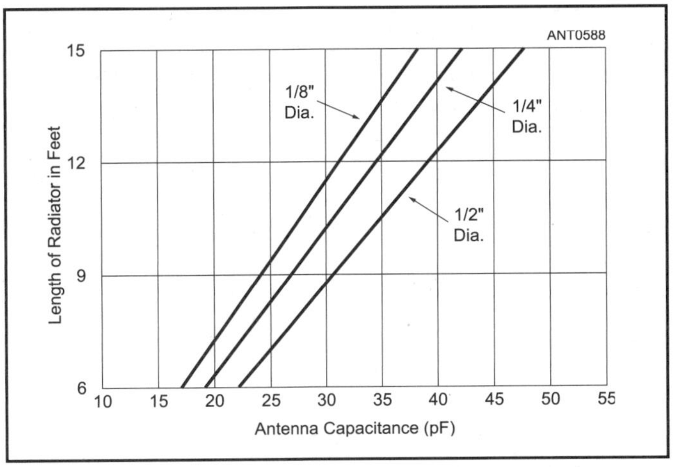

Figure 21.3 — Graph showing the approximate capacitance of short vertical antennas for various diameters and lengths. These values should be approximately halved for a center-loaded antenna.

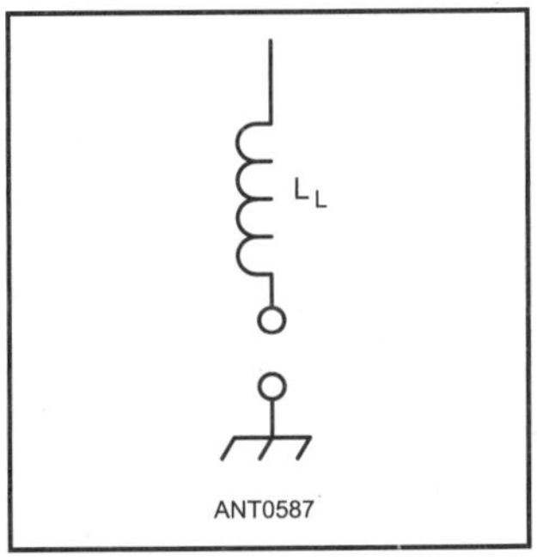

Figure 21.4 — The capacitive reactance at frequencies below the resonant frequency of the whip can be canceled by adding an equivalent inductive reactance in the form of a loading coil in series with the antenna.

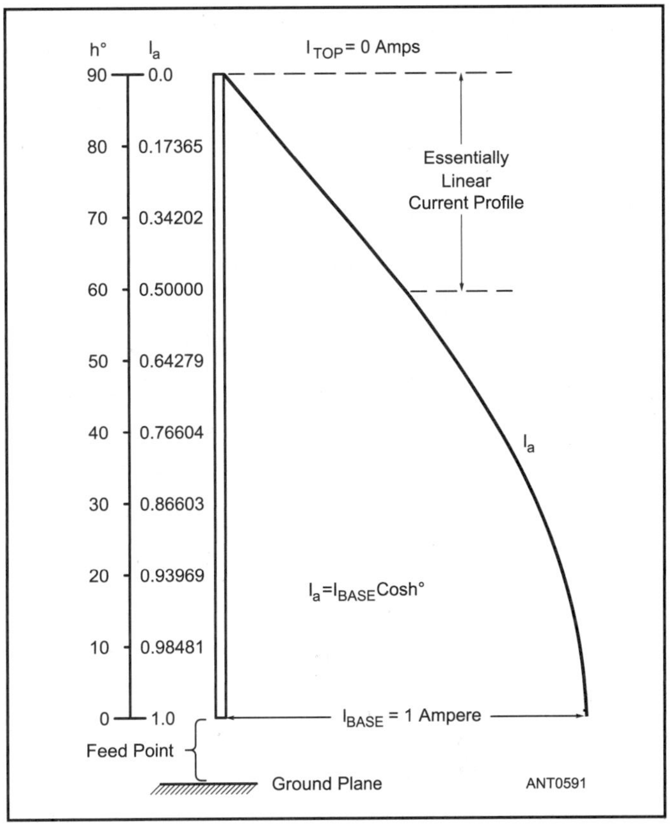

Figure 21.5 — Relative current distribution on a vertical antenna of height h = 90 electrical degrees.

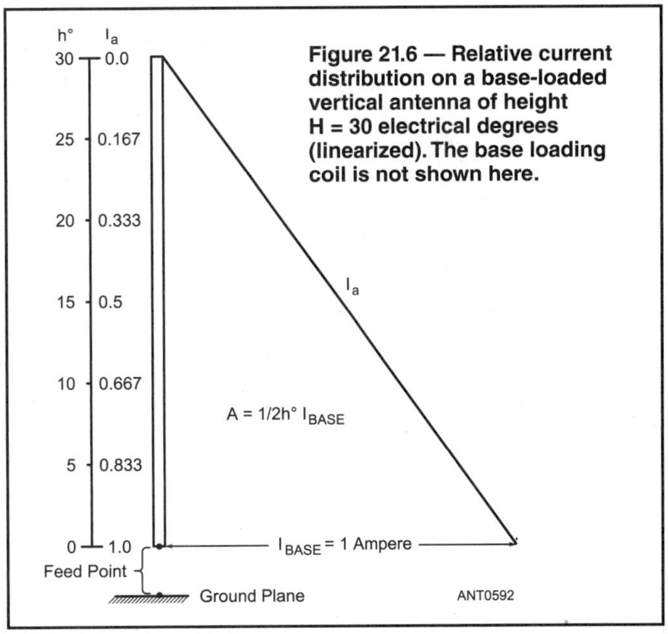

Figure 21.6 — Relative current distribution on a base-loaded vertical antenna of height H = 30 electrical degrees (linearized). The base loading coil is not shown here.

In an unloaded λ/4 whip (electrically 90 degrees long), current is maximum at the base in the feed point (see **Figure 21.5**). It follows a sinusoidal distribution with electrical height (h_{elec}) in degrees or radians, $I = I_{base} \cosh (h_{elec})$, tapering to zero at the top of the whip. Note that most of the current flows in the bottom section of the antenna.

Now add the loading inductor. The inductor is a lumped constant inductance and maintains constant current throughout the coil. As a result, the current at the top and bottom of a coil (ignoring losses for now) is the same. This "forces" more current into the top section than would flow in the equivalent section of a full, 90-degree whip. Current is still a maximum at the base and in the loading coil, tapering to zero at the top of the whip as shown in **Figure 21.6**. This increases losses in the coil and associated ground system for current returning to the feed point. The point of maximum radiation from the antenna is also at the lowest point of the antenna.

CENTER LOADING

One method of improving the current distribution and radiated field strength over base loading is to place the loading coil farther up the whip, as shown in **Figure 21.7**, creating a *center-loaded* antenna. The position of the coil that creates maximum efficiency varies depending on several factors, including the frequency of operation, coil Q, and resistive ground losses. However, mounting the coil at about 40% of the antenna's height (measured from the base) is a good compromise, and yields the best overall average in antenna efficiency across the HF bands.

Table 21.1 shows the approximate loading coil inductance for the various amateur bands for both base-loaded and center-

Table 21.1
Approximate Values for 8-foot Mobile Whip

f(MHz)	*Loading L (μH)*	*R_C(Q50) (Ω)*	*R_C(Q300) (Ω)*	*R_R (Ω)*	*Feed R* (Ω)*	*Matching L (μH)*
Base Loading						
1.8	345	77	13	0.1	23	3
3.8	77	37	6.1	0.35	16	1.2
7.2	20	18	3	1.35	15	0.6
10.1	9.5	12	2	2.8	12	0.4
14.2	4.5	7.7	1.3	5.7	12	0.28
18.1	3.0	5.0	1.0	10.0	14	0.28
21.25	1.25	3.4	0.5	14.8	16	0.28
24.9	0.9	2.6	—	20.0	22	0.25
29.0	—	—	—	—	36	0.23
Center Loading						
1.8	700	158	23	0.2	34	3.7
3.8	150	72	12	0.8	22	1.4
7.2	40	36	6	3.0	19	0.7
10.1	20	22	4.2	5.8	18	0.5
14.2	8.6	15	2.5	11.0	19	0.35
18.1	4.4	9.2	1.5	19.0	22	0.31
21.25	2.5	6.6	1.1	27.0	29	0.29

R_C = loading coil resistance; R_R = radiation resistance.
*Assuming loading coil Q = 300 and including estimated ground-loss resistance.

Table 21.2
Suggested Loading Coil Dimensions

Req'd L (μH)	*Turns*	*Wire Size*	*Dia. (Inches)*	*Length (Inches)*
700	190	22	3	10
345	135	18	3	10
150	100	16	2.5	10
77	75	14	2.5	10
77	29	12	5	4.25
40	28	16	2.5	2
40	34	12	2.5	4.25
20	17	16	2.5	1.25
20	22	12	2.5	2.75
8.6	16	14	2	2
8.6	15	12	2.5	3
4.5	10	14	2	1.25
4.5	12	12	2.5	4
2.5	8	12	2	2
2.5	8	6	2.375	4.5
1.25	6	12	1.75	2
1.25	6	6	2.375	4.5

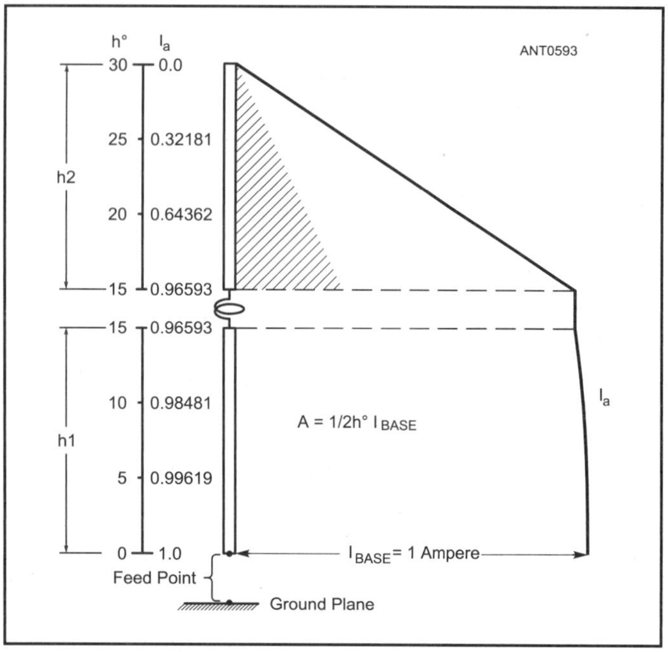

Figure 21.7 — Relative current distribution on a center-loaded antenna with base and top sections each equal to 15 electrical degrees in length. The cross-hatched area shows the current distribution that would exist in the top 15 degrees of a 90-degree-high vertical fed with 1 ampere at the base.

loading whips. Also shown in the table are approximate values of radiation resistance to be expected with an 8-foot whip, and the resistances of loading coils — one group having a Q of 50, the other a Q of 300. A comparison of radiation and coil resistances will show the importance of reducing the coil resistance to a minimum, especially on the three lower frequency bands. **Table 21.2** shows suggested loading-coil dimensions for the inductance values given in Table 21.1.

LOADING COIL LOSSES

Minimizing loading coil resistive losses also increases efficiency, particularly important on heavily loaded antennas for the lower HF bands. To accomplish this, the loading coil should have a high ratio of reactance-to-resistance (that is, a high unloaded Q). Loading coil loss resistance is a function of the coil Q:

$$R_{COIL} = \frac{X_L}{Q}$$

where R_{COIL} is the loss resistance, X_L is the reactance, and Q is coil quality factor.

A loading coil for use at 4 MHz, wound with small wire on a small-diameter solid form of average quality and enclosed in a metal protector, may have a Q as low as 50, with a loss resistance of 50 Ω or more. High-Q coils require a large conductor, air-wound construction, large spacing between turns, and the best insulating material available. A diameter not less than half the length of the coil (but no larger than ≈3 inches), and a minimum of metal in the magnetic field of the coil are also necessities for optimum efficiency. Such a coil may show a Q of 300 or more at 4 MHz, with a resistance of 12 Ω or less.

Higher Q values can be obtained by using larger diameter coils having a diameter-to-length ratio of two, by using larger diameter wire, by using more spacing between turns, and by using low-loss supporting and enclosure materials. In theory, loading coil turns should not be shorted for tuning purposes because shorted turns somewhat degrade Q. Pruning to resonance should be done by removing turns from the coil.

In fairness, it should be pointed out that many practical mobile antennas use large diameter loading coils with shorted turns to achieve resonance. The popular "Texas Bug Catcher" coils and screwdriver antenna types come to mind here. (See the section "HF Mobile Antenna Types.") Despite general cautions against shorting turns, these systems are often more efficient than antennas with small, relatively low-Q, fixed loading coils.

TUNING THE LOADING COIL

Pruning the antenna to resonance should be done by removing coil turns, rather than by shorting turns or shortening the whip section excessively. Shortening the whip reduces radiation efficiency, by both shortening the antenna and moving the optimum coil position. Shorting turns in the loading coil reduces the Q of the coil.

21.1.3 Capacitive Loading

Another way to increase efficiency is to increase the capacitance in the top portion of the antenna through the use of a *capacitance hat or capacity hat*, as discussed in the chapter on **Dipoles and Monopoles**. This is also referred to as *top loading*. Unfortunately, the wind resistance of a capacity hat makes it somewhat unwieldy for mobile use. If a capacity hat is used to increase efficiency, it must be properly mounted at the very top of the antenna. Beside the increased wind loading, the chances of snagging on a tree limb or other obstruction are also increased.

No matter where the hat is located, the added capacitance will be the same. However, if placed too close to the coil, the added capacitance will decrease efficiency by increasing current losses in the coil. The most effective position is at the very top of the antenna. This requires robust antenna construction and mounting techniques but the increase in performance is worth the effort.

At a minimum, hats should be placed at least half their diameter above the coil and as far away from vehicle metal as possible. If the hat is mounted near the loading coil, there will be an *appearance* of greater efficiency, increased bandwidth, and higher input impedance. But it will be due to increased losses in the loading coil!

21.1.4 Ground Loss

In a short, coil-loaded mobile antenna, a large portion of the power fed to the antenna is dissipated in ground and coil resistances. (Remember that "ground" refers to the entire system of the vehicle body and soil around the vehicle.) A relatively insignificant amount of power is also dissipated in the antenna conductor resistance and in the leakage resistance of the base insulator. Because these last two losses are both very small and difficult to estimate, they are neglected in considerations of radiation efficiency.

Ground loss is a function of vehicle size, placement of the antenna on the vehicle, and conductivity of the ground over which the vehicle is traveling. It is only feasible to control the first two variables. Larger vehicles provide better ground planes than smaller ones. The ground plane created by the vehicle is only partial, so the result is considerable RF current flow (and loss) in the ground around and under the vehicle.

By raising the antenna base as high as possible on the vehicle, ground losses are decreased. This results from a decrease in antenna capacitance to ground that also increases the capacitive reactance to ground. This, in turn, reduces currents and losses in the actual ground around the vehicle.

Since R_r for short whip antennas is quite low, loss resistance increases the feed point impedance, making it closer to 50 Ω. This reduces SWR and creates a false sense that the antenna is functioning well without impedance matching. As a general observation, HF mobile antennas for bands below 20 MHz that do not need matching to create a low SWR are probably inefficient due to loss resistance.

21.1.5 Impedance Matching

The base impedance of short, high-Q coil-loaded antennas is quite low. For example, an 8-foot antenna optimized for 3.9 MHz with an unloaded coil Q of 300 and a ground-loss resistance of 2 Ω has a base input impedance of about 13 Ω. This low impedance value causes a standing wave ratio of 4:1 in 50-Ω coax at resonance. This high SWR is not compatible with the requirements of solid-state transmitters. Also, the bandwidth of shortened vertical antennas is very narrow. This severely limits the capability to maintain transmitter loading over even a small frequency.

You can transform the low resistance of the whip to a value suitable for a 50-Ω system with a shunt-feed arrangement, such as an L network. The latter may only require a shunt coil or shunt capacitor at the base of the whip since the net series capacitive or inductive reactance of the antenna and its loading coil may be used as part of the network (see **Figure 21.8**). This is similar to the hairpin or beta match on an HF Yagi as described in the **Transmission Line System Techniques**

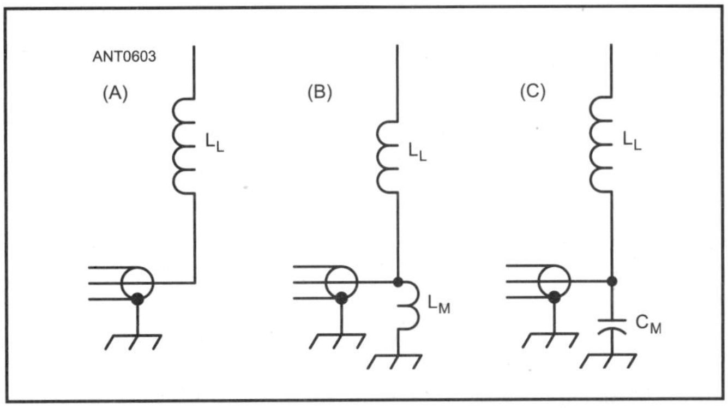

Figure 21.8 — At A, a whip antenna that is resonated with a center loading coil. At B and C, the value of the loading coil has been altered slightly to make the feed point impedance appear reactive, and a matching component is added in shunt to cancel the reactance. This provides an impedance transformation to match the Z_0 of the feed line. An equally acceptable procedure, rather than altering the loading coil inductance, is to adjust the length of the top section above the loading coil for the best match.

chapter. Matching networks should be designed for minimum loss to maximize the transmitter power available at the antenna.

The use of a shunt coil in parallel with feed point is the preferred matching methodology for two reasons. First, it provides a dc ground for the antenna which helps control static buildup. Second, once adjusted, no further adjustment is needed to cover all the HF bands as you can see from the calculated values for L in Table 21.1. Thus, it is an ideal matching scenario for remotely tuned antennas.

The value of the canceling shunt reactance, X_P, may be found from the formula:

$$X_P = \frac{R_f Z_0}{\sqrt{R_f (Z_0 - R_f)}}$$

where X_P is the reactance in Ω, R_f is the feed point resistance, and Z_0 is the feed line impedance. For $Z_0 = 50\ \Omega$ and $R_f = 13\ \Omega$, $X_P = 29.6\ \Omega$. At 3.9 MHz, the inductance required is $L = X_P / 2\pi f = 0.53\ \mu H$.

TUNING WITH A SHUNT REACTANCE

Continuing with the example above, an inductive shunt matching will be used with the antenna as in Figure 21.8B, where 29.6 Ω is needed for L_M. at 3.9 MHz. This requires a coil of 0.53 μH placed from the whip feed point terminal to ground.

The adjustable whip section above the loading coil should be set for minimum height. Use an antenna analyzer or vector impedance analyzer to check the SWR across the band to find where a minimum occurs. Assuming it is below the desired frequency, shorten the whip slightly and check again. It should be moved approximately ¼ inch at a time until the SWR reaches a minimum at the center of the desired range. If the frequency at which the minimum SWR occurs is above the desired frequency, repeat the procedure above, but lengthen the whip only slightly.

If a shunt capacitor is used instead, start with the adjustable whip section at maximum length and shorten it gradually in small steps. In either case, move away from the whip when checking SWR and conduct the tuning process with the antenna in the clear.

USING AN AUTOMATIC TUNER

High-frequency mobile antennas have limited bandwidth, especially on the lower bands, where small changes in frequency result in large increases in SWR due to their high Q. In these cases, an automatic antenna tuner may be used if it is not operated too far from resonance. On the lower HF bands, this allowable range may be no more than a few tens of kilohertz. When possible, the tuner should be mounted as close to the antenna as possible to minimize high SWR losses in the feed line.

21.2 HF Mobile Antenna Types

21.2.1 The Screwdriver Antenna

No doubt the biggest change in HF mobile operation has been brought about by the screwdriver antenna. Originally conceived by Don Johnson, W6AAQ, the basic design has become ubiquitous, available from many different manufacturers. They consist of a large, hollow lower mast, an extendable coil assembly, and a whip, typically 60 to 96 inches long.

The unused portion of the coil is stored in the mast of the antenna. Finger stock at the top of the mast contacts the coil across one or two turns. A dc motor, controlled remotely, drives a screw arrangement that extends or retracts the coil to tune lower or higher in frequency, respectively. That tuning can be done while in motion is an attractive feature, hence their popularity.

A decent quality, high-Q, screwdriver antenna is not inexpensive and can cost upward of $1000, although most are about half this amount. They're relatively heavy and require both a feed line (coax), and a motor control cable. Some varieties also use a reed switch to count the turns of the screw (see the "Mobile Antenna Controllers" section).

Shortened versions of the screwdriver are available from several manufacturers and have become very popular. Their light weight, short length, and ease of mounting, account for their popularity. However, because of their short overall length and low-Q coils, they take a big hit in performance over their full-sized cousins, especially when mounted on lip mounts. They also require some special considerations when coupled to automatic antenna controllers, as covered later.

It should be noted that not all models use the same mounting scheme. Some use standard ⅜-24 mounts, and at least one uses a ¾-inch mount. Some form of base insulator is also required in most cases.

If you wish to build your own screwdriver antenna, a project is included with this book's online material.

21.2.2 Monoband Antennas

There are several types of monoband antennas, including the "bug catcher", linear-loaded varieties, and the ever-popular Hustler series.

BUG-CATCHER ANTENNAS

The "bug catcher" shown in **Figure 21.9** in which a large air-wound loading coil is used for center loading, can be the most efficient of all the mobile antenna types, if mounted

Figure 21.9 — A "bug catcher" style antenna showing the large, air-wound center-loading coil in the center of the antenna with a capacitance-hat at the top. This antenna was designed and constructed by VE6AB.

correctly. (The name derives from the tendency of the coil to "catch bugs" while in motion.) However, it has several drawbacks, not the least of which is wind loading, especially when equipped with a capacitive top-hat, which is discussed later. The design tends to be heavier than other monoband antennas, requiring heavy-duty mounting and base springs — even guys to keep them stable at highway speeds. Bug-catcher antennas, are monoband by nature but can be made multiband. The usual practice is to make the coil large enough in reactance to resonate the antenna on 80 meters. Then a jumper wire is used to short coil turns to resonate the antenna on the higher bands. However, shorting turns reduces coil Q and lowers efficiency.

HELICAL-WOUND ANTENNAS

These lightweight antennas, referred to by the trade name "Hamsticks," are quite popular due to their low cost and reasonable performance. They look like the continuously loaded antennas in the next section except most of the inductance is created by a single, fixed-value loading coil.

The antenna itself is a fiberglass tube or rod with a small-gauge wire wound around it in a few turns, creating a bottom section of the antenna that is approximately straight. At the top of the tube, the wire winding changes to close-wound, creating a loading coil and the antenna is topped off with a short, adjustable-length whip, commonly referred to as a *stinger*. The lower the frequency of operation, the longer the section of close-wound wire. On 80 and 75 meters, the close-wound section covers most of the tube, leaving only the stinger as the radiating section of the antenna.

Due to their light weight, a mag-mount, angle, or trunk lip mount may be used with surprisingly good results considering their low Q, and relatively short length (≈7 feet). Changing bands requires changing the complete antenna, but most models have quick-disconnects available making the task quicker and easier. As a rule, they don't require impedance matching, as their overall losses bring the input impedance very close to 50 Ω.

CONTINUOUSLY LOADED ANTENNAS

There are several manufacturers of both monoband and multiband antennas that could be described as continuously loaded. (Sometimes referred to as "linear loaded," this is not the linear loading technique used to shorten dipoles and beam antennas.) For these antennas, loading is done using multiple fixed-value inductors spaced over the length of the antenna or winding a continuous coil with a large pitch (ratio of turn length to turn diameter) along the antenna.

The multiband versions use what is commonly called a "flying lead" connected at the base, which in turn connects to taps between the coils placed along the body of the antenna to select the band.

Proponents incorrectly argue that the large length-to-diameter, up to 25 to 1, allows the coil to radiate, thus increasing efficiency. However, what little advantage this form of loading has, it is more than offset by the low coil Q, and short overall length (4 to 7 feet).

These antennas typically do not require matching, but a few models exhibit input impedances of greater than 100 Ω and thus need to be matched.

SHORTENED DIPOLES

A few amateurs opt to purchase two identical mobile antennas and mount them in a V configuration. Knowing that ground loss is the dominate factor in determining antenna efficiency, they reason that replacing the ground loss with a second antenna is a viable solution. Brackets that mount on a small mast are available for mounting two mobile whips with an SO-239 connector for attaching a feed line.

While they're correct that it increases radiation resistance as well as the feed point input impedance, efficiency remains largely the same because ground loss has been replaced with the second antenna's loss of about the same magnitude. Gain claims are often unrealistic, as well. A full-size, lossless dipole in free space has a maximum theoretical gain of 2.15 dBi — higher values assume the presence of ground reflections and antenna heights of ½ wavelength or more which are impractical at best for a mobile station.

STAINLESS STEEL WHIPS

Almost without exception, most whips referred to as "CB whips" are made from 17-7 stainless steel wire. Their overall length is 102 inches but at one time 108- and 120-inch versions were available. They are made from wire about 0.220 to 0.250 inch in diameter that is straightened and ground down to an OD of 0.200 inch. Beginning at about 60 inches above the base, they're tapered down to 0.100-inch OD at the tip. The whip is finished off with a swaged-on ⅜-24 threaded brass base fitting and a small corona ball added at the tip.

Stainless steel isn't the best of RF conductors, especially on the lower HF bands. When compared to an aluminum conductor of the same size, the additional resistive losses may reduce the ERP (effective radiated power) by ≈3 dB on 160 meters, depending on the overall length of the whip in use.

The unfortunate truth is, there is no viable alternative with the strength and flexibility of stainless steel! Whips can be copper plated (a costly step) but the improvement is minimal. Covering the whip with silver-plated copper braid is easy to do, but again, the ERP improvement versus the additional wind loading might not be worth the effort.

CORONA BALLS

The small corona balls supplied atop standard CB whips provide a slight amount of eye protection but their effect on reducing corona is questionable. What is corona and how does a corona ball prevent it?

The highest RF voltage occurs at the very top of the whip. Under the right weather conditions, it is possible to see the corona discharge from the end of a pointed whip even when running modest power levels. *Corona discharge* is caused by the small radius of the whip's tip creating large differences in voltage (voltage *gradients*) that exceed the breakdown voltage of air across small distances. This causes the air to ionize and conduct. The discharge then extends away from the antenna as "streamers" until voltage is reduced below the level of ionization. Static discharges from the pointed tip can also become a problem on receive. If in contact with or very near dry vegetation, the discharge can start a fire, as well.

The solution is to replace the pointed end with a smoother, larger surface. The corona ball's smooth, round surface reduces voltage changes with distance that cause corona discharge. The corona ball must be large enough to be effective — at least 0.5 inch in diameter and preferably 1 inch — and are available from several *QST* advertisers. Above 1 inch, wind loading becomes a problem.

CAPACITANCE HATS

The addition of a capacitance hat (discussed earlier) to an HF mobile antenna has both benefits, and drawbacks. Several of the benefits are greater efficiency, increased bandwidth, and higher input impedance which makes matching easier. Some of the drawbacks are increased wind loading and complexity, higher weight, and the requirement of greater overall structural strength of the antenna and mounting hardware. For more practical information on capacity hats, visit **k0bg.com**.

Adding capacitance to the portion of the antenna above the loading coil effectively increases the overall electrical length which raises the point of maximum current from the base further towards the loading coil's position. This increases the radiation resistance, making the antenna more efficient, and to a lesser degree, increases the bandwidth.

The hat may consist of a single stiff wire, two or more wires, a disc made up of several more wires like the spokes of a wheel, a set of loops, or wire arranged as the spokes of a wheel as shown in **Figure 21.10**. The larger the hat (physically), the greater the capacitance and the greater the effective increase in electrical length. Since less inductance is required to resonate the electrically longer antenna, coil losses will also decrease. Plans for a capacitive hat hub designed and made by KØHL are provided with this book's online information and include suggestions on where to buy materials. The supporting whip in this case is a 102-inch CB whip that has been cut down to 60 inches.

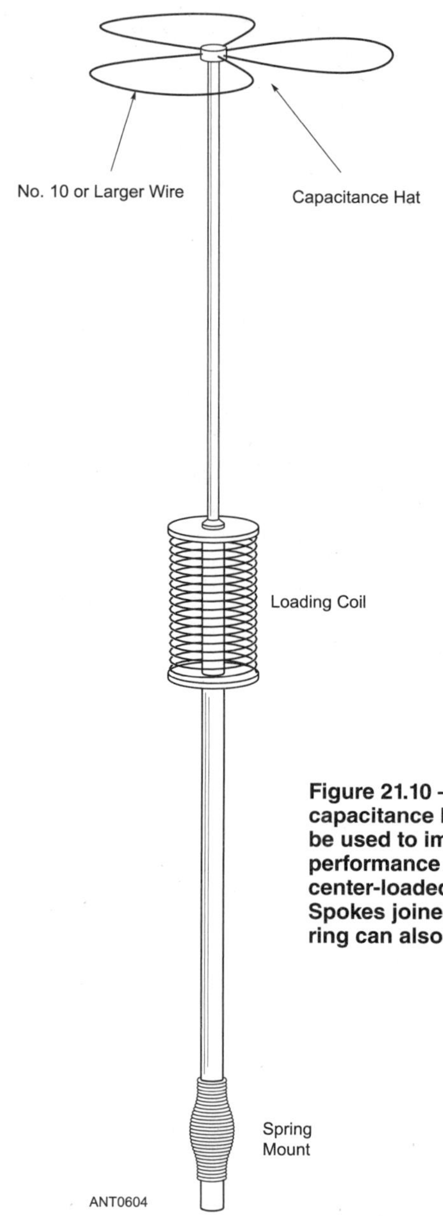

Figure 21.10 — A capacitance hat can be used to improve the performance of base- or center-loaded whips. Spokes joined by an outer ring can also be used.

When this hat is mounted atop a Scorpion 680 screwdriver antenna, 80- through 17-meter operation is possible. Measured field strength improvement over an unloaded 102-inch whip is between 3 dB and 6 dB, depending on the band.

21.2.3 HF Antenna Mounts

Antenna mounts for HF antennas come in so many different styles that it is difficult to decide which is best for any specific installation. Several popular styles are discussed below. Feed line connections may be simple wire lugs, an SO-239 connector, or a coaxial cable with a PL-259 or another RF connector installed. Mounts are available that attach directly to the vehicle, clamp on to a part of the vehicle, or use a magnet to hold the antenna. (See the chapter **VHF and UHF Mobile and Rover Antennas** for information about mounts for those bands.)

Which mount you pick and where you install it depends on many factors. Among them are weight, overall length, frequency of operation, the vehicle in question, and personal preferences. Weight may be as much as 20 pounds for a full-sized screwdriver or bug-catcher antenna. The length may be as much as 13 feet or more for a full-sized HF whip. The key phrase for mounting the antenna is: *It is the metal mass directly under the antenna, not what's alongside, that counts the most!*

It is important to mention that modern vehicles often use aluminum or composite materials, rather than steel for body panels. Aluminum, while durable and lightweight, does not have the structural strength, nor the resistance to vibration of steel. Before installing body-style mounts of any kind on aluminum bodied vehicles, consult the manufacturer's published data for proper methods. Mounting antennas directly on composite panels *should not* be attempted since doing so may create cracks or tears and the non-conductive composite does not provide any ground-plane surface.

Regardless of which mount you use, remember that the maximum legal height for vehicles, including the antenna, is 13½ feet. Gas stations, garages, and tree branches can be considerably lower and inflict serious damage to the antenna and sometimes the vehicle. You will become vigilant about clearance while driving with a mobile antenna!

Another often-overlooked requirement is deciding on which side of the vehicle the antenna should be mounted. For rear-mounted antennas, the driver's side of the vehicle is preferred. This can be very important if you live in an area with low bridges and overhanging trees as there is typically more clearance toward the center of the street. Further, it is easier to see the antenna in the side mirrors if they are on the driver's side. If you've chosen front mounting, common when pulling a trailer or RV, then it should be mounted to the right to avoid distraction or obstruction of your vision.

Whatever method you choose for mounting your antenna, it must be sturdy enough to hold the weight and withstand the wind loading imposed by the antenna without too much flexing. It should be attached in such a way to maximize what little ground plane a vehicle represents. Keep in mind, no matter what the antenna, permanent and secure mounting maximizes performance and safety.

3/8-INCH THREADED HARDWARE

Many mobile antenna mounts use a male or female 3/8-24 threaded stud and receptable. Ball mounts, clip and lip mounts, and mag mounts are frequently supplied with this type of threaded base.

The studs themselves are often stainless steel, but some are mild steel or brass. If the antenna in question is heavy or particularly tall, a strong stud is in order. A replacement stud can be easily made from a 2-inch, Class 8 bolt by cutting off and redressing the threaded portion. The resulting stud has over twice the strength of the stainless-steel version.

BALL MOUNTS

Ball mounts as shown in **Figure 21.11** require a vertical or near-vertical surface on a sturdy metal panel. Commercially available mounts come with the base insulator and backing washers or plates for a sturdy installation. Current model vehicles may use thin sheet metal or composite materials for body panels so be sure of the strength and type of material before installing a ball mount.

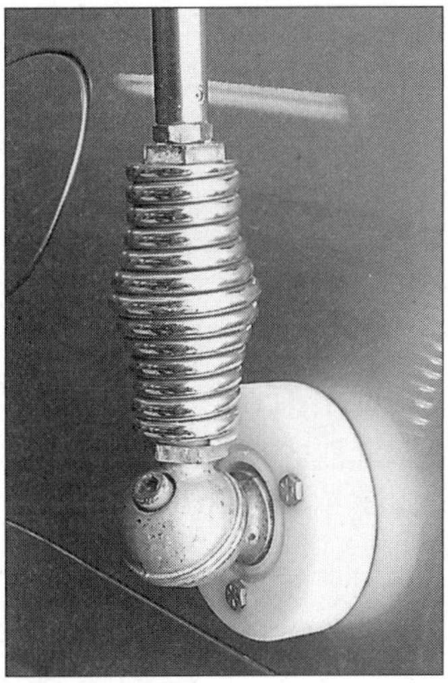

Figure 21.11 — A ball mount is attached to a vertical or nearly-vertical vehicle panel and can be adjusted so that the antenna is vertical. The spring shown in this photo may or may not be included with the mount. The length of the spring must be included in the antenna's total length.

CLIP OR LIP MOUNTS

Clip mounts avoid drilling holes in sheet metal and mount on a trunk, hood, or door edge or lip. They are adaptable to any surface angle. If you're careful in closing the door or hatch on which they're mounted, they work quite well. Clearance between the mount and the vehicle body structure should be checked before purchase, however. Some are provided with extra thin coaxial cable feed lines that avoid damage from being closed in doors and hatches. Take care to protect the feed line as it enters the vehicle and is routed to the transceiver.

Typical clip mounts are secured by setscrews. These screws often require backing plates to provide additional strength and should be used even when difficult to attach. The folded-over sheet metal of the car body to which the set screws make contact may not offer a secure mechanical connection. Even modest and lightweight antennas tend to stress the connection. When the connection loosens, intermittent SWR and RFI problems are often the result. Therefore, as a rule, clip mounts should be restricted to antennas weighing less than 2 pounds. Larger antennas can be used if guyed or otherwise stabilized above the mount. It is recommended to run a bonding wire or strap from the mount to a nearby body screw. This improves contact between the mount and body metal considerably.

All modern vehicles are dipped in a zinc compound before final assembly and painting. When exposed to air, zinc rapidly oxidizes but in this case the oxidation is a good thing! When a piece of road debris nicks the paint down to the zinc layer, it quickly oxidizes, and protects the base metal underneath. Do not remove this zinc coating to bare metal! This removes the protective coating, allowing the underlying steel to rust and creates an intermittent connection.

These mounts bring the coax cable into the trunk or passenger cabin through the weather seal potentially allowing water to enter. The problem is often exacerbated by the larger control cable most screwdriver antennas require. Take care to dress the cables and seals to direct water toward a drain hole or other exit.

ANGLE BRACKETS

Angle brackets come in a variety of sizes, shapes, angles, hole size, attachment style, strength, and colors. They work well for lightweight antennas. There are special hood and trunk seam versions for trucks and other vehicles. They require holes for attachment screws. Some brackets can be clamped on mirror arms or other tubes and struts common on larger pickup and commercial trucks.

MAGNET "MAG" MOUNTS

Magnet or "mag" mounts are available that can secure just about any size antenna. Although they're meant for temporary mounting, it is common for them to be used as permanent mounts to avoid drilling holes in the car body. Most mag mounts are designed to attach to a horizontal surface such as a vehicle roof, trunk, or cargo bed.

Mag mounts are convenient for temporary use but have several drawbacks. Regardless of the number or size of the magnets, the ultimate holding power relies on the metal surface. For example, newer vehicles often use aluminum and/or steel-reinforced composite materials. In these cases, mag mounts *cannot be used since there is little or no holding force for the magnet and composite materials will not act as a ground plane for the antenna. M*ounts are available with three or four magnets for larger HF antennas and highway speeds. These mounts tend to be heavy and are difficult to install and remove. The magnets also tend to collect metallic road debris and dust that eventually get under the magnet and mar the vehicle's finish.

Regardless of the number of magnets, for safety, large antennas should be tethered or guyed to keep them in place while in motion. Monofilament nylon fishing line is insulating and not sensitive to RF. A plastic clamp can also provide an attachment point for guy lines. How the line is securely attached, depends on the antenna, the vehicle and mounting location.

Mag mounts rely on capacitive coupling to the car body for return current to the feed point. Most mounts provide about 100 pF per magnet. The capacitive reactance of a single magnet is 227 Ω at 7 MHz, 57 Ω at 28 MHz, and 2.7 Ω at 146 MHz. Divide the reactance by the number of magnets on the mount. This is an acceptable amount of reactance at VHF and UHF but even a four-magnet mount presents 57 Ω at 7 MHz. This reactance will result in a significant increase in common-mode current on the feed line shield at HF. This can cause RFI problems inside the vehicle and distorts the expected omni-directional radiation patter. The recommended solution at HF is to install a ground strap or wire to the nearest chassis "hard point" such as a body screw. If no attachment point is available a small screw can be installed under the vehicle door's weather seal.

To minimize common-mode current, a Type 31 ferrite split core, snapped over a few turns of coax will often suffice. Type 43 material is better at VHF and UHF. The core should be mounted close to the base of the antenna, and outside, not inside, the vehicle. Wrapping the core with electrical tape will protect it from weather. If possible, arrange the core so that it is off of the vehicle surface and the vibration will not scratch the paint.

Routing the coax feed line for mag mounts can be challenging. Users typically route the coax through rubberized trunk, door, and window seals that can result in water leakage. Where possible, the coax should be routed under trunk seals, where additional body sealing material may be used to minimize water leaks. If possible, route the coax so that water running along the cable will be directed to a drain channel or drip from a low point before entering the vehicle.

THROUGH-HOLE MOUNTS

A through-hole mount is study and makes a good body panel connection. For example, the NMO-style mount is often preferred, as it provides the best ground connection to the panel's inside surface. If the connections are secure, common-mode current will be minimized without the use of ferrite split beads since the feed line immediately enters and is shielded by the vehicle body panel. NMO mounts are most common with VHF/UHF antennas and small HF whips.

TRAILER HITCH AND STAKE MOUNTS

Many operators using large screwdriver or whip antennas for HF use a commercial trailer hitch mount (usually a ⅜-24 mount) attached to a hitch shank in place of a trailer ball. The shank slides into a standard hitch receiver and is secured with a pin. The coax feed line extends from the side or front of the shank. (See **curtmfg.com/basic-towing-components** for a diagram of trailer hitch components.)

It is important that shank be securely attached electrically to the vehicle body, either with a bolt or strap. The base of the antenna will be very close to the vehicle which will affect antenna tuning and may block some signals from the direction of the front of the vehicle. Extending the antenna base section above the vehicle may help if the total antenna height remains below the maximum highway limit of 13½ feet. Be aware that the antenna may also interfere with opening the rear door, tailgate, or hatch. Quick disconnect mounts are available for trailer hitch mounts.

As an alternative to the trailer hitch mount, **Figure 21.12** shows a heavy screwdriver antenna on a custom mount made by Joe McEneaney, KG6PCI. The 18-pound antenna is supported by a steel mast welded to a frame extension. There is a stainless-steel plate at the top of the mast, bolted to the top

Figure 21.12 — A Scorpion 680 screwdriver antenna mounted on the truck of KG6PCI. (Photo courtesy of Alan Applegate, KØBG and Ron Douglass, NI7J)

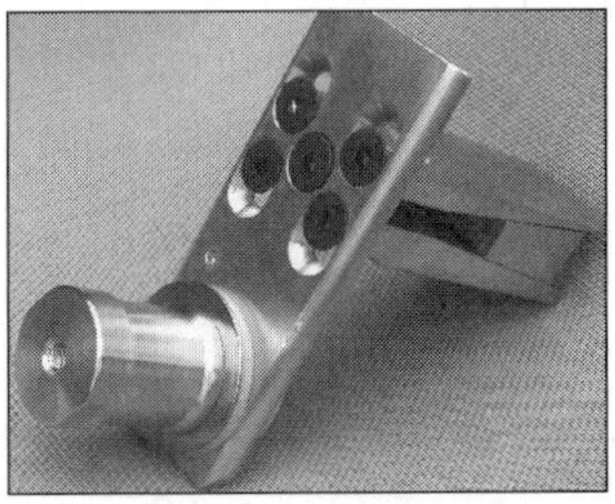

Figure 21.13 — Stake-pocket mounts are designed to fit into the square holes in the walls of a pickup truck's bed. An offset mount as shown in the photo will also clear most bed covers.

of the bed rail, that secures the antenna and reduces ground losses. A quick disconnect at the base of the antenna facilitates removal when desired.

For pickup trucks, stake pocket mounts in the top of the bed rail or in the bed offer more efficient operation. A stake pocket mount like the Breedlove model shown in **Figure 21.13** is a good, no-holes choice. Its offset design allows it to extend from beneath most bed covers. A separate ground strap or wire must be attached to create an effective current return path.

21.2.4 Controlling Common-Mode Current

In the mobile environment, the vehicle is part of the antenna system. As a result, RF common-mode current picked up from the transmitted signal will flow on the *outside* of the coax shield. This surface also acts as a "third wire" connected directly to one side of an antenna. The common-mode RF current will radiate a signal of its own, just like any conductor carrying RF current, and it can cause RFI to your equipment and to the vehicle's electronic systems.

In the case of HF mobile antennas, the magnitude of common-mode current on feed lines and other cables increases as ground impedance increases which also increases ground losses. As a result, the coax and control cables running to clamp- or lip-mount and mag-mount antennas will typically carry more common-mode current than body-mounted antennas. This is why permanent mounts bonded to the vehicle's metal surface are recommended. This shields the feed line from the strong RF fields at the antenna feed point and provides a low-impedance path for return current other than the coax shield's outer surface.

Because of the potential for RFI from common-mode currents, it is prudent to add RF chokes to reduce common-mode currents in a mobile installation, even though there may be no direct indication of a problem. The best place to install a common-mode RF choke is at the base of the antenna where the feed line is connected and not inside the vehicle.

The most convenient way to create an RF choke is to use the "split core" or "snap-on" ferrite cores. A Type 31, ¾-inch ID split core may be utilized with great effect. Depending on the coax size, between five and seven turns of either RG-58 or RG-8X can be wound through that size core as shown in Figure 21.16B. The impedance will be somewhat greater than 1.8 kΩ at 10 MHz which is adequate in most cases. Adding a second split core doubles the impedance. Take care not to bend the coaxial cable too sharply in making the choke, particularly for foam-insulation cables, as the center conductor can "migrate" (be forced through) the center insulation over time, creating a short circuit. For more information on ferrite common-mode chokes, see the **Transmission Line System Techniques** chapter.

21.2.5 Screwdriver Antenna Controllers

Screwdriver antennas have become very popular in part because their operating frequency can be changed while in motion. Most manufacturers offer some form of manual control box as an option. However, manual controllers require the operator to watch either an internal or external SWR indicator during tuning, which isn't safe while in motion. Fortunately, there is a solution — the automatic antenna controller.

There are two basic types with several variations, SWR-sensing and turn counters. Both types require special attention with respect to RF on the antenna's control leads. Most also have a built-in *park* feature which retracts the coil all the way into the mast. If you have garage or carport clearance issues, this is a nice feature.

One clear advantage of most automatic controllers is that they store previous operating frequencies. When you change frequency, the controller always adjusts the antenna in the correct direction, saving wear and tear on the motor assembly. The controllers also have manual modes that allow an operator to adjust the screwdriver length for initial setup or fine-tuning.

SWR-SENSING CONTROLLERS

The West Mountain Radio TARGETuner (**westmountainradio.com**) shown in **Figure 21.14** is a typical automatic controller that can retune an antenna based on SWR measurements from a separate sensing unit or based on frequency data directly from a radio's computer control port. Commanding the radio to activate a low-power TUNE function varies with the manufacturer and/or radio.

Figure 21.14 — An SWR-sensing controller adjusts the length of the screwdriver coil for minimum SWR automatically.

Figure 21.15 — A turns-counting controller keeps track of coil position by counting switch closures from a reed switch mounted on the antenna.

Full power should never be used while tuning a screwdriver antenna, especially models with low-Q loading coils. Using too much power during tuning can cause arcing between the coil turns, thus destroying the loading coil. Some tuners can put the transceiver into a low-power mode automatically.

TURN-COUNTER CONTROLLERS

Most screwdriver antennas come equipped with a turns counter, usually in the form of a magnet attached to the drive assembly that closes a magnetic reed switch. As the motor turns, the switch opens and closes once or twice every 360°. The controller counts the closures and moves the antenna to a *predetermined* length stored in the controller's memory. **Figure 21.15**, an Ameritron SDC-104, is an example of this type of turns-counting controller. "Jog" buttons are included to touch up the SWR once the predetermined point is reached.

CONTROL LEAD RF CHOKES

All screwdriver antennas have one thing in common: Their control motor and any reed switches are housed inside the antenna. Therefore, the control leads will be "hot" with RF during transmissions. This RF must be prevented from reaching the controller or erratic operation may result. This is especially important when utilizing short antennas on clip mounts with their inherent ground losses. Running the cables through trays in the vehicle body also reduces common-mode RF by acting as a shield.

Figure **21.16A** shows a motor lead choke utilizing a ¾-inch ID, Type 31 split core. The core shown is wound with 13 turns of #18, nylon insulated wire with an OD of 0.068 inches. Larger diameter wire will not allow enough turns to be wound on the core. It is important that the turns not be overlapped or twisted as this will reduce the choke's effective impedance. In this case, the choke presents approximately 10 kΩ of impedance at 10 MHz, an amount adequate in all but the most severe cases. It is important to wind as many non-overlapping turns on the core as possible.

(A)

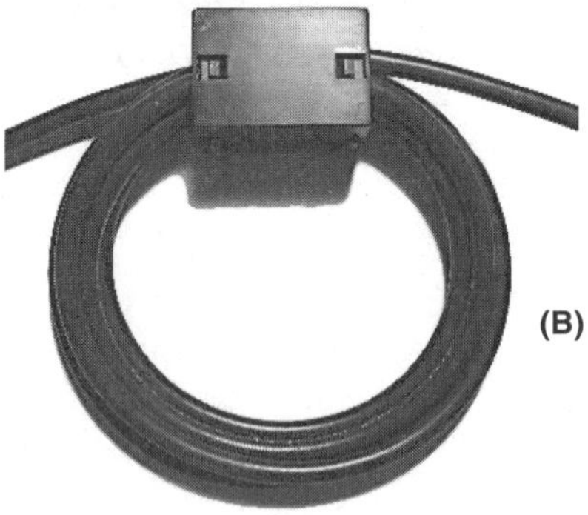

(B)

Figure 21.16 — At A, dc power leads are wound around a split ferrite bead to form an RF choke. B shows how coaxial cable can be wound on a split ferrite bead to form an RF choke on the outside of the cable shield. Wind coax loosely to avoid forcing the center conductor through the center insulation.

21.3 References and Bibliography HF Mobile Antennas

Source material and more extended discussions of topics covered in this chapter can be found in the references given below and, in the textbooks listed at the end of the **Antenna Fundamentals** chapter.

Belrose, J., "Short Antennas for Mobile Operation," *QST*, Sep. 1953, pp. 30 – 35.

Brown, B., "Optimum Design of Short Coil-Loaded High-Frequency Mobile Antennas," *ARRL Antenna Compendium Volume 1* (ARRL, 1985), p. 108.

Frazell, C., and Allison, T., "Another Look at an Old Subject: The Bug Catcher," *QST*, Dec. 1980, pp. 30 – 32.

21.4 HF Antennas for Sail and Power Boats

21.4.1 Planning Your Installation

Many of the mobile antennas discussed earlier in this chapter can be applied to sailboats. (For readers who might not be fully conversant with nautical jargon, the Wikipedia's online glossary of nautical terms at **en.wikipedia.org/wiki/Glossary_of_nautical_terms** will help you keep port and starboard straight.) However, the presence of the mast and rigging, plus the prevalence of nonconducting fiberglass hulls complicates the issue:

- On most boats the spars, standing rigging and some running rigging will be conductors. Stranded stainless steel wire is usually used for standing rigging and aluminum for spars.
- Running rigging such as topping lifts, running backstays, jackstays, etc may also be made from stranded stainless wire on occasion and often change position while the boat is underway. This changes the configuration of the rigging and may affect radiation patterns and feed point impedances. For example, when tacking you may discover that the SWR on starboard tack is quite different from that on port tack.
- The antennas on a boat will always be close (in terms of wavelength) to the mast and rigging. Some antennas may in fact be part of the rigging. This means very tight electrical coupling between the antenna and the rigging. This means the entire rigging is effectively the "antenna".
- The feed point impedance, SWR and radiation pattern can be strongly influenced by the presence of spars and rigging.
- The behavior of a given antenna will depend on the details of the rigging on a particular vessel. The performance of a given antenna can vary widely on different boats, due to differences in dimensions and arrangement of the rigging.
- Even though you may be floating on a sea of saltwater, grounding still requires careful attention!
- The radio will typically be an HF transceiver with an output power of 100 W. This low power operation means you must pay careful attention to the efficiency of the "antenna system" and take into account the radiation pattern which will normally be asymmetric with significant signal reduction in some directions.

THE FIRST STEP

An effective antenna system for a sailboat can require a good deal of effort and some expense. It may be necessary for example, to modify the rigging and do considerable work inside the hull to install a grounding system. For this reason, it is important at the beginning to define your goals: Do you simply want to have a little fun at anchor on a summer vacation or are you planning to go blue water cruising and possibly need to communicate back home from the middle of the Indian Ocean? Is the installation primarily for emergencies to summon assistance or will you want to have daily communications with other boats and shore stations? Or do you want all these plus lots of time for just DXing or chatting with friends back home?

You need to think about what bands you want to operate on. As we'll see shortly, multiband operation poses some problems. Your intended use for amateur radio will determine the time, effort and money you have to invest in the antenna system, and it will also directly impact your final choice of antenna.

Note the use of the words "antenna system" above. This includes not only the antenna itself but the grounding system, the feed arrangements and possibly an antenna tuner. All of these components interact and affect the final result.

ANTENNA MODELING

Because of the strong interaction between the rigging and the antenna, accurate prediction of radiation patterns and a reasonable guess at feed point impedances requires that you model both the antenna and the rigging with CAD software. Fortunately, easy-to-use antenna modeling software such as *EZNEC* (**eznec.com**) and *4nec2* (**qsl.net/4nec2/**) are available free. Modeling allows you to try several different ideas and see which approach works best for your installation. Because of the wide variation between boats, even those of the same class, each new installation is unique and should be analyzed separately.

While the software is very helpful, it must be used with some care:

1) Unless you accurately model the system, considerable cut-and-try may be needed and even then, you won't have any real idea of how your system is performing. Cut-and-try can be expensive when it must be done in 1 × 19 stainless steel wire with $300 swaged insulator fittings!

2) In addition to the rigging, lifelines, stanchions, and

pulpits and any grounding connections between these should be included in the modeling.

3) Take the time to carefully measure the actual dimensions on the boat.

4) Modeling software with ask you to select the characteristics of the "ground" over which the antenna is installed. Saltwater is much more conductive than any normal soil but is still not a perfect conductor. However, for the purposes of selecting a design it is much simpler to use the perfect ground option. The software computations will also run faster when perfect ground is used, and the accuracy of the predictions will be more than adequate.

5) The connections between the spars and rigging will have many small intersection angles and radically different conductor diameters — this can cause some modeling problems. In general, sufficient accuracy can be obtained by using the same diameter for all the parts of the *NEC* model including the spars. Make all the conductors 0.25 inch which is typical for standing rigging.

6) Be careful to make the segment lengths at a junction the same for each wire connected to that junction.

7) For more information on antenna modeling, see the **Antenna Modeling** chapter.

From *NEC* modeling, you can expect the predicted radiation patterns to be close to reality, but the feed point impedance predictions will be approximate. Some final adjustment will usually be required. *NEC* modeling with *EZNEC-Pro/4* will be used for much of the following discussion. The model uses the dimensions and rigging arrangements for a Crealock 37 sailboat. The author (N6LF) and his wife lived aboard this boat for many years and cruised offshore extensively. Some of the ideas shown are taken directly from experience on this boat, other boats he has owned and boats belonging to fellow cruisers.

PRE-INSTALLATION EVALUATION

When the antenna is going to be integrated into the standing rigging, it's a very good idea (after modeling) to try your designs out at the dock. For example, suppose you want to insulate part of your backstay and use it as your primary antenna. Temporarily you could replace the backstay with a stout Dacron line and use wire and inexpensive insulators for the initial tests to determine the antenna final dimensions. When you are satisfied finalize the backstay in stainless wire and swaged insulators. This approach can save a lot of money and aggravation.

A SAFETY NOTE

Ungrounded rigging near deck level can have high RF potentials when you transmit. For example, the shrouds on a fiberglass boat connect to chainplates bolted to the hull, but these may not be grounded. Ungrounded, the lower ends of the shrouds can inflict painful RF burns on the unwary while transmitting, even while operating at low power. This is not hypothetical! As a rule, all rigging, spars, and lifelines near deck level should be grounded. This also makes good sense

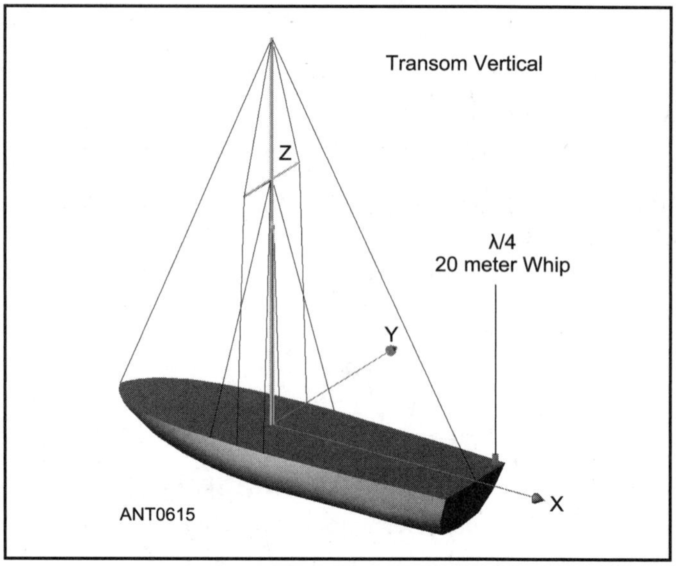

Figure 21.17 — An example of a 20 meter λ/4 whip mounted on the transom. A local ground system must also be provided, as described in the section on grounding.

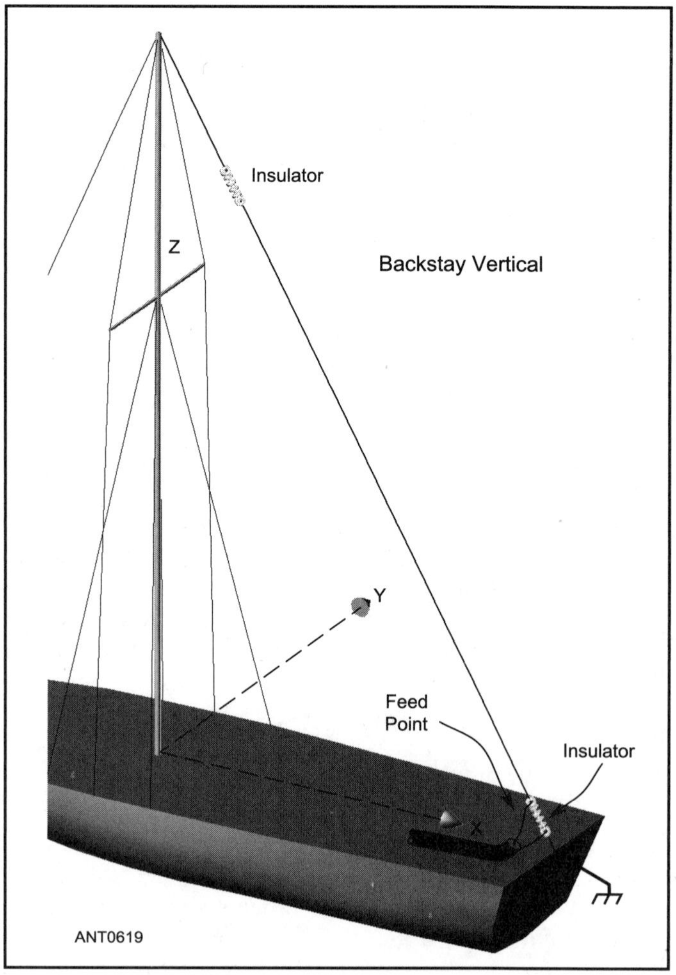

Figure 21.18 — An example of a backstay vertical fed at deck level. A local ground point must be established on the transom next to the base of the backstay.

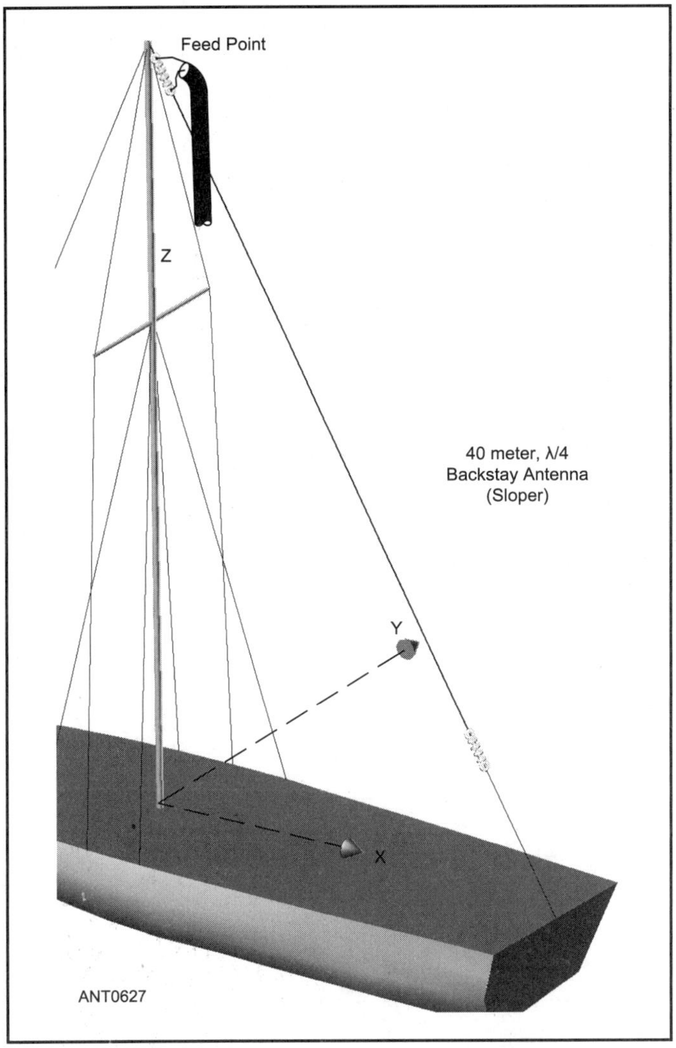

Figure 21.19 — An insulated stay 40 meter half-sloper fed at the masthead.

Figure 21.20 — A rigid dipole can be made from aluminum tubing, fiberglass poles or a combination of these and attached to the mast such as is visible in the photo at the top of the mast.

for lightning protection. For antennas with parts near deck level that can be touched, a sleeve of schedule 80 PVC pipe can be placed over the lower end as a protective shield. It's not uncommon to stand at the stern with a hand grasping the backstay. You don't want to be able to grasp the backstay above the insulator without an insulating shield over it! Many commercial verticals for marine use are insulated.

As shown in the chapter **Effects of Ground**, it is possible to determine in advance the potentials that may exist on a given system using the near-field calculations provided by most software combined with some simple calculations using a spreadsheet.

21.4.2 Antenna Options

There are a number of possibilities for antennas on a sailboat. One of the simplest is to install a separate vertical as shown in **Figure 21.17.** An alternative is to insulate a portion of the backstay and use that as a vertical as shown in **Figures 21.18** and **21.19**. The backstay vertical can be fed at deck level or at the masthead which is the same idea as the λ/4-sloper discussed in the chapter on **General Purpose MF and HF Antennas**. One problem with this antenna is that the lower end of the antenna is a very high potential point. You don't want the lower end of the sloper to be anywhere it could be reached from the deck. Another possibility is to place a self-supporting dipole at the masthead as shown in **Figure 21.20**.

These basic antennas can be applied in several ways:

1) For single-band operation you can make the vertical shown in Figure 21.18 λ/4 resonant or insulate a portion of the backstay that is λ/4 resonant (Figure 21.18 or 21.19). If the

length of the backstay or the vertical is not long enough to reach resonance on the desired band, you can use the loading techniques described earlier in this chapter for mobile antennas and there is also some useful information regarding loading in the chapter **General Purpose MF and HF Antennas**.

2) Another single-band option is the use of a self-supporting dipole at the masthead as shown in Figure 21.31. The antenna shown was fabricated from a pair of 12-foot fiberglass fly-fishing rod blanks (with a copper wire inside!) that were attached to ¾ inch by 6-foot aluminum tubes to make them 18 feet long each for resonance on 20 meters. Although it looks a bit ungainly this antenna survived several years of cruising and two 24-day passages in the North Pacific including the long beat back from Hawaii. The antenna was very effective for the 20 meter marine nets. A 15-meter version of this antenna was installed on another boat for a passage from Australia back to the US via South Africa. With this masthead dipole they were able to work back to the US regularly from the Indian Ocean. One half of this antenna would make a good homebrew vertical on the transom.

3) For multiband operation it is possible to build or purchase multiband antennas, some of which are intended for mobile operation (see the **Multiband HF Antennas** chapter and material on mobile antennas earlier in this chapter). These come in many forms: multiple traps, replaceable upper sections, interchangeable loading coils for each band or motorized tuning of a loading coil. Unfortunately, most commercial products of this type are not intended for a marine environment. In addition, close proximity to the rigging can have a strong effect on multiband trap verticals, preventing them from being tuned properly.

4) Another option for multiband operation is the SteppIR family of self-adjusting verticals (**steppir.com**). The antenna consists of a fiberglass tube, 18 feet or 34 feet long, inside of which is a variable length of metal tape. The tape is motor driven so that its length can be adjusted to be resonant at any frequency from 40 or 20 meters (depending on the tube length) through 6 meters. It is even possible to purchase a tuning unit for operation on 80 meters. The antenna controller comes with pre-programmed length settings for the amateur bands, but these can be custom adjusted to compensate for the interaction with the rigging. These antennas can be quite efficient, and a tuner is not needed in most installations.

5) A common solution for multiband operation is to use a fixed length antenna, such as a vertical mounted on the transom or integrated into the backstay, combined with a tuner to provide a match to the transmitter. One note of caution: Automatic antenna tuners intended for marine use are readily available although relatively expensive. They can provide an acceptable match between the transmitter and fixed length antenna over a wide range of frequencies. This can be a very convenient solution. However, these low-power tuners can be relatively inefficient, reducing the radiated power significantly. A single-band antenna with a dedicated matching network can usually provide better performance although that requires more effort.

6) It is also possible to use more than one antenna. For example, you could use an insulated backstay resonant on 40 meters combined with a shorter transom vertical for the higher bands.

TEMPORARY ANTENNAS

Not everyone needs a permanent antenna. A variety of temporary antennas can be arranged. A few of these are shown in **Figures 21.21**, **21.22**, and **21.23**. All of these options will

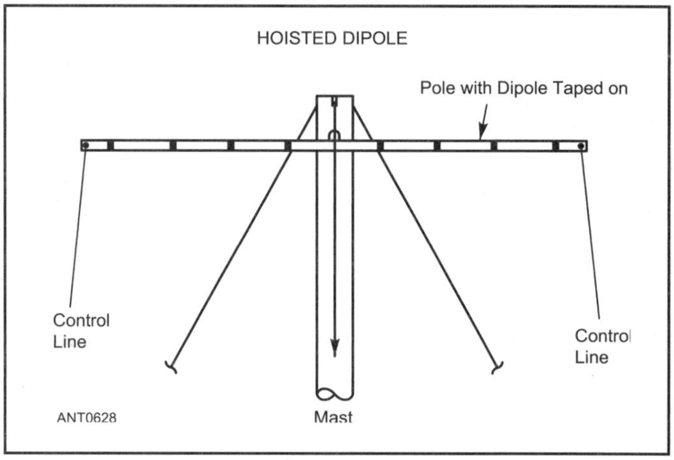

Figure 21.21 — A dipole can be taped to a wood or bamboo pole and hoisted to the masthead with the main halyard while at anchor. It is possible to make this a multiband dipole.

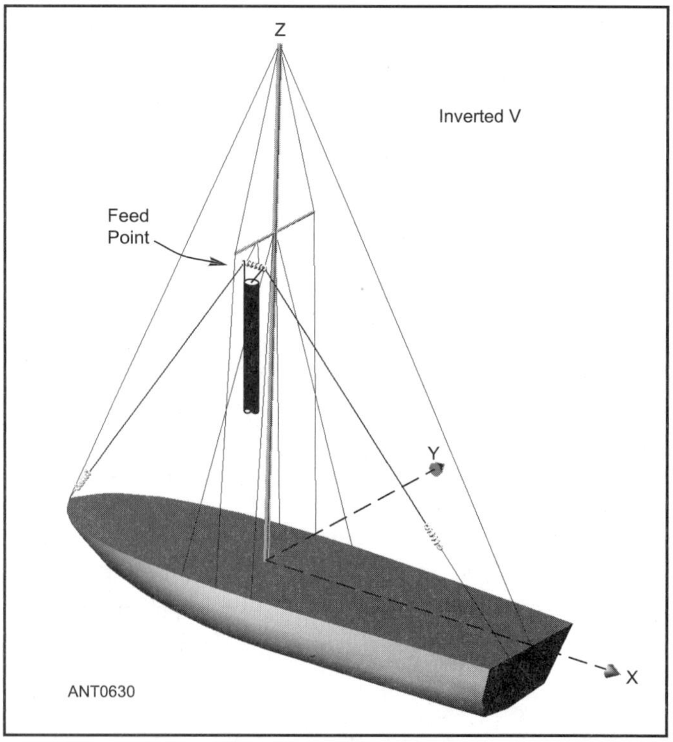

Figure 21.22 — The flag halyard can be used to hoist the center of an inverted V to the spreaders, or alternatively, the main halyard can be used to hoist the center of the antenna to the masthead. Interaction between the rigging and the antenna will be very pronounced and the length of the antenna will have to be adjusted on a cut-and-try basis.

be strongly affected by their close proximity to the rigging but by employing a tuner, they may work well for temporary operation. You can also try altering the wire lengths to get a better match.

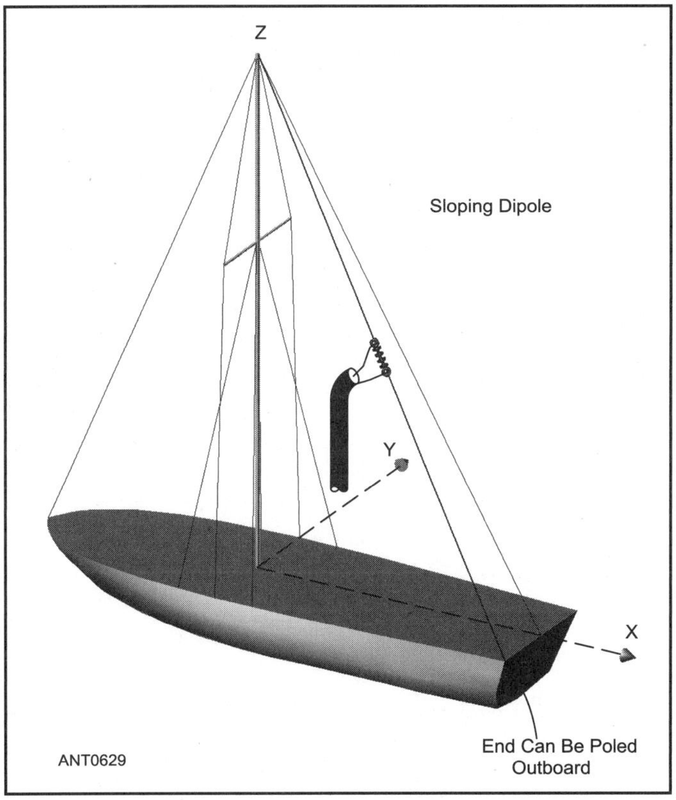

Figure 21.23 — One end of dipole can be attached to the main halyard and pulled up to the masthead. The bottom end of the dipole should be pulled out away from the rigging as much as possible to reduce the impact of the rigging on the impedance.

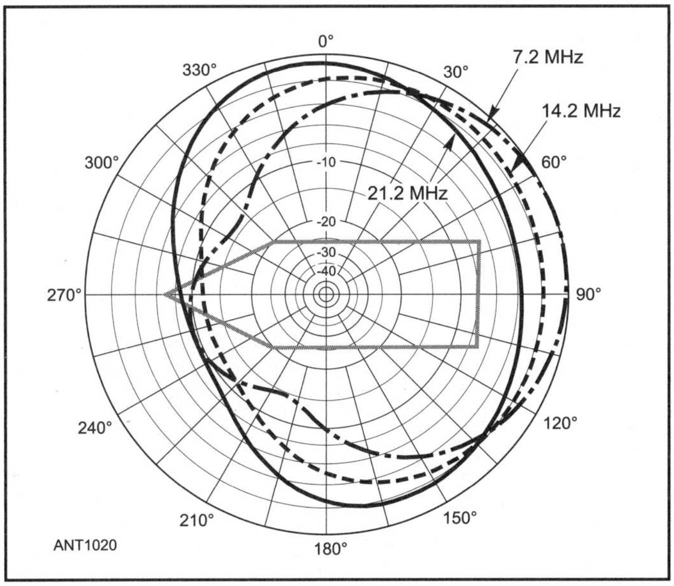

Figure 21.24 — Azimuth radiation pattern of a vertical at 15° elevation at 7.2, 14.2 and 21.2 MHz.

21.4.3 The Effect of Mast and Rigging

A vertical can be placed on the transom as shown in Figure 21.17. (Note that the vertical is offset a short distance from the backstay to reduce coupling to the rigging slightly). This vertical could be a mobile whip, a fixed length commercial marine vertical or an insulated section of backstay. It turns out that the length of the antenna and whether it's part of the backstay or separate has only a modest effect on the radiation pattern so we will use 23-foot independent vertical that will give us a general idea what to expect. **Figure 21.24** shows the

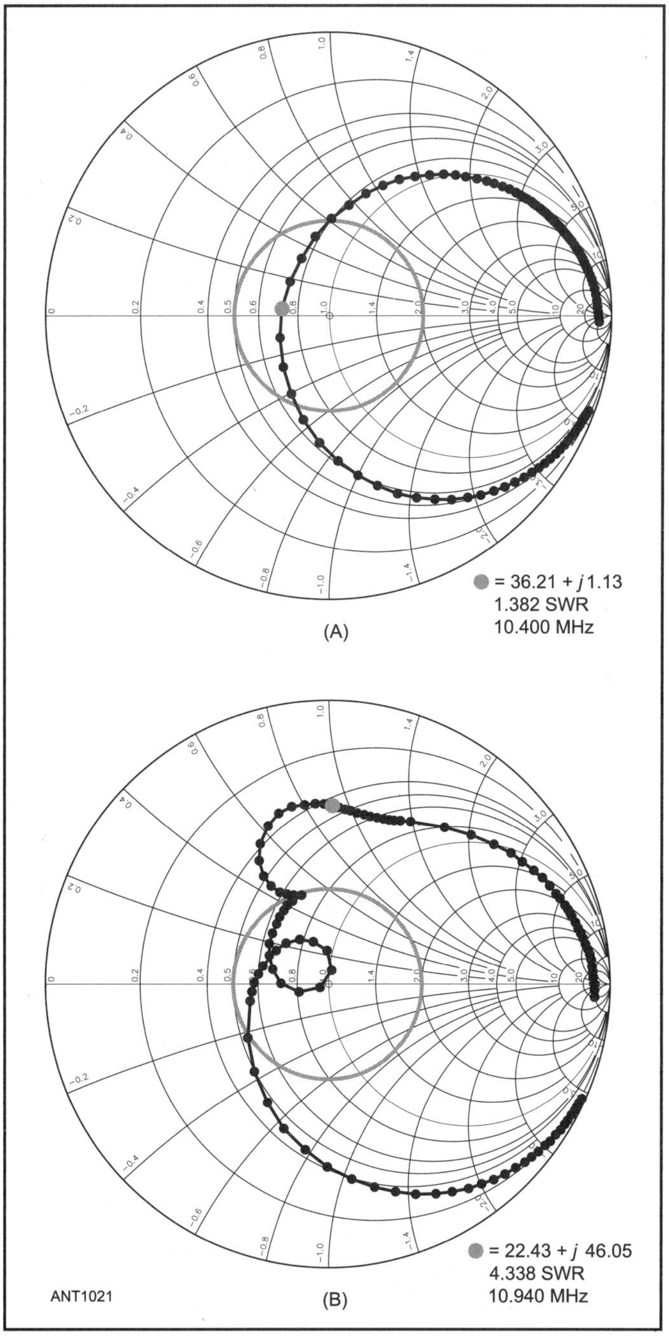

Figure 21.25 — Feed point impedance of a 23 foot free-standing vertical with the mast and rigging present. (Z_0 = 50 Ω)

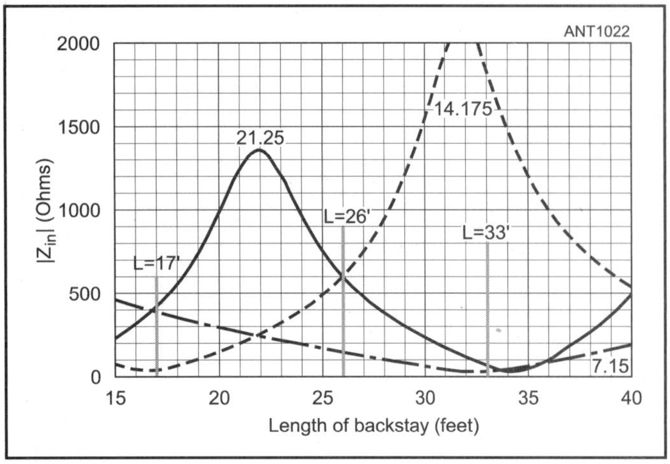

Figure 21.26 — Feed point impedance as a function of vertical length at 7.150, 14.175 and 21.250 MHz. (Z_0 = 50 Ω)

radiation patterns for this antenna at 7.2, 14.2 and 21.25 MHz.

Unlike a vertical standing alone, this antenna doesn't have an omnidirectional pattern. It is asymmetrical, with pattern distortion of 8-10 dB depending on the band. Further, the pattern is offset in the direction the antenna is placed on the transom. With the backstay vertical that offset is absent. The pattern distortion shown in Figure 21.35 is very typical for a wide range of boats. The directive gain can be useful but only if you point the boat in the right direction! Otherwise, you may have significant reduction in your signal.

Figure 21.25 shows Smith chart graphs for the feed point impedance at the base of a 23-foot vertical with and without the rigging. Figures 21.24 and 21.25 are very good examples of the profound effect the mast and rigging can have on an antenna installed on a sailboat.

What if we chose a length other than 23 feet for either the vertical or an insulated backstay? Is there a better choice? **Figure 21.26** shows Z_{in} for various vertical lengths from 15 to 40 feet on 40, 20 and 15 meters. For a backstay vertical it would be common to set L=33 feet which gives a good match on 40 and 15 meters. Usually, no tuner would be needed or at least the internal tuner found in most transceivers would have little difficulty matching those bands. However, L=33 feet is a very poor length for 20 meters — the impedance is very high and even the best tuner might have difficulty matching to that load. Instead of 33 feet you could set L=17 feet which will have $Z_{in} = 11 - j384$ Ω at 7.15 MHz, $36 + j8$ Ω at 14.175 MHz and $220 + j451$ Ω at 21.25 MHz. On 20 meters a tuner is not required and the impedances on 40 and 15 meters are reasonable for an automatic tuner.

Common lengths for commercial marine antennas intended for HF SSB service are 23 feet and 28 feet. From Figure 21.26 we can see these lengths have impedances that are a bit high (though not impossible) for many automatic tuners. A better choice would be 26 feet. However, this observation applies only to this particular boat and rigging! Other boats, with different rigging dimensions might be better (or worse) with a given vertical length. That is why it is a good idea to model each boat individually before choosing an antenna. Each installation will be unique!

The message here is that some lengths are better than others for verticals or insulated backstay antennas and these lengths may not be resonant on any of the bands. The choice of length will depend on the specifics of the boat, the desired operating bands and whether a tuner is used.

21.4.4 Antennas for Power Boats

Power boaters are not usually faced with the problems and opportunities created by the mast and rigging on a sailboat. A powerboat may have a small mast, but usually not on the same scale as a sailboat. Antennas for power boats have much more in common with automotive mobile operation, but the motion of a powerboat, especially in rough seas, can be quite severe. This places additional mechanical strain on the antennas and exposure to wet and possibly saltwater environments.

The simplest situation for HF is to install a regular mobile vertical on the bow-pulpit of a cabin cruiser. The bow-pulpit and any attached bonding conductor act as a counterpoise for the vertical. Band-changing then becomes a simple matter of replacing the antenna or attaching a different resonator. The ground system then becomes a critical part of the antenna system as discussed in the following section.

Sometimes several radial wires are used with a vertical, much like that for a ground-plane antenna. This is not a very good idea unless the "wires" are wide copper foil strips that can lower the Q substantially. The problem is the high voltage present at the ends of the radials. On a boat these radials are likely to be near the cabin, which in turn contains both people and electronic equipment. The high voltage at the ends of the radials is both a safety hazard and can result in RF coupling back into the equipment, including ham gear, navigational instruments, and entertainment devices. Decoupling the radials from the transmission line, as discussed in the Mobile section of this chapter can be very helpful in keeping RF out of other equipment.

One way to avoid many of problems associated with grounding is to use a rigid dipole antenna as suggested in Figure 21.20. For short-range communication, a low dipole over saltwater can be effective. However, if long-range communication is needed, then a well-designed vertical, operating over seawater, will work much better. For these to work, of course, you must have the ground system associated with a vertical.

It is not uncommon for large powerboats to have a two or three-element multiband Yagi installed on a short mast. While these can be effective, if they are not mounted high above the waterline (> λ/2) they may be disappointing for longer-range communication. Over saltwater, vertical polarization is very effective for longer distances. A simple, well-designed, vertical system on a boat may outperform a low Yagi.

Remember that in the case of a thunderstorm, a VHF/marine SSB/ham antenna may be the highest thing on the water for a mile or so and therefore liable to be struck by lightning. Antennas should be lowered if possible. A direct strike on antennas will do a lot of damage to the entire RF system.

21.4.5 Ground Systems

You may be sitting in the middle of thousands of miles of saltwater. This is great for propagation, but you will still have to connect to that ground, particularly if you want to use a vertical antenna. If the boat has a steel or aluminum hull, no additional ground system is required. For wooden or fiberglass hulls, there are many possibilities, but the scheme shown in **Figure 21.27** is representative for sailboats.

First, a wire, strap, or most preferably 3-inch by 0.003-inch ground foil, is installed as a grounding conductor from bow-to-stern on each side. If strap or foil is not available, a pair of parallel wires (such as #12 AWG) spaced a few inches apart will have an impedance similar to a wide copper strap and may be easier to install. This system couples to the water capacitively through the hull and is not directly immersed. Do not use braided strap as it will corrode when exposed to water, fresh or salt. Some fiberglass hulls have embedded copper mesh that is used for RF bonding.

Bond the lifeline stanchions, chain plates, bow and stern pulpits, and any rails. On sailboats, include the forestay and backstay chain plates and create a common connection at the base of the mast.

The bonding conductor can also be attached to the engine and to the keel bolts. It is not recommended to bond everything below the waterline, as that may result in unexpected additional electrolysis. (Marine literature is inconsistent on this point.) This must be dealt with on a case-by-case basis. If the protective zinc sacrificial anodes (**boatus.com/boattech/casey/sacrificial-zincs.asp**) deplete more rapidly after a ground system is installed or modified, change it by disconnecting some part of the system — the engine-shaft-propeller, for example. Ground systems vary with every installation and must be customized to each vessel. However, just as on shore, the better the ground system, the better the performance of a vertical antenna!

A common recommendation for powerboat grounds is two or three porous-zinc through-hull ground plates. These must be professionally installed with leak proof techniques. Bonded through-hulls using #8 AWG wire are recommended by the America Boat and Yacht Council for controlling galvanic corrosion and the effects of nearby (not direct) lightning strikes. To connect the bonding foil or strap, wire-brush the post, wrap the foil or strap around it, and tighten with a stainless-steel hose clamp. There is no need for soldering or welding.

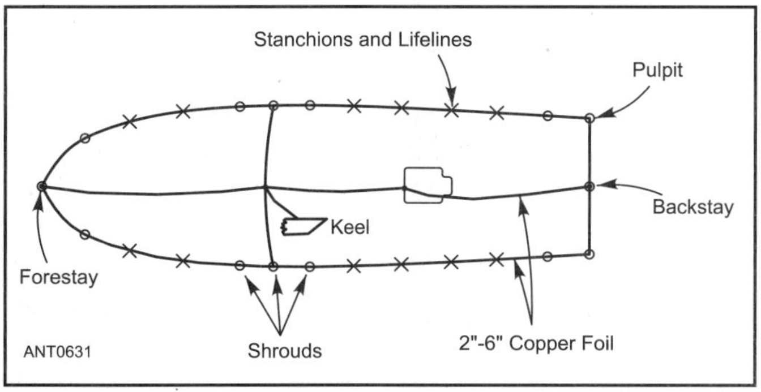

Figure 21.27 — A typical sailboat grounding scheme.

Consult with your ship builder before connecting the grounding system to though-hull ground plates installed at the factory. The completed grounding system should be inspected by a certified marine electrician to ensure that it does not interfere with the boat's anti-galvanic corrosion system.

Some power boats have a ground-plane equivalent built into the roof of a flying bridge. The bridge is the most common location of RF communications equipment, including VHF ship-to-shore, marine SSB, and ham radio equipment. This built-in ground plane should be connected to the ground system with foil or strap.

In modern cabin cruisers, the ability to install a bonding conductor in the bow or passenger compartment of the boat is limited, due to the extensive woodwork involved in the typical cabin cruiser. However, an equivalent ground might be created in a more accessible portion of the hull, particularly the engine compartment.

A ground conductor can be attached with adhesive to the inside of the engine compartment or just formed to the interior of the engine compartment. Using adhesive is preferable to avoid having unsecured items in the engine compartment. The ground system should not be connected directly to the negative battery terminal. If practical run a separate grounding conductor from an antenna mount directly to the through-hull. This minimizes inductance of the connection.

Icom recommends that HF transceivers be connected to the ground system via foil or strap. The foil can be folded so that it is easy to remove the radio for servicing, but this also increases the inductance of the connection substantially. Keep the conductor as short as possible while still allowing the radio to be removed for service.

The negative lead of many HF radios is fused. This can allow false ground paths from winches, etc., to blow the fuse rather than damaging the expensive radio. Be careful to route the ground conductor in a way that it does not interfere with the power connections.

When transmitting, it is common to see meters reacting to voice or CW peaks. With the antenna mounted directly on the boat, the strong RF field is rectified by dissimilar-metal or corroded connections. This creates dc currents that affect metering circuits.

21.4.6 Antenna Tuners on Boats

Antenna tuners are covered elsewhere in this book, such as the **Transmission Line System Techniques** chapter. Another good resource is *The ARRL Guide to Antenna Tuners* by Joel Hallas, W1ZR. This section presents several issues that are of particular concern to antenna systems on boats.

Tuners can only match a limited range of impedances. In general, very low and very high impedances lead to higher voltages and/or currents in the tuner components, which can lead to much lower tuner efficiency. The worst case is usually when the resistive component at the feed point is very low, and the reactive component is high. This happens when whip antennas are used at frequencies below their λ/4 resonance (see Table 21.1 for examples of feed point resistance as an 8-foot whip is excited at lower frequencies). As the antenna is made longer and approaches λ/2 resonance, the resistive part of Z_{in} can become very large, >1000 Ω. From the point of view of tuner efficiency and the ability to provide a match, the antenna feed point impedance should be kept between 10 Ω and 500 Ω, if possible.

The tuner should be placed physically as close to the antenna feed point as possible. The best design is to have a good ground connection immediately adjacent to the feed point and tuner. Using a remote tuner at the base of a ham/marine-SSB antenna will also help eliminate RF feedback and "hot spots" such as on a microphone or enclosure.

Running an insulated wire from the feed point back through the boat to a tuner at or in the transceiver is a very bad practice. There is the danger of exposure to high potentials on the wire and the probability of RF coupling to the boat's wiring and other electronics. *Do not do this*!

If you have a good ground connection next to the feed point and another at the transmitter, it is possible to use a length of coaxial cable to connect the feed point to the tuner, allowing you to use a conventional manual tuner collocated with the transceiver. However, the coax is a transmission line, and it will transform the feed point impedance to some new value that may or may not be suitable for the tuner. (See the **Transmission Lines** chapter for more on impedance transformation by feed lines.) In addition, there can be very high voltages on the transmission line. The best general advice is to locate the tuner as close as possible to the antenna feed point!

Locating the tuner close to the feed point may have disadvantages, however. The tuner may need to be installed in a locker or cabinet that may not be completely shielded from the weather, so you must use a weather-tight tuner. Such a location makes it difficult to use a manual tuner since you may have to reach into the locker to adjust the tuner for a new band. Typically, weather-resistant automatic tuners are chosen for this application.

TABLE OF CONTENTS

Chapter 22—Online Material

Articles

- "A Four-Way DFer" by Malcolm Mallette, WA9BVS
- "A Fox-Hunting DF Twin Tenna" by R.F Gillette, W9PE
- "A Reversible LF and MF EWE Receive Antenna for Small Lots" by Michael Sapp, WA3TTS
- "Active Antennas" by Ulrich Rohde, N1UL
- "Beverages in Echelon"
- "Design, Construction and Evaluation of the Eight Circle Vertical Array for Low Band Receiving" by Joel Harrison, W5ZN and Bob McGwier, N4HY
- "Flag, Pennants and Other Ground-Independent Low-Band Receiving Antennas" by Earl Cunningham, K6SE
- "Ferrite-Core Loop Antennas"
- "Introducing the Shared Apex Loop Array" by Mark Bauman, KB7GF
- "Is This EWE for You?" by Floyd Koontz, WA2WVL
- "K6STI Low-Noise Receiving Antenna for 80 and 160 Meters" by Brian Beezley, K6STI
- "Modeling the K9AY Loop" by Gary Breed, K9AY
- "More EWEs for You" by Floyd Koontz, WA2WVL
- "Rebuilding a Receiving Flag Antenna for 160 Meters" by Steve Lawrence, WB6RSE
- "Simple Direction-Finding Receiver for 80 Meters" by Dale Hunt, WB6BYU
- "The AMRAD Active LF Antenna" by Frank Gentges, KØBRA
- "Double-Ducky Direction Finder" by David Geiser, WA2ANU
- "A Simple Direction-Finding Receiver for 80 Meters" by Dale Hunt, WB6BYU
- "Build the HANDI-Finder!" Bob Leskovec, K8DTS
- "RDF System Calibration and Testing"
- "Chokes and Isolation Transformers for Receiving Antennas" Jim Brown, K9YC
- "Noise in Receiving Systems"
- "Portable Flag Antenna for MF/HF Radio Direction Finding" Don Kirk, WD8DSB
- "Active Loop Aerials for HF Reception Part 1: Practical Loop Aerial Design," Chris Trask, N7ZWY
- "Active Loop Aerials for HF Reception Part 2: High Dynamic Range Aerial Amplifier Design," Chris Trask, N7ZWY

Chapter 22

Receiving Antennas

There are many instances in amateur radio when it is important to focus on antennas used only for receiving. Not all antennas are used for transmitting! This chapter covers three such applications for antennas: increasing the receiving signal-to-noise ratio on the MF and HF bands; creating a controlled radiation pattern for precisely determining the direction to a transmitter; and making measurements of astronomical or cosmic signals for scientific purposes.

The chapter's first section has been updated to include the results of improved antenna modeling and extensive testing that has produced new small-antenna designs that rival the storied Beverage below 10 MHz. The second section which addresses the challenges of direction-finding at VHF and HF has been brought up to current practices by Dale Hunt, WB6BYU, and Charles Scharlau, NZØI. Finally, a group from the Society of Amateur Radio Astronomers (SARA) has contributed an overview of antennas used for measuring astronomical and geophysical phenomena. Since the beginnings of radio, amateurs have supported research and conducted experiments entirely on their own: this new section continues that tradition.

22.1 HF and MF Receiving Antennas

The following introduction is excerpted from the section "Introduction to Receiving Antennas" written by Robye Lahlum, W1MK, in *ON4UN's Low-Band DXing*.

Separate antennas are necessary because optimum receiving and transmitting have different requirements. For a transmit antenna, we want maximum possible field strength in a given direction (or directions) at the most useful elevation (wave) angles. We cannot tolerate unnecessary power loss in a transmit antenna, because any amount of transmitting loss decreases signal-to-noise ratio at the distant receiver.

A receiving antenna on the other hand has a different design priority. The goal is obtaining a signal that can be read comfortably, which means having the greatest possible signal-to-noise (S/N) and signal-to-QRM ratio. Receiving antennas providing the best performance can and will be different under different circumstances, even at the same or similar locations. There is no such thing as a universal "best low-band receiving antenna."

Typical low band receiving antennas like the Beverage require more space that most hams have available. In recent years, computer modeling has enabled the development of small loops and arrays that provide meaningful improvements in receiving ability without requiring large areas or overly specialized construction techniques.

22.1.1 Directivity and Coupling

Directivity is the main concern for a receiving antenna on the low bands. There are currently two methods to quantify this directivity described in the fifth edition of ON4UN's *Low-Band DXing — Directivity Merit Figure* and *Receiving Directivity Factor*. In addition, Jukka Klemola, OH6LI, develops the idea of Noise Margin and Leaking Index in his presentation made available by the World Wide Radio Operators Foundation (WWROF) at **wwrof.org/wp-content/uploads/2018/02/Receiving-Antenna-Metrics-With-Examples-v20p.pdf**. The presentation includes a detailed comparison of the performance for popular receiving antennas.

DIRECTIVITY MERIT FIGURE (DMF)

The average front-to-back (the peak forward lobe versus what happens in the back 180° over the entire elevation angle range) gives a good indication of directivity. The DMF is the forward gain of the antenna at a chosen elevation angle (usually the elevation angle producing maximum gain) minus the average back half-hemisphere's gain. This is the area between 90° and 270° azimuth — provided the forward lobe is aiming at 0° azimuth — and 0° to 90° elevation. (DMF can be calculated from the table of pattern gain values and using a spreadsheet or other software to perform the averaging function. W8WWV's *DBDXView* will perform the calculations from *EZNEC* data files and is available with *Low-Band DXing*.)

This method of evaluating a receive antenna applies to a case where a dominant noise arrives from a relatively wide half-hemisphere. If the noise is evenly distributed in all directions (e.g., in a very quiet location), the RDF metric discussed below should be used.

Many noise sources vary in direction, arrival angle and polarization. The same is true for desired signals. Because of this, we really only are considering "average" results over time. Averages are not foolproof under every condition. For example, if you have a strong single-point noise and if that noise arrives in a deep notch in your receiving antenna pattern, the S/N improvement may be much greater than expected. If noise arrives predominantly from a higher antenna response area, the S/N improvement will be proportionally less. Another important thing to consider: Signals almost never arrive from a single angle or direction. A range of angles is involved, and a single-angle evaluation does not fully represent the real world.

RECEIVING DIRECTIVITY FACTOR (RDF)

Developed by Tom Rauch, W8JI (**w8ji.com**), RDF goes a step further and compares the forward lobe gain to the average gain of the antenna in all directions (both azimuth and elevation).

While the Directivity Merit Factor (DMF) compares forward gain at the desired wave angle to the average gain in the rear half hemisphere, RDF compares forward gain at a desired direction and elevation angle to average gain over the entire hemisphere above ground. RDF includes all areas around and above the antenna, considering noise to be evenly distributed and aligned with the antenna polarization. RDF tells you not only how good the average front-to-back ratio is, but also how narrow your forward (wanted) lobe is.

Losses are factored out, and we find the directivity of the array. If noise, on average, is evenly distributed in all directions (including forward and side lobe areas) this method provides an accurate picture of receiving ability. (Keep in mind most antenna modeling programs used by amateurs calculate pattern at infinite distances and ignore ground wave response. RDF models, like DMF models, are not reliable when ground wave noise dominates skywave noise.)

For everything but an omnidirectional antenna, the RDF will be different from the DMF. You have to decide if your location has dominant skywave noise in the rearward area (DMF), or if skywave noise is evenly distributed on average (RDF). Do not compare RDF with DMF.

Calculating the RDF with *EZNEC* is very simple. After ensuring the model is correct, model the antenna with lossy elements and real ground and plot the 3D pattern. The main *EZNEC* window shows average gain at the very bottom. Now, go to a two-dimensional elevation or azimuth pattern and select the desired elevation angle and/or azimuth of the desired signal with the gain cursor and note the gain. The difference between the overall average gain and gain at the desired direction and elevation angle is the RDF. The front lobe does not have to align with the desired signal. You can also move the cursor around and look at the RDF for off-path signals. (W8WWV's *LBDXView* software will also calculate RDF from *EZNEC* tables.)

RDF is not the only metric useful in evaluating receiving antennas, but it is still very useful. **Table 22.1** provides a list of common receiving antennas with their nominal RDF. This will help the station designer make antenna choices based on circumstances and need.

USING DMF AND RDF

Both evaluation systems have their merits. If you're in a location that's always very quiet, with no specific noise or QRM sources from a particular direction, then RDF is most meaningful. The exception would be if you always had grossly

Diversity Reception

Because signal characteristics are constantly changing, various schemes for taking advantage of the changes to improve reception performance have been created. Called "diversity reception," there are several systems based on different aspects of the signals or channels, such as time, frequency, location or space, polarization, etc.

The most common system used by amateurs is antenna diversity that uses the signals from two or more antennas. It can be used to reduce fading and co-channel interference. For instance, a signal that fluctuates in strength may be stronger at one antenna and weaker at another at any given moment.

The simplest diversity system is for the operator to manually switch between the antennas for the best signal-to-noise ratio. Another common system is a "voting receiver" with circuits that continually evaluate and select the antenna with the strongest signal. Another option now available in some amateur transceivers is to use separate antennas with two receiver sub-systems. The resulting output signals can be selected by a voting system, or the operator can listen to either or both signals. Some operators listen to one signal in each ear and train themselves to focus on whichever is easier to copy.

The antennas used for diversity reception should be chosen so that fading or interference have different effects on the received signal. This can be accomplished by using antennas with opposite polarizations or that are far enough apart (500 feet or more) for the signals to be relatively independent. If a multi-receiver approach is used, the receivers must be phase-locked so that each signal is received with the same frequency and phase characteristics. Tom Rauch, W8JI presents a good discussion of diversity systems for amateur radio at **w8ji.com/polarization_and_diversity.htm**.

Table 22.1
Receiving Table RDF Performance Summary

Small Receiving Antennas (RDF 4 to 11 dB)	
4 dB	Bidirectional 8-foot diameter “magnetic” loop *close to the ground*
5 dB	Single vertical antenna (short vertical or ¼ wavelength vertical)
6 dB	225-foot Beverage on Ground (BOG)
7 dB	250-foot Beverage about 7 feet high better low angle response
7 dB	Unidirectional terminated small loop *close to the ground* (flag, pennant, EWE, VE3DO)
8 dB	Two switchable small, terminated loops at right angles to each other (K9AY Array, Shared Apex Loop Array)
8 dB	Pair of 250-foot staggered Beverages about 7 feet high
9 dB	Two phased short verticals with 60 to 80-foot spacing
9 dB	Triangle array of phased short verticals with 60 to 80-foot spacing
10 dB	LIXA double-triangle, 85 feet long by 23 feet high
11 dB	Vertical Waller Flag, two phased vertical loops *close to the ground*
High-Performance Receiving Antennas (RDF 10 to 14 dB)	
Large antennas are less effective than small antennas for suppressing local RFI sources within about 1,000 feet	
10 dB	Pair of 400-foot staggered Beverages about 7 feet high
10 dB	500 to 600-foot Beverage about 7 feet high ideal for both 160 and 80 meters
11 dB	Two or three close spaced 500 to 600-foot Beverages, staggered 125 feet
11 dB	Vertical Waller Flag, 2 phased close spaced vertical loops close to the ground
12 dB	750 to 1000-foot Beverage about 7 feet high
12 dB	4-square array of active or passive short verticals 80 x 80 ft
12 dB	3-element YCCC tri-band array of short active verticals, 120 ft long
12 dB	5-element YCCC tri-band array of short active verticals, 84 x 84 ft
12 dB	9-circle YCCC tri-band array of short active verticals 120-foot diameter
12 dB	Horizontal Waller Flag, 2 phased horizontal loops
12 dB	2x LIRA (Pair of LIXA), 272 feet long
13 dB	BSEF array of 4 short verticals switchable in two directions, 350 feet x 65 feet
13 dB	8-circle array of short verticals with 106-degree phasing, 200-foot diameter
13 dB	8-circle BSEF array of short passive verticals 350-foot diameter + radials
14 dB	Four broadside/end-fire 750-1000-foot Beverages 750 feet x 330 feet
15 dB	Staggered pair of 1000-foot Beverages, 1150 feet x 330 feet
15 dB	4x LIFA (Four LIXA), 706 feet long
Single Small Loop Antennas (RDF 4 to 7 dB, 120 to 150-degree beamwidth)	
Best choice for reducing RFI from sources within about 1,000 feet	
4 dB	8-foot diameter bidirectional “magnetic” loop
6 – 7 dB	Unidirectional terminated small loop antennas (Flag, Pennant, EWE, K9AY, VE3DO; 120-degree beamwidth)
6 – 7 dB	Mechanically rotatable unidirectional terminated small loop antenna (rotatable flag, 120-degree beamwidth)

Information based on 2022 Contest University presentation “Easy to Build Low Band Receiving Antennas for Small and Large Lot” by W3LPL

dominant noise (or QRM) only from one direction. For a front-to-rear (F/R) selection to be valid, the dominant noise would have to be so strong as to consistently exceed distributed background noise by the null-depth ratio between an antenna selected by RDF compared to one selected by F/R.

John Kaufmann, W1FV, also made the following observation on the Topband email reflector (**lists.contesting.com/mailman/listinfo/Topband**): “As RDF gets higher, the beamwidth of the antenna system generally gets narrower. By making the RDF very high, you are necessarily restricting the angular sector over which the antenna delivers its best performance. This is fine as long as the angular sector coincides with a direction that is important to you. The flip side is you give up some of that performance outside that sector. For switched arrays with a finite number of selectable directions, that could be a disadvantage when a direction of interest falls halfway between contiguous switching directions. Looking at the pattern of the array will tell you what you give up in the “in between” directions.”

Polarization of the signals and the noise are assumed to be the same on average for RDF calculations. If the signal and noise have different polarizations, the antenna will have different responses to each, and the RDF metric is not valid. For example, if your local noise source has a different polarization than the sky-wave signals you are trying to receive, RDF can be greatly misleading. However, most local noise is propagated by vertically polarized ground wave.

COUPLING

Most antenna models are developed and evaluated without other antennas or conductive surfaces nearby except for ground under the antenna. This is rarely the case in the real world, with transmitting antennas, metal surfaces and structures, power lines, and numerous other conductors in the vicinity. Especially on the low bands with their long wavelengths, it is common for other antennas to be as close as a few hundredths of a wavelength away. As a result, there will likely be a significant amount of interaction. As W8JI observed, “If [the

Choosing a Receive Antenna

There are so many different receive antennas, how do you choose one that will work for your station? The important criteria in most cases are the band(s) of use, the available space, and noise levels and directions. Even then, there might be several designs available. An excellent presentation that summarizes available choices is provided by Frank Donovan, W3LPL, a contributor to the *Antenna Book* and HF station design expert. "Easy to Build Low Band Receiving antennas for Small & Large Lots" is available as downloadable slides: see **contestuniversity.com/files** in the group for 2022.

antenna] receives, it will receive from the mess of things all around it from the dirt below it to the wires down the road."

Coupling can significantly distort an antenna's radiation pattern, whether receiving or transmitting. Separating the antenna from whatever it is coupling to is the best remedy but that is not an option in many cases. De-tuning a transmitting antenna when not in use by shifting its resonance out of band is a common technique of reducing coupling. The exact technique depends on the antenna.

Coupling can also result in significant amounts of power being picked up and overloading or damaging receivers. Out-of-band energy can be rejected with filters, but in-band coupling is harder to manage. Front-end protection circuits may be required, or a relay to interrupt the signal path during transmit periods is often used.

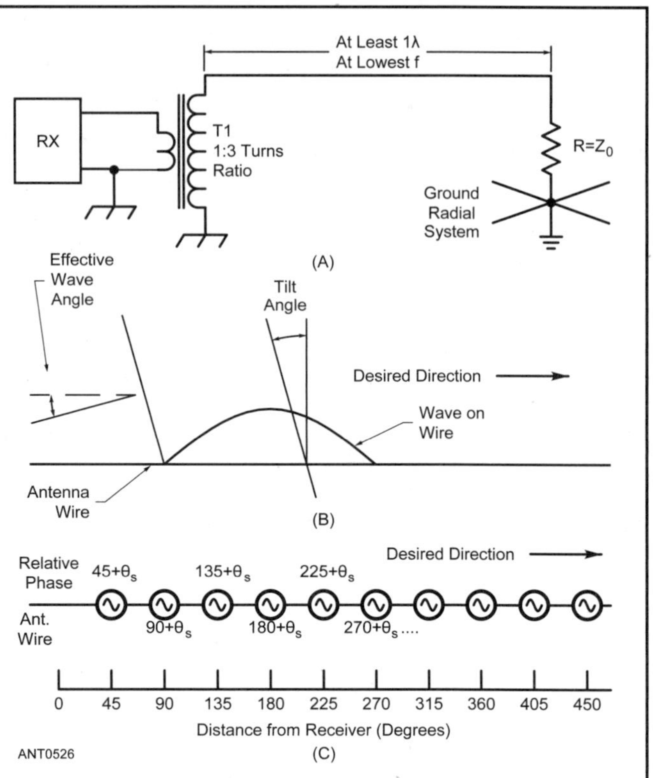

Figure 22.1 — At A, a simple one-wire Beverage antenna with a variable termination impedance and a 9:1 impedance matching transformer for the receiver impedance. Ground radials at the termination are optional. At B, a portion of a wave from the desired direction is shown traveling down the antenna wire. Its tilt angle and effective takeoff angle are also shown. At C, a situation analogous to the action of a Beverage on an incoming wave is shown. See text for discussion.

22.1.2 The Beverage Antenna

Perhaps the best-known type of wave antenna is the *Beverage*. Many 160 meter enthusiasts have used Beverage antennas to enhance the signal-to-noise ratio while attempting to extract weak signals from the often high levels of atmospheric noise and interference on the low bands. Alternative antenna systems have been developed and used over the years, such as loops and long spans of unterminated wire on or slightly above the ground, but the Beverage antenna has proven to be one of the best for 160 meter weak-signal reception. The information in this section was prepared originally by Rus Healy, K2UA.

A Beverage is simply a directional wire antenna, at least one wavelength long, supported along its length at a fairly low height and terminated at the far end in its characteristic impedance. This antenna is shown in **Figure 22.1A**. It takes its name from its inventor, Harold Beverage, W2BML.

Many amateurs choose to use a single-wire Beverage because they are easy to install, and they work well. The drawback is that Beverages are physically long and they do require that you have the necessary amount of real estate to install them. Sometimes, a neighbor will allow you to put up a temporary Beverage for a particular contest or DXpedition, particularly during the winter months.

Beverage antennas can be useful into the HF range, but they are most effective at lower frequencies, mainly on 160 through 40 meters. The antenna is responsive mostly to low-angle incoming waves that have significant vertical polarization. These conditions are nearly always satisfied on 160 meters, and most of the time on 80 meters. On higher frequency bands, polarization of received signals is elliptical and there is almost always enough vertical polarization for Beverages to perform well up to 30 MHz or more. Many amateurs have reported excellent performance from Beverage antennas at frequencies as high as 14 MHz, especially when rain or snow (precipitation) static prevents good reception on the Yagi or dipole transmitting antennas used on the higher frequencies.

Even though Beverage antennas have excellent directive patterns if terminated properly, gain never exceeds about –3 dBi in most practical installations. However, the directivity that the Beverage provides results in a much higher signal-to-noise ratio for signals in the desired direction than almost any other real-world antenna used at low frequencies.

A typical situation might be a station located in the US Northwest (W7), trying to receive 160 meter signals from Japan to the northwest, while thunderstorms from the rear in the US Southwest (W5) are creating huge static crashes. Instead of listening to an S7 signal with 10-dB over S9 noise and interference on a vertical, the directivity of a Beverage will typically allow copying the same signal at perhaps S5 with only S3 (or lower) noise and interference. This is certainly a worthwhile improvement. However, in the middle of a thunderstorm, or if there is a thunderstorm in the direction of the signal, no Beverage is going to help!

BEVERAGE OPERATION

The Beverage antenna acts like a long transmission line with one lossy conductor (the ground), and one good conductor (the wire). Beverages have excellent directivity if erected properly, but they are quite inefficient because they are mounted close to the ground. This is in contrast with the terminated long-wire antennas described earlier, which are typically mounted high off the ground. In most cases, Beverage antennas are not suitable for use as transmitting antennas.

Because the Beverage is a traveling wave, terminated antenna, it has no standing waves resulting from radio signals. As a wave strikes the end of the Beverage from the desired direction, the wave induces voltages along the antenna and continues traveling in the surrounding space adjacent to the antenna and close to the ground as well. Figure 22.1B shows part of a wave on the antenna resulting from a desired signal. This diagram also shows the tilt of the wave. The signal induces equal voltages in both directions. The resulting currents are equal and travel in both directions. The component traveling toward the termination end moves against the wave and thus builds down to a very low level at the termination end. Any residual signal resulting from this direction of current flow will be absorbed in the termination (if the termination is approximately equal to the antenna impedance). The component of the signal flowing in the other direction, as we will see, becomes a part of the received signal coupled into the feed line.

This process can be likened to a series of signal generators lined up on the wire, with phase differences corresponding to their respective spacings on the wire (Figure 22.1C). At the receiver end, a maximum voltage is produced by these voltages adding in phase. For example, the wave component induced at the receiver end of the antenna will be in phase (at the receiver end) with a component of the same wave induced, say, 270° (or any other distance) down the antenna, after it travels to the receiver end.

In practice, there is some phase shift of the wave propagating on the wire with respect to the wave arriving at the antenna. This phase shift results from the velocity factor of the antenna. (As with any transmission line, the signal velocity on the Beverage is somewhat less than in free space.) Velocity of propagation on a Beverage is typically between 85 and 98% of that in free space. As antenna height is increased to a certain optimum height (typically about 10 feet for 160 meters), the velocity factor increases. Beyond this height, only minimal improvement is afforded, as shown in **Figure 22.2**. These curves are the result of experimental work done in 1922 by RCA and reported in a *QST* article (November 1922) entitled "The Wave Antenna for 200-Meter Reception," by H. H. Beverage. The curve for 160 meters was extrapolated from the other curves.

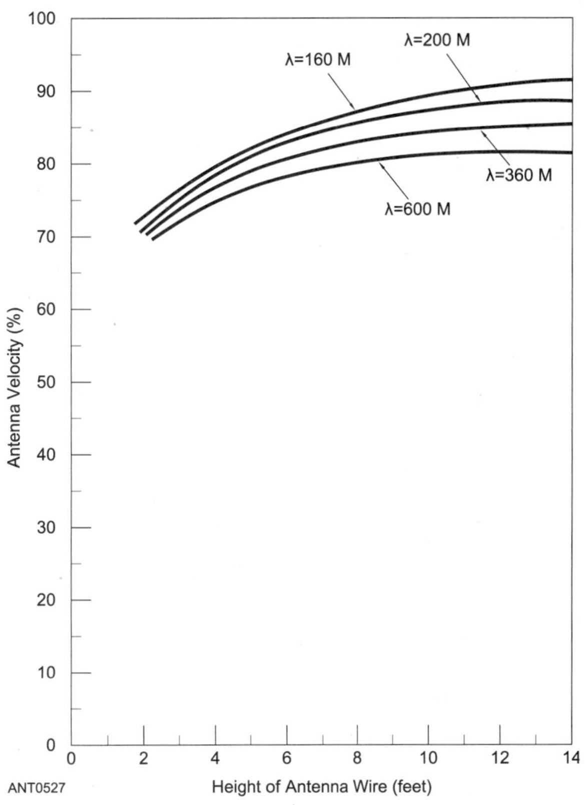

Figure 22.2 — Signal velocity on a Beverage increases with height above ground and reaches a practical maximum at about 10 feet. Improvement is minimal above this height. (100% represents the velocity of light.)

Phase shift (per wavelength) is shown as a function of velocity factor in **Figure 22.3**, and is given by:

$$\theta = 360\left(\frac{100}{k} - 1\right)$$

where k = velocity factor of the antenna in percent.

The signals present on and around a Beverage antenna are shown graphically in A through D of **Figure 22.4**. These curves show relative voltage levels over a number of periods of the wave in space and their relative effects in terms of the total signal at the receiver end of the antenna.

PERFORMANCE IN OTHER DIRECTIONS

The performance of a Beverage antenna in directions other than the favored one is quite different than previously discussed. Take, for instance, the case of a signal arriving perpendicular to the wire (90° either side of the favored direction). In this case, the wave induces voltages along the wire that are essentially *in phase*, so that they arrive at the receiver end more or less out of phase, and thus cancel. (This can be likened to a series of signal generators lined up along the antenna as before but having no progressive phase differences.)

As a result of this cancellation, Beverages exhibit deep nulls off the sides, provided that the antenna is low enough to

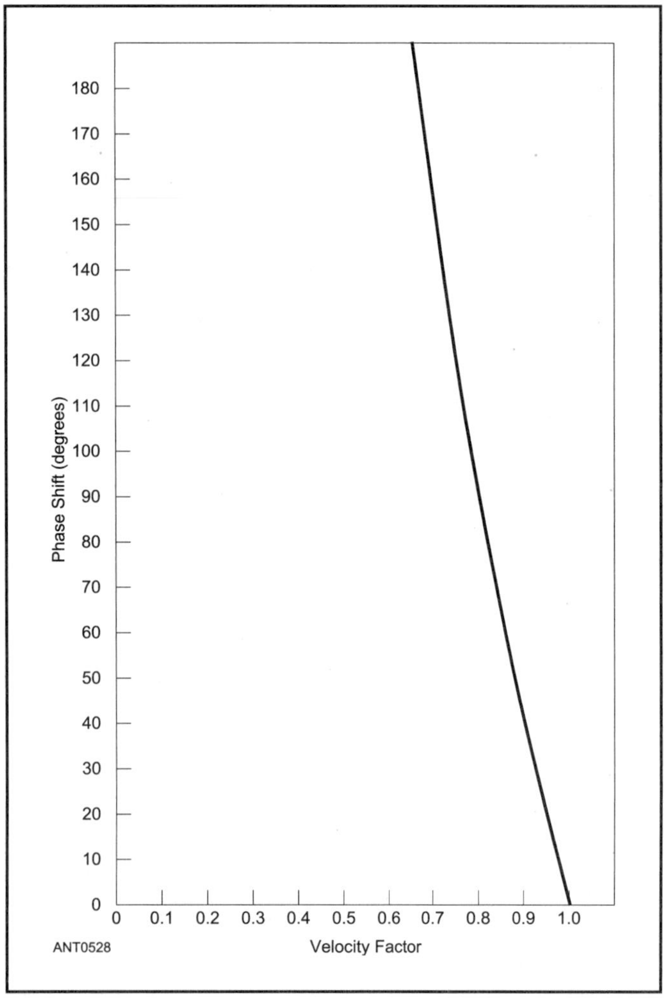

Figure 22.3 — This curve shows phase shift (per wavelength) as a function of velocity factor on a Beverage antenna. Once the phase shift for the antenna goes beyond 90°, the gain drops off from its peak value, and any increase in antenna length will decrease gain.

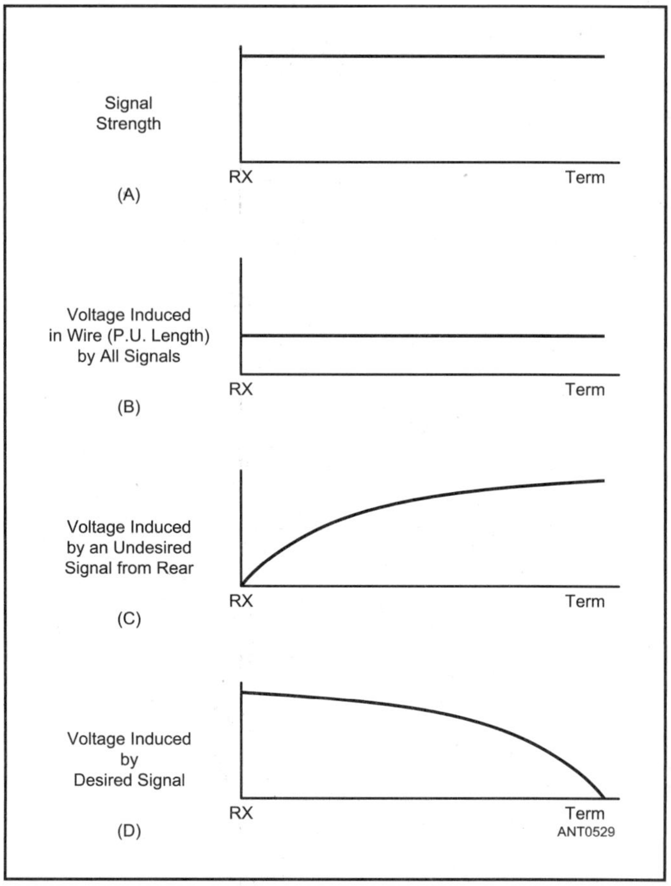

Figure 22.4 — These curves show the voltages that appear in a Beverage antenna over a period of several cycles of the wave. Signal strength (at A) is constant over the length of the antenna during this period, as is voltage induced per unit length (P.U.) in the wire (at B). (The voltage induced in any section of the antenna is the same as the voltage induced in any other section of the same size, over the same period of time.) At C, the voltages induced by an undesired signal from the rearward direction add in phase and build to a maximum at the termination end (TERM), where they are dissipated in the termination (if $Z_{term} = Z_0$). The voltages resulting from a desired signal are shown at D. The wave on the wire travels closely with the wave in space, and the voltages resulting add in phase to a maximum at the receiver end (RX) of the antenna.

minimize reception of horizontally polarized signals from the sides. Some minor sidelobes will exist, as with other long-wire antennas, and will increase in number with the length of the antenna.

In the case of a signal arriving from the rear of the antenna, the behavior of the antenna is very similar to its performance in the favored direction. The major difference is that the signal from the rear adds in phase at the termination end and is absorbed by the termination impedance. **Figure 22.5** compares the azimuth and elevation patterns for a 2-wavelength (1062 foot) and a 1-wavelength (531 foot) Beverage at 1.83 MHz. The wire is mounted 8 feet above flat ground (to keep it above deer antlers and away from humans too) and is terminated with a 500-Ω resistor in each case, although the exact value of the terminating resistance is not critical. The ground constants assumed in this computer model are conductivity of 5 mS/m and a dielectric constant of 13. Beverages operated over saltwater or highly conductive soil have very low signal levels and very poor directivity.

For most effective operation, the Beverage should be terminated in an impedance equal to the characteristic impedance Z_{ANT} of the antenna. For maximum signal transfer to the receiver, you should also match the receiver's input impedance to the antenna. If the termination impedance is not equal to the characteristic impedance of the antenna, some part of the signal from the rear will be reflected back toward the receiver end of the antenna.

If the termination impedance is merely an open circuit (no terminating resistor), total reflection will result, and the antenna will exhibit a nearly bidirectional pattern (still with deep nulls off the sides). An unterminated Beverage will not have the same response to signals in the rearward direction as it exhibits to signals in the forward direction because of attenuation and re-radiation of part of the reflected wave as it travels back toward the receiver end. **Figure 22.6** compares the response from two 2-λ Beverages, one terminated and the

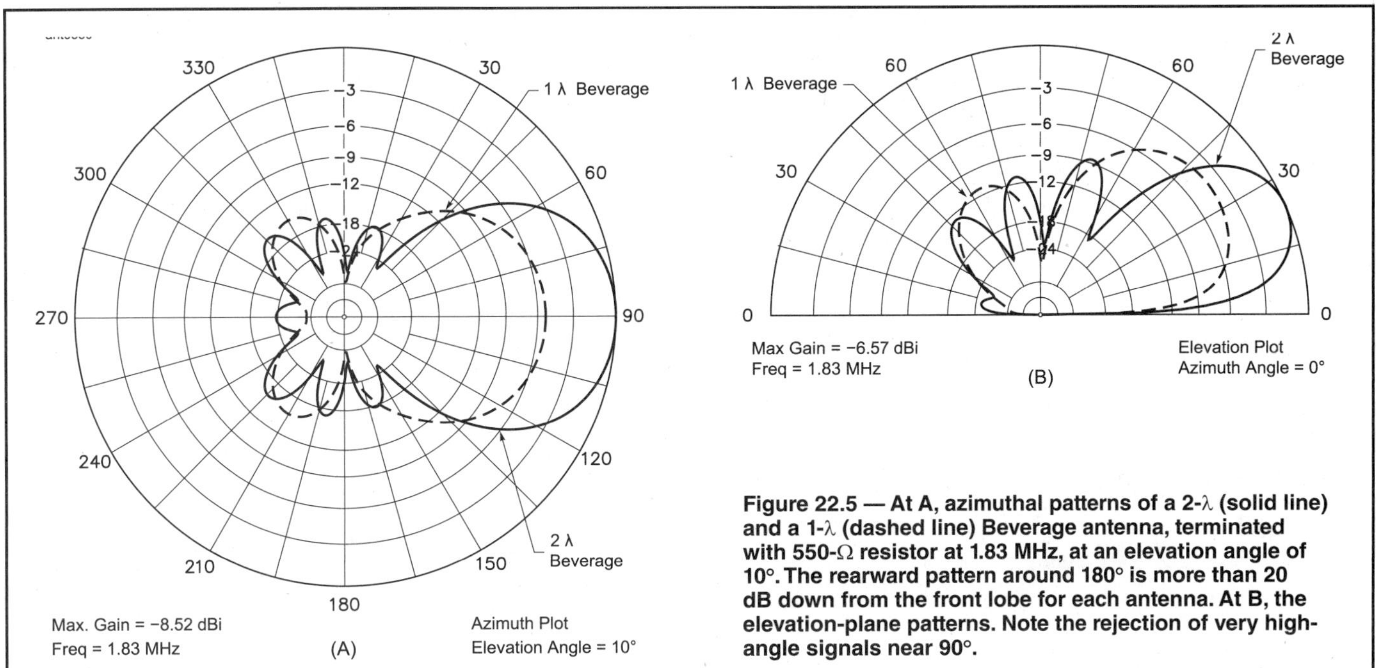

Figure 22.5 — At A, azimuthal patterns of a 2-λ (solid line) and a 1-λ (dashed line) Beverage antenna, terminated with 550-Ω resistor at 1.83 MHz, at an elevation angle of 10°. The rearward pattern around 180° is more than 20 dB down from the front lobe for each antenna. At B, the elevation-plane patterns. Note the rejection of very high-angle signals near 90°.

other unterminated. Just like a terminated long-wire transmitting antenna (which is mounted higher off the ground than a Beverage, which is normally used only for receiving), the terminated Beverage has a reduced forward lobe compared to an unterminated Beverage. The unterminated Beverage exhibits about a 5 dB front-to-back ratio for this length because of the radiation and wire and ground losses that occur before the forward wave gets to the end of the wire.

To determine the appropriate value for a terminating resistor, you need to know the characteristic impedance (surge impedance), Z_{ANT}, of the Beverage. It is interesting to note that Z_{ANT} is not a function of the length, just like a transmission line.

$$Z_{ANT} = 138 \times \log\left(\frac{4h}{d}\right)\ \Omega$$

where

Z_{ANT} = characteristic impedance of the Beverage = terminating resistance needed

h = wire height above ground

d = wire diameter (in the same units as h)

Another aspect of terminating the Beverage is the quality of the RF ground used for the termination. For most types of soil, a ground rod is sufficient, since the optimum value for the termination resistance is in the range of 400 to 600 Ω for typical Beverages and the ground-loss resistance is in series with this. Even if the ground-loss resistance at the termination point is as high as 40 or 50 Ω, it still is not an appreciable fraction of the overall terminating resistance. For soil with very poor conductivity, however, (such as sand or rock) you can achieve a better ground termination by laying radial wires on the ground at both the receiver and termination ends. These wires need not be resonant quarter-wave in length, since the ground detunes them anyway. Like the ground counterpoise for a vertical antenna, a number of short radials is better than a few long ones. Some amateurs use chicken-wire ground screens for their ground terminations.

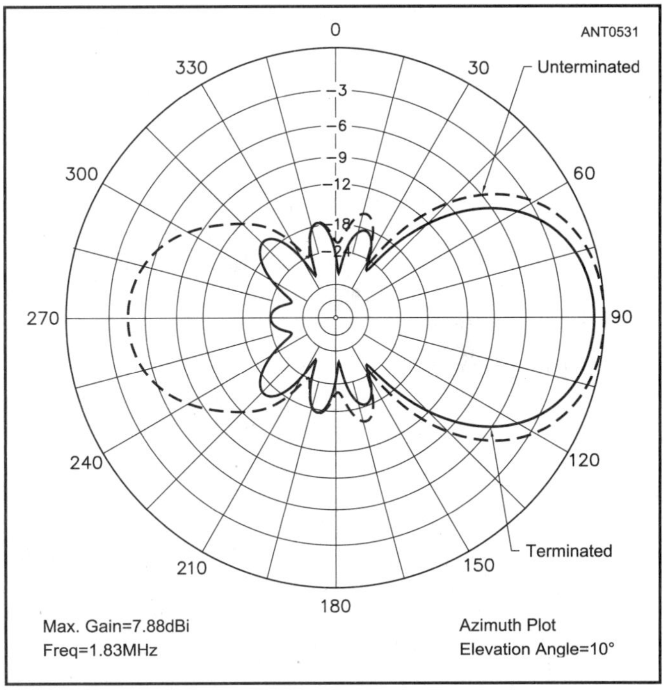

Figure 22.6 — Comparing the azimuthal patterns for a 2-λ Beverage, terminated (solid line) and unterminated (dashed line).

As with many other antennas, improved directivity and gain can be achieved by lengthening the antenna and by arranging several antennas into an array. One item that must be kept in mind is that by virtue of the velocity factor of the antenna, there is some phase shift of the wave traveling on the antenna compared to the wave arriving at the antenna. Because of this phase shift, although the directivity may continue to sharpen with increased length, there will be some optimum length at which the gain of the antenna will peak. Beyond this length, the voltages arriving at the receiver end of the antenna will no longer be in phase and will not add to produce a maximum signal at the receiver end. This optimum length is a function of velocity factor and frequency, and is given by:

$$L = \frac{\lambda}{4\left(\frac{100}{k} - 1\right)}$$

where

L = maximum effective length (same units as λ)
λ = signal wavelength in free space
k = velocity factor of the antenna in percent

Because velocity factor increases with height (to a point, as mentioned earlier), optimum length is somewhat longer if the antenna height is increased but at the expense of front-to-side ratio. The maximum effective length also increases with the number of wires in the antenna system. For example, for a two-wire Beverage like the bidirectional version the maximum effective length is about 20% longer than the single-wire version. A typical length for single-wire 1.8-MHz Beverage antennas (made of #16 AWG wire and erected 10 feet above ground) is about 500 to 1200 feet for optimum performance on 160 meters and 300 to 600 feet for optimum performance on 80 meters.

FEED POINT TRANSFORMERS FOR SINGLE-WIRE BEVERAGES

The usual concept of SWR is applies to an impedance mismatch at the load end of a feed line. This is not the case here where the signal source is the Beverage antenna, and the feed line termination is the receiver. Impedance matching of the source to the feed line is the most important issue for receiving antennas.

As an example, assume that the Z_{ANT} of a particular Beverage is 525 Ω and the terminating resistance is equal to that value. If a 3:1 turns-ratio transformer (a $3^2 = 9:1$ impedance transformer) is used between a 50 Ω feed line and the receiver end of the antenna, the nominal impedance presented to the antenna would be 50 × 9 = 450 Ω. The mismatch of the feed line to the receiver would be 525/450 = 1.27:1, not enough to be concerned about.

Matching transformer T1 in Figure 22.1 is easily constructed as a flux-coupled transformer or as an autotransformer. Small toroidal ferrite cores are best for this application, with those of high permeability (μ_i = 125 to 5000, type 77 ferrite is recommended for 160 meters) being the easiest to wind (requiring fewest turns) and having the best high-frequency response (because few turns are used).

A 9:1 transformer can be made from a pair of ferrite beads as described on the K9AY website at **aytechnologies.com/TechData/9-to-1_XFMR.htm**. (Trifilar-wound autotransformers are convenient but do not provide galvanic isolation and have significant distributed capacitance between the primary and secondary windings.) **Figure 22.7** shows the basic two-bead design. If a binocular core is available, that simplifies construction. If high-frequency noise or signals are present, additional isolation between primary and secondary can be obtained by using a toroidal core and placing the windings on opposite sides.

THE TWO-WIRE BEVERAGE

The two-wire antenna shown in **Figure 22.8** has the major advantage of having signals from both directions available at the receiver at the flip of a switch between J1 and J2. Also, because there are two wires in the system, greater signal voltages will be produced. (Equal amounts of signal voltage are induced in both wires) The April 2006 *QST* article "A Cool Beverage Four Pack" by Ward Silver, NØAX, describes a four-directional array created from a pair of two-wire Beverages at right angles.

A signal from the left direction in Figure 22.8 induces equal voltages in both wires, and common-mode currents flow as a result. The *reflection transformer* (T3 at the right-hand end of the antenna) then combines the common-mode currents and sends them back down the antenna toward the receiver as a differential-mode signal, using the antenna wires as a balanced open-wire transmission line. This signal is then transformed by T1 to the input impedance of the receiver (50 Ω) at J1.

Signals traveling from right to left also induce equal common-mode voltages in each wire, and they travel toward the receiver end, through T1, and into T2. Signals from this direction are available at J2.

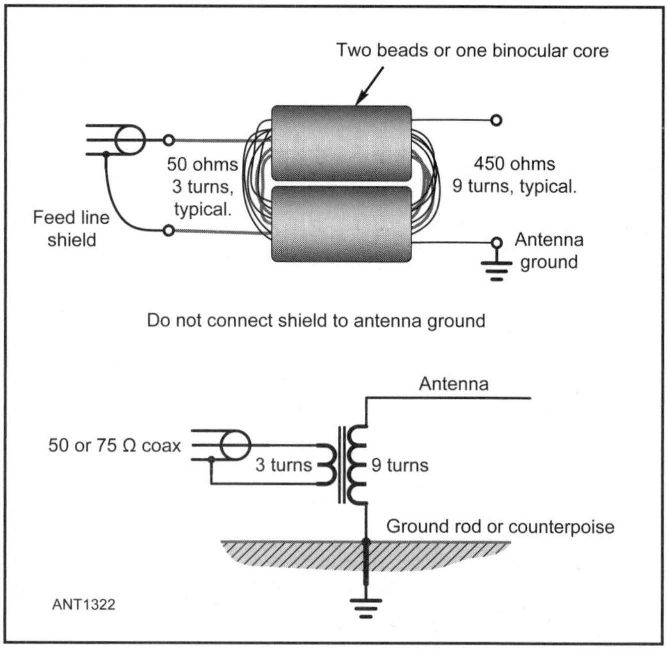

Figure 22.7 — A two-bead or binocular core 9:1 impedance transformer for receiving antennas with a 3:1 turns ratio. See text for details.

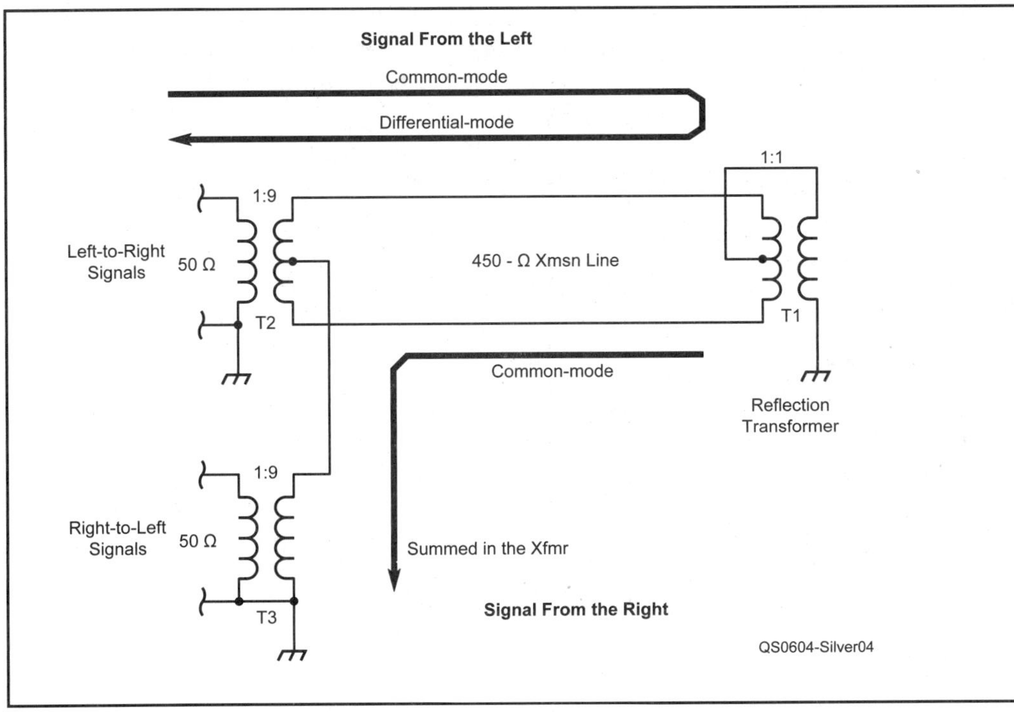

Figure 22.8 — A two-wire Beverage antenna that can receive signals from either direction by switching between the 9:1 impedance transformer outputs.

T1 and T2 are standard 9:1 wideband transformers capable of operating from 1.8 to at least 10 MHz. Like any two parallel wires making up a transmission line, the two-wire Beverage has a certain characteristic impedance — we'll call it Z_1 here — depending on the spacing between the two wires and the insulation between them. T3 transforms the terminating resistance needed at the end of the line to Z_1. Keep in mind that this terminating resistance is equal to the characteristic impedance Z_{ANT} of the Beverage — that is, the impedance of the parallel wires over the images in the ground below. For example, if Z_1 of the Beverage wire is 300 Ω (that is, you used TV twin-lead for the two Beverage wires), T3 must transform the balanced 300 Ω to the unbalanced 500 Ω Z_{ANT} impedance used to terminate the Beverage.

The design and construction of the reflection transformer used in a two-wire Beverage is more demanding than that for the straightforward matching transformer T1 because the exact value of terminating impedance is more critical for good F/B. See the **Receiving Antennas** chapter in *ON4UN's Low-Band DXing* for details on winding the reflection transformers for a two-wire Beverage.

Another convenient feature of the two-wire Beverage is the ability to steer the nulls off either end of the antenna while receiving in the opposite direction. For instance, if the series RLC network in Figure 22.28 is connected to the transformer output for signals coming from the right and adjusted while signals from the left are being received through the other transformer, interference coming from the right can be partially or completely nulled. The nulls can be steered over a 60° (or more) area off the right-hand end of the antenna.

The two-wire Beverage is typically erected at the same height as a single-wire version. The two wires are at the same height and are spaced uniformly — typically 12 to 18 inches apart for discrete wires. Some amateurs construct two-wire Beverages using "window" ladder-line, twisting the line about three twists per foot for electrical balance and mechanical stability in the wind.

The characteristic impedance Z_{ANT} of a Beverage made using two discrete wires with air insulation between them depends on the wire size, spacing and height and is given by:

$$Z_{ANT} = 69 \log \left[\frac{4h}{d} \sqrt{1 + \left(\frac{2h}{S} \right)^2} \right] \Omega$$

where

Z_{ANT} = Beverage impedance = desired terminating resistance

S = wire spacing

h = height above ground

d = wire diameter (same units for S, h, and d)

BEVERAGE ON GROUND (BOG)

A number of low-band DXers have reported improved received signal-to-noise ratios using a Beverage On Ground (BOG). This consists of a wire just a few inches above the ground. BOG performance is significantly degraded if the wire is in direct contact with the ground. Results are mixed as discussed by Guy Olinger, K2AV, in the following excerpt from a discussion on the Topband reflector with input from Frank Donovan, W3LPL: "What is often called a BOG is really a ground-mounted low-velocity-factor receive antenna, which has its own set of rules. The technique of terminating the far end of a wire in what amounts to a characteristic impedance, to dissipate the standing wave on the wire, does not produce an optimum BOG.

"160 meter BOGs longer than 220 feet do not perform well. One can easily model a longer BOG that has a pattern *reversal*. The various serious quirks of BOGs make them [difficult to use] because their performance is strongly affected by local ground characteristics.

"The BOG's pattern will also vary with the ground's water content, which is in turn varying the velocity factor and the best termination strategy. This effect, along with the wire gradually growing down into the grass, can be responsible for the difficulty in obtaining repeatable and satisfactory results."

CONSTRUCTION CONSIDERATIONS

There are a few basic principles that must be kept in mind when erecting Beverage antennas if optimum performance is to be realized. Start by considering the complete project and plan thoroughly.

1) Choose an antenna length consistent with good performance on the bands you will operate.

Recommended Beverage Lengths:

160 meters	500-1,200 feet
80 meters	300-600 feet
40 meters	200-500 feet

500 to 600 feet provides a good compromise between 160 and 80 meter performance.

2) Keep the antenna as straight and as nearly level as possible over its entire run. Avoid following the terrain under the antenna too closely — keep the antenna level with the average terrain. Variations in height smaller than and extending for less than 1/10 wavelength will have little effect on performance.

3) Either 50 or 75 Ω feed line can be used with little effect on performance. Be sure to weatherproof the transformers, termination connections, and feed line connectors.

4) Use a noninductive resistor for terminating a single-wire Beverage. If you live in an area where lightning is common, use 2 W metal oxide, non-inductive terminating resistors, which can better survive surges due to nearby lightning strikes.

5) Use high-quality insulators for the Beverage wire where it comes into contact with the supports. Plastic insulators designed for electric fences are inexpensive and effective.

6) Keep the Beverage away from parallel conductors such as electric power and telephone lines for a distance of at least 200 feet. Approximately perpendicular conductors, including other Beverages, may be crossed within a few feet with relatively little interaction, but do not cross any conductors that may pose a safety hazard.

7) Run the coaxial feed line to the Beverage so that it is not directly under the span of the wire. This prevents common-mode currents from appearing on the shield of the coax. It is best to install a common-mode choke at the end of the feed line adjacent to its connection to the Beverage. Do not connect the feed line shield to the ground system used by the antenna.

8) If you use elevated radials in your transmitting antenna system, keep your Beverage feed lines well away from them to avoid stray pickup that are likely to disrupt the Beverage's directivity.

9) If lightning is a problem in your area, add a small spark gap across the terminating resistor. The simplest method is to bypass the resistor with a short piece of heavy wire and cutting the wire in the middle with diagonal or side cutters, creating a small gap with sharp edges. Similar gaps can be created where the antenna wires are connected to an enclosure as shown by W8JI at **w8ji.com/lightning_strikes.htm**. During lightning season, check the protective components in your system regularly to be sure they are still present and functioning.

22.1.3 Tuned Small Loops

To be considered an electrically small loop, the total length of conductor in the loop must not exceed about 0.085 λ so the current will have the same amplitude and phase in every part of the loop. This results in a bidirectional, figure-eight pattern with deep nulls broadside to the plane of the loop. (See the extensive discussion of small loops in the **Loop Antennas** chapter for more about the theory of these antennas.) Amateur applications of these loops include direction finding and low-noise directional receiving antennas for 3.5 MHz and below. (See the section on Direction-Finding Antennas later in this chapter.)

Maintaining symmetry creates electrical balance around the loop which is important to preserving the depth of the pattern's nulls. Balanced loops are not affected noticeably by nearby objects and can be installed indoors or out after being tuned to resonance. Moving them from one place to another does not significantly affect the tuning. Using flexible cable to build small receiving loops will achieve satisfactory results but even better performance and stability result from using semi-rigid 50 or 75 Ω hardline cable. The semi-rigid cable will also maintain loop shape and symmetry better than for flexible cable.

For receiving applications, it is not necessary to match the feed line to the loop, though doing so may enhance the performance somewhat. The builder can use 50- or 75-Ω coax feed line and no difference in performance will be observed.

PROPAGATION EFFECTS ON NULL DEPTH

After building a balanced loop you are likely to find it does not approach the theoretical performance in the null depth. This problem may result from propagation effects. Tilting the loop away from a vertical plane may improve performance under some propagation conditions, to account for the vertical angle of arrival. Basically, the loop performs as described above only when the signal is arriving with vertical polarization perpendicular to the axis of rotation of the loop.

At incidence angles other than perpendicular, the position and depth of the nulls deteriorate. Bond explained this issue in his book on direction finding in 1944 along with the math to calculate the performance. The problem can be even further influenced by the fact that if the loop is situated over less than perfectly conductive ground, the wave front will appear to tilt or bend.

Another cause of apparent poor performance in the null depth can be from polarization error. Small loop antennas have no directivity for horizontally polarized signals. If the polarization of the received signal is not completely vertical, the nulls will not be sharp. In fact, for elliptically polarized signals, the loop might appear to have almost no nulls. Mount the loop antenna close to the ground to minimize its susceptibility to horizontally polarized signals. Propagation effects are discussed further in the sections on direction finding.

SITING EFFECTS ON SMALL LOOPS

The location of the loop has an influence on its performance that at times may become quite noticeable. For ideal performance the loop should be located outdoors and clear of any large conductors, such as metallic downspouts and towers. A loop tuned for VLF reception, when mounted this way, will show good sharp nulls spaced 180° apart if the loop is well-balanced. This is because the major propagation mode at VLF is by ground wave. At frequencies in the HF region, a significant portion of the signal is propagated by sky wave, and nulls are often only partial.

Most hams locate their loop antennas near their operating position. If you choose to locate a small loop indoors, its performance may show nulls of less than the expected depth, and some skewing of the pattern. For precision direction finding there may be some errors associated with wiring, plumbing, and other metallic construction members in the building. Also, a strong local signal may be reradiated from the surrounding conductors so that it cannot be nulled with any positioning of the loop. There appears to be no known method of curing this type of problem. All this should not discourage you from locating a loop indoors; this information is presented here only to give you an idea of some pitfalls. Many hams have reported excellent results with indoor mounted loops, in spite of some of the problems.

Locating a receiving loop in the field of a transmitting antenna may cause a large voltage to appear at the receiver antenna terminals. This may be sufficient to destroy sensitive RF amplifier transistors or front-end protection diodes. This can be solved by disconnecting your loop from the receiver during transmit periods. This can obviously be done automatically with a relay that opens when the transmitter is activated but timed correctly so that even a few milliseconds of transmitted signal cannot enter the receiver.

PROJECT: A RECEIVING LOOP FOR 1.8 MHZ

loop of **Figure 22.9** has a conductor length of 20 feet. At 1.81 MHz, 20 feet is 0.037 λ. With this style of loop, 0.037 λ is about the maximum practical dimension if you want to tune the element to resonance. This limitation results from the distributed capacitance between the shield and inner conductor of the loop. RG-59 was used for the loop element in this example. The capacitance per foot for this cable is 21 pF, resulting in a total distributed capacitance of 420 pF. An additional 100 pF was needed to resonate the loop at 1.810 MHz.

Therefore, the approximate inductance of the loop is 15 µH. The effect of the capacitance becomes less pronounced at the higher end of the HF spectrum, provided the same percentage of a wavelength is used in computing the conductor length. The ratio between the distributed capacitance and the lumped capacitance used at the feed point becomes greater at resonance. These facts should be contemplated when scaling the loop to those bands above 1.8 MHz.

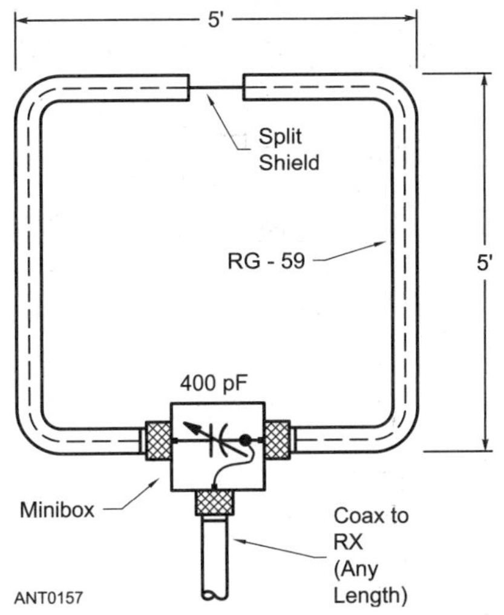

Figure 22.9 — Schematic diagram of the loop antenna. The dimensions are not critical provided overall length of the loop element does not exceed approximately 0.1 λ. Small loops which are one half or less the size of this one will prove useful where limited space is a consideration.

There will not be a major difference in the construction requirements of the loop if coaxial cables other than RG-59 are used. The line impedance is not significant with respect to the loop element. Various types of coaxial line exhibit different amounts of capacitance per foot, however, thereby requiring more or less capacitance across the feed point to establish resonance. Remove the shield of the loop coax for one inch directly opposite the feed point. Treat the exposed areas with a sealing compound once this is done. Covering the gap with a non-conductive plastic tube also helps provide mechanical strength at this point.

A supporting structure was fashioned from bamboo poles. The X frame is held together at the center with two U bolts. The loop element is taped to the cross-arms to form a square. You could likely use metal cross arms without seriously degrading the antenna performance. Alternatively, wood can be used for the supporting frame. A wooden or plastic center mast is sufficient to hold a loop made from hardline, even up to several feet in diameter.

An aluminum project box was used at the feed point of the loop to hold the resonating variable capacitor. In this model a 50 to 400-pF compression trimmer was used to establish resonance. You must weatherproof the box for outdoor installations.

The Q of this loop is sufficiently low to allow the operator to peak it for resonance at 1.9 MHz and use it across the entire 160 meter band. The degradation in performance at 1.8 and 2 MHz will be so slight that it will be difficult to discern.

22.1.4 Resistively Loaded Small Loops

Loop receiving antennas with resistive loading are popular because they can provide useful broadband directivity with very simple construction. A wide range of sizes and shapes are seen in practice: the K9AY Loop, flags, and pennants are the most popular because they are simple to build. Rotatable versions of the flag antenna can also be constructed. This section explains the basic theory of how the antennas work and summarizes several types. Construction articles are provided in the online material.

DIRECTIVITY FROM RESISTIVE LOADING

The shape of the loop is not of primary importance as a wide range of shapes can be successfully used as dictated by mechanical convenience, available supports, etc. What unites this class of antennas is how the normal pattern of a small loop is changed to a cardioid with a single useful null by judiciously adding series resistance into the loop. (An alternative approach is presented in the section describing the K9AY Loop.)

In unloaded small loops (<1/8-wavelength circumference) the current amplitude around the loop is essentially constant with little phase shift. Adding series resistance, the current amplitude remains relatively constant but there is significant phase shift around the loop. The non-uniform phase of the current around the loop changes the radiation pattern. The amount of phase shift is a function of loop inductance and load resistance: the loop is behaving like a series L-R circuit.

We can illustrate this with an example like that shown in **Figure 22.10**. The source is represented by a circle and the loading resistor by a square. The loop is 14 feet on each side and the frequency is 1.8 MHz, so the width of the loop is about 9.2 degrees. This is the phase delay between the vertical arms for a signal passing transversally across the loop.

A clockwise current direction convention was used in the model so the current direction in the load wire is the opposite of the source wire, i.e., 180 degrees out of phase in the unloaded loop. The vertical arms of the loop produce a pattern very much like the two-element phased array with the elements 180 degrees out of phase in the **Phased Arrays** chapter (see the collection of H-plane patterns with ϕ=180°). **Figure 22.11** shows the azimuthal pattern, at 0° elevation in free space without loading.

Changing the phase relationship between currents in the two arms changes the pattern. To produce a single sharp null in a two-element phased array with equal element currents 14 feet apart, the phase difference would have to be 180 – 9.2 ≈ 171 degrees.

With a load resistance of 675 Ω the pattern has become substantially unidirectional with a 25 dB null off the back (see **Figure 22.12**). Note however, that the peak gain has fallen from +1.73 dBi to –39.2 dBi. That's the penalty for loading a small loop to achieve the necessary phase relationship but this is often acceptable for receiving antennas. A preamplifier can

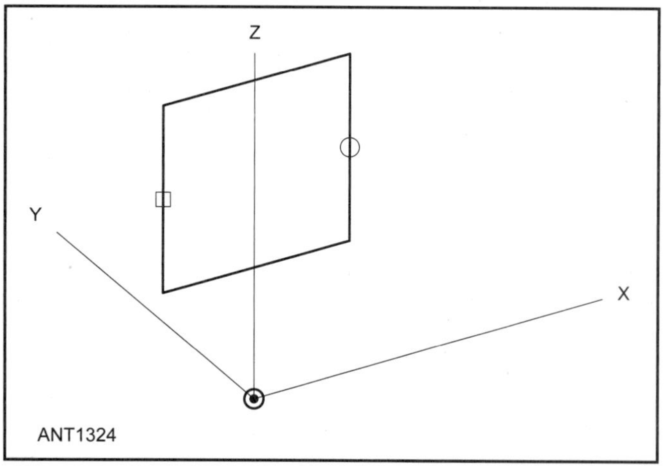

Figure 22.10 — Vertical square loop with no loading.

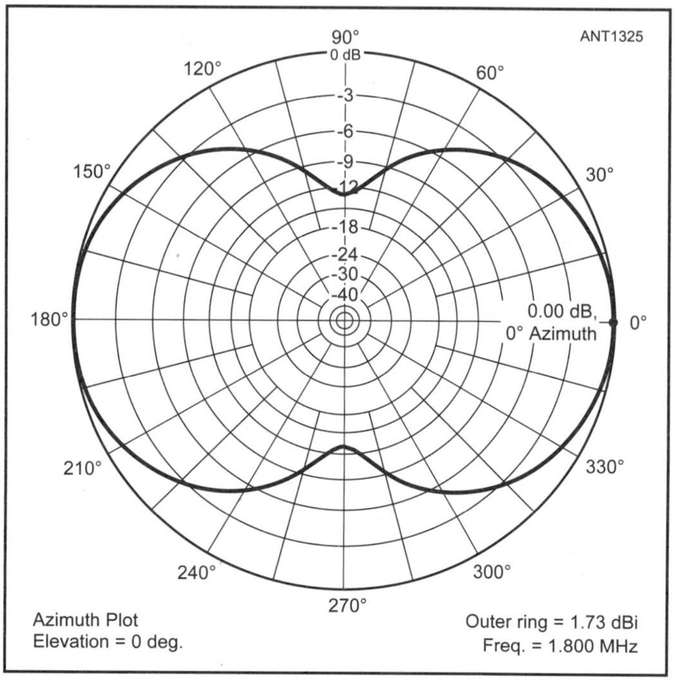

Figure 22.11 — The unloaded loop's azimuthal pattern at 0 degrees in free space.

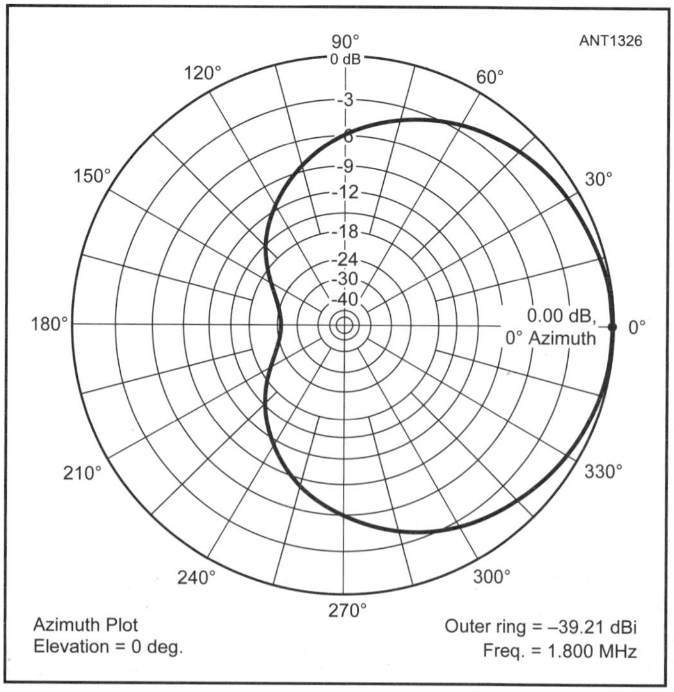

Figure 22.12 — The loop's pattern with a 675 Ω loading resistor.

be used to recover the signal level, if necessary.

Figures 22.13 and **22.14** compare the loop current amplitude and phase with and without loading. Adding loading changes the current amplitude around the loop very little but the phase is very different. The feed point phase is 0 degrees, and the load point phase is ≈-13 degrees. Note that this is not very much different from the 9.2° needed in an ordinary two element array. In this example the loop the current amplitudes are not exactly the same and the phase is not constant over the length of on side so the effective phase becomes an average.

This example was designed for a fixed frequency, 1.8 MHz but one of the attractive features of this family of antennas is that while the current distribution remains quite uniform the current phase changes in a way that tracks the electrical size of the loop maintaining the null over a wide bandwidth. This is an example of *crossfire phasing* described in the **Phased Array** chapter.

At 1.8 MHz with a 675 Ω load the input impedance at the feed point is: Z_i=709 + *j*144 Ω. Modeling the loop as a series L-R circuit and calculating the phase shift as arctan(X/R) = arctan (144/709) ≈ 11 degrees of phase shift which is consistent with the earlier discussion. (Arctan is the same as $\tan^{-1}$)

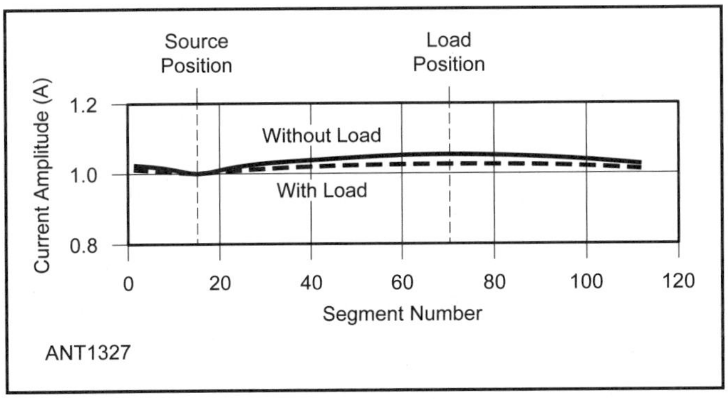

Figure 22.13 — Loop current amplitude with (dashed line) and without (solid line) loading.

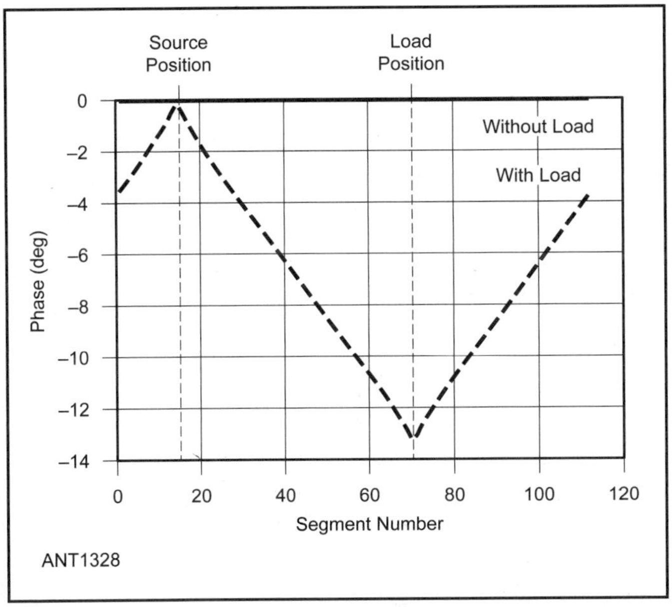

Figure 22.14 — Loop current phase with (dashed) and without (solid) loading.

ALTERNATE LOOP SHAPES, FEED POINTS, AND LOAD POINTS

In Figure 22.10 the loop was shown as square and there is nothing special about that. The shape is frequently a rectangle or a triangle, often referred to as "flags", "pennants," or "EWE's.: The shape chosen will affect the optimum value for R. Given the infinite variety of shapes and dimensions R is most practically determined from modeling.

Figure 22.10 showed the load and source located at the midpoint of the vertical arms. For convenience, both the load and feed point can be shifted to the bottom of the loop as shown in **Figure 22.15**. The optimum value for R will change somewhat and can be determined by modeling.

There is great flexibility in the location of the lower wire as indicated in **Figure 22.16**. The lower wire can be elevated above ground, typically eight feet or so, or it can be laid directly on the ground surface or just below. (Note that if the lower wire is directly in contact with or at the surface of the ground, changes in ground conductivity will affect antenna performance.) It is also possible to use ground stakes at either end

Figure 22.15 — Alternative feed (Source) and load points at the bottom of the loop.

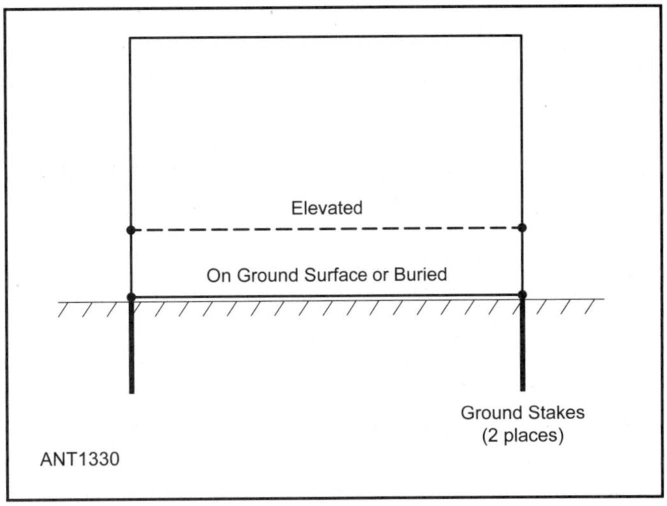

Figure 22.16 — Alternate lower wire locations.

to complete the loop with ground resistance as with the EWE antennas discussed below. However, the impedance of the ground stakes affects the value for R and is likely to change as soil moisture changes with seasons. An interconnecting ground wire will stabilize the ground impedance.

PROJECT: EWE ANTENNA

The EWE antenna invented by Floyd Koontz, WA2WVL, combines two short vertical wires and one horizontal wire as shown in **Figure 22.17** (see the References and Bibliography). The EWE is essentially a two-element driven array. The antenna receives best in the plane of the array in the direction opposite the termination. The pattern is a broad cardioid with a null in the direction of the terminated "rear" element. The horizontally polarized gain of the antenna is about 20 dB lower than the vertically polarized gain and is directed at a high angle off the side. As with all small loop antennas, the received signal level of an EWE antenna is very low and requires both a common-mode choke on the feed line and a high-gain, low noise figure preamplifier.

The version in Figure 22.9 is designed to operate from 1.8 to 4.0 MHz with a front-to-back ratio of greater than 25 dB without adjustment. The EWE can be bottom fed as shown in the figure or at the top of the front vertical element. The autotransformers used in the original article have been changed to isolation transformers with a 3:1 turns ratio. This reduces common-mode noise picked up on the feed line shield. If a separate ground connection is required for the feed line, place the feed line choke between the transformer and the ground connection.

If separate feed lines and transformers are used for each of the vertical elements, a termination resistor can be switched in, opposite to the feed point, to create a reversible pattern. If two of these reversible antennas are positioned at right angles, a four-way receiving antenna system is obtained.

Switching the antenna requires 75 Ω TV-type A/B switches which automatically terminate the unused port in 75 Ω. (See the *QST* article describing the LF/MF EWE in the next section.) This allows separate receivers to be used on the individual EWE antennas. The 75 Ω impedance is multiplied in the transformer by 9 to create a 675 Ω termination. A two-port 180° combiner makes it possible to obtain a bi-directional pattern aimed between the main lobes of the individual antennas.

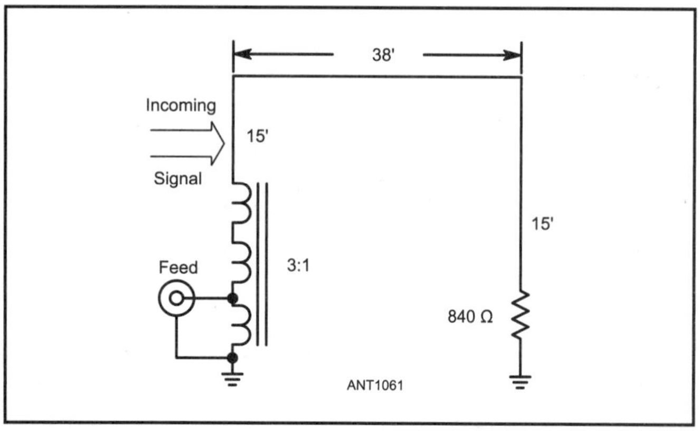

Figure 22.17 — The EWE antenna designed for use on 160 and 80 meters.

PROJECT: LF AND MF REVERSIBLE EWE

This version of the EWE designed by Mike Sapp, WA3TTS, was optimized for weak signal reception on the 2200 and 630 meter bands. It is also useful on the 160 and 80 meter bands with a typical SWR of 1.3:1 throughout its design range. It can be used down into the 30 kHz range, as well. As with other EWE antennas, the dimensions are not critical and can be reduced to fit a small lot with some corresponding reduction in signal capture. The full article, "A Reversible LF and MF EWE Receive Antenna for Small Lots" is included in the online material and includes detailed construction directions and complete descriptions of the specialized components associated with this antenna.

Because the frequency of operation is much lower than most amateur receiving antennas, the impedance transformer and common-mode choke construction use multiple ferrite cores taped together. In addition, special common-mode chokes are used, and careful attention is paid to block common-mode noise and transmit signal pickup on the receive feed lines. See the original article for detailed information about construction of the chokes and transformer.

PROJECT: K9AY LOOP

Described here by its inventor, Gary Breed, K9AY, the K9AY Loop is a hybrid that combines two antenna types. Referring to **Figure 22.18**, if the termination resistor is zero — a short circuit — the antenna becomes a classic "small loop" (usually defined as less than 0.1 λ diameter). The near-field response of small loops is predominantly to the magnetic

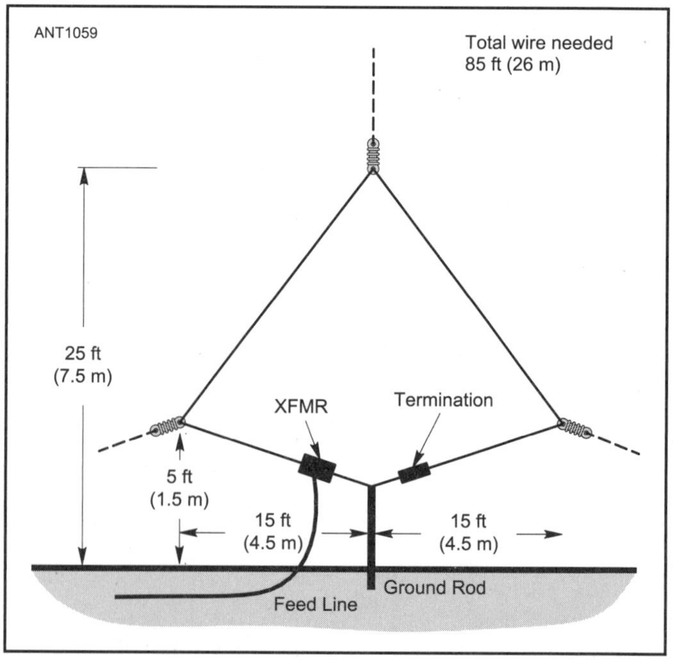

Figure 22.18 — Configuration of the K9AY Loop at the maximum size that allows coverage of both 160 and 80 meter ham bands with a resistive termination.

field (H-field) component of an electromagnetic wave. Next, with an infinite resistor — an open circuit — the antenna becomes a short, bent monopole. Short monopole antennas respond most strongly to the electric field (E-field) component of an electromagnetic wave. (This is an alternative analysis to the two-vertical approach described previously.)

In the K9AY Loop, the terminating resistor serves to balance the ratio of the small loop and monopole responses, with energy from the two modes summed at the feed point. When the value of the resistor is adjusted to the optimum value (typically near 400 Ω), there is cancellation of arriving signals in one of the directions in line with the plane of the loop. This cancellation occurs because of the rotational "sense" of the H-field. While the E-field is one-dimensional (amplitude only), the H-field obeys the "right hand rule" that can be visualized as spiral rotation as a wave travels through space. Waves arriving from opposite directions will thus have opposite rotation. From one direction, the E- and H-field contributions are summed at the feed point. But for signals from the opposite direction, the antenna output is the difference of these contributions. (See the References and Bibliography for additional information about the antenna.) This same type of behavior is present in two other devices familiar to hams; a directional coupler such as those used in the familiar Bird wattmeter, and the direction-finding (DF) loop with sense antenna described in the section on Direction-Finding Antennas later in this chapter.

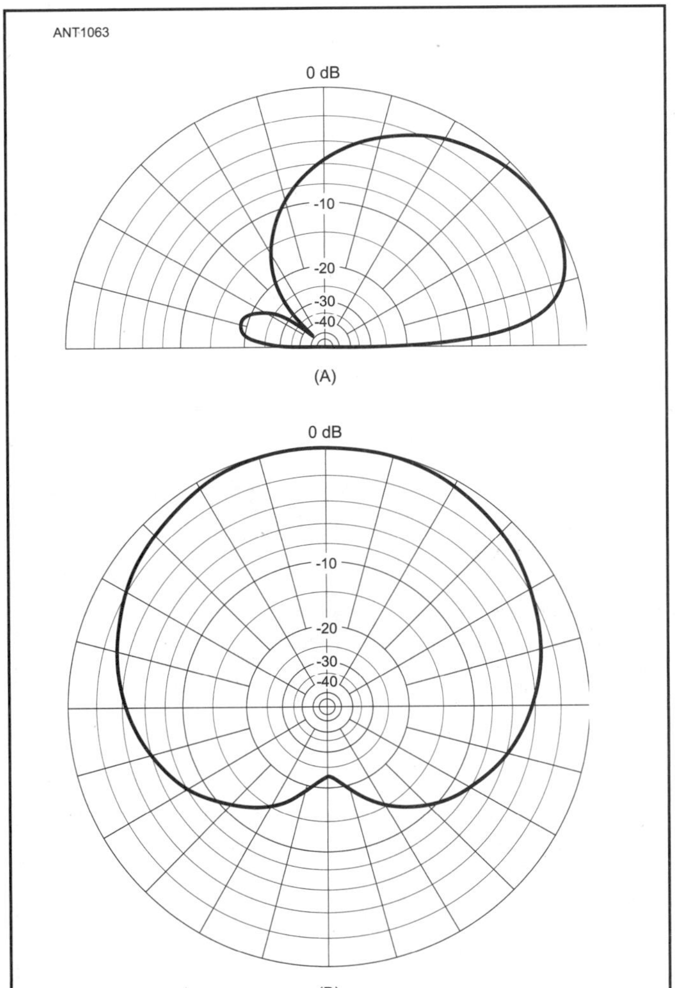

Figure 22.19 — Vertical (A) and horizontal (B) radiation patterns for the K9AY Loop at 1.825 MHz.

The tradeoff for obtaining a directional pattern with small loop size is low efficiency. With the dimensions given above, the K9AY Loop has a gain of approximately –26 dBi. For comparison, a ¼-wave vertical has a gain near 0 dBi, and a typical one-wavelength Beverage antenna has a gain about –11 dBi. The loop should be used with a good high gain, high dynamic range, low noise figure preamplifier for best results. It is not suitable for transmitting, since most of the RF energy will be absorbed by the resistor.

For the chosen shape of the loop, and with the influence of lossy ground, the resulting null appears at an angle about 45° above the horizon, in line with the plane of the loop and toward the side with the resistor. This is shown in the pattern plots of **Figure 22.19**.

As designed, the size is the maximum for 80 meter use. If made larger, the rearward null could not be obtained with just a resistor as the termination. If made smaller, the directional pattern will remain the same, but the signal level will be lower. The voltage (or current) at the feed point is proportional to the area enclosed by the loop. For example, a loop with half-size dimensions will have ¼ the area, and thus, 12 dB lower signal level. A smaller version of the K9AY Loop scaled to the 30 and 40 meter bands was developed by Bob Lombardi, W4ATM. (See the References and Bibliography entry for Lombardi.) K9AY has also done some experimentation with multi-turn versions of the loop as noted in the References and Bibliography.

The model of the antenna uses the *MININEC* ground option, which assumes perfect ground when calculating impedance. Ground losses are simulated by placing a resistor in the ground connection. A little trial-and-error determined that a resistor in the range of 100 to 150 Ω results in a pattern that matched the free-space model (and on-air behavior, as best as it can be determined). **Figure 22.20** is a diagram showing the modeling dimensions and parameters. This model has proven accurate for modeling loops of different sizes and shapes, and for arrays of loops. (K9AY updated his model for the loop in the article "Modeling the K9AY Loop" in the March/April 2015 issue of the *National Contest Journal* which is included with this book's online material.)

Construction

Construction of the K9AY Loop is shown in Figure 22.18. Approximately 85 feet of wire is arranged into a four-sided shape that is almost triangular. This shape was chosen primarily for its mechanical arrangement — it has a single center support approximately 25 feet high, and it can share that support with a second loop installed at right angles (see **Figure 22.21**).

Connections are made at the bottom. One end of the loop wire goes to the high impedance side of a 9:1 matching transformer; the other end to a resistor with an optimum value that

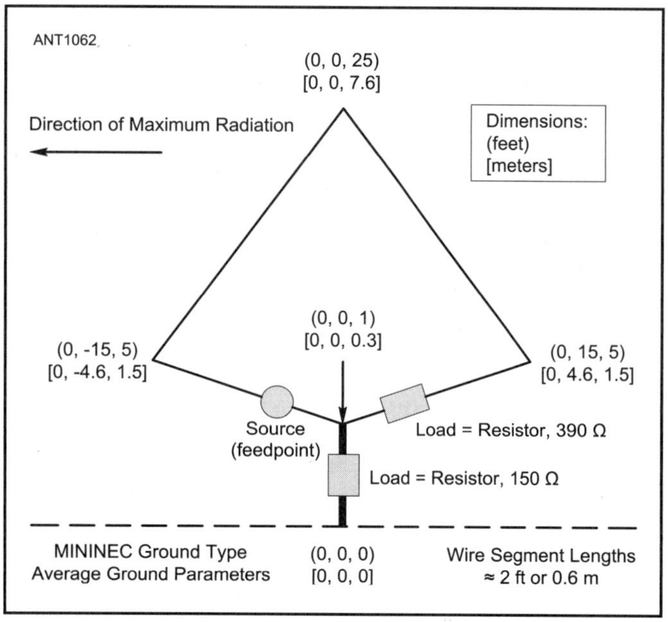

Figure 22.20 — Diagram of the K9AY Loop with dimensions and parameters for computer modeling.

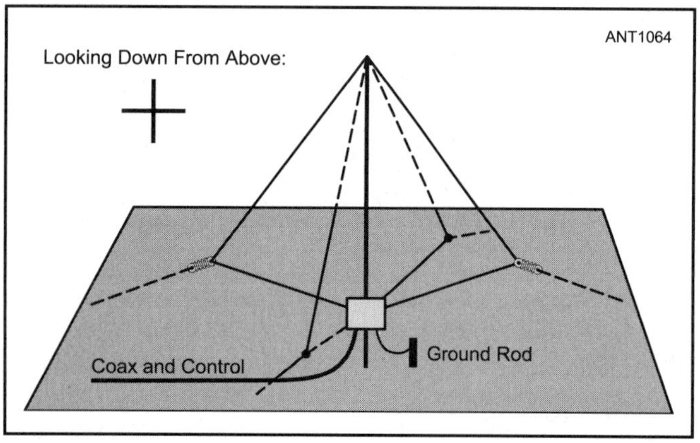

Figure 22.21 — Two loops can be installed with the same central support, creating a two-loop system that can be switched to cover four different directions. In a typical installation for 160 and 80 meter operation, the loops are 25 feet high and ±15 feet from the center (30 feet across).

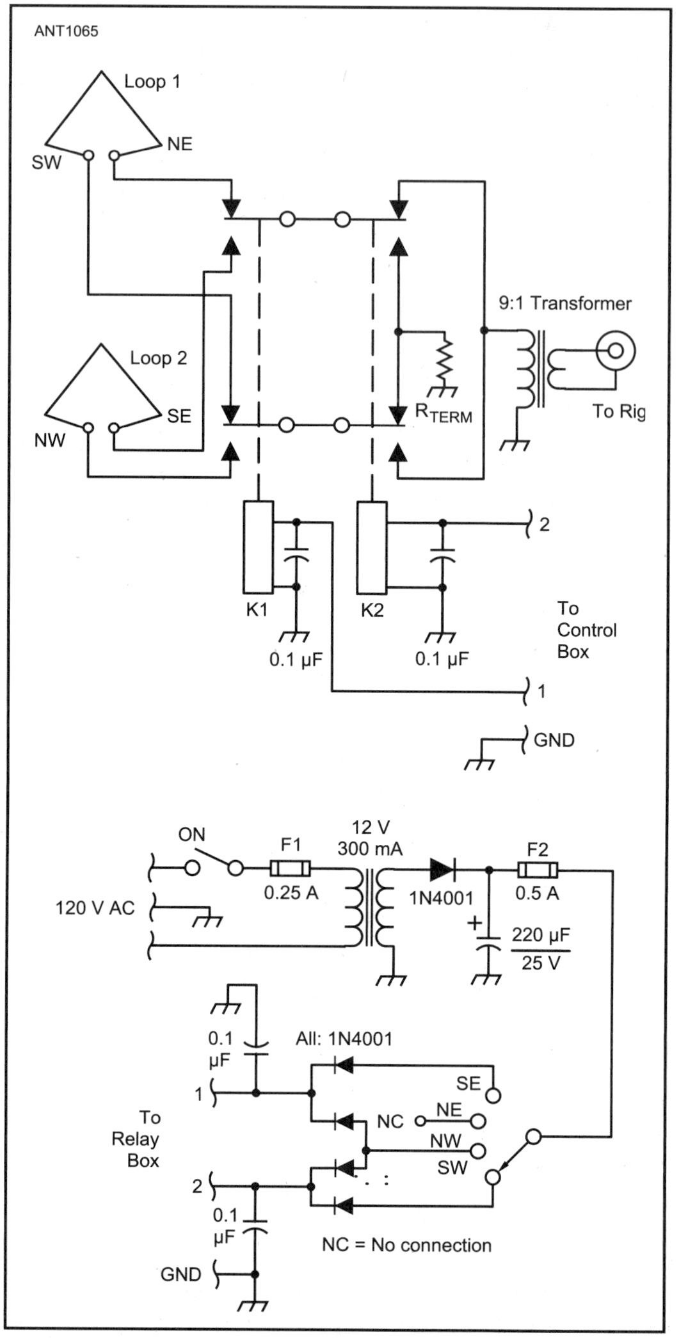

Figure 22.22 — Outdoor antenna switching (top) and indoor control (bottom) circuits for a four-direction, two-loop system. All rectifiers should be bypassed with a 0.01 or 0.001 µF capacitor.

is typically about 400 Ω. (See the previous section "Feed Point Transformers for Single-Wire Beverages" for more information on the transformer design.) Because the connections to each end are at a central point, it is a simple matter to include a relay at this point to reverse the connections, which reverses the directional pattern of the loop. As noted above, a second loop can be installed. Since its connections are also located in the same place, a switching system with four directions is easily implemented. The ability to switch the pattern to several directions is the primary advantage of the K9AY Loop over other small receiving antenna designs. A schematic diagram of four-direction relay switching is shown in **Figure 22.22**.

VE3DO LOOP

Figure 22.23 shows the VE3DO loop which functions similarly to the K9AY Loop. The antenna receives in the direction of the side of the loop with the matching transformer. The transformer uses a BN73-202 binocular core. For 50 Ω feed line, use a 3:1 turns ratio and for 75 Ω use a 5:2 turns ratio. Note that the secondary of the transformer connects between one side of the bottom horizontal wire and ground while the terminating resistor connects between the other side of the bottom horizontal wire and ground. The shield of the coax must not be connected to the common ground of the

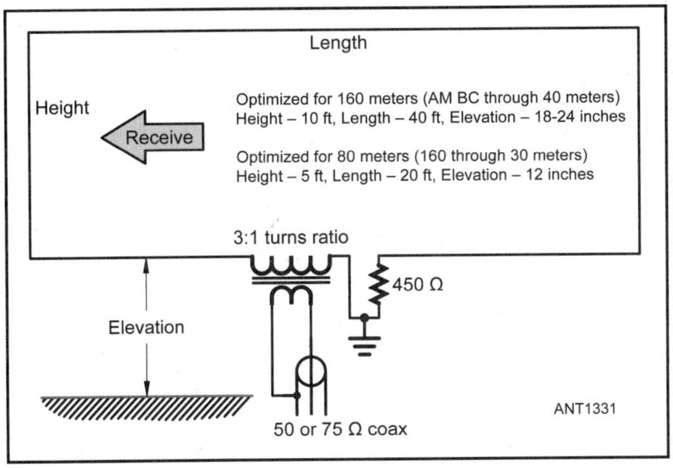

Figure 22.23 — The VE3DO loop with dimensions optimized for 160 and 80 meters.

transformer. A feed line choke should be used at the transformer. While a ground is required, a single ground rod is sufficient, supplemented by a few short radials if necessary for poor or dry ground. Lower elevations above ground may increase directivity at the expense of lowering received signal levels.

A preamplifier of 18-20 dB gain with input filtering to reject AM BC band signals is a must. Loops can be reversed, and a pair installed at right angles with a relay system as described for the K9AY Loop. More information about the VE3DO Loop is available at **ok1rr.com/index.php/antennas/8-the-ve3do-receiving-loop** and in a presentation by K9YC at **audiosystemsgroup.com/VE3DO.pdf**.

PROJECT: FLAG AND PENNANT ANTENNAS

Jose Mata, EA3VY, and Earl Cunningham, K6SE, developed the pennant and flag receiving antennas in **Figure 22.24** which have become popular for the low band DXer. The antennas were developed to eliminate the need for a good ground for predictable low noise directional reception. Their small size makes them practical for those DXers without the room to construct a Beverage or Four-Square antenna. The basic premise for these antennas is to create a hybrid of the small loop pattern and a bent monopole pattern that has useful directivity. (See the previous section on Directivity from Resistive Loading for more information.)An online search for flag and pennant designs will return a large number.

Pennant and flag antennas have a feed point impedance in the range of 945 Ω (the termination opposite the feed point is also 945 Ω). The flag version shows about 5.5 dB higher signal level than the pennant version. Their directivity is toward the feed point direction and appears cardioidal. The front-to-back ratio is in excess of 35 dB. A simple 16 to 1 toroidal or balun transformer can be used to couple to low impedance coax lines.

THE FLAG ANTENNA

While many dimensions can be used for the antenna, constructed as a rectangle, optimized values provide the best directivity over a wide frequency range with a single termination resistor. The standard dimensions developed by EA3VY and K6SE are shown in **Figure 22.25**: 4.27 meters (14 feet)

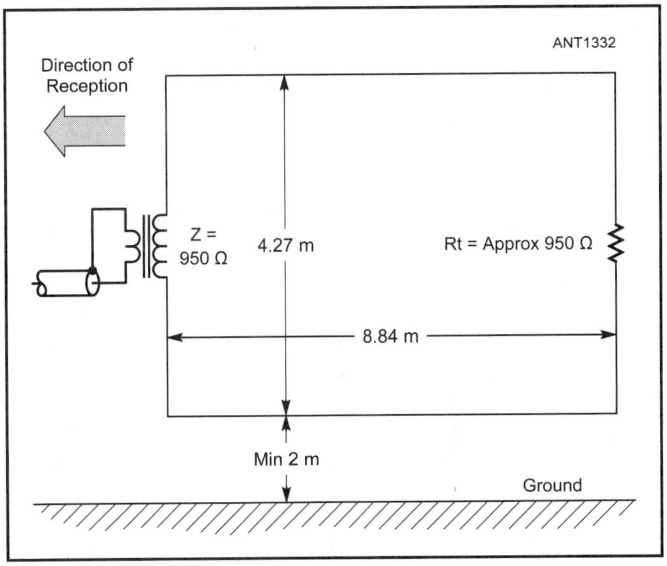

Figure 22.25 — Optimized dimensions for the 160/80 meter flag antenna.

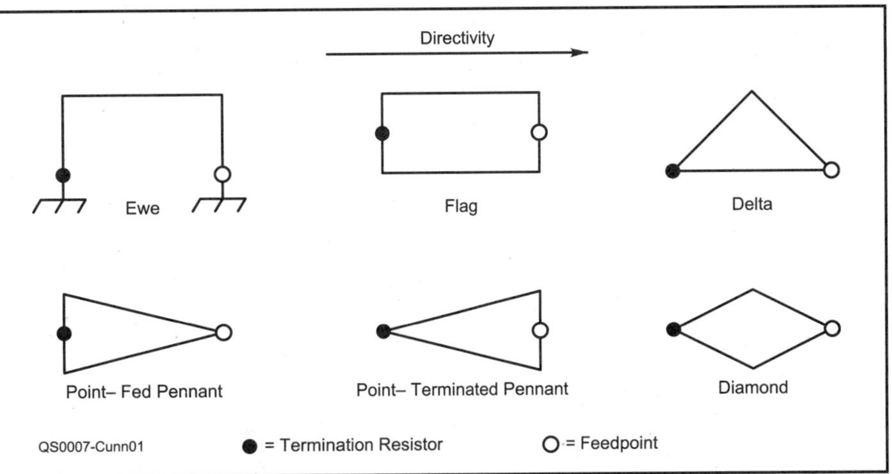

Figure 22.24 — Configurations of the flag and pennant antennas. The dimensions of the flag, both pennants, and the diamond (a modification of the flag) are 29 feet by 14 feet. The delta (a type of half-diamond) is 17 feet high and 28 feet long. The ground-independent antennas are designed to be installed 6 feet above ground.

high by 8.84 meters (29 feet) wide, with a bottom wire height of 2 meters (6 feet) above ground. These dimensions result in an antenna that has excellent characteristics from 7.5 MHz and down. The antenna was designed to be broadband with minimum feed point reactance over a wide frequency range. This requires the termination resistor to be equal to the feed point resistance with the specific values for height and width. This design has a high F/B ratio over any type of soil and at a wide range of heights above ground.

This configuration has a gain of approximately –28 dBi on 160 meters, –18 dBi on 80 meters, and –10 dBi on 40 meters. The termination resistor is 950 Ω and is opposite the feed point which is in the center of the other vertical section as shown in the figure. The input impedance on 160 meters is 950 Ω with a small reactive component of less than 50 Ω.

REVERSIBLE FLAG

Mark Connelly, WA1ION, (**qsl.net/wa1ion**) has modified the flag antenna to be electrically reversed in direction and to allow remote optimization of the termination. In his version 16:1 transformers are put at both the termination and feed point locations and a coax cable is brought from the low impedance winding of both of these into the station. The user can then attach one of these to the receiver and the other to a noninductive potentiometer and adjust the potentiometer so that it is in the range of 55 to 70 Ω to see an impedance at the antenna in the 880 to 1120 Ω range (when the transformer ratio is taken into effect). This allows an in-station switching box to be constructed to allow these receiver and termination connections to be reversed to allow the null to be moved in the opposite direction.

ROTATABLE FLAG

Steve Lawrence, WB6RSE, took the steering solution to the next level and designed a flag antenna that is mechanically rotatable. The article "Rebuilding a Receiving Flag Antenna for 160 Meters" describes a 29-by-14-foot flag with a frame made from telescoping fiberglass poles. The assembly is sturdy enough to be turned with a small rotator. The full article is included in the online material.

WALLER FLAG

A type of flag array, the Waller Flag (named for Carlos da Silva, N4IS) consists of two small flag antennas in the same plane, connected out of phase by inverting one feed line where the loop signals are combined. The basic design is illustrated in **Figure 22.26**. The array's overall dimensions of 26 feet by 16 feet allow it to be rotated — it is approximately the same size as a 4-element 10 meter Yagi. With a gain of –53 dBi, the signal level is very low and requires a 30-40 dB, low-noise preamp. A horizontally polarized version has also been designed but must be mounted well above the ground. More information

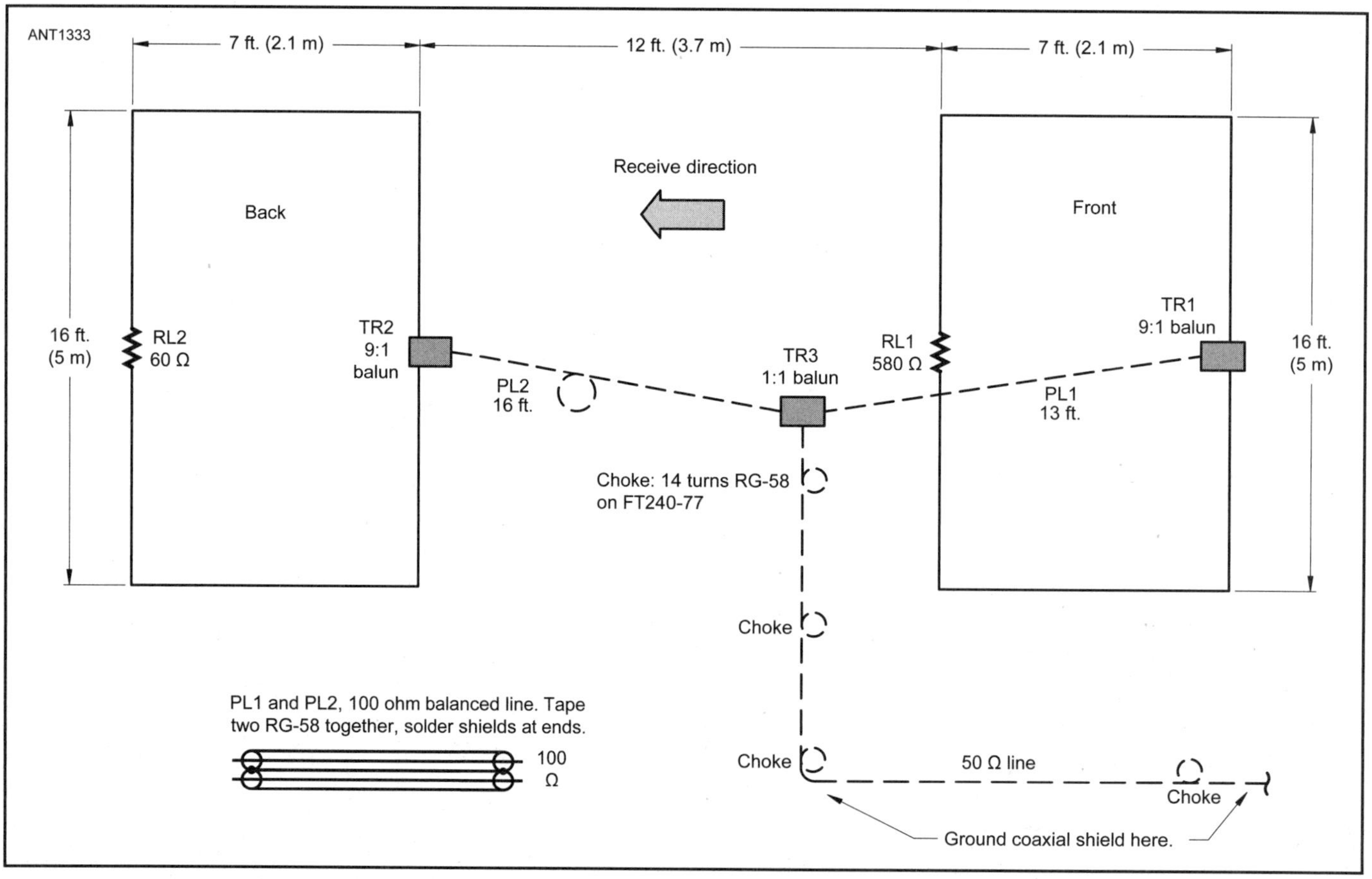

Figure 22.26 — The Waller Flag antenna is an array of two flag antennas in an end-fire configuration. The loops are typically oriented vertically, 12 feet apart. (Graphic from the 2011 Dayton Hamvention Antenna Forum presentation.)

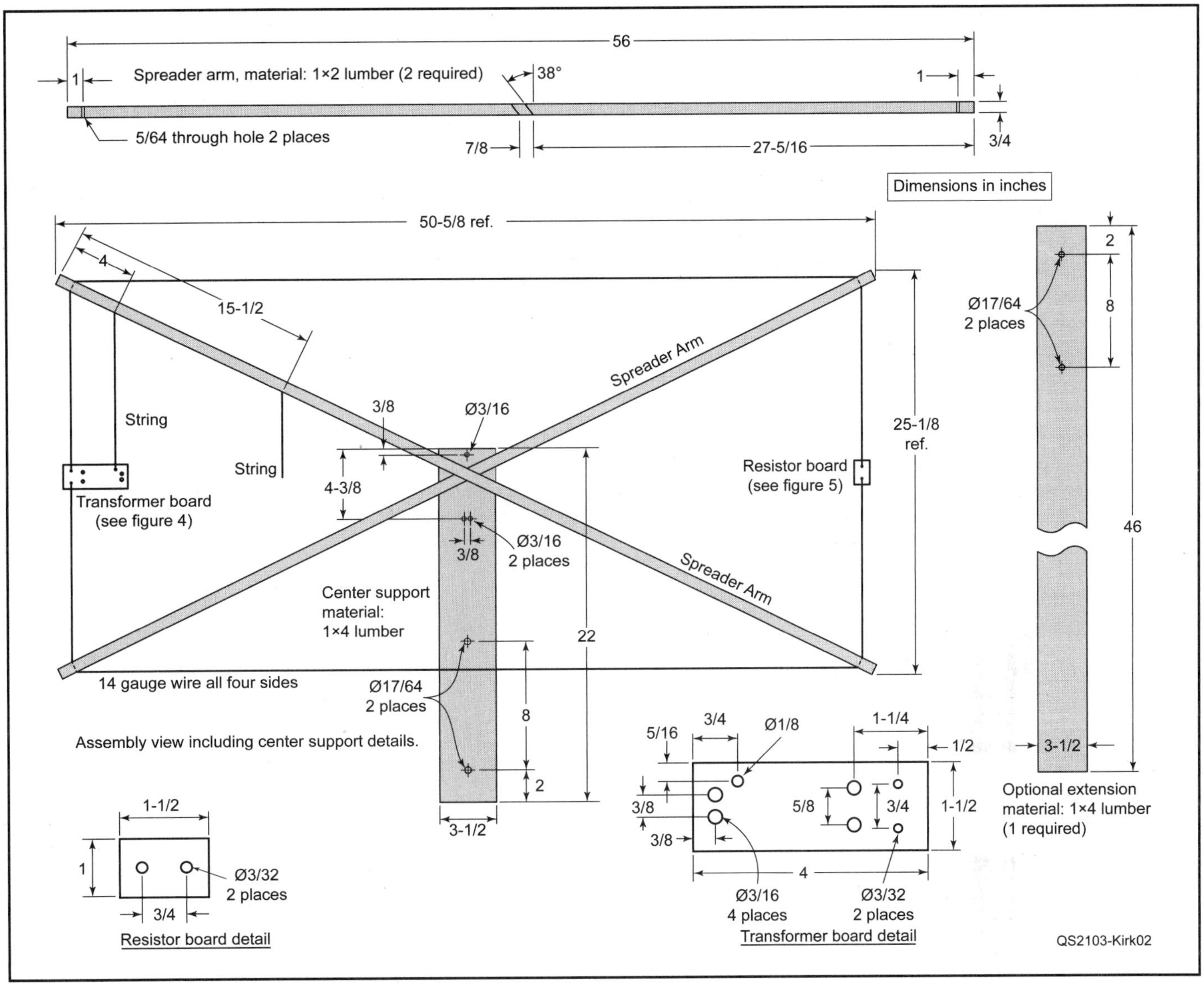

Figure 22.27 — The WD8DSB portable flag antenna is well-suited to RFI tracking and direction finding.

on this antenna is available in a presentation from the 2011 Dayton Hamvention Antenna Forum at **kkn.net/dayton2011/N4ISWallerFlag.pdf** and in a 2016 WWROF webinar at **wwrof.org/wp-content/uploads/2016/03/WWROF-WEB-NAIR-RX-Antennas-for-a-Small-Lot-.pdf**.

PORTABLE FLAG

Don Kirk, WD8DSB, has developed a miniature version of the flag antenna for use in direction-finding and RFI tracking. (See **Figure 22.27** and the article "Portable Flag Antenna for MF/HF Radio Direction Finding" in the online material.) Measuring 2 by 4 feet, the antenna is small enough to fit in a car and weighs only a few pounds. It maintains a cardioid pattern from 1.8 to 30 MHz with a front-to-back ratio of 12 to 21 dB.

THE PENNANT ANTENNA

Derived from the rectangular flag antenna, the pennant antenna has a triangular shape that resembles a flag pennant. **Figure 22.28** shows the optimized dimensions for the pennant antenna for use from 160 through 40 meters. The termination resistor is 900 Ω and can be placed either at the "point" of the triangle or in the center of the vertical section. The feed point is then placed at the opposite location with equivalent results.

Approximate gain on 160 meters is about –34 dBi (about 6 dB less than the flag antenna), –24 dBi on 80 meters, and –16 dBi on 40 meters. Note that the lower gain is proportional to the smaller area enclosed by the pennant compared to the flag: ½ that of the flag. This results in ½ the received voltage and ¼ the received power, which is a difference of –6 dB.

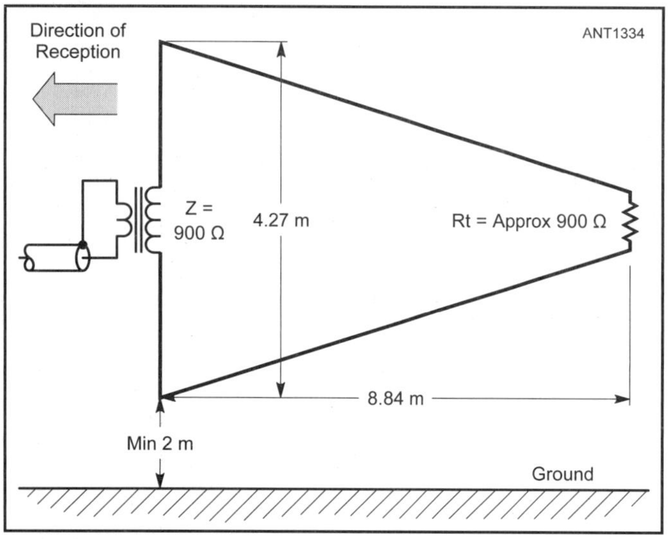

Figure 22.28 — Optimized dimensions for the 160/80-meter pennant antenna.

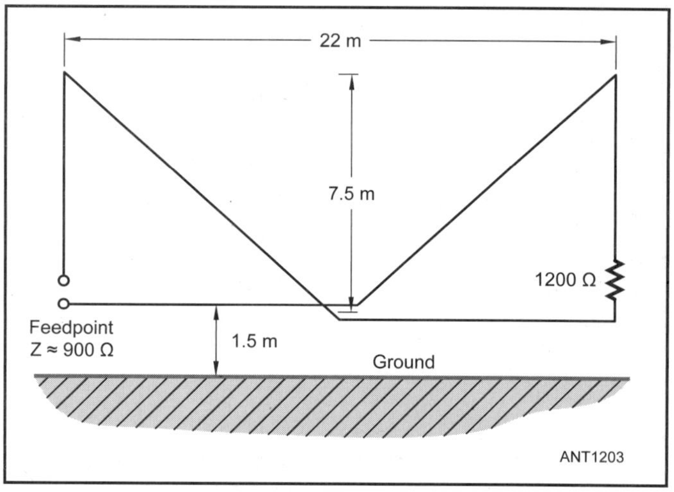

Figure 22.29 — The Double Half-Delta Loop (DHDL) antenna designed by AA7JV is an improved version of the flag and pennant receiving antennas. Note that the loops cross in the center of the antenna without a connection between them.

DOUBLE HALF DELTA LOOP (DHDL)

George Wallner, AA7JV, developed a variation on the pennant antenna known as the Double Half Delta Loop (DHDL), shown in **Figure 22.29**. A complete description of the antenna by AA7JV is available at **ok1rr.com/index.php/antennas/42-double-half-delta-loop-rx-antenna**. An illustration of how the antenna is installed at contest station ED1R was published by Tobias Wellnitz, DH1TW, at **dh1tw.de/double-half-delta-loop-dhdl-receiving-antenna**. The improvement in RDF over a flag antenna of similar size is about 2.5 dB.

PROJECT: LIXA DOUBLE LOOP

Jukka Klemola, OH6LI, extended the DHDL as a pair of apex-up triangles to create the LIXA (Linear Inline Target Antenna) shown in **Figure 22.30**. The additional separation improved the RDF to approximately 10 dB with a maximum gain of -33.5 dBi. The development and configuration for the LIXA antenna is provided along with pattern comparisons to Beverage antennas at **wwrof.org/wp-content/uploads/2018/02/Receiving-Antenna-Metrics-With-Examples-v20p.pdf**.

INSTALLATION AND OPERATING NOTES

Although these notes were originally written with the K9AY Loop in mind, they apply just as well to all small, terminated loops.

Location — Because receiving loops will often be installed where there is limited space, there may be interaction with

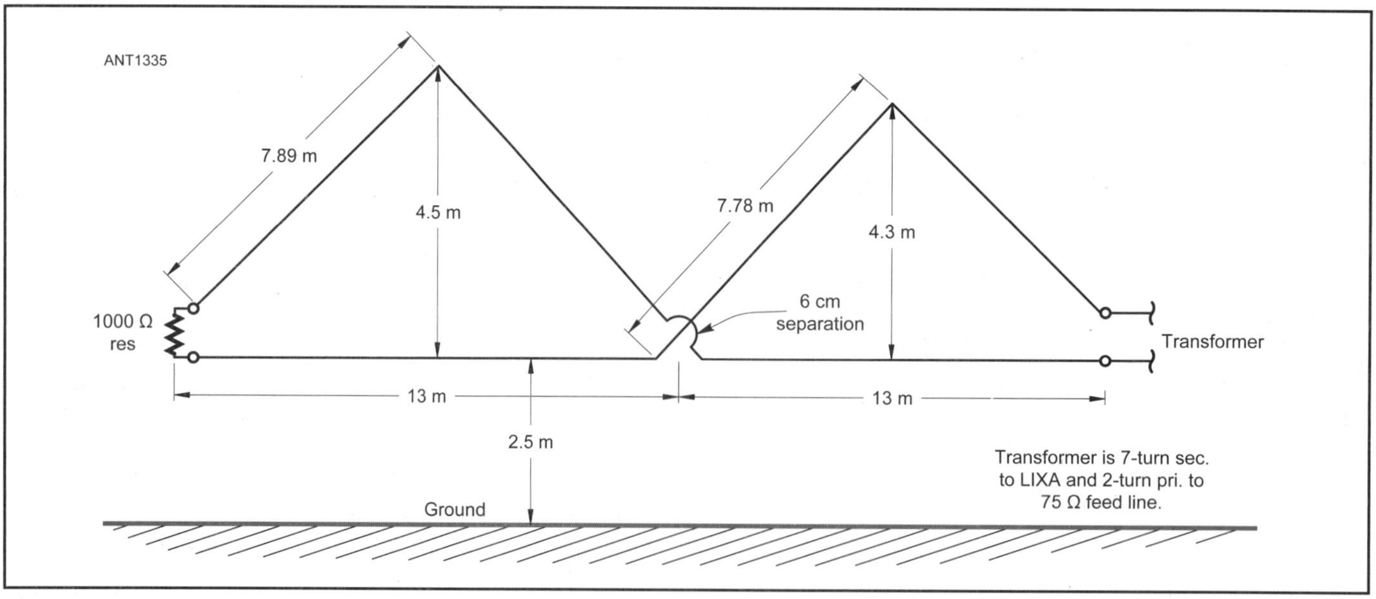

Figure 22.30 — Dimensions for the Linear Inline Target Antenna (LIXA) designed by OH6LI.

nearby objects. Other antennas, house wiring, metal siding and gutters, overhead utilities, metal fences and other conductors are likely to distort the pattern and reduce the depth of the null. The key test for proper operation is good front-to-back ratio. If F/B is poor, you will need to identify the problem. It is usually easiest to change the loop location compared to changing the surroundings!

Transmitting Antennas — Proximity to transmitting antennas may result in high RF levels on the loop, sent into the station on the feed line. Your receiver should be protected! Protective devices are available from ham radio dealers, or you can make a simple relay box that disconnects the feed line when transmitting. Operating the relay must be timed properly so that the transmitted signal cannot enter the receiver even for a few milliseconds. It's best to open both the center conductor and shield connections.

Ground Connection — For loops requiring a connection to or that depend on a ground plane, experience has shown that locations with almost any type of "real dirt" soil only require a single ground rod for proper operation. However, some installations may experience seasonal changes in soil moisture. Desert and saltwater installations will change the behavior, too. It sometimes helps to install additional ground radials to maintain consistent performance. Four or eight short radials are sufficient. Make them the same length and place the first four directly under the loop wires. Radials should extend 10 feet or so beyond the footprint of the loop.

Common-Mode Isolation — While many installations will work just fine with feed line and antenna both connected to the ground rod, it is good practice to provide better isolation to avoid having the feed line shield become part of the antenna. Impedance matching transformers should have separate primary and secondary windings with no direct (galvanic) connection between the winding ground connections, with the antenna side connected to the ground rod.

The feed line may work well "floating," although another ground rod for the feed line may be wise, especially with long feed lines. Feed lines that are buried or placed directly on the ground will be the least susceptible to common-mode problems. If possible, avoid elevating feed lines above ground (along fences or on posts, for example).

A feed line choke between any ground connection of the feed line and transformer is recommended. Preamps or other electronics should be on the feed line side of the choke. See the K9YC paper on receiving chokes referenced previously for suitable designs.

Lack of directivity — If you don't see a deep rearward null and you're sure there is no installation problem, coupling to nearby antennas, towers, and buildings, or common-mode issues with feed line and control lines, or you see obvious changes with the seasons (typically in dry summer or with winter frost), then install some radials to stabilize the ground connection as described in the previous paragraphs.

22.1.5 Multi-Turn Loops for MF and LF

(The following section was contributed by Rudy Severns, N6LF. His full treatment of multi-turn loops, including photographs of suggested construction methods, is included in the online material as "Multi-Turn LF and MF Receiving Loops".) At HF, single-turn loop receiving antennas usually provide adequate signal output (v) but at MF and especially LF that is not the case because for the same incoming signal strength loop voltage decreases with frequency. Given practical limits on loop diameter the usual solution is to add more turns to get more signal. Initially this works but as turns are added the rate of increase will plateau and then start to fall. For a given diameter there will be a broad optimum number of turns for maximum signal output at a given frequency. Loop diameter and number of turns are key choices for loop design at LF and MF.

LOOP SENSITIVITY

We can get a feeling for the signal output from loops by comparing them to vertical E-probes. How does the open circuit output (v) of a loop compare to a vertical whip for the same incident vertical E-field?

$v=E*h_e$

where h_e is the *effective height* in meters and E is the field strength in V/m. (See the **Dipoles and Monopoles** chapter for an explanation of effective height.)

For a simple vertical of physical height h:

$h_e=h/2$

For a loop:

$h_e=2\pi A_c N/\lambda$

where A_c is the loop area, N is the number of turns, and λ the wavelength at the operating frequency (f_o). For example, if h=20 feet, for the vertical h_e=10 feet. A 10-turn loop with a diameter of 10' at 475 kHz (where λ=2072'), has $h_e \approx 9.5'$. For the same incident field, we would expect similar output from either antenna. At 137 kHz, he for the whip remains 10 feet but for the loop h_e=2.75 feet. The loop output will be down ≈–11 dB compared to the whip. That's one reason 2200 meter loops need to be larger in diameter and/or have more turns than those for 630 meters.

There's a lot of practical information in equation for loop he. Output voltage, v, is a linear function of N and proportional to the square of the diameter, D. As is shown later, due to self-resonance the maximum useful number of turns is limited but increasing the diameter is very effective. For example, going from D=6 to 8 feet improves the output by ≈5 dB. Increasing D to 10 feet yields another ≈4 dB. Practical exam-

Measuring Noise Margin (NM)

The simplest way to check NM for a given receiver-antenna combination is to set the receive frequency to a part of the band without signals, turn off the AGC, place an RMS voltmeter on the audio output and disconnect the antenna, using the gain control set the output to a convenient level. Then reconnect the antenna and read the new output level. The difference between the two readings (in dB) is the NM. If a true-RMS meter is not available a normal peak reading meter can be used, usually without too much error.

ples of D=24-foot loops are given later. Compared to a 6-foot loop, D=24 feet increases output by +24 dB. Loops this large are not needed for 630 meters but can be very useful on 2200 meters.

LOOP OUTPUT

With very low radiated power limits and very high atmospheric noise levels, reception at LF and MF is often focused on decoding very weak digital signals buried deep in noise. The most basic requirement for a receiving antenna is that, for a given ambient noise level, it provides an output at least 10 dB above the receiver noise floor so that receiver noise is not a limiting factor. This is referred to as the *noise margin* (*NM*). In this context the "receiver" includes all of the cabling, matching networks, filters, amplifiers, etc., between the loop output terminals and the receiver input. Atmospheric and local RFI levels vary greatly between location, time of day, and season. At a noisy urban location, a 10 dB NM might be easy but at a quiet rural location with much lower noise significantly more antenna output may be needed. A good rule is to aim for >10 dB of NM at the lowest noise level likely at a given location. A direct measurement of noise margin is not difficult as explained in the sidebar "Measuring Noise Margin".

Much of the discussion that follows is focused on maximizing loop output, but we need to be careful — there can be too much of a good thing. A 10 dB NM is necessary but 30 – 40 dB is not and may be counterproductive. Besides the desired weak signals buried in noise, there will very likely be strong signals close in frequency and/or very strong lightning crashes with the potential to overdrive the receiver creating distortion which can degrade weak signal reception. W7IUV has proposed a practical compromise, suggesting that while receiving normal noise levels without strong signals present, the input to the receiver should be high enough to show a little activity at the low end of the S-meter range, but no more. This allows the full dynamic range of the receiver to be used, limiting distortion when strong signals appear.

LOOP SHAPES

There are many possible loop shapes, but the diamond and octagon are the most common. Irregular shapes can be used but symmetric shapes have better pattern nulls. Two winding configurations are in general use:

1) Solenoidal, with all of the turns having the same diameter as an ordinary air-wound inductor.

2) A flat spiral with the turns all in the plane of the loop with progressively decreasing turn diameter, creating a flat inward spiral.

There are tradeoffs between these choices: a flat spiral is simpler and does not need slotted wire support combs at the ends of the support arms. In a solenoidal winding each turn has the same area whereas in a flat spiral the area of each turn decreases, reducing output. Spiral windings tend to have lower Q than solenoidal which also reduces the output. However, when the number of turns and wire spacing are small and the diameter large, the signal reduction with a spiral is modest. Examples of each of these configurations are given later.

RESONANT LOOPS

Over an extended range of frequencies, the impedance measured between the open ends of a loop will have multiple alternating resonances and antiresonances like dipoles. Loops are usually used at frequencies below the lowest resonance, referred to as the self-resonant frequency (f_r). Loops may be untuned for broadband use or as an element in a phased array or resonated with a capacitor, C_r, (as in a small, tuned loop) to maximize output at a chosen operating frequency, f_o.

A multi-turn loop is simply a coil, and we can express its Q in the usual way:

$$Q=(2\pi fL_a)/R_a$$

where L_a is the loop's inductance and R_a is the loop's resistance. The output voltage, with the loop tuned to resonance, will then be:

$$v_o=H_0(NQ)A_cf$$

where H_0 is the peak field intensity in A/m, A_c is the area of the coil in square meters, and f is the frequency.

Note that the open-loop voltage is multiplied by the Q. Qs of several hundred are possible, leading to the possibility of a large increase in v_o. For example, a Q of 300 would, in theory at least, increase the output by ≈50 dB which is a primary reason for resonating a loop. The real world is not so generous. The equation gives the open circuit output voltage with an infinite impedance load. Most of the time we will want to connect the loop output to the receiver via 50 or 75 Ω cables. The loading can substantially reduce the effective Q depending on how it is connected to the loop.

Besides increasing v_o, resonating the loop reduces the bandwidth allowing the loop to act as a filter, improving rejection of out-of-band signals. Using larger wire or increasing the diameter could increase Q further but again we have to be wary of too much of a good thing. There is a downside to narrow bandwidth: the 630 and 2200 meter bands are narrow enough that fixed value for C_r can usually be used but on 160 meters and higher the bands are proportionately much wider so a variable C_r will likely be needed if the loop is used over a significant part these bands.

LOOP-TO-FEED LINE MATCHING

The impedance of a resonant loop can be very high, typically hundreds of kΩ. How do we effectively couple that to a 50 or 75 Ω feed line? A transformer would need a turns ratio of 100–150:1 which is not practical. A balanced amplifier with high impedance differential inputs and low impedance balanced outputs has been used for impedance conversion but commercial units are not available.

There is another practical problem, the ends of the loop are very sensitive to stray capacitance to a feed line and/or nearby conductors. The feed line connected directly to the loop acts as a simple vertical with its output adding to and overwhelming the loop output. This is an extreme example, but even much smaller couplings can degrade the pattern. Instead of a shunt capacitor across the ends of the coil a series capacitor can be used to resonate the loop. Two possible connections are shown in **Figure 22.31A**.

The original high impedance parallel resonance at f_r is still

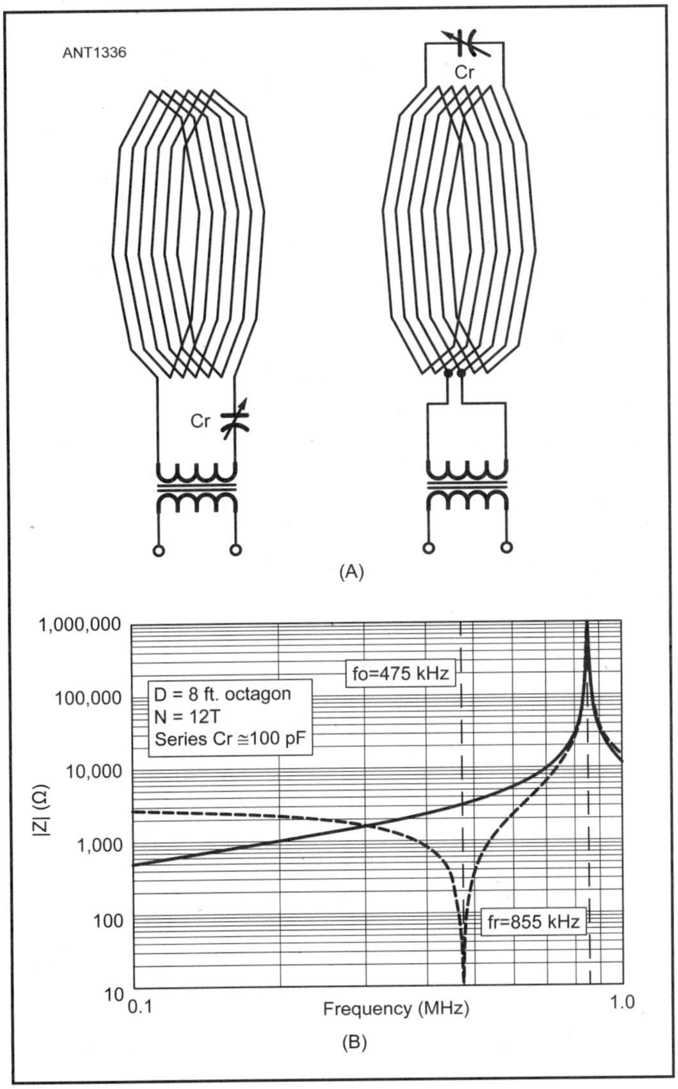

Figure 22.31 — Connecting the resonating capacitor in series with a multi-turn coil (A) creates a low impedance series resonance that is suitable for transformer coupling to a feed line (B).

present but adding C_r in series has introduced a low impedance series resonance at f_0 in the range of 5–100 Ω, very suitable for a matching transformer as shown in Figure 22.31B. Typically, the transformer will be a few turns on a small binocular ferrite core. Besides providing matching, the transformer can help to decouple the loop from the feed line. The usual inter-winding capacitance (between the primary and secondary) will be of the order of 10 – 15 pF which is adequate isolation for 630- and 2200-meter loops and may be acceptable for 160 meters. For 80-meter loops this may be too much capacitance. (Note that decoupling requires there be no common connection between the primary and secondary windings, such as to a metallic enclosure.)

CONSTRUCTION EXAMPLES

The supporting frame for a loop can be fabricated from inexpensive PVC pipe and fittings. Suitable pipe sizes vary from ½-inch to 1-inch and are available in different wall thickness: thin-wall class 1120 and heavier Schedules 40 and 80. For most loops, 1120 will be lighter and less expensive but still have adequate strength. For smaller loops ½-inch pipe is ok but for 8–12-foot loops, ¾-inch or 1-inch will provide a more durable structure. Alternative materials, such as wood, can also be used. Mechanically, the simplest form is a flat spiral diamond wound on a PVC pipe cross. Octagonal loops are more complicated to fabricate but are usually more robust and provide better performance. In particular the increased number of supports for the wire and the smaller span between supports help to make the loop more resistant to ice damage.

The multi-turn loops typical at LF and MF often need several hundred feet of wire. The wire size is not critical: Anything from #14 to #22 will work. Larger wire diameters yield higher loop Q but in general, #18 or #20 wire works well and is relatively economical. Some of the least expensive wire is intended for buried wire "dog fences" and available in 500-foot rolls. Materials for high-volume applications like dog fencing can be dramatically less expensive than by-the-foot pricing.

22.1.6 Active Antennas and Preamplifiers

The following material is based on the September 2001 *QST* article, "The AMRAD Active LF Antenna," by Frank Gentges, KØBRA. (This article is also included with this book's online material.) A detailed treatment of active whip antennas and several active impedance-conversion circuits was also published by Dr Ulrich Rhode, N1UL, in *RF Design* (see the References and Bibliography) and he has published an excellent overview presentation, "Electrically Short Antennas" with co-authors Salazar-Palma and Sarkar at **synergymwave.com/articles/2016/Antenna_presentation.pdf**.

An active antenna is an electrically and physically small antenna combined with an active electronic circuit, such as an amplifier. An active antenna uses a small whip — one that is a fraction of a wavelength long at the desired frequency — connected to an active impedance-conversion circuit. Power loss is not a significant concern for all but the smallest receiving antenna. This allows short verticals to be used in a receiving array rather than much more efficient ¼-wave verticals.

An electrically short whip has a high output impedance. For example, a 1-meter whip at 100 kHz has an input impedance higher than 100 kΩ, mostly capacitive reactance. If such a whip were connected directly to a 50-Ω load, signals would be attenuated more than 80 dB than those from a 50-Ω antenna! Thus, active impedance-conversion is required, usually a high-input-impedance FET-based amplifier.

Signal-to-noise ratio (SNR) is a primary concern for active antennas due to the antenna's small size. Nevertheless, if the noise contributed by the transistor is less than the noise picked up by the antenna, SNR can be comparable to an optimized passive antenna for the same frequency. Below about 4 MHz, atmospheric and man-made noise dominates the antenna output signal. Above 4 MHz, a circuit using an FET with a noise figure of 1 – 2 dB or less will provide satisfactory results.

The recently opened amateur bands of 630 and 2200 meters can also benefit from active antennas, since full-size antennas are quite large. The active whips described above are useful on these low frequencies. Preamps and impedance converters can make use of op amps and other analog ICs designed for use below 1 MHz. For example, the active antenna project by Robert Dildine, W6SFH (see the References and Bibliography entry for R. Dildine) uses a 1-meter dipole and an op amp signal conditioning circuit. The lower frequency also allows the use of common CAT5 network cable between the antenna package and receiver.

The major challenges to the impedance conversion circuit are nonlinearity and the resulting intermodulation distortion products. Intermodulation products generated in the signal conditioning circuit can create a significant amount of noise and other interference. This is a particularly difficult issue close to transmitting antennas and filters may be required.

PREAMPLIFIERS

The professional antenna literature on active receiving antennas focuses on noise, sensitivity, and bandwidth. The newer literature on active integrated antennas is about putting transmit and receive electronics at a single antenna or many antennas in an array. The amateur literature focuses on construction projects that combine antennas and LNAs for reception. Older designs used discrete components. The trend in modern circuit design is modular. A circuit using an op-amp or a gain block is simplest. Candidate devices are Analog Devices ADA4817, Qorvo TQP9M3028, or TriQuint gain blocks, to name a few. Parts can be purchased from Digi-Key and other vendors.

In his paper, W7IUV notes the primary requirements for low-band preamps: The preamp should have sufficient gain to allow use of the typically low-output receiving antennas by most modern transceivers (at least 20 dB). At the same time, the noise figure must be sufficiently low as to not degrade the system noise temperature, which includes the receiver, the antenna, the transmission line, and all the noise sources the antenna sees. In addition, it must be a relatively high-power amplifier so that local AM BC stations and other strong signals on the amateur bands do not cause IMD products to be generated in the preamp.

Bandwidth or frequency response should be determined by the intended use of the preamp. W7IUV's design is primarily intended to be used for 160 and 80 meters. In his circuit, the operational bandwidth is limited at the high end by the gain-bandwidth product (f_T or GBW) of the transistor used and at the low end by the coupling capacitors. In practice, when using a high frequency device like the 2N5109, high-end roll off at around 30 MHz is due to the ferrite core. When using a low frequency device like the DCP68, the high end starts rolling off around 7 MHz.

When a high-level RX antenna such as a long Beverage is used, a broadcast-reject filter will be required ahead of the preamp. In many cases, the preamp doesn't need the filter and will amplify the broadcast signal, but the radio may overload. To prevent overload, a high-pass filter is required. Simple high-pass filters are available from a variety of vendors. The filters are also easy to build with common parts, usually don't require any alignment to function properly, and aren't too sensitive to input and output terminations. A 7th-order Chebychev high-pass, with a 0.1 to 1 dB pass band ripple, will normally be all that's required to use with this preamp. (A suitable design is provided in W7IUV's paper.)

Chris Trask, N7ZWY, has published the design of a broadband preamp for active antennas covering 30 kHz to 70 MHz (see the References and Bibliography section for Active Antennas). The input amplifier is a pair of U310 JFETs in cascode followed by a 2N2222/2N2905 cascode. The article is in German, but the schematic is easy to read, including a power-over-feed line circuit.

Another widely used preamplifier design for the lower HF bands was created by Larry Molitor, W7IUV and is described, including schematics and parts lists, in "Low Band High Performance Preamp" at **mtmscientific.com/preamp.pdf**. (The preamp is also available as a commercial product from MTM Scientific.) An array using the preamp is also described at **sites.google.com/site/rxpreamps**.

22.1.7 Receive Arrays

ARRAYS OF K9AY LOOPS

Although the K9AY Loop has useful directivity, its pattern is modest compared to most Beverage antennas. One way to improve performance, while keeping most of the antenna's limited-space appeal, is to combine two or more of them in an array. One of the simplest arrays is to install two crossed-loop sets with a spacing of ½-wavelength (140 feet on 80 meters, 270 feet on 160 meters). For simplicity, a phase shift of 0° for broadside operation and 180° for end-fire operation can be used to avoid the need for additional phase shift circuitry — phasing can be accomplished by simply reversing the windings of one matching transformer when the array is in the end-fire mode.

Figure 22.32 compares the radiation patterns of a single loop and the two-elements in line with the loops (end-fire mode, phasing = 180°). The array adds two very deep side nulls to the horizontal pattern and increases the gain by 3 dB. Also, the vertical directivity is enhanced with a deep overhead null. The main forward lobe is narrower than a single loop but remains quite wide.

Figure 22.33 shows the horizontal pattern for the broadside mode (phase shift = 0°). The main forward lobe is much narrower than a single loop, and good side nulls are present. The vertical pattern is not shown because it is the same shape as a single loop, plus the 3 dB array gain.

Of course, other arrays with different spacings and phase shifts can be designed. The K9AY Loop is a good candidate for an array element. Its inherent directivity results in performance that is better than the same array using omnidirectional elements such as verticals. The loops also have a low VSWR on the feed line, which simplifies the design of a phasing network. The technique of creating an array of vertical elements by using loops is discussed in the article "Introducing the Shared-Apex Loop Array" by Mark Bauman, KB7GF that is included with this book's online material.

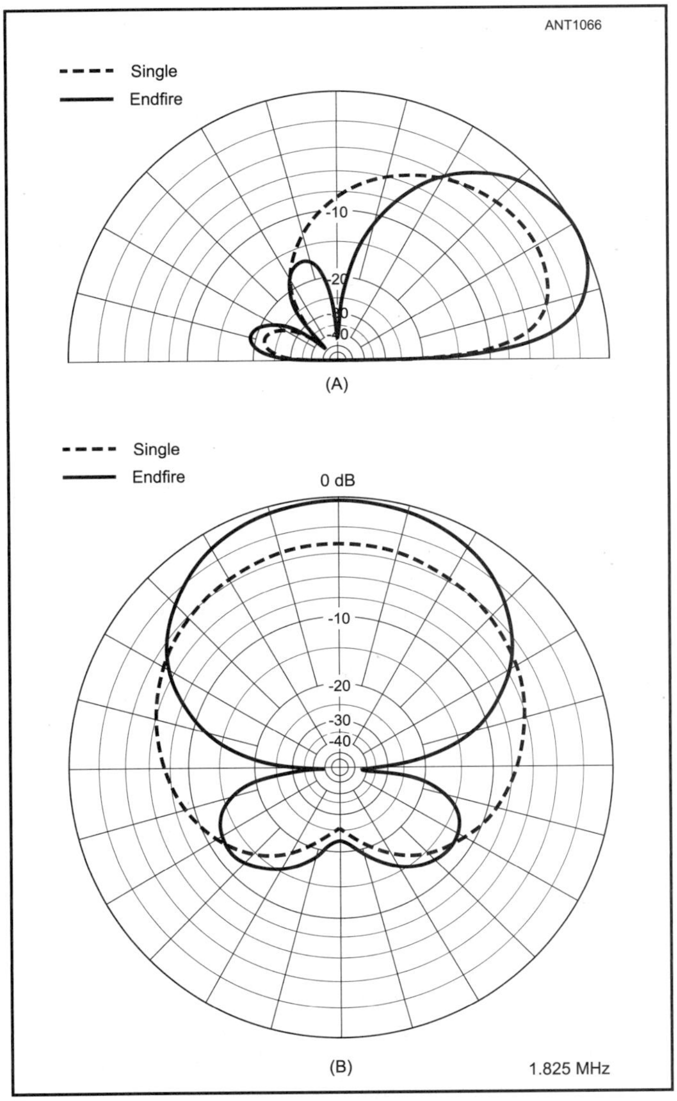

Figure 22.32 — Vertical (A) and horizontal (B) radiation patterns for two K9AY Loops, spaced ½ λ, fed in end-fire mode with 180° phasing. Frequency is 1.825 MHz

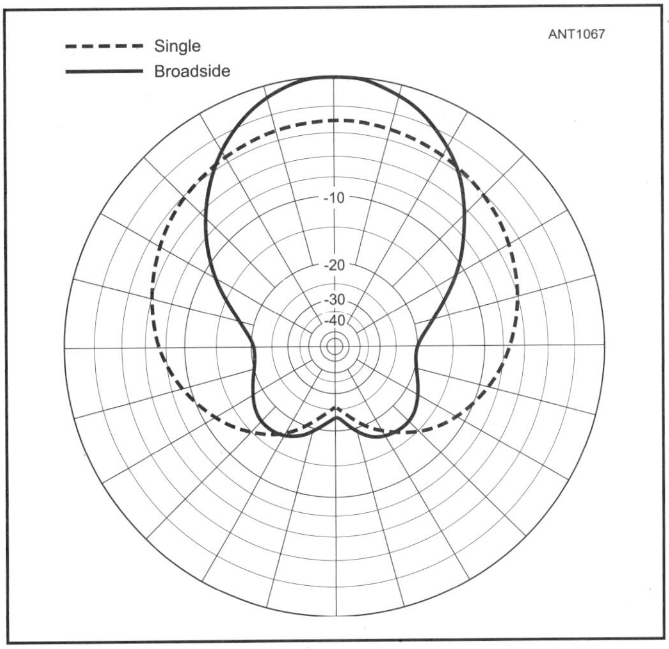

Figure 22.33 — Horizontal pattern for two K9AY Loops, spaced ½ λ, fed as a broadside array with 0° phasing. Frequency is 1.825 MHz.

PENNANT ARRAY

WD8DSB has designed a three-element, point-fed pennant array (**sites.google.com/site/pennantflagantennas**). The antennas have a common feed point with all antenna "points" in the center of the array. A single BN73-202 binocular core transformer is used to match whichever antenna is selected. Two relays are used for antenna switching with a single control line supplying +12/0/–12 V. This same basic switching controller design can be used with any balanced antenna design.

LIRA ARRAY

The LIRA array is composed of LIXAs separated by approximately 25 meters. The 2x LIRA (Linear Inline Receiving Antenna) with a pair of LIXAs has an excellent RDF of 12.1 dB. The 4x LIRA, which is approximately 216 meters long, achieves an RDF of approximately 14.8 dB, similar to two staggered 320-meter long Beverages (see the article "Beverages in Echelon" in the online material). The development and configuration for the LIXA antenna is provided along with pattern comparisons to Beverage antennas at **wwrof.org/wp-content/uploads/2018/02/Receiving-Antenna-Metrics-With-Examples-v20p.pdf**.

CIRCLE ARRAYS

"Circle arrays" of three (a triangle array), four (a four-square array) and all the way to nine vertical antennas have become popular, using active whip antennas as described in the previous section. A number of examples can be seen in the Dayton Hamvention Antenna Forum presentations by Lee Strahan, K7TJR, and Mark Bauman, KB7GF, at **kkn.net/dayton2014/dayton-2014-antenna-forum.html** and in the PowerPoint presentation "Easy to Build Low Band Receiving Antennas for Small and Large Lots" " by Frank Donovan, W3LPL, from the 2014 Contest University at **contestuniversity.com/wp-content/uploads/2022/05/W3LPL-Easy-to-Build-Low-Band-Receiving-Antennas-for-Small-and-Large-Lots-2022.pdf.** These designs provide an unprecedented ability to reject noise and improve receive SNR without requiring large pieces of property. The small footprint (electrically small) of these arrays requires careful attention to design and construction detail, however.

The design and construction of an 8-element array was detailed in an exhaustive article by Joel Harrison, W5ZN, and Bob McGwier, N4HY, in the 2010 *QEX* article "Design, Construction and Evaluation of the Eight Circle Vertical Array for Low Band Receiving" that is included with this book's online material and shown schematically in **Figure 22.34**. The issues encountered when designing and building this system apply to smaller systems, as well.

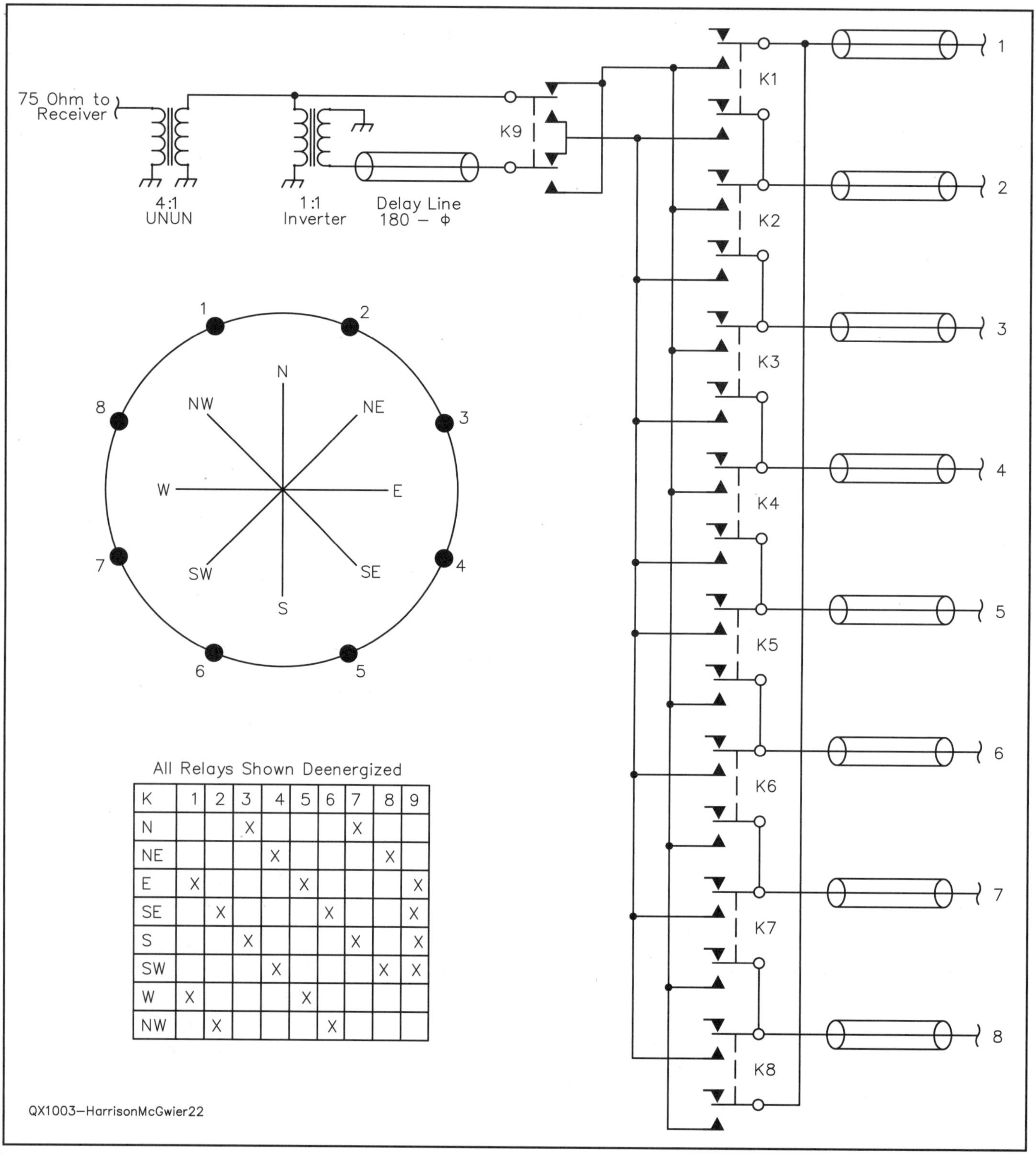

K	1	2	3	4	5	6	7	8	9
N			X				X		
NE				X				X	
E	X				X				X
SE		X				X			X
S			X				X		X
SW				X				X	X
W	X				X				
NW		X				X			

Figure 22.34 — The schematic of the eight-circle receiving array at W5ZN.

Dan Maguire, AC6LA, has done some modeling of various circle arrays and published comparative radiation patterns at **ac6la.com/adhoc** — look for filenames beginning with "8circle." Dan also provided additional discussion and links to models in his Topband reflector post from 23 Dec 2014 (**lists.contesting.com/_topband/2014-12/msg00379.html**). Commercial versions of circle arrays are produced from time to time. Currently (late-2022) an 8-circle array for 160 and 80 meters is available as the Hi-Z Antennas 4-8P-LV2-85 from DX Engineering (**dxengineering.com**).

You can also find performance comparisons of circle arrays in the W3LPL presentation at **contestuniversity.com/wp-content/uploads/2022/05/W3LPL-Easy-to-Build-Low-Band-Receiving-Antennas-for-Small-and-Large-Lots-2022.pdf**.

22.1.8 Chokes for Receiving Antennas

(These few notes are from K9YC's Mar/Apr 2019 NCJ article, "Chokes and Isolation Transformers for Receiving Antennas," included in the online material for this chapter. The article is based on K9YC's paper of the same name which is downloadable from ***k9yc.com/RXChokesTransformers.pdf****. The article and paper include application and design information.*) A feed line behaves as a receiving antenna for noise current, possibly even as a parasitic element of another antenna nearby. If the feed line is coaxial cable, this current flows on the outer surface of the shield; on two-wire feed line, it appears as the difference of currents in the two conductors, which would otherwise be equal and opposite.

The current can then get into the feed line at a termination or directly by the mechanism of *transfer impedance*. It is particularly important to ensure that common-mode current on the feed line shield is blocked from entering the feed line where it mixes with the desired signal and cannot be removed. Ferrite chokes at the end of the cable can be quite effective against noise *ingress* from coupling. Do not connect the shield of a receiving antenna feed line to the antenna ground because that will allow common-mode noise or signals to combine with the desired signal.

Transformers provide an alternate means of blocking common-mode current. Carefully wound to minimize capacitance between windings, they add a very small capacitance — and thus a very high impedance — in series with the common-mode circuit. Transformers that are used to carry high power, i.e., for transmitting antennas, usually have bifilar windings, with the primary and secondary wound close together to maximize coupling and minimize loss and excessive heating. Too much capacitance between primary and secondary provides a path for common-mode current; for this reason, bifilar transformer windings should be avoided with receive transformers. The *ARRL Handbook* and the chapter **Receiving Antennas** of *ON4UN's Low-Band DXing* book are also good sources of more information on winding toroidal transformers.

Effective common-mode chokes are formed by winding multiple turns of a feed line through a suitable ferrite core to form a parallel RLC circuit with a low Q resonance near the operating frequency. In this "near resonance" region, the choke "looks like" a high value of resistance to common-mode current, effectively blocking it. We achieve this by choosing a ferrite mix that's very lossy in the desired frequency range, and by winding the right number of turns around the right size core to place the resonance near the middle of the desired frequency range.

The lossy core makes the resonance very broad. Q values of 0.5 – 1 are typical of good chokes. The differential circuit (the inside of the coax) doesn't see the choke (except as the added feed line length needed to wind it). **Table 22.2** summarizes K9YC's choke designs for the 630 meter through 40 meter bands using one twisted pair removed from good quality CAT6 cable. (CAT6 cable consists of four molded twisted-pair wires, each pair forming a high-bandwidth transmission line.)

Multiple chokes can be placed in series to increase choking impedance and to cover a wider frequency range. For example, 18-21 turns on two #75A cores in series with 27 turns on one #43 core would provide excellent choking from 480 kHz to 10 MHz (including the AM broadcast band).

The cores for the chokes are small toroids, typically about 1-inch OD and 0.3125-inches thick and are identified by their Fair-Rite part numbers. Cores were chosen on the basis of suitability for the frequency ranges and easy availability at low cost. See the referenced articles and online paper for more information about construction and performance of both chokes and transformers.

Table 22.2
Receiving Chokes

		Choking Impedance Rs (ohms) on Band (meters)					
Turns	*Core*	*630*	*160*	*80*	*40*	*30*	*20*
18	Single–#75A/5975001401	3K	7.7K	5.2K	3.2K	2.5K	
16	Double–#75A /5975001401	3.8K	8.2K	5.5K			
17		5K	11K	6.3K	2.9K		
18		5.8K	11.5K	6.2K	2.5K		
19		6.5K	12.5K	5.9K	2.1K		
20		7.2K	12.5K	5K	1.7K		
21		7.8K	13K	5.8K	2K		
16	Single–#75B/2675821502	4.5K	6K	4.1K	2.5K		
18		5.8K	7.2K	4.6K	2.6K		
20		7.5K	8K	4.7K	2.2K		
22		9.7K	8K	4.2K	1.6K		
26		15.6K	8K	3.6K	1.1K		
15	Single–#43/5943001601		550	1.7K	3.3K	4.5K	6K
27			2.2K	9K	19K	8.5K	1.5K

22.1.9 MF and HF Receiving Antennas References and Bibliography

Source material and more extended discussion of topics covered in this chapter can be found in the references given below and, in the textbooks, listed at the end of the **Antenna Fundamentals** chapter.

ACTIVE ANTENNAS

Professional literature

S. R. Best, "Noise Figure of Electrically Small Antennas," *36th Allerton Antenna Applications Symposium* (AAS), Monticello, IL, Sep. 18-20, 2012.

S. R. Best, "Realized Noise Figure of the General Receiving Antenna," *IEEE Antennas and Wireless Propagation Letters*, Vol. 12, May 2013, pp. 702-705.

K. Chang, R. A. York, P. S. Hall, and T. Itoh, "Active Integrated Antennas," *IEEE Transactions on Microwave Theory and Techniques*, Vol. 50, no. 3, Mar. 2002, pp. 937-944.

J. Hopf and H. Lindenmeier, "Active Loop Antennas," *IEEE International Symposium on Antennas and Propagation*, Albuquerque, NM, May 24-28, 1982, pp. 560-563.

H. Lindenmeier, "Active Receiving Antennas for Very Low Frequencies (4 kHz - 400 kHz)," *IEEE International Symposium on Antennas and Propagation*, Williamsburg, VA, Dec. 11-14, 1972, pp. 344-347.

H. K. Lindenmeier, "The Active Receiving Antenna: An Appropriate Element for HF-Radio Reception," *4th IEE International Conference on HF Radio Systems and Techniques* (HFRST), London, UK, Apr. 11-14, 1988 pp. 151-155.

H. H. Meinke, "Aktive Antennen," *Nachrichtentechnische Zeitschrift*, Dec. 1966, pp. 697-705.

H. H. Meinke, "Active Receiving Antennas at Microwave Frequencies," *5th European Microwave Conference*, Hamburg, Germany, Sep. 1-4, 1975, pp. 337-347.

E. H. Nordholt and D. Van Willigen, "A New Approach to Active Antenna Design," *IEEE Transactions on Antennas and Propagation*, Vol. 28, no. 6, Nov. 1980, pp. 904-910.

U. L. Rohde, "Active Antennas," *RF Design*, May/June 1981, pp. 38-42.

R. A. Sainati, "Active Antenna Performance Limitation," *IEEE Transactions on Antennas and Propagation*, Vol. 30, no. 6, Nov, 1982, pp. 1265-1267.

M. S. Sharawi and O. Hammi, *Design and Applications of Active Integrated Antennas*, Artech House, 2018.

Amateur/hobbyist Literature (construction projects)

G. Baars, "Wideband Active Loop Antenna for General-Coverage Receivers," *Elektor Electronics*, Jan. 2000, pp. 20-21.

J. Becker, DJ8IL, "Wideband Active Rod Antenna," *Elektor Electronics*, May 1991, pp. 49-53.

J. Becker, DJ8IL, "Active Magnetic Antennas: Have General Coverage Receiver, Will Travel," *Elektor Electronics*, Sep. 1998, pp. 22-27.

P. J. Bertini K1ZJH, "Active Antenna Covers 0.5-30 MHz," *Ham Radio*, May 1985, pp. 37-39 and 41-43. Comment by R. C. Hansen, July 1985, p 10.

I. Braithwaite, G4COL, "An Active Antenna for 160 to 4 metres," *RadCom*, Oct. 2001, pp. 52-54.

R. W. Burhans, "Active Antenna Preamplifiers," *Ham Radio*, May 1986, pp. 47-50 and 53-54.

M. A. Covington, N4TMI, "AM-FM-SW Active Antenna," *Popular Electronics*, July 1989, pp. 73 and 106.

D. DeMaw, W1FB, "Build An Active Antenna," *Monitoring Times*, Apr. 1992, pp. 98-99.

B. Dildine, W6SFH, "An Active Dipole for Long- and Medium-Wave Frequencies," *QST*, Oct. 2018, pp. 30-34.

J. Fisk, W1DTY, "Voltage-Probe Receiving Antenna," *Ham Radio*, Oct. 1970, pp. 22-21.

F. Gentges, KØBRA, "The AMRAD Active LF Antenna," *QST*, Sep. 2001, pp. 31-37.

P. Hawker, G3VA, "HF Active Receiving Loop Antenna," *RadCom*, June 1986, pp. 419-420.

A. J. Henk, "Loop Antennas: Fact, Not Fiction," Part 1, *RadCom*, Sep. 1991, pp. 51-53; Part 2, *RadCom*, Oct. 1991, pp. 47-50.

C. Kluttz, W4TMR, "The Flag on Ground (FoG) Antenna," *QST*, Sep. 2017, pp. 30-31.

A. Knott, G6KSN, "A Tuned Active Antenna," *Practical Wireless*, Jan. 1990, pp. 50-52.

R. A. Lambert, G3FNZ, "A Directional Active Loop Receiving Antenna System," *RadCom*, Nov. 1982, pp. 944-949.

W. Sheets, K2MQJ, and R. F. Graf, KA2CWL, "A 100-kHz-to-30-MHz Active Antenna," *Popular Electronics*, Aug. 1997, pp. 48-53, 76.

C. Trask, N7ZWY, "Active Loop Aerials for HF Reception Part 1: Practical Loop Aerial Design," *QEX*, July-Aug. 2003 pp. 35-42.

C. Trask, N7ZWY, "Active Loop Aerials for HF Reception Part 2: High Dynamic Range Aerial Amplifier Design," QEX, Sep./Oct. 2003, pp. 44-49.

C. Trask, N7ZWY, "A High Dynamic Range Amplifier for Active Short Monopole Antennas," Jan. 30, 2008. Available from **electronicprojectsforfun.files.wordpress.com/2017/11/activemonopoleamplifierbychristrask.pdf**

C. Trask, N7ZWY, "An Evaluation of Junction Field-Effect Transistors Suitable for Active Antenna Applications," Dec. 4, 2008. Contact author ctrask@ieee.org.

C. Trask, N7ZWY, "An Evaluation of Bipolar Transistors Suitable for Active Antenna Applications," rev. 3, Dec. 15, 2008. Contact author ctrask@ieee.org.

C. Trask, N7ZWY, "Complementary Push-Pull Amplifiers for Active Antennas: A Critical Review," rev. 4, Sep. 15, 2013. Contact author ctrask@ieee.org.

BEVERAGE ANTENNAS

A. Bailey, S. W. Dean and W. T. Wintringham, "The Receiving System for Long-Wave Transatlantic Radio Telephony," *The Bell System Technical Journal*, Apr. 1929.

J. S. Belrose, "Beverage Antennas for Amateur Communications," Technical Correspondence, *QST*, Sep. 1981, p 51.

H. Beverage, C. Rice, and E. Kellogg, "The Wave Antenna — A New Type of Highly Directive Antenna," *Transactions of the AIEE*, Feb. 1923, pp. 215-266.

H. H. Beverage, "Antennas," *RCA Review*, July 1939.

H. H. Beverage and D. DeMaw, "The Classic Beverage Antenna Revisited," *QST*, Jan. 1982, pp. 11-17.

B. Boothe, "Weak-Signal Reception on 160 — Some Antenna Notes," *QST*, June 1977, pp. 35-39.

J. Brown, "Chokes and Isolation Transformers for Receiving Antennas," *National Contest Journal*, Mar./Apr. 2019, pp. 7-10.

M. F. DeMaw, *Ferromagnetic-Core Design and Application Handbook* (Englewood Cliffs, NJ: Prentice-Hall Inc, 1981).

J. Devoldere, *ON4UN's Low-Band DXing, Fifth Edition* (Newington: ARRL, 2010). See the chapter **Receiving Antennas**, for many practical details on Beverage and terminated loop antennas.

F. Donovan and W. Silver, "The Beverage Antenna, 100 Years Later," *QST*, Nov. 2021, pp. 55-57.

V. A. Misek, *The Beverage Antenna Handbook* (Wason Rd., Hudson, NH: W1WCR, 1977).

W. Silver, "A Cool Beverage Four Pack," *QST*, Apr. 2006, pp. 33-36.

LOOPS, FLAGS, AND PENNANTS

D. Bond, *Radio Direction Finders*, 1st ed. (New York: McGraw-Hill Book Co, 1944).

G. Bramslev, "Loop Aerial Reception," *Wireless World*, Nov. 1952, pp. 469-472.

G. Breed, "The K9AY Terminated Loop — A Compact, Directional Receiving Antenna," *QST*, Sep. 1997, pp. 43-46.

G. Breed, "Hum Problems When Switching the K9AY Loops," Technical Correspondence, *QST*, May 1998, p. 73.

G. Breed, "Introduction to Multi-Wire Loops," *QRP Quarterly*, Jan. 2019, pp. 36-38.

G. Breed, Additional notes on the K9AY Loop are available at **k9ay.com** under the "Tech Notes" tab.

R. Burhans, "Experimental Loop Antennas for 60 kHz to 200 kHz," *Technical Memorandum (NASA) 71*, (Athens, OH: Ohio Univ, Dept of Electrical Engr), Dec 1979.

R. Burhans, "Loop Antennas for VLF-LF," *Radio-Electronics*, June 1983, pp. 83-87.

M. Connelly, "New Termination Control Method for Flag, Pennant and Similar Antennas," International Radio Club of America reprint A162, Nov. 2002.

M. Connelly, "Pennant Antenna with Remote Termination Control," **qsl.net/wa1ion/pennant.htm**.

E. Cunningham, "Flag, Pennants and Other Ground-Independent Low-Band Receiving Antennas," *QST*, July 2000, pp. 34-37.

R. Devore and P. Bohley, "The Electrically Small Magnetically Loaded Multiturn Loop Antenna," *IEEE Trans on Ant and Prop*, July 1977, pp. 496-505.

F. Donovan, "Easy to Build Low Band Receiving Antennas for Small and Large Lots," **contestuniversity.com/wp-content/uploads/2022/05/W3LPL-Easy-to-Build-Low-Band-Receiving-Antennas-for-Small-and-Large-Lots-2022.pdf**

R. J. Edmunds, Ed. "An FET Loop Amplifier with Coaxial Output," *N.R.C. Antenna Reference Manual, Vol. 2*, 1st ed. (Cambridge, WI: National Radio Club, Oct. 1982), pp. 17-20.

S. Goldman, "A Shielded Loop for Low Noise Broadcast Reception," *Electronics*, Oct. 1938, pp. 20-22.

J. V. Hagan, "A Large Aperture Ferrite Core Loop Antenna for Long and Medium Wave Reception," *Loop Antennas Design and Theory*, M.G. Knitter, Ed. (Cambridge, WI: National Radio Club, 1983), pp. 37-49.

F. M. Howes and F. M. Wood, "Note on the Bearing Error and Sensitivity of a Loop Antenna in an Abnormally Polarized Field," *Proc IRE*, Apr. 1944, pp. 231-233.

F. Koontz, "Is this EWE for You?," *QST*, Feb. 1995, pp. 31-33. See also Feedback, Apr. 1995 *QST*, p. 75.

F. Koontz, "More EWEs for You," *QST*, Jan. 1996, pp. 32-34.

F. Koontz, "The Horizontal EWE Antenna," *QST*, Dec. 2006, pp. 37-38.

S. Lawrence, "Rebuilding a Receiving Flag Antenna for 160 Meters," *QST*, July 2015, pp. 35-38.

G. Levy, "Loop Antennas for Aircraft," *Proc IRE*, Feb. 1943, pp. 56-66. Also see correction, *Proc IRE*, July 1943, p 384.

R. Lombardi, "Field Deployable Mini-K9AY Loop," *QST*, Feb. 2019, pp. 39-41.

R. C. Pettengill, H. T. Garland and J. D. Meindl, "Receiving Antenna Design for Miniature Receivers," *IEEE Trans on Ant and Prop*, July 1977, pp. 528-530.

W. J. Polydoroff, *High Frequency Magnetic Materials — Their Characteristics and Principal Applications* (New York: John Wiley and Sons, Inc, 1960).

E. Robberson, "QRM? Get Looped," *Radio and Television News*, Aug. 1955, pp. 52-54, 126.

M. Sapp, "A Reversible LF and MF EWE Receive Antenna for Small Lots," *QST*, Apr. 2019, pp. 37-43.

D. Sinclair, "Flag and Pennant Antenna Compendium," **angelfire.com/md/k3ky**.

G. S. Smith, "Radiation Efficiency of Electrically Small Multiturn Loop Antennas," *IEEE Trans on Ant and Prop*, Sep. 1972, pp. 656-657.

E. C. Snelling, *Soft Ferrites — Properties and Applications* (Cleveland, OH: CRC Press, 1969).

C. R. Sullivan, "Optimal Choice for the Number of Strands in a Litz-Wire Transformer Winding," *IEEE Trans on Power Electronics*, Vol. 14 No. 2, Mar. 1999, pp. 283-291 (also available online at **engineering.dartmouth.edu/inductor/papers.shtml**).

G. Thomas, "The Hot Rod — An Inexpensive Ferrite Booster Antenna," *Loop Antennas Theory and Design*, M. G. Knitter, Ed. (Cambridge, WI: National Radio Club, 1983), pp. 57-62.

MULTI-TURN LOOP ANTENNAS

M. Harper and M. K. Underhill, "Measurements of the Radiation and Loss Resistances of Small HF Multi-Turn Multi-Resonant Tuned Loops," *IEE 9th International Conference on HF Radio Systems and Techniques* (HFRST), Bath, UK, June 23-26, 2003, pp. 57-63.

V. Leenerts, WØINK, "Loop Antennas – The Factor 'N'," *QEX*, Jan./Feb 2011, pp. 35-38.

G. S. Smith, *The Radiation Efficiency of Electrically Small Multiturn Loop Antennas*, Technical Report No. 612, DTIC AD0709154, Harvard University, Jun 1970. Also published as "Radiation Efficiency of Electrically Small Multiturn Loop Antennas," *IEEE Transactions on Antennas and Propagation*, Vol. 20, no. 5, Sep. 1972, pp. 656-657.

G. S. Smith, *The Proximity Effect in Systems of Parallel Conductors and Electrically Small Multiturn Loop Antennas*, Technical Report No. 624, DTIC AD0736984, Harvard University, Dec 1971. Also published as "Proximity Effect in Systems of Parallel Conductors," *Journal of Applied Physics*, Vol. 43, no. 5, May 1972, pp. 2196-2203.

C. D. Taylor and C. W. Harrison, Jr., "On Thin-Wire Multiturn Loop Antennas," *IEEE Transactions on Antennas and Propagation*, Vol. 22, no. 3, May 1974, pp. 407-413.

22.2 Radio Direction-Finding Antennas

This section describes the antennas and methods suitable for a variety of *radio direction finding* (*RDF*) uses from lower HF bands through UHF. Describing RDF methods helps explain the key design features for specific antenna types. Popular RDF antennas and systems used by amateurs are covered here, with a project or referenced article included for each.

RDF is an activity that has been part of amateur radio since its earliest days. Amateurs participate in RDF exercises to develop skills for use in support of public service (see the sidebar), search-and-rescue, competitive events, or simply because it is fun. Performing RDF involves knowledge of propagation, topography, orienteering, antenna systems, and use of portable receiving equipment.

The most common application of RDF for amateurs is hidden transmitter hunting (also known as *foxhunting* or *bunny hunting*). Transmitter hunts are often conducted from vehicles as informal events organized by local clubs, while on foot hunts in a park can be a fun activity as part of a club picnic. This is excellent practice for locating sources of RF interference (intentional or otherwise), tracking and recovering balloon and rocket payloads, and other signal-tracking applications. Coordinated efforts by several amateurs with RDF skills can be quite effective in locating transmitters over wide areas. These exercises can involve frequencies from 160 meters into the UHF spectrum. RFI tracking and source identification is discussed in the *ARRL Handbook's* chapter on **RFI and EMC**. The "Noise Loop" — a portable flag antenna for RFI applications — is covered in the MF and HF Receiving Antenna section of this chapter.

Transmitter hunting has also developed into an international competitive sport called Amateur Radio Direction Finding (ARDF), or *radio orienteering* (see the sidebar). This sport takes place on foot, usually in wooded areas. IARU World Championship events bring together teams representing their IARU societies to compete for individual and team championship titles. Conducted on either 2 meters or 80 meters using small loops or Yagis, ARDF requires competitors to use only a map, magnetic compass, and their RDF receiver to navigate the course. ARDF competitors use integrated receiver/antenna combinations that optimize ergonomics and reduce the amount of gear a competitor must carry. Examples of this type of gear can be found on the Homing In website (**homingin.com**).

22.2.1 Triangulation and Homing

There are two general approaches to RDF. When the receiving sites are at fixed locations, azimuth bearings are plotted from two or more sites and the approximate location of the transmitter is thus determined by *triangulation*. When portable or mobile receivers relocate to take multiple bearings from various locations as they approach the transmitter location, this is called *homing*. Each approach has its own requirements for equipment and accuracy. Transmitter hunters often use a combination of both methods.

TRIANGULATION

It is impossible to pinpoint the whereabouts of a transmitter from a single azimuth bearing. With a directional antenna you can determine the direction of a signal source, but not how far away it is. Triangulation uses bearings taken from multiple locations to locate a signal source.

For fixed location receiving stations, multiple bearings are obtained from two or more different receiving sites. Alternatively, a mobile receiver can take bearings from different locations. The bearings are then plotted on an area map from the site at which it was taken. The approximate location of the transmitter is indicated by the crossing points of the bearing lines.

Errors due to reflections are particularly common at VHF. With just two bearing locations, there is no check on the accuracy of the bearings, and a single bad bearing could cause

History of Radio Orienteering

Also known as Amateur Radio Direction Finding (ARDF), radio orienteering got its start shortly after World War II. For the first time, portable tube-type radio technology was widely available on the military surplus market. Its low cost removed a barrier to entry into a new radio activity.

The first descriptions of competitive RDF are from Sweden around 1948. The large size of the receivers and weight of their lead-acid batteries required that the first competitions take place by bicycle or by car. By 1952 the Swedish national society for radio amateurs, SSA, organized the first Swedish RDF Championship.

The popularity of radio orienteering on foot accelerated in the 1970's with the advent of solid-state technology. The resulting smaller receivers and transmitters could run on smaller, lighter, batteries. The sport spread across national borders. Rules were established and by 1980 the 1st ARDF World Championships were held in Wladyslawowo, Poland, with ten nations in attendance.

Today, radio orienteering spans much of the globe. Organized ARDF competitions can be found in almost every European country, much of Asia, and in Canada, and the United States. World Championships are held biannually. For more information visit **arrl.org/ardf**.

the bearing lines to not intersect at all. Three bearing lines will usually cross to form a triangle on the map rather than at a single point, with the transmitter somewhere near the triangle. With four bearings, a single bad bearing can be discarded if the remaining three bearings intersect close together. Additional information on the technique of triangulation and much more on RDF techniques may be found at the Homing In website mentioned above.

Bearing accuracy is critical to the usefulness of triangulation used alone, especially when the receiving sites are far from the signal source. A 1-degree offset results in a location error of about 2% of the distance to the transmitter: that is, if the transmitter is 10 miles away, the bearing would miss the target by 0.2 miles. Especially at HF, antennas using nulls are generally preferred because a sharp null provides a more precise bearing than the main (forward) lobe of an antenna. Note that all components of accuracy must be considered: not just the sharpness of the antenna pattern, but the ability of the receiver to detect changes in signal strength, the ability to measure the pointing direction of the antenna, and the accuracy with which a bearing can be plotted on a map.

It is important to note that the directions determined by an RDF receiver can be affected by skew paths (HF) and reflections (VHF and UHF). In addition, signals arriving by skywave can appear to be coming from different azimuths than by ground wave. Avoiding these errors are part of successful RDF.

HOMING

Homing is an RDF technique in which participants proceed from a starting point toward the transmitter location. Whether in a vehicle, on foot, or a combination of the two. Bearings are taken in motion or when stopped at intermediate points. Homing is the only technique used in ARDF events.

Because multiple bearings are taken as the hunters approach the transmitter, bearing accuracy isn't as important for homing as it is for triangulation. If bearings are sufficiently accurate to bring hunters reliably closer to the transmitter, the hunters will eventually arrive at the signal source. In mobile and portable RDF, accuracy of 5 or 10 degrees is adequate. While this might sound large, as the distance to the transmitter is reduced, the resulting distance error also shrinks. Even errors of 15 or 20 degrees can still get you to the transmitter, although not necessarily by the most direct route.

In competitive events where the most common technique is to move progressively toward peak signal, it is more important to be able to take a reading quickly and consistently. With an intermittent transmitter signal, it is useful to be able to follow a compass bearing while the transmitter is off the air, to continue making progress toward the transmitter even when no signal is present.

Bearing accuracy depends on more than just the antenna. It is also affected by the detector type and signal strength indicator. For example, consider a typical 3-element Yagi with a half-power H-plane beamwidth of ±50 degrees (perpendicular to the plane of the elements) or ±32 degrees in the E-plane. With a signal-strength resolution of 1 dB, the beam-

Non-Amateur Uses of RDF

RDF has real-world applications and is a necessary skill in some fields. For example, wildlife biologists have used low-power transmitters attached to birds and other animals to study migration patterns and rely on hams and other volunteers to monitor and track the signals. While many modern tags relay data via cellular phone systems instead, the older beacons around 216 MHz are still in use.

RDF is also useful in air or marine *Search and Rescue* (*SAR*) and in law enforcement. "All certified aircraft and marine vessels over 36 feet, or vessels that venture more than 2 nautical miles from shore, are required to have an emergency beacon that transmits on 406 MHz directly to the COSPAS-SARSAT constellation with a unique serial number ID and GPS coordinates, or on the previously used standard frequency of 121.5 MHz.

"As of 2019, the older 121.5 MHz-only beacons are no longer being sold but most aircraft beacons in the US General Aviation fleet, called *Emergency Locator Transmitters* (*ELTs*), are still on 121.5 MHz or are dual-band 121.5/406 MHz units. These are currently allowed until replaced.

"Activations of 121.5 MHz beacons must be investigated promptly, no matter the time or the weather. Locating these beacons almost always come down to "old school" RDF-ing, and present many challenges, especially from unconventional propagation. Understanding the underlying physics of electronic theory and radio propagation has helped me immensely in my volunteer service with Civil Air Patrol."

Maj. Lowell Silver, WW7SAR, Seattle Composite Squadron, Civil Air Patrol, U.S. Air Force Auxiliary width between display increments is closer to ±20 degrees.

A typical 2-meter mobile FM transceiver with a bar-graph signal strength meter may have an overall range of about 12 dB, often covered in 5 to 7 steps even if the meter appears to have more divisions. The result is a signal strength resolution of about 2 dB per step. If we rotate the antenna to find the directions where the highest bar on the meter just turns on, and where it just turns off again, we can estimate the actual bearing is located at the direction midway between the two. This is often referred to as "eyeball averaging" and provides a more accurate bearing given the relatively small change in signal strength across the peak of the beam.

Audible signal strength indication is commonly used with purpose-built receivers for ARDF. A dc bias on an AM detector might be used to create a threshold effect. Or the signal strength indication voltage might be used to drive an "audio S-meter" — a voltage-controlled oscillator that changes tone pitch with signal strength. It is easier for most people to hear small differences in pitch than variations in audio volume. Pitch can indicate differences in signal strength less than 0.25 dB, or roughly ±10 degrees with a typical 3-element Yagi, and the audio equivalent of "eyeball averaging" can resolve it even more closely.

Antennas for homing have different mechanical requirements, depending on their applications. Often, the same types of beam antennas used for normal two-way communications will work for RDF. If the forward beamwidth is not narrow enough for the RDF application, then an antenna with a deep null may provide a more accurate bearing. In mobile hunts where measurements are made from various stopping points, the antennas (and mounts) must support getting the antenna into and out of the vehicle with minimal effort. For operation while in motion, they must be able to withstand normal driving speeds and be capable of rotation against wind resistance. Rugged design to survive overhanging tree branches and complying with local requirements for allowable height and overhang off the sides of the vehicle are also important.

Antennas hand-carried in ARDF competitions are often made of pieces of steel tape-measure so the elements will bend, then snap back into place when they hit a branch while moving through brush or trees. They also need to be ergonomic and lightweight, so it is comfortable to carry them in a long competition.

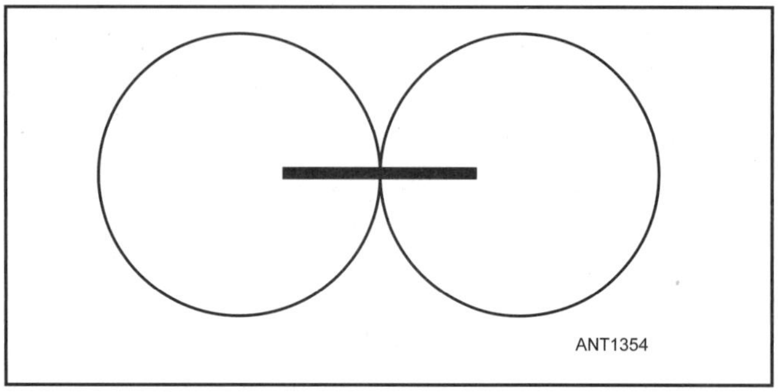

Figure 22.35 — The pattern of a small, well-balanced loop showing two sharp nulls 180 degrees apart.

22.2.2 Small Loop Antennas

Small loop antennas are popular for HF RDF work due to their size and portability. Several factors must be considered in the design of an RDF loop. The loop must be small in circumference compared with the wavelength. Generally, the conductor length should be less than 0.08λ long. Maximum response from the small loop antenna is in the plane of the loop, with sharp nulls exhibited at right angles to that plane. (A more detailed treatment is presented in the **Loop Antennas** chapter.)

Decreasing the physical size of a small loop doesn't affect the pattern. The smaller the loop, however, the lower its efficiency. This is because its aperture samples a smaller section of the wavefront. Thus, if you use loops that are very small in terms of wavelength, you will need preamplifiers to compensate for the reduced efficiency.

Small loop antennas may be either tuned or untuned. Tuned loops typically use a parallel capacitor, and the resulting circuit has a high impedance across the capacitor. Tapping the loop, or adding a coupling loop, will lower the impedance. Depending on the Q of the loop, it may need to be re-tuned to cover more than a narrow frequency range. Untuned loops work well for wideband coverage and exhibit a low impedance.

The theoretical small loop pattern is illustrated in **Figure 22.35**. When properly balanced, the loop exhibits two nulls 180° apart. Thus, a single null reading with a small loop antenna will not indicate the exact direction toward the transmitter — only the line along which the transmitter lies in two directions from the antenna. Methods of overcoming this ambiguity are discussed later in this section.

The loop is held vertically so the null is in the horizontal plane at right angles to the loop. It is then rotated to point the pattern null at the signal source. Because the loop is omnidirectional in the vertical plane, it doesn't work well for RDFing signals arriving at high elevation angles unless it can be rotated in elevation as well as azimuth.

A loop must be balanced electrostatically with respect to ground to obtain the sharpest nulls that provide the most accurate bearings. If unbalanced, the loop will exhibit two modes of operation. One is the mode of a true loop described above, while the other is that of an essentially nondirectional vertical antenna of small dimensions. This second mode is called the *antenna effect*. The voltages introduced by the two modes are seldom in phase and will distort the pattern of the loop.

Electrostatic balance can be obtained by shielding the loop, as described in this section's project, "Receiving Loop Antenna for 1.8 MHz." The shield, represented by the broken lines in the drawing, eliminates the antenna effect. The response of a well-constructed shielded loop is quite close to the ideal pattern shown in Figure 22.35.

On the low-frequency amateur HF bands, the smaller size of multi-turn loops makes them more convenient for portable RDF operation. Such a loop is shown in **Figure 22.36.** This loop may also be shielded and if the total conductor length remains below 0.08λ, the directional pattern is that of Figure 22.35. A sense element may also be used with a multi-turn loop.

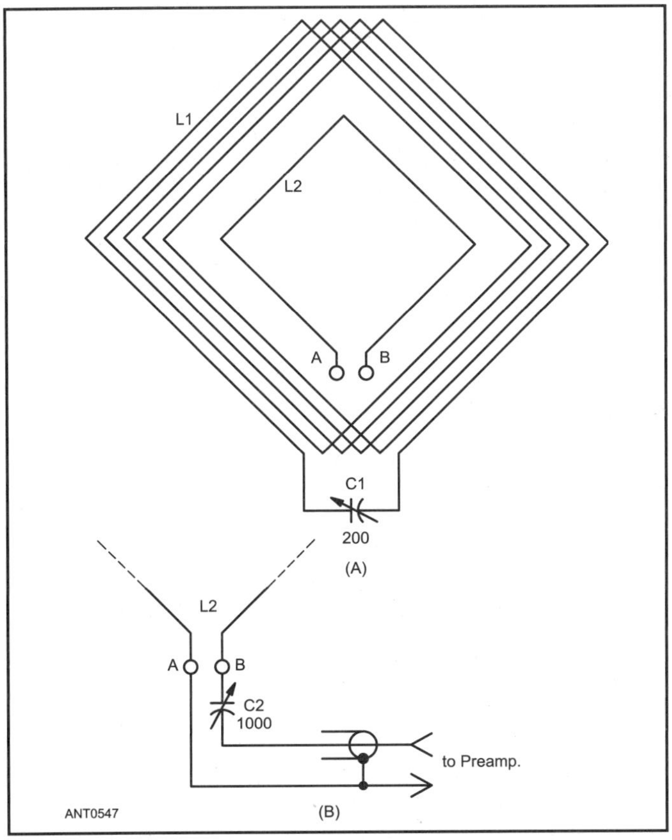

Figure 22.36 — A multi-turn small loop (A) consisting of several turns of wire (L1) with total length much less than 1λ. Maximum response is in the plane of the loop with nulls broadside to the loop. L2 is a coupling loop connected to a preamplifier. C1 is tuned for maximum signal strength by resonating the loop. C2 is a coupling capacitor that adjusts antenna Q and bandwidth.

Small loops can be constructed by winding the loop on a suitable ferrite rod. In that case, the wire is wound into a long, single-layer, thin (solenoidal) coil. The null in the pattern is along the axis of the coil — imagine each turn as a very small loop with the pattern from each turn adding together along the coil. Design of ferrite-core loop antennas is described in the article "Ferrite-Core Loops" included in this book's online material. Construction examples are described later in this chapter.

22.2.3 Sense Antennas

A small loop antenna pattern has two nulls 180 degrees apart, so ambiguity exists as to which one indicates the true direction toward the transmitter. For example, a single east-west bearing provides no way of determining whether the transmitter lies to the east or west of the receiving location. If bearings are taken from more than one location, the ambiguity may be removed using triangulation, as described previously. However, it is sometimes important to determine the correct direction using readings taken at a single location.

A *sense antenna* can be added to a small loop antenna to obtain an antenna pattern with a single null and a single maximum. To accomplish that, the sense antenna by itself must have an omnidirectional pattern, and its output must be adjusted to provide the same signal strength as the loop and an appropriate phase relative to that of the loop. The outputs of the loop and sense antennas are combined, with their relative phases adjusted to combine constructively in one of the loop's peak directions (and therefore destructively in the opposite direction). The result is a cardioid pattern exhibiting only one peak and one null, as shown in **Figure 22.37**.

Figure 22.37B shows a circuit for adding a sense antenna to a loop. R1 and L1 are adjusted experimentally during setup for the best null. Because R1 functions as an attenuator, the sense antenna must be long enough to pick up at least as much signal as the loop does. (Alternatively, a preamp can be used on the sense antenna.) L1 adjusts the phase of the signal from the sense antenna. In practice, the null of the cardioid is not as

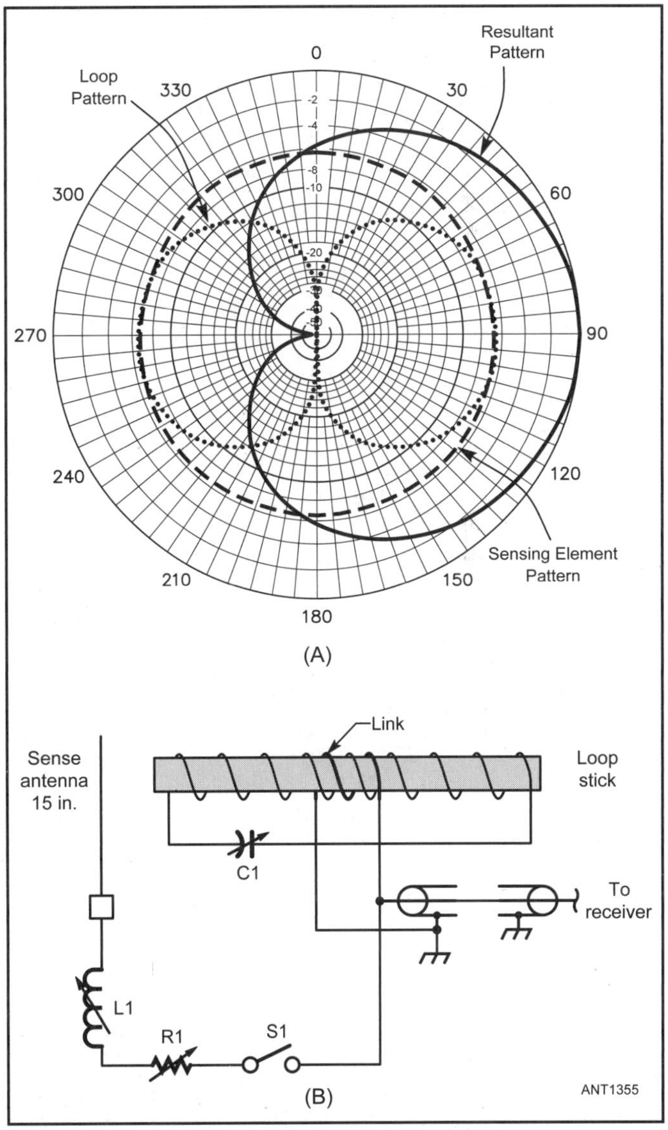

Figure 22.37 — Figure A is the pattern of a loop antenna with a sense antenna. At B is a typical circuit for combining the loop and sense antenna signals. R1 is adjusted for equal amplitudes from both antennas, L1 adjusts the phase of the sense antenna, and C1 resonates the loop at the frequency of use.

sharp as that of the loop, so the usual measurement procedure is to first switch out the sense antenna and use the loop alone to obtain a precise bearing reading. Then the sense antenna is switched in and another reading is taken to resolve the ambiguity. The peak and null directions of the cardioid pattern are at 90 degrees to the nulls of the loop's bidirectional pattern.

22.2.4 Adcock Antennas

Perhaps the simplest RDF array is the Adcock antenna shown in **Figure 22.38**. If two vertical dipoles are mounted in parallel and fed out of phase with equal length feed lines, the signals will cancel perpendicularly to the plane of the two elements, creating a distinct null. For multiband use, the antennas may be fed with open wire lines, carefully trimmed to equal length. This array has a bidirectional null, like that of a loop, but is capable of nulling signals arriving at higher elevation angles as well.

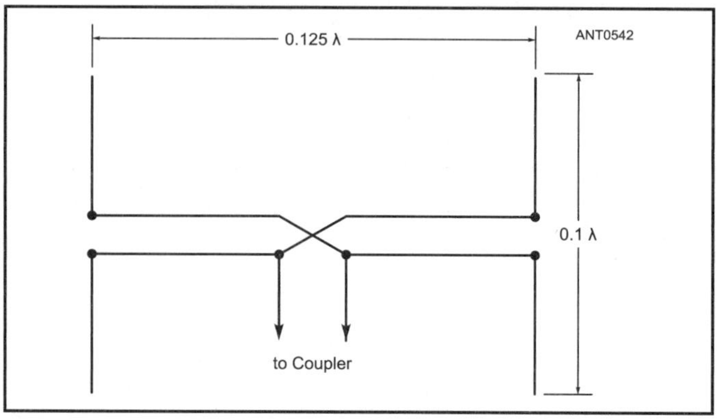

Figure 22.38 — A simple Adcock antenna.

The radiation pattern of the Adcock is shown in **Figure 22.39A**. The nulls are in directions broadside to the array and become sharper with greater element spacings. However, with an element spacing greater than 0.75λ, the pattern begins to take on additional nulls in the directions off the ends of the array axis. At a spacing of 1λ the pattern is that of Figure 22.39B, and the array becomes unsuitable for RDF applications.

LONG-BASELINE INTERFEROMETER

The same principle of the Adcock — parallel elements in a common plane connected out of phase — can be extended to wider spacings for more accuracy. However, because there will be multiple nulls in the pattern, this must be done carefully to ensure that the proper null is used. This is called a *long-baseline interferometer*. On 2 meters, a spacing of 20 feet can give better than 1-degree accuracy, and 50 feet is a reasonable maximum distance for measuring the angle with hand-held equipment. A more detailed explanation is given in the referenced article by Cowen and Beery.

22.2.5 Beam Antennas

Most types of beam antennas can be used for RDF work, especially at VHF and above where dimensions are more suitable for portable, mobile, or hand-held use. Yagis, quads, phased arrays (like the HB9CV), and log periodics are all popular. Standard antennas used for ham communications are generally adequate, although there may be some specific physical requirements to consider.

For fixed stations, horizontally stacked (side by side) arrays of beam antennas will give the sharpest patterns as the azimuth pattern is narrowed. For mobile hunting, wind drag, and the hazards of overhanging tree branches need to be considered in the mechanical design, as well as local restrictions on how far an antenna can extend past the edge of a vehicle. For vertical polarization, a quad doesn't extend as far above the roof as a Yagi does. When hunting on foot, weight and ergonomics become more important, along with flexible elements to withstand running through undergrowth.

Common beam antennas are the 3-element Yagi, 2 and 3-element quads, 2-element Moxons, and the 2-element HB9CV. (See the chapter on **HF Beam Antennas**.) Sample patterns for horizontal and vertical polarization are shown in **Figure 22.40**. While the 3-element Yagi has slightly more gain and smaller beamwidth, the differences among the patterns are comparatively small, as the minor lobes are relatively well controlled. These antennas are all commonly used for RDF.

In all cases, the patterns for horizontal polarization are

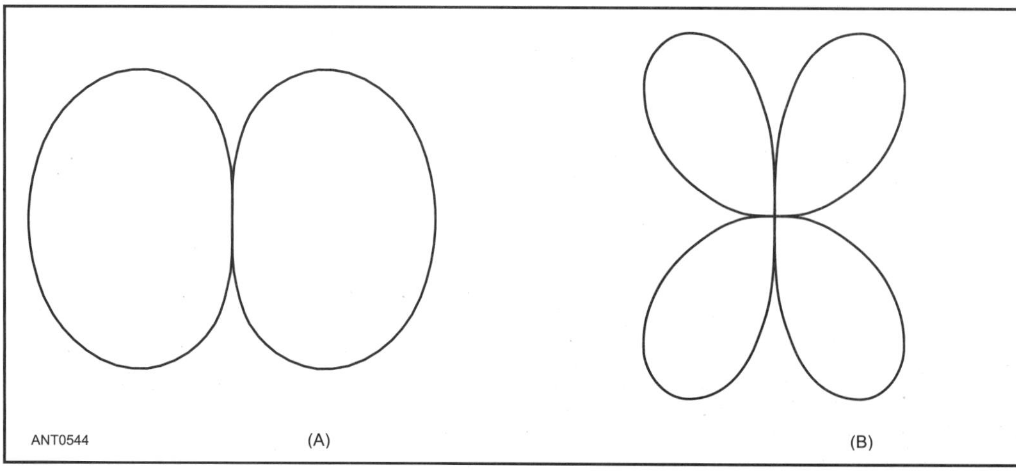

Figure 22.39 — At A, the pattern of the Adcock antenna with an element spacing of ½ λ. The elements are horizontal for this pattern (in and out of the page). As element spacing is increased beyond ½ λ, additional lobes appear (B) making the antenna unsuitable for RDF.

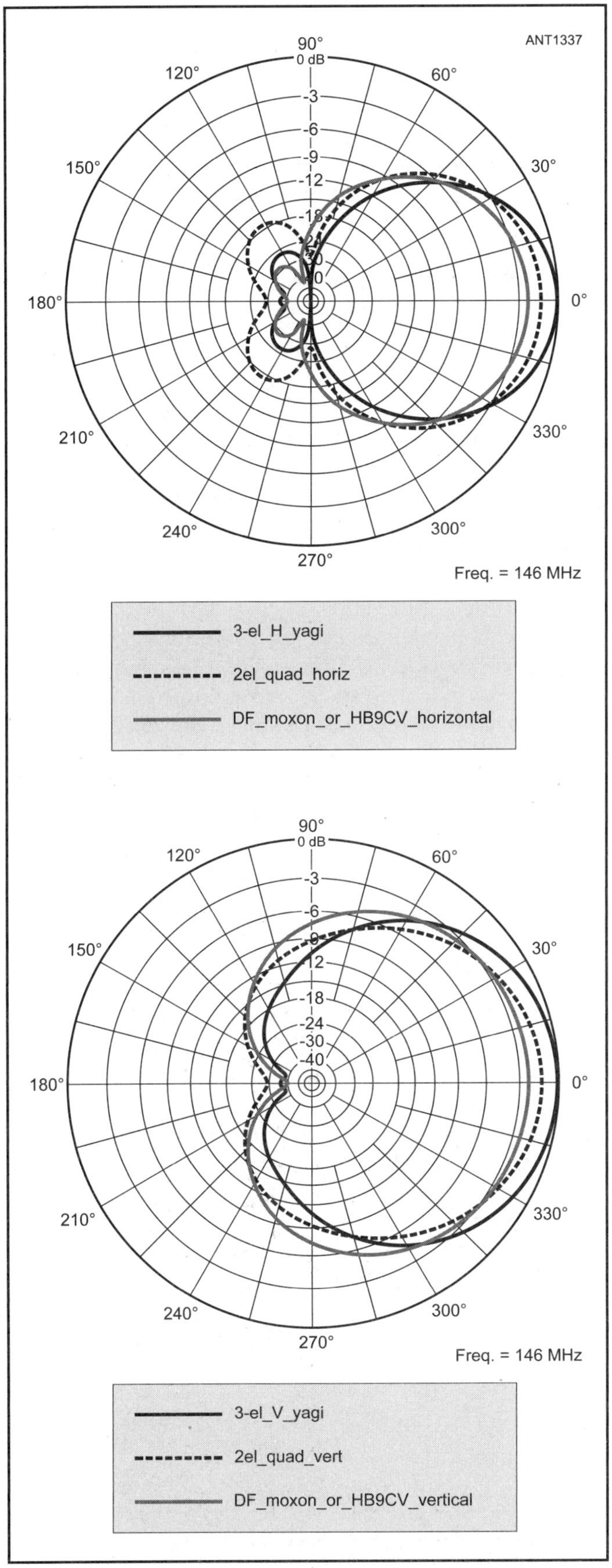

Figure 22.40 — At A, the azimuth patterns for a horizontally polarized 3-element Yagi (solid trace), a 2-element cubical quad (dashed trace), and a Moxon or HB9CV (gray trace). B shows the same antennas vertically polarized.

RDF System Calibration and Testing

Like any precision measuring device, RDF systems need to be calibrated for them to provide accurate bearings. Planning and preparation can make system check-out and calibration go more smoothly. "RDF System Calibration and Testing" in the online material discusses how to go about this important process.

sharper than for vertical polarization. In some cases, for vertical polarization, the rear null may give a better bearing when signals are strong enough, but it is more easily confused by reflections. Otherwise, the peak of the main lobe may be more reliable.

22.2.6 Simple Direction-Finding Systems

WATSON-WATT RDF SYSTEM

The Watson-Watt system consists of a pair of Adcock (or loop) antennas at right angles to each other, each feeding one of two matched receivers. The IF outputs are used to drive the horizontal and vertical deflection inputs of an oscilloscope. The patterns of the two antennas are shown in **Figure 22.41**.

Basically, one antenna provides a signal proportional to the sine of the bearing, and the other to the cosine: the resulting plot with RF applied draws a line across the display in the

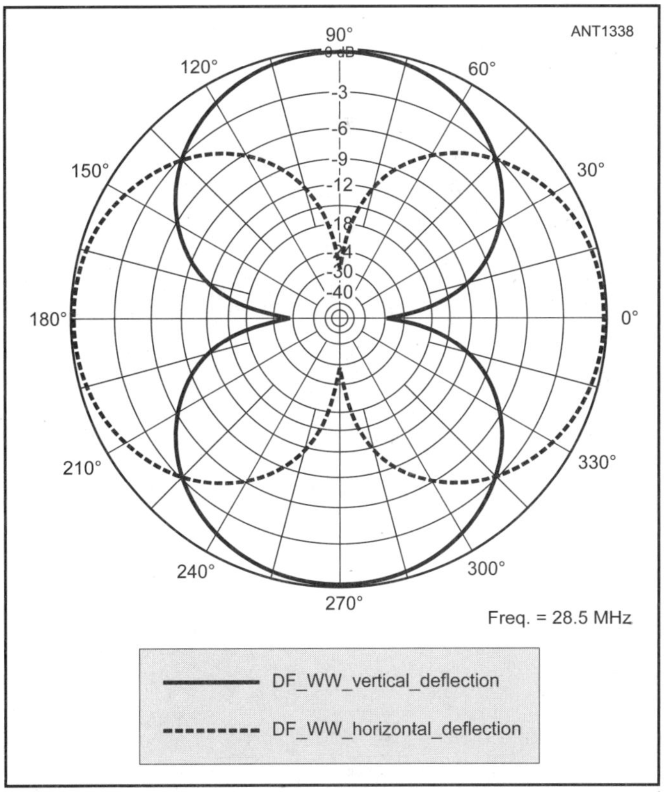

Figure 22.41 — The pattern of a Watson-Watt RDF system antenna array.

direction of the signal. The amplitude of the beam can be modulated by a signal from a sense antenna for a unidirectional display. The perimeter of the display is calibrated in degrees. This provides an instantaneous determination of direction with no moving parts. A standard oscilloscope can be used for the display, or the processing can be done in software. Further information is available from Jasik and by Moell and Curlee (see References and Bibliography).

AMPLITUDE COMPARISON (SWITCHED PATTERN) SYSTEMS

Amplitude comparison or *switched pattern* systems switch back and forth between two different antenna patterns. The indicator is often a zero-center meter that shows the difference in signal strength between the two. The antenna is then rotated until the meter needle is centered, indicating the receiving signal amplitudes are equal. While the meter can be centered when pointing directly toward or away from the source, any small deviation will give a "turn right" or "turn left" indication to bring the antenna to the proper direction. **Figure 22.42** shows an example: the meter will be centered only when the transmitter is directly ahead or behind, where the two patterns have the same strength. Otherwise, the direction of the needle will indicate which direction to turn the antenna.

The switched patterns can be generated by two different antennas or by switching the characteristics of a single antenna. For example, a common VHF implementation uses a 2-element Yagi with each element tuned by the coax feed line length to act as a reflector when the other element is being driven. At HF, the phase of a sense antenna can be switched to change the direction of the cardioid pattern of a loop antenna. It is important that the two patterns be relatively "clean", so there are only two locations (front and back) where they have the same strength. Further information is available in the reference by Jasik and the book by Moell and Curlee.

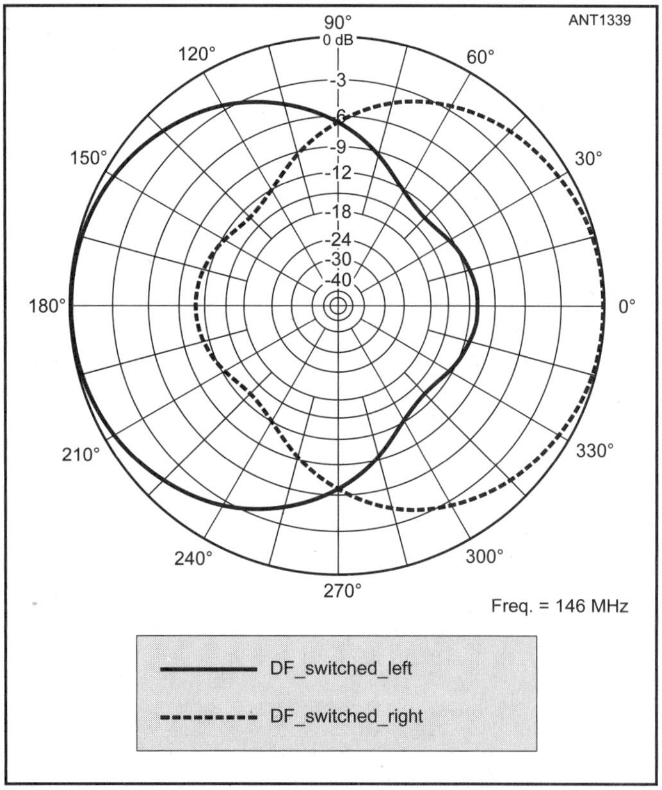

Figure 22.42 — Typical patterns for a switched-pattern system. A bearing to the transmitter is obtained when the amplitudes of a signal received by each antenna are equal.

22.2.7 Electronic Antenna Rotation

With an array of many fixed elements, beam formation and rotation can be performed electronically by sampling and combining signals from various individual elements in the array. Contingent upon the total number of elements in the system and their physical arrangement, almost any desired antenna pattern can be formed by summing the sampled signals in appropriate amplitude and phase relationships. Delay networks are used for some of the elements before the summation is performed. In addition, attenuators may be used for some elements to develop patterns such as from an array with binomial current distribution.

For the moment, consider just two elements of such an antenna, shown as A and B in **Figure 22.43**. Also shown is the wavefront of a radio signal arriving from a distant transmitter. As drawn, the wavefront strikes element A first, and must travel somewhat farther before it strikes element B. There is a finite time delay before the wavefront reaches element B.

The propagation delay may be measured by delaying the signal received at element A before summing it with that from element B. If the two signals are combined directly, the amplitude of the resultant signal will be maximum when the delay for element A exactly equals the propagation delay. This results in an in-phase condition at the summation point. Or if one of the signals is inverted and the two are summed, a null will exist when the element-A delay equals the propagation delay; the signals will combine in a 180° out-of-phase relationship. Either way, once the time delay is known, it may be converted to distance. Then the direction from which the wave is arriving may be determined by trigonometry.

By altering the delay in small increments, the peak of the

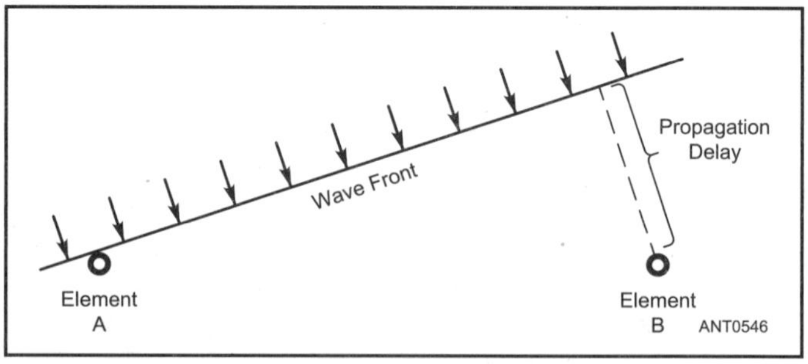

Figure 22.43 — One method of electronic beam forming. By delaying the signal from element A by an amount equal to the propagation delay, the two signals may be summed precisely in phase, even though the signal is not arriving from the broadside direction. Because the time delay is the same for all frequencies, the system is not frequency sensitive.

antenna lobe (or the null) can be steered in azimuth. This is true without regard to the frequency of the incoming wave. Thus, if the delay is less than the period of one RF cycle, the system is not frequency sensitive, other than for the frequency range that may be covered satisfactorily by the array elements themselves. Surface acoustic wave (SAW) devices or lumped-constant networks can be used for delay lines in such systems if the system is used only for receiving. Rolls of coaxial cable of various lengths are used in installations for transmitting. In this case, the lines are considered for the time delay they provide, rather than as simple phasing lines. The difference is that a phasing line is ordinarily designed for a single frequency (or for an amateur band), while a delay line offers essentially the same time delay at all frequencies.

A four-element, electronically rotating RDF antenna system for amateur RDF was described in November 1995 *QST* (see the References and Bibliography entry for Mallette) and is included with this book's online material. The system is designed to be used while mobile and is based on time-difference-of-arrival techniques described later in this section.

The Wullenweber antenna, also known as a Circularly Disposed Antenna Array or CDAA (**navy-radio.com/frd10.htm**), was used until recently by the military for HF direction-finding. A Wullenweber consists of a very large number of elements arranged in a circle, usually outside of (or in front of) a circular reflecting screen. Delay lines and electronic switches create a beam-forming network that can be steered in any direction and with a wide variety of patterns. The Wullenweber design has been replaced by more sophisticated systems that are faster and more accurate, but it is a good example of the basic techniques involved.

22.2.8 TDOA Direction Finder Systems

To understand the principle of *time-difference of arrival* (*TDOA*) direction finding, consider identical omnidirectional antennas placed some distance apart, as shown in **Figure 22.44**. A signal will generally arrive at the antennas at slightly different times simply because each antenna is at a different distance from the signal source.

The signal received at multiple receiving stations can be compared to determine a difference in the signal's arrival time. Any time-varying property of the source signal (e.g., modulation it might exhibit) can serve as an identifying marker to correlate the signals and derive the arrival time difference between the antennas.

TDOA systems typically employ multiple receiving stations separated by several kilometers or more. All stations record and forward their received data to a central location for processing. A computer then correlates the data received from each station and uses the results to calculate the time delays. When three or more receiving stations are employed, these systems may derive an accurate location estimate for the signal source, not simply the angle of arrival of the received signal. Even with a low-cost TDOA system, accurate localization results can be obtained as described in the References and Bibliography entry for Scholl.

SWITCHED TDOA DIRECTION FINDERS

Switched dual-antenna TDOA direction finders operate based on signal phase measurements instead of signal amplitude. By taking advantage of an FM receiver's ability to detect phase changes, a hand-held FM receiver can be used in a simple but effective radio direction finder for determining the angle of arrival for a received signal. RDF designs using switched TDOA include the classic "Double-Ducky" direction finder and the HANDI-Finder™. All of them work on the principle described below. Both articles are included in this book's online material and under Geiser and Leskovec in the References and Bibliography.

Dual-antenna TDOA radio direction finders utilize only two receiving antennas. This simple approach makes for easy-to-build designs with small parts counts and low cost. A signal's phase is the time-varying property that is analyzed to detect the presence of a time delay.

For direct-path signals, the phase of the signal received at the antennas will differ (as illustrated in **Figure 22.45**), provided that the signal source is not equidistant from the two antennas. Observing no difference in phase, then, is the telltale sign that the signal source lies somewhere along the plane of equidistance between the two receiving antennas.

Note that although a radio signal's phase varies with time, it also repeats with each period of a sinusoidal signal. Each sine wave period is identical to the previous ones and to those that follow. Furthermore, each half-period of a sine wave differs from the previous half-period only by its sign, so the magnitude of the phase difference between two waves is identical with a half-period periodicity. Consequently, it is essential to ensure that the two receiving antennas receive the same half period of the signal wavefront. Failure to do that

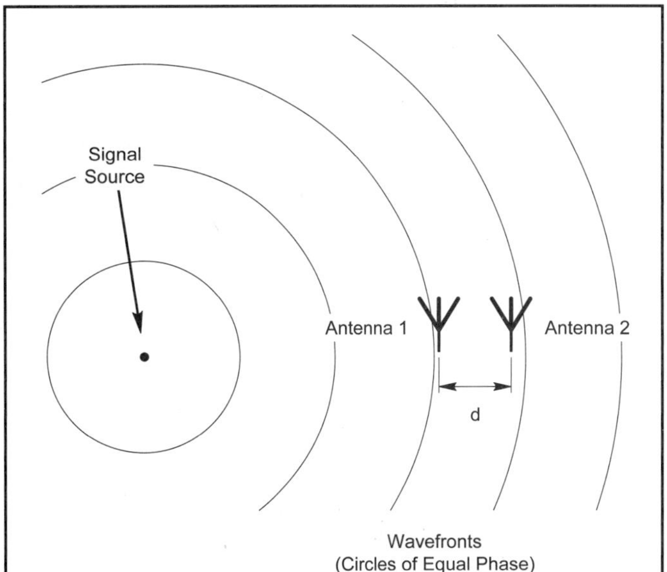

Figure 22.44 — A signal from a distant transmitter received by two identical receiving antennas separated by a distance, d.

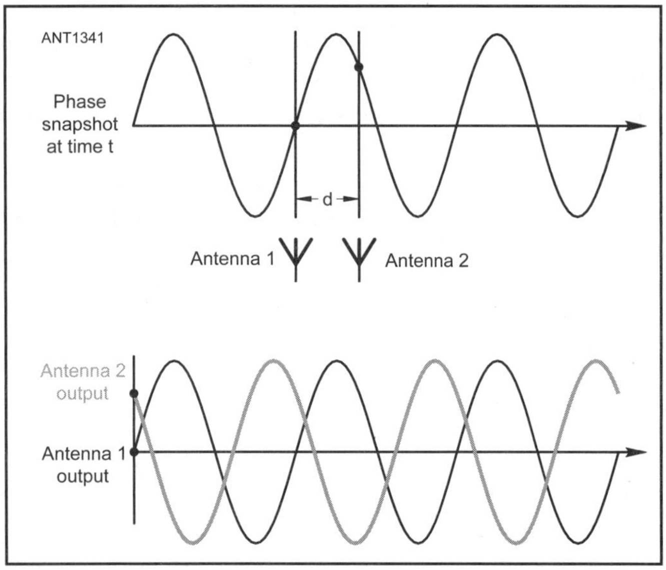

Figure 22.45 — Top: A snapshot at time t of the arriving wavefront at two antennas: one located a distance d farther from the signal source. Bottom: Signals from the antennas at time t and onward.

would result in multiple angles of arrival providing identical phase differences between the two antennas. This problem is easily avoided by ensuring that the two receiving antennas are separated by less than one-half the received signal's wavelength so that $d<\lambda/2$, where d is the distance between receiving antennas and λ is the wavelength of the received signal.

Switched TDOA antennas may be separated by an arbitrary distance less than $\lambda/2$, but the maximum phase deviation decreases as the antennas are brought closer together. If d is too small, the FM receiver will provide only a weak audio tone signal. Wider antenna separation also improves azimuthal bearing accuracy, so the widest practical separation should be used.

A switched TDOA typically uses an FM receiver to detect phase difference. High-speed RF switches repeatedly connect one antenna and then the other to an FM receiver's antenna input. The switching is done at an audio rate (e.g., 500 Hz) suitable for the FM receiver to demodulate and send to its speaker. The result is an audio tone from the receiver whenever a signal within its passband is present at both antennas, and there is a detectable phase difference between them. Importantly for radio direction finding, no audio signal will be present (a "tone-null") when the received signal arrives at both antennas simultaneously and, therefore, at equal phase. The antennas can be rotated in unison to find the tone-null direction and, thus, the bearing direction toward the transmitter.

As described, a dual-antenna TDOA direction finder is bi-directional: its tone nulls occur both toward and away from the signal's origin. The ambiguity can be resolved using the triangulation direction-finding approach described earlier in this chapter. There is also the option of adding a left/right indication circuit, informing the operator which null is the one toward the signal source. **Figure 22.46** illustrates a dual-antenna TDOA direction finder design.

The vertical antennas can be dipoles, rubber ducks, or whip antennas placed above a ground plane. The feed lines running from each antenna to the antenna switching unit must have identical electrical lengths. The switching unit should connect each antenna to the receiver with a 50% duty cycle at an audio rate that the FM receiver (and the operator) can easily detect. Multiple RF switch devices are typically used to implement a double-throw antenna switch. This system is not intended to be used for transmitting.

Switched dual-antenna TDOA direction finders for VHF frequencies and above can be quite compact and easily carried by hand if the antennas are rigidly mounted together. The antennas are rotated as a unit until a tone-null is achieved, indicating that the source of the signal lies in the plane between the two antennas.

The antenna switching unit uses solid-state switches to achieve an audio switching rate. Integrated circuit RF switches, PIN diodes, or even standard high-speed switching diodes have been used successfully to implement the RF switches. Within the antenna switching unit, a simple audio square-wave generator such as a 555 timer IC drives the switches.

With synchronized sampling of the FM receiver's output and suitable audio processing to detect the sign of the tone's amplitude, it is possible to drive a center-scale meter or an LED indicator to display which direction to turn to face the transmitter. Such a left/right indicator removes the 180-degree directional ambiguity and simplifies operation.

Becoming adept at using switched TDOA direction finders requires some practice. Learning to recognize multipath signals' effects on the audio tone is important for avoiding con-

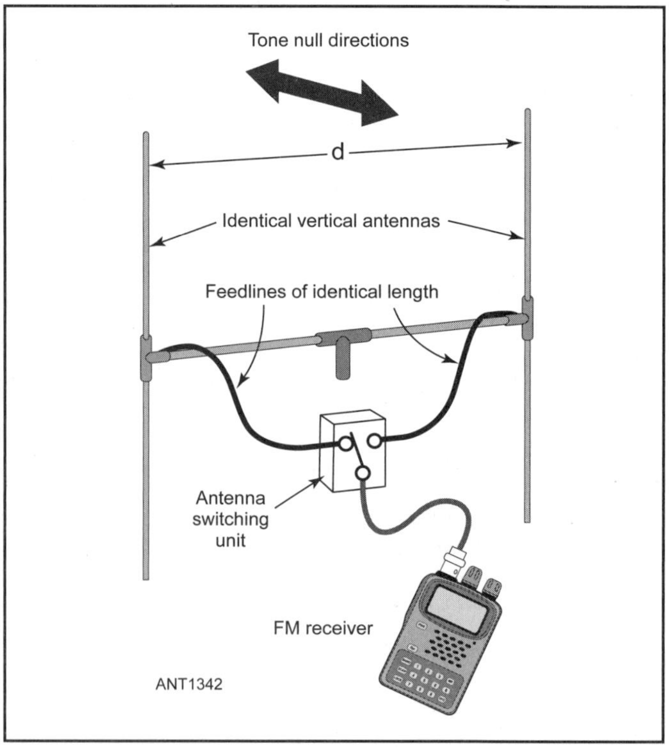

Figure 22.46 — A simple switched TDOA direction finder.

fusion from the vague tone nulls they can create. The operator should practice with the direction finder to become familiar with how the switched TDOA behaves under known signal direction, power, and frequency situations. An operator's skill for recognizing when *not* to trust the direction finder's output can be just as important as steering toward the tone null.

Switched Dual-Antenna TDOA Advantages

- Directional accuracy of ±5 degrees under ideal conditions
- Simple to build
- Straightforward to use
- Works especially well for RDFing modulation formats containing a strong carrier component (CW, FM, AM)
- Works best for RDFing while in motion

Switched Dual-Antenna TDOA Disadvantages

- Does not work well for RDFing horizontally polarized signals
- Can be confused by multi-path signals, particularly when stationary
- Modulation on the hunted signal can confuse the operator
- Susceptible to damage if used as a transmitting antenna
- Does not provide antenna gain for hunting weak signals

22.2.9 Doppler Direction Finder Systems

The familiar Doppler effect produces a shift toward a lower frequency when a transmission source and receiver move apart. A shift toward a higher frequency occurs when the source and receiver move toward one another.

Note that the Doppler effect occurs due to the relative motion of the signal source and the receiver so the receiving antenna can be moved to create a Doppler shift. The transmitting antenna need not move. That shift in frequency can then be measured to determine the direction toward the transmitting antenna: the greatest shift upward in frequency will occur when the receiving antenna moves directly toward the source of transmissions, and the greatest downward shift for motion directly away.

The classic explanation of Doppler direction finder operation examines a single vertical receiving antenna moving at a constant rate in a circular path around a central axis. **Figure 22.47** shows a 1/4-wavelength vertical antenna in uniform circular motion at a distance R from the axis of rotation. The antenna's instantaneous velocity toward a distant signal source can be shown to vary sinusoidally:

$$V = KR\omega \sin(\theta)$$

where V is the antenna's component of velocity toward an arriving wavefront, K is a constant chosen to agree with the units used for the other variables, R is the antenna's distance from the axis of rotation, ω is the antenna's rotational velocity in degrees/second, and θ is the antenna's angular position (in degrees). **Figure 22.48** illustrates how the velocity toward the transmitting antenna changes sinusoidally as the receiving antenna rotates. Motion away from the transmitted signal is assigned a negative value.

By carefully selecting the appropriate rotational velocity (ω) and radius (R), a frequency-modulated signal from the rotating antenna can be achieved that is suitable for demodulation by an FM receiver. For example, to obtain an FM modulation frequency of 750 Hz, a rotational velocity of 45,000 RPM (750 revolutions per second) can be selected. To achieve a Doppler-induced frequency deviation of ±1 kHz on a 146 MHz signal, a rotation radius of 50 centimeters can be chosen. In response to a received signal, an attached FM receiver would then produce a 750 Hz audio sine wave at its speaker output.

Determining the azimuth (angle of arrival) for the received signal can be accomplished by detecting the zero-crossing of the detected audio signal and determining its position in time relative to the antenna's angular motion. Mechanical Doppler systems are impractical to construct, but pseudo-Doppler systems, described next, can provide identical results without physically rotating the antenna.

PSEUDO-DOPPLER DIRECTION FINDER

In practice, *pseudo-Doppler* direction finders (aka, *synthetic Dopplers*) use three or more stationary antennas spaced equidistantly around a circle, as illustrated in **Figure 22.49**. Antenna

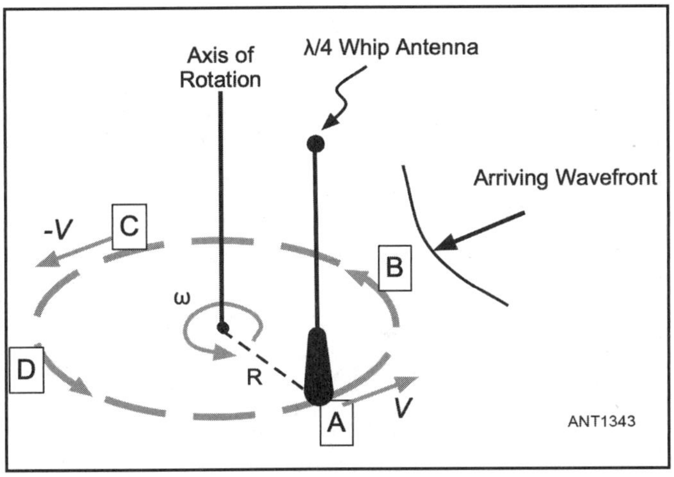

Figure 22.47 — A theoretical Doppler antenna circles around the axis of rotation, repeatedly moving toward and away from the signal source at an audio rate.

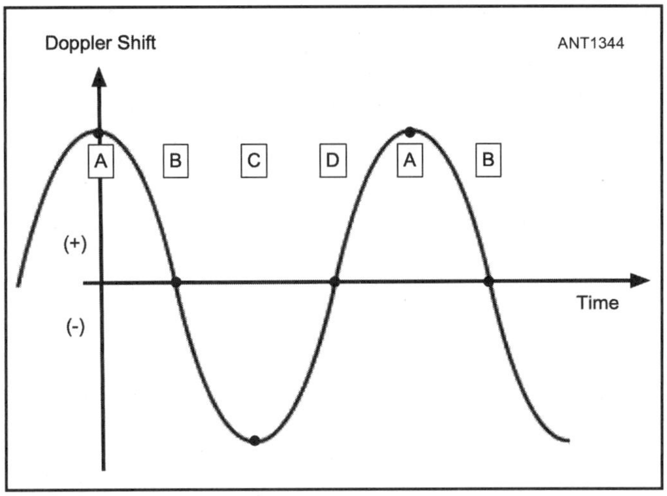

Figure 22.48 — Frequency shift versus time produced by the rotating antenna movement toward and away from the signal source.

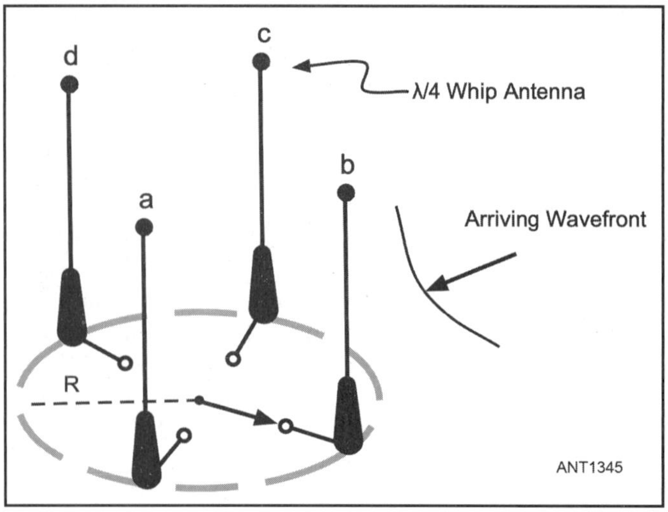

Figure 22.49 — A four-antenna pseudo-Doppler antenna array simulates a rotating antenna.

motion is then simulated by switching rapidly between the antennas in a circular pattern using high-speed electronic RF switches. The antenna switching rate is chosen to achieve a simulated rotation rate in the same manner as was done for the mechanical Doppler system described previously. The outputs from the antennas are fed sequentially into an FM receiver.

Each discrete step between antennas modulates the received signal according to the phase change caused by the different arrival times of the received signal at each antenna position. Just as a switched dual-antenna TDOA direction finder causes phase changes each time the antenna is switched, the pseudo-Doppler induces a phase shift with each step between antennas. Two consecutively switched antenna's alignment with the arriving wavefront determines the magnitude and sign of each phase step. A pseudo-Doppler generates a discrete horizontal (azimuthal) sweep of phase difference measurements: one for each switch between antennas.

As with dual-antenna TDOA designs, spacing between adjacent pseudo-Doppler antennas must be kept below λ/2 to avoid ambiguity in the measured angle of arrival. As the value of R increases, more antennas must be added to keep adjacent antenna spacing below λ/2. Increasing the number of antennas helps average out any random differences between antennas, thereby reducing the system's bearing error caused by errors in antenna placement and feed line lengths. However, adding more antennas increases system cost, complexity, and weight. All those factors must be considered when choosing the number of antennas for a pseudo-Doppler design.

Selecting a larger circular radius R increases the area of the sampled wavefront, which should generally result in greater bearing accuracy from a pseudo-Doppler antenna system. The choice for R also determines the minimum number of antennas required to maintain a λ/2 maximum separation between consecutively switched antennas. Those factors, and the total space available for the antenna system, should be considered when choosing the optimum radius of a pseudo-Doppler antenna design.

A pseudo-Doppler's antenna switching is accomplished using solid-state RF switches configured to isolate all but the active antenna from the FM receiver antenna input. PIN diodes or high-speed switching diodes are typically used to implement the antenna switches. Because the switching diodes are connected directly to the RF signal path of the antennas, strong external signals (including out-of-band signals) generate mixing products that can interfere with the operation of the pseudo-Doppler. This problem can be addressed by installing suitable low-pass or band-pass filters on each antenna.

The FM receiver functioning as the pseudo-Doppler's detector generates a series of audio pulses, depicted simplistically as rectangular pulses in **Figure 22.50**, in response to the phase shifts as it switches sequentially through the array of antennas. The audio pulses are then passed through a narrow audio filter centered at the rotational frequency. The audio filter integrates and removes the high frequency "steps" from the pulsed audio, effectively extracting a continuous sinusoidal waveform that is equivalent to the signal from a mechanically rotated system.

Like a mechanical Doppler, a zero-crossing of the filtered audio signal can be used to determine the angle of arrival for the received signal. Using a zero-crossing is advantageous because changes in audio signal amplitude will not affect the zero-cross position. The bearing direction is determined by comparing the time of the zero-crossing relative to the antenna array's switching sequence.

A pseudo-Doppler system must be calibrated beforehand using a test signal at a known direction (designated zero degrees). Calibration is needed, in part, because the FM receiver will affect the shape, amplitude, and duration of the detected phase pulses (due primarily to differences in IF filtering), thus altering the phase of the filtered audio sinusoid. But the absolute timing of the zero crossing is unimportant: only its timing relative to the antenna switching sequence determines the displayed bearing direction, and that relative timing is precisely set during calibration.

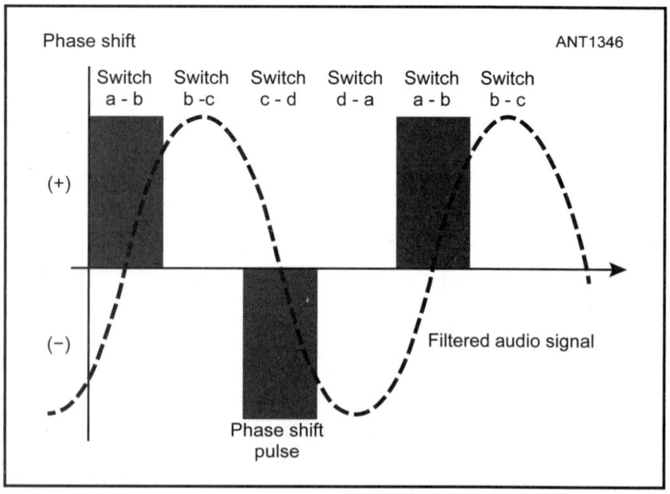

Figure 22.50 — Four-antenna pseudo-Doppler phase shift pulses for a radio wavefront arriving perpendicular to the plane containing antennas "a" and "b".

For mobile use, a metal plate can serve as a ground plane and support platform to hold the antenna array in place, or the antennas can be affixed individually to the metal roof of the vehicle. In either case, the wind load of a pseudo-Doppler array is generally much less than that of a beam antenna, and the system is relatively inconspicuous compared to a beam antenna poking up above the car roof. Pseudo-Doppler antenna arrays designed for VHF use tend to be too large for portable use. However, a pseudo-Doppler built for UHF frequencies and above can be small and light enough to be carried by one person or even by a drone (see the References and Bibliography entry for W. E. Gerhard III). For use at a fixed location, horizontally polarized omnidirectional antennas might be substituted for vertical whips, enhancing the pseudo-Doppler's ability to RDF horizontally polarized signals.

Pseudo-Dopplers are ideal for tracking down sources of malicious interference to amateur FM repeaters because they are effective at tracking the strong vertically polarized signals that repeater jammers usually transmit. Also, because an accurate bearing direction can be displayed after just a few antenna switching cycles, pseudo-Dopplers can track signals of very short duration: well under 1 second.

Pseudo-Doppler Advantages

• Provides bearing directions even for signals of very short duration (~10 msec)

• Directional resolution as fine as 1 degree

• Directional accuracy of ±5 degrees under ideal conditions

• Simple to use

• Works especially well for RDFing modulation formats containing a strong carrier component (CW, FM, AM)

• Works best for RDFing while in motion

• Stealthier than a beam antenna

• Small wind profile and no moving parts facilitate use at highway speeds

• Interfaces readily to computing devices for enhanced signal analysis or recording

Pseudo-Doppler Disadvantages

• Doesn't work well for RDFing horizontally polarized signals

• Can be confused by multi-path signals, particularly when stationary

• Certain phase-modulated signals may confuse a pseudo-Doppler

• Susceptible to damage if used as a transmitting antenna

• Antennas do not provide gain for hunting weak signals

PROJECT: A MULTI-TURN FRAME LOOP ANTENNA

The earliest style of receiving loops was the multi-turn frame antenna. Figure 22.36 previously illustrated the details of a practical frame type of loop antenna. This antenna was described in *QST* for July 1977 (see the references for DeMaw). The circuit in Figure 22.36A is a 5-turn system tuned to resonance by C1. If the layout is symmetrical, good balance should be obtained. L2 helps to achieve this objective by eliminating the need for direct coupling to the feed terminals of L1. If the loop feed were attached in parallel with C1, a common practice, the loop would require a high-impedance balanced feed to prevent imbalance.

L2 can be situated just inside or slightly outside of L1, and a 1-inch separation was used in the original. The receiver or preamplifier can be connected to terminals A and B of L2. C2 controls the amount of coupling between the loop and the preamplifier. The lighter the coupling, the higher is the loop Q, the narrower is the frequency response, and the greater is the gain requirement from the preamplifier. Even with the coupling loop, the feed point impedance is still high: no attempt is made to match the loop impedance to the preamplifier. The impedance can be lowered by reducing the size of L2 relative to L1, and/or using more turns on L1 to change the turns ratio. Making L2 about half the diameter of L1 gives an impedance around 200 Ω.

A supporting frame for the loop of can be constructed of wood, as shown in **Figure 22.51**. The dimensions given are for a 1.8-MHz frame antenna. For use on 75 or 40 meters, L1 will require fewer turns, or the size of the wooden frame should be made somewhat smaller than that in the figure.

If electrostatic shielding is desired, the design shown in **Figures 22.52** and **22.53** can be used. In this example, the loop conductor and the single-turn coupling loop are made from RG-58 coaxial cable. The number of loop turns should be sufficient to resonate with the tuning capacitor and the effective capacitance between the center conductor and the shield of the coax (which may be several hundred pF) at the operating frequency. Alternatively, just L2 can be shielded, which adds less capacitance. Antenna resonance can be checked by coupling a dip meter to the loop and tuning C1 through its range.

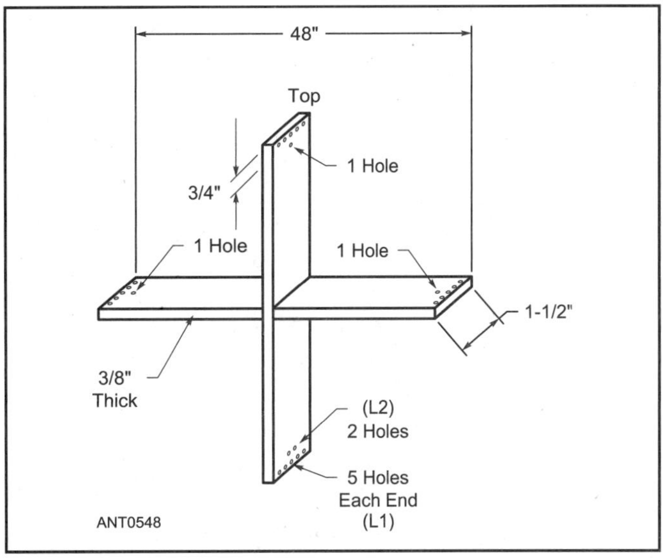

Figure 22.51 — A wooden frame can be used to hold the loop wire.

Figure 22.52 — A table-top version of the electrostatically shielded loop using RG-58 coaxial cable.

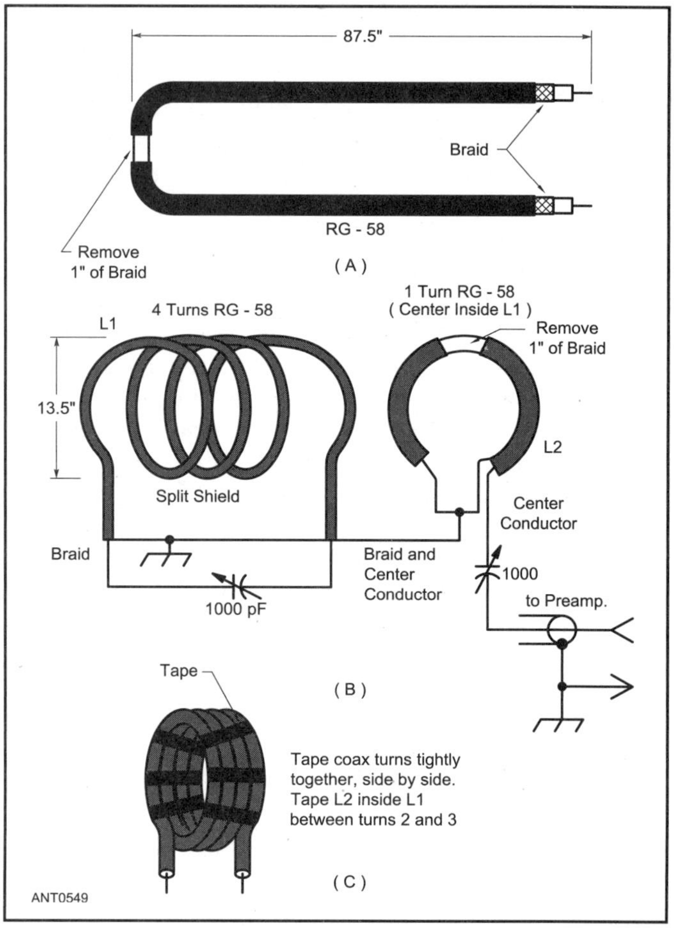

Figure 22.53 — Components and assembly details of the shielded loop shown in Figure 22.41. The dimensions and values given are for 1.8 MHz operation.

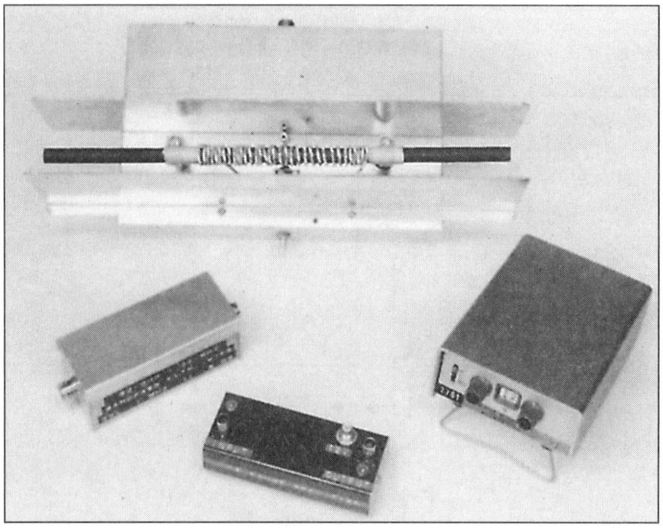

Figure 22.54 — A shielded ferrite-rod loop for 160 is shown at the top of the photograph. Two rods have been glued end to end as described in the text. The other units are a low-pass filter (lower left), broadband preamp (center), and step attenuator (lower right).

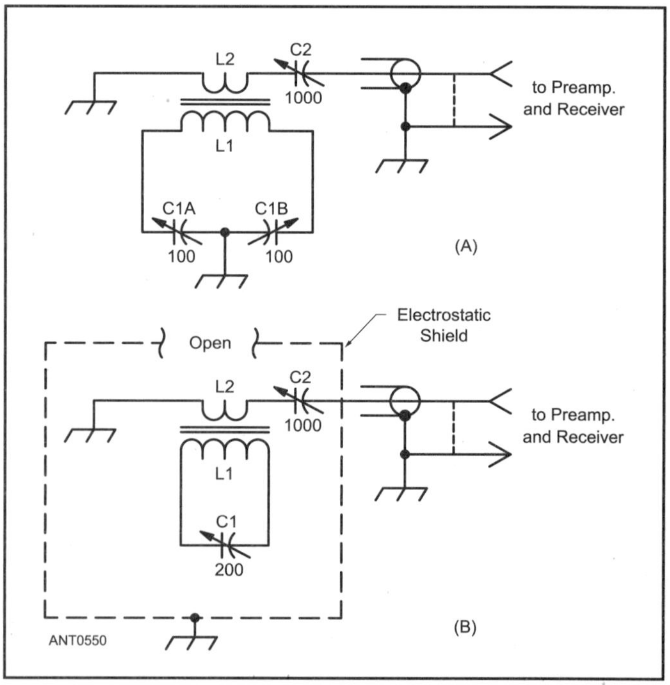

Figure 22.55 — At A is the circuit diagram of the ferrite loop. C1 is a dual-section air-variable capacitor. The schematic at B shows the ferrite rod contained in an electrostatic shield channel (see text).

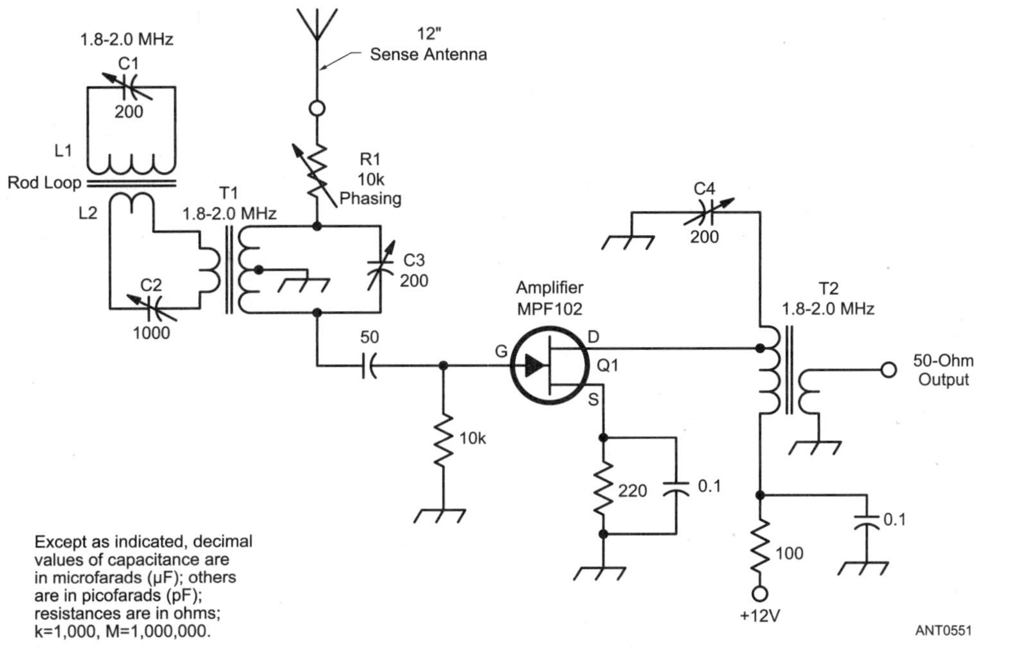

Figure 22.56 — Schematic diagram of a rod-loop antenna with a cardioid pattern. The sensing antenna, phasing network, and a preamplifier are shown. The secondary of T1 and the primary of T2 are tuned to resonance at the operating frequency of the loop. Amidon T-68-2 to T-68-6 toroid cores are suitable for both transformers. NTE457 and J113 are direct replacements for the MPF102, if needed.

PROJECT: A FERRITE-CORE LOOP FOR 160 METERS

Figures 22.54 and **22.55** show a ferrite rod loop (loopstick antenna). This antenna was also described in July 1977 *QST* by DeMaw. The article "Ferrite-Core Loop Antennas" analyzes this antenna in more detail, including the effects of rod permeability and winding configuration. The article is available in this book's online material.

The winding (L1) has the appropriate number of turns to permit resonance with C1 at the operating frequency. L1 should be spread over approximately 1⁄3 of the core center. Litz wire will yield the best Q on 160 meters, but enameled magnet wire can be used if desired. A layer of electrical tape on the rods is recommended as a covering for the core before adding the wire since ferrite is somewhat abrasive.

L2 functions as a coupling link over the exact center of L1. C1 is a dual-section variable capacitor, although a small differential capacitor might be added in parallel with it to optimize balance. The loop Q is controlled by means of C2, which is a mica-compression trimmer.

Electrostatic shielding of rod loops can be achieved by centering the rod in a U-shaped channel of non-magnetic material such as aluminum, brass, or copper, extending slightly beyond the ends of the rod loop (1 inch is suitable). The open side (top) of the channel can't be closed, as that would constitute a shorted turn and render the antenna useless. This can be demonstrated by shorting across the center of the channel with a screwdriver blade when the loop is tuned to an incoming signal. The shield-braid gap in a coaxial cable loop antenna is maintained for the same reason.

Figure 22.53 shows the shielded rod loop assembly. This antenna was developed experimentally for 160 meters and uses two 7-inch ferrite rods, glued together end-to-end with epoxy cement. The longer core resulted in improved sensitivity for weak-signal reception. The other items in the photograph were used during the evaluation tests. This loop and the frame loop discussed in the previous section have bidirectional nulls.

OBTAINING A CARDIOID PATTERN

Although the bidirectional pattern of loop antennas can be used effectively in tracking down signal sources by means of triangulation, an essentially unidirectional loop response will help to reduce the time spent finding the fox. Adding a sense antenna to the loop is simple to do, and it will provide the desired cardioid response. The theoretical pattern for this combination was shown previously in Figure 22.37.

Figure 22.56 shows how a sense element signal can be combined with a loop or loopstick antenna. The link from the loop is connected by coaxial cable to the primary of T1, which is a tuned toroidal transformer with a split secondary winding. C3 is adjusted for peak signal response at the frequency of interest (as is C4), then R1 is adjusted for minimum back response of the loop. It will be necessary to readjust C3 and R1 several times to compensate for the interaction of these controls. The adjustments are repeated until no further null depth can be obtained. Tests by the ARRL showed that null depths as great as 40 dB could be obtained with the circuit of Figure 22.50 on 80 meters. A near-field weak signal source was used during the tests. (Because the ratio of the E- and H-field intensities varies in the near field, as well as with height above ground, final adjustment should use a signal source at least 1λ from the transmitter.)

The greater the null depth, the lower the signal output from the system, so plan to include a preamplifier with 25 to 40 dB of gain. Q1 shown in **Figure 22.57** will deliver approximately 15 dB of gain. In the interest of maintaining a good noise figure, even at 1.8 MHz, Q1 should be a low-noise device such as a 2N4416. If more gain is required, the circuit of Figure 22.55

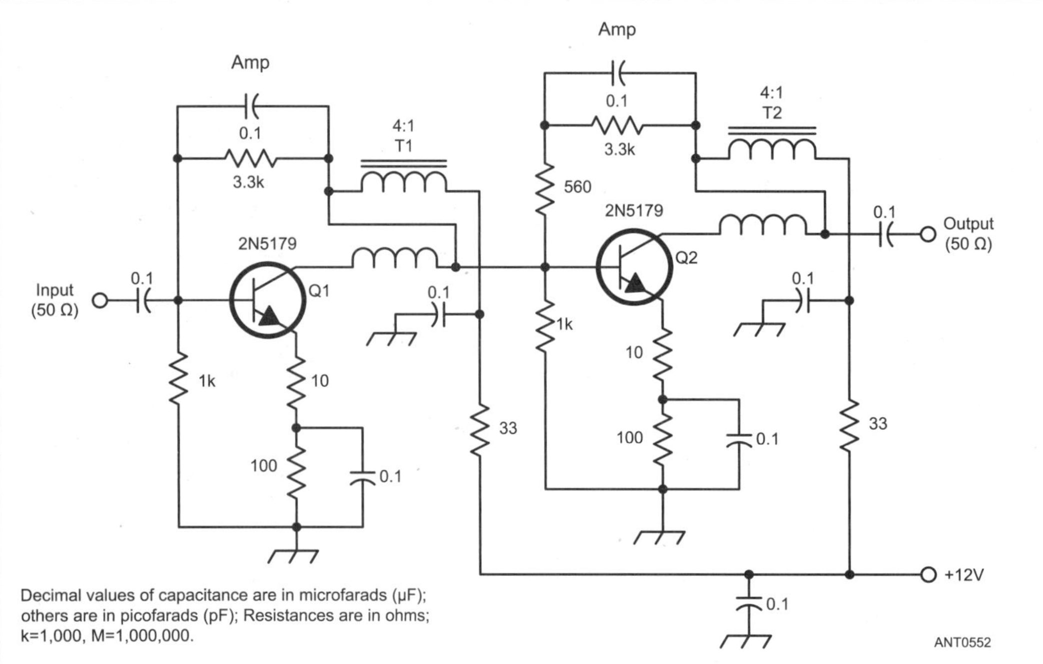

Figure 22.57 — Schematic diagram of a two-stage broadband amplifier patterned after a design by W7ZOI. T1 and T2 have a 4:1 impedance ration and are wound on Amidon FT-50-61 toroid cores which have a permeability (µ) of 125. Each transformer has 12 bifilar turns of #24 AWG enameled wire. Capacitors are disc or monolithic ceramic. The amplifier should be built on double-sided circuit board for best stability.

can be used following T2. The sense antenna can be mounted from a few mm to 6 inches from the loop. The vertical whip need not be more than 12 inches long. Some experimenting is necessary in order to obtain the best results. Optimization will also change with the operating frequency of the antenna.

PROJECT: A SIMPLE DIRECTION-FINDING SYSTEM FOR 80 METERS

This section gives an overview of the article by the same name in September 2005 *QST*. (See the referenced article by Hunt.) The full article is included with this book's online material. The antenna (a multi-turn loop) and receiver are combined into a single package as shown in **Figure 22.58**. The receiver was designed to hear a 1 W signal from >5 miles away, to have low battery drain and to be lightweight and rugged for competitive RDF use.

The loop antenna had to be easy to build with readily available parts and be able to withstand hard use in the field. While a ferrite rod would make the loop much smaller, it didn't meet the project's objective for parts availability. Threading wires through a piece of polyethylene tubing, then gluing it into a hole in each side of the receiver case, makes a very sturdy and light loop.

The loop itself uses an even number of turns for the main

Figure 22.58 — The integrated antenna, handle, and receiver are built into an aluminum box at A. The controls are designed to be operated with one hand while using the antenna. The loop wiring and sense amplifier schematics are included with the article in the online material.

tuned winding, so the center tap can be grounded and the tuning capacitor mounted inside the case. An additional winding serves as a coupling link to the cascode RF stage, which has an input impedance around 1500 Ω. The Q is such that a 100 kHz segment of the 80 meter band can be covered without needing to gang the tuning of the loop with the receiver VFO, although signal strengths are somewhat lower at the ends of the range.

In this case, shielding just the coupling loop (by using miniature coax) provides the same balance benefits as shielding the entire loop. An advantage is reduced capacitance between the tuned winding and the shield, which improves performance and makes it easier to tune. While ideally the shield of the coupling loop would be broken at the top center, having the gap at one end of the loop doesn't cause any obvious problems in performance.

A separate winding provides coupling for the sense antenna. While previous ferrite-core loops worked well with a 6-inch sense antenna, this loop required a sense antenna over 5 feet tall to get the proper pattern. Instead, a preamp was used to permit a more practical sense antenna length. (An FET would have been a better choice than a bipolar transistor, but the original design was constrained to use more common parts.) Adding more turns, or making the loop larger in diameter, will further increase sensitivity.

Many sense antennas circuits have separate adjustments for phase shift and amplitude, requiring a lot of back-and-forth in the tuning process. Because the required 90-degree phase shift is provided by a transformer in this case (the coupling between the sense link and the main loop), only the amplitude requires adjustment (by adjusting the gain of the preamp on the sense antenna.) That makes it much easier to adjust.

Another issue with some sense antenna circuits is that the output of the loop varies with frequency when the tuning is fixed, and that affects the setting of the sense antenna required to match the amplitude. With this circuit, the sense antenna is coupled through the loop, so any change in amplitude due to changing frequency will affect both at the same time, thereby providing a good null over a wider bandwidth.

Note that the relative amplitudes of the E and H fields are not constant in the near field of the transmitting antenna, and they also vary with height above ground. That affects the signal strengths from the loop and the sense antenna, and hence the depth of the null. Adjusting the sense antenna at a distance of about 1λ from the signal source provides a reasonable balance between near- and far-field performance, and the adjustment should be made at the same height above ground as the antenna will be used.

PROJECT: A COMBINED YAGI – TDOA VHF ANTENNA

Switched dual-antenna TDOA direction finders can give sharp bearings, but they lack sensitivity for long-distance work. Yagis are sensitive, but they provide relatively broad bearings. The Oct 1998 *QST* article by Gillette, "A Fox-Hunting DF Twin 'Tenna" describes a three-element Yagi antenna that blends both on a single boom to cover both ends of the hunt. Being rigid, the elements of the antenna described in the article make it somewhat impractical for competitive RDF-ing in brushy or wooded areas, but the design provides a starting point for experimentation and modification. The article is included with this book's online material.

This antenna uses slide switches to configure it as either a Yagi or a single-channel TDOA as shown in **Figure 22.59**. When used as a TDOA, a GaAs RF microcircuit switches the FM receiver between two matched dipoles at an audio frequency. To make the antenna compact, W9PE used hinged, telescopic whips as the elements; they collapse and fold parallel to the boom for storage.

To form the TDOA, the two end elements are converted to dipoles and the center element is disabled. The feed line to the receiver is switched from the center element to the RF switch output, and the end elements are connected via feed lines to the RF switch inputs.

If both TDOA coax cables are of equal length (between the antennas and switch) and the two antennas are the same distance from the transmitter (broadside to it), the signals from both antennas will be in phase. No phase difference will be detected when switching from one antenna to the other. If one antenna is a little closer to the transmitter than the other, however, there will be a phase shift when we switch antennas. When the antenna switch is at an audio rate, say 700 Hz, the repeated phase shifts result in a set of 700 Hz modulation that can be heard by the operator as in the preceding switched dual-antenna TDOA description.

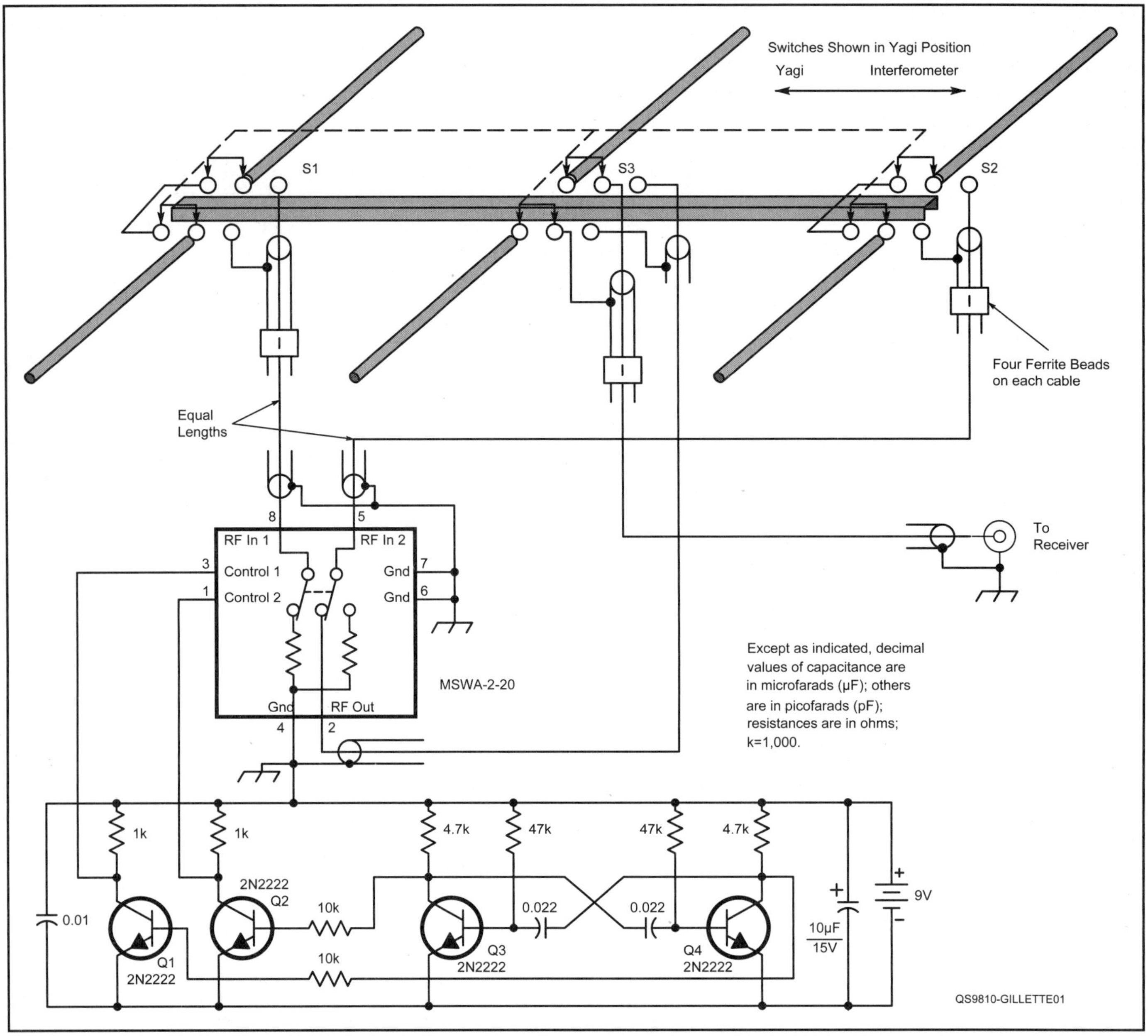

Figure 22.59 — Schematic of the Yagi/Interferometer system.

PROJECT: A TAPE-MEASURE ELEMENT YAGI FOR 2 METERS

This antenna was designed by WB2HOL while searching for a beam with a good front-to-back ratio to use in hidden transmitter hunts. It exhibits a very clean pattern and is perfect for RDF use. This beam can be constructed using only simple hand tools.

Steel "tape measure" elements fold easily when putting the antenna into a car and yet are self-supporting. They also hold up well while moving through brush. This antenna is not designed for use on a moving vehicle.

Three elements keep the boom of schedule-40 PVC from getting too long. Pipe, crosses, and tees can be found at any hardware store for the boom and element supports. A simple hairpin match consists of a 5-inch length of #14 AWG solid wire bent into a U-shape, with the two legs about ¾ inch apart. This gives a very good match across the 2-meter band with a 1-inch distance between the driven element halves.

The 1-inch-wide tape-measure elements can be cut with a pair of shears, chamfering the ends of the elements. Be careful — the edges are very sharp. Use sandpaper to dull the sharp edges and remove burrs. Electrical tape or conformal coating such as Plasti-Dip on the ends of the elements will protect against getting cut. Wear safety glasses while cutting the elements. See **Figure 22.60** for dimensions. Be cautious of the internal spring tension when disassembling the tape measure.

Wider tape measures will provide stiffer elements or stacking thinner elements. Covering the entire element with heat shrink provides additional stiffness and comes in a variety of colors. A handheld-size receiver can be mounted to the boom of a beam with plastic brackets or hook-and-loop fasteners to further integrate the package.

Scrape or sand the paint off the tape-measure elements where the feed line is attached. Most tape measures have a very durable paint finish designed to stand up to heavy use. Tin the elements before soldering the feed line to the driven element halves, then mount the driven element to the boom.

Two alternative methods can be used to attach the feed line. One method employs ring terminals on the end of the coax. The ring terminals are then secured under self-tapping screws or with 6-32 bolts and nuts into holes drilled in the driven-element halves. However, with this method, you cannot fine-tune the antenna by moving the halves of the driven element in and out.

The simplest method is simply to slide the ends of the feed line under 1½-inch stainless-steel hose clamps and tighten the clamps to hold the ends of the coax against the driven elements on the PVC cross as shown in **Figure 22.61**.

This allows fine tuning the driven element for lowest SWR

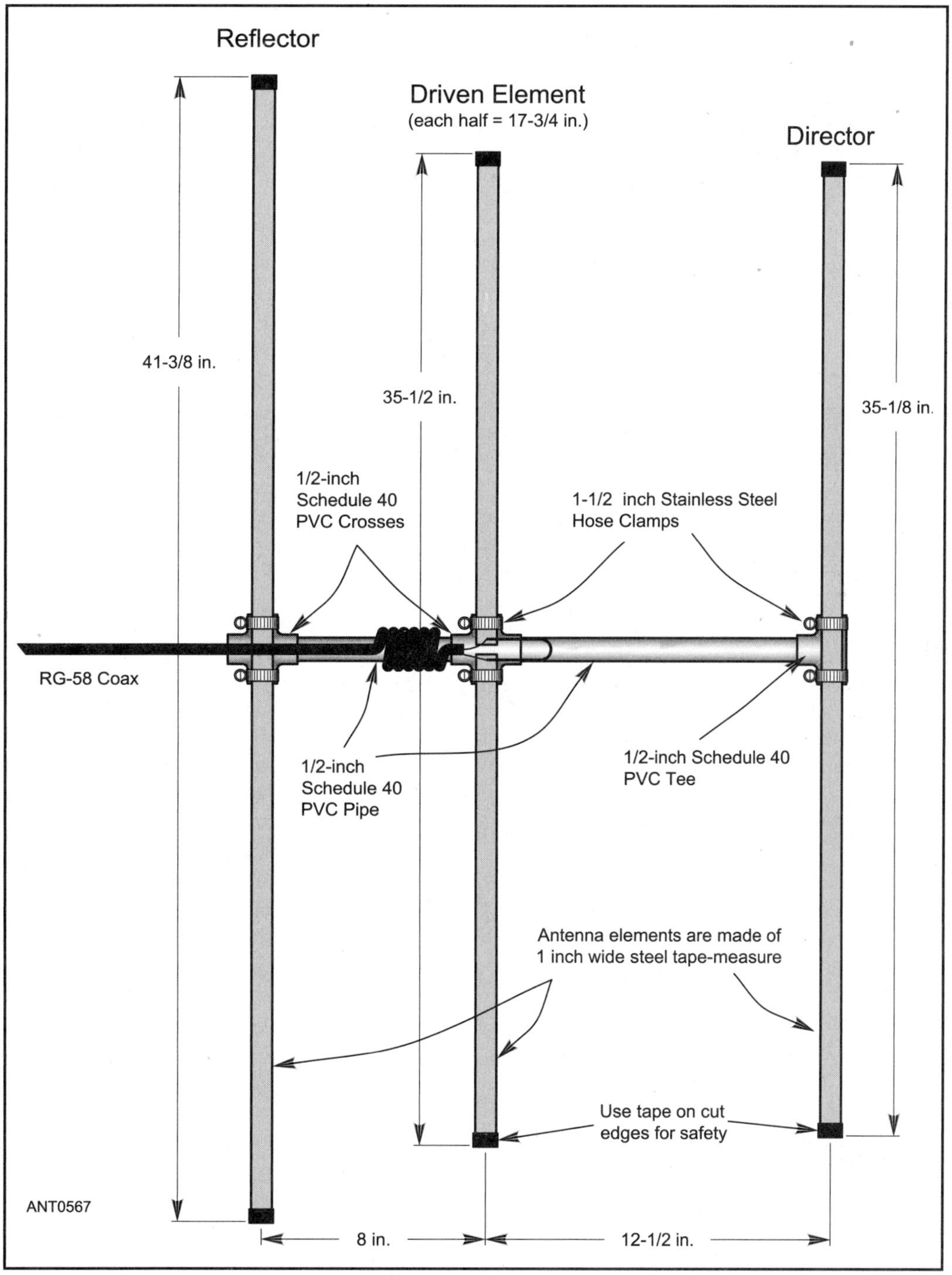

Figure 22.60 — Tape-measure beam dimensions.

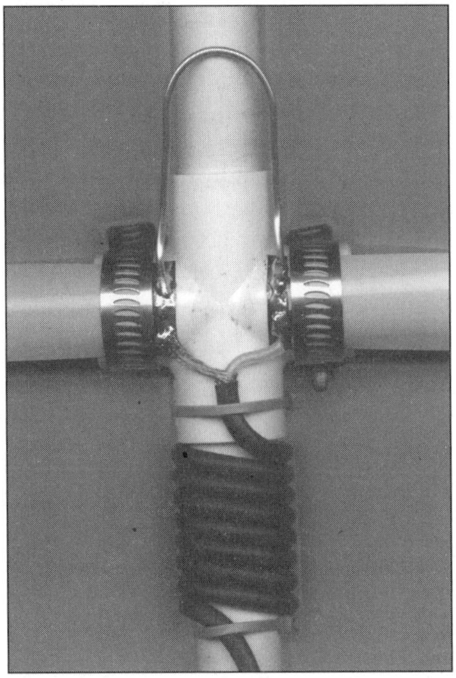

Figure 22.61 — Photo of the driven element halves mounted to PVC cross using hose clamps. The hairpin match is shown soldered to the elements along with the coaxial feed line.

Figure 22.62 — Photo of completed tape-measure beam.

simply by loosening the hose clamps and sliding the halves of the driven element in or out to lengthen or shorten the element. A 1:1 SWR can be achieved with the two elements spaced about 1 inch apart. **Figure 22.62** shows the completed antenna. For a lighter antenna, use ½" thin-wall PVC pipe for the antenna, and fiberglass strapping tape to attach the elements rather than hose clamps. A 3D-printer model file for a bracket to mount tape measure or rod elements on ½-inch PVC pipe is available online (see References and Bibliography entry for Boyd). Numerous examples of alternative methods of construction can be found online.

A balun is not essential for this antenna design when the feed line is routed perpendicularly away from the driven element. But, if desired, 8 turns of the coax feed line can be wound around the boom as shown in the photo, creating a choke to prevent feed line interaction from distorting the antenna pattern. RG-174 coax can be substituted to save weight without significantly increasing losses in the short length of feed line. The coil can be covered with electrical tape or a tennis racket grip to secure the coils to the boom and provide a non-slip handhold. An alternative to the coil approach is to slip several ferrite beads (Amidon FB-43-6301 or similar) over the outside of the coax feed line as close as possible to the feed point.

Note that almost any VHF Yagi can be built using tape measure elements. This design is optimized for a deep rear null, but other designs with higher gain and narrower beamwidth are often used. When modeling Yagis with tape measure elements, the diameter of the equivalent round element is about half of the width of the tape measure element.

PROJECT: A PORTABLE 2 METER HIGH-ACCURACY RDF SYSTEM

This is a portable RDF system that can be used while parked on a hilltop or other suitable spot. Different modes of operation provide different levels of accuracy, depending on the specific needs.

The equipment is simple: a pair of 3-element Yagis, each with a support mast (PVC pipe or telescoping painter poles), some coaxial cable and a T connector, and a few PVC pipe fittings (see **Figure 22.63A**).

If the elements are attached to the boom with clips, they are easier to remove for transport, although this is not a requirement. Other construction methods, as well as most commercial antennas, are suitable, with minor variations in the mounting hardware. The coax cables should be routed perpendicular to the elements off the back of the boom behind the reflector, to prevent distortion of the radiation pattern.

The patterns for three configurations of the system using vertical polarization are shown in Figure 22.63. For a single Yagi (Figure 22.63A), the half-power beamwidth is about 118 degrees with a free-space gain of 7.2 dBi. When the second antenna is added with 48" spacing using a PVC crossbar (Figure 22.63B), the gain increases to 10.6 dBi and the half-power beamwidth narrows to 47 degrees. This gives higher accuracy and more gain for weak signals. Wider spacings result in a narrower beamwidth, but increased side lobes. Exact gain and beamwidth values will depend on the specific antennas used, but these are representative.

Inverting one antenna at the same spacing, as shown in Figure 22.63C, creates a deep forward null and strong forward lobes at 41 degrees on either side. The lobes make it possible to resolve the 180-degree ambiguity of an Adcock system, while providing a narrow null for taking a bearing. In this configuration, the system can give better than 5-degree resolution, depending on the signal strength and receiver sensitivity.

By mounting the two antennas on separate supports and extending the cables, they can be used as a long-baseline interferometer with up to 50-foot spacing. This requires more space and time but is capable of very accurate bearings when used with a surveyor's sighting compass having ½-degree resolution.

PROJECT: A SIMPLE MOBILE MAST MOUNT

This mounting method in **Figure 22.64** makes it relatively easy to install a rotatable antenna mast for transmitter hunting in many types of vehicles. The primary requirement is that the window glass tapers inwards at the top of the window, and there is a metal section between the top of the window glass and the top of the door, which can still be opened. Specific details and dimensions will need to be determined for each vehicle. (Other mounting methods are described in the book by Moell and Curlee listed in the References and Bibliography.)

There are two parts to the mount: a base attached to the inside of the door, to support the weight of the mast and the antenna and act as a pivot; and a top bushing or sleeve to take most of the horizontal force due to wind resistance while driving.

The top sleeve can be a short piece of any sort of plastic pipe or tubing with an inside diameter that allows the mast to rotate inside it. The sleeve needs to be stiff and firm enough for the mast to pass through it and rotate smoothly inside it. A short piece of larger PVC pipe, or a straight coupler, works well. It must be secured to the top of the door so it can't slip backwards. Tie-wraps, nylon straps, or duct tape have all been used. When the door is closed, the additional pressure of the door weather stripping will help hold the mast in place. Depending on the size of the antenna and vehicle speed, the forces at this point can be high due to the sideways pressure on the mast from wind drag on the antenna.

The base portion needs to be positioned so that the mast is (nearly) vertical and at a convenient location for the operator to turn it. Often this is determined by the configuration of the inside door handle or arm rest, or whatever else is available as an attachment. If the arm rest has a hole in it or there is a map pocket, the mount can be inserted into it or a bracket can be used. Again, this must be customized for each vehicle, but Figure 22.64B suggests an idea.

The socket at the bottom of the mast can be a PVC pipe cap, with a short piece of pipe if needed. A metal washer inside the socket, or a rounded wooden plug in the bottom of the mast lubricated with candle wax, makes the mast easier to turn.

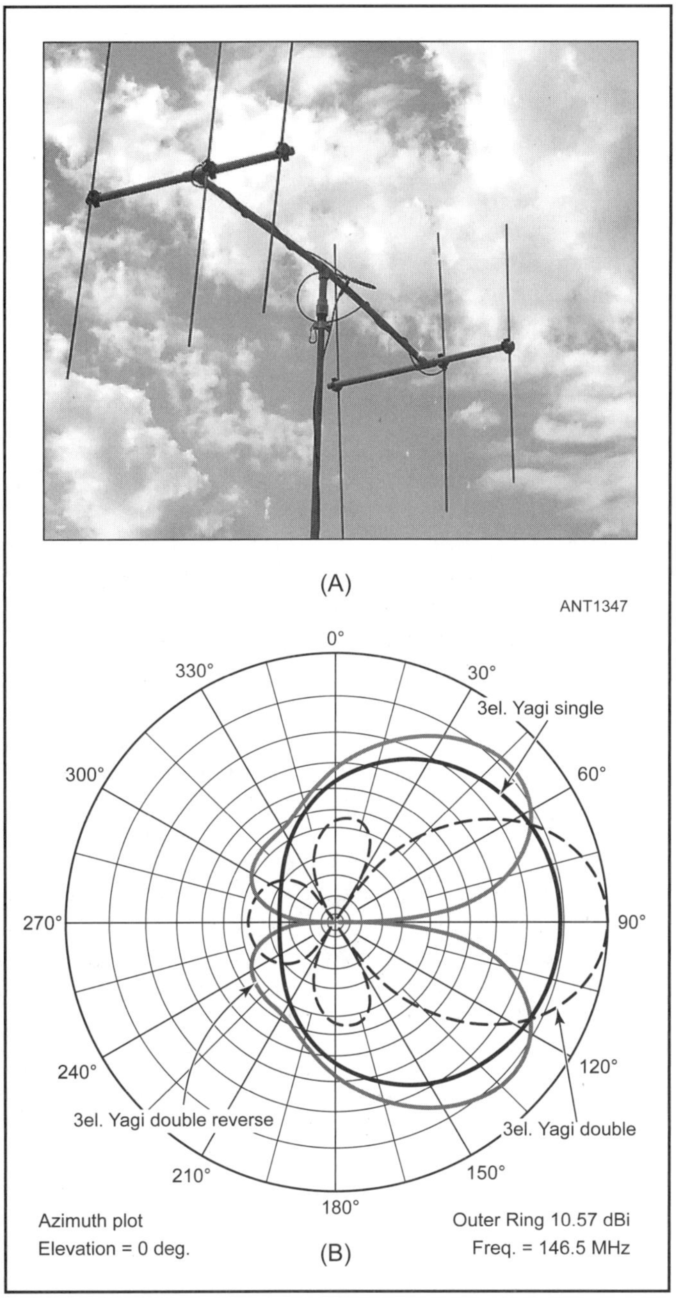

Figure 22.63 — A shows a complete two-Yagi system. The solid trace is the radiation pattern of a single vertically polarized 3-element Yagi. The dashed trace shows the narrower pattern obtained with two Yagis spaced 48" apart, fed in phase, as shown in A. The gray trace shows the pattern of the array with one antenna inverted (turned over with respect to the other Yagi) to produce a null in the forward direction with two side lobes, which can be used to distinguish between the front and rear nulls.

Figure 22.64 — A method of securing a vertical mast in a car door for RDF-ing. A shows the mast held in place by a sleeve at the top of the window frame. B shows a method of supporting the mast in the door handle.

Besides being able to open the door with the antenna mounted, this method also permits rolling the window up part way. A piece of clear acrylic or polycarbonate sheet can be cut to fit the remaining gap in the window with a slot for the mast. Some sort of rain shield on the mast can help to keep rain from running down the mast and into the car.

PVC masts may require reinforcement with a dowel or mop handle inside, depending on the size of the antenna array. The mast should also have an indicator on the mast for which way the antenna is pointing. A screw or nail stuck through the mast allows the operator to determine direction by feel. Be sure to align the antenna and mast direction indicator.

22.2.10 Direction Finding References and Bibliography

Source material and more extended discussion of topics covered in this chapter can be found in the references given below and in the textbooks listed in the References and Bibliography for the **Antenna Fundamentals** chapter.

C. F. W. Anderson, "A Crossed-Loop/Goniometer DF Antenna for 160 Meters," *The ARRL Antenna Compendium, Vol. 1,* ARRL, 1985, pp. 127-132.

G. Bonaguide, "HF DF — A Technique for Volunteer Monitoring," *QST*, Mar. 1984, pp 34-36.

D. S. Bond, *Radio Direction Finders,* 1st edition (New York: McGraw-Hill Book Co., 1944).

G. Boyd, "3D-Printed Yagi Antenna Element Bracket", **openardf.org/open-links/3d-projects-for-ardf**

R. E. Cowan and T. A. Beery, "Direction Finding with the Interferometer," *QST*, Nov. 1985, pp. 33-37.

D. DeMaw, "Beat the Noise with a Scoop Loop," *QST*, July 1977, pp 30-34.

D. DeMaw, "Maverick Trackdown," *QST*, July 1980, pp. 22-25.

T. Dorbuck, "Radio Direction-Finding Techniques," *QST*, Aug. 1975, pp. 30-36.

D. T. Geiser, "Double-Ducky Direction Finder," *QST*, July 1981, pp. 11-14.

D. T. Geiser, "The Simple Seeker," *The ARRL Antenna Compendium*, Vol. 3, p. 126.

G. Gercke, "Radio Direction/Range Finder," *73*, Dec. 1971, pp. 29-30.

W. E. Gerhard III, "Pseudo Doppler Direction Finding System for Localizing Non-Cooperative VHF Transmitters with a Hybrid UAS", Master's Thesis, Virginia Polytechnic Institute and State University, June 27, 2019

R. Gillette, "A Fox-Hunting DF Twin 'Tenna," *QST*, Oct. 1998, pp. 41-44.

N. K. Holter, "Radio Foxhunting in Europe," Parts 1 and 2, *QST*, Aug. 1976, pp. 53-57 and Nov. 1976, pp. 43-46.

D. Hunt, "A Simple Direction-Finding Receiver for 80 Meters," *QST*, Sep. 2005, pp. 36-41.

J. Isaacs, "Transmitter Hunting on 75 Meters," *QST*, June 1958, pp. 38-41.

H. Jasik, *Antenna Engineering Handbook*, 1st edition (New York: McGraw-Hill, 1961).

R. Keen, *Wireless Direction Finding*, 3rd edition (London: Wireless World).

D. Kirk, "Portable Flag Antenna for MF/HF Radio Direction Finding," *QST*, Mar. 2021, pp. 33-36.

J. Kraus, *Antennas*, 2nd edition (New York: McGraw-Hill Book Co., 1988).

J. Kraus, *Electromagnetics*, 4th edition (New York: McGraw-Hill Book Co., 1992).

B. Leskovec, "Build the HANDI-Finder!", *QST*, May 1993, p. 35. (**handi-finder.com**)

M. C. Mallette, "The Four-Way DFer," *QST*, Nov. 1995, pp. 29-35.

P. O'Dell, "Simple Antenna and S-Meter Modification for 2-Meter FM Direction Finding," Basic Amateur Radio, *QST*, Mar. 1981, pp. 43-47.

Ramo and Whinnery, Fields and Waves in Modern Radio (New York: John Wiley & Sons, 1944).

S. Scholl, DC9ST, "Introduction and Experiments on Transmitter Localization with TDOA", Software Defined Radio Academy, Friedrichshafen, Germany, July 2017 (**panoradio-sdr.de/wp-content/uploads/2017/07/sdr_tdoa_localization_online.pdf, youtube.com/watch?v=Km4TU17b05s**)

F. Terman, Electronic and Radio Engineering (McGraw-Hill Book Co., 1955).

For more information on direction finding, see *Radio Orienteering-The ARDF Handbook* by Bob Titterington, G3ORY, David Williams, M3WDD and David Deane, G3ZOI and *Transmitter Hunting: Radio Direction Finding Simplified*, by Joe Moell, KØOV, and Thomas Curlee, WB6UZZ. These books are available from your local dealer or can be ordered directly from ARRL (**arrl.org/shop**).

22.3 Amateur Radio Astronomy Antennas

The title of this section could be read in two ways: does this section apply to amateur radio operators doing astronomy or to those who are amateurs at radio astronomy? It applies to both! This section will list several radio astronomy applications and then give a summary description of antennas that are used for them. The material here is extracted from a much more extensive document in the online material, "Antennas for Radio Astronomy," developed by authors affiliated with the Society of Amateur Radio Astronomers (SARA: **radio-astronomy.org**). It includes a complete list of references for the material in this section.

In 1937 Grote Reber, W9GZF, become very interested in radio discoveries by Karl Jansky and, capitalizing on his amateur radio know-how, built his own radio telescope consisting of a parabolic dish of 31-foot (9.5 meters) in diameter in his backyard and was able to publish a series of articles in the *Astrophysical Journal*. In 1944, Reber developed a contour radio map of the sky, with brighter areas indicating richer radio sources, the brightest being the center of the Milky Way: radio astronomy was born!

Today, scientifically minded radio amateurs are involved in a number of astronomical and space weather programs. Some, including the popular Solar Eclipse QSO Parties and Eclipse and Frequency Measurement Festivals are coordinated through the HamSCI collective at **hamsci.org**. Other programs, such as HAARP (**haarp.gi.alaska.edu**), utilize radio amateurs to make observations and submit measurements. Amateurs observe and measure numerous solar and geophysical phenomena. The Radio Jove Project (**radiojove.gsfc.nasa.gov**) involves solar and planetary astronomy. Beyond the solar system, amateurs observe pulsars, Fast Radio Bursts, interstellar hydrogen emissions, and more. Each area places different requirements on the antennas and antenna systems.

The following amateur radio astronomers contributed to this section: Peter East; Wolfgang Herrmann; Dan Layne, ADØCY; Richard Marsden; Eduard Mol; Mario Natali, IØNAA; Steve Olney, VK2XV; Charles Osborne, K4CSO; Jonathan Pettingale; Alex Pettit, KK4VB; Bruce Randall, NT4RT; Whitham Reeve; Richard Russel, ACØUB; Chip Sufitchi, N2YO; Chuck Higgins; Dave Typinski, AJ4CO; and Ray Uberecken, AAØL.

Excellent introductions to radio astronomy can be found at the SARA YouTube channel maintained by Rich Russel, ACØUB, given by Ed Harfmann (**youtu.be/AOgvjRXnins**) and Dr. Wolfgang Herrmann (**youtu.be/8j1bVpC6M94**).

This section refers to Yagi, dish, and horn antennas which are described in this book's chapter **VHF, UHF, and Microwave Antennas**.

22.3.1 Overview and Theory

This sub-section was contributed by Mario Natali, IØNAA.

Radio astronomical sources can be broadly classified into two categories; thermal and nonthermal.

Thermal radiation is obtained when a black body is heated and is governed by Planck's law. The peak emission frequency depends on the temperature.

Most of the nonthermal radiation is either synchrotron radiation or Bremsstrahlung radiation, produced by a sudden slowing down or deflection of charged particles (especially electrons) passing through matter in the vicinity of the strong electric fields of atomic nuclei.

Even if radio astronomical sources can have very different mechanisms of emissions, all of them are very weak sources of radio waves and have power flux densities many orders of magnitude below those we are familiar with.

SIGNAL STRENGTH

Most cosmic radio sources generate broadband signals and thus the power received depends on the total receiver bandwidth (Total Power). This fact, connected with the need to be able to compare measures performed with antennas with different area of captures, pushed radio astronomers to use a dedicated unit of measure to specify cosmic sources signal strength. This unit is the "Jansky" (abbreviated Jy) and was named after Karl G. Jansky.

The Jy is a unit of measure of power per unit bandwidth per unit area:

$$1Jy = 10^{(-26)} Watt\ m^{(-2)} Hz^{(-1)}$$

The –26 exponent indicates the radiation must be extremely weak. Expressed as text, 1 jansky is equal to one-hundredth of one-trillionth of a trillionth of a watt per square meter per hertz!

The Jy compares with the well-known dBm (decibels above 1 mW). As an example, EME operation routinely deals with very weak signals. A typical EME signal on 1296 MHz, after a 2000 W EIRP (63 dBm) transmitted signal is reflected from the Moon, incurring a 270 dB path loss, is received with a strength of –207 dBm. If the receiving antenna has an aperture of $\lambda^2/4\pi$ and a 3000 Hz bandwidth, the –207 dBm signal is equivalent to about 2,500 Jy. Only the Sun exceeds 2500 Jy at 1400 MHz all other "strong" sources are below 2000 Jy. The strongest pulsars have a signal strength of 1 Jy, and all the others are in the range of milli Jy and micro-Jy! Thus, the receiving antenna is quite important!

RECEIVED NOISE

The analysis of thermal noise in the system will help us in understanding the concept of *antenna temperature*, which is a common way of comparing noise levels for receiving antenna systems. In a resistor at a certain temperature the so-called thermal noise is due to the random motion of electrons. (For a more complete discussion, see the expanded version of this section in the online material and the article "Noise In Receiving Systems" from the *ARRL Handbook*.)

The thermal noise voltage effective value is:

$$V_{rms} = \sqrt{4kTBR}$$

where

k = Boltzmann constant (1.38×10^{-23} J/K)
T = Temperature in Kelvin
B = Bandwidth (Hz)
R = Resistance (Ω)

Therefore, the power generated will be:

$$P = \frac{V_{rms}^{\;2}}{4R} = kTB$$

Thus, P (noise power) is proportional to T (temperature) and the term *equivalent temperature* can be used to quantify the noise.

In radio astronomy the equivalent noise temperature of an antenna that observes a non-polarized noise source at temperature T_{src} depends on the ratio between the solid angles of the source and of the antenna as shown in **Figure 22.65**. The equation that links all the parameters is:

$$T_{ant} = T_{src}\left(\frac{\Omega_S}{\Omega_A}\right)$$

Note that the symbol Ω is a solid angle and not resistance.

Now we have all the elements to measure the noise power from a cosmic source and we will use the Y-factor method of specifying noise power levels. This is done by measuring noise when pointing the antenna alternately to a reference source (usually a cold sky area) and to the source:

$$Y = \frac{P_{ON}}{P_{OFF}}$$

where

P_{ON} = Noise power when pointing the antenna to the source
P_{OFF} = Noise power when pointing the antenna to a cold sky area

We can now write the formula for noise power as Y_T from the source entirely in terms of temperatures:

$$Y_T = \frac{\left(T_{src} + T_{sys}\right)}{\left(T_{sky} + T_{sys}\right)}$$

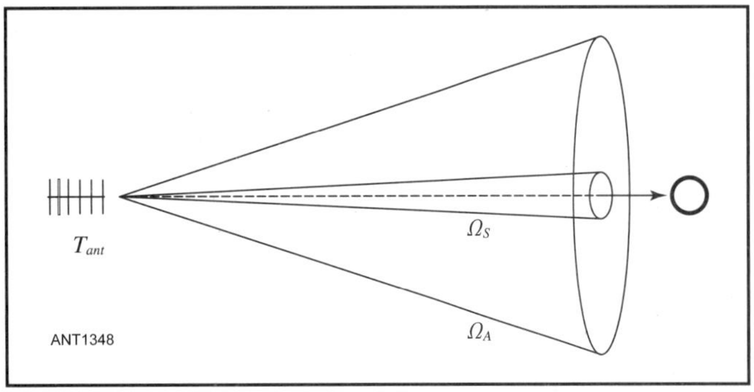

Figure 22.65 — Determining the equivalent noise temperature of an antenna using solid angles. See text for explanation.

where

T_{src} = Antenna equivalent temperature while pointing cosmic source to be analyzed
T_{sys} = Receiving system total noise temperature
T_{sky} = Antenna equivalent temperature while pointing at a cold sky area (this factor can be neglected most of the time)

Y can also be expressed in dB as $10 \log_{10} Y_T$.

PREDICTING SOURCE DETECTABILITY

MURMUR (**i0naa.altervista.org/index.php**) is one of several programs that can help in predicting what cosmic sources are detectable with a certain set-up. It has the capability to predict the expected signal strength of strong cosmic sources such as the Sun, Moon, Cassiopeia A, Cygnus A, Taurus A, Sagittarius A, Virgo A and Quasar 3C273.

Inputs to *MURMUR* include the basic characteristics of the antenna and of the receiving system and, based on those inputs, shows predictions of Pulsar detectability, and expected Y-factor noise of several noise sources. **Figure 22.66** shows a typical main screen of *MURMUR*.

22.3.2 Solar Radio Emissions and Aurora Radio Reflections

This subsection was contributed by Whitham D. Reeve.

SOLAR RADIO EMISSIONS

Solar radio emissions are a component of space weather and have a very wide frequency spectrum; however, depending on the intervening ionosphere's condition, the emissions are blocked by the ionosphere below around 15 MHz. The blockage can occur at lower or higher frequencies, but observations as low as 5 MHz are very rare at most locations on Earth.

Solar radio emissions are more intense at lower frequencies, so HF and low-VHF antennas are the best types for solar observations. Specific frequency bands have been set aside for radio astronomy purposes and observers may wish to try listening to the Sun in the center of those bands shown in **Table 22.3**. However, above around 85 MHz interference from terrestrial transmitters, such as FM and TV broadcast transmitters and mobile telephone systems, becomes a serious impediment to observations of wideband emissions.

The ideal antenna for solar radio observations is a wideband, steerable, dual-polarized, directional beam antenna operating from 10 to 85 MHz. A rotator for elevation and azimuth may be used to track the Sun but a fixed antenna pointed south may be used in a drift-scan mode in which the Sun crosses the antenna beam each day as Earth rotates. The drift-scan mode works best with antennas that have relative wide horizontal and vertical beamwidths. At higher latitudes, the antenna could be made adjustable in elevation to compensate for the Sun's elevation as the seasons change, but this may not be necessary if the antenna's vertical beamwidth is large enough to encompass the Sun's year-around elevation changes.

Most solar radio emissions are unpolarized, but some are

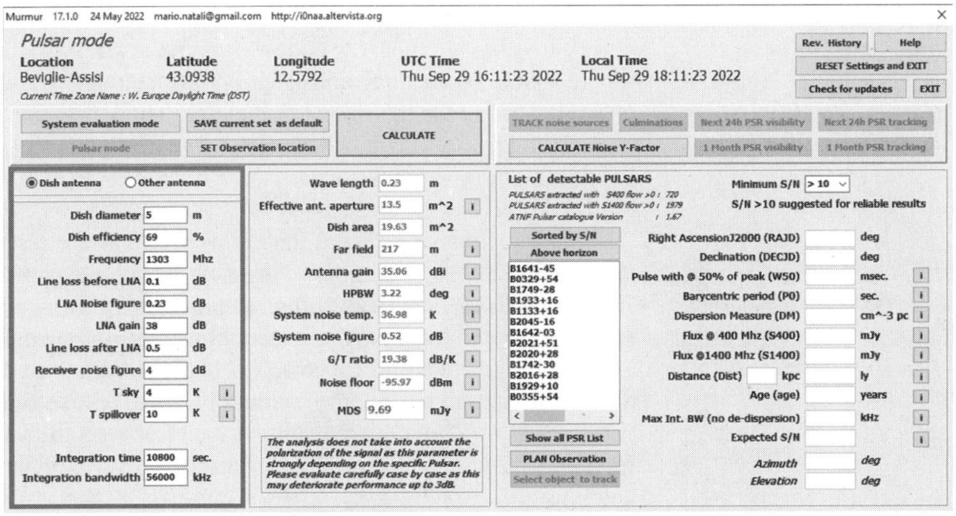

Figure 22.66 — A typical main screen for *MURMUR*, which is used to predict cosmic source detectability.

Table 22.3
Radio Astronomy Frequency Allocations, USA only

13.360-13.410 MHz	25.550-25.670 MHz	37.5-38.0 MHz	73.0-74.6 MHz	406.1-410.0 MHz
608-614 MHz	1400-1427 MHz	1610.6-1613.8 MHz	1660.0-1670.0 MHz	2655-2690 MHz
4990-5000 MHz	10.68-10.7 GHz	15.35-15.4 GHz	22.21-22.5 GHz	23.6-24.0 GHz
31.3-31.8 GHz	42.5-43.5 GHz	51.4-54.25 GHz	58.2-59 GHz	64-65 GHz
86-92 GHz	105-116 GHz	164-168 GHz	182-185 GHz	217-231 GHz
265-275 GHz				

characterized by significant right or left circular polarization. A linear polarized antenna may be used for most observations but, if polarization is important to the observer, circular polarized antennas are needed. Circular polarizations may be derived from linear crossed-dipoles or crossed multielement antennas with suitable coupling components such as a quadrature coupler.

High gain antennas are not usually necessary at the lower frequencies because solar radio emissions can be quite intense, rising 30 to 40 dB above the HF background noise during strong solar flares. However, solar radio emissions at VHF and higher are relatively weak except for an occasional strong flare. For observations in the UHF band, antenna arrays will improve observations success.

Because of their wideband nature, Log Periodic Dipole Array (LPDA) antennas work quite well for receiving solar radio emissions in linear polarization. See **Figure 22.67** and **22.68** for examples of LPDAs used for radio astronomy. The gain of typical LPDA antennas is modest, on the order of 6 to 8 dB when well clear of the ground and up to 5 to 6 dB higher when within several wavelengths of the ground. Two identical LPDA antennas installed with cross polarization (for example, one vertical and the other horizontal) and coupled with a quadrature coupler may be used to receive circular polarized emissions. See the chapter **Frequency-Independent Antennas** for more information on LPDAs.

The Long Wavelength Array (LWA) antenna in **Figure 22.69** is an omnidirectional, tied-fork, active cross-dipole antenna with an operating frequency range of about 5 to above 100 MHz that also works quite well for receiving solar radio emissions. Because of FM broadcast transmitter interference, the antenna usually is not used above 85 MHz. The LWA antenna has the advantage of being ground mounted, so no

Figure 22.67 — Tower-mounted, horizontally polarized, rotatable LPDA antenna with 8 elements and design frequency range of 18-32 MHz. (Photo by Whitham Reeve)

tower or elevated structure is needed. It can be configured for circular polarizations by connecting the output from each dipole through a broadband quadrature coupler. The peak gain of the LWA antenna is about 8 dB over moderate ground; the antenna pattern is mushroom-shaped with a vertical 3 dB beamwidth of approximately 100°.

Figure 22.68 — Gable-mounted, Sun-tracking, 21-element LPDA antenna with design frequency range of 50 to 1300 MHz used in the e-CALLISTO solar radio spectrometer network. (Photo by Whitham Reeve)

Figure 22.69 — The Long Wavelength Array (LWA) Antenna is a ground-mounted, crossed-dipole about 1.5 m high. The horizontal support structure fastened to the middle of the mast is made from non-conductive fiberglass rods. An important part of the installation is the 3 × 3 m ground screen made from galvanized fence wire. This antenna is multipurpose and is used for solar radio observations in the e-CALLISTO solar radio spectrometer network and HF radio propagation experiments. (Photo by Whitham Reeve)

Simple half-wavelength dipole antennas, folded dipoles and many other configurations of wire antennas work well for observing relatively narrow bandwidths in the HF band. The dipole should be cut for a consistently quiet frequency above 15 MHz found by experimentation. A frequency between 20 and 25 MHz with a half-wavelength from 7.5 to 6.0 meters, is a good starting point at many locations. The axis of the dipole should be oriented east-west.

If observations of weaker solar radio emissions are desired at VHF and above, where there are many more weak emissions than strong ones, a low noise amplifier is recommended at the antenna to improve the system noise performance. For example, the Front-End Electronics (FEE) circuitry used in the LWA antenna has an approximately 2.7 dB noise figure and 35 dB gain. The high gain allows the FEE to set the noise figure of the antenna-receiver system and ensures that the antenna does not limit system sensitivity. Because of the FEE's high gain, attenuators are generally needed at the receiver RF input to prevent overdriving the receiver, something that needs to be considered for any amplified antenna system. Low noise amplifiers are almost always used with LPDA antennas that operate in the VHF band. More information about the LWA is available at **reeve.com/RadioScience/Antennas/ActiveCrossed-Dipole/LWA_Antenna.htm**.

AURORA RADIO REFLECTIONS

Aurora radio reflections are an interesting phenomenon that involves propagation of a signal from a transmitter to an active aurora region where the signal is reflected towards a receiver, a form of bistatic radar. The incident path usually is along a narrow northerly azimuth with the reflection path along a similarly narrow southerly azimuth. (The aurora is discussed in more detail in the **Propagation of Radio Waves** chapter.)

Aurora radio reflections have been observed over wide frequency ranges from HF to UHF. Observers at latitudes above about 50° have a better chance of observing aurora radio reflections during modest geomagnetic disturbances but stronger storms move the aurora to lower latitudes, which allows the reflections to be detected by lower-latitude observers.

The reflections take place in the E region at altitudes of approximately 100 to 120 km. Except in the HF band, line-of-site propagation is required between the transmitter and reflection region and between the reflection region and the receiver. Distances of 500 to 1000 km or more from the receiver to the reflection point are typical. Because of the long distances involved, an antenna that works well at low elevation angles is best.

The ideal antenna for aurora radio reflections is a linear polarized, narrowband, narrow beamwidth antenna, such as a single multielement Yagi antenna or Yagi array. Crossed-Yagi antennas setup for circular polarization also may be used. The same antennas used for solar radio observations discussed above have been used successfully for observations of aurora radio reflections in the HF band. Because of their relatively low gain, single dipole antennas and similar wire antennas may not work well for aurora radio observations.

If observations of the phenomenon, and not communications, are the only goal, omnidirectional radio beacon transmitters can be monitored for reflections with a directional receive antenna pointed northward. However, the beacon transmitter and receiver stations should be approximately along a north-south line for best results. Spectrum observations are best made with very narrow post-detection (audio) bandwidths on the order of below 50 to around 200 Hz. Software used for observing meteor trail reflections also works for aurora radio reflections.

22.3.3 Active Antenna for HF Radio Astronomy

This subsection was contributed by Bruce Randall, NT4RT.

An active antenna is an antenna where an active part of the receiver (an amplifier) is an integral part of the antenna itself. (Active antennas are also discussed in this chapter's section on MF and HF Receiving Antennas.) The Long Wavelength Array (LWA) described in the previous sub-section on Solar Radio Emissions is a good example of an active antenna for radio astronomy at 20 to 80 MHz. One of these antennas occupies a 2.5-meter diameter circle on the ground and is about 1.5 meters tall. The Murchison Widefield Array (MWA) covers 70 to 300 MHz in a manner similar to the LWA. This sub-section describes a prototype active antenna that is used for observations between 15 and 40 MHz.

Horizontal polarization is generally more appropriate for radio astronomy. A vertical polarization antenna close to the ground has a strong response at the horizon and a null overhead. A horizontal polarized antenna has the opposite. HF sky wave signals arrive at low angles, so the null at the horizon helps reduce this interference and atmospheric static. The path through the ionosphere for radio astronomy signals is unobstructed at the high angles where the horizontal polarization performs the best. This subsection is focused on antennas for use between 15 MHz and 40 MHz.

A receiving short dipole or monopole probe much shorter than a wavelength ($<< \lambda$) has a capacitive source impedance with a very low series resistive part. A preamplifier that has very high capacitive input impedance is needed. The length and diameter of the elements set the impedance. This source impedance and the preamp make a voltage divider that loses some signal level. The dipole source impedance should be lower (more capacitance), and the preamp impedance should be higher (less capacitance) for the lowest loss. (A detailed analysis of the preamp requirements and circuits is presented in "Antennas for Radio Astronomy" which is available in the online material.)

The dipole elements used are each 0.6 meter long for a total length of 1.2 meters. They are made of US "1/2 inch" electrical conduit which is 18 mm outside diameter. This conduit is also sold as "1/2-inch EMT" It is supported by a frame of PVC plumbing pipe. **Figure 22.70** shows the 18 mm tubing and the PVC plumbing pipe. Notice PVC pipe is lashed to a camera tripod for testing. The figure shows how the prototype preamp assembly is attached to the dipole. A more substantial mounting and a weatherproof box are needed for unattended observations. The cable to the building where the SDR and computer are located is about 30 meters of low loss 75 Ω RG11 coaxial cable.

Figure 22.71A shows the active antenna system consisting of the antenna equivalent circuit, a filter, and FET amplifier input impedance. Because these active antennas cover a very wide range of frequencies, preamp overload could be a problem if a broadcast site is close by. A filter is needed to limit input signal strength in the AM broadcast band and above 54 MHz where TV and FM broadcast stations are located.

Each half of the dipole is treated as a separate antenna and combined in a differential circuit as shown in Figure 22.71B. The preamplifier modules used for prototype evaluation are self-contained commercial "mini-whip" units purchased online. The output of the modules, labeled "MWEB" in Figure 22.71C, are combined in the differential input circuit shown in Figure 22.71C. The output of the MMIC buffer amplifier then drives the RG-11 feed line to the receiver.

22.3.4 Sudden Ionospheric Disturbances

This subsection was contributed by Jonathan Pettingale and Richard Marsden.

Sudden Ionospheric Disturbances (*SIDs*) are caused by X-rays and extreme ultraviolet radiation (EUV) from solar flares. (See the **Propagation of Radio Waves** chapter for more information on SIDs and related phenomena.) The effects are measured by tracking changes in the signal strength of Very Low Frequency (VLF) radio transmissions as they are reflected from the ionosphere. The VLF signals come from transmitters used to communicate with submarines and are of constant power. The received signal strength of these VLF waves changes as the flares affect the ionosphere by adding extra ionization — thus changing where the VLF waves are reflected in the ionosphere. Continuously tracking the received signal strength of the sources allows changes to be detected and hence the effects of the solar flares to be detected.

The transmitter stations are usually very large, covering many kilometers. since the wavelength of the frequency being transmitted, typically 10 to 50 kHz, is about 6 to 30 kilometers. A suitable antenna for observing SIDs is a wire-loop antenna.

Figure 22.70 — The active dipole is constructed from ½-inch (18-mm) EMT and mounted on PVC pipe. The antenna preamp is attached directly to the feed point. (Photo by Bruce Randall, NT4RT)

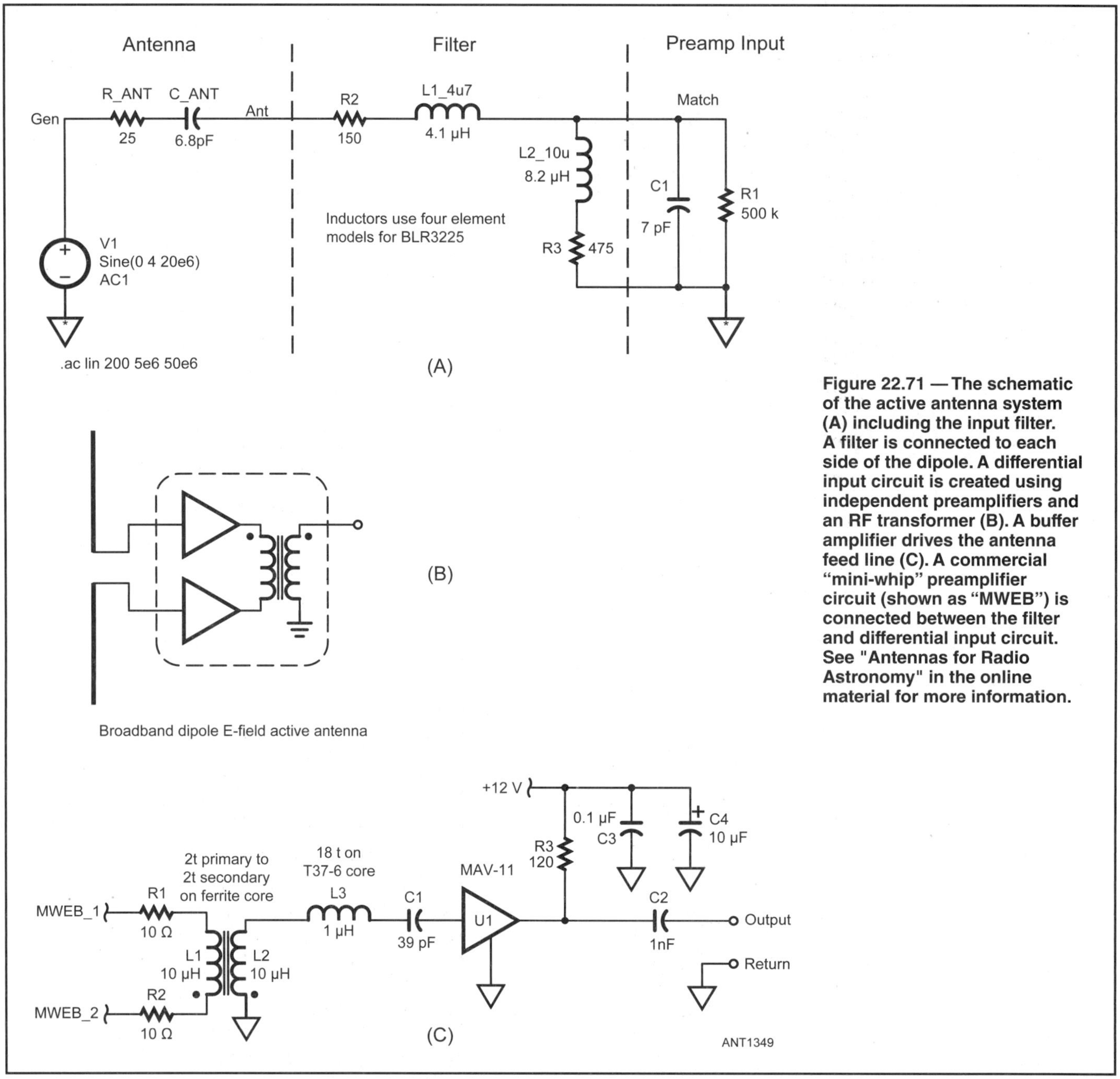

Figure 22.71 — The schematic of the active antenna system (A) including the input filter. A filter is connected to each side of the dipole. A differential input circuit is created using independent preamplifiers and an RF transformer (B). A buffer amplifier drives the antenna feed line (C). A commercial "mini-whip" preamplifier circuit (shown as "MWEB") is connected between the filter and differential input circuit. See "Antennas for Radio Astronomy" in the online material for more information.

Figure 22.72 — Three examples of multi-turn frame loops used for receiving VLF signals to study SIDs.

There is no standard size or shape of antenna. The loop does not need to be built to precise dimensional specifications and exact tolerances. A loop antenna can be built using easily acquired parts and supplies. (Frame-type loops are discussed in the previous sections of this chapter.) A small (1 meter wide) antenna with lots of loops of wire or a large antenna (2 or more meters wide) with fewer loops of wire is satisfactory. Typical loop antennas for receiving SIDs are shown in **Figure 22.72**.

Typical signals received from VLF transmitters are on the order of ~0.1 millivolts. Receiving signal strength can be improved by increasing the number of turns or enlarging the size of the loop. As the number of turns increases, the distributed capacitance also increases, which lowers the resonant frequency. Also, when the number of turns increases, the resistance of the wire also increases, causing the amplitude of the signal to drop. A tuning circuit can also be added, to tune the loop to the frequency of interest.

A suitable receiver for the loop antenna is a computer sound card. A preamplifier is required due to the low voltage from the antenna. A commercially available antenna and preamp with software for data analysis is available from the Society of Amateur Radio Astronomers (SARA) under their SuperSID program. Instructions for building a SuperSID antenna can be found at **solar-center.stanford.edu/SID/docs/SID_Antenna.pdf.**

An example of signals received during an M-class solar flare are shown in **Figure 22.73**. The transmitting stations were located in Maine (NAA), Washington (NLK), and North Dakota (NML). The receiver and antenna were location in Wichita Falls, Texas.

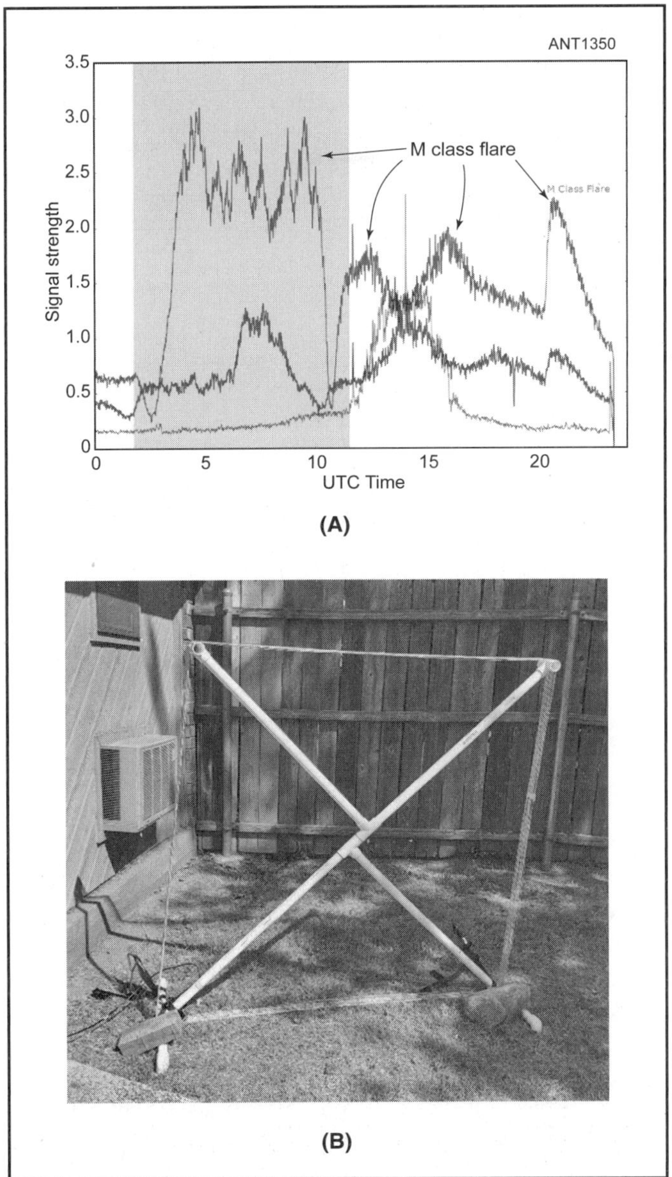

Figure 22.73 — VLF signals received (A) from stations NAA, NLK, and NML during an M-class solar flare and the SuperSID antenna (B). (Photos by Richard Marsden)

22.3.5 Meteor Detection

This sub-section was written by Chip Sufitchi, N2YO.

Meteor echoes are signal received after reflecting from an ionized meteor trail. (See the **Propagation of Radio Waves** chapter for information on meteor scatter propagation.) The reflected signals are from a powerful transmitter in a VHF band (ideally a tower broadcasting analog TV on channels 2-5) located far enough away that direct signals are not received but within range of a meteor scatter reflection. A standard VHF TV antenna is used for receiving the signals.

The meteor detector at **livemeteors.com** is located in the Washington, DC metropolitan area. The 4-element receiving Yagi antenna shown in **Figure 22.74** is aimed at a TV tower in Toronto, Canada broadcasting analog TV on channel 2 around 55.24 MHz. Another transmitter on channel 3 analog TV, around 61.260 MHz, is located near Timmins, Ontario. The receiver is an RTL-SDR and the display software is *SDR#*. Live streaming can be watched at **livemeteors.com** and on YouTube Live.

The full system consists of a 5-element VHF Yagi antenna pointing to Ontario, a VHF TV preamplifier, and 50 feet of 75 Ω RG-6 coaxial cable to the RTL-SDR receiver. Any preamplifier with a noise figure of 1 dB or less will work. The system uses *Radio-SkyPipe* as a "strip chart" style recording program to capture meteor detections. The program runs in server mode so that other *Radio-SkyPipe* users can connect remotely to the system and receive information in real time.

The strength of the signal will vary according to the distance from transmitter and the power of the transmitter. For the low VHF channels (2-6), the antenna should provide a good match between 54 and 88 MHz. A 70 MHz (4-meter band in Europe) Yagi will work for these channels. A simple dipole with adjustable telescopic arms will receive meteor echoes even without a preamplifier. The dipole, RTL/SDR, and a laptop make a good portable solution to provide demonstrations or use the system in the field.

Figure 22.74 — A 4-element Yagi for low-VHF channels on a 15-foot mast is suitable for receiving meteor echoes. The height is not critical. (Photo by Chip Sufitchi, N2YO)

22.3.6 Radio Jupiter Project

This sub-section was contributed by Chuck Higgins and Dave Typinski, AJ4CO.

Because of a strong magnetic field, energetic radiation belts, and a rich environment of plasma, Jupiter emits a broad spectrum of radio emissions from below 1 kHz to above 300 GHz. Called *Jovian decameter* (*DAM*) emission, the range occurs from 3 MHz to 39.5 MHz having a peak spectral power at about 10 MHz. The lower limit on observations from ground-based observatories is generally above 15 MHz due to attenuation by the Earth's ionosphere. NASA's Radio JOVE Project (**radiojove.gsfc.nasa.gov**) was created to encourage students and amateur scientists to receive and study these emissions with their own easy to construct radio telescopes.

Jovian DAM is most often emitted from points along the plasma flux tube within the Jovian magnetic field that connects Jupiter and its satellite Io. Common spectral features in Jovian radio emissions include frequency envelopes, spectral arc structures, L-bursts, S-bursts, N events, and modulation lanes. These features depend both on the frequency and the Io/non-Io source parameters. An excellent observation of a Jovian Io-B is shown in **Figure 22.75**.

Due to increasing ionospheric absorption "cutting off" signals below 15 MHz, and due to the Jupiter emission signal strength decreasing above 24 MHz, the optimal frequency range for ground-based Jupiter observations is from 18 to 22 MHz. Therefore, antennas designed for a center frequency near 20 MHz (wavelength = 15 m) are ideal for Jupiter, and beneficially, also work very well to observe solar radio emissions. A single half-wave wire dipole antenna is a simple and inexpensive antenna to detect the strongest Jupiter radio signals. Other antennas that work well include a 2-element Moxon, a 2- or 3-element Yagi, quads, log periodics, helixes, and polarimeters.

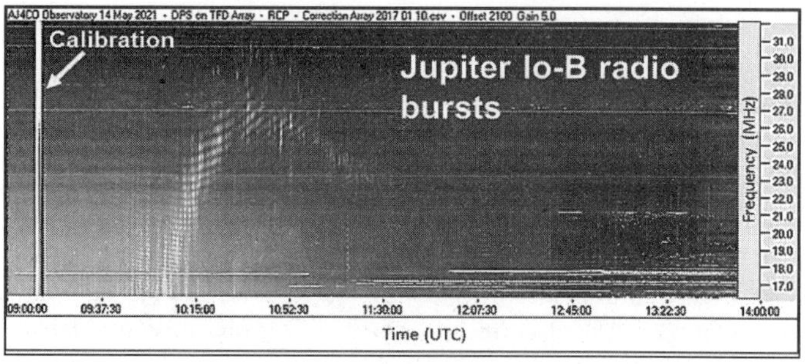

Figure 22.75 — A frequency-time spectrogram showing radio emissions from Jupiter in the range of 16 – 32 MHz over a time-span of five hours showing common spectral features like arc structures, L-bursts. The curved bands are Faraday lanes caused by propagation through Earth's ionosphere. (Graphic courtesy of Dave Typinski, AJ4CO, and Chuck Higgins)

For a 20 MHz dipole, the tip-to-tip length is 23.4 ft (7.1 m). To achieve an antenna beaming pattern (i.e., maximum gain) pointing upward, the dipole is mounted horizontally a quarter wavelength (λ/4) above the ground. The added benefit of a horizontal dipole with an upward-pointing beam is that it is less sensitive to terrestrial interference, most of which comes from the horizon. The λ/4 height is optimal to account for reflected waves off the ground adding together in phase (constructive interference). The ground acts like a reflector to radio waves if the conductivity of the soil is of good quality; a moist, rich soil is very good quality. Changing

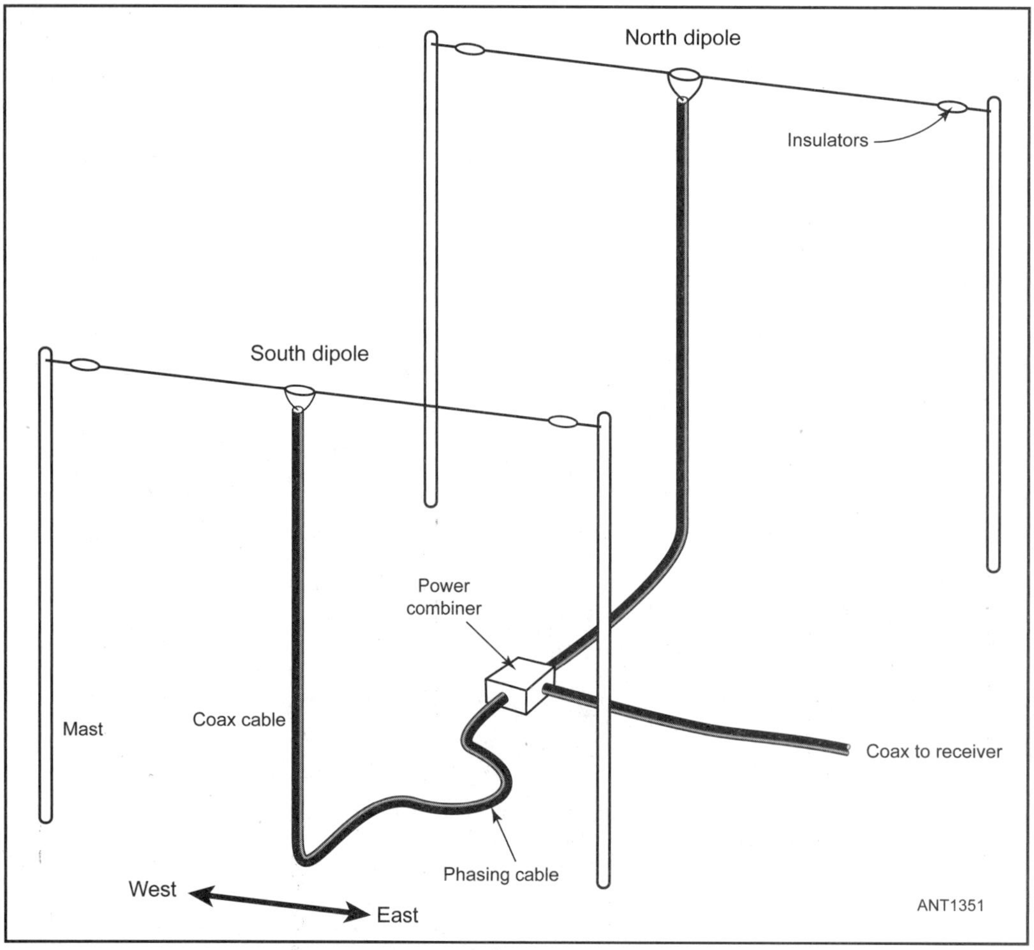

Figure 22.76 — The Radio JOVE dual dipole array with a phasing cable inserted in the transmission line leading from the south dipole to the power combiner. This is a configuration for northern hemisphere observers. For an observer in the southern hemisphere the phasing cable would be installed in the line leading from the north dipole to the power combiner.

the height of the dipole antenna will change the beam pattern. For example, a dipole located a half wavelength ($\lambda/2$) above ground will cause a null overhead and a split beam 30° above the horizon.

To detect weaker radio emissions Radio JOVE developed an antenna array using two dipole antennas to achieve almost twice the gain of a single dipole as shown in **Figure 22.76**. Without a phasing cable, the two antennas produce an overhead beam, somewhat narrower than that of a single dipole alone. It is an important principle of antennas that the higher the gain the narrower will be the antenna beam. The power combiner adds the two signals together and since they are in-phase with one another the resulting signal sent to the receiver is twice that of a single dipole alone.

The array pattern can be steered to the proper elevation with a *phasing cable* as shown in the figure. By delaying the signal from the south dipole by the proper amount of time, the waves from each antenna will arrive in-phase at the combiner. The correct amount of delay depends on the location where the array will be erected. (See the Radio JOVE website for more information.)

Jupiter's DAM radio emissions are highly circularly polarized. A crossed-Yagi or crossed log periodic antenna gives the ability to detect right-hand (RCP) and left-hand circular (LCP) polarization. A square array of four dipoles can be made into a polarimeter (an instrument that shows RCP and LCP signals separately) by combining the signals from the four dipoles using a hybrid ring.

SDR receivers with a wide bandwidth can be matched with wideband antennas to create a radio spectrograph displaying frequency-time data as in Figure 22.75. The advantage is that spectral information about the radio emitter leads to a much better understanding of the physics behind the radio wave generation and propagation. These multifrequency radios can be matched with wideband antennas providing excellent spectral coverage of Jupiter or solar radio emissions. Wire dipoles allow for 3-4 MHz of bandwidth, so an excellent spectrograph can be made of an SDR radio and a dual dipole antenna (see the Radio JOVE 2.0 system). For wider bandwidths, a *terminated folded dipole* (*TFD*) square array can provide excellent spectral coverage and polarization. However, adding polarization and beam steering to wideband systems makes them a bit more complicated and expensive.

22.3.7 Hydrogen 21-cm Line

This sub-section was contributed by Charles Osborne, K4CSO.

Neutral hydrogen (H1) is one of the most abundant elements in the universe. H1 emits a signal on 1420.4057 MHz that is found in every direction. Because it is such an abundant element, by mapping where its emission signal is found, we also learn the location of many cosmic sources and structures. This sub-section contains descriptions of several antenna systems used to receive the neutral hydrogen signal, including several dishes and feed systems.

DRIFT SCANNING

Radio astronomers use techniques not unlike optical astronomers, taking time exposure pictures. In radio this involves averaging sometimes hundreds of thousands of measurements to reduce the random noise, gradually exposing the hydrogen signal at more and more distance. The simplest technique called *drift scanning* just allows the sky to move in front of a dish fixed pointed at a particular elevation corresponding to declination. The sky is moving by at 15° per hour, so integration times longer than a few minutes begins to smear out details.

By detecting the various spiral arms of the Milky Way galaxy one can gradually improve the system performance until we are seeing just beyond the galactic center at 30,000 to 40,000 light years. (By comparison, moonbounce is a distance of 500,000 miles, which is only 2.6 light seconds.)

More advanced amateur radio astronomers use tracking antennas to follow a portion of the sky sometimes for many hours. Larger systems can detect objects millions of light years away by integration for hours instead of minutes. The challenges and rewards come from building system electronics stable and sensitive enough to make measurements over hours that can be added in software to achieve the desired accuracy and sensitivity.

PROJECT: HORN AND 3.7-METER PARABOLIC DISH SYSTEM

The horn antenna in **Figure 22.77** is a *Standard Gain Horn* (*SGH*) normally used to compare gains on an antenna range. Its gain is 16.05 dBi. The horn dimensions are 26.25" × 20.33" at the mouth. The horn is 22" deep where it enters the 3.25"

Figure 22.77 — A simple horn antenna for detecting neutral hydrogen emissions and a parabolic 3.7-meter dish with a septum polarized feed. (Photos by Charles Osborne, K4CSO)

Table 22.4
Antenna Analysis by K4CSO

	Standard Gain Horn	*3.7-Meter Dish*
T_{hot} (85°F = 302° K)	–66.28dB	–66.63dB
Sun Noise (Solar Flux 124)	1.03dB	11.05 dB
T_{cold} (15° Kelvin)	–68.78dB	–69.39dB
Y-Factor	2.5dB	2.76dB

× 6.5" ID waveguide section with a length is 8". The probe is placed 2.22" from the back wall short centered on the wide dimension of the waveguide. The horn is approximately equivalent to a 24" dish giving a beamwidth of 26 degrees. It can detect hydrogen emissions from strong sources like the galactic center near the constellation of Sagittarius.

The parabolic dish in the background of Figure 22.77 is a GigaSat FA-370 with a focal length of 54 inches, resulting in a 0.375 *focus to diameter ratio* (*F/D*) at prime focus. It has an estimated 31.5 dBi gain, 4.3-degree beam width (11 dB Sun noise at a solar flux index of 124).

The feed is a Septum Polarized (circular polarized for 1296 EME TX/RX) based on an OK1DFC design (**ok1dfc.com/eme/Technic/septum/W1GHZanalysis.pdf**). The feed is 6 × 6 × 24-inch square aluminum with an 18-inch diameter x 3-inch deep cake pan for the scalar choke ring. Positioning the choke ring fore and aft a few centimeters from the throat of the horn helps match the feed beamwidth to the angle needed for the dish focal length to get the best signal to noise ratio. Moving it forward on the feed narrows the feed beamwidth. Pulling it back widens the feed beamwidth.

The dish uses an Ocean Server OS5000 3axis magnetometer for pointing readout. Positioning is elevation over azimuth driven by 18VDC cordless drill motors with jackscrews for elevation and a chain drive for azimuth control.

The RF receive chain consists of:

LNA: SAWBird+H1 40 dB gain with 0.6 dB NF (noise figure)

Feedline: 100 feet RG-214 (-15dB loss)

PostAmp: NoElec LaNA 16 dB gain with 1 dB NF

Receiver: RTL-SDR.com V3

Software: *SDR#*

Antenna analysis was conducted on the horn and dish antennas with the results shown in **Table 22.4**.

Results show the *SDR#* screen with the H1 detection of the galactic Milky Way plane. Multiple spiral arms are seen. Emissions are also Doppler shifted. The peaks below 1420.405 MHz are red-shifted lower in frequency because that material is receding from us at up to 100 km/sec. The other peak above 1420.405 is blue-shifted higher in frequency because it is moving toward us at similar speeds.

PROJECT: PARABOLIC DISH REFLECTOR AND LOOP FEED CHOKE RINGED REFLECTOR

This sub-section was contributed by Alex Pettit, KK4VB and is partially derived from the work of Rastislav Galuscak, OM6AA.

One of the more easily observed radio frequency structures is RF radiation at 21 centimeters from the large neutral hydrogen clouds within the Milky Way. Although not a trivial task, shape, intensity, and velocity quantitative measurements can be performed with parabolic reflectors as small as 1 meter in diameter.

A 31-page document by OM6AA (**om6aa.eu/Loop_Feed_with_enhanced_performance.pdf**) describes a 23 cm/13 cm dish loop feed system in sufficient detail to scale to 21 cm radio telescope reception. It consists of a soldered assembly of copper PC board base, lathe turned feed-through, and sheet brass choke ring. It is time consuming to construct but performed extremely well. The dimensions and the constructed model are shown in **Figure 22.78A** and **B**.

KK4VB experimented with more off-the-shelf items to derive an antenna matching size and performance of the OM6AA design and found an easily constructed alternative (see Figure 22.63C) with a total parts cost of approximately $25. Operational tests have shown its performance equal to the more complex copper/brass OM6AA antenna. Construction details and instructions are given in the document "Antennas for Radio Astronomy" in the online material.

With this feed system mounted to a 1-meter diameter reflector and the appropriate electronics and software, you can make measurements of signal strength and plot regions of neutral hydrogen clouds within the Milky Way such as in **Figure 22.79**.

PROJECT: HYDROGEN LINE BEGINNER'S TELESCOPE

This sub-section was contributed by Michiel Klaasen.

The hardware of the telescope (receiving antenna) consists of an obsolete satellite TV dish, and a paint bucket. The electronic components are a low-cost preamplifier, a satellite inline amplifier used as a power inserter, and an RTL-SDR receiver. The preamplifier could be replaced by also an inline amplifier.

Figure 22.80A shows the completed telescope. Complete instructions are available in "Antennas for Radio Astronomy" in the online material. An example of a 5-minute integrated sample is shown in Figure 22.80B. By using the drift scanning method and adjusting the telescope elevation a map of the sky at 21 cm wavelengths can be made by this modest instrument.

Another simple system is described in the online *IEEE Spectrum* article, "Build your own radio telescope: Track the movement of the Milky Way" by David Schneider at (**ieeexplore.ieee.org/document/8847581**) The author describes the use of aluminum flashing and a rectangular solvent can to build 1420 MHz horn antenna, including placement of the coaxial transition probe. An inexpensive SDR "dongle" and *HPSDR* software are used as the receiver.

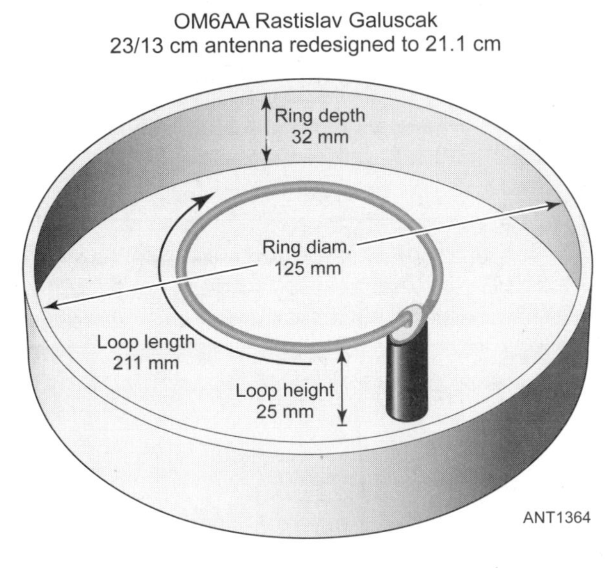

(A)

(B)

(C)

Figure 22.78 — The original dimensions of the OM6AA loop feed system (A). The constructed feed system is shown at B and a "cake pan" derivative is shown at C. (Photos by Alex Pettit, KK4VB)

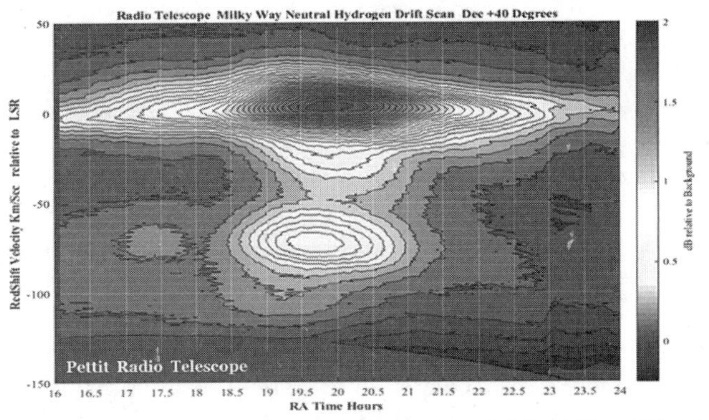

Figure 22.79 — A sample of 21-cm measurements taken with the OM6AA-derived feed system and a 1-meter reflector dish.

(A)

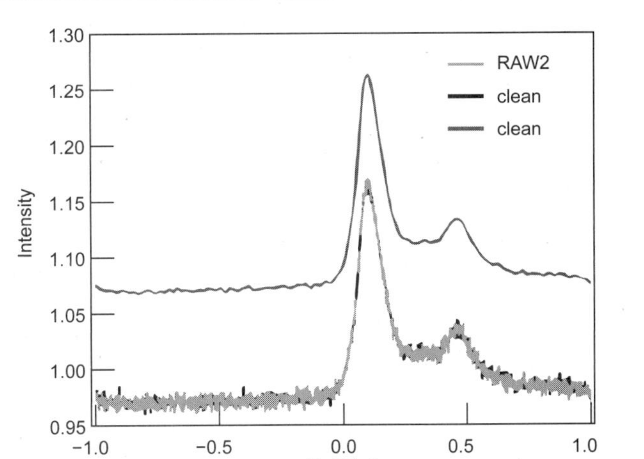

(B)

Figure 22.80 — The completed beginner's 21-cm telescope (A) and a sample of data taken with the instrument (B). (Photos by Michel Klaasen)

22.3.8 Pulsar Detection

This sub-section was created from material contributed by Mario Natali, IØNAA; Peter East; Steve Olney, VK2XV; Wolfgang Herrmann; Ray Uberecken, AAØL, and Dan Layne, ADØCY.

Pulsars, whose name is originated from the contraction of the two words "PULSating StAR", are a special class of so-called "neutron stars" that are created by a catastrophic stellar supernova. They have physical dimensions of a few tens of kilometers and are characterized not only by the extraordinary compactness, but also by extremely powerful magnetic and gravitational fields. They have a high rate of rotation on their own axis with very short periods ranging from a few milliseconds to a few seconds. Pulsars have very stable periods and can be used as celestial clocks. Pulse intensities vary widely, partly due to scintillation from scattering in the ionized interstellar medium.

The combination of these factors produces many effects and what interests us is that they emit a rotating beam of radio waves that extends to a large part of the spectrum and that is more intense at lower frequencies. These rotating beams are received as very accurately timed pulses with repetition rates of milliseconds to several seconds.

With the advent of SDR technology, detecting a known pulsar is now within the reach of amateur radio astronomers. For example, B0329+54, the brightest pulsar in the northern hemisphere, can be detected using RTL-SDRs with a 3-meter dish or a twin-Yagi. Accurate tracking is required due to extended integration times. For fainter pulsars a larger dish and wider bandwidth SDR is needed.

Pulse period-matched synchronous integration or period-folding of the detected signal is the most effective technique in recovering a true pulsar from galactic and receiver noise. The main characteristics are very accurate pulse timing, broadband noise transmission with much more power at low frequencies; the energy scintillates and is dispersed in frequency due to electron interaction along the interstellar path. It is not easy for amateurs to detect and recognize. The typical system requirements over the frequency range 300 MHz to 1400 MHz are a few square meters of antenna aperture, a few MHz up to 50 MHz of RF bandwidth, a few hours of data integration, a system noise temperature around or below 100 K and, not the least, a low-RFI environment.

PULSAR DETECTION WITH DSP

Pulsars are very weak radio sources and for amateur radio astronomers it is almost impossible to detect even the strongest one in real time. The approach used is to record the signal and use specialized techniques of DSP in order to increase the signal-to-noise (S/N) ratio (or SNR) to be able to detect the pulses.

The DSP technique used is called "folding"; this process can be understood by imagining that the signal is recorded on a continuous paper strip. Capitalizing on the fact that we know from the literature the frequency of the pulsar under investigation we fold the paper in small pieces of the length of the pulsar period (see **Figure 22.81**). By repeating this "folding" operation we allow the small contributions of the pulsars signals to add together until the pulses emerge from the background noise. Since the background noise is random, it is reduced by the process of adding the data together.

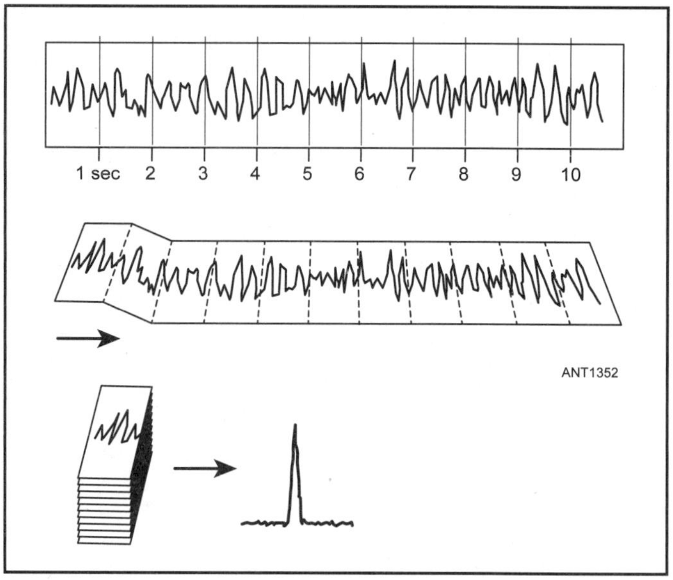

Figure 22.81 — The process called "folding" adds together data at intervals of the pulsar period. This allows the pulsar emissions to emerge from the random background noise.

The process to sample and record the signal must be done with extreme stability and precision to allow the post-recording "folding" process to work properly. The sampling precision starts from the receiver that must be very stable (a GPSDO or lock to a rubidium standard) and continues with pre-processing and recording that requires a PC with adequate processing power. The minimum requirement for processing up to 20 MHz bandwidth data is an I5 with clock frequency > 3 GHz, quad core, and fast USB, while for 50 MHz bandwidth an I7 with clock frequency > 4 GHz is required. The data is then stored as files on a hard drive.

Once the file is recorded, it must be processed and converted to a "filter bank" (.fil) format in order to be ready to go through the analysis session that starts with determination of the exact pulsar period (frequency). This task is performed with a program called *TEMPO* that uses geographical coordinates of the observation site to calculate the exact data that will be used in the subsequent phase. The final analysis is performed with a suite of programs called *PRESTO* (PulsaR Exploration and Search TOolkit) that will tell us if we were able to detect the pulsar. **Figure 22.82** shows a typical output screen from a *PRESTO* analysis.

The detection of pulsars is viewed as a major achievement by many in Citizen Scientist Radio Astronomy circles. Despite the difficulty, there are many examples of successful pulsar detection by citizen scientists which comply with the scientific method and, as such, are good sources of information.

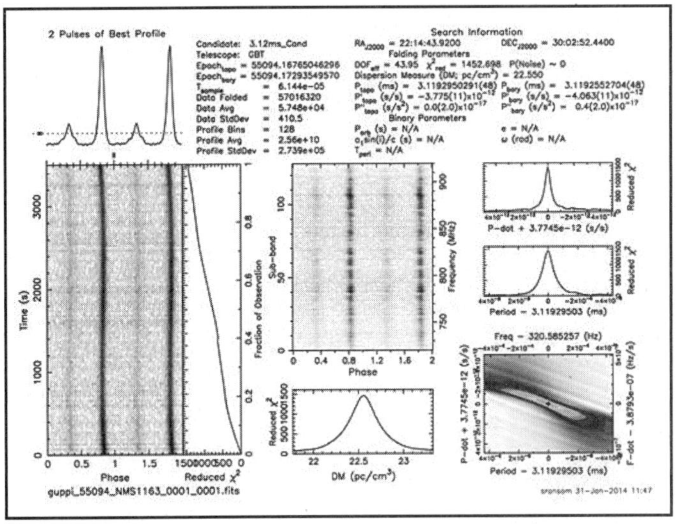

Figure 22.82 — The output of the *PRESTO* software that analyzes data to see if a pulsar has been detected. This screen shot shows two peaks of a pulsar emission at the upper left with supporting data in the other windows.

ANTENNAS FOR PULSAR DETECTION – AN EXAMPLE

The following paragraphs describe the antenna system used for the first amateur detection (by VK2XV) of a pulsar "glitch" in which its period abruptly changes. While antennas up to very large dishes are used to detect pulsars by amateurs, this example shows that meaningful measurements can be made using antenna systems similar to those used for amateur satellite and moonbounce operation.

At the Hawkesbury Radio Astronomy (HawkRAO) two antenna configurations have been used for Vela pulsar observation. A 2-by-2 Yagi array is currently used to make Vela pulsar observations. This pulsar passes almost directly overhead and so the best type of antenna to build up sufficient aperture in the restricted space available at the observatory is a long Yagi — not common at professional observatories — but common for amateur radio stations. The Vela Pulsar also has the highest signal strength at 430 MHz of any pulsar.

The Vela pulsar signal is almost completely polarized, with linear polarization being the dominant mode. This means there is the potential for the pulsar signal and a linearly-polarized receiving antenna to be cross-polarized, resulting in loss in received signal level. The last stage of the signal's journey through the ionosphere introduces a variable amount of polarization twist due to Faraday rotation. Therefore, any attempt at alignment of a linear-polarized antenna to be coincident to that fixed orientation in space of the Vela pulsar signal is made ineffective by this last variable "twist". To avoid the effects of an unknown polarization orientation for the incoming Vela signal it was decided to utilize a circularly polarized antenna - which responds to linearly polarized signals from all orientations.

The selected M2 436CP42UG antenna boom length is about 5.7 meters long and has 42 elements. Circular polarization is produced by introducing a 1/4 λ physical offset between

(A)

(B)

Figure 22.83 — The single Yagi (A) used to detect the Vela Pulsar at the Hawkesbury Radio Astronomy Observatory. Later, the antenna was expanded to the 2-by-2 array of Yagis (B). (Photos by Steve Olney, VK2XV)

two crossed Yagis with the notional vertical polarized Yagi placed forward relative to the horizontal polarized Yagi. The initial successful detection of Vela Pulsar signals was achieved by using drift scanning with this single Yagi antenna mounted vertically as shown in **Figure 22.83A**. Later, the antenna was expanded to a 2-by-2 array of the same antenna.

22.3.9 Masers

This sub-section was contributed by Eduard Mol.

A *maser* (Microwave Amplification by Stimulation of Electromagnetic Radiation: **en.wikipedia.org/wiki/Maser**) operates at radio frequencies similarly to a laser. Astrophysical masers (**en.wikipedia.org/wiki/Astrophysical_maser**) occur naturally, for example, in interstellar molecular clouds. The frequencies at which these natural masers operate are referred to as "lines" for their single-signal emissions.

Water masers emit an amplified spectral line of water at 22.235 GHz. They are commonly found in star forming regions and in the gas envelopes of evolved stars. Water masers are among the brightest sources in the sky at microwave frequencies: the flux densities of the strongest water masers often exceed 10000 Jansky. Water masers are also highly variable, with spectral components often changing in flux density and velocity over timescales of weeks to years. One of the most exciting aspects of water masers is their flaring behavior: occasionally, a spectral component in a water maser may become several times stronger and fade away again over the course of a few months or even weeks. The variability and flaring behavior of water masers makes them interesting targets for long-term observing programs, especially with amateurs supplementing professional observatories.

Several astronomical objects with strong water maser signals and a project for receiving the 22 GHz signal are described in the online document "Antennas for Radio Astronomy." Maser signals produced by OH (hydroxyl) on 1665 MHz and CH_3OH (alcohol) on 12.18 GHz can also be received and measured by amateurs.

Receiving maser emissions requires a dish for the frequency of the maser with accurate pointing and tracking. **Figure 22.84** shows a high-quality, solid 1-meter dish mounted on an HEQ5 telescope mount, used for receiving maser signals from interstellar water molecules.

As of April 2023, eight water maser sources have been successfully observed with this setup: W49, W51, W3-IRS5, Orion KL, W75, Cepheus A, G34.403+0.232, and NML Cygni. Most of these sources are associated with major star forming complexes, except for NML Cygni which is a red giant star. The strongest two sources, W51 and W49, were observed nearly every month for over a year in order to detect variability and flaring. The results of the W49 observing program are summarized in the previously referenced online document.

Figure 22.84 — A 1-meter offset feed dish on an HEQ5 tracking telescope mount. This antenna is used for receiving 22 GHz signals from water masers. (Photo by Eduard Mol)

These observations show it is possible to detect several of the strongest water maser sources with a dish as small as 1 meter and off-the-shelf equipment. Furthermore, by doing monthly observations, their variability has been successfully observed. Despite the technical challenges and limitations, the observation of water masers with small dishes presents new and interesting opportunities for radio astronomy enthusiasts.

TABLE OF CONTENTS

Chapter 23 — Online Material

Articles

- "Coaxial RF Connectors for Microwaves" by Tom Williams, WA1MBA
- "Hands-On Radio: Open Wire Transmission Lines" by Ward Silver, NØAX
- "Hands-On Radio: SWR and Transmission Line Loss" by Ward Silver, NØAX
- "Hands-On Radio: Choosing a Feed Line" by Ward Silver, NØAX
- "Hands-On Radio: Feed Line Comparison" by Ward Silver, NØAX
- "Installing Coax Crimp Connectors" by Dino Papas, KLØS
- "Microwave Plumbing" by Paul Wade, W1GHZ
- "Multiband Operation with Open-wire Line" by George Cutsogeorge, W2VJN
- "My Feedline Tunes My Antenna" by Byron Goodman W1DX
- RF Connectors and Transmission Line Information
- Smith Chart supplement
- "The Doctor Is In: Yes, Window Line Can be Spliced — If You Must" by Joel Hallas, W1ZR
- "Using RG58 coaxial crimp connectors with RG6 cable" by Garth Jenkinson, VK3BBK
- "Visualizing Microwaves" by Paul Wade, W1GHZ
- "Demystifying the Smith Chart or How to train your antenna" by Michael Tola, K3MT
- "Voltage, Current, Power, and Loss Equations for General Transmission Lines" by Steve Stearns, K6OIK
- Spreadsheet for Converting Rs/Xs to Rp/Xp

Chapter 23

Transmission Lines

23.1 Basic Theory of Transmission Lines

The connecting link between a source of ac power, such as a transmitter, and a load, such as an antenna, is a *transmission line*, *feeder* or *feed line*. Its purpose is to carry the power from one place to another and to do it as efficiently as possible. That is, the ratio of the power *transferred* by the line to the power *lost* in or from it should be as large as the circumstances permit. This is the goal, whether the ac power is RF or low-frequency ac utility power.

23.1.1 Current Flow in Long Lines

The simplest transmission line is a pair of parallel conductors, so we will develop our theory based on that model. In **Figure 23.1**, imagine that the connection between the battery and the two wires is made instantaneously and then broken. During the time the wires are in contact with the battery terminals, electrons in wire 1 will be attracted to the positive battery terminal and an equal number of electrons in wire 2 will be repelled from the negative terminal. This happens only near the battery terminals at first, because electromagnetic waves do not travel at infinite speed. Some time does elapse before the currents flow at the more extreme parts of the wires. By ordinary standards, the elapsed time is very short. Because the speed of wave travel along the wires may approach the speed of light at 300,000,000 meters per second, it becomes necessary to measure time in millionths of a second (microseconds, µs).

For example, suppose that the contact with the battery is so short that it can be measured in a very small fraction of a microsecond. Then the "pulse" of current that flows at the battery terminals during this time can be represented by the vertical line in **Figure 23.2**. At the speed of light this pulse travels 30 meters along the line in 0.1 µs, 60 meters in 0.2 µs, 90 meters in 0.3 µs, and so on, as far as the line reaches.

The current does not exist all along the wires; it is only present at the point that the pulse has reached in its travel. At this point it is present in both wires, with the electrons moving in one direction in one wire and in the other direction in the other wire. If the line is infinitely long and has no resistance (or other cause of energy loss), the pulse will travel undiminished forever.

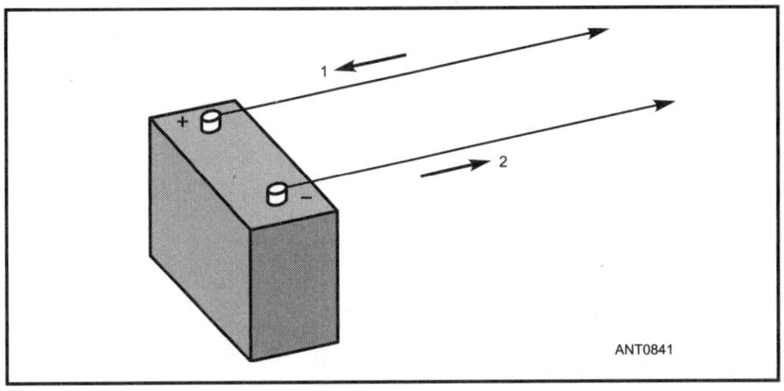

Figure 23.1 — A representation of current flow on a long transmission line.

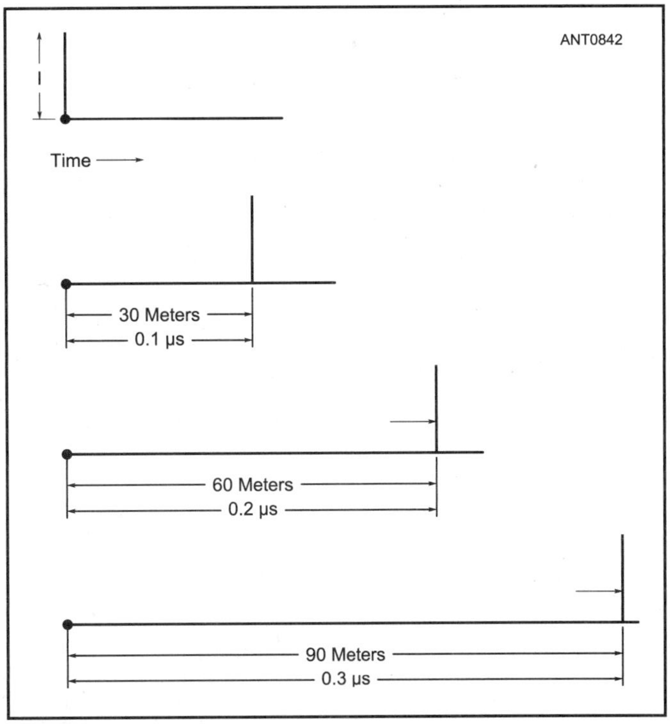

Figure 23.2 — A current pulse traveling along a transmission line at the speed of light would reach the successive positions shown at intervals of 0.1 µs.

By extending the example of Figure 23.2, it is not hard to see that if, instead of one pulse, a whole series of them were started on the line at equal time intervals, the pulses would travel along the line with the same time and distance spacing between them, each pulse independent of the others. In fact, each pulse could even have a different amplitude if the battery voltage were varied between pulses. Furthermore, the pulses could be so closely spaced that they touched each other, in which case current would be present everywhere along the line simultaneously.

It follows from this that an alternating voltage applied to the line would give rise to the sort of current flow shown in **Figure 23.3**. If the frequency of the ac voltage is 10,000,000 hertz or 10 MHz, each cycle occupies 0.1 ms, so a complete cycle of current will be present along each 30 meters of line. This is a distance of one wavelength. Any currents at points B and D on the two conductors occur one cycle later in time than the currents at A and C. Put another way, the currents initiated at A and C do not appear at B and D, one wavelength away, until the applied voltage has gone through a complete cycle.

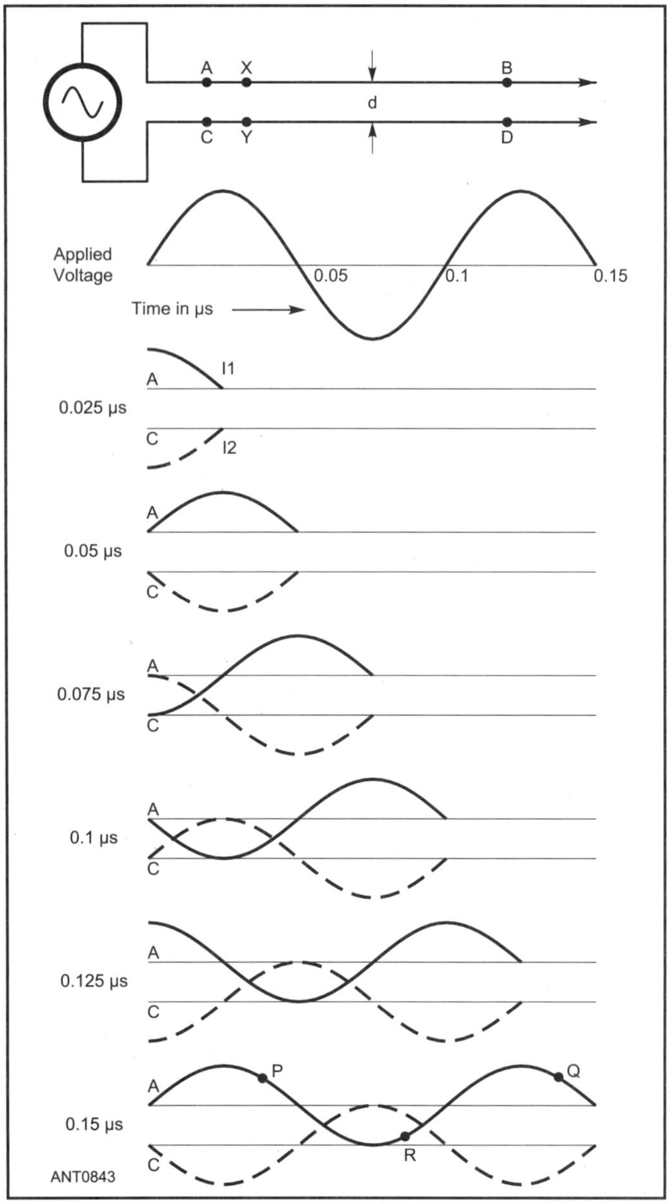

Figure 23.3 — Instantaneous current along a transmission line at successive time intervals. The frequency is 10 MHz; the time for each complete cycle is 0.1 μs.

Because the applied voltage is always changing, the currents at A and C change in proportion. The current a short distance away from A and C — for instance, at X and Y — is not the same as the current at A and C. This is because the current at X and Y was caused by a value of voltage that occurred slightly earlier in the cycle. This situation holds true all along the line; at any instant the current anywhere along the line from A to B and C to D is different from the current at any other point on that section of the line.

The remaining series of drawings in Figure 23.3 shows how the instantaneous currents might be distributed if we could take snapshots of them at intervals of ¼ cycle. The current travels out from the input end of the line in waves. At any given point on the line, the current goes through its complete range of ac values in one cycle, just as it does at the input end. Therefore (if there are no losses) an ammeter inserted in either conductor reads exactly the same current at any point along the line, because the ammeter averages the current over a whole cycle. (The phases of the currents at any two separate points are different, but the ammeter cannot show phase.)

23.1.2 Velocity of Propagation

In the example above it was assumed that energy travels along the line at the velocity of light. The actual velocity is very close to that of light only in lines in which the insulation between conductors is air. The presence of dielectrics other than air reduces the velocity.

Current flows at the speed of light only in a vacuum, although the speed in air is close to that in a vacuum. Therefore, the time required for a signal of a given frequency to travel down a length of practical transmission line is *longer* than the time required for the same signal to travel the same distance in free space. Because of this propagation delay, 360° of a given wave exists in a physically shorter distance on a given transmission line than in free space. The exact delay for a given transmission line is a function of the properties of the line, mainly the dielectric constant of the insulating material between the conductors. This delay is expressed in terms of the speed of light (either as a percentage or a decimal fraction), and is referred to as velocity factor (VF). The velocity factor is related to the dielectric constant (ε) by

$$VF = \frac{1}{\sqrt{\varepsilon}} \tag{1}$$

The wavelength in a practical line is always shorter than the wavelength in free space, which has a dielectric constant ε = 1.0. Whenever reference is made to a line as being a half wavelength or quarter wavelength long (λ/2 or λ/4), it is understood that what is meant by this is the *electrical* length of the line. The physical length corresponding to an electrical wavelength on a given line is given by

$$\lambda\ (\text{feet}) = \frac{983.6}{f} \times VF \qquad (2)$$

where
  f = frequency in MHz
  VF = velocity factor

Values of VF for several common types of lines are given later in this chapter. The actual VF of a given cable varies slightly from one production run or manufacturer to another, even though the cables may have exactly the same specifications.

As we shall see later, a quarter-wavelength line is frequently used as an impedance transformer, and so it is convenient to calculate the length of a quarter-wave line directly by

$$\lambda / 4 = \frac{245.9}{f} \times VF \qquad (2A)$$

It is important to note that Equation 1 is based on some simplifying assumptions about the cable and the frequency of use. The VF of any transmission line is not constant — it varies with frequency although a nominal VF is given in cable specifications. At the lowest audio frequencies, VF is quite a bit lower than the nominal value, rising rapidly throughout the audio spectrum and continuing to increase through the radio spectrum until it reaches a nearly constant value in the VHF range. It is this constant value that is computed by simple equations for VF that don't take frequency into account. The nominal VF and other characteristics of many types of lines, both coax and twin lead, are shown in **Table 23.1** later in this chapter. (Excerpted from Jim Brown, K9YC's "A Ham's Guide to RFI, Ferrites, Baluns, and Audio Interfacing" at **k9yc.com/publish.htm** which has more information.)

For most cables, VF at 2 MHz is typically 1-2% lower than the nominal value. In other words, an actual transmission line is 1-2% longer electrically than using the nominal value that the simplified equation for VF predicts. Because of this change, the physical length of a stub for the lower frequency bands will be 1-2% shorter than predicted from the specified value. **Figure 23.4** illustrates the behavior of both VF and loss for a typical coaxial cable.

Always measure the actual VF of cables at the frequency of use before calculating electrical lengths for stubs or other length-sensitive uses. This is generally not an issue at amateur frequencies (except for the 2200 meter band) but should be considered if coax or twisted-pair lines are used for software-defined radio applications at low frequencies. (See "Transmission Lines at Audio Frequencies and a Bit of History" by Jim Brown, K9YC, in the References and Bibliography.)

But Why 50 Ohms?

Coaxial cable burst on the scene as ham radio re-booted after World War II and the 50 Ω characteristic impedance of RG-8 became the de facto standard from then on. But why 50 Ω? The answer comes from Volume 9 of the MIT Radiation Lab Series, *Microwave Transmission Circuits*, by George L. Ragan, published in 1948. (**web.mit.edu/klund/www/books/radlab.html**) On page 147, after several pages deriving the optimum geometries, Ragan writes, "Obvious economy both in test equipment and in design work can be achieved if a single impedance can be chosen as a compromise standard. It has been found convenient to adopt 50 ohms as an impedance level offering a satisfactory compromise." His Table 4.2 shows the relative loss and power-handling capability loss of 50 Ω air- and polyethylene-insulated lines. The latter achieves better than 50% of the optimum value based either on wavelength or outer conductor size, including 100% of the optimum attenuation. Thus, 50 Ω was selected based on available types and sizes of materials to give good (but mostly not best) performance for both power and loss. (Thanks to Gene Pentecost, W4IMT, for researching this question.)

23.1.3 Characteristic Impedance

A perfectly lossless transmission line may be represented by a whole series of small inductors and capacitors connected in an infinitely long line, as shown in Figure 23.4A. (We first consider this special case because we need not consider how the line is terminated at its end, since there is no end.)

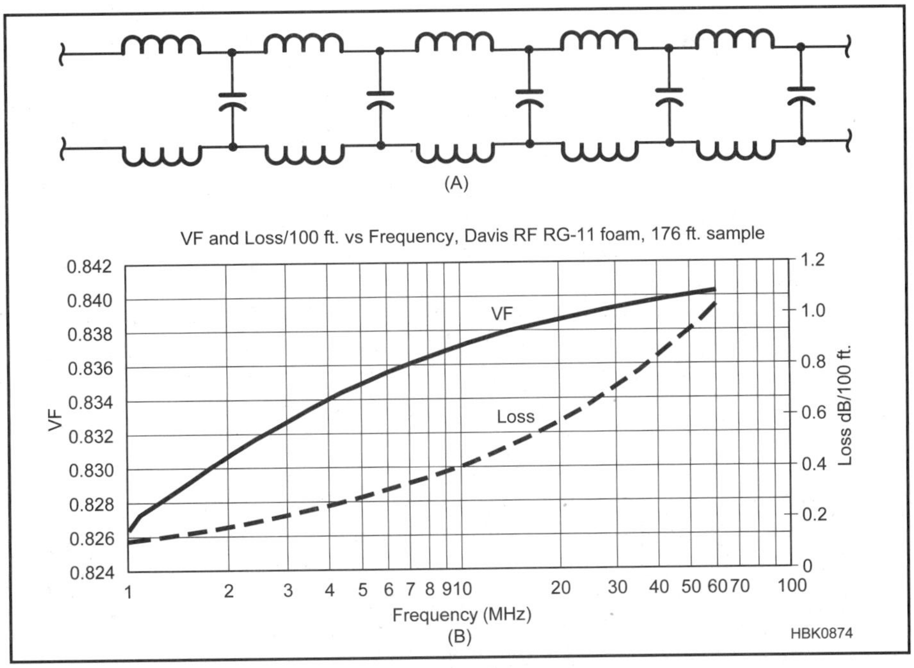

Figure 23.4 — Equivalent circuit of an infinitely long lossless transmission line using lumped circuit constants (A) along with typical VF and loss with frequency (B). (See text).

Each inductor in Figure 23.4A represents the inductance of a very short section of one wire and each capacitor represents the capacitance between two such short sections. The inductance and capacitance values per unit of line depend on the size of the conductors and the spacing between them. Each series inductor acts to limit the rate at which current can charge the following shunt capacitor, and in so doing establishes a very important property of a transmission line: its *surge impedance*, more commonly known as its *characteristic impedance*. This is usually abbreviated as Z_0,

$$Z_0 \approx \sqrt{L / C} \tag{3A}$$

where L and C are the inductance and capacitance per unit length of line. The characteristic impedance of an air-insulated parallel-conductor line, neglecting the effect of the insulating spacers, is given by

$$Z_0 = \frac{120}{\sqrt{\varepsilon}} \cosh^{-1} \frac{S}{d} \tag{3B}$$

where

Z_0 = characteristic impedance

S = center to center distance between the conductors

d = diameter of conductors in the same units as S

When S□ d, the approximation $Z_0 = 276 \log_{10} (2S/d)$ may be used but for $S < 2d$ gives values that are significantly higher than the correct value, such as is often the case when wires are twisted together to form a transmission line for impedance transformers.

The characteristic impedance of an air-insulated coaxial line is given by

$$Z_0 = 138 \log_{10}(b/a) \tag{3C}$$

where

Z_0 = characteristic impedance

b = inside diameter of outer conductors

a = outside diameter of inner conductor (in same units as b).

It does not matter what units are used for S, d, a or b, as long as they are the *same* units. A line with closely spaced, large conductors will have a low characteristic impedance, while one with widely spaced, small conductors will have a relatively high characteristic impedance. Practical open-wire lines exhibit characteristic impedances ranging from about 200 to 800 Ω, while coax cables have Z_0 values between 25 to 100 Ω. Except in special instances, coax used in Amateur Radio has an impedance of 50 or 75 Ω.

All practical transmission lines exhibit some power loss. These losses occur in the resistance that is inherent in the conductors that make up the line, and from leakage currents flowing in the dielectric material between the conductors. We'll next consider what happens when a real transmission line, which is not infinitely long, is terminated in an actual load impedance, such as an antenna.

It should be noted that Z_0 also varies with frequency and below VHF is complex — that is, not a pure resistance, and is slightly capacitive. The *TLW* program (Transmission Line for Windows by N6BV), included in this book's online material, provides Z_0 data for most commonly used cables, and can plot voltage and current along the line. These plots clearly show standing waves on a line at 2 MHz when the termination is only resistive. The mismatch is small and the effect on attenuation is insignificant, but it clearly shows up in carefully made measurements of long cable lengths over a range of frequencies as a small ripple in attenuation values.

The simplified calculations given in this section make simplifying assumptions about conductor and insulation characteristics that give useful values at MF through low VHF. At lower and higher frequencies the actual values become significantly different.

23.1.4 Terminated Lines

The value of the characteristic impedance is equal to $\sqrt{L/C}$ in a perfect line — that is, one in which the conductors have no resistance and there is no leakage between them — where L and C are the inductance and capacitance, respectively, per unit length of line. The inductance decreases with increasing conductor diameter, and the capacitance decreases with increasing spacing between the conductors. Hence a line with closely spaced large conductors has relatively low characteristic impedance, while one with widely spaced thin conductors has high impedance. Practical values of Z_0 for parallel-conductor lines range from about 200 to 800 Ω. Typical coaxial lines have characteristic impedances from 30 to 100 Ω. Physical constraints on practical wire diameters and spacings limit Z_0 values to these ranges.

In the earlier discussion of current traveling along a transmission line, we assumed that the line was infinitely long. Practical lines have a definite length, and they are terminated in a load at the output or load end (the end to which the power is delivered). In **Figure 23.5**, if the load is a pure resistance of a value equal to the characteristic impedance of a perfect, lossless line, the current traveling along the line to the load finds that the load simply "looks like" more transmission line of the same characteristic impedance.

The reason for this can be more easily understood by considering it from another viewpoint. Along a transmission line, power is transferred successively from one elementary section in Figure 23.4 to the next. When the line is infinitely long, this power transfer goes on in one direction — away from the source of power.

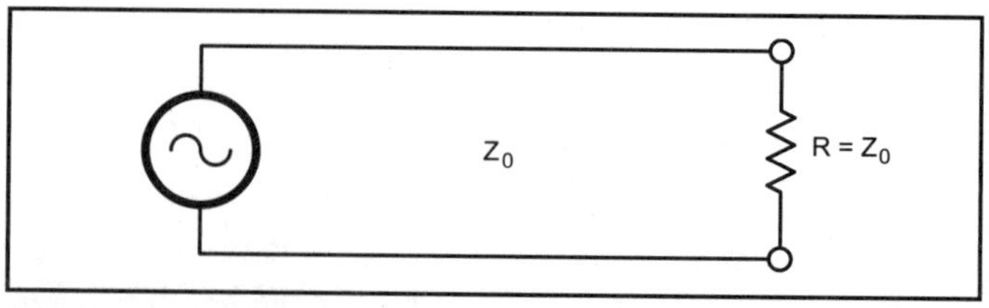

Figure 23.5 — A transmission line terminated in a resistive load equal to the characteristic impedance of the line.

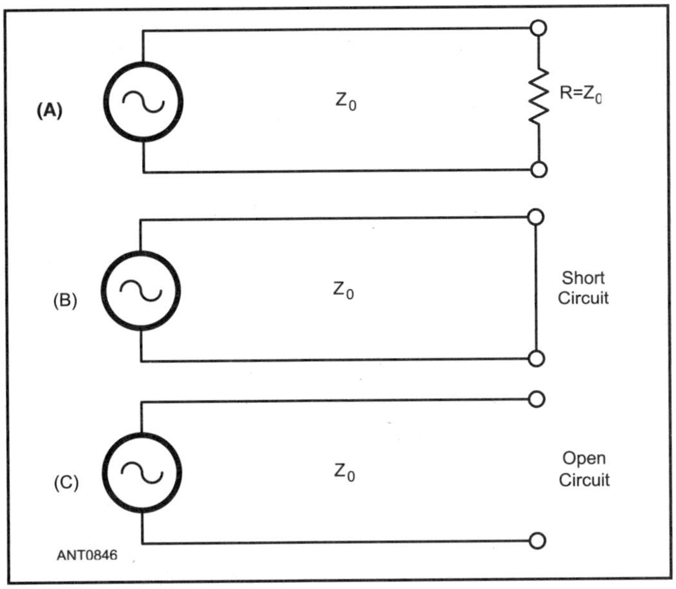

Figure 23.6 — Mismatched lines; extreme cases. At A, termination not equal to Z_0; at B, short-circuited line; At C, open-circuited line.

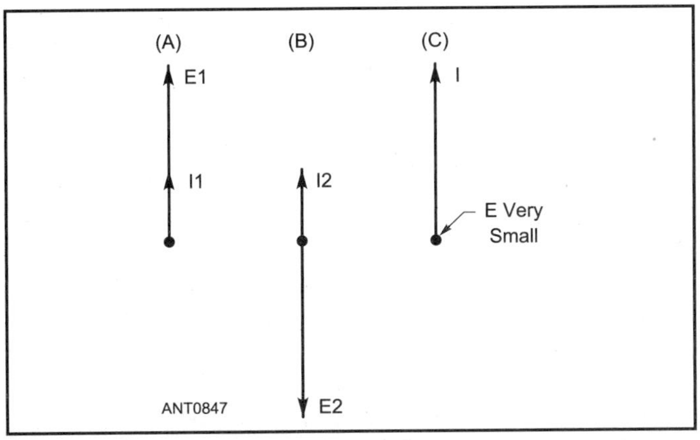

Figure 23.7 — Voltage and current at the short circuit on a short-circuited line. These vectors show how the incident voltage and current (A) combine with the reflected voltage and current (B) to result in high current and very low voltage in the short circuit (C).

From the standpoint of Section B, Figure 23.4, for instance, the power transferred to section C has simply disappeared in C. As far as section B is concerned, it makes no difference whether C has absorbed the power itself or has transferred it along to more transmission line. Consequently, if we substitute a load for section C that has the same electrical characteristics as the transmission line, section B will transfer power into it just as if it were more transmission line. A pure resistance equal to the characteristic impedance of C, which is also the characteristic impedance of the line, meets this condition. It absorbs all the power just as the infinitely long line absorbs all the power transferred by section B.

MATCHED LINES

A line terminated in a load equal to the complex characteristic line impedance is said to be *matched*. In a matched transmission line, power is transferred outward along the line from the source until it reaches the load, where it is completely absorbed. Thus with either the infinitely long line or its matched counterpart, the impedance presented to the source of power (the line-input impedance) is the same *regardless of the line length*. It is simply equal to the characteristic impedance of the line. The current in such a line is equal to the applied voltage divided by the characteristic impedance, and the power put into it is E^2/Z_0 or I^2Z_0, by Ohm's law.

MISMATCHED LINES

Now take the case where the terminating load is *not* equal to Z_0, as in **Figure 23.6**. The load no longer looks like more line to the section of line immediately adjacent. Such a line is said to be *mismatched*. The more the load impedance differs from Z_0, the greater the mismatch. The power reaching the load is not totally absorbed, as it was when the load was equal to Z_0, because the load requires a voltage to current ratio that is different from the one traveling along the line. The result is that the load absorbs only part of the power reaching it (the *incident* power); the remainder acts as though it had bounced off a wall and starts back along the line toward the source. This is known as *reflected power*, and the greater the mismatch, the larger the percentage of the incident power that is reflected. In the extreme case where the load is zero (a short circuit) or infinity (an open circuit), *all* of the power reaching the end of the line is reflected back toward the source.

Whenever there is a mismatch, power is transferred in both directions along the line. The voltage to current ratio is the same for the reflected power as for the incident power, because this ratio is determined by the Z_0 of the line. The voltage and current travel along the line in both directions in the same wave motion shown in Figure 23.3. If the source of power is an ac generator, the incident (outgoing) voltage and the reflected (returning) voltage are simultaneously present all along the line. The actual voltage at any point along the line is the vector sum of the two components, taking into account the *phases* of each component. The same is true of the current.

The effect of the incident and reflected components on the behavior of the line can be understood more readily by considering first the two limiting cases — the short-circuited line and the open-circuited line. If the line is short-circuited as in

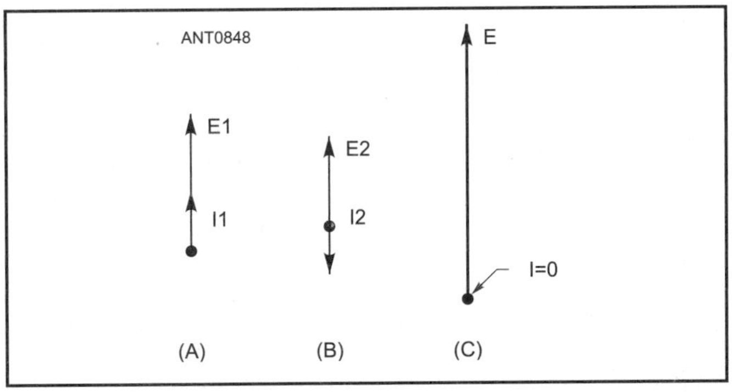

Figure 23.8 — Voltage and current at the end of an open-circuited line. At A, incident voltage and current; At B, reflected voltage and current; At C, resulting voltage and current.

Voltage and Current Vectors

The vector arrows in Figures 23.7 and 23.8 are used to illustrate how incident and reflected voltage and current combine. The length of the vector from its head (dot) to the end (arrowhead) represent the amplitude of the voltage or current. The direction of the vector represents phase with 0 degrees being straight up and 180 degrees being straight down. For more information on vectors, phasors, and other math topics, see the entry for "Radio Mathematics" online at **arrl.org/arrl-antenna-book-reference**.

Figure 23.6B, the voltage at the end must be zero. Thus the incident voltage must disappear suddenly at the short. It can do this only if the reflected voltage is opposite in phase and of the same amplitude. This is shown by the vectors in **Figure 23.7**. The current, however, does not disappear in the short circuit. In fact, the incident current flows through the short and in addition, there is the reflected component in phase of the same amplitude as the incident current.

The reflected voltage and current must have the same amplitudes as the incident voltage and current, because no power is dissipated in the short circuit; all the power starts back toward the source. Reversing the phase of *either* the current or voltage (but not both) reverses the direction of power flow. In the short-circuited case the phase of the voltage is reversed on reflection, but the phase of the current is not.

If the line is open-circuited (Figure 23.6C) the current must be zero at the end of the line. In this case the reflected current is 180° out of phase with the incident current and has the same amplitude. By reasoning similar to that used in the short-circuited case, the reflected voltage must be in phase with the incident voltage, and must have the same amplitude. Vectors for the open-circuited case are shown in **Figure 23.8**.

Where there is a finite value of resistance (or a combination of resistance and reactance) at the end of the line, as in Figure 23.6A, only part of the power reaching the end of the line is reflected. That is, the reflected voltage and current are smaller than the incident voltage and current. If R is less than Z_0, the reflected and incident voltage are 180° out of phase, just as in the case of the short-circuited line, but the amplitudes are not equal because all of the voltage does not disappear at R. Similarly, if R is greater than Z_0, the reflected and incident currents are 180° out of phase (as they were in the open-circuited line), but all of the current does not appear in R. The amplitudes of the two components are therefore not equal. These two cases are shown in **Figure 23.9**. Note that the resultant current and voltage are in phase in R, because R is a pure resistance.

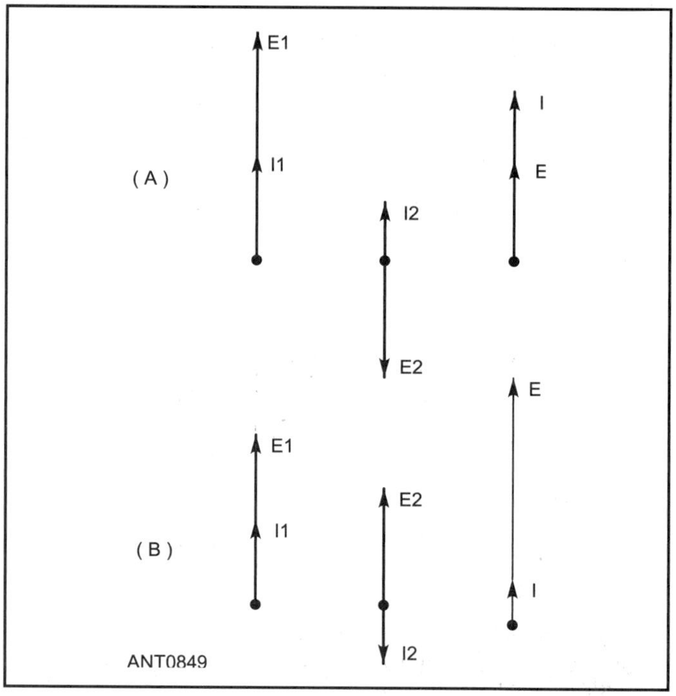

Figure 23.9 — Incident and reflected components of voltage and current when the line is terminated in a pure resistance R not equal to Z_0. In the case shown, the reflected components have half the amplitude of the incident components. At A, R less than Z_0; at B, R greater than Z_0.

NON-RESISTIVE TERMINATIONS

In most of the preceding discussions, we considered loads containing only resistance. Furthermore, our transmission line was considered to be lossless. Such a resistive load will consume some, if not all, of the power that has been transferred along the line. However, a non-resistive load such as a pure reactance can also terminate a length of line. Such terminations, of course, will consume no power, but will reflect all of the energy arriving at the end of the line. In this case the theoretical SWR (covered later) in the line will be infinite, but in practice, losses in the line will limit the SWR to some finite value at line positions back toward the source.

At first you might think there is little or no point in terminating a line with a non-resistive load. In a later section we shall examine this in more detail, but the value of input impedance depends on the value of the load impedance, on the length of the line, the losses in a practical line, and on the characteristic impedance of the line. There are times when a line terminated in a non-resistive load can be used to advantage, such as in phasing or matching applications. Remote switching of reactive terminations on sections of line can be used to reverse the beam heading of an antenna array, for example. The point of this brief discussion is that a line need not always be terminated in a load that will consume power.

23.2 Practical Transmission Lines

Transmission lines consisting of two parallel conductors as in **Figure 23.10**, parts E, F, and G are called *open- or parallel-wire lines*, *parallel-conductor lines* or *two-wire lines*. The specific styles shown here are called *twin-lead* (E), *ladder line* (F), and *window line* (G). Current flowing on one conductor is balanced by an equal-and-opposite current flowing on the other conductor. In almost all cases, both conductors have an equal impedance to the system's ground reference and so these are referred to as *balanced lines*.

A second general type of line construction called *coaxial cable* or coax (pronounced "KOH-ax") or *concentric line* is shown in Figures 23.10A, B, C, and D. In coax, one of the conductors is tube-shaped and encloses the other conductor. Current flowing on the inner conductor is balanced by an equal current flowing in the opposite direction on the inside surface of the outer conductor. Because of skin effect, the current on the inner surface of the outer conductor does not penetrate far enough to appear on the outside surface. In fact, the total electromagnetic field outside the coaxial line (as a result of currents flowing on the conductors inside) is always zero, because the outer conductor acts as a shield at radio frequencies, reducing radiation from coax to nearly zero. The separation between the inner conductor and the outer conductor is therefore unimportant from the standpoint of reducing radiation. (This is not true at very low frequencies where the skin depth is greater than the shield thickness and at microwave frequencies where openings in the braided shield of flexible coax becomes significant with respect to a wavelength.)

A third general type of transmission line is the *waveguide* which is not shown here. Waveguides are discussed in the chapter **VHF, UHF, and Microwave Antenna Systems**.

The equations presented in the preceding and following sections make some simplifying assumptions, particularly concerning loss and the complex characteristics impedance and propagation constant. A fully general treatment is provided in the paper "Voltage, Current, Power, and Loss Equations for

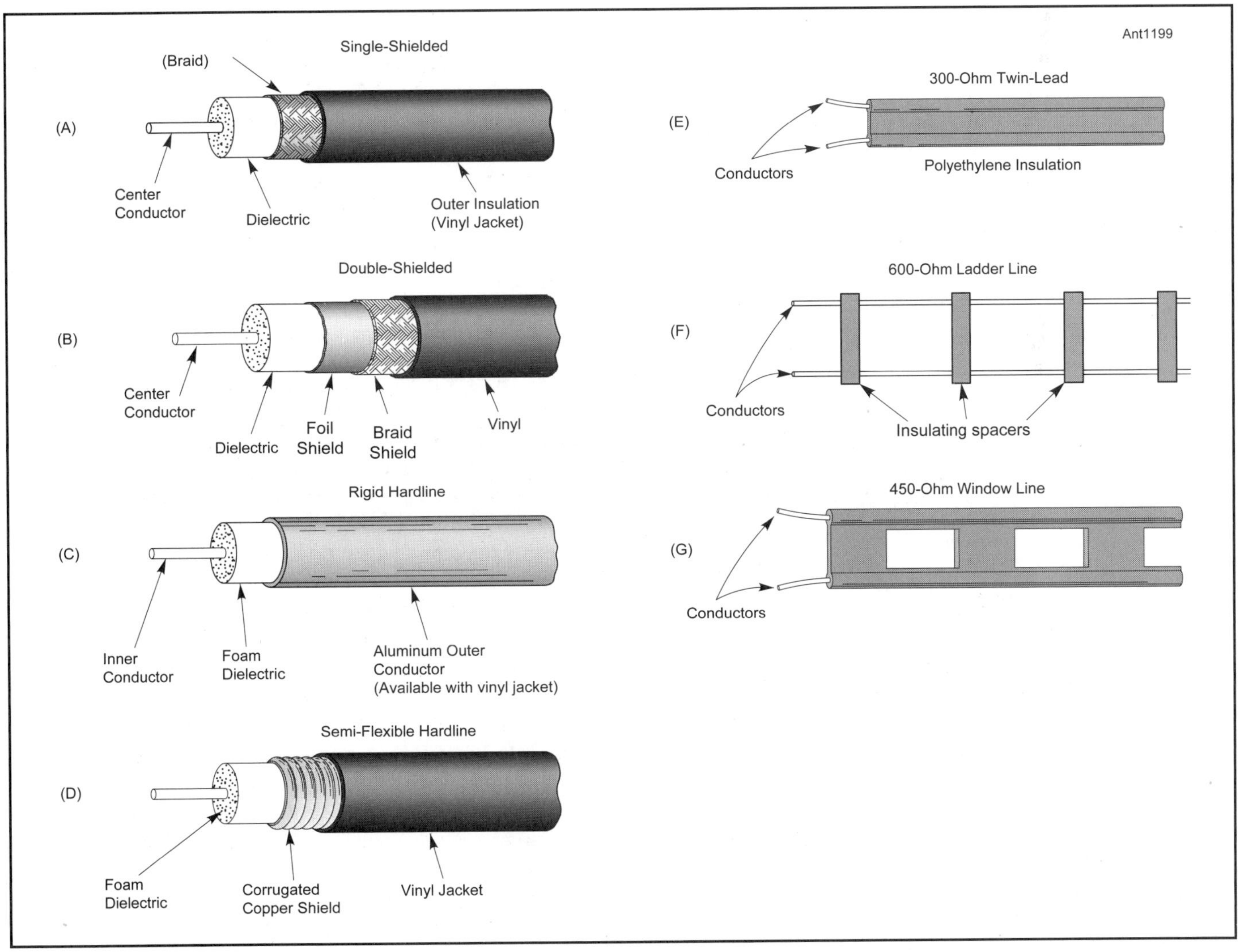

Figure 23.10 — Common types of transmission lines used by amateurs below microwave frequencies. Coaxial cables are shown at A, B, C, and D. Parallel-conductor lines are shown at E, F, and G.

General Transmission Lines" by Steve Stearns, K6OIK, which is included in the online material.

COMMON-MODE AND DIFFERENTIAL-MODE CURRENT

It is important to recognize the two types of currents that may flow in and on transmission lines: differential-mode (DM) and common-mode (CM). **Figure 23.11** shows DM and CM current for typical unshielded paired conductors at A and a coaxial line at B.

DM signals are what we often think of as "balanced" in that the signal consists of identical currents flowing in opposite directions along two closely-matched paths, neither of which is connected directly to ground or a grounded enclosure. CM signals flow equally on all conductors of a multi-conductor cable or on the common (shield) conductor of a coaxial or shielded cable.

Taking a close look at Figure 23.11B, you can see that a single cable can support both DM and CM signals at the same time. In fact, at RF the outside of a braided or foil shield is electrically independent from the inside because the skin effect restricts ac current flow to the exterior surfaces of a conductor. At frequencies above 1 MHz, current penetrates copper or aluminum less than 0.1 mm.

CM current is often caused by the conductors acting as an antenna and picking up a transmitted signal. It can also result from signals being present on a ground conductor or enclosure or the signal can leak from an enclosure. As discussed in the next section, CM current can be converted to a DM signal by the cable's transfer impedance. CM current also radiates a signal just as current on an antenna does.

Every practical line will have some inherent loss, partly because of the resistance of the conductors, partly because power is consumed in the dielectric used for insulating the conductors, and partly because in many cases a small amount of power escapes from the line by radiation.

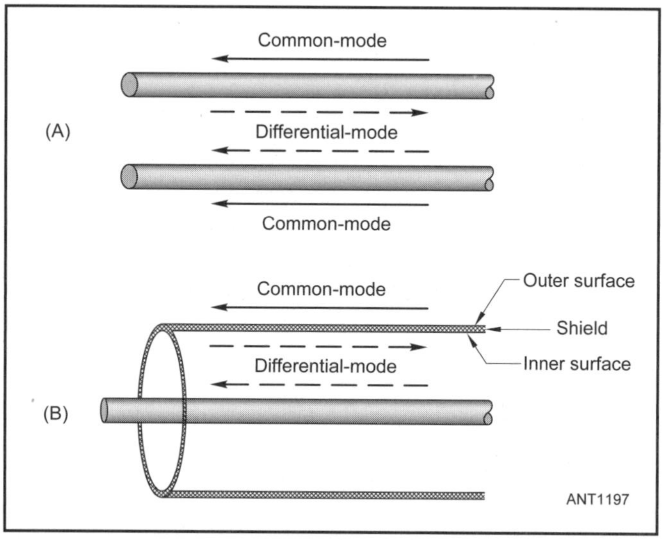

Figure 23.11 — Common-mode (CM) and differential-mode (DM) current can flow on parallel-conductor and coaxial cables at the same time. CM current can be converted to a DM signal by the cable's transfer impedance.

LINE RADIATION AND TRANSFER IMPEDANCE

At RF, every conductor that has appreciable length compared with the wavelength in use *radiates* power — every conductor is an antenna. Special care must be used, therefore, to minimize radiation from the conductors used in RF transmission lines. Without such care, the power radiated by the line may be much larger than that which is lost in the resistance of conductors and dielectrics (insulating materials). Power loss in resistance is inescapable, at least to a degree, but loss by radiation is largely avoidable.

Radiation loss from differential-mode signals carried by transmission lines can be prevented by using two conductors arranged and operated so the electromagnetic field from one is balanced everywhere by an equal and opposite field from the other. In such a case, the resultant field is zero everywhere in space — there is no radiation from the line. This requires that the spacing between the conductors making up the line be very small compared with the wavelength of the energy flowing in the line. Through the UHF range, the transmission lines used by amateurs satisfy this requirement with plenty of margin and line radiation is not significant.

Figure 23.3 shows two parallel conductors having currents I1 and I2 flowing in opposite directions. If the current I1 at point Y on the upper conductor has the same amplitude as the current I2 at the corresponding point X on the lower conductor, the fields set up by the two currents are equal in magnitude. Because the two currents are flowing in opposite directions, the field from I1 at Y is 180° out of phase with the field from I2 at X. However, it takes a measurable interval of time for the field from X to travel to Y.

If I1 and I2 are alternating currents, the phase of the field from I1 at Y changes in such a time interval, so at the instant the field from X reaches Y, the two fields at Y are not exactly 180° out of phase. The two fields are exactly 180° out of phase at every point in space only when the two conductors occupy the same space — an obviously impossible condition if they are to remain separate conductors.

The best that can be done is to make the two fields cancel each other as completely as possible. This can be achieved by keeping the distance d between the two conductors small enough so the time interval during which the field from X is moving to Y is a very small part of a cycle. When this is the case, the phase difference between the two fields at any given point is so close to 180° that cancellation is nearly complete.

Practical values of d (the separation between the two conductors) are determined by the physical limitations of line construction. A separation that meets the condition of being "very small" at one frequency may be quite large at another. For example, if d is 6 inches, the phase difference between the two fields at Y is only a fraction of a degree if the frequency is 3.5 MHz. This is because a distance of 6 inches is such a small fraction of a wavelength (1 λ = 281 feet) at 3.5 MHz. But at 144 MHz, the phase difference is 26°, and at 420 MHz, it is 77°. In neither of these cases could the two fields be considered to "cancel" each other. Conductor separation must be very small in comparison with the wavelength used; it should never exceed 1% of the wavelength, and smaller separations are desirable.

Common-mode current flowing on the outside of a coaxial line's shield can also create differential-mode signals inside the line due to *transfer impedance*. (See the referenced entry for Jim Brown, K9YC on "A Ham's Guide to RFI, Ferrites, Baluns, and Audio Interfacing" and by Brown and Bill Whitlock on "Common-Mode to Differential-Mode Conversion in Shielded Twisted-Pair Cables (Shield-Current-Induced Noise)".) From Brown's paper, transfer impedance is defined as ratio of the differential voltage induced inside the cable to common-mode current on the shield. Its units are ohms, a low value is better, and the lower limit is the resistance of the shield at the frequency of interest. The overall quality, percent coverage, and uniformity of the shield also contribute to the transfer impedance — a less dense braid or a shield with poor uniformity raise the transfer impedance, causing more noise to couple by this method. Transfer impedance varies with frequency and its effect is significant below a few MHz, particularly for inexpensive audio cables used in consumer equipment.

23.2.1 Attenuation

MATCHED-LINE LOSSES

The most important causes of transmission line loss for amateurs are conductor and dielectric losses. Power lost in a transmission line is not directly proportional to the line length, but varies logarithmically with the length. That is, if 10% of the input power is lost in a section of line of certain length, 10% of the remaining power will be lost in the next section of the same length, and so on. For this reason it is customary to express line losses in terms of decibels per unit length, since the decibel is a unit of logarithmic ratios. Calculations are very simple because the total loss in a line is found by multiplying the decibel loss per unit length by the total length of the line.

The power lost in a matched line (that is, where the load is equal to the characteristic impedance of the line) is called *matched-line loss*. Matched-line loss is usually expressed in decibels per 100 feet. It is necessary to specify the frequency for which the loss applies, because the loss does vary with frequency.

Conductor and dielectric loss both increase as the operating frequency is increased, but not in the same way. This, together with the fact that the relative amount of each type of loss depends on the actual construction of the line, makes it impossible to give a specific relationship between loss and frequency that will apply to all types of lines.

One relationship that does apply is that for lines made of the same materials (for example, copper and solid polyethylene) higher impedance lines will have lower losses. This is because the current is lower in a higher impedance line, reducing resistive (I^2R) losses.

In practice, when selecting a feed line, each type of line must be considered individually. Actual loss values for practical lines are given in a later section of this chapter along with a discussion of how to select a feed line.

One effect of matched-line loss in a real transmission line is that the characteristic impedance, Z_0, becomes complex, with a non-zero reactive component X_0. Thus,

$$Z_0 = R_0 - jX_0 \tag{4A}$$

$$X_0 = -R_0 \frac{\alpha}{\beta} \tag{4B}$$

where

$$\alpha = \frac{\text{Attenuation (dB / 100 feet)} \times 0.1151 \text{ (nepers / dB)}}{\text{100 feet}}$$

the matched-line attenuation, in nepers per unit length. (Nepers are a unitless non-logarithmic radio and 1 neper = 8.686 dB.)

$\beta = \frac{2\pi}{\lambda}$, the phase constant in radians/unit length.

The reactive portion of the complex characteristic impedance is always capacitive (that is, its sign is negative) and the value of X_0 is usually small compared to the resistive portion R_0.

23.2.2 Reflection Coefficient

The ratio of the reflected voltage at a given point on a transmission line to the incident voltage is called the *voltage reflection coefficient*. The voltage reflection coefficient is also equal to the ratio of the incident and reflected currents. Thus

$$\rho = \frac{E_r}{E_f} = \frac{I_r}{I_f} \tag{5}$$

where

ρ = reflection coefficient
E_r = reflected voltage
E_f = forward (incident) voltage
I_r = reflected current
I_f = forward (incident) current

The reflection coefficient is determined by the relationship between the line Z_0 and the actual load at the terminated end of the line. In most cases, the actual load is not entirely resistive — that is, the load is a complex impedance, consisting of a resistance in series with a reactance, as is the complex characteristic impedance of the transmission line.

The reflection coefficient is thus a complex quantity, having both amplitude and phase, and is generally designated by the Greek letter ρ (rho), or sometimes as Γ (Gamma). The relationship between R_a (the load resistance), X_a (the load reactance), Z_0 (the complex line characteristic impedance, whose real part is R_0 and whose reactive part is X_0) and the complex reflection coefficient ρ is

Coaxial Feed Line Loss Coefficients

High-precision calculations of loss in coaxial feed lines require three constants, K0, K1, and K2, which are specified by manufacturers for each type of cable. You may encounter these coefficients in online calculators and other tools for determining feed line characteristics, loss, and so on.

- K0 is associated with the dc resistance of the conductors and does not vary with frequency.
- K1 is associated with the skin effect of the conductors which varies in proportion to the square root of frequency.
- K2 is associated with the dielectric loss which varies directly with frequency.

$$\rho = \frac{Z_a - Z_0}{Z_a + Z_0} = \frac{(R_a \pm jX_a) - (R_0 \pm jX_0)}{(R_a \pm jX_a) + (R_0 \pm jX_0)} \quad (6)$$

For high-quality, low-loss transmission lines at low frequencies, the characteristic impedance Z_0 is almost completely resistive, meaning that $Z_0 \cong R_0$ and $X_0 \cong 0$. The magnitude of the complex reflection coefficient in Eq 6 then simplifies to:

$$|\rho| = \sqrt{\frac{(R_a - R_0)^2 + X_a^2}{(R_a + R_0)^2 + X_a^2}} \quad (7)$$

For example, if the characteristic impedance of a coaxial line at a low operating frequency is 50 Ω and the load impedance is 120 Ω in series with a capacitive reactance of –90 Ω, the magnitude of the reflection coefficient is

$$|\rho| = \sqrt{\frac{(120-50)^2 + (-90)^2}{(120+50)^2 + (-90)^2}} = 0.593$$

Note that the vertical bars on each side of ρ mean the *magnitude* of rho. If R_a in Eq 7 is equal to R_0 and if X_a is 0, the reflection coefficient, ρ, also is 0. This represents a *matched condition*, where all the energy in the incident wave is transferred to the load. On the other hand, if R_a is 0, meaning that the load has no real resistive part, the reflection coefficient is 1.0, regardless of the value of R_0. This means that all the forward power is reflected, since the load is completely reactive. As we shall see later on, the concept of reflection coefficient is a very useful one to evaluate the impedance seen looking into the input of a mismatched transmission line.

Another representation of the reflection coefficient concept is the *return loss*, which is the reflection coefficient expressed in dB.

$$RL = -20 \log |\rho| \text{ dB} \quad (8)$$

For example, a reflection coefficient of 0.593 is a return loss of –20 log (0.593) = 4.5 dB. (Note that some texts express return loss as negative numbers, but most define it as positive.)

23.2.3 Standing Waves

As might be expected, reflection cannot occur at the load without some effect on the voltages and currents all along the line. To keep things simple for a while longer, let us continue to consider only resistive loads, without any reactance. The conclusions we shall reach are valid for transmission lines terminated in complex impedances as well.

The effects are most simply shown by vector diagrams. **Figure 23.12** is an example where the terminating resistance R is less than Z_0. The voltage and current vectors at R are shown in the reference position; they correspond with the vectors in Figure 23.9A, turned 90°. Back along the line from R toward the power source, the incident vectors, E1 and I1, lead the vectors at the load according to their position along the line measured in electrical degrees. (The corresponding distances in fractions of a wavelength are also shown.) The vectors representing reflected voltage and current, E2 and I2, successively lag the same vectors at the load.

This lag is the natural consequence of the direction in which the incident and reflected components are traveling, together with the fact that it takes time for power to be transferred along the line. The resultant voltage E and current I at each of these positions is shown as a dotted arrow. Although the incident and reflected components maintain their respective amplitudes (the reflected component is shown at half the incident-component amplitude in this drawing), their phase relationships vary with position along the line. The phase shift causes both

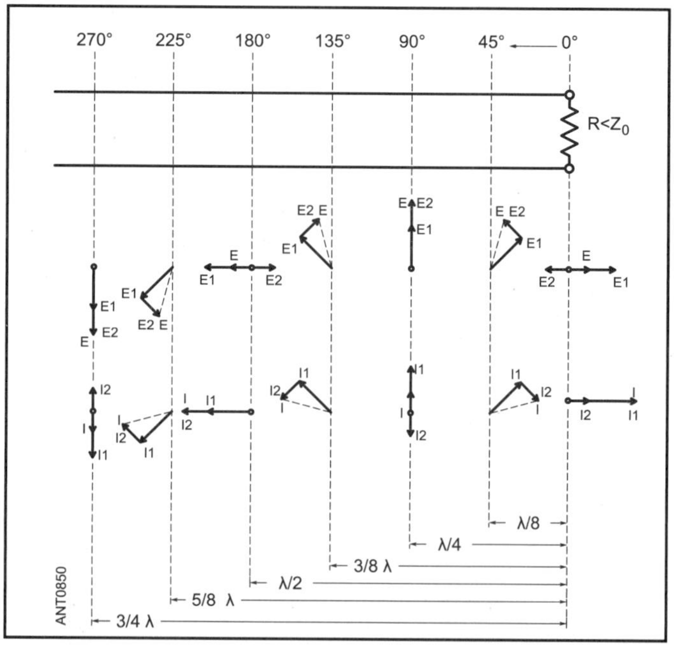

Figure 23.12 — Incident and reflected components at various positions along the transmission line, together with resultant voltages and currents at the same positions. The case shown is for R less than Z_0.

Visualizing Transmission Line Action

Equations and vector diagrams can be hard to imagine as actual waves so it is very helpful to have a visual presentation of what's actually going on "in there." Although old, the video "Similarities in Wave Behavior" uses a simple counter-top apparatus, the Shive Wave Machine, to show basic transmission line mechanics. Concepts such as reflection, absorption, and SWR, are illustrated using a minimum of simple math. You can find it on the YouTube AT&T Archives channel at **youtube.com/@ATTTechChannel**. To demonstrate waves and fields in coaxial lines and waveguides see the paper "Visualizing Microwaves" by Paul Wade, W1GHZ, that is included in the online material. It shows how to set up simple demonstrations of waves in transmission lines. Finally, Lecher lines (an open-wire feed line used for measurements) can also be used to demonstrate wave behavior in transmission lines at UHF using simple equipment. (**hackaday.com/2017/02/07/using-a-lecher-line-to-measure-high-frequency**)

the amplitude and phase of the *resultants* to vary with position on the line.

If the amplitude variations (disregarding phase) of the resultant voltage and current are plotted against position along the line, graphs like those of **Figure 23.13A** will result. If we could go along the line with a voltmeter and ammeter measuring the current and voltage at each point, plotting the collected data would give curves like these. In contrast, if the load matched the Z_0 of the line, similar measurements along the line would show that the voltage is the same everywhere (and similarly for the current). The mismatch between load and line is responsible for the variations in amplitude which, because of their stationary, wave-like appearance, are called *standing waves*.

Some general conclusions can be drawn from inspection of the standing-wave curves: At a position 180° ($\lambda/2$) from the load, the voltage and current have the same values they do at the load. At a position 90° from the load, the voltage and current are "inverted." That is, if the voltage is lowest and current highest at the load (when R is less than Z_0), then 90° from the load the voltage reaches its highest value. The current reaches its lowest value at the same point. In the case where R is greater than Z_0, so the voltage is highest and the current lowest at the load, the voltage is lowest and the current is highest 90° from the load.

Note that the conditions at the 90° point also exist at the 270° point ($3\lambda/4$). If the graph were continued on toward the source of power it would be found that this duplication occurs at every point that is an odd multiple of 90° (odd multiple of $\lambda/4$) from the load. Similarly, the voltage and current are the same at every point that is a multiple of 180° (any multiple of $\lambda/2$) away from the load.

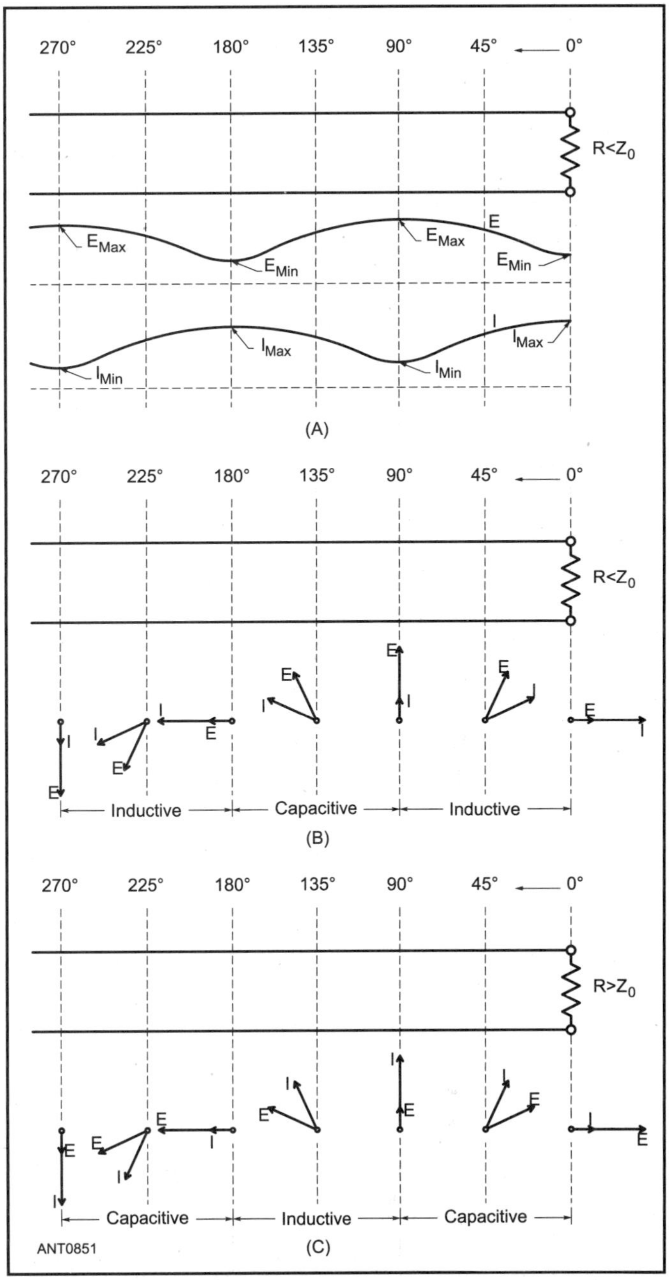

Figure 23.13 — Standing waves of current and voltage along the line for R less than Z_0. At A, resultant voltages and currents along a mismatched line are shown at B and C. At B, R less than Z_0; At C, R greater than Z_0.

STANDING-WAVE RATIO

The ratio of the maximum voltage (resulting from the interaction of incident and reflected voltages along the line) to the minimum voltage — that is, the ratio of E_{max} to E_{min} in Figure 23.13A, is defined as the *voltage standing-wave ratio* (VSWR) or simply *standing-wave ratio* (SWR).

$$SWR = \frac{E_{max}}{E_{min}} = \frac{I_{max}}{I_{min}} \tag{9}$$

The ratio of the maximum current to the minimum current is the same as the VSWR, so either current or voltage can be measured to determine the standing-wave ratio. The standing-wave ratio is an index of many of the properties of a mismatched line. It can be measured with fairly simple equipment, so it is a convenient quantity to use in making calculations on line performance.

The SWR is related to the magnitude of the complex reflection coefficient by

$$\text{SWR} = \frac{1+|\rho|}{1-|\rho|} \qquad (10)$$

and conversely the reflection coefficient magnitude may be defined from a measurement of SWR as

$$|\rho| = \frac{\text{SWR}-1}{\text{SWR}+1} \qquad (11)$$

We may also express the reflection coefficient in terms of forward and reflected power, quantities which can be easily measured using a directional RF wattmeter. The reflection coefficient may be computed as

$$\rho = \sqrt{\frac{P_r}{P_f}} \qquad (12)$$

where

P_r = power in the reflected wave

P_f = power in the forward wave.

From Eq 11, SWR is related to the forward and reflected power by

$$\text{SWR} = \frac{1+|\rho|}{1-|\rho|} = \frac{1+\sqrt{P_r/P_f}}{1-\sqrt{P_r/P_f}} \qquad (13)$$

Figure 23.14 converts Eq 13 into a convenient nomograph. In the simple case where the load contains no reactance, the SWR is numerically equal to the ratio between the load resistance R and the characteristic impedance of the line. When R is greater than Z_0,

$$\text{SWR} = \frac{R}{Z_0} \qquad (14)$$

When R is less than Z_0,

$$\text{SWR} = \frac{Z_0}{R} \qquad (15)$$

(The smaller quantity is always used in the denominator of the fraction so the ratio will be a number greater than 1).

It is important to note that in a lossless transmission line, SWR does not change with length of the line or along the line. While the values of voltage and current do change along the line, the ratio of their maximum and minimum values does not. The value of SWR shown by typical amateur SWR measuring instruments may change with line length but that can result from a number of causes; inaccuracy of the voltage or current sensing circuits, common-mode current on the outside of a coaxial feed line shield, and signals from a nearby transmitter upsetting the voltage or current measurement being the most common reasons.

FLAT LINES

As discussed earlier, all the power that is transferred along a transmission line is absorbed in the load if that load is a resistance value equal to the Z_0 of the line. In this case, the line is said to be *perfectly matched.* None of the power is reflected back toward the source. As a result, no standing waves of current or voltage will be developed along the line. For a line operating in this condition, the waveforms drawn in Figure 23.13A become straight lines, representing the voltage and current delivered by the source. The voltage along the line is constant, so the minimum value is the same as the maximum value. The voltage standing-wave ratio is therefore 1:1. Because a plot of the voltage standing wave is a straight line, the matched line is also said to be *flat.*

23.2.4 Additional Power Loss Due to SWR

The power lost in a given line is least when the line is terminated in a resistance equal to its characteristic impedance, and as stated previously, that is called the *matched-line loss.* There is however an *additional loss* that increases with an increase in the SWR. (Modern transmitters will also reduce output power to protect the solid-state output devices from

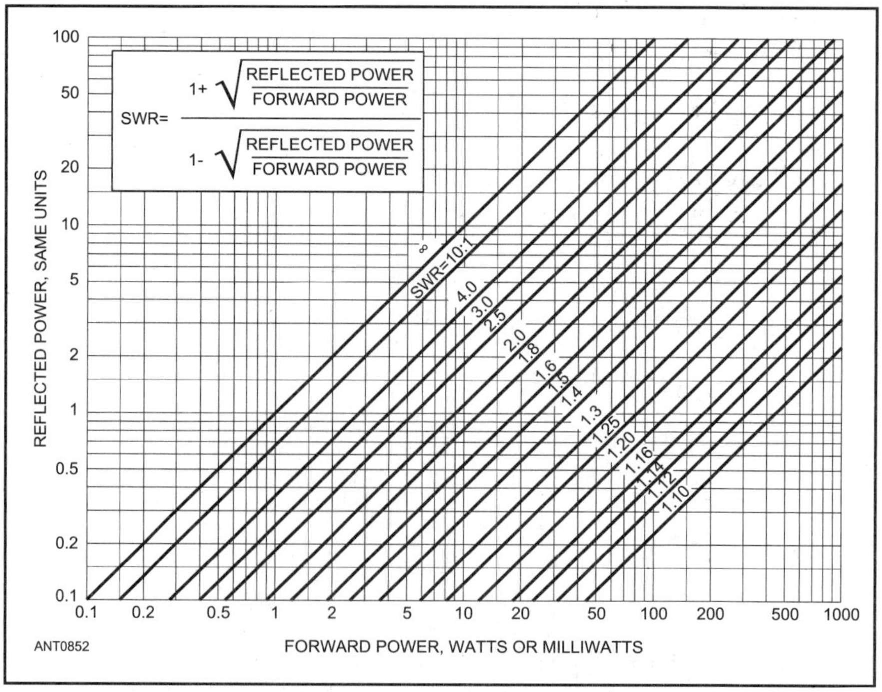

Figure 23.14 — SWR as a function of forward and reflected power.

SWR and Resonance

It is a common misunderstanding that for a transmission line connected to an antenna, minimum SWR occurs when the antenna is resonant. In a general sense, this is not true — minimum SWR occurs when the magnitude of the load's reflection coefficient, $|\rho|$, is at a minimum (see Eq 7). Viewing the load impedance on a Smith chart as in **Figure 23.A**, the value of $|\rho|$ is represented by the distance from the origin (center) to the point representing the load impedance. (The Smith chart is explored in the PDF supplement, "The Smith Chart" and the RSGB Radcom article, "Demystifying the Smith Chart or How to train your antenna" by Michael Tola, K3MT, that are included in the online material.)

As the frequency changes, the impedance of an antenna changes. The example in Figure 23.A shows points A, B and C — three plausible load impedances for an antenna at different frequencies. Point O is the origin. The antenna is resonant at both A and C since the points are on the X=0 line through the middle of the chart. At point A the impedance is $0.2 + j0$ or 10 Ω in a 50-Ω system and C represents $4.0 + j0$ Ω or 200 Ω. The magnitude of ρ at A is 0.67 and the SWR = 5:1. The magnitude of ρ at C is 0.6 and the SWR = 4:1. Point B represents the normalized load impedance $0.8 + j0.8$, which is $40 + j40$ Ω in a 50-Ω system. The magnitude of ρ at B is 0.42 and the SWR = 2.44. Even though the load impedance at B is reactive (nonresonant) the SWR is lower than at either of the two resonant points at A and C.

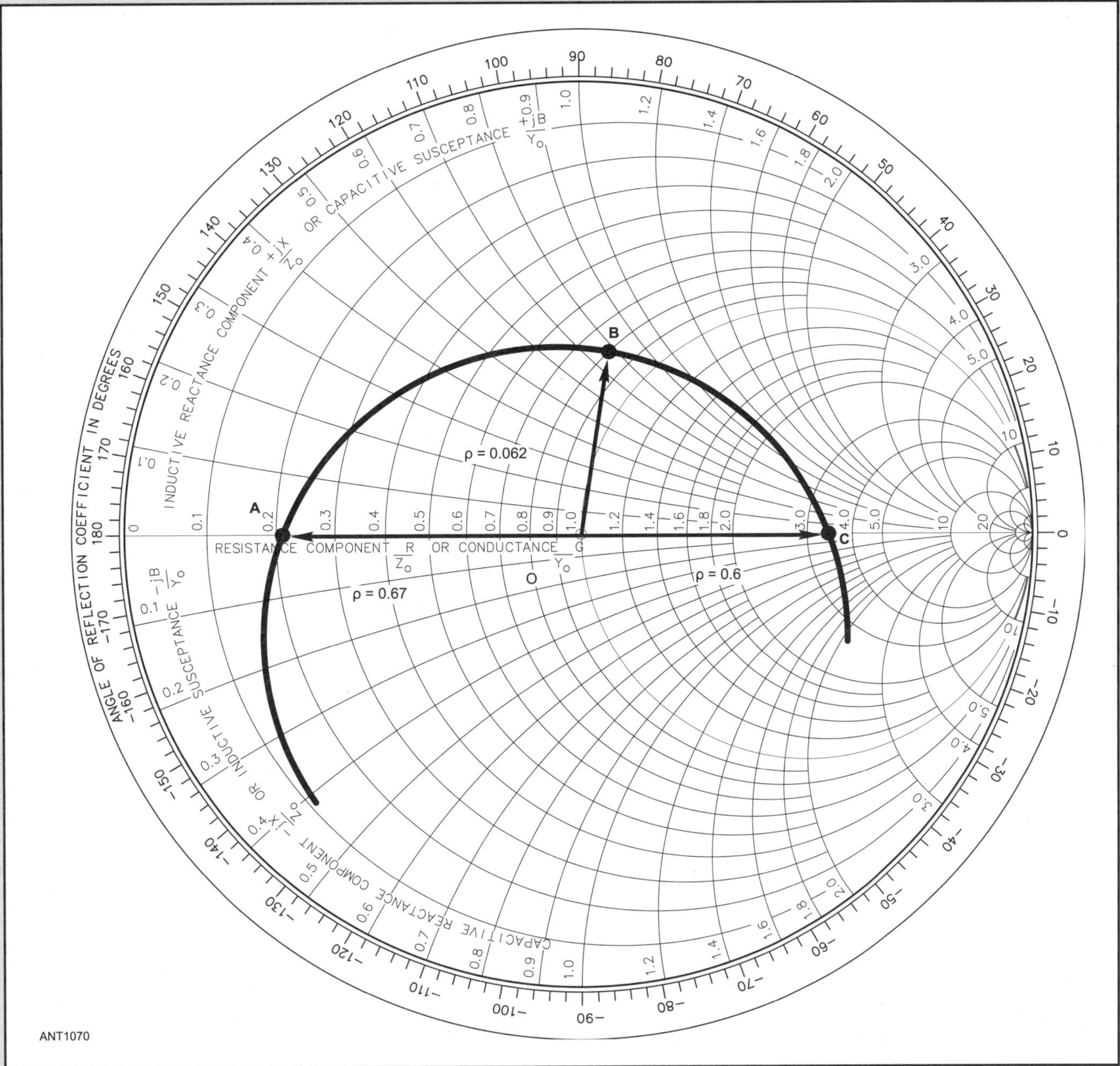

Figure 23.A — Load impedance viewed on a Smith chart.

the higher voltages and currents caused by elevated SWR but this is not power lost in the feed line.)

Additional loss in the line occurs because the effective values of both current and voltage become greater on lines with standing waves. The increase in effective current raises the ohmic losses (I^2R) in the conductors, and the increase in effective voltage increases the losses in the dielectric (E^2/R). (The nature of feed line loss is discussed at length in *Reflections* by W2DU — see the referenced entries for M. W. Maxwell.)

The increased loss caused by an SWR greater than 1:1 may or may not be serious. If the SWR at the load is not greater than 2:1, the additional loss caused by the standing waves, as compared with the loss when the line is perfectly matched, does not amount to more than about ½ dB, even on very long lines. One-half dB is an undetectable change in signal strength. Therefore, it can be said that, from a practical standpoint in the HF bands, an SWR of 2:1 or less is every bit as good as a perfect match, so far as additional losses due to SWR are concerned.

As is illustrated by the examples of a 100-foot-long doublet and a 66-foot-long Inverted V at the beginning of the chapter on **Transmission Line System Techniques**, both non-resonant antennas that are in widespread use on HF, the impedance mismatch and SWR can be quite high. In such cases, losses in even modest lengths of feed line can be unacceptably high. (See the online article "Multiband Operation with Open-wire Line" by George Cutsogeorge, W2VJN, with this book's online material.)

Above 30 MHz, in the VHF and especially the UHF range, where low receiver noise figures are essential for effective weak-signal work, matched-line losses for commonly available types of coax can be relatively high. This means that even a slight mismatch may become a concern regarding overall transmission line losses. At UHF one-half dB of additional loss may be considered intolerable!

The total loss in a line, including matched-line and the additional loss due to standing waves may be calculated from Eq 16 below for moderate levels of SWR (less than 20:1).

$$\text{Total Loss (dB)} = 10 \log \left(\frac{a^2 - |\rho|^2}{a\,(1 - |\rho|^2)} \right) \qquad (16)$$

where

$a = 10^{0.1\,ML}$ = matched-line loss ratio

ML = the matched-line loss in dB for the particular length of line

$|\rho|$ = the reflection coefficient at the load, calculated as in Eq 7

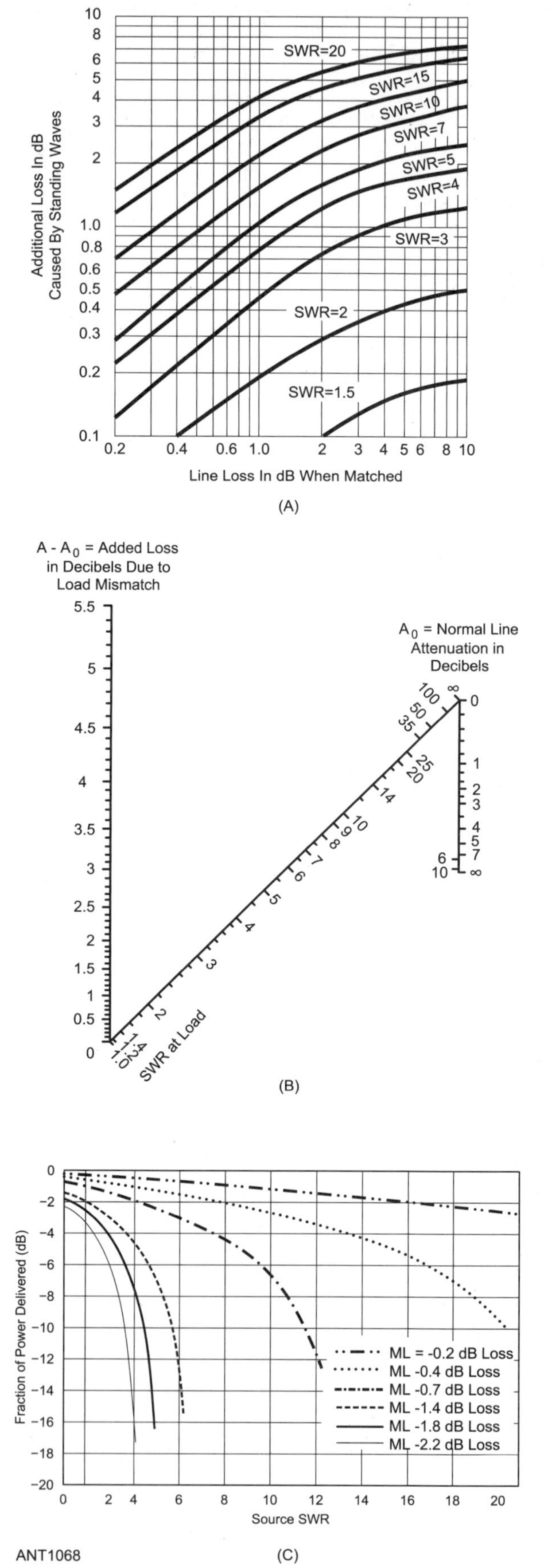

Figure 23.15 — (A) Additional line loss due to standing waves (SWR, measured at the load). See Figure 23.24 for matched-line loss. To determine the total loss in dB, add the matched-line loss to the value from this graph. (B) Nomograph showing Added Loss in dB due to mismatch (SWR at Load) with a known line attenuation. Place a straightedge along the points representing load SWR and line attenuation. Read additional loss on the left-hand scale. (C) Fractional amount of the input power delivered to the load given source or input SWR and line attenuation. (Graph provided courtesy of Refined Audiometrics Laboratory, LLC by David McLain, N7AIG.)

and reflected power is assumed to be re-reflected at the source. Thus, the additional loss caused by the standing waves is calculated from:

Additional Loss (dB) = Total Loss – ML (17)

For example, RG-213 coax at 14.2 MHz is rated at 0.795 dB of matched-line loss per 100 feet. A 150-foot length of RG-213 would have an overall matched-line loss of

$$(0.795/100) \times 150 = 1.193 \text{ dB}$$

Thus, if the SWR at the load end of the RG-213 is 4:1,

$$\alpha = 10^{1.193/10} = 1.316$$

$$|\rho| = \frac{4-1}{4+1} = 0.600$$

and the total line loss

$$= 10 \log \left(\frac{1.316^2 - 0.600^2}{1.316\,(1-0.600^2)} \right) = 2.12 \text{ dB}$$

The additional loss due to the SWR of 4:1 is 2.12 – 1.19 = 0.93 dB. **Figure 23.15A** is a graph of additional loss versus SWR. Figure 23.15B is a nomograph equivalent to Figure 23.15A. Figure 23.15C is an alternative graph that shows the fraction of input power actually delivered to the load for a given source SWR and line Matched Loss (ML).

23.2.5 Line Voltages and Currents

It is often desirable to know the maximum voltages and currents that are developed in a line operating with standing waves. (We'll cover the determination of the exact voltages and currents along a transmission line later.) The voltage maximum may be calculated from the equations below, and the other values determined from the result.

The following equation is the standard for calculating peak RMS voltage as a function of SWR at the load:

$$E_{max} = \left(1 + \frac{SWR - 1}{SWR + 1}\right)\sqrt{P \times Z_0} \qquad (18A)$$

where

E_{max} = voltage maximum along the line in the presence of standing waves

P = power delivered by the source to the line input in watts

Z_0 = characteristic impedance of the line in ohms

SWR = SWR at the load

For example, if P = 100 W in a 50 Ω line with an SWR of 4:1,

$$E_{max} = \left(1 + \frac{4-1}{4+1}\right)\sqrt{100 \times 50} = 113 \text{ V}$$

The value of E_{max} for an infinite SWR is twice the incident voltage according to this equation. Strictly speaking, this value of E_{max} only applies near the load in the case of lines with appreciable losses. However, the resultant values are the maximum possible that can exist along the line under normal circumstances. For this reason the value is useful as a rule-of-thumb in determining whether or not a particular line can operate safely with a given SWR. Voltage ratings for various cable types are given in a later section.

Figure 23.16 shows the peak ratio of current or voltage, in the presence of standing waves, to the current or voltage that would exist with the same power in a perfectly matched line. As with Eq 18 and related calculations, the curve literally applies only near the load.

An alternate calculation applies if P is the net input power, which on a directional wattmeter equals $P_{fwd} - P_{refl}$, and none of the reflected power is absorbed by the source (such as a transmitter's output stage) or by line loss. In such a case, power is continually "pumped" into the line. If the termination is infinite, such as for a short or open, power is only dissipated by line loss and voltage can become very high.

$$E_{max} = \sqrt{P \times Z_0 \times SWR} \qquad (18B)$$

An alternate equation provided by Bob Zavrel, W7SX, is:

$$E_{max} = \left(\frac{1}{1 - |\rho|}\right)\sqrt{P \times Z_0} \qquad (18C)$$

If $P_{fwd} - P_{refl}$ = 100 W of power is applied to the same 50-Ω line with an SWR at the load of 4:1, using equation 18b the maximum voltage is:

$$E_{max} = \sqrt{100 \times 50 \times 4} = 141.4 \text{ V}$$

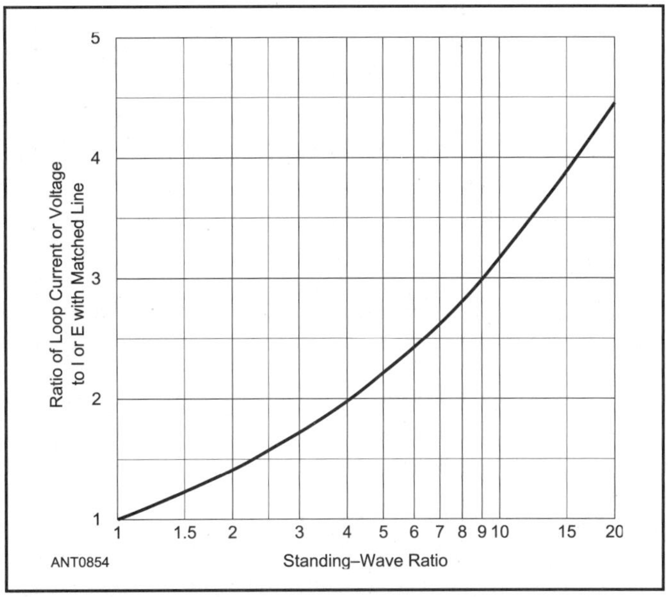

Figure 23.16 — Increase in maximum value of current or voltage on a line with standing waves, as referred to the current or voltage on a perfectly matched line, for the same power delivered to the load. Voltage and current at minimum points are given by the reciprocals of the values along the vertical axis. The curve is plotted from the relationship, current (or voltage) ratio = the square root of SWR.

In practice, when SWR is very high, line losses and transmitter output amplifier protection circuitry limit the peak line voltage caused by standing waves to a lower value.

Regardless of which equation is used, from Eq 9, E_{min}, the minimum voltage along the line equals E_{max}/SWR. The maximum current may be found by using Ohm's law. $I_{max} = E_{max}/Z_0$. The minimum current equals I_{max}/SWR.

The voltages determined in the various forms of Eq 18 are RMS values — that is, the voltages that would be measured with an ordinary RF voltmeter. If voltage breakdown is a consideration, the value from Eq 18 should be converted to an *instantaneous peak voltage* by multiplying by 1.414 and by 2.828 to find the instantaneous peak-to-peak voltage.

23.2.6 Input Impedance

The effects of incident and reflected voltage and current along a mismatched transmission line can be difficult to envision, particularly when the load at the end of the transmission line is not purely resistive, and when the line is not perfectly lossless.

If we can put aside for a moment all the complexities of reflections, SWR and line losses, a transmission line can simply be considered to be an *impedance transformer*. A certain value of load impedance, consisting of a resistance and reactance, at the end of a particular transmission line is transformed into another value of impedance at the input of the line. The amount of transformation is determined by the electrical length of the line, its characteristic impedance, and by the losses inherent in the line. The input impedance of a real, lossy transmission line is computed using the following equation, called the *Transmission Line Equation*, which uses the hyperbolic cosine and sine functions.

$$Z_{in} = Z_0 \frac{Z_L \cosh(\gamma\ell) + Z_0 \sinh(\gamma\ell)}{Z_L \sinh(\gamma\ell) + Z_0 \cosh(\gamma\ell)} \qquad (19)$$

where

Z_{in} = complex impedance at input of line

Z_L = complex load impedance at end of line = $R_a \pm j\,X_a$

Z_0 = characteristic impedance of line = $R_0 - j\,X_0$

ℓ = physical length of line

γ = complex loss coefficient = $\alpha + j\,\beta$

α = matched-line loss attenuation constant, in nepers/unit length (1 neper = 8.686 dB; cables are rated in dB/100 ft)

β = phase constant of line in radians/unit length (related to physical length of line ℓ by the fact that 2π radians = one wavelength, and by Eq 2)

$$\beta = \frac{2\pi}{VF \times 983.6 / f(MHz)} \text{ for } \ell \text{ in feet}$$

VF = velocity factor

For example, assume that a half-wave dipole terminates a 50-foot long piece of RG-213 coax. This dipole is assumed to have an impedance of 43 + j 30 Ω at 7.15 MHz, and its velocity factor is 0.66. The matched-line loss at 7.15 MHz is 0.54 dB/100 feet, and the characteristic impedance Z_0 for this type of cable at this frequency is 50 – j 0.45 Ω. Using Eq 19, we compute the impedance at the input of the line as 65.8 + j 32.0 Ω.

Solving this equation manually is quite tedious, but it may be solved using a traditional paper Smith chart or a computer program. (The PDF file "The Smith Chart" explains how to use the chart and is available with this book's online material.) *SimSmith* by AE6TY (**ae6ty.com/Smith_Charts.html**) is available for free download and there are several on-line calculators available if you search for "smith chart calculator" on the Internet. *TLW* (Transmission Line for Windows) is an ARRL program that performs this transformation, but without Smith chart graphics. *TLW* is available with this book's online material.

One caution should be noted when using any of these computational tools to calculate the impedance at the input of a mismatched transmission line — the velocity factor of practical transmission lines can vary significantly between manufacturing runs of the same type of cable. For highest accuracy, you should measure the velocity factor of a particular length of cable before using it to compute the impedance at the end of the cable. See the chapter **Antenna and Transmission Line Measurements** for details on measurements of line characteristics.

INPUT SWR AND LINE LOSS

If the line is not perfectly matched to the load the loss in the line reduces the amount of reflected power that returns to the source end of the line. This makes SWR appear lower at the source (transmitter) end of the line than it is at the load (antenna) end of the line. The longer the line or the higher the loss, the more power is dissipated as heat and the lower the input SWR. In fact, a long (many wavelengths) lossy transmission line can be used as a dummy load at VHF and higher frequencies.

A nomograph is given in **Figure 23.17** that relates load SWR, line attenuation, and load SWR. If you know any two of those three parameters, place a ruler between those two points and read the third from the intersection of the ruler with the scale for the unknown parameter.

SERIES AND PARALLEL EQUIVALENT CIRCUITS

Once the series-form impedance $R_S \pm j\,X_S$ at the input of a particular line has been determined, either by measurement or by computation, you may wish to determine the equivalent parallel circuit $R_P \parallel \pm j\,X_P$, which is equivalent to the series form only at a single frequency. (|| is an abbreviation for "in parallel with.") The equivalent parallel circuit is often useful when designing a matching circuit (such as an antenna tuner, for example) to transform the impedance at the input of the cable to another impedance. The following equations are used

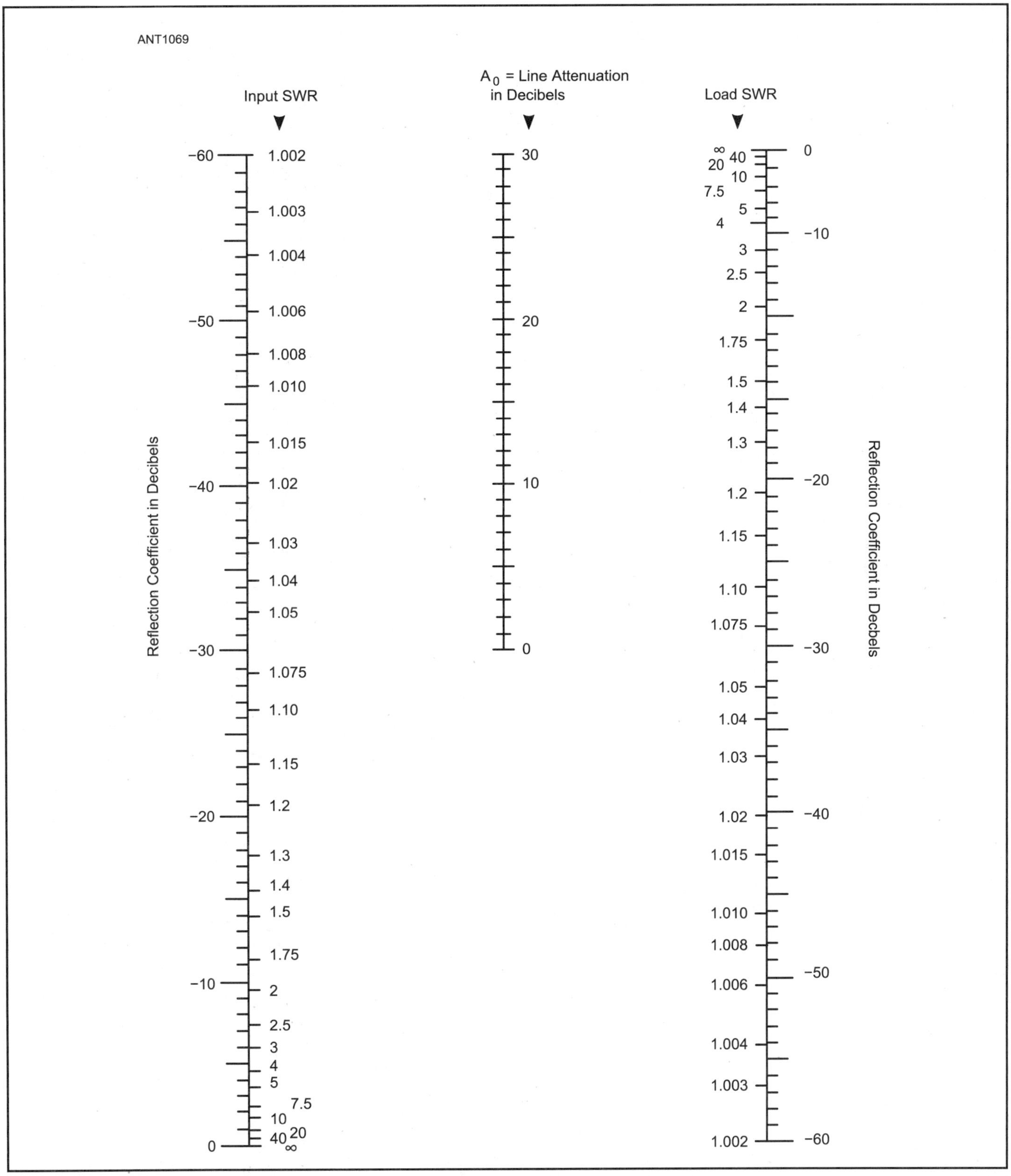

Figure 23.17 — Nomograph showing that load SWR, line attenuation or input SWR can be determined if two of the values are known. Place a straightedge between the two known values and read the value of the third where the straightedge crosses the scale for the third parameter.

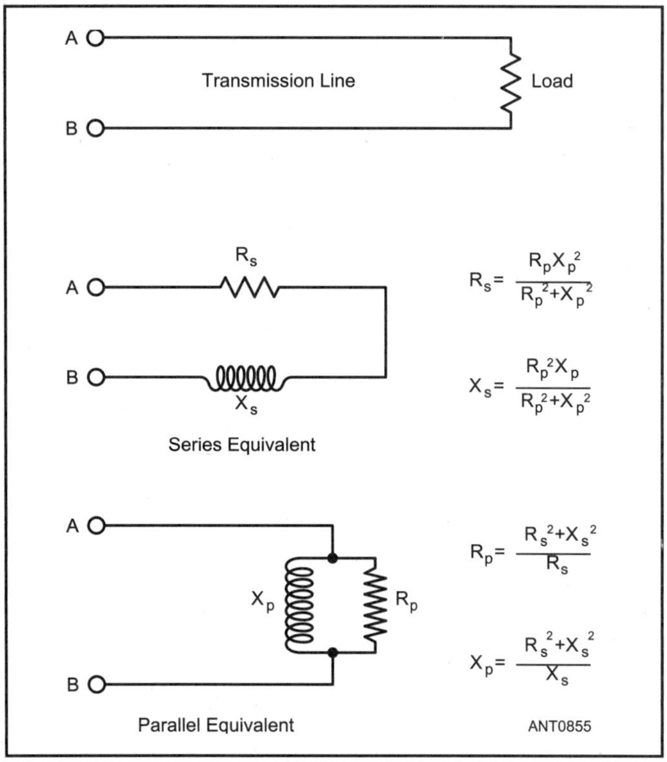

Figure 23.18 — Input impedance of a line terminated in a resistance. This impedance can be represented by either a resistance and reactance in series, or a resistance and reactance in parallel, at a single frequency. The relationships between the R and X values in the series and parallel equivalents are given by the equations shown. X may be either inductive or capacitive, depending on the line length, Z_0 and the load impedance, which need not be purely resistive.

to make the transformation from series to parallel and from parallel to series. See **Figure 23.18**.

$$R_p = \frac{R_s^2 + X_s^2}{R_s} \qquad (20A)$$

$$X_p = \frac{R_s^2 + X_s^2}{X_s} \qquad (20B)$$

and

$$R_s = \frac{R_p X_p^2}{R_p^2 + X_p^2} \qquad (21A)$$

$$X_s = \frac{R_p^2 X_p}{R_p^2 + X_p^2} \qquad (21B)$$

The individual values in the parallel circuit are not the same as those in the series circuit (although the overall result is the same, but only at one frequency), but are related to the series-circuit values by these equations. For example, let us continue the example in the section above, where the impedance at the input of the 50 feet of RG-213 at 7.15 MHz is 65.8 + *j* 32.0 Ω. The equivalent parallel circuit at 7.15 MHz is

$$R_p = \frac{65.8^2 + 32.1^2}{65.8} = 81.46\ \Omega$$

$$X_p = \frac{65.8^2 + 31.2^2}{31.2} = 169.97\ \Omega$$

If we were to put 100 W of power into this parallel equivalent circuit, the voltage across the parallel components would be

$$\text{Since } P = \frac{E^2}{R},\quad E = \sqrt{P \times R} = \sqrt{100 \times 81.46} = 90.26\ \text{V}$$

Thus, the current through the inductive part of the parallel circuit would be

$$I = \frac{E}{X_p} = \frac{90.26}{169.97} = 0.53\ \text{A}$$

HIGHLY REACTIVE LOADS

When highly reactive loads are used with practical transmission lines, especially coax lines, the overall loss can reach staggering levels. For example, a popular multiband antenna is a 100-foot long center-fed dipole located some 50 feet over average ground. At 1.83 MHz, such an antenna will exhibit a feed-point impedance of 4.5 – *j* 1673 Ω, according to the analysis program *EZNEC*. The high value of capacitive reactance indicates that the antenna is extremely short electrically — after all, a half-wave dipole at 1.83 MHz is almost 270 feet long, compared to this 100 foot long antenna. If an amateur attempts to feed such a multiband antenna directly with 100 feet of RG-213 50-Ω coaxial cable, the SWR at the antenna terminals would be (using the *TLW* program from this book's online material) 1740:1. An SWR of more than 1700 to one is a very high level of SWR indeed! At 1.83 MHz the matched-line loss of 100 feet of the RG-213 coax by itself is only 0.26 dB. However, the total line loss due to this extreme level of SWR is 26 dB.

This means that if 100 W is fed into the input of this line, the amount of power at the antenna is reduced to only 0.25 W. Admittedly this is an extreme case. It is more likely that an amateur would feed such a multiband antenna with open-wire ladder or window line than coaxial cable. The matched-line loss characteristics for 450-Ω window open-wire line are far better than coax, but the SWR at the end of this line is still 793:1, resulting in an overall loss of 8.9 dB. Even for low-loss open-wire line, the total loss is significant because of the extreme SWR.

This means that only about 13% of the power from the transmitter is getting to the antenna, and although this is not very desirable, it is a lot better than the losses in coax cable feeding the same antenna. However, at a transmitter power level of 1500 W, the maximum voltage in a typical antenna tuner used to match this line impedance is almost 9200V with the open-wire line, a level which will certainly cause arcing or burning inside. (As a small compensation for all the loss in coax under this extreme condition, so much power is lost that the voltages present in the antenna tuner are not excessive.) Keep in mind also that an antenna tuner can lose significant power in internal losses for very high impedance levels, even if it has sufficient range to match such impedances in the first place.

Clearly, it would be far better to use a longer antenna at this 160 meter frequency. Another alternative would be to resonate a short antenna with loading coils (at the antenna). Either strategy would help avoid excessive feed line loss, even with low-loss line.

23.2.7 Special Cases

Beside the primary purpose of transporting power from one point to another, transmission lines have properties that are useful in a variety of ways. One such special case is a line an exact multiple of λ/4 (90°) long. As shown earlier, such a line will have a purely resistive input impedance when the termination is a pure resistance. Also, short-circuited or open-circuited lines can be used in place of conventional inductors and capacitors since such lines have an input impedance that is substantially a pure reactance when the line losses are low. (An alternate way of explaining the interesting behavior of transmission lines — "My Feedline Tunes My Antenna!" by Byron Goodman, W1DX — is included with this book's online material. Originally published in 1956, this classic *QST* article is still useful today.)

THE HALF-WAVELENGTH LINE

When the line length is a multiple of 180° (that is, a multiple of λ/2), the input resistance is equal to the load resistance, regardless of the line Z_0. As a matter of fact, a line an exact multiple of λ/2 in length (disregarding line losses) simply repeats, at its input or sending end, whatever impedance exists at its output or receiving end. It does not matter whether the impedance at the receiving end is resistive, reactive, or a combination of both. Sections of line having such length can be added or removed without changing any of the operating conditions, at least when the losses in the line itself are negligible.

IMPEDANCE TRANSFORMATION WITH QUARTER-WAVE LINES

The input impedance of a line an odd multiple of λ/4 long is

$$Z_i = \frac{Z_0^2}{Z_L} \quad (22)$$

where Z_i is the input impedance and Z_L is the load impedance. If Z_L is a pure resistance, Z_i will also be a pure resistance. Rearranging this equation gives

$$Z_0 = \sqrt{Z_i Z_L} \quad (23)$$

This means that if we have two values of impedance that we wish to "match," we can do so if we connect them together by a λ/4 transmission line having a characteristic impedance equal to the square root of their product.

A λ/4 line is, in effect, a transformer, and in fact is often referred to as a *quarter-wave transformer*. It is frequently used as such in antenna work when it is desired, for example, to transform the impedance of an antenna to a new value that will match a given transmission line. This subject is considered in greater detail in the **Transmission Line System Techniques** chapter section "Quarter-Wave Transformers."

LINES AS CIRCUIT ELEMENTS

Two types of non-resistive line terminations are quite useful — short and open circuits. The impedance of the short-circuit termination is 0 + *j*0, and the impedance of the open-circuit termination is infinite. Such terminations are used in *stub matching* as described in the **Transmission Line System Techniques** chapter. Applications of line sections as circuit elements in connection with antenna and transmission-line systems are discussed in later chapters.

An open- or short-circuited line does not deliver any power to a load, and for that reason is not, strictly speaking a "transmission" line. However, the fact that a line of the proper length has inductive reactance makes it possible to substitute the line for a coil in an ordinary circuit. Likewise, another line of appropriate length having capacitive reactance can be substituted for a capacitor.

Sections of lines used as circuit elements are usually λ/4 or shorter. The desired type of reactance (inductive or capacitive) or the desired type of resonance (series or parallel) is obtained by shorting or opening the far end of the line. The circuit equivalents of various types of line sections are shown in **Figure 23.19**. Longer lengths of line are not necessary since any value of impedance available from a particular type of feed line is attainable in λ/4 or less.

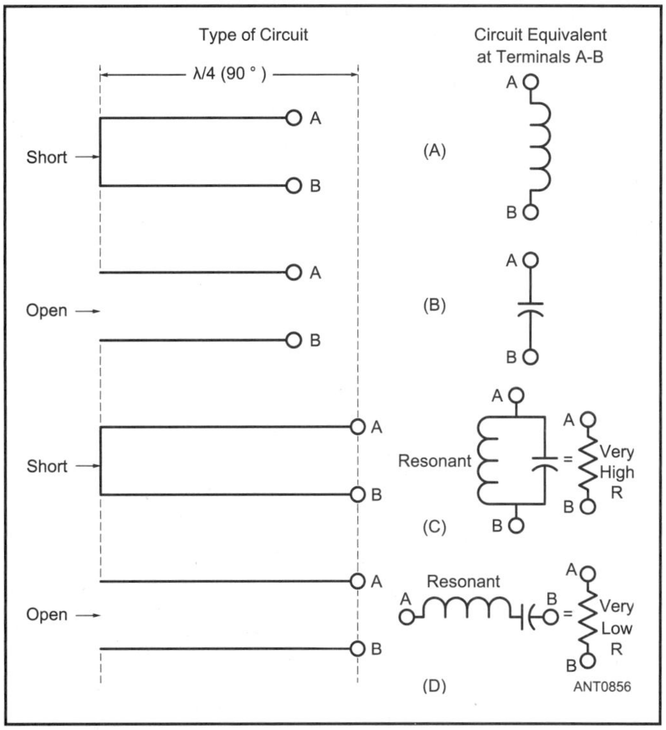

Figure 23.19 — Lumped-constant circuit equivalents of open- and short-circuited transmission lines.

When a line section is used as a reactance, the amount of reactance is determined by the characteristic impedance and the electrical length of the line. The type of reactance exhibited at the input terminals of a line of given length depends on whether it is open- or short-circuited at the far end.

The equivalent *lumped* value for any inductor or capacitor may be determined with the aid of the Smith chart or the Transmission Line Equation, Eq 19. Line losses may be taken into account if desired, as explained for Eq 19. In the case of a line having no losses, and to a close approximation when the losses are small, the inductive reactance of a short-circuited line less than λ/4 in length is

$$X_L \text{ in } \Omega = Z_0 \tan \ell \qquad (24)$$

where ℓ is the length of the line in electrical degrees and Z_0 is the characteristic impedance of the line.

The capacitive reactance of an open-circuited line less than λ/4 in length is

$$X_C \text{ in } \Omega = Z_0 \cot \ell \qquad (25)$$

Lengths of line that are exact multiples of λ/4 have the properties of resonant circuits. With an open-circuit termination, the input impedance of the line acts like a series-resonant circuit. With a short-circuit termination, the line input simulates a parallel-resonant circuit. The effective Q of such linear resonant circuits is very high if the line losses, both in resistance and by radiation, are kept down. This can be done without much difficulty, particularly in coaxial lines, if air insulation is used between the conductors. Air-insulated open-wire lines are likewise very good at frequencies for which the conductor spacing is very small in terms of wavelength.

23.2.8 Voltage and Current Along a Line

The voltage and current along a transmission line will vary in a predictable manner, whether that line is matched or mismatched at its load end. (The voltage and current along a matched line vary because of loss in the line.) Eq 26 below describes the voltage at point ℓ, while Eq 27 describes the current at point ℓ, each as a function of the voltage at the input of the line.

$$E_x = E_{in}\left(\cosh \gamma\ell - \frac{Z_0}{Z_{in}} \sinh \gamma\ell\right) \text{volts} \qquad (26)$$

$$I_x = \frac{E_{in}}{Z_{in}}\left(\cosh \gamma\ell - \frac{Z_{in}}{Z_0} \sinh \gamma\ell\right) \text{amperes} \qquad (27)$$

where γ = complex loss coefficient used in Eq 19, and cosh and sinh are the hyperbolic cosine and sine functions. The load end of the transmission line is, by definition, at a length of ℓ.

A useful identity for working with the $\cosh^{-1}$ or acosh function encountered in transmission line calculations is:

$$\cosh^{-1}(x) = \ln\left(x + \sqrt{x^2 - 1}\right)$$

The inverse hyperbolic cosine (cosh) is sometimes accessed on calculators by using the INV (inverse) key before COSH.

The power at the input and the output of a transmission line may be calculated using Eq 28 and Eq 29 below.

$$P_{in} = |E_{in}|^2\, G_{in} \text{ watts} \qquad (28)$$

$$P_{load} = |E_{load}|^2\, G_{load} \text{ watts} \qquad (29)$$

where G_{in} and G_{load} are the admittance at the input (the real part of $1/Z_{in}$) and the admittance at the load (the real part of $1/Z_{load}$) ends respectively of the line. Z_{in} is calculated using Eq 19 for a length of ℓ.

The power loss in the transmission line in dB is:

$$P_{loss} = 10 \log\left(\frac{P_{in}}{P_{load}}\right) \text{dB} \qquad (30)$$

23.2.9 Magnetic Fields and Twisted Pair Lines

(*From K9YC's tutorial, "A Ham's Guide to RFI, Ferrites, Baluns, and Audio Interfacing" at* ***k9yc.com/publish.htm***.) A coaxial cable shield prevents electric field (capacitive) coupling, but it has little effect on magnetic fields (that is, inductive coupling). This is true at low frequencies because cable shields are not made of magnetic material. It is true at high frequencies because of imperfections in the shield that decrease the uniformity of current flow on the shield.

A transmission line does reject magnetic fields, but it does this by virtue of the mutual coupling between the conductors that causes the current and voltage induced in them by an external field to be equal and opposite, so they cancel at the input circuit to which the cable is connected. The degree of this equality depends on the coupling coefficient k, which is typically on the order of 0.7 for a closely spaced twisted pair. An ideal coaxial cable, however, has a coupling coefficient of 1 above the cutoff frequency of the shield (see below). So, the shield of a coaxial cable is not a magnetic shield, it is an electric shield. Magnetic noise rejection is the result of mutual coupling between the center conductor and the shield, not because of shielding.

Another important fact explains why coaxial cables don't reject magnetically coupled low frequency hum and buzz. Cables don't exhibit mutual coupling at frequencies where the resistance of the conductor is greater than its inductive reactance. The low frequency at which this transition occurs is called the *shield cutoff frequency*. For most cables, this is between about 1 kHz (coax with a heavy double copper braid shield) and 20 kHz (coax with a foil/drain shield).

Twisting works to reject noise from the magnetic field because it causes the voltage induced in the two conductors to be more nearly equal. It also reduces electric field coupling

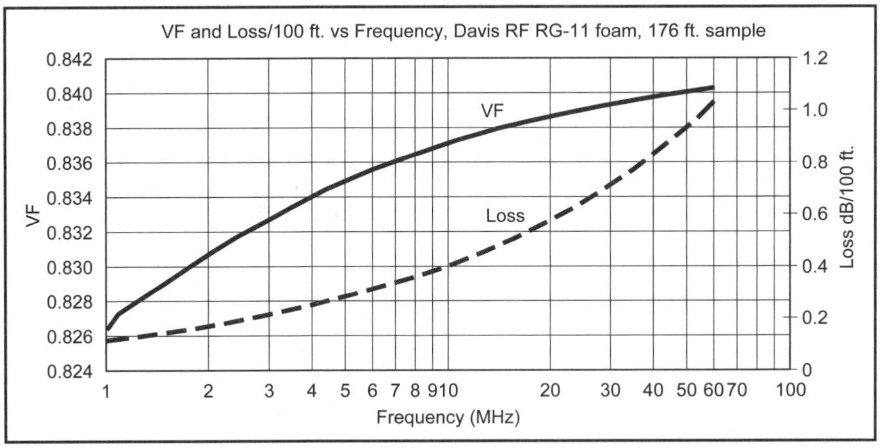

Figure 23.20 — The actual performance of transmission lines varies with frequency. For precision use of a cable, the exact value of Z_0, VF, and loss should be measured at the frequency of use.

in balanced circuits. In general, the "tighter" the twist, the more equal the induced voltage will be to the highest frequency. That's because any interfering field will vary with position based on the wavelength of the field.

To understand how twisting rejects magnetic noise, consider an interfering source such as a transformer with a two-conductor cable running past it. If the cable is not twisted, one conductor will be closer to the source, so more noise will be coupled to it than the other conductor. If the conductors are twisted, one conductor will be closer at one point along the cable, but one half twist further along the cable, the other conductor will be closer. The difference in spacing between the conductors may not sound like it should cause much difference in level, but if we need 100 dB of cancellation, the two voltages must be equal within .0001%, a very small margin of error. Balancing the noise voltage that is induced in each conductor keeps it a common-mode voltage and prevents it from becoming a differential-mode signal in the cable which would interfere with the desired signal.

For example, when using software to transform antenna measurements made in the station to the actual impedance at the feed point, the variability of VF must be applied to data for antennas for the lower bands (14 MHz and below). AC6LA's free *Zplots* utility software (**ac6la.com/zplots1.html**) plots VF, Z_0, and attenuation versus frequency from measurements of a known length of a transmission made with the far end open and again with the far end shorted.

Figure 23.20 is a plot of VF and attenuation computed by *ZPlots* from such measurements on a 176-foot length of RG-11 cable with a #14 AWG solid copper center conductor, a foam dielectric, and a copper braid shield. This behavior and general curve shape are typical of all transmission lines as predicted by fundamental transmission line equations. Exact values for each line will differ based on their physical dimensions and their dielectric.

23.3 Feed Line Construction and Operating Characteristics

The two basic types of transmission lines, parallel conductor and coaxial, can be constructed in a variety of forms. Both types can be divided into two classes, (1) those in which the majority of the insulation between the conductors is air, where only the minimum of solid dielectric necessary for mechanical support is used, and (2) those in which the conductors are embedded in and separated by a solid dielectric. The first variety (air-insulated) has the lowest loss per unit length, because there is no power loss in dry air if the voltage between conductors is below the level at which corona forms. At the maximum power permitted for amateur transmitters, it is seldom necessary to consider corona unless the SWR on the line is very high.

Transmission lines in which the conductors are separated by a flexible dielectric have a number of advantages over the air-insulated type. They are less bulky, weigh less in comparable types and maintain more uniform spacing between conductors. They are also generally easier to install, and are neater in appearance. Both parallel conductor and coaxial lines are available with flexible insulation.

The chief disadvantage of such lines is that the power loss per unit length is greater than in air-insulated lines. Power is lost in heating of the dielectric, and if the heating is great enough (as it may be with high power and a high SWR) the line may break down mechanically and electrically.

23.3.1 Air-Insulated Lines

Figure 23.21 shows four different types of air-insulated transmission lines. The two-wire and coaxial lines are common in amateur use. The four-wire line is most common at high-

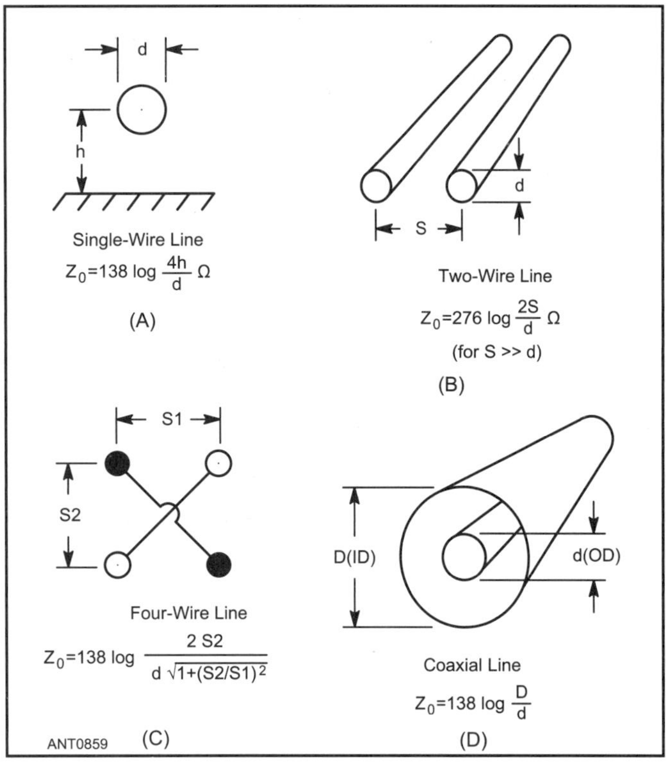

Figure 23.21 — **Construction of air-insulated transmission lines.**

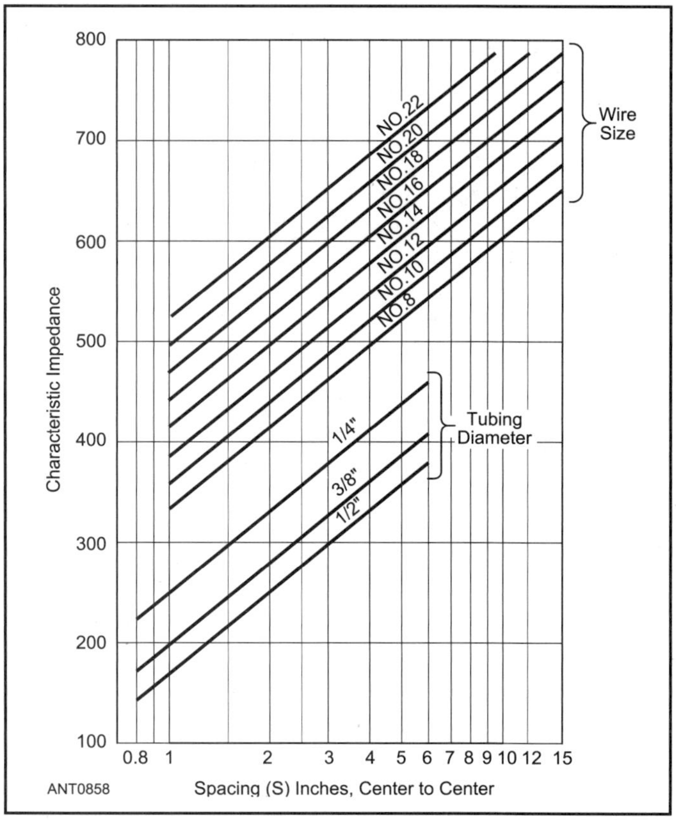

Figure 23.22 — **Characteristic impedance as a function of conductor spacing and size for parallel conductor lines.**

power commercial and military installations. The single-wire line is useful in some types of point-to-point construction.

The characteristic impedance of an air-insulated parallel conductor line, neglecting the effect of the spacers, is given by

$$Z_0 = \frac{120}{\sqrt{\varepsilon}} \cosh^{-1}\left(\frac{S}{d}\right) = \frac{276}{\sqrt{\varepsilon}} \log\left[\frac{S}{d} + \sqrt{\left(\frac{S}{d}\right)^2 - 1}\right] \qquad (31A)$$

where

Z_0 = characteristic impedance in ohms

ε = relative permittivity of insulating medium (1 for dry air)

S = center-to-center distance between conductors

d = outer diameter of conductor (in the same units as S)

An approximation that can be used when S >> d and ε=1 is:

$$Z_0 = 276 \log\left(\frac{2S}{d}\right) \qquad (31B)$$

The error of the approximation becomes significant for S/d < 3.

For single-wire lines, similar formulas are used with the same caveat about errors for 2h/d < 3:

$$Z_0 = 60 \cosh^{-1}\left(\frac{2h}{d}\right) = 138 \log\left(\frac{4h}{d}\right) \qquad (31C)$$

Impedances for two-wire lines using common sizes of conductors over a range of spacings are given in **Figure 23.22**.

At very close spacings, such as for the parallel-wire lines used for winding chokes and baluns, the exact formula should be used. **Figure 23.23** shows the difference in calculated values for very close spacings.

FOUR-WIRE LINES

Another parallel conductor line that is useful in some applications is the four-wire line (Figure 23.21C). In cross section, the conductors of the four-wire line are at the corners of a square. Spacings are on the same order as those used in two-wire lines. The conductors at opposite corners of the square are connected to operate in parallel. This type of line has a lower characteristic impedance than the simple two-wire type. Also, because of the more symmetrical construction, it has better electrical balance to ground and other objects that are close to the line. The spacers for a four-wire line may be discs of insulating material, X-shaped members, etc.

AIR-INSULATED COAXIAL LINES

In air-insulated coaxial lines (Figure 23.21D), a considerable proportion of the insulation between conductors may actually be a solid dielectric, because the separation between the inner and outer conductors must be constant. This is particularly likely to be true in small diameter lines. The inner conductor, usually a solid copper wire, is supported at the center of the copper tubing outer conductor by insulating beads or a helically wound strip of insulating material. The beads are usually a ceramic such as isolantite or Steatite, and the wire is generally crimped on each side of each bead to prevent the beads from sliding. The material of which the beads are made, and the number of beads per unit length of line, will affect the characteristic impedance of the line. The greater the number of beads in a given length, the lower the characteristic impedance compared with the value obtained with air insulation only. Teflon is ordinarily used as a helically wound support for the center conductor. A tighter helical winding lowers the characteristic impedance.

The presence of the solid dielectric also increases the losses in the line. On the whole, however, a coaxial line of this type tends to have lower actual loss, at frequencies up to about 100 MHz, than any other line construction, provided the air inside the line can be kept dry. This usually means that air-tight seals must be used at the ends of the line and at every joint. The characteristic impedance of an air-insulated coaxial line is given by

$$Z_0 = 138 \log \frac{D}{d} \qquad (32)$$

where

Z_0 = characteristic impedance in ohms

D = inside diameter of outer conductor

d = outside diameter of inner conductor (in same units as D)

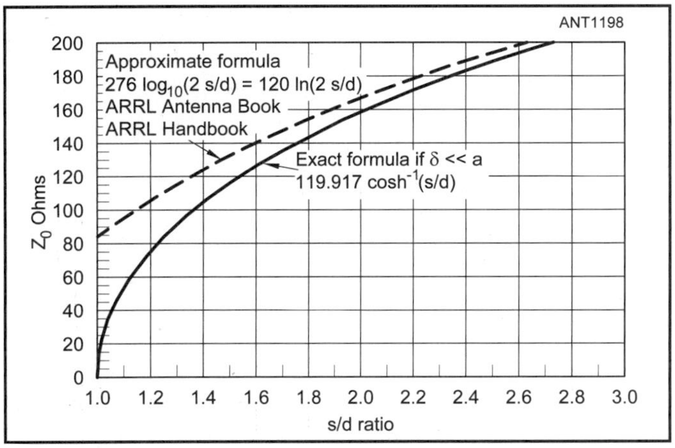

Figure 23.23 — A graph showing the approximate and the exact calculations of characteristic impedance for close-spaced parallel-wire lines. [Contributed by Steve Stearns, K6OIK, Pacificon, Oct 2010]

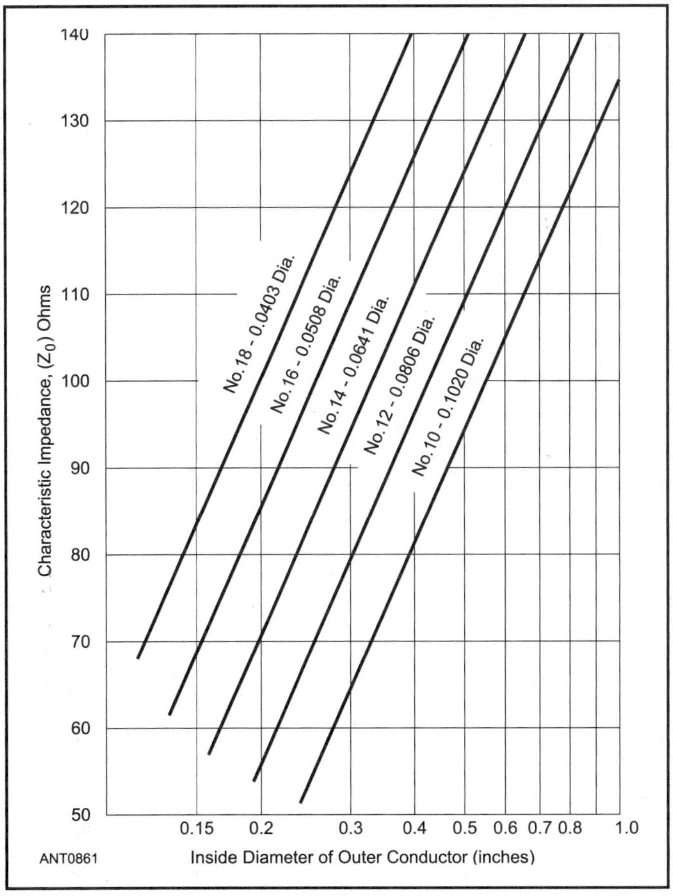

Figure 23.24 — Characteristic impedance of typical air insulated coaxial lines.

Values for typical conductor sizes are graphed in **Figure 23.24**. The equation and the graph for coaxial lines are approximately correct for lines in which bead spacers are used, provided the beads are not too closely spaced.

23.3.2 Parallel-Conductor Lines

For common *twin-lead* (see Figure 23.10E) the conductors are stranded wire equivalent to #20 AWG in cross-sectional area, and are molded in the edges of a polyethylene ribbon about ½-inch wide that keeps the wires spaced a constant amount away from each other. The effective dielectric is partly solid and partly air, and the presence of the solid dielectric lowers the characteristic impedance of the line as compared with the same conductors in air. The resulting impedance is approximately 300 Ω. This type of feed line is most commonly used for TV and broadcast FM receiving antennas.

Because part of the field between the conductors exists outside the solid dielectric, dirt and moisture on the surface of the ribbon tend to change the characteristic impedance of the line. The operation of the line is therefore affected by weather conditions. The effect will not be very serious in a line terminated in its characteristic impedance, but if there is a considerable mismatch, a small change in Z_0 may cause wide fluctuations of the input impedance. Weather effects can be minimized by cleaning the line occasionally and giving it a thin coating of a water repellent material such as silicone grease or car wax.

To overcome the effects of weather on the characteristic impedance and attenuation of ribbon type line, another type of twin-lead is made using an oval polyethylene tube with an air core or a foamed dielectric core. The conductors are molded diametrically opposite each other in the walls. This increases the leakage path across the dielectric surface. Also, much of the electric field between the conductors is in the hollow (or foam-filled) center of the tube. This type of line is fairly

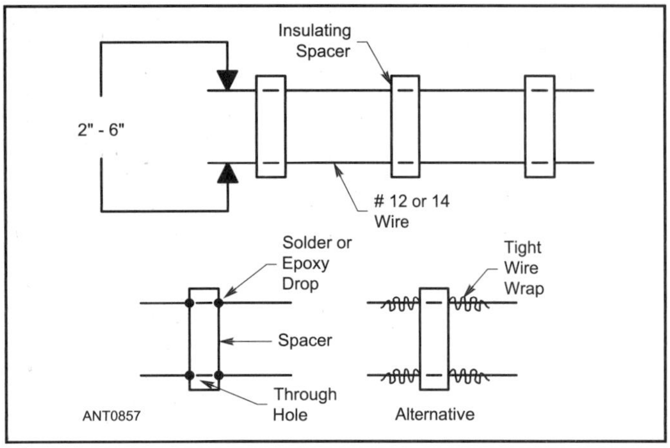

Figure 23.25 — Typical open-wire line construction. The spacers may be held in place by beads of solder or epoxy cement. Wire wraps can also be used, as shown.

impervious to weather effects. Care should be used when installing it, however, so any moisture that condenses on the inside with changes in temperature and humidity can drain out at the bottom end of the tube and not be trapped in one section. This type of line is made in two conductor sizes (with different tube diameters), one for receiving applications and the other for transmitting.

Ladder line as shown in Figure 23.10F is one of the oldest forms of transmission lines used by amateur. Although once

Table 23.1
Nominal Characteristics of Commonly Used Transmission Lines

RG or Type	*Part Number*	*Nom. Z_0 Ω*	*VF %*	*Cap. pF/ft*	*Cent. Cond. AWG*	*Diel. Type*	*Shield Type*	*Jacket Matl*	*OD inches*	*Max V (RMS)*	*Matched Loss (dB/100') 1 MHz*	*10*	*100*	*1000*
RG-6	Belden 1694A	75	82	16.2	#18 Solid BC	FPE	FC	P1	0.275	300	0.3	.7	1.8	5.9
RG-6	Belden 8215	75	66	20.5	#21 Solid CCS	PE	D	PE	0.332	2700	0.4	0.8	2.7	9.8
RG-8	Belden 7810A	50	86	23.0	#10 Solid BC	FPE	FC	PE	0.405	300	0.1	0.4	1.2	4.0
RG-8	TMS LMR400	50	85	23.9	#10 Solid CCA	FPE	FC	PE	0.405	600	0.1	0.4	1.3	4.1
RG-8	Belden 9913	50	84	24.6	#10 Solid BC	ASPE	FC	P1	0.405	300	0.1	0.4	1.3	4.5
RG-8	CXP1318FX	50	84	24.0	#10 Flex BC	FPE	FC	P2N	0.405	600	0.1	0.4	1.3	4.5
RG-8	Belden 9913F	50	83	24.6	#11 Flex BC	FPE	FC	P1	0.405	300	0.2	0.6	1.5	4.8
RG-8	Belden 9914	50	82	24.8	#10 Solid BC	FPE	FC	P1	0.405	300	0.2	0.5	1.5	4.8
RG-8	TMS LMR400UF	50	85	23.9	#10 Flex BC	FPE	FC	PE	0.405	600	0.1	0.4	1.4	4.9
RG-8	DRF-BF	50	84	24.5	#9.5 Flex BC	FPE	FC	PE	0.405	600	0.1	0.5	1.6	5.2
RG-8	WM CQ106	50	84	24.5	#9.5 Flex BC	FPE	FC	P2N	0.405	600	0.2	0.6	1.8	5.3
RG-8	CXP008	50	78	26.0	#13 Flex BC	FPE	S	P1	0.405	600	0.1	0.5	1.8	7.1
RG-8	Belden 8237	52	66	29.5	#13 Flex BC	PE	S	P1	0.405	3700	0.2	0.6	1.9	7.4
RG-8X	Belden 7808A	50	86	23.5	#15 Solid BC	FPE	FC	PE	0.240	300	0.2	0.7	2.3	7.4
RG-8X	TMS LMR240	50	84	24.2	#15 Solid BC	FPE	FC	PE	0.242	300	0.2	0.8	2.5	8.0
RG-8X	WM CQ118	50	82	25.0	#16 Flex BC	FPE	FC	P2N	0.242	300	0.3	0.9	2.8	8.4
RG-8X	TMS LMR240UF	50	84	24.2	#15 Flex BC	FPE	FC	PE	0.242	300	0.2	0.8	2.8	9.6
RG-8X	Belden 9258	50	82	24.8	#16 Flex BC	FPE	S	P1	0.242	300	0.3	0.9	3.2	11.2
RG-8X	CXP08XB	50	80	25.3	#16 Flex BC	FPE	S	P1	0.242	300	0.3	1.0	3.1	14.0
RG-9	Belden 8242	51	66	30.0	#13 Flex SPC	PE	SCBC	P2N	0.420	5000	0.2	0.6	2.1	8.2
RG-11	Belden 8213	75	84	16.1	#14 Solid BC	FPE	S	PE	0.405	300	0.1	0.4	1.3	5.2
RG-11	Belden 8238	75	66	20.5	#18 Flex TC	PE	S	P1	0.405	300	0.2	0.7	2.0	7.1
RG-58	Belden 7807A	50	85	23.7	#18 Solid BC	FPE	FC	PE	0.195	300	0.3	1.0	3.0	9.7
RG-58	TMS LMR200	50	83	24.5	#17 Solid BC	FPE	FC	PE	0.195	300	0.3	1.0	3.2	10.5
RG-58	WM CQ124	52	66	28.5	#20 Solid BC	PE	S	PE	0.195	1400	0.4	1.3	4.3	14.3
RG-58	Belden 8240	52	66	29.9	#20 Solid BC	PE	S	P1	0.193	1400	0.3	1.1	3.8	14.5
RG-58A	Belden 8219	53	73	26.5	#20 Flex TC	FPE	S	P1	0.195	300	0.4	1.3	4.5	18.1
RG-58C	Belden 8262	50	66	30.8	#20 Flex TC	PE	S	P2N	0.195	1400	0.4	1.4	4.9	21.5
RG-58A	Belden 8259	50	66	30.8	#20 Flex TC	PE	S	P1	0.192	1400	0.5	1.5	5.4	22.8
RG-59	Belden 1426A	75	83	16.3	#20 Solid BC	FPE	S	P1	0.242	300	0.3	0.9	2.6	8.5
RG-59	CXP 0815	75	82	16.2	#20 Solid BC	FPE	S	P1	0.232	300	0.5	0.9	2.2	9.1
RG-59	Belden 8212	75	78	17.3	#20 Solid CCS	FPE	S	P1	0.242	300	0.2	1.0	3.0	10.9
RG-59	Belden 8241	75	66	20.4	#23 Solid CCS	PE	S	P1	0.242	1700	0.6	1.1	3.4	12.0
RG-62A	Belden 9269	93	84	13.5	#22 Solid CCS	ASPE	S	P1	0.240	750	0.3	0.9	2.7	8.7
RG-62B	Belden 8255	93	84	13.5	#24 Flex CCS	ASPE	S	P2N	0.242	750	0.3	0.9	2.9	11.0
RG-63B	Belden 9857	125	84	9.7	#22 Solid CCS	ASPE	S	P2N	0.405	750	0.2	0.5	1.5	5.8
RG-83	WM165	35	66	44.0	#10 Solid BC	PE	S	P2	0.405	2000	0.23	0.8	2.8	9.6
RG-142	CXP 183242	50	69.5	29.4	#19 Solid SCCS	TFE	D	FEP	0.195	1900	0.3	1.1	3.8	12.8
RG-142B	Belden 83242	50	69.5	29.0	#19 Solid SCCS	TFE	D	TFE	0.195	1400	0.3	1.1	3.9	13.5
RG-174	Belden 7805R	50	73.5	26.2	#25 Solid BC	FPE	FC	P1	0.110	300	0.6	2.0	6.5	21.3
RG-174	Belden 8216	50	66	30.8	#26 Flex CCS	PE	S	P1	0.110	1100	0.8	2.5	8.6	33.7
RG-179	Belden MRG1791	75	66	67	#30 Flex SCCS	PE	TC	PVC	0.110	1000	n/a	4.9	8.9	27.9
RG-213	Belden 8267	50	66	30.8	#13 Flex BC	PE	S	P2N	0.405	3700	0.2	0.6	2.1	8.0
RG-213	CXP213	50	66	30.8	#13 Flex BC	PE	S	P2N	0.405	600	0.2	0.6	2.0	8.2
RG-214	Belden 8268	50	66	30.8	#13 Flex SPC	PE	D	P2N	0.425	3700	0.2	0.7	2.2	8.0
RG-216	Belden 9850	75	66	20.5	#18 Flex TC	PE	D	P2N	0.425	3700	0.2	0.7	2.0	7.1
RG-217	WM CQ217F	50	66	30.8	#10 Flex BC	PE	D	PE	0.545	7000	0.1	0.4	1.4	5.2
RG-217	M17/78-RG217	50	66	30.8	#10 Solid BC	PE	D	P2N	0.545	7000	0.1	0.4	1.4	5.2
RG-218	M17/79-RG218	50	66	29.5	#4.5 Solid BC	PE	S	P2N	0.870	11000	0.1	0.2	0.8	3.4
RG-223	Belden 9273	50	66	30.8	#19 Solid SPC	PE	D	P2N	0.212	1400	0.4	1.2	4.1	14.5
RG-303	Belden 84303	50	69.5	29.0	#18 Solid SCCS	TFE	S	TFE	0.170	1400	0.3	1.1	3.9	13.5

used nearly exclusively, such homemade lines are enjoying a renaissance of sorts because of their high efficiency and low cost. A typical construction technique is shown in **Figure 23.25**. The two wires are supported a fixed distance apart by means of insulating spacers. Spacers may be made from material such as polycarbonate, phenolic, polystyrene, or ABS plastics. Ceramic spacers such as isolantite or Steatite are also used and may be found on the surplus market or at flea markets. Several vendors also sell spacers designed specifically for building open-wire line. The spacer length varies from 2 to 6 inches. Smaller spacings are desirable at higher frequencies (28 MHz and above) so radiation from the transmission line is minimized.

Spacers must be used at small enough intervals along the line to keep the two wires from moving appreciably with respect to each other. For amateur purposes, lines using this construction ordinarily have #12 AWG or #14 AWG conductors (such as THHN wire used for house wiring and discussed in the chapter **Antenna Materials and Construction**), and the characteristic impedance is between 500 to 600 Ω.

Where an air-insulated line with still lower characteristic impedance is needed, metal tubing from ¼ to ½-inch diameter is frequently used. With the larger conductor diameter and relatively close spacing, it is possible to build a line having a characteristic impedance as low as about 200 Ω. This construction technique is principally used for λ/4 matching transformers at

RG or Type	*Part Number*	*Nom. Z_0 Ω*	*VF %*	*Cap. pF/ft*	*Cent. Cond. AWG*	*Diel. Type*	*Shield Type*	*Jacket Matl*	*OD inches*	*Max V (RMS)*	*Matched Loss (dB/100') 1 MHz*	*10*	*100*	*1000*
RG-316	CXP TJ1316	50	69.5	29.4	#26 Flex BC	TFE	S	FEP	0.098	1200	1.2	2.7	8.0	26.1
RG-316	Belden 84316	50	69.5	29.0	#26 Flex SCCS	TFE	S	FEP	0.096	900	0.8	2.5	8.3	26.0
RG-393	M17/127-RG393	50	69.5	29.4	#12 Flex SPC	TFE	D	FEP	0.390	5000	0.2	0.5	1.7	6.1
RG-400	M17/128-RG400	50	69.5	29.4	#20 Flex SPC	TFE	D	FEP	0.195	1400	0.4	1.3	4.3	15.0
LMR240	TMS 54201	50	83	24.2	#16 Solid BC	FPE	TC	PE	0.240	1000	n/a	0.8	2.3	8
LMR400	TMS 54001	50	84	23.9	#10 Solid BC	FPE	TC	PE	0.405	8000	n/a	0.4	1.2	1.5
LMR500	TMS LMR500UF	50	85	23.9	#7 Flex BC	FPE	FC	PE	0.500	2500	0.1	0.4	1.2	4.0
LMR500	TMS LMR500	50	85	23.9	#7 Solid CCA	FPE	FC	PE	0.500	2500	0.1	0.3	0.9	3.3
LMR600	TMS LMR600	50	86	23.4	#5.5 Solid CCA	FPE	FC	PE	0.590	4000	0.1	0.2	0.8	2.7
LMR600	TMS LMR600UF	50	86	23.4	#5.5 Flex BC	FPE	FC	PE	0.590	4000	0.1	0.2	0.8	2.7
LMR1200	TMS LMR1200	50	88	23.1	#0 Copper Tube	FPE	FC	PE	1.200	4500	0.04	0.1	0.4	1.3
Hardline														
1/2"	CATV Hardline	50	81	25.0	#5.5 BC	FPE	SM	none	0.500	2500	0.05	0.2	0.8	3.2
1/2"	CATV Hardline	75	81	16.7	#11.5 BC	FPE	SM	none	0.500	2500	0.1	0.2	0.8	3.2
7/8"	CATV Hardline	50	81	25.0	#1 BC	FPE	SM	none	0.875	4000	0.03	0.1	0.6	2.9
7/8"	CATV Hardline	75	81	16.7	#5.5 BC	FPE	SM	none	0.875	4000	0.03	0.1	0.6	2.9
LDF4-50A	Heliax – ½"	50	88	25.9	#5 Solid BC	FPE	CC	PE	0.630	1400	0.02	0.2	0.6	2.4
LDF5-50A	Heliax – ⅞"	50	88	25.9	0.355" BC	FPE	CC	PE	1.090	2100	0.03	0.10	0.4	1.3
LDF6-50A	Heliax – 1¼"	50	88	25.9	0.516" BC	FPE	CC	PE	1.550	3200	0.02	0.08	0.3	1.1
Parallel Lines														
TV Twinlead (Belden 9085)		300	80	4.5	#22 Flex CCS	PE	none	P1	0.400	**	0.1	0.3	1.4	5.9
Twinlead (Belden 8225)		300	80	4.4	#20 Flex BC	PE	none	P1	0.400	8000	0.1	0.2	1.1	4.8
Twinlead	RFC 1321	300	91		#18 Flex CCS	PE	none	PE	0.400	n/a	n/a	n/a	n/a	n/a
TV twinlead	RFC1320	300	91		#20 Flex BC	PE	none	PE	0.400	n/a	n/a	n/a	n/a	n/a
Ladder Line	RFC 552	420	91.7		#16 Flex CCS	PE	none	PE	0.930	n/a	n/a	n/a	n/a	n/a
	RFC 551	450	90.2		#18 Sol CCS	PE	none	PE	0.930	n/a				
	RFC 554	390	91		#14 Flex CCS	PE	none	PE	0.930	n/a	n/a	n/a	n/a	n/a
Open Wire Line		600	0.95-99**	1.7	#12 BC	none	none	none	**	12000	0.02	0.06	0.2	-

Note: RFC part numbers from the RF Connection are typical of parallel conductor lines from several sources

Approximate Power Handling Capability (1:1 SWR, 40°C Ambient):

	1.8 MHz	*7*	*14*	*30*	*50*	*150*	*220*	*450*	*1 GHz*
RG-58 Style	1350	700	500	350	250	150	120	100	50
RG-59 Style	2300	1100	800	550	400	250	200	130	90
RG-8X Style	1830	840	560	360	270	145	115	80	50
RG-8/213 Style	5900	3000	2000	1500	1000	600	500	350	250
RG-217 Style	20000	9200	6100	3900	2900	1500	1200	800	500
LDF4-50A	38000	18000	13000	8200	6200	3400	2800	1900	1200
LDF5-50A	67000	32000	22000	14000	11000	5900	4800	3200	2100
LMR500	18000	9200	6500	4400	3400	1900	1600	1100	700
LMR1200	52000	26000	19000	13000	10000	5500	4500	3000	2000

Legend:

**	Not Available or varies
***	Varies with spacer material and spacing
ASPE	Air Spaced Polyethylene
BC	Bare Copper
CC	Corrugated Copper
CCA	Copper Cover Aluminum
CCS	Copper Covered Steel
CXP	Cable X-Perts, Inc.
D	Double Copper Braids
DRF	Davis RF
FC	Foil + Tinned Copper Braid
FEP	Teflon ® Type IX
Flex	Flexible Stranded Wire
FPE	Foamed Polyethylene
Heliax	Andrew Corp Heliax
N	Non-Contaminating
P1	PVC, Class 1
P2	PVC, Class 2
PE	Polyethylene
S	Single Braided Shield
SC	Silver Coated Braid
SCCS	Silver Plated Copper Coated Steel
SM	Smooth Aluminum
SPC	Silver Plated Copper
TC	Tinned Copper
TFE	Teflon®
TMS	Times Microwave Systems
UF	Ultra Flex
WM	Wireman

the higher frequencies and for use with log-periodic dipole arrays having feed point impedances near 200 Ω.

A third type of commercial parallel-line is so-called *window line*, illustrated in Figure 23.10G. This is a variation of twin-lead construction, except that *windows* are cut in the polyethylene insulation at regular intervals. This reduces weight of the line, and also breaks up the amount of surface area where dirt, dust and moisture can accumulate. Such window line is commonly available with a nominal characteristic impedance of 450 Ω, although actual impedance varies from about 390 to 450 Ω. A conductor spacing of about 1 inch is used in the 450-Ω line with a conductor size of about #18 AWG. The impedances of such lines are somewhat lower than given by Figure 23.22 for the same conductor size and spacing, because of the effect of the dielectric constant of the spacer material used. The attenuation is quite low and lines of this type are entirely satisfactory for transmitting applications at amateur power levels.

23.3.3 Coaxial Cables

Coaxial cable is available in flexible and semi-flexible varieties. The fundamental design is the same in all types, as shown in Figure 23.10. The outer diameter varies from 0.06 inch to over 5 inches. Power handling capability and cable size are directly proportional, as larger dielectric thickness and larger conductor sizes can handle higher voltages and currents. Generally, losses decrease as cable diameter increases. The extent to which this is true is dependent on the properties of the insulating material.

Some coaxial cables have stranded wire center conductors while others use a solid copper conductor. Similarly, the outer conductor (shield) may be a single layer of copper braid, a double layer of braid (more effective shielding), solid aluminum (hardline and Heliax), aluminum foil or aluminized mylar, or a combination of these.

VOLTAGE, POWER AND LOSS SPECIFICATIONS

Selection of the correct coaxial cable for a particular application is not a casual matter. Not only is the attenuation loss of significance, but breakdown and heating (voltage and power) also need to be considered. If a cable were lossless, the power handling capability would be limited only by the breakdown voltage. There are two types of power ratings: *peak power* and *average power*. The peak power rating is limited by a voltage breakdown between the inner and outer conductors and is independent of frequency. The average power rating is governed by the safe long-term operating temperature of the dielectric material and decreases as the frequency increases. Excessive RF operating voltage in a coaxial cable can cause noise generation, dielectric damage and eventual breakdown between the conductors.

The power handling capability and loss characteristics of coaxial cable depend largely on the dielectric material between the conductors and the size of the conductors. The commonly used cables and many of their properties are listed in **Table 23.1**. The pertinent characteristics of unmarked coaxial cables can be determined from the equations in **Table 23.2**. The most common impedance values are 50, 75 and 95 Ω. However, impedances from 25 to 125 Ω are available in special types of manufactured line. The 25-Ω cable (miniature) is used extensively in magnetic-core broadband transformers.

In practical coaxial cables the copper and dielectric losses, rather than breakdown voltage, limit the maximum power than can be accommodated. If 1000 W is applied to a cable having a loss of 3 dB, only 500 W is delivered to the load. The remaining 500 W must be dissipated in the cable. The dielectric and outer jacket are good thermal insulators, which prevent the

Table 23.2
Coaxial Cable Equations

$$C\ (\text{pF/foot}) = \frac{7.26\varepsilon}{\log(D/d)} \qquad \text{(Eq A)}$$

$$L\ (\mu\text{H/foot}) = 0.14 \log\frac{D}{d} \qquad \text{(Eq B)}$$

$$Z_0\ (\text{ohms}) = \sqrt{\frac{L}{C}} = \left(\frac{138}{\sqrt{\varepsilon}}\right)\left(\log\frac{D}{d}\right) \qquad \text{(Eq C)}$$

$$\text{VF \% (velocity factor, ref. speed of light)} = \frac{100}{\sqrt{\varepsilon}} \qquad \text{(Eq D)}$$

$$\text{Time delay (ns/foot)} = 1.016\sqrt{\varepsilon} \qquad \text{(Eq E)}$$

$$f\ (\text{cutoff/GHz}) = \frac{7.50}{\sqrt{\varepsilon}\,(D+d)} \qquad \text{(Eq F)}$$

$$\text{Reflection Coefficient} = |\rho| = \frac{Z_L - Z_0}{Z_L + Z_0} = \frac{\text{SWR}-1}{\text{SWR}+1} \qquad \text{(Eq G)}$$

$$\text{Return Loss (dB)} = -20 \log|\rho| \qquad \text{(Eq H)}$$

$$\text{SWR} = \frac{1+|\rho|}{1-|\rho|} \qquad \text{(Eq I)}$$

$$V\ \text{peak} = \frac{(1.15\ S\ d)(\log D/d)}{K} \qquad \text{(Eq J)}$$

$$A = \frac{0.435}{Z_0 D}\left(\frac{D}{d}(K1+K2)\right)\sqrt{f} + 2.78\sqrt{\varepsilon}\,(PF)(f) \qquad \text{(Eq K)}$$

where
- A = attenuation in dB/100 foot
- d = OD of inner conductor
- D = ID of outer conductor
- S = max voltage gradient of insulation in volts/mil
- ε = dielectric constant
- K = safety factor
- K1 = strand factor
- K2 = braid factor
- f = freq in MHz
- PF = power factor

Note: Obtain K1 and K2 data from manufacturer.

conductors from efficiently transferring the heat to free air. As a result the cable can heat up, softening the plastic insulation and allowing the geometry of the conductors and the characteristic impedance to change or even short-circuit. Many amateur transmitter duty cycles are so low that substantial overload is permissible on current peaks so long as the SWR is relatively low, such as less than 2:1. **Figure 23.26** is a graph of the matched-line attenuation characteristics versus frequency for the most popular lines

A cable with a solid dielectric will handle higher power than a cable with a foam dielectric. RG-8/U with a solid dielectric will handle 5000 V maximum while the same cable with foam dielectric only has a 600 V rating. In addition, heating of the center conductor from cable loss can soften the center insulation. (See the following section on Center Conductor Migration.)

As the operating frequency increases, the power-handling capability of a cable decreases because of increasing conductor loss (skin effect) and dielectric loss. RG-58 with foam dielectric has a breakdown rating of only 300 V, yet it can handle substantially more power than its ordinary solid dielectric counterpart because of the lower losses. Normally, the loss is inconsequential (except as it affects power handling capability) below 10 MHz in amateur applications. This is true unless extremely long runs of cable are used.

In general, full legal amateur power can be safely applied to inexpensive RG-58 coax in the bands below 10 MHz. RG-8 and similar cables can withstand full amateur power through the VHF spectrum, but connectors must be carefully chosen in these applications. Connector choice is discussed in a later section.

As inexpensive RG-6-type cables gain wider use for receiving antennas, cable loss on the MF and LF bands becomes more important, particularly with copper-clad steel (CCS) center conductors. These cables are designed for use at VHF and higher frequencies, so the copper plating on the center conductor may be extremely thin. This increases resistive loss on the lower frequency bands and may also cause problems

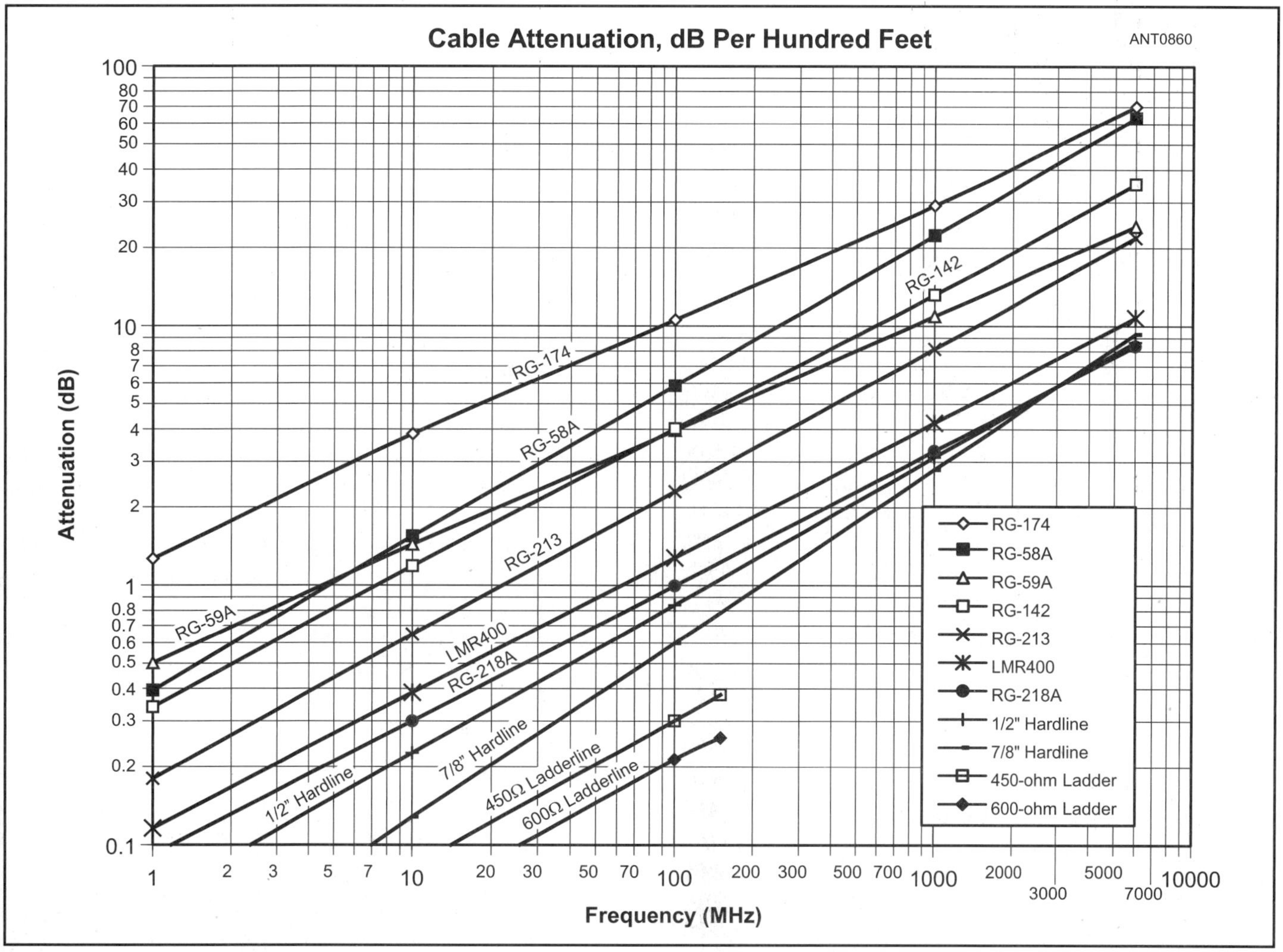

Figure 23.26 — Nominal matched-line attenuation in decibels per 100 feet of various common transmission lines. Total attenuation is directly proportional to length. Attenuation will vary somewhat in actual cable samples, and generally increases with age in coaxial cables having a type 1 jacket. Cables grouped together in the above chart have approximately the same attenuation. Types having foam polyethylene dielectric have slightly lower loss than equivalent solid types, when not specifically shown above.

RG-8, RG-213 and Type Cables

The most common coax used for amateur applications is RG-8/U — a 50-Ω cable approximately 0.4 inch in diameter, with solid or foamed polyethylene center insulation, and capable of handling full legal power. A close second to RG-8/U is RG-213/U, also a 50-Ω cable and nearly identical. The two cable types are almost identical as seen in Table 23.1, but RG-213/U is slightly lossier than RG-8.

Many amateurs are unaware that RG-8/U is an obsolete military specification designation, meaning that the part number RG-8/U does not confer any particular level of quality or performance on the cable. RG-213/U, on the other hand, is a current military designation that can only be used for cables manufactured to the military specification for that cable, both for materials as well as manufacturing processes. This results in a more consistent product.

It is also common for manufacturers to add "type" after a military specification label, such as "RG-8 Type" or "RG-213 Type." This means that the cable has much the same performance characteristics as the "non-type" cable but is not guaranteed to meet that higher level of performance.

Should you decide to use RG-8/U or a "type" cable, read the specifications carefully. The shield coverage (the percentage of the center insulator covered by the copper braid shield) should be from 95 to 97% for a high-quality cable. You should not be able to easily see the center insulation through holes in the shield.

Another advantage of RG-213/U is that the jacket is made from non-contaminating PVC and many types of RG-213/U are rated for direct burial.

if dc power is supplied through the cable. Be particularly wary of surplus or off-brand cable that is intended for TV and data use. It is recommended that a long run of the cable be tested for loss and resistance before being placed into service. Cable with a solid-copper center conductor is more expensive but avoids low-frequency and resistance problems.

DETERIORATION

Deterioration of coaxial cable is most commonly caused by water or moisture infiltration which causes corrosion of the shield, dramatically increasing its losses. This usually occurs at the ends of cables where connectors are installed or the cable is separated into two conductors for attachment to an antenna.

Exposure of the inner insulating material to moisture and chemicals over time contaminates the center insulation and increases cable losses. Newer types of foam-dielectric cables are less prone to contamination than are older types of solid-polyethylene insulated cables.

Impregnated cables, such as Times Wire LMR-400-DB, are immune to water and chemical damage, and may be buried if desired. They also have a self-healing property that is valuable when rodents chew into the line. Cable loss should be checked at least every two years if the cable has been outdoors or buried. See the section on testing transmission lines.

The outer insulating jacket of the cable (usually PVC) is used solely as protection from dirt, moisture and chemicals. (The jacket's only electrical function is compressing the shield braid to keep the strands in good contact with each other.) If the jacket is breached, it generally leads to corrosion of the shield and contamination of the center insulation, again causing high losses.

The ultra-violet (UV) radiation in sunlight causes a chemical reaction in standard PVC jacket material that causes the plastic to break down into products that migrate from the jacket into the braid and center insulation, degrading the electrical properties of both. If your cable will be exposed to strong sunlight, use a cable with a non-contaminating jacket.

CABLE CAPACITANCE

The capacitance between the conductors of coaxial cable varies with the impedance and dielectric constant of the line. Therefore, the lower the impedance, the higher the capacitance per foot, because the conductor spacing is decreased. Capacitance also increases with dielectric constant.

BENDING RADIUS

A normal amateur installation will create bends and turns in the feed line run. It is common to wind coax into a coil to form a common-mode RF choke or to store excess cable. Bending coax is acceptable as long as the *minimum bending radius* is not violated. A typical minimum bending radius is a multiple of the coax diameter. For example, a common minimum bending radius specification for RG-8 is 4 inches, which is a multiple of 8 (½ inch OD × 8). Coax with more rigid shield materials such as hardline or Heliax will have a larger minimum bending radius.

If the cable will be subjected to regular flexing, such as if it is attached to a rotating antenna, use a cable with a stranded center conductor. When repeatedly bent or flexed, solid center conductors will develop *metal fatigue* and break.

Miniature and sub-miniature TFE-insulated cables such as RG-400 are often used for winding choke baluns. The cable is wound around a toroid core or rod, usually with a turn radius several times smaller than the minimum specified. There are few reports of failure from this practice in both commercial and home-made chokes. While no specification is available, the consensus of experienced antenna system builders is that if the power carried by the cable is well below its maximum rating, not at an elevated temperature, and not repeatedly flexed, smaller radius bends do not lead to failure of this type of cable.

CENTER CONDUCTOR MIGRATION

The most common center insulation materials are solid polyethylene (PE), extended or "foamed" polyethylene (FPE), and solid Teflon (TFE). Teflon dielectric coax is usually trouble-free and often used at VHF and UHF frequencies due to its low loss characteristics.

Foam polyethylene dielectric coax is used extensively on

the HF bands. RG-8X and RG-11/U (Belden 8213) are examples found in many stations. An unfortunate property of the foam dielectric coax is a lack of mechanical stability under some conditions. The center conductor in foam coax can migrate toward the shield causing an "impedance bump," or worse, a center conductor-to-shield short.

Several user-created conditions can lead to foam coax developing a short circuit. (Problems associated with center conductor migration are also addressed in the material on wound-coax chokes and baluns in the **Transmission Line System Techniques** chapter.) A major culprit is bending or coiling foam coax with a tight radius. For example, RF choke baluns are often made by wrapping several turns of coax into a tight bundle with a tight radius. Coaxial cable stubs are also wrapped into a coil of small radius to keep them small overall and out of the way. Coax is sometimes coiled up just to use up extra length. These practices are all potential trouble.

An additive factor is the self-heating caused by the cable's loss — a direct function of the amount of power applied and SWR. RG-8X is not rated for 1500 W, but lots of amateurs use it successfully at that power level. RG-8X gets warm to the touch at 1500 W. Increasing internal temperature softens the foam which facilitates center conductor migration. Tight radius bends taken together with heating are a recipe for an eventual short circuit. Tightly coiled baluns used outdoors receive solar heating in addition to self-heating and a tight bend radius. A balun made and used this way has a very high probability of shorting out over time, particularly when used at high power.

To avoid center conductor migration: don't use sharp bends, particularly at high power. Use solid dielectric coax to make tightly coiled coaxial baluns and if stubs must be coiled up, use solid dielectric coax for those too. Use up spare foam coax length by laying it flat on the floor and avoiding sharp radius turns or bends.

PARALLELED LINES

In order to obtain feed lines with intermediate or unusual characteristic impedances, identical lengths of line with Z_0 can be connected in parallel. The resulting characteristic impedance, $Z_{COMB} = Z_0 / N$, where N is the number of lines in parallel. For example, to create a section of line with Z_0 = 37.5 Ω, two sections of 75 Ω RG-11 or RG-59 can be connected in parallel to create a λ/4 matching section for a 25 Ω load. Paralleled cables have the same loss as a single cable would with an equal degree of mismatch.

Either coaxial or parallel-conductor lines may be combined in parallel. When using paralleled coaxial lines, if standard connectors and adaptors are not used and lines are spliced together, precautions must be taken to maintain shielding at the junctions or RF chokes must be placed on the line to block noise currents on the shield from entering the line and to prevent signals from inside the line escaping to flow on the outside of the shield. If parallel-conductor lines are combined they must be kept well apart (at least one line width) to avoid coupling between the lines.

Splicing Window Line

In keeping with the amateur ethic of re-use, feed lines are often spliced. While connectors can be installed on coaxial line to join sections, that luxury is not available for the common window line. The ARRL's take on splicing window line is included in the online material from "The Doctor Is In" column in *QST*.

Waveguide and Microwave Cable

Rigid waveguide is used above 1 GHz and is uncommon below 10 GHz in amateur installations. Amateurs use special low-loss coaxial cables for short runs, along with special connectors such as the SMA family and others developed for consumer use in mobile networks and other microwave systems. The special techniques for working with these transmission lines at microwave frequencies are introduced in the chapter on **VHF, UHF, and Microwave Antenna Systems**. See the article "Microwave Plumbing" in this book's online material.

Other useful references include the RSGB's *International Microwave Handbook* and the ARRL's *UHF/Microwave Experimenter's Manual*, which is out of print but available used (see the References and Bibliography). In addition, *QST*'s "Microwavelengths" column by Paul Wade, W1GHZ, often often contains information about working with transmission lines above 1 GHz.

SHIELDED BALANCED LINES

Shielded balanced lines made from parallel coaxial cables have several advantages over open-wire lines. They can be buried and they can be routed through metal buildings or inside metal piping the same as for single coaxial lines. The outer surface of the shields can pick up noise and common-mode signals just as for single coaxial lines, as well.

The shields are connected together (see **Figure 23.27A**), and the two inner conductors constitute the balanced line. At the input, the coaxial shields should be connected to chassis ground; at the output (the antenna side), they are joined but left floating. (See the previous section's caution about blocking shield current at the open end of the cable.)

The characteristic impedance of a balanced shielded line is twice that of each single line — as if they were in series. Shielded balanced lines having impedances of 140 or 100 Ω can be constructed from two equal lengths of 70-Ω or 50-Ω cable (RG-59 or RG-58 would be satisfactory for amateur power levels). Paralleled RG-63 (125-Ω) cable would make a balanced transmission line more in accord with traditional 300-Ω twin-lead feed line (Z_0 = 250 Ω). Note that the losses for these shielded types of balanced lines will generally be higher than those for classic open-wire lines.

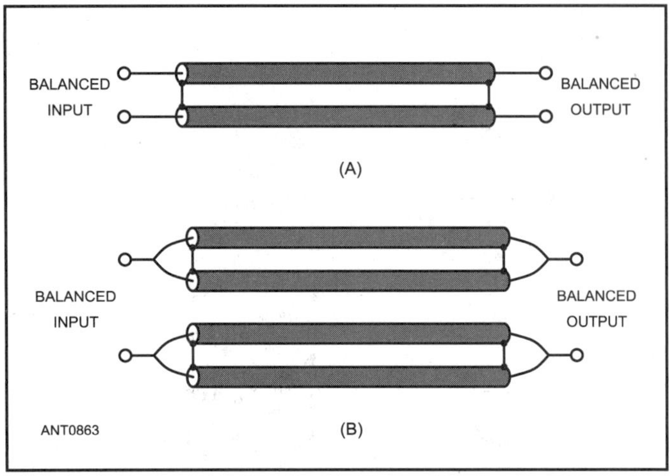

Figure 23.27 — Shielded balanced transmission lines utilizing standard small-size coaxial cable, such as RG-58 or RG-59. These balanced lines may be routed inside metal conduit or near large metal objects without adverse effects.

A high power, low-loss, low-impedance 70-Ω (or 50-Ω) balanced line can be constructed from four coaxial cables as in Figure 23.27B. The characteristic impedance of each pair of cables is one-half that of the single lines as described in the previous section. The net result is that the overall characteristic impedance is that of a single cable. Again, the shields are all connected together. The center conductors of the two sets of coaxial cables that are connected in parallel provide the balanced feed.

23.4 RF Connectors

There are many different types of RF connectors for coaxial cable, but the three most common for amateur use are the UHF, Type N and BNC families. Type F connectors are becoming popular for use with receiving antennas and low-loss RG-6 coaxial cable. Type SMA connectors are commonly found on hand-held transceivers and microwave equipment. The type of connector used for a specific job depends on the size of the cable, the frequency of operation and the power levels involved.

If the connector is to be exposed to the weather, select a waterproof design such as Type N or take care to thoroughly waterproof the connector as discussed in the chapter **Building Antenna Systems and Towers.**

23.4.1 UHF Connectors

The so-called UHF connector (the series name is not related to frequency) is found on most HF and some VHF equipment. PL-259 is another name for the UHF male, and the female is also known as the SO-239. These connectors are rated for full legal amateur power at HF and can be used through VHF without concerns. Above the 70 cm band, the connectors are poor for UHF work because of variable impedance and inconsistent insulator characteristics of different brands. PL-259 connectors are designed to fit RG-8 and RG-11 size cable (0.405-inch OD). Adapters are available for use with smaller

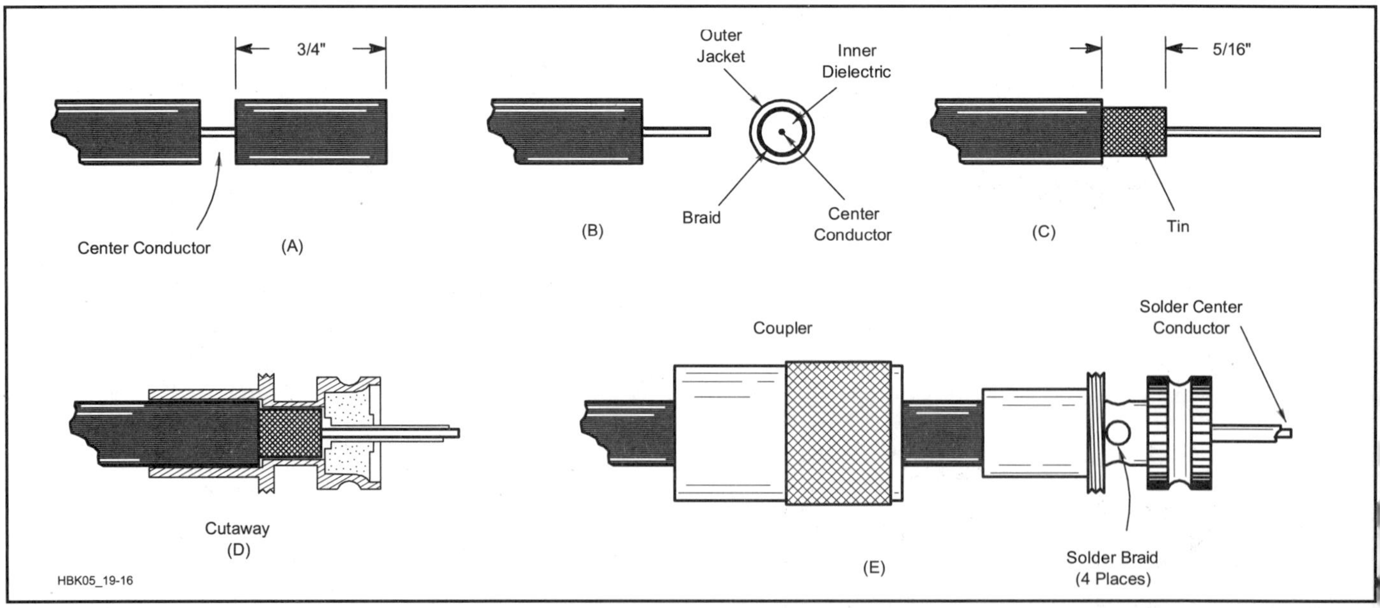

Figure 23.28 — The PL-259 plug of the UHF family of connectors is almost universal for amateur HF use and is popular for equipment operating in the VHF range. Steps A through E are described in detail in the text.

RG-58, RG-59 and RG-8X size cable. UHF connectors are not weatherproof.

Figure 23.28 shows how to install the solder type of PL-259 on RG-8 cable. Note that this is only one of many different methods hams have developed to attach these popular connectors. The key to any successful solder-based method is to have a large soldering gun or iron that can heat the connector body quickly and thoroughly without melting the center insulation from having to apply heat for a long time. For soldered connectors, do not pay attention to suggestions that it is sufficient to capture braid in the connector threads or between the connector body and adaptors. Such an installation will inevitably fail and presents a poor connection on VHF and UHF bands from the outset. If you don't want to solder a PL-259, use good-quality crimp connectors with the proper installation tools.

Proper preparation of the cable end is the key to success. Follow these simple steps. Measure back about ¾-inch from the cable end and slightly score the outer jacket around its circumference. With a sharp knife, cut through the outer jacket, through the braid, and through the dielectric — almost to the center conductor. Be careful not to score the center conductor. Cutting through all outer layers at once keeps the braid from separating. (Using a coax stripping tool with preset blade depth makes this and subsequent trimming steps much easier.)

Pull the severed outer jacket, braid and dielectric off the end of the cable as one piece. Inspect the area around the cut, looking for any strands of braid hanging loose and snip them off. There won't be any if your knife was sharp enough. Next, score the outer jacket about 5⁄16-inch back from the first cut. Cut through the jacket lightly; do not score the braid. This step takes practice. If you score the braid, start again. Remove the outer jacket.

Tin the exposed braid and center conductor, but apply the solder sparingly and avoid melting the dielectric. Slide the coupling ring onto the cable. Screw the connector body onto the cable. If you prepared the cable to the right dimensions, the center conductor will protrude through the center pin, the braid will show through the solder holes, and the body will actually thread onto the outer cable jacket. A very small amount of lubricant on the cable jacket will help the threading process.

Solder the braid through the solder holes. Solder through all four holes; poor connection to the braid is the most common form of PL-259 failure. A good connection between connector and braid is just as important as that between the center conductor and connector. Use a large soldering iron for this job. With practice, you'll learn how much heat to use. If you use too little heat, the solder will bead up, not really flowing onto the connector body. If you use too much heat, the dielectric will melt, letting the braid and center conductor touch. Most PL-259s are nickel plated, but silver-plated connectors are much easier to solder and only slightly more expensive.

Solder the center conductor to the center pin. The solder should flow on the inside, not the outside, of the center pin. If you wait until the connector body cools off from soldering the braid, you'll have less trouble with the dielectric melting. Trim the center conductor to be even with the end of the center pin. Use a small file to round the end, removing any solder that built up on the outer surface of the center pin. Use a sharp knife, very fine sandpaper or steel wool to remove any solder flux from the outer surface of the center pin. Screw the coupling ring onto the body, and you're finished.

Figure 23.29 shows how to install a PL-259 connector on RG-58 or RG-59 cable. An adapter is used for the smaller cable with standard RG-8 size PL-259s. (UG-175 for RG-58 and UG-176 for RG-59) Prepare the cable as shown. Once

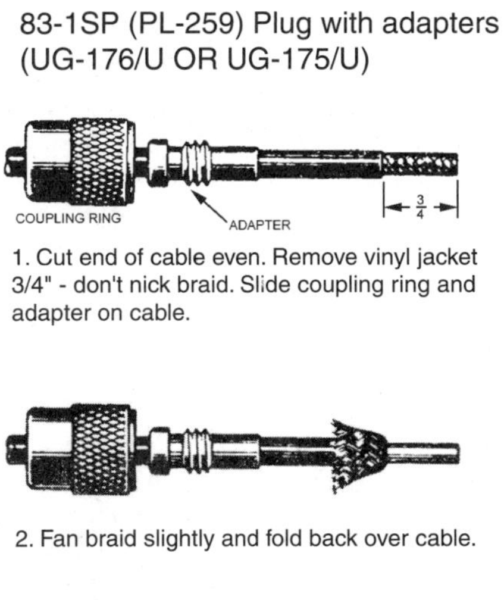

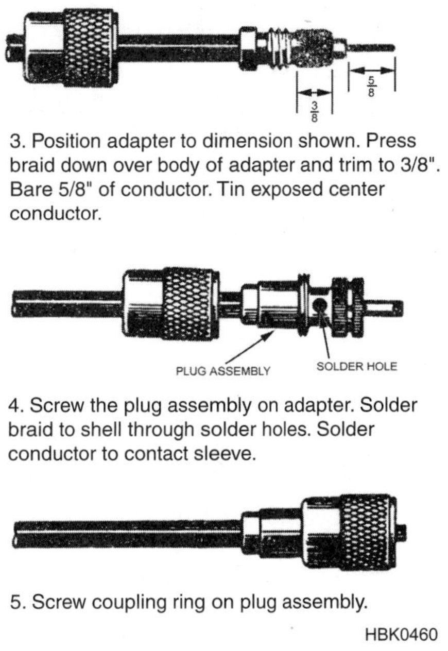

Figure 23.29 — Installing PL-259 plugs on RG-58 or RG-59 cable requires the use of UG-175 or UG-176 reducing adapters, respectively. The adapter screws into the plug body using the threads of the connector to grip the jacket on larger cables. *(Courtesy Amphenol Electronic Components)*

UHF Connectors

Braid Crimp - Solder Center Contact

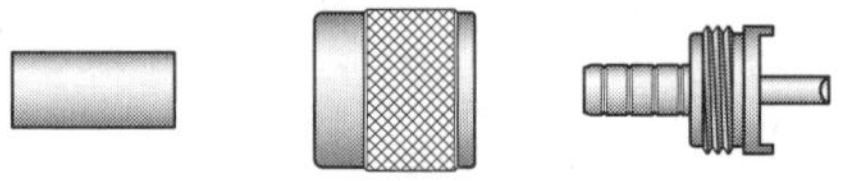

Amphenol	Cable RG-/U	Cable Attachment		Hex Crimp Data			Stripping Dims, inches (mm)		
		Outer	Inner	Cavity for Outer Ferrule	Die Set Tool 227-994	CTL Series Tool No.	a	b	c
83-58SP	58, 141	Crimp	Solder	0.213(5.4)	227-1221-11	CTL-1	1.14 (29.0)	0.780 (19.9)	0.250 (6.4)
83-58SP-1002	400	Crimp	Solder	0.213(5.4)	227-1221-11	CTL-1	1.14 (29.0)	0.780 (19.9)	0.250 (6.4)
83-59DCP-RFX	59	Crimp	Solder	0255(6.5)	227-1221-13	CTL-1	1.22 (30.9)	0.890* (22.6)	0.543 (13.8)
83-58SCP-RFX	58	Crimp	Solder	0.213(5.4)	227-1221-11	CTL-1	1.22 (30.9)	0.890* (22.6)	0.543 (13.8)
83-59SP	59	Crimp	Solder	0.255(6.5)	227-1221-13	CTL-1	1.22 (30.9)	0.890* (22.6)	0.543 (13.8)
83-8SP-RFX	8	Crimp	Solder	0.429(10.9)	227-1221-25	CTL-3	1.22 (30.9)	0.890* (22.6)	0.543 (13.8)

See www.AmphenolRF.com for assembly instructions for all other connectore types. These dimensions only apply to Amphenol connectors and may not be correct for other manufacturers.
* Manufacturer's assembly dimensions incorrectly show 0.574 inches.

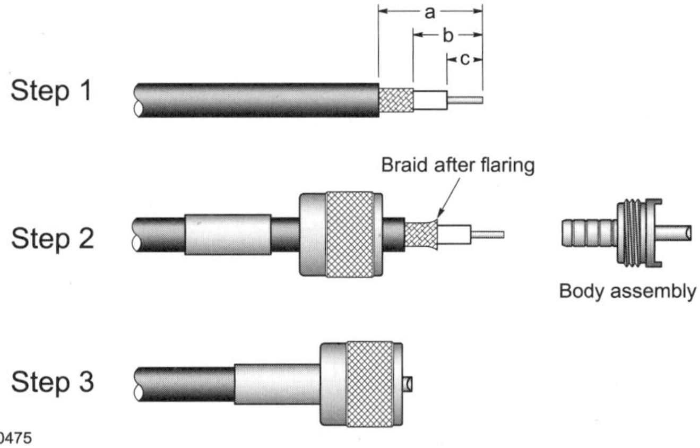

Step 1 Cut end of cable even. Strip cable to dimensions shown in table. All cuts are to be sharp and square. Do not nick braid, dielectric or center conductor. Tin center conductor avoiding excessive heat.

Step 2 Slide coupling nut and ferrule over cable jacket. Flair braid slightly as shown. Install cable into body assembly, so inner ferrule portion slides under braid, until braid butts shoulder. Slide outer ferrule over braid until it butts shoulder. Crimp ferrule with tool and die set indicated in table.

Step 3 Soft solder center conductor to contact. Avoid heating contact excessively to prevent damaging insulator. Slide/screw coupling nut over body.

HBK0475

Figure 23.30 — Crimp-on UHF connectors are available for all sizes of popular coaxial cable and save considerable time over soldered connectors. The performance and reliability of these connectors is equivalent to soldered connectors, if crimped properly. ***(Courtesy Amphenol Electronic Components)***

the braid is prepared, screw the adapter into the PL-259 shell and finish the job as you would a PL-259 on RG-8 cable.

Figure 23.30 shows the instructions and dimensions for crimp-on UHF connectors that fit all common sizes of coaxial cable.

While amateurs have been reluctant to adopt crimp-on connectors, the availability of good quality connectors and inexpensive crimping tools make crimp technology a good choice, even for connectors used outside. Soldering the center conductor after crimping in the connector tip is optional. The crimping process is illustrated in the article "Installing Coax Crimp Connectors" by Dino Papas, KLØS, that is included with the online material.

23.4.2 Other RF Connectors

BNC CONNECTORS

The BNC connectors illustrated in **Figure 23.31** are popular for low power levels at VHF and UHF. They accept RG-58 and RG-59 cable and are available for cable mounting in both male and female versions. Several different styles are available, so be sure to use the dimensions for the type you have. Follow the installation instructions carefully. If you prepare the cable to the wrong dimensions, the center pin will not seat properly with connectors of the opposite gender. Sharp scissors are a big help for trimming the braid evenly. Crimp-on BNC connectors are also available, with a large number of variations, including a twist-on version. A guide to installing these connectors is available with this book's online material.

TYPE N CONNECTORS

The Type N connector, illustrated in **Figure 23.32**, is a must for high-power VHF and UHF operation. N connectors are available in male and female versions for cable mounting and are designed for RG-8 size cable. Unlike UHF connectors, they are designed to maintain a constant impedance at cable joints. Like BNC connectors, it is important to prepare the cable to the right dimensions. The center pin must be positioned correctly to mate with the center pin of connectors of the opposite gender. Use the right dimensions for the connector style you have. Crimp-on N connectors are also available,

Coax Connectors — Not as Simple as They Appear

"You get what you pay for" was never more true than when it comes to common UHF connectors, including PL-259s, SO-239s, adapters, and so on. Every hamfest seems to have at least one vendor selling "mystery" UHF connectors, sometimes for as little as $1.00 each. What are you buying when you buy a $1.00 PL-259? It's pretty much a guess. For the difference of a dollar or two, "mystery" UHF connectors are a very poor investment.

PL-259s have four parts: the outer sleeve called the "knurled nut," the connector body, the insulator/dielectric and the center pin. All four components can be compromised to the point of making a bargain connector useless.

Problems frequently encountered:

- Finish: Bargain connectors sometimes have a finish you can't solder to! They may have a chrome-like appearance, but the plating may not take solder well and has to be filed down for a good connection.
- Threading: The internal threads at the rear of the body are there to accept a UG-style insert that narrows the connector barrel to accept smaller diameter coax such as RG-8X or RG-58. The threads may be metric! UG inserts also sometimes appear in the US market with metric threads. Either way, the insert will not screw into the body.
- Dielectric: Good connectors use quality phenolic or Teflon insulation between the center pin and the body. Bargain connectors might use anything, including materials like polystyrene, which will melt when the center pin is soldered.
- Center pin diameter: This is one of the most common and insidious problems in mystery PL-259s. The center pin ODs are almost always slightly smaller than they should be and it's hard to notice. The center pin connection between a PL-259 and an SO-239 or barrel connector depends on the male side pin OD being correct and the matching fingers on the female side being the correct diameter and made of the proper spring material.
- Center socket spring tension: If the SO-239 socket metal relaxes over time and/or temperature, an intermittent connection will be created that can be very hard to track down.
- Mating indentions: The indentations on the end of the SO-239 that mates to a PL-259 (the annulus flange) may only have four indentations to match up with the short prongs on the body of the male connector. A quality SO-239 or barrel connector has indentations all the way around. If the PL-259 and SO-239 don't seat completely, an intermittent connection is likely to develop.
- Tee and right-angle (elbow) UHF adapters: The center conductor makes a right-angle turn inside the shell. In poor-quality adapters the right-angle connection is done with a spring contact — these do not hold up. Quality tee and right-angle adapters are reliable because the internal conductors are tapped and threaded — the conductors are screwed together within the body at the right-angle junction.

How can we tell the good connectors? If the price is too good to be true — well, it is. PL-259s with good silver plating have a dull appearance. Good connectors have a part number and manufacturer's name stamped into them. You can look up the connector's specifications if it's marked. An example is the connectors made by Amphenol — all of which have parts numbers such as 83-1SP (PL-259) or 83-1R (SO-239) stamped into or onto the connector body. *[Contributed by Hal Kennedy, N4GG]*

again with a large number of variations. A guide to installing these connectors is available with this book's online material.

TYPE F CONNECTORS

Type F connectors, used primarily on cable TV connections, are also popular for receive-only antennas and can be used with RG-59 or the increasingly popular RG-6 cable available at low cost. Crimp-on is the only option for these connectors and **Figure 23.33** shows a general guide for installing them. The exact dimensions vary between connector styles and manufacturers — information on crimping is generally provided with the connectors. There are two styles of crimp — ferrule and compression. The ferrule crimp method is similar to that for UHF, BNC and N connectors in which a metal ring is compressed around the exposed coax shield. The compression crimp forces a bushing into the back of the connector, clamping the shield against the connector body. In all cases, the exposed center conductor of the cable — a solid wire — must end flush with the end of the connector. A center conductor that is too short may not make a good connection.

SMA CONNECTORS

The SMA connector in **Figure 23.34** is the most common microwave connector. The cable center insulation is taken directly to the connector interface without air gaps. A standard SMA is rated for use to 12.4 GHz but high-quality connectors, properly installed, can be used to 24 GHz. For more information about SMA and other microwave connectors, see the References and Bibliography entry for Williams (the article is also available with this book's online material).

SMA connectors have become popular on handheld VHF/UHF transceivers. Some models use a "reverse SMA" that requires a double-receptacle adapter for a feed line terminated in an SMA plug to be attached.

TNC COAXIAL CONNECTORS

The TNC (Threaded — Neill — Concelman) is essentially a BNC with a threaded rather than a bayonet backshell. It thus is essentially a smaller Type N connector, but with the inner connecting surfaces the same size. It extends the 2 GHz frequency limit of the BNC up to 10 GHz or higher and takes

BNC CONNECTORS

Standard Clamp

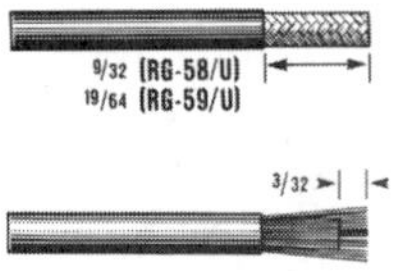

1. Cut cable even. Strip jacket. Fray braid and strip dielectric. ***Don't nick braid or center conductor.*** Tin center conductor.

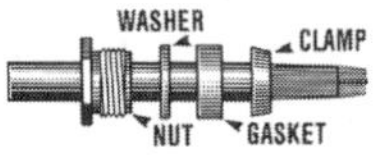

2. Taper braid. Slide nut, washer, gasket and clamp over braid. Clamp inner shoulder should fit squarely against end of jacket.

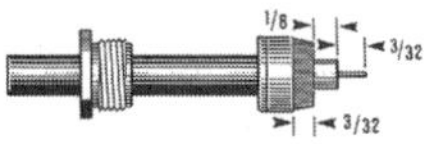

3. With clamp in place, comb out braid, fold back smooth as shown. Trim center conductor.

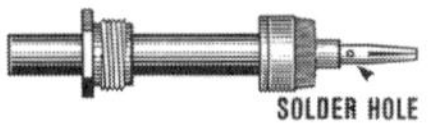

4. Solder contact on conductor through solder hole. Contact should butt against dielectric. Remove excess solder from outside of contact. Avoid excess heat to prevent swollen dielectric which would interfere with connector body.

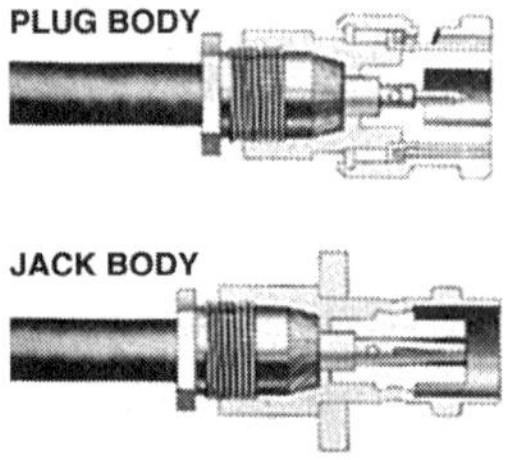

5. Push assembly into body. Screw nut into body with wrench until tight. ***Don't rotate body on cable to tighten.***

Improved Clamp

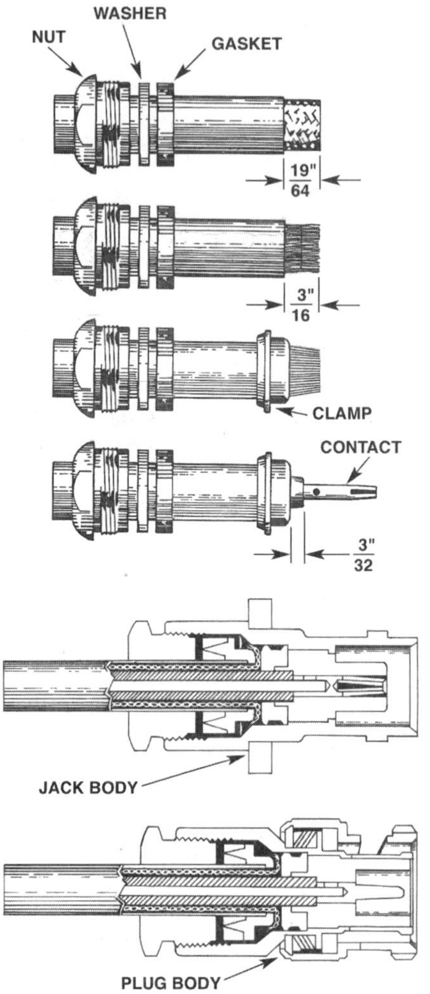

Follow 1, 2, 3 and 4 in BNC connectors (standard clamp) exceptas noted. Strip cable as shown. Slide gasket on cable *with groove facing clamp.* Slide clamp *with sharp edge facing gasket.* Clamp *should* cut gasket to seal properly.

HBK05_19-18

C. C. Clamp

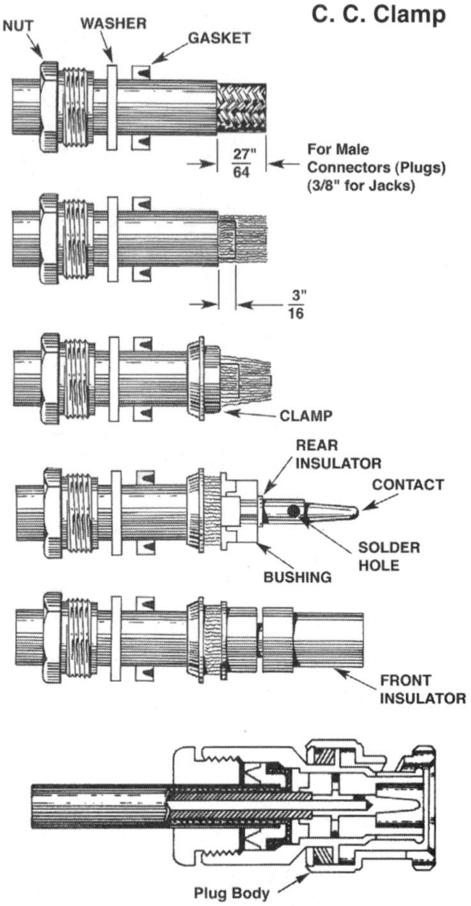

1. Follow steps 1, 2, and 3 as outlined for the standard-clamp BNC connector.

2. Slide on bushing, rear insulator and contact. The parts must butt securely against each other, as shown.

3. Solder the center conductor to the contact. Remove flux and excess solder.

4. Slide the front insulator over the contact, making sure it butts against the contact shoulder.

5. Insert the prepared cable end into the connector body and tighten the nut. Make sure the sharp edge of the clamp seats properly in the gasket.

Figure 23.31 — BNC connectors are common on VHF and UHF equipment at low power levels. *(Courtesy Amphenol Electronic Components)*

Type N assembly instructions

HBK05_19-19

CLAMP TYPES

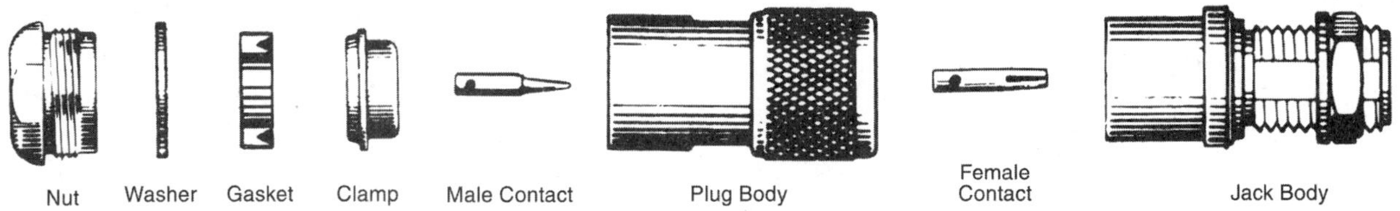

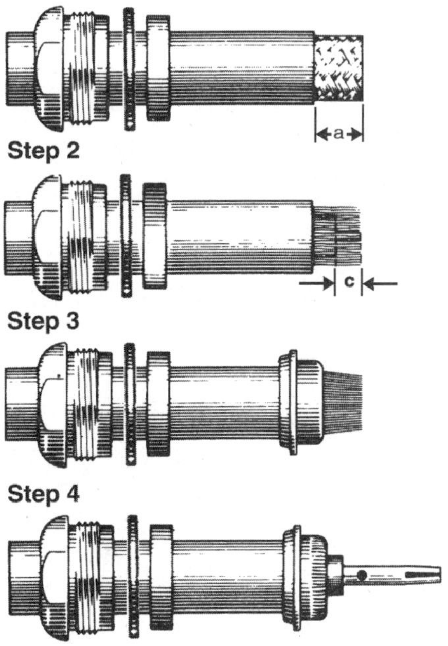

Amphenol Number	Connector Type	Cable RG-/U	Strip Dims., inches (mm)	
			a	c
82-61	N Plug	8, 9, 144, 165, 213, 214, 216, 225	0.359(9.1)	0.234(6.0)
82-62	N Panel Jack		0.312(7.9)	0.187(4.7)
82-63	N Jack	8, 9, 87A, 144, 165, 213, 214, 216, 225	0.281(7.1)	0.156(4.0)
82-67	N Bulkhead Jack			
82-202	N Plug	8, 9, 144, 165, 213, 214, 216, 225	0.359(9.1)	0.234(6.0)
82-202-RFX	N Plug	8, 213, 214	0.315(8.0)	0.177(4.5)
82-202-1006	N Plug	Belden 9913	0.359(9.1)	0.234(6.0)
82-835	N Angle Plug	8, 9, 87A, 144, 165, 213, 214, 216, 225	0.281(7.1)	0.156(4.0)
18750	N Angle Plug	58, 141, 142	0.484(12.3)	0.234(5.9)
34025	N Plug		0.390(9.9)	0.203(5.2)
34525	N Plug	59, 62, 71, 140, 210	0.410(10.4)	0.230(5.8)
35025	N Jack	58, 141, 142	0.375(9.5)	0.187(4.7)
36500	N Jack	59, 62, 71, 140, 210	0.484(12.3)	0.200(5.1)

See **AmphenolRF.com** for assembly instructions for all other connector types. These dimensions only apply to Amphenol connectors and may not be correct for other manufacturers.

Step 1 Place nut, washer, and gasket, with "V" groove toward clamp, over cable and cut off jacket to dimension a.

Step 2 Comb out braid and fold out. Cut off cable dielectric to dim. c as shown.

Step 3 Pull braid wires forward and taper toward center conductor. Place clamp over braid and push back against cable jacket.

Step 4 Fold back braid wires as shown, trim braid to proper length and form over clamp as shown. Solder contact to center conductor.

Step 5 Insert cable and parts into connector body. Make sure sharp edge of clamp seats properly in gasket. Tighten nut.

Step 5

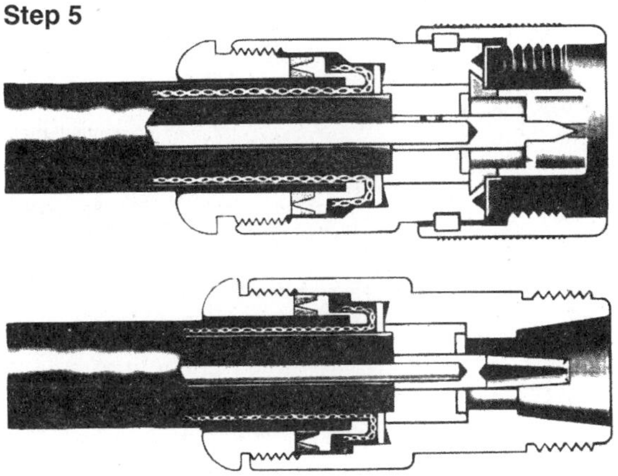

Figure 23.32 — Type N connectors are required for high-power VHF and UHF operation. ***(Courtesy Amphenol Electronic Components)***

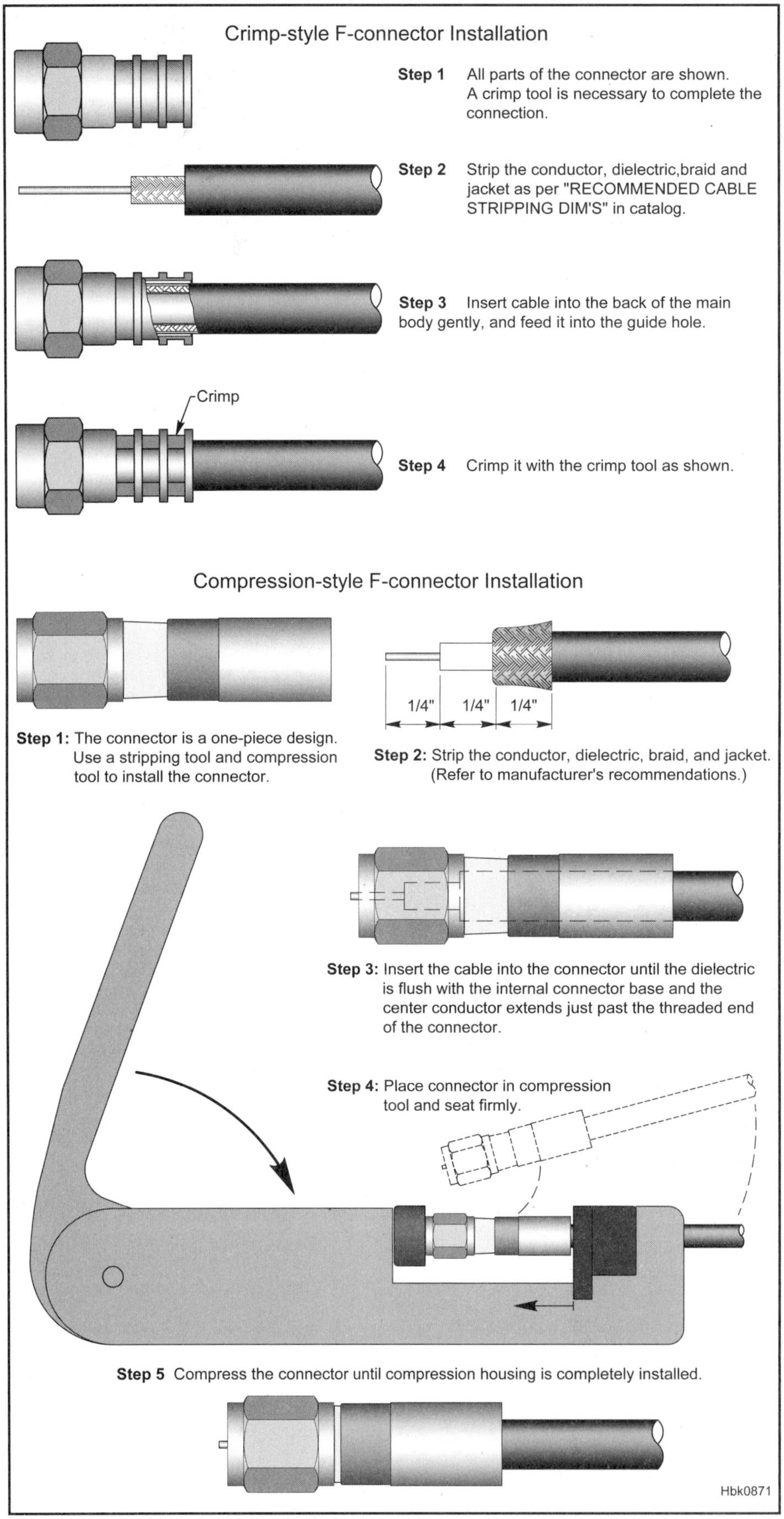

Figure 23.33 — Type F connectors, commonly used for cable TV connections, can be used for receive-only antennas with inexpensive RG-59 and RG-6 cable.

Figure 23.34 — A pair of SMA connectors, with male on the left and female on the right. SMA connectors are available in nickel, stainless steel, or gold finish.

less panel space. It is a natural for heavy duty requirements with smaller cables.

TYPE C COAXIAL CONNECTORS

This connector, honoring just Concelman, is essentially a TNC for larger cables. It is about the size of a Type N, but with a bayonet backshell and larger diameter inner components. It would seem to be a natural for patch panels for those running high power, but it has never caught on in the amateur community.

TYPE HN COAXIAL CONNECTORS

The Type HN connector is similar in design and layout to the Type N but is a bit larger. It has higher voltage breakdown and power ratings than the type N. It is a good match to the cables that are somewhat larger than RG-8 size and finds some amateur use in high power stations with long cable runs.

GENERAL RADIO CONNECTORS

The General Radio type 874 or GR genderless connector is most frequently seen on test equipment made by that company, later GenRad through the 1970s. Both the inner and outer connection arrangements are made of four spring leaves in two pairs, with one pair of each separated further than the other. In this way, by rotating 90 degrees, any two connectors can be mated resulting in a solid, matched connection without the need for gender converters. There is no locking arrangement, so it's not particularly suitable for long-term connections, but it's fine for lab use.

HARDLINE CONNECTORS

Surplus hardline cable comes in various sizes (½, ⅝, ¾, 1 inch and so on) that are not compatible with standard RF connectors such as UHF or N. There have been dozens of inventive schemes published over the years that use plumbing hardware or other materials to fabricate an adaptor compatible with a standard connector. If you decide to make your own adapter, be cautious about using dissimilar metals and waterproof the connector carefully. Otherwise, use the recommended connectors from the manufacturer — these are often available as surplus on Internet websites.

USING RG-6 WITH RG-58 CRIMP CONNECTORS

RG-6 coaxial cable is readily and cheaply available as it is commonly used for domestic cable and satellite TV. Crimp-type BNC, N, PL-259 and others are readily obtainable for RG-58 cables. Crimp connectors for RG-6 other than Type F are becoming difficult to find. However RG-58 crimp connectors can be satisfactorily used on RG-6 and some other cables as described on the article by Garth Jenkinson, VK3BBK, with this book's online material.

23.4.3 Connector Identifier and Range Chart

Table 23.3 provides a list of the military and industry part numbers for the most common RF connectors and adaptors used by amateurs on the MF/HF, VHF, and UHF bands.

Figure 23.35 provides dimensions and side views to help identify the different types of connectors used for RF through microwave frequencies. Dimensions are provided in both imperial and metric units as appropriate. For mm-wave and microwave connectors, calipers or a micrometer may be required to provide an accurate measurement capable of distinguishing between similar connectors. These specifications are intended for connector identification only and should not be the sole dimensions used when laying out a circuit board or drilling a mounting hole. **Figure 23.36** shows the frequency ranges appropriate for popular connector types.

These figures and chart were provided by Pasternack (**pasternack.com**), a major distributor of coaxial connectors, cable, tools, and other RF materials and supplies.

Table 23.3
Coaxial Cable Connectors

UHF Connectors

Military No.	*Style*	*Cable RG- or Description*
PL-259	Str (m)	8, 9, 11, 13, 63, 87, 149, 213, 214, 216, 225
UG-111	Str (m)	59, 62, 71, 140, 210
SO-239	Pnl (f)	Std, mica/phenolic insulation
UG-266	Blkhd (f)	Rear mount, pressurized, copolymer of styrene ins.

Adapters

PL-258	Str (f/f)	Polystyrene ins.
UG-224,363	Blkhd (f/f)	Polystyrene ins.
UG-646	Ang (f/m)	Polystyrene ins.
M-359A	Ang (m/f)	Polystyrene ins.
M-358	T (f/m/f)	Polystyrene ins.

Reducers

UG-175		55, 58, 141, 142 (except 55A)
UG-176		59, 62, 71, 140, 210

Family Characteristics:

All are nonweatherproof and have a nonconstant impedance. Frequency range: 0-500 MHz. Maximum voltage rating: 500 V (peak).

N Connectors

Military No.	*Style*	*Cable RG-*	*Notes*
UG-21	Str (m)	8, 9, 213, 214	50 Ω
UG-94A	Str (m)	11, 13, 149, 216	70 Ω
UG-536	Str (m)	58, 141, 142	50 Ω
UG-603	Str (m)	59, 62, 71, 140, 210	50 Ω
UG-23, B-E	Str (f)	8, 9, 87, 213, 214, 225	50 Ω
UG-602	Str (f)	59, 62, 71, 140, 210	—
UG-228B, D, E	Pnl (f)	8, 9, 87, 213, 214, 225	—
UG-1052	Pnl (f)	58, 141, 142	50 Ω
UG-593	Pnl (f)	59, 62, 71, 140, 210	50 Ω
UG-160A, B, D	Blkhd (f)	8, 9, 87, 213, 214, 225	50 Ω
UG-556	Blkhd (f)	58, 141, 142	50 Ω
UG-58, A	Pnl (f)		50 Ω
UG-997A	Ang (f)		50 Ω

Panel mount (f) with clearance above panel

M39012/04-	Blkhd (f)	Front mount hermetically sealed
UG-680	Blkhd (f)	Front mount pressurized

N Adapters

Military No.	*Style*	*Notes*
UG-29,A,B	Str (f/f)	50 Ω, TFE ins.
UG-57A.B	Str (m/m)	50 Ω, TFE ins.
UG-27A,B	Ang (f/m)	Mitre body
UG-212A	Ang (f/m)	Mitre body
UG-107A	T (f/m/f)	—
UG-28A	T (f/f/f)	—
UG-107B	T (f/m/f)	—

Family Characteristics:

N connectors with gaskets are weatherproof. RF leakage: –90 dB min @ 3 GHz. Temperature limits: TFE: –67° to 390°F (–55° to 199°C). Insertion loss 0.15 dB max @ 10 GHz. Copolymer of styrene: –67° to 185°F (–55° to 85°C). Frequency range: 0-11 GHz. Maximum voltage rating: 1500 V P-P. Dielectric withstanding voltage 2500 V RMS. SWR (MIL-C-39012 cable connectors) 1.3 max 0-11 GHz.

BNC Connectors

Military No.	*Style*	*Cable RG-*	*Notes*
UG-88C	Str (m)	55, 58, 141, 142, 223, 400	

Military No.	*Style*	*Cable RG-*	*Notes*
UG-959	Str (m)	8, 9	
UG-260,A	Str (m)	59, 62, 71, 140, 210	Rexolite ins.
UG-262	Pnl (f)	59, 62, 71, 140, 210	Rexolite ins.
UG-262A	Pnl (f)	59, 62, 71, 140, 210	nwx, Rexolite ins.
UG-291	Pnl (f)	55, 58, 141, 142, 223, 400	
UG-291A	Pnl (f)	55, 58, 141, 142, 223, 400	nwx
UG-624	Blkhd (f)	59, 62, 71, 140, 210	Front mount Rexolite ins.
UG-1094A	Blkhd		Standard
UG-625B	Receptacle		
UG-625			

BNC Adapters

Military No.	*Style*	*Notes*
UG-491,A	Str (m/m)	
UG-491B	Str (m/m)	Berylium, outer contact
UG-914	Str (f/f)	
UG-306	Ang (f/m)	
UG-306A,B	Ang (f/m)	Berylium outer contact
UG-414,A	Pnl (f/f)	# 3-56 tapped flange holes
UG-306	Ang (f/m)	
UG-306A,B	Ang (f/m)	Berylium outer contact
UG-274	T (f/m/f)	
UG-274A,B	T (f/m/f)	Berylium outer contact

Family Characteristics:

Z = 50 Ω. Frequency range: 0-4 GHz w/low reflection; usable to 11 GHz. Voltage rating: 500 V P-P. Dielectric withstanding voltage 500 V RMS. SWR: 1.3 max 0-4 GHz. RF leakage –55 dB min @ 3 GHz. Insertion loss: 0.2 dB max @ 3 GHz. Temperature limits: TFE: –67° to 390°F (–55° to 199°C); Rexolite insulators: –67° to 185°F (–55° to 85°C). "Nwx" = not weatherproof.

HN Connectors

Military No.	*Style*	*Cable RG-*	*Notes*
UG-59A	Str (m)	8, 9, 213, 214	
UG-1214	Str (f)	8, 9, 87, 213, 214, 225	Captivated contact
UG-60A	Str (f)	8, 9, 213, 214	Copolymer of styrene ins.
UG-1215	Pnl (f)	8, 9, 87, 213, 214, 225	Captivated contact
UG-560	Pnl (f)		
UG-496	Pnl (f)		
UG-212C	Ang (f/m)		Berylium outer contact

Family Characteristics:

Connector Styles: Str = straight; Pnl = panel; Ang = Angle; Blkhd = bulkhead. Z = 50 Ω. Frequency range = 0-4 GHz. Maximum voltage rating = 1500 V P-P. Dielectric withstanding voltage = 5000 V RMS SWR = 1.3. All HN series are weatherproof. Temperature limits: TFE: –67° to 390°F (–55° to 199°C); copolymer of styrene: –67° to 185°F (–55° to 85°C).

Cross-Family Adapters

Families	*Description*	*Military No.*
HN to BNC	HN-m/BNC-f	UG-309
N to BNC	N-m/BNC-f	UG-201,A
	N-f/BNC-m	UG-349,A
	N-m/BNC-m	UG-1034
N to UHF	N-m/UHF-f	UG-146
	N-f/UHF-m	UG-83,B
	N-m/UHF-m	UG-318
UHF to BNC	UHF-m/BNC-f	UG-273
	UHF-f/BNC-m	UG-255

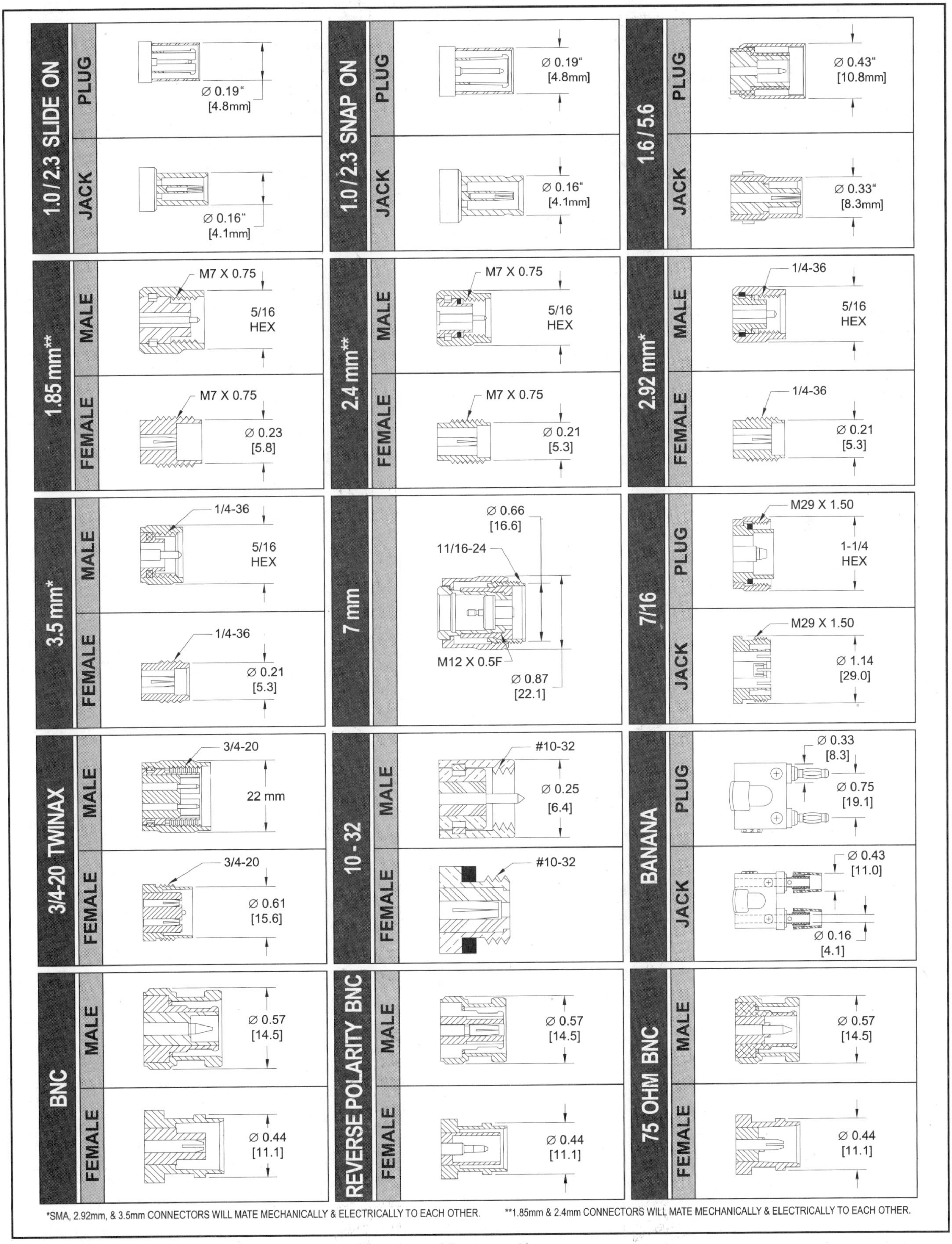

Figure 23.35A – Connector side views, set 1 of 4. (Courtesy of Pasternack)

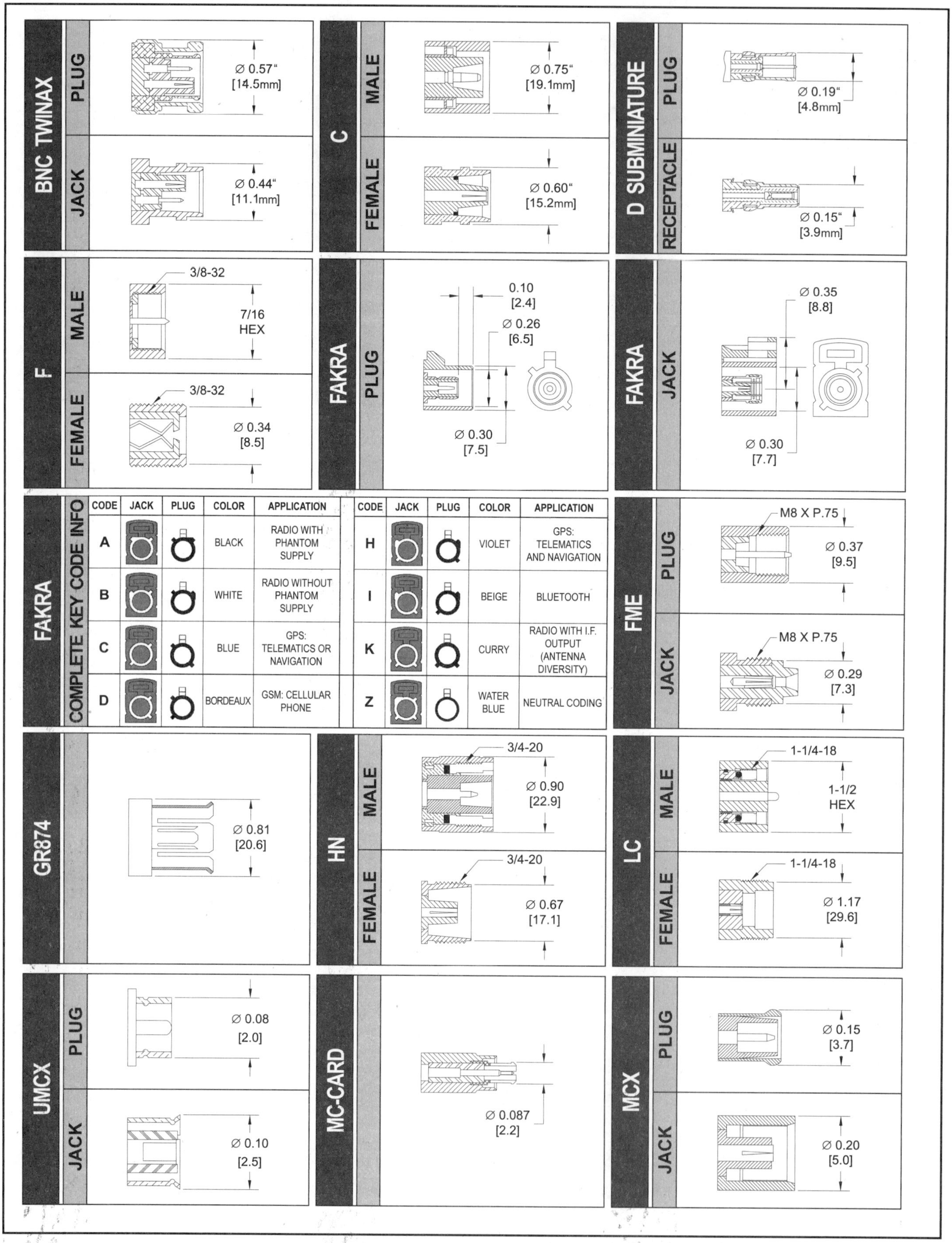

Figure 23.35B – Connector side views, set 2 of 4. (Courtesy of Pasternack)

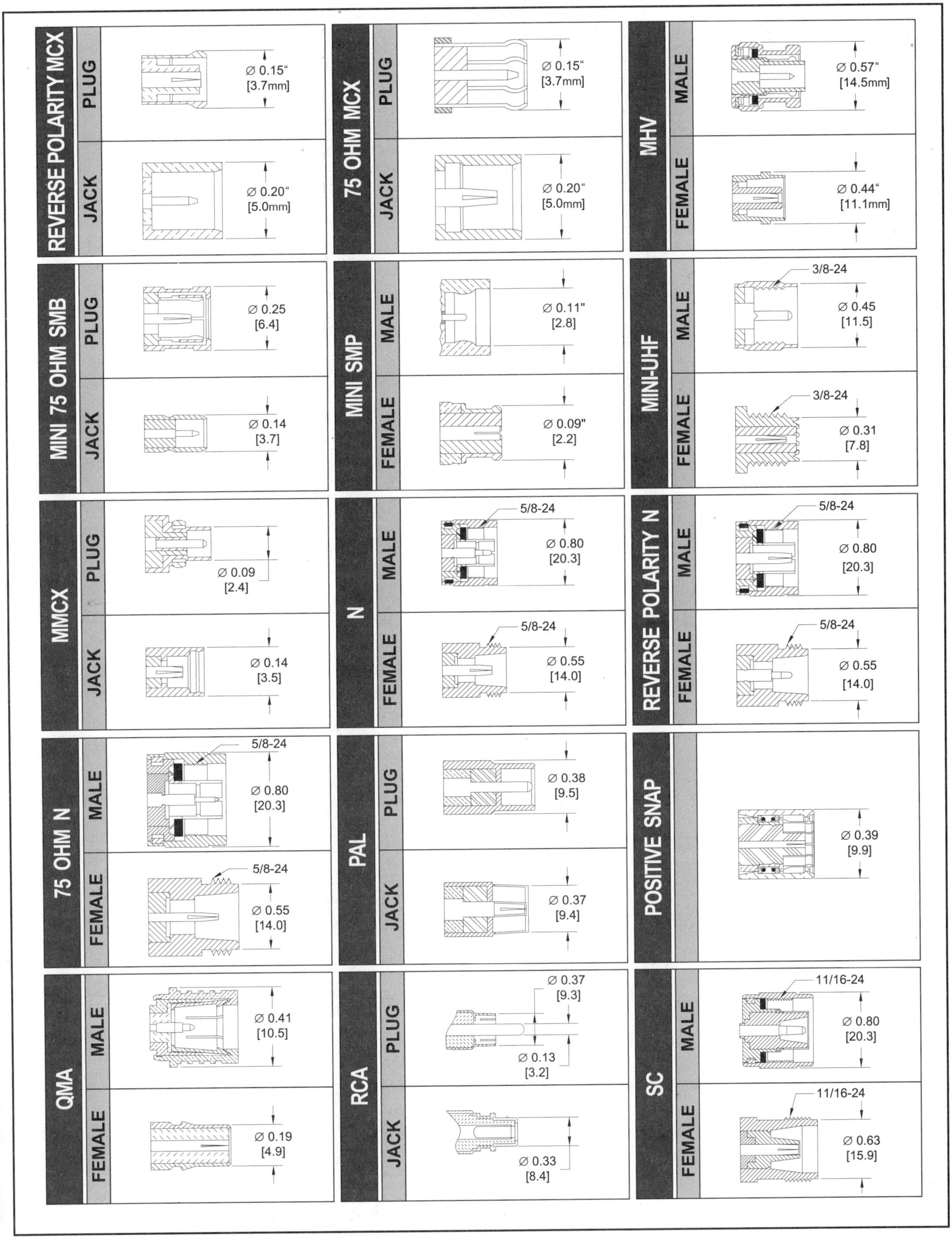

Figure 23.35C – Connector side views, set 3 of 4. (Courtesy of Pasternack)

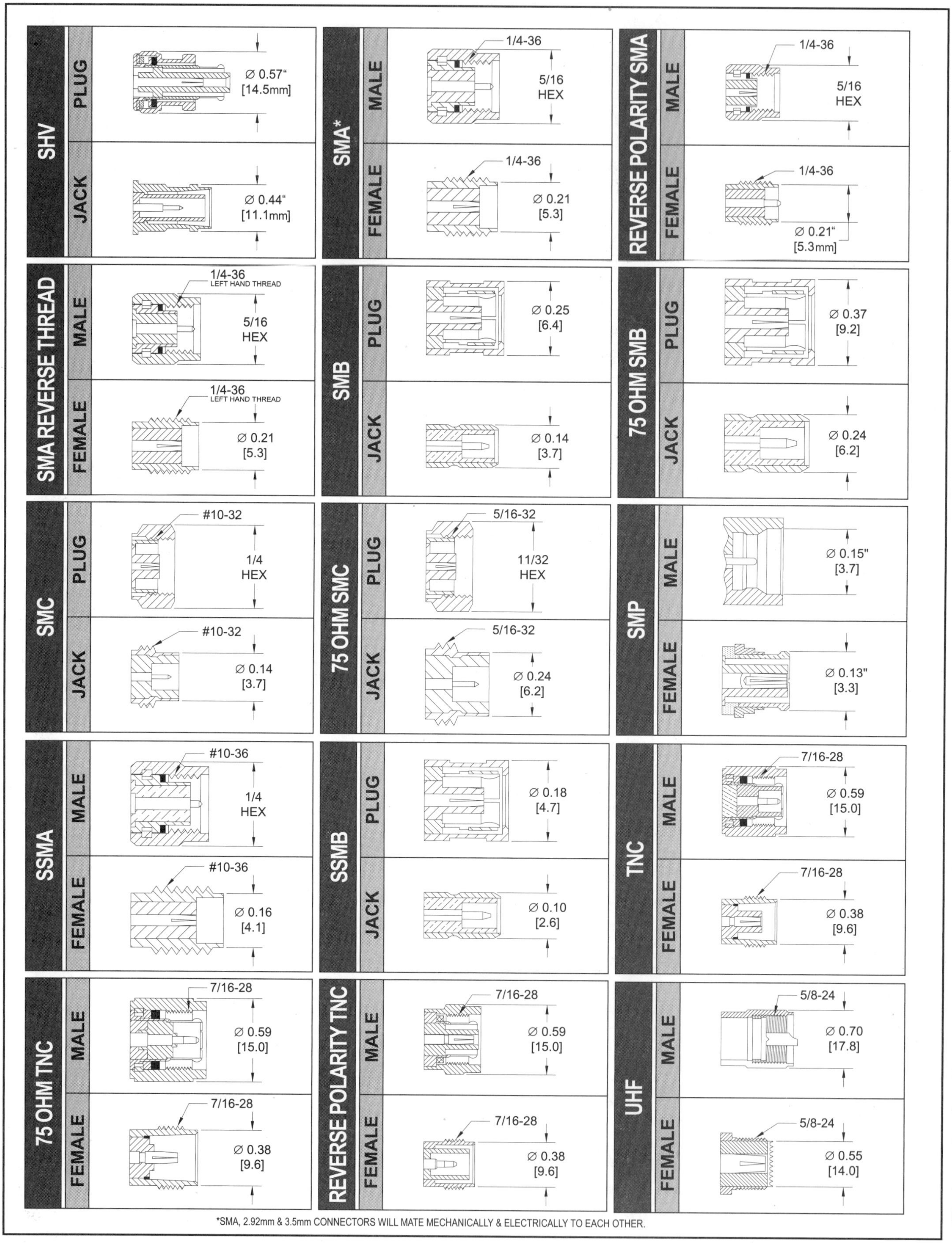

Figure 23.35D – Connector side views, set 4 of 4. (Courtesy of Pasternack)

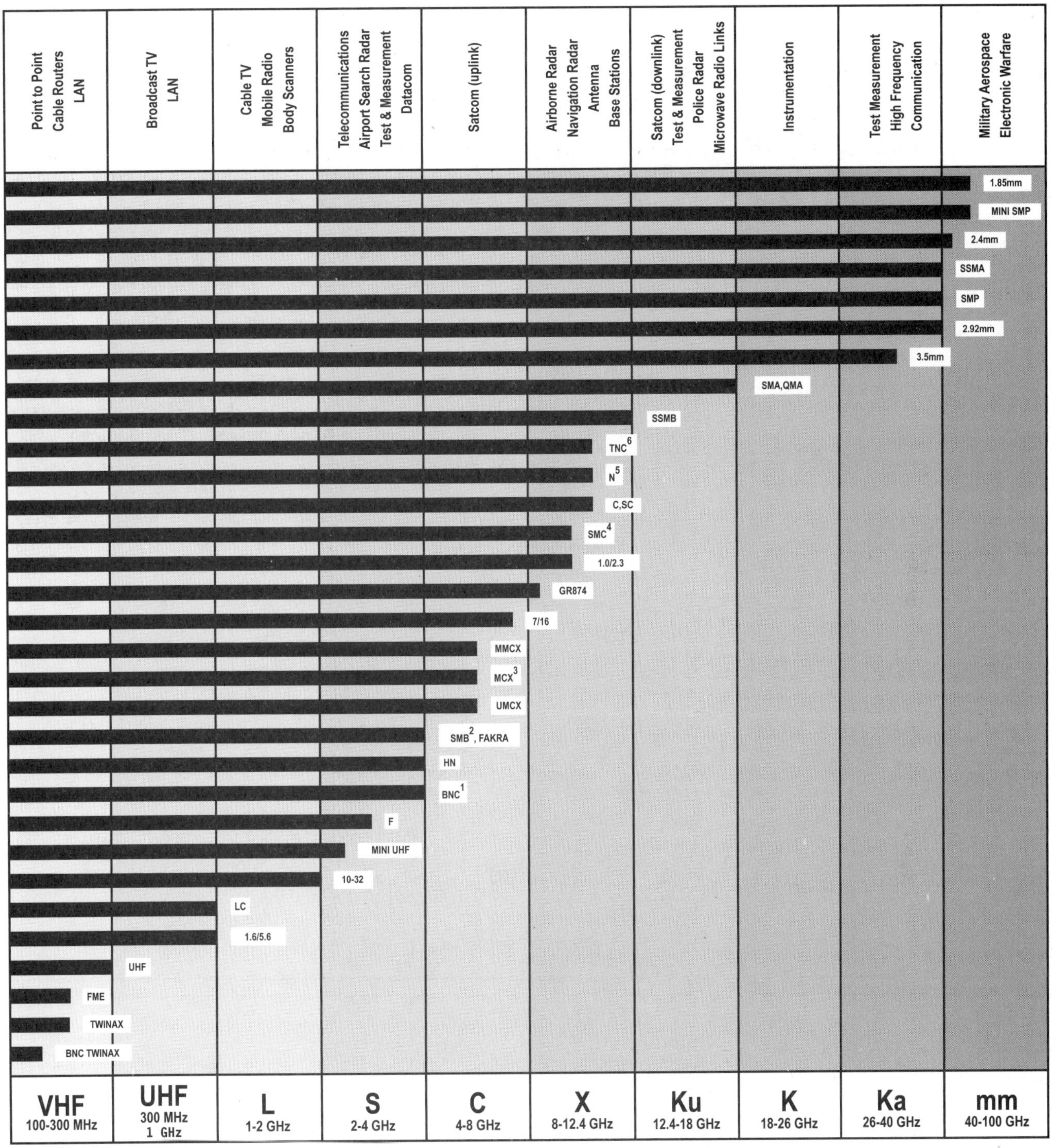

<u>Notes:</u>

1: BNC-75 Ohm connectors operate up to 1 GHz
2: SMB-75 Ohm & Mini SMB-75 Ohm connectors operate up to 4 GHz
3: MCX-75 Ohm connectors operate up to 6 GHz
4: SMC-75 Ohm connectors operate up to 10 GHz
5: N-75 Ohm connectors operate up to 1.5 GHz
6: TNC-75 Ohm connectors operate up to 1 GHz

Figure 23.36 – Recommended frequency ranges by connector type. (Courtesy of Pasternack)

23.5 Choosing And Installing Feed Lines

23.5.1 Comparing Feed Lines

Begin by studying the section on Transmission Line System Design in the chapter **Transmission Line System Techniques**. It is important to understand the requirements for your feed line before making a purchase. By approaching your antenna and feed line as a whole, you may be able to improve performance and save money at the same time. At the least, you will have a better appreciation for the different parts of your antenna system.

The usual two primary considerations for choosing a feed line are loss at the frequency of use and cost. Starting with the impedance of the load attached to the feed line (usually an antenna feed point) determine the matched loss for types of feed line you are considering. **Table 23.4** and **Table 23.5**, published by Frank Donovan, W3LPL in 2008 give typical losses for various types of coaxial cable at frequencies in the amateur bands by using a calculator by VK1OD. (Most manufacturers specify losses at 1, 10, 100 and 1000 MHz.) Table 23.5 specifies the length of line that will exhibit a loss of 1 dB.

To use Table 23.4, multiply the loss figure by the length of your feed line divided by 100 feet. For example, to find the loss of a 250-foot run of RG-213 at 28.4 MHz, multiply the table loss (1.2 dB) by 250/100 = 1.2 × 2.5 = 3.0 dB. Now use Equation 16 or one of the charts in Figure 23.15 to determine the total loss of the line at that frequency and SWR. If one of the cables is acceptable to you in performance and affordability, your job is done.

If you are operating with full power, you must also consider the peak voltage and power handling capability of the line. There may be other considerations in special circumstances. For example, operators who carry QRP equipment may elect to use RG-174 coax, even though it has high losses, because of its low weight.

Table 23.4
Cable Attenuation (dB per 100 feet)

MHz	*1.8*	*3.6*	*7.1*	*14.2*	*21.2*	*28.4*	*50.1*	*144*	*440*	*1296*
LDF7-50A	0.03	0.04	0.06	0.08	0.10	0.12	0.16	0.27	0.5	0.9
FHJ-7	0.03	0.05	0.07	0.10	0.12	0.15	0.20	0.37	0.8	1.7
LDF5-50A	0.04	0.06	0.09	0.14	0.17	0.19	0.26	0.45	0.8	1.5
FXA78-50J	0.06	0.08	0.13	0.17	0.23	0.27	0.39	0.77	1.4	2.8
3/4" CATV	0.06	0.08	0.13	0.17	0.23	0.26	0.38	0.62	1.7	3.0
LDF4-50A	0.09	0.13	0.17	0.25	0.31	0.36	0.48	0.84	1.4	2.5
RG-17	0.10	0.13	0.18	0.27	0.34	0.40	0.50	1.3	2.5	5.0
LMR-600	0.10	0.15	0.20	0.29	0.35	0.41	0.55	0.94	1.7	3.1
SLA12-50J	0.11	0.15	0.20	0.28	0.35	0.42	0.56	1.0	1.9	3.0
FXA12-50J	0.12	0.16	0.22	0.33	0.40	0.47	0.65	1.2	2.1	4.0
FXA38-50J	0.16	0.23	0.31	0.45	0.53	0.64	0.85	1.5	2.7	4.9
9913	0.16	0.23	0.31	0.45	0.53	0.64	0.92	1.6	2.7	5.0
LMR-400	0.16	0.23	0.32	0.46	0.56	0.65	0.87	1.5	2.7	4.7
RG-213	0.25	0.37	0.55	0.75	1.0	1.2	1.6	2.8	5.1	10.0
RG-8X	0.49	0.68	1.0	1.4	1.7	1.9	2.5	4.5	8.4	13.2
RG-58	0.56	0.82	1.2	1.7	2.0	2.4	3.2	5.6	10.5	20.0
RG-174	1.1	1.5	2.1	3.1	3.8	4.4	5.9	10.2	18.7	34.8

Table 23.5
Cable Attenuation (feet per dB)

MHz	*1.8*	*3.6*	*7.1*	*14.2*	*21.2*	*28.4*	*50.1*	*144*	*440*	*1296*
LDF7-50A	3333	2500	1666	1250	1000	833	625	370	200	110
FHJ-7	2775	2080	1390	1040	833	667	520	310	165	92
LDF5-50A	2108	1490	1064	750	611	526	393	227	125	69
FXA78-50J	1666	1250	769	588	435	370	256	130	71	36
3/4" CATV	1666	1250	769	588	435	385	275	161	59	33
LDF4-50A	1145	809	579	409	333	287	215	125	70	39
RG-17	1000	769	556	370	294	250	200	77	40	20
LMR-600	973	688	492	347	283	244	182	106	59	33
SLA12-50J	909	667	500	355	285	235	175	100	53	34
FXA12-50J	834	625	455	300	250	210	150	83	48	25
FXA38-50J	625	435	320	220	190	155	115	67	37	20
9913	625	435	320	220	190	155	110	62	37	20
LMR-400	613	436	310	219	179	154	115	67	38	21
RG-213	397	279	197	137	111	95	69	38	19	9
RG-8X	257	181	128	90	74	63	47	27	14	8
RG-58	179	122	83	59	50	42	30	18	9	5
RG-174	91	67	48	32	26	23	17	10	5	3

Table 23.6
Advantage from Upgrading Feed Line

Feet Required For 1 dB Advantage If Replaced By LDF5-50A (7/8-inch Heliax)

MHz	*1.8*	*3.6*	*7.1*	*14.2*	*21.2*	*28.4*	*50.1*	*144*	*440*	*1296*
LDF4-50A	2500	1430	1250	910	715	625	475	279	158	90
RG-17	1666	1430	1110	770	560	475	420	120	60	30
FXA12-50J	1250	1000	770	525	435	355	255	120	75	40
9913	935	590	455	320	280	220	150	85	53	29

Feet Required For 1 dB Advantage If Replaced By LDF4-50A (1/2-inch Heliax)

MHz	*1.8*	*3.6*	*7.1*	*14.2*	*21.2*	*28.4*	*50.1*	*144*	*440*	*1296*
RG-17	–	–	–	–	–	–	–	220	90	40
FXA12-50J	–	–	2000	1250	1100	835	625	250	145	65
9913	1430	1000	715	500	455	345	235	135	75	40
RG-213	618	434	306	212	171	146	106	58	29	14

For situations in which SWR is very high (such as for a nonresonant doublet used on multiple bands) or a very long run of feed line is required, open-wire line may be the best solution. Be sure to include the cost of impedance transformers in your system budget to connect the higher-impedance open-wire line to 50-Ω equipment and antennas.

If you are considering replacing a long run of cable with hardline or Heliax, **Table 23.6** should be helpful. This is a common situation for stations with antennas far from the transceiver and for VHF/UHF stations of any size. The cable lengths in the table are the lengths for which replacing them with Heliax would yield a 1-dB benefit. For example, replacing a 146-foot run of RG-213 with ½-inch Heliax would yield a 1 dB benefit on 10 meters. Similarly, an 85-foot run of Belden 9913 used on 2 meters could be replaced by ⅞-inch Heliax for a 1 dB benefit. The longer the cable run, the greater the benefit of replacing them with the lower loss of Heliax. (LDF4-50A and LDF5-50A are available at reasonable prices on auction websites, ham websites such as **eham.net** or **qrz.com**, and at hamfests.)

23.5.2 Installing Coaxial Cable

One great advantage of flexible coaxial line is that it can be installed with almost no regard for its surroundings. It requires no insulation, can be run on or in the ground or in piping, can be bent around corners with a reasonable radius, and can be snaked through places such as the space between walls where it would be impractical to use other types of lines. In addition, coaxial lines are unaffected by proximity to other conductors and can be run inside metal conduit or attached to metal structures.

Coax must still be treated with care as described in the following paragraphs, especially when being pulled through a conduit. Cable grips should be used to spread the gripping force over a large area of the cable's surface and the amount of force should be limited to prevent distorting the cable's cross section.

JACKET PROTECTION

When installing coaxial cable, it is important to protect the cable jacket to prevent water from entering the cable at any point. First, handle the cable with care during storage and

Coaxial Feed Line Loss Calculators

Should you need exact loss calculations for a specific feed line, the loss may be found by using ARRL's *TLW* software available from this book's online material. A good online feed line loss calculator is provided by Times-Microwave at **timesmicrowave.com/calculator**. Another free calculator has been created by Dan McGuire, AC6LA, at **ac6la.com/tldetails1.html**.

Using Coax Braid

It is common to loosen and strip the shield braid from old coax and reuse it as a ground strap. Unfortunately, cable braid is not a very good RF conductor without its jacket! What makes braid work well in coaxial cable is the continuous pressure of the jacket that compresses the braid, keeps all of the strands in good contact, and protects it from water. This allows the braid to act as a continuous conducting surface.

When braid is removed from the cable, the jacket is no longer present to protect and compress the strands. This allows them to move away from each other and for the strand surfaces to corrode, greatly reducing the effectiveness of the braid at RF. This is why the commercial and military standard for this type of connection is solid copper strap or heavy solid copper wire.

Used coax braid may be used for dc and low-frequency connections as long as it is protected from the weather but for a reliable RF connection use copper strap or heavy wire. Flat-weave tinned braid designed for unprotected use may be used as an RF conductor but never where it is exposed to water.

Coaxial cable inner conductor and center insulation can be used as a high-voltage wire to the rating of the coaxial cable as long as the insulation is not cracked or compromised in some other way.

installation so that the jacket is not damaged. If damage to the jacket is noticed immediately and no water is allowed to enter the cable, limited amounts of damage can be repaired using the same technique for waterproofing splices made with RF connectors as described in the **Building Antenna Systems and Towers** chapter.

Secure the cable after it has been connected to the antenna so that the jacket is not abraded or chafed by motion due to wind or antenna rotation. Cables hanging vertically should be supported in such a way that any bending is gradual and with a radius comfortably above the minimum bending radius. Cable grips are available that clamp over a short length, spreading the pressure and avoiding damage to the jacket. If wire or plastic cable ties are used, do not over-tighten them so that the jacket is crimped.

An important part of jacket protection is the waterproofing of RF connectors. Exposed coaxial cable braid will act as a wick, drawing in moisture. To a lesser extent, cables with stranded center conductors or partially hollow center insulation will draw in moisture as well. Coaxial cable infiltrated by water or moisture, either in the braid or center conductor, rapidly becomes unusable due to loss. Coax with a discolored or tarnished shield is not repairable and should be discarded.

BURYING COAX

There are several reasons why you might choose to bury coaxial cable feed lines. One is that buried cable is virtually free from storm and UV damage, and usually has lower maintenance costs than cable that is exposed to the weather. Another reason might be that underground cable interacts less with the radiation pattern of antennas, picks up less noise, and carries less common-mode RF on the outside of the shield. A buried cable will be aesthetically acceptable in almost all communities, as well.

Although any cable can be buried, a cable that is specifically designed for burial will have a longer life. *Direct-burial* cable has a high-density polyethylene jacket because it is both nonporous and will withstand a relatively high amount of compressive loads. In impregnated direct burial cables, an additional moisture barrier of polyethylene grease may be applied under the jacket; this allows the material to leak out, thus "healing" small jacket penetrations. These are referred to as "flooded" cables and the grease can make installing connectors more difficult. Neither RG-8/U or RG-213/U are automatically rated for direct burial — the cable vendor must specify the direct burial rating. The cable jacket is usually stamped with "Direct Burial" or the equivalent.

Here are some direct burial tips:

1) Because the outer jacket is the cable's first line of defense, any steps which can be taken to prevent damage to it will go a long way toward maintaining cable quality.

2) Bury the cable in sand or finely pulverized soil, free of sharp stones, cinders or rubble. If the soil in the trench does not meet these requirements, tamp four to six inches of sand into the trench and lay the cable. Tamp in another six to eleven inches of sand above the cable. Place a creosoted or pressure-treated board in the trench above the sand prior to the final filling of the trench. This will provide some protection against damage that could be caused by digging or driving stakes.

3) When laying buried cable, leave some slack in the cable. A tightly stretched cable is more likely to be damaged as it is being covered with fill material.

4) Examine the cable as it is being installed to be sure the jacket has not been damaged during storage or by being dragged over sharp edges.

5) It is important that burial is below the frost line to avoid damage by the expansion and contraction of the soil and water during freezing and thawing cycles.

USING CONDUIT

You may want to consider burying the coax in plastic pipe or electrical conduit. While plastic pipe provides a mechanical barrier, water incursion is practically guaranteed — water will either leak in directly or will condense from moisture in the air. Be careful to drill holes in the bottom of solid conduit at all low spots so that any moisture can drain out or use the perforated pipe that allows the water to drain out into the surrounding ground.

Whether the conduit is above or below ground, use large-radius sweeps to create bends instead of elbows. It is much easier to pull cable through the gradual bend of a sweep and pulling cables through too sharp a bend can damage it. Metal conduit and fittings frequently have sharp edges and burrs that will cut or even strip the jacket from coax being pulled over them. Before assembling each section, file off sharp or rough edges.

When choosing the size of the conduit, leave plenty of extra space — at least double the expected total diameter of your cable bundle. A 3 to 4 inch-diameter pipe is recommended. This greatly eases the pulling process and gives the cables plenty of room to move around connectors and joints in the conduit. Be sure to include a "fish rope" or "fish wire" with the final cable you pull so you can add or replace cables later.

If you also have rotator or other control cables, there may be local building codes that limit the number and type of cables that can share the same conduit.

23.5.3 Installing Parallel-Conductor Line

OPEN-WIRE LINE

In installing an open-wire line, care must be used to prevent it from being affected by moisture, snow and ice. If the line is home-made, only spacers that are impervious to moisture and are unaffected by sunlight and weather should be used on air-insulated lines. Ceramic spacers meet this requirement although they are somewhat heavy. The wider the line spacing, the longer the leakage path across the spacers, but this cannot be carried too far without running into line radiation, particularly at the higher frequencies. Six inches should be considered a maximum practical spacing for HF use.

The line should be kept away from other conductors, including downspouts, metal window frames, flashing, etc, by a distance of two or three times the line spacing. Conductors that are very close to the line will be coupled to it to some degree, and the effect is that of placing an additional load across the line at the point where the coupling occurs. Reflections take place from this coupled load, raising the SWR. The effect is at its worst when one wire is closer than the other to the external conductor. In such a case one wire carries a heavier load than the other, with the result that the line currents are no longer equal. The line then becomes unbalanced.

TWIN-LEAD AND WINDOW LINES

Solid dielectric, two-wire lines have a relatively small external field because of the small spacing, and can be mounted within a few inches of other conductors without much danger of coupling between the line and such conductors. Standoff insulators are available for supporting lines of this type when run along walls or similar structures.

As with open-wire lines, avoid installing the line in such a way that snow, ice, or liquid water can build up on the line. This presents an additional dielectric to the conductors and can change the line impedance or create loss.

PARALLEL LINE CONNECTORS

Considering how much longer balanced transmission line has been in use than coaxial cable, there aren't many choices of connector, but a few standards have evolved over the years.

Screw Terminals—Most vintage amateur radio equipment designed for balanced transmission line offered screw terminals. Screw terminals have the advantage of being nearly universal, in that virtually any reasonably sized wire size can fit under the screw head and may stay in place and not short during tightening. Still, the connection is not terribly reliable. A better solution is the use of crimped or soldered spade lugs under the screw terminals.

Double Banana Plug and Jack—A banana plug is a robust spring-loaded plug of a size that happens to fit nicely into the center conductor of a UHF socket. A popular test equipment connectivity arrangement is two banana plugs within a common insulating housing spaced 0.75 inches. This spacing is very convenient for use with most window-type transmission line.

Jacks are available in various forms, including panel mounting types and even combination plug and jack sets that also have screw terminals to clamp wire leads. Another handy arrangement is a kind of terminal that is sometimes called a "five-in-one." This mounts through a single hole into a panel and has a banana socket surrounded by a nut arrangement that surrounds a threaded surface that includes a hole for wire or tip insertion. Thus, it can accept a banana plug, a spade lug, a wire bent around the threads, or a wire pushed through the perpendicular hole. If two are installed on 3⁄4-inch centers, it will also accept the double banana plug, but can deal with loose wire ends, or lugs as well.

Powerpole Connectors—Popular for dc power connections in amateur radio equipment, these genderless connectors have a crimp-on terminal in a rectangular housing. (**andersonpower.com/us/en/resources/PowerPoleResourcesPage.html**) Like the banana plug, there is no locking mechanism so the connectors can pull apart. (Pins and locking clips are available to hold the connectors together.) The PP30 is the standard series for power connections. The PP10 and PP15 will work for transmission lines.

MECHANICAL ISSUES

Where a parallel-wire line must be anchored to a building or other structure, standoff insulators of a height comparable with the line spacing should be used if mounted in a spot that is open to the weather. Electric fence insulators are an excellent source of standoffs for this type of feed line. They are available from farm supply dealers and are fairly inexpensive.

Lead-in bushings for bringing the line into a building also should have a long leakage path. You may want to install a feed line feedthrough panel designed to fit in a window frame. Ceramic feed-through insulators can be used and are available as replacement parts from the panel vendors.

When running any kind of parallel-wire line down the side of a tower or other conducting surface, balance can be preserved by twisting the line every few feet. This results in approximately equal coupling by each conductor. Twisting the line also reduces the tendency of the line to move in the wind.

Parallel-line also has more wind resistance than coaxial cable and tends to move quite a bit more. The continual flexing can cause the conductors to break at soldered or otherwise fixed joints. This is a particular problem for lines with solid conductors as is common with window line. Support the line where it is attached to an antenna with insulators designed to provide stress relief to parallel-wire lines. (See the **Antenna Materials and Construction** chapter.)

Sharp bends should be avoided in any type of parallel-wire line, because it causes a change in the characteristic impedance at that point. The result is that reflections take place from each bend. This is of less importance when the SWR is high than when an attempt is being made to match the load to the line Z_0. It may be impossible to get the SWR to the desired figure until bends in the line are made very gradual.

23.6 References and Bibliography

Source material and more extended discussion of topics covered in this chapter can be found in the references given below and in the textbooks listed at the end of Chapter 2 **Dipoles and Monopoles**.

A. Barter, *International Microwave Handbook*, 2nd edition, RSGB, 2008.

C. Brainard and K. Smith, "Coaxial Cable — The Neglected Link," *QST*, Apr. 1981, pp. 28-31.

J. Brown, "A Ham's Guide to RFI, Ferrites, Baluns, and Audio Interfacing," Jan. 2019, Audio Systems Group (**audiosystemsgroup.com**).

J. Brown, "Transmission Lines at Audio Frequencies, and a Bit of History," Audio Systems Group (**audiosystemsgroup.com**).

J. Brown and B. Whitlock, "Common-Mode to Differential-Mode Conversion in Shielded Twisted-Pair Cables (Shield-Current-Induced Noise), AES Preprint 5747," Audio Systems Group (**audiosystemsgroup.com**).

D. DeMaw, "In-Line RF Power Metering," *QST*, Dec. 1969, pp. 11-16.

A. Ferreira, Jr., W. Pereira, J. Ribeiro, "Determine Twisted-Line Characteristic Impedance," *Microwaves & RF*, Jan. 2008, **mwrf.com/test-and-measurement/determine-twisted-line-characteristic-impedance**.

D. Geiser, "Resistive Impedance Matching with Quarter-Wave Lines," *QST*, Feb. 1963, pp. 56-57.

R. C. Johnson and H. Jasik, *Antenna Engineering Handbook*, 2nd ed. (New York: McGraw-Hill, 1984), pp. 43-27 to 43-31.

E. Jordan, Ed., *Reference Data for Engineers: Radio, Electronics, Computer, and Communications*, 7th Edition (Howard W. Sams, 1985).

R. W. P. King, H. R. Mimno and A. H. Wing, *Transmission Lines, Antennas and Waveguides* (New York: Dover Publications, Inc., 1965).

J. D. Kraus, *Antennas* (New York: McGraw-Hill Book Co., 1950).

Kurokawa, "Power Waves and the Scattering Matrix," *IEEE Transactions on Microwave Theory and Techniques*, Vol MTT-13, Mar. 1965, pp. 194-202.

Z. Lau, "RF: Mounting RF Connectors," *QEX*, Nov. 1996, pp. 21-22.

M. W. Maxwell, "Another Look at Reflections (Parts 1-7)," *QST*, Apr. 1973, pp. 35-41; June 1973, pp. 20-23, 27; Aug. 1973, pp. 36-43; Oct 1973, pp. 22-29; Apr. 1974, pp. 26-29, 160-165; Dec. 1974, pp. 11-14, 158-166; Aug. 1976, pp. 15-20.

M. W. Maxwell, *Reflections III* (New York: CQ Communications, 2010; available on CD from **store.cq-amateur-radio.com/shop/**).

T. McMullen, "The Line Sampler, an RF Power Monitor for VHF and UHF," *QST*, Apr. 1972, pp. 21-25.

D. Papas, "Installing Coax Crimp Connectors," *QST*, Feb. 2019, pp. 44-46.

J. Reisert, "RF Connectors, Part I and Part II," *Ham Radio*, Sep. 1986, pp. 77-80, and Oct. 1986, pp. 59-64.

H. H. Skilling, *Electric Transmission Lines* (New York: McGraw-Hill Book Co, Inc, 1951).

W. Silver, "Hands-On Radio: Experiment 94 — SWR and Transmission Line Loss," *QST*, Nov. 2010, pp. 63-64.

W. Silver, "Hands-On Radio: Experiment 96 — Open Wire Transmission Lines," *QST*, Jan. 2011, pp. 59-60.

W. Silver, "Hands-On Radio: Experiment 137 — Choosing a Feed Line," *QST*, June 2014, pp. 55-56.

W. Silver, "Hands-On Radio: Experiment 177 — Feed Line Comparison," *QST*, Oct. 2017, pp. 71-72.

G. Southworth, *Principles and Applications of Waveguide Transmission* (New York: D. Van Nostrand Co, 1950).

UHF/Microwave Experimenter's Manual, ARRL, 2000 (out of print).

H. Weinstein, "RF Transmission Cable for Microwave Applications," *Ham Radio*, May 1985, pp. 106-112.

T. Williams, "Microwavelengths: Coaxial RF Connectors for Microwaves," *QST*, Nov. 2004, pp. 92-94.

TABLE OF CONTENTS

Chapter 24 — Online Material

Articles

- "Baluns in Matching Units" by Robert Neece, KØKR
- "Broadband Antenna Matching"
- "Build a 9:1 Unun Transformer," By Stan Johnson, WØSJ
- "Coiled-Coax Balun Measurements" by Ed Gilbert, K2SQ
- "Compact 100-W Z-Match Antenna Tuner" by Phil Salas, AD5X
- "Don't Blow Up Your Balun" by Dean Straw, N6BV
- "Factors to be Considered in Matching Unit Design" by Robert Neece, KØKR
- "Hairpin Tuners for Matching Balanced Antenna Systems" by John Stanley, K4ERO
- "High-Power ARRL Antenna Tuner" by Dean Straw, N6BV
- "Matching with Inductive Coupling"
- "Matching-Unit Circuit Comparison Table" by Robert Neece, KØKR
- "Optimizing the Performance of Harmonic Attenuation Stubs" by George Cutsogeorge, W2VJN
- "Tapered Lines"
- "The AAT — Analyze Antenna Tuner — Program" by Dean Straw, N6BV
- "The EZ Tuner — Parts 1, 2, and 3," by Jim Garland, W8ZR
- "The Quest for the Ideal Antenna Tuner" by Jack Belrose, VE2CV
- "Why Do Baluns Burn Up?" by Zack Lau, W1VT

Chapter 24

Transmission Line System Techniques

The **Transmission Lines** chapter presented the fundamentals of transmission line operation and characteristics. This chapter covers methods of getting energy into and out of the transmission line at the transmitter and at the antenna. This requires *coupling* — the transfer of energy between two systems — from a transmitter to the feed line or from the feed line to the antenna. For coupling to be the most efficient, both systems should have the same ratio of voltage to current (impedance) wherever the two systems meet so that no energy is reflected at that interface. This often requires *impedance matching* to convert energy at one ratio of voltage to current to another ratio — all as efficiently as possible. This can be done with LC circuits, special structures, and even transmission lines themselves.

The initial portions of this chapter discuss methods used at the transmitter to effectively transfer power into the antenna system feed line using LC impedance-matching circuits and antenna tuners. The subject then turns to choosing a transmission line and deciding the best configuration of feed line and impedance-matching devices. Finally, at the "other end" of the feed line, several sections address methods of impedance matching at the antenna and minimizing unwanted interaction between the feed line and antenna.

24.1 Coupling the Transmitter and Line

A lot of effort is expended to ensure that the impedance presented to the transmitter by the antenna system feed line is close to 50 Ω. Is all that effort worthwhile? Like most broadly phrased questions, the answer begins, "It depends…" Vacuum-tube transmitters, with the wide adjustment range of the output amplifier's pi-network, could comfortably deliver rated output power into a wide variety of loads. The drawback was that the output network needed to be readjusted whenever the operating frequency changed significantly.

The modern amateur transceiver does not require output tuning adjustment at all for its broadband, untuned solid-state final amplifiers that are designed to operate into 50 Ω. Such a transmitter is able to deliver its rated output power — at the rated level of distortion — only when it is operated into the load for which it was designed. Generating full power from such a transmitter into loads far from 50 Ω can result in distortion products causing interference to other stations.

Further, modern radios often employ protection circuitry to reduce output power automatically if the SWR rises above 2:1. Protective circuits are needed because the higher voltages or currents encountered at such loads can quickly destroy solid-state amplifier transistors. Modern solid-state transceivers often include built-in antenna tuners to match impedances when the SWR isn't 1:1.

The impedance at the input of a transmission line is determined by the frequency, the characteristic impedance (Z_0) of the line, the physical length, velocity factor and the matched-line loss of the line, as well as the impedance of the load (the antenna) at the output end of the line. The section on Transmission Line System Design later in this chapter presents an example of this effect for a typical multiband dipole. (See the **Transmission Lines** chapter for an explanation.)

If the impedance at the input of the transmission line connected to the transmitter differs appreciably from the load resistance into which the transmitter output circuit is designed to operate, an impedance-matching circuit must be inserted between the transmitter and the line input terminals.

These circuits, called *networks* in professional literature, have one of several configurations with the L, pi, and T being the most common. The name of the network reflects the letter (L, π or T) that the usual shape of the circuit schematic most closely resembles.

The use of impedance-matching networks in a standalone piece of equipment is usually referred to as an *antenna tuner* or just *tuner*. This is somewhat of a misnomer since the network does not "tune" the antenna at all, even if located directly at the terminals of the antenna. The network only transforms the impedance presented to its output terminals into a different impedance at its input terminals. Many modern transceivers feature an internal antenna tuner that can compensate for SWR up to 3:1 (sometimes more).

In many publications, such an impedance-matching network is often called a *transmatch*, meaning a "transmitter matching" network. Another common name is *matchbox* (after the E.F. Johnson product line). A network operated automatically by a microprocessor is often called an *auto tuner*. Regardless of the name, the function of an antenna tuner is to transform the impedance at the input end of the transmission line — whatever it may be — to the 50 Ω needed for the transmitter to operate properly. An antenna tuner does *not* alter the SWR between its output terminals and the load, such as on the transmission line going to the antenna. It only ensures that the transmitter sees the 50-Ω load for which it was designed.

Antenna tuners come in three basic styles: *manual* (adjusted by the operator), *automatic* (adjusted under the control of a microprocessor) and *remote* (an automatic version designed to be mounted away from the operating position). Manual tuners are the most common and often include an SWR or power meter to aid the operator in adjusting the tuner. Automatic tuners may be internal to the transmitter or external, standalone equipment. Since the controlling microprocessor measures SWR on its own, there is rarely a need for power or SWR metering on automatic antenna tuners. Automatic models are available that are activated manually, or that sense the RF frequency and tune immediately, or that tune based on a computer control input or control link to the host transceiver. Remote antenna tuners are essentially automatic antenna tuners in enclosures designed to be mounted outside or out of sight of the operator and have no operating controls or displays.

As an example of the impedance-matching task, column one of **Tables 24.1** and **24.2** list the computed impedance at the center of two common dipoles mounted over average ground (with a conductivity of 5 mS/m and a dielectric constant of 13). The dipole in Table 24.1 is 100 feet long, and is mounted as a flattop, 50 feet high. The dipole in Table 24.2 is 66 feet long overall, mounted as an inverted-V whose apex is 50 feet high and whose legs have an included angle of 120°. The second column in Tables 24.1 and 24.2 shows the computed impedance at the transmitter end of a 100-foot long transmission line using 450-Ω window open-wire line. Please recognize that there is nothing special or "magic" about these antennas — they are merely representative of typical antennas used by real-world amateurs.

The intent of the tables is to show that the impedance at the input of the transmission line varies over an extremely wide range when antennas like these are used over the entire range of amateur bands from 160 to 10 meters. The impedance at the input of the line (that is, at the antenna tuner's output terminals) *will be different* if the length of the line or the frequency of operation is changed. It should be obvious that an antenna tuner used with such a system must be very flexible to match the wide range of impedances encountered under ordinary circumstances — and it must do so without arcing from high voltage or overheating from high current.

Table 24.1
Impedance of Center-Fed 100 Foot Flattop Dipole, 50 Feet High Over Average Ground

Frequency (MHz)	*Antenna Feed point Impedance (Ω)*	*Impedance at Input of 100 ft 450-Ω Line (Ω)*
1.83	4.5 – *j* 1673	2.0 – *j* 20
3.8	39 – *j* 362	888 – *j* 2265
7.1	481 + *j* 964	64 – *j* 24
10.1	2584 – *j* 3292	62 – *j* 447
14.1	85 – *j* 123	84 – *j* 65
18.1	2097 + *j* 1552	2666 – *j* 884
21.1	345 – *j* 1073	156 + *j* 614
24.9	202 + *j* 367	149 – *j* 231
28.4	2493 – *j* 1375	68 – *j* 174

Table 24.2
Impedance of Center-Fed 66 Foot Inv-V Dipole, 50 Feet at Apex, 120° Included Angle Over Average Ground

Frequency (MHz)	*Antenna Feed point Impedance (Ω)*	*Impedance at Input of 100 ft 450-Ω Line (Ω)*
1.83	1.6 – *j* 2257	1.6 – *j* 44
3.8	10 – *j* 879	2275 + *j* 8980
7.1	65 – *j* 41	1223 – *j* 1183
10.1	22 + *j* 648	157 – *j* 1579
14.1	5287 – *j* 1310	148 – *j* 734
18.1	198 – *j* 820	138 – *j* 595
21.1	103 – *j* 181	896 – *j* 857
24.9	269 + *j* 570	99 – *j* 140
28.4	3089 + *j* 774	74 – *j* 223

24.1.1 The Impedance Matching System

Over the years, radio amateurs have derived a number of circuits for use as antenna tuners. At one time, when parallel-conductor transmission line was more widely used, link-coupled tuned circuits were in vogue. With the increasing popularity of coaxial cable used as feed lines, other circuits have become more prevalent. The most common form of antenna tuner in recent years is some variation of a *T-network* configuration.

The basic system of a transmitter, impedance-matching network, transmission line and antenna is shown in **Figure 24.1**. As usual, we assume that the transmitter is designed to deliver its rated power into a load of 50 Ω. The problem is one of designing a matching circuit that will transform the actual line impedance at the input of the transmission line into a resistive impedance of 50 + *j*0 Ω. This impedance will be unbalanced; that is, one side will be grounded, since modern transmitters universally ground one side of the output connector to the chassis. The line to the antenna, however, may be unbalanced (coaxial cable) or balanced (parallel-conductor line), depending on whether the antenna itself is unbalanced or balanced.

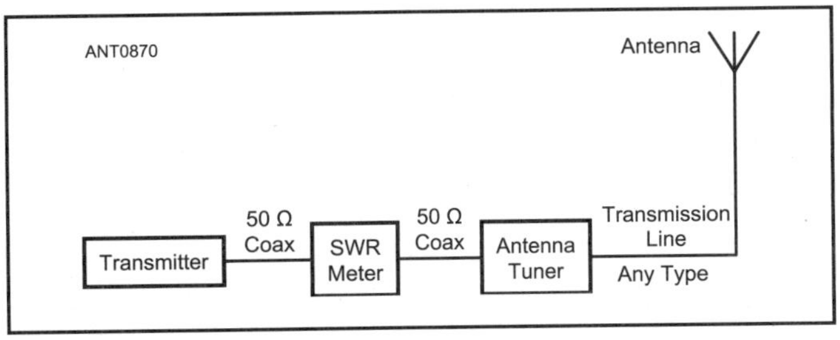

Figure 24.1 — Essentials of an impedance-matching system between transmitter and transmission line. The SWR meter indicates the quality of the match provided by the antenna tuner and may be part of the antenna tuner or the transmitter.

The antenna tuner in such a system may only consist of the LC network necessary to transform impedance. This is typical of custom LC networks constructed to match an antenna used on a single band that may be located away from the transmitter. An antenna tuner used on multiple bands and located in the station usually includes some type of SWR bridge or meter. (See the **Antenna and Transmission Line Measurements** chapter.)

Other features common in commercial antenna tuners include directional wattmeters, switches for the use of multiple feed lines and for bypassing the tuner and balanced and single-wire outputs. An overview of antenna tuner functions and features is provided in *The ARRL Guide to Antenna Tuners* by Joel Hallas, W1ZR (see References and Bibliography).

24.1.2 Harmonic Attenuation

This is a good place to bring up the topic of harmonic attenuation, as it is related to antenna tuners. One potentially desirable characteristic of an antenna tuner is the degree of extra harmonic attenuation it can provide by acting as a tuned circuit. While this is desirable in theory, it is not always achieved in practice. For example, if an antenna tuner is used with a single, fixed-length antenna on multiple bands, the impedances presented to the tuner at the fundamental frequency and at the harmonics will often be radically different as shown in Table 24.2. For example, at 7.1 MHz, the impedance seen by the antenna tuner for the 66-foot inverted-V dipole is 1223 – j 1183 Ω. At 14.1 MHz, roughly the second harmonic, the impedance is 148 – j 734 Ω. The amount of harmonic attenuation for a particular network will vary dramatically with the impedances presented at the different frequencies.

HARMONICS AND MULTIBAND ANTENNAS

There are some antennas for which the impedance at the second harmonic is essentially the same as that for the fundamental. This often involves trap antenna systems or wideband log-periodic designs. For example, a system used by many amateurs is a triband Yagi that works on 20, 15 and 10 meters. The second harmonic of a 20-meter transmitter feeding such a tribander can be objectionably strong for nearby amateurs operating on 10 meters such as at a Field Day or other multi-position special event or contest station, even with the approximately 60 dB of attenuation of the second harmonic provided by the low-pass filters at the output of modern solid-state transceivers. The third harmonic of a 144.2 MHz fundamental can cause interference on the 432 MHz band, as well. A linear amplifier can exacerbate the problem, since its second harmonic may be suppressed only about 46 dB by the typical pi-network output circuit used in many older amplifiers.

Most amateur antenna tuners will not attenuate the 10-meter harmonic much at all, especially if the tuner uses a high-pass T-network. This is the most common network used commercially because of the wide range of impedances it will match. Some T-network designs have attempted to improve the harmonic attenuation using parallel inductors and capacitors instead of a single inductor for the center part of the tee. Unfortunately, this often leads to more loss and more critical tuning at the fundamental, while providing little, if any, additional harmonic suppression in actual installations. The lesson here is to not depend on the antenna tuner for harmonic suppression — use filters at the transmitter.

HARMONICS AND PI-NETWORK TUNERS

If a low-pass pi-network is used for an antenna tuner, there will be additional attenuation of harmonics, perhaps as much as 30 dB for a loaded Q of 3. The exact degree of harmonic attenuation, however, is often limited due to the stray inductance and capacitance present in most tuners at harmonic frequencies. Further, the matching range for a pi-network tuner is fairly limited because of the range of input and output capacitance needed for widely varying loads.

HARMONICS AND STUBS

Far more reliable suppression of harmonics can be achieved using quarter-wave and half-wave transmission line stubs at the transmitter output. For example, a typical 20-meter $\lambda/4$ shorted stub (which is an open circuit at 20 meters, but a short circuit at 10 meters) will provide about 25 dB of attenuation to the second harmonic. It will handle full legal amateur power too. The characteristics of such stubs are covered in the sections of this chapter on the use of stubs as filters and on impedance matching at the antenna. The use of stubs as filters is also covered in excellent book *Managing Interstation Interference* by George Cutsogeorge, W2VJN (see References and Bibliography).

24.1.3 Myths About SWR

There are some enduring and quite misleading myths in Amateur Radio concerning SWR.

• Despite some claims to the contrary, a high SWR *does not by itself* cause RF interference, or TVI or telephone interference. While it is true that an antenna located close to such devices can cause overload and interference, the SWR in the feed line to that antenna has nothing to do with it, providing of course that the tuner, feed line or connectors are not arcing. The antenna is merely doing its job, which is to radiate. The transmission line is doing its job, which is to convey power from the transmitter to the radiator.

• A second myth, often stated in the same breath as the first one above, is that a high SWR will cause radiation from a transmission line. SWR has nothing to do with excessive radiation from a line. Common-mode currents on feed lines do radiate just like on antennas, but they are not directly related to SWR. An asymmetric arrangement of a transmission line and antenna can result in common-mode currents being induced on the outside of the shield of coax or as an imbalance of currents in an open-wire line. Common-mode current will radiate just as if it were on an antenna. If that current is flowing close to electronic equipment such as a telephone or entertainment system, RFI can result. A *choke (*also called a *choke balun)* is used on coaxial feed lines to reduce these currents as described in the section "Current and Choke Baluns" later in this chapter.

• A third and perhaps even more prevalent myth is that you can't "get out" if the SWR on your transmission line is higher than 1.5:1 or 2:1 or some other such arbitrary figure. On the HF bands, if you use reasonable lengths of good coaxial cable (or even better yet, open-wire line), the truth is that you need not be overly concerned if the SWR at the load is kept below about 6:1. This sounds pretty radical to some amateurs who have heard horror story after horror story about SWR. The fact is that if you can load up your transmitter without any arcing inside, or if you use a tuner to make sure your transmitter is operating into its rated load resistance, you can enjoy a very effective station, using antennas with feed lines having high values of SWR. For example, a 450-Ω open-wire line connected to the multiband dipole shown in Table 24.1 would have a 19:1 SWR on it at 3.8 MHz. Yet time and again this antenna has proven to be a great performer at many installations.

• A fourth myth is that changing the length of a feed line changes the SWR. Changing a feed line's length does *not* change the SWR (except for losses) inside the line. When someone tells you that adding or subtracting length changes the SWR, they are really telling you that their SWR meter reading was affected by the changing impedance in the line or that common-mode currents were affecting the measurement. Changing the feed line length can affect the impedance of the line to common-mode current and thus how much common-mode current is flowing at a particular point, including at the antenna's feed point.

24.2 Impedance Matching Networks

This section reviews the operation of several common impedance matching networks that are used as antenna tuners. As a supplement to this chapter, a review of impedance-matching circuit designs and characteristics contributed by Robert Neece, KØKR is included with this book's online material. It includes:

• Factors to be Considered in Creating or Assessing Matching-Unit Designs for the MF/HF Spectrum

• Comparison Table of Matching-Unit Designs

• Baluns in Matching Units

Along with the discussion is an extensive collection of references. The student of impedance matching will find the material to supplement and complement the material here, giving examples of commercial equipment and addressing the general advantages and disadvantages of each type. The student will also enjoy the excellent three-part series of articles by George Grammer, W1DF, listed in the References and Bibliography.

When designing and constructing impedance matching networks, particularly for power levels of 100 W and higher, it is important to take into account the high voltages and currents that may be present. The larger the difference between the input and output impedances, the higher those voltages and currents will be. Inductors should be constructed from low-loss wire or tubing. Variable inductors should be rated for transmitting applications. Capacitors should have sufficient voltage rating and variable capacitors should have heavy contacts to the moving plates. Switches must be heavy enough to handle both the current and voltage. Connections between components should be made with short lengths of heavy wire or strap. For more information on these heavy-duty components and wiring techniques, see the *ARRL Handbook* chapter on **RF Power Amplifiers** and projects for building high-power equipment.

24.2.1 The L-Network

A comparatively simple but very useful matching circuit for unbalanced loads is the L-network, as shown in **Figure 24.2A**. L-network antenna tuners are normally used for only a single band of operation, although multiband versions can be made with switched or variable coil taps. To determine the range of circuit values for a matched condition, the input and load impedance values must be known or assumed. Otherwise, a match may be found by trial and error.

There are several versions of the L-network. In Figure 24.2A, L is shown as the series reactance, X_S, and C1 as the shunt or parallel reactance, X_P. However, a capacitor may be used for the series reactance and an inductor for the shunt reactance, to satisfy mechanical or other considerations. The version shown in Figure 24.2A is the most popular with amateurs because of its low-pass characteristics that reduce harmonics, reasonable component values, and convenient construction from available component styles. A complete discussion of L-networks is available in the *ARRL Handbook*.

The ratio of the series reactance to the series resistance, X_S/R_S, is defined as the network Q. The four variables, R_S, R_P, X_S and X_P, for lossless components are related as given in the equations below. When any two values are known, the other two may be calculated.

$$Q = \sqrt{\frac{R_P}{R_S} - 1} = \frac{X_S}{R_S} = \frac{R_P}{X_P} \quad (1)$$

$$X_S = QR_S = \frac{QR_P}{1+Q^2} \quad (2)$$

$$X_P = \frac{R_P}{Q} = \frac{R_P R_S}{X_S} = \frac{R_S^{\ 2} + X_S^{\ 2}}{X_S} \quad (3)$$

$$R_S = \frac{R_P}{Q^2+1} = \frac{X_S X_P}{R_P} \quad (4)$$

$$R_P = R_S(1+Q^2) = QX_P = \frac{R_S^{\ 2} + X_S^{\ 2}}{R_S} \quad (5)$$

The reactance of loads that are not purely resistive may be taken into account and absorbed or compensated for in the reactances of the matching network. Inductive and capacitive reactance values may be converted to inductor and capacitor values for the operating frequency with standard reactance equations.

It is important to recognize that Eq 1 through 5 are for *lossless* components. When real components with real unloaded Qs are used, the transformation changes and you must compensate for the losses. Real coils are represented by a perfect inductor in series with a loss resistance, and real capacitors by a perfect capacitor in parallel with a loss resistance. At HF, a physical coil will have an unloaded Q_U between 100 and 400, with an average value of about 200 for a high-quality airwound coil mounted in a spacious metal enclosure. A variable capacitor used in an antenna tuner will have an unloaded Q_U of about 1000 for a typical air-variable capacitor with wiper contacts. An expensive vacuum-variable capacitor can have an unloaded Q_U as high as 5000.

The power loss in coils is generally larger than in variable capacitors used in practical antenna tuners. The circulating RF current in both coils and capacitors can also cause severe heating. The ARRL Laboratory has seen coils forms made of plastic melt when pushing antenna tuners to their extreme limits during product testing. The RF voltages developed across the capacitors can be pretty spectacular at times, leading to severe arcing.

Note that L-networks cannot match all impedances to 50 Ω. The load and source impedances must have the proper relationship for the equations to solve to obtainable component values. The reactance at the load must also be cancellable by the reactance of the L-network. If the load impedance is such that it cannot be matched by an L-network, try (a) reversing the network or (b) adding λ/8 to λ/4 of transmission line between the load and network. This does not change the SWR, but it does transform the load impedance to a new combination of resistance and reactance that the L-network may be able to match.

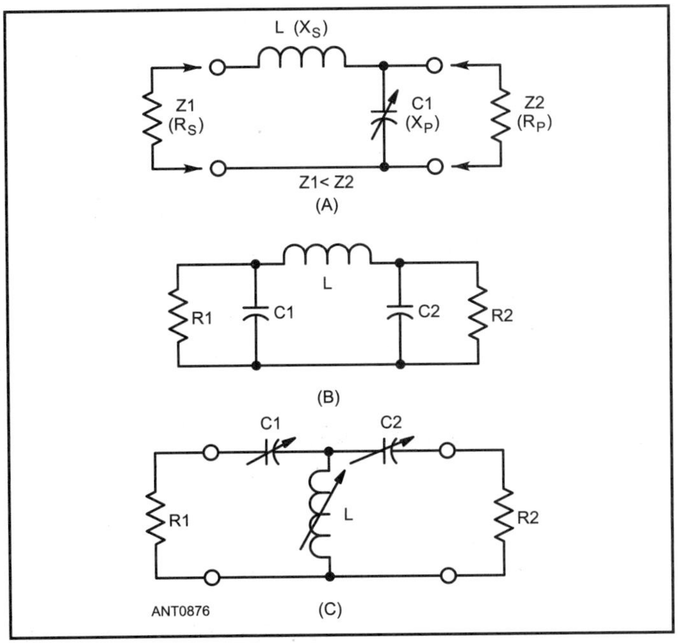

Figure 24.2 — At A, the L-matching network, consisting of L and C1, to match Z1 and Z2. The lower of the two impedances to be matched, Z1, must always be connected to the series-arm side of the network and the higher impedance, Z2, to the shunt-arm side. The positions of the inductor and capacitor may be interchanged in the network. At B, the pi-network tuner, matching R1 to R2. The pi-network provides more flexibility than the L as an antenna-tuner circuit. See equations in the text for calculating component values. At C, the T-network tuner. This has more flexibility in that components with practical values can match a wide variety of loads. The drawback is that this network can be inefficient, particularly when the output capacitor is small.

L-NETWORK CONSTRUCTION

Building an L-network is straightforward and there have been many construction articles about constructing antenna tuners based on an L-network. If you are trying to match an antenna for a single band, the network can be constructed with fixed-value components as in **Figure 24.3A** if you know the impedance to be matched and are willing to do the calculations. (See the References and Bibliography entry for Hands-On Radio Experiment 157 by Silver.)

Dick Sanders, K5QY, uses the variable, re-configurable L-network in Figure 24.3B as a test set. (See his References and Bibliography entry.) He connects the L-network to the antenna and an antenna analyzer to the input of the network. Then he adjusts the network for the best match, measures the value of the L-network components, and builds an L-network with those values.

The L-network can form the basis of an adjustable antenna tuner for high or low power. The article "On the Quest for an Ideal Antenna Tuner" by Jack Belrose, VE2CV, begins with a simple, reversible L-network and extends it to a more versatile configuration that can place the L and C in both series and shunt. (The article is included in the online material for this chapter.)

Finally, the L-network can be tuned automatically by a microcontroller. Most automatic antenna tuners are built this way. Relays are used to select from a wide variety of fixed-value components. If a match is not reached, other relays "turn

(A)

(B)

Figure 24.3 — Two examples of L-networks. At A is a full-power L-network for matching a base-fed tower on 160 meters using a vacuum variable capacitor and inductor wound from 1/4-inch refrigerator tubing. At B is a low-power L-network that is used as an adjustable test set for determining what component values are required for matching a load impedance. [Dick Sander, K5QY, photo]

the network around" and move the shunt component to the other end of the network.

24.2.2 The Pi-Network

The impedances at the feed point of an antenna used on multiple HF bands varies over a very wide range, particularly if thin wire is used. This was described in detail in the **Dipoles and Monopoles** chapter. The transmission line feeding the antenna transforms the wide range of impedances at the antenna's feed point to another wide range of impedances at the transmission line's input. This often mandates the use of a more flexible antenna tuner than an L-network.

The pi-network, shown in Figure 24.2B, offers more flexibility than the L-network, since there are three variables instead of two. The only limitation on the circuit values that may be used is that the reactance of the series arm, the inductor L in the figure, must not be greater than the square root of the product of the two values of resistive impedance to be matched. The following equations are for lossless components in a pi-network.

For R1 > R2

$$X_{C1} = \frac{R_1}{Q} \tag{6}$$

$$X_{C2} = R2\sqrt{\frac{R1/R2}{Q^2+1-R1/R2}} \tag{7}$$

$$X_L = \frac{(Q \times R1) + \dfrac{R1 \times R2}{X_{C2}}}{Q^2+1} \tag{8}$$

The pi-network may be used to match a low impedance to a rather high one, such as 50 to several thousand ohms. Conversely, it may be used to match 50 Ω to a quite low value, such as 1 Ω or less. For antenna-tuner applications, C1 and C2 may be independently variable. L may be a roller inductor or a coil with switchable taps.

Alternatively, a lead fitted with a suitable clip may be used to short out turns of a fixed inductor. In this way, a match may be obtained through trial. It will be possible to match two values of impedances with several different settings of L, C1 and C2. This results because the Q of the network is being changed. If a match is maintained with other adjustments, the Q of the circuit rises with increased capacitance at C1.

Of course, the load usually has a reactive component along with resistance. You can compensate for the effect of these reactive components by changing one of the reactive elements in the matching network. For example, if some reactance were shunted across R2, the setting of C2 could be changed to compensate for inductive or capacitive shunt reactance.

As with the L-network, the effects of real-world unloaded Q for each component must be taken into account in the pi-network to evaluate real-world losses.

Pi-networks are used in vacuum-tube amplifiers to match the high tube output impedance to the 50-Ω impedance of most feed lines and antenna systems. See the *ARRL Handbook* chapter **RF Power Amplifiers** for more information on and design software for the pi-network.

24.2.3 The T-Network

Both the pi-network and the L-network often require unwieldy values of capacitance — that is, *large* capacitances are often required at the lower frequencies — to make the desired transformation to 50 Ω. Often, the range of capacitance from minimum to maximum must be quite wide when the impedance at the output of the network varies radically with frequency, as is common for multiband, single-wire antennas.

The high-pass T-network shown in Figure 24.2C is capable of matching a wide range of load impedances and uses practical values for the components. However, as in almost everything in radio, there is a price to be paid for this flexibility. The T-network can be very lossy compared to other network types. This is particularly true at the lower frequencies, whenever the load resistance is low. Loss can be severe if the maximum capacitance of the output capacitor C2 in Figure 24.2C is low.

For example, **Figure 24.4** shows the computed values for the components at 1.8 MHz for four types of networks into a load of $5 + j\,0\ \Omega$. In each case, the unloaded Q of the inductor used is assumed to be 200, and the unloaded Q of the capacitor(s) used is 1000. The component values were computed using the program *TLW* (described later in this chapter).

Figure 24.4A is a low-pass L-network; Figure 24.4B is a high-pass L-network and Figure 24.3C is a pi-network. At more than 5200 pF, the capacitance values are pretty unwieldy for the first three networks. The loaded Q_L for all three is only 3.0, indicating that the network loss is small. In fact, the loss is only 1.8% for all three because the loaded Q_L is much smaller than the unloaded Q_U of the components used.

The T-network in Figure 24.4D uses more practical, realizable component values. Note that the output capacitor C2 has been set to 500 pF and that dictates the values for the other two components. The drawback is that the loaded Q in this configuration has risen to 34.2, with an attendant loss of 22.4% of the power delivered to the input of the network. For the legal limit of 1500 W, the loss in the network is 335 W. Of this, 280 W ends up in the inductor, which will probably melt! Even if the inductor doesn't burn up, the output capacitor C2 might well arc over, since it has more than 3800 V peak across it at 1500 W into the network.

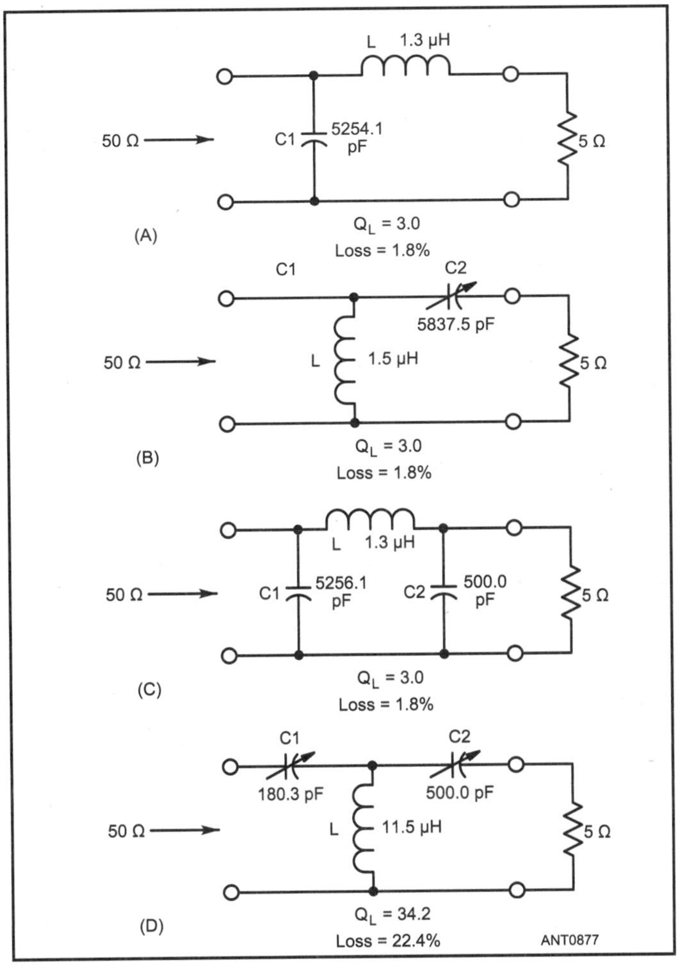

Figure 24.4 — Computed values for real components (Q_U = 200 for coil, Q_U = 1000 for capacitor) to match 5-Ω load resistance to 50-Ω line. At A, low-pass L-network, with shunt input capacitor, series inductor. At B, high-pass L-network, with shunt input inductor, series capacitor. Note how large the capacitance is for these L-networks. At C, low-pass pi-network and at D, high-pass T-network. The component values for the T-network are practical, although the loss is highest for this particular network, at 22.4% of the input power.

Due to the losses in the components in a T-network, it is quite possible to "load it up into itself," causing real damage inside. For example, *TLW* analyzed a T-network loaded up into a short circuit at 1.8 MHz. The component values look quite reasonable; C_{IN} = 78 pF, L = 13 µH, C_{OUT} = 500 pF, but unfortunately *all* the power is dissipated in the network itself. The current through the output capacitor C2 at 1500 W input to the antenna tuner would be 35 A, creating a peak voltage of more than 8700 V across C2. Either C1 (also at more than 8700 V peak) or C2 will probably arc over before the power loss is sufficient to destroy the coil. However, the loud arcing might frighten the operator pretty badly.

The point you should remember is that the T-network is indeed very flexible in terms of matching to a wide variety of loads. However, it must be used judiciously, lest it burn itself up. Even if it doesn't fry itself, it can waste that precious RF power you'd rather put into your antenna. Additional discussion of the T-network as an antenna tuner is provided in the article by Sabin listed in the References and Bibliography. A fully-automated, full-power T-network, was described by Jim Garland, W8ZR, in his series of *QST* articles "The EZ Tuner" which are included in the online material.

ADJUSTING T-NETWORK ANTENNA TUNERS

The process of adjusting an antenna tuner can be simplified greatly by using a process that not only results in minimum SWR to the transmitter, but also minimizes power losses in the tuner circuitry. If you have a commercial tuner and read the user's manual, the manufacturer will likely provide a method of adjustment that you should follow, including initial settings. If you do not have a user's manual, first open the tuner and determine the circuit for the tuner. To adjust a T-network type of tuner:

1) Set the series capacitors to maximum value. This may not correspond to the highest number on the control scale — verify that the capacitor's plates are fully meshed.

2) Set the inductor to maximum value. This corresponds to placing a switch tap or roller inductor contact so that it is electrically closest to circuit ground.

3) If you have an SWR analyzer, connect it to the **TRANSMITTER** connector of the tuner. Otherwise, connect the transceiver and tune it to the desired frequency, but do not transmit.

4) Adjust the inductor throughout its range watching the SWR analyzer for a dip in the SWR or listen for a peak in the received noise. Return the inductor to the setting for lowest SWR or highest received noise.

a) If no SWR minimum or noise peak is detected, reduce

the value of the capacitor closest to the transmitter in steps of about 20% and repeat.

b) If still no SWR minimum or noise peak is detected, return the input capacitor to maximum value and reduce the output capacitor value in steps of about 20%.

c) If still no SWR minimum or noise peak is detected, return the output capacitor to maximum value and reduce both input and output capacitors in 20% steps.

5) Once a combination of settings is found with a definite SWR minimum or noise peak:

a) If you are using an SWR analyzer, make small adjustments to find the combination of settings that produce minimum SWR with the maximum value of input and output capacitance.

b) If you do not have an SWR analyzer, set the transmitter output power to about 10 W, ensure that you won't cause interference, identify with your call sign, and transmit a steady carrier by making the same adjustments as in step 5a.

c) For certain impedances, the tuner may not be able to reduce the SWR to an acceptable value. In this case, try adding feed line at the output of the tuner from ⅛- to ½ λ electrical wavelength long. This will not change the feed line SWR, but it may transform the impedance to a value more suitable for the tuner components.

In general, for any type of tuner, begin with the maximum reactance to ground (maximum inductance or minimum capacitance) and the minimum series reactance between the source and load (minimum inductance or maximum capacitance). The configuration that produces the minimum SWR with maximum reactance to ground and minimum series reactance will generally have the highest efficiency and broadest tuning bandwidth.

24.2.4 Tuning Electrically Short Whips

This section is extracted from the article "Tuning Electrically Short Antennas for Field Operation" by Kai Siwiak, KE4PT, and Ulrich Rohde, N1UL. The full article, including a number of references, was originally published by *Microwave Journal* and is available online at **microwavejournal.com/articles/32231-tuning-electrically-short-antennas-for-field-operation**. Also see the **Dipoles and Monopoles** chapter for a discussion of key characteristics of short monopoles or whips and various loading methods to increase their electrical size.

Portable and mobile operation are becoming more popular, and this often results in the use of electrically small antennas for convenience. The most common antennas are loaded and unloaded whips with a set of ground radials, a counterpoise, or some other type of grounding. To match the impedance of these antennas to the 50 Ω expected by the transmitter, an antenna tuner must be used. This section focuses on monopoles (whips) but many of the same ideas apply to electrically short dipoles.

The efficiency of an antenna, $\eta = R_r / (R_r + R_{loss})$, where R_r is the radiation resistance that represents radiated power and R_{loss} represents the total effective loss resistance from all types of losses. R_r for electrically short antennas can be very low, a few ohms or much less at MF. Electrically short antennas, typically λ/10 or shorter, look like a capacitor with a typical capacitance of 25 pF/m of length, e.g., 75 pF for a 3-meter rod. From a presentation "Electrically Short Antennas" by Rohde, Salazar-Palma, and Sarkar, a 10.5-foot whip antenna exhibits typical impedances and efficiency shown in **Table 24.3**.

Table 24.3
Characteristics Of a 10.5-Foot Whip Antenna

F (MHz)	*C (pF)*	R_r *(Ω)*	*Z (Ω)*	*η (%)*	*L (μH)*
1.8	30.1	0.146	13.72-j2716	1.064	240
3.5	30.6	0.55	7.43-j1375	7.4	62.5
7.0	32.8	2.2	7.04-j644	31.2	14.6
10.0	36.5	4.5	6.5-j408	69.2	6.49
14.0	46.5	8.8	10-j232	88.0	2.64

The inductance, L, is the base loading required to resonate the whip.

Longer antennas that might be used on a ship or boat also present highly reactive impedances until they begin to approach λ/4 as shown in **Figure 24.5**.

The inductances for tuning are found in commercial input/output switchable antenna tuners operating from 1.5 to 30 MHz. The circuit is an L-network (see previous section) where the switched shunt capacitors can be connected to either side of the inductors. The capacitors are typically low-loss mica transmitting units.

Figure 24.6A shows the matching ranges of the tuner with the capacitors on each side of the inductors, and Figure 24.6B shows a simplified schematic of the main capacitor bank that is switched to either the input or output side of the inductors. The inductors are wound with 0.048-inch diameter, enameled copper wire and have approximately 0.04 μH step size. The capacitor step size is 9.375 pF. This tuner has nine switchable inductors, 10 switchable capacitors and two positions for one

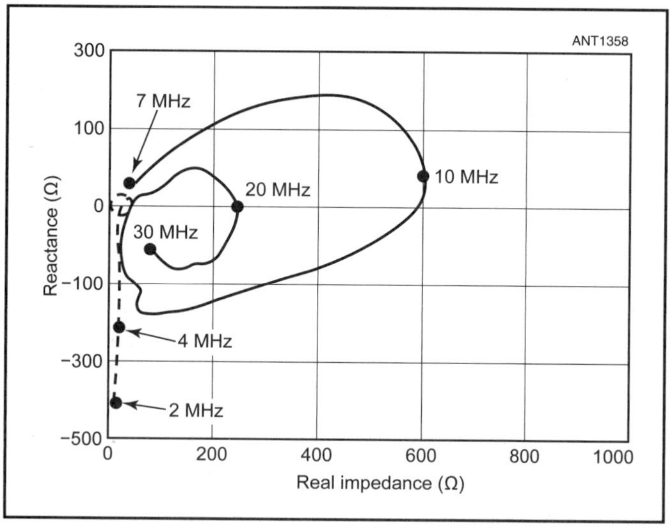

Figure 24.5 — Measure impedance of a 35-foot whip antenna on a large boat.

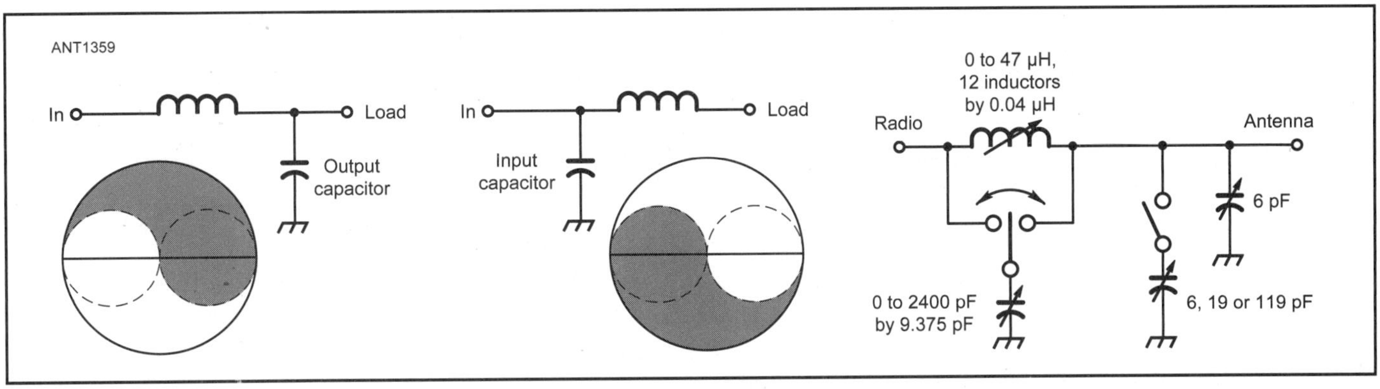

Figure 24.6 — Smith charts showing tuner matching options the right capacitor bank is used when the load resistance is > 50 Ω, and the left capacitor bank is used when the load resistance is < 50 Ω (a). Tuning network is similar to that of the ICOM AT-130.

of the capacitor banks (i.e., on either side of the inductors), yielding 1,048,576 tuning combinations. The 6 pF capacitor at the output represents the ceramic antenna mount or connector. For best performance, antenna tuners use air core coils or very low permeability powdered iron cores.

Some tuner designs use a high-pass, T-configuration. (See **Figure 24.7**). LC1 forms one resonant circuit, LC2 forms the other circuit and the two are tuned to resonate at the frequency of operation. Generally, when the value of C2 is too small, input resonance occurs yet there is no loading and no output power obtained. This is the flaw of the T-configuration: the left loop can be in resonance, and no output power (voltage) is available in the right loop. This is referred to as "tuning up into itself." In this condition, the tuner can be damaged by high voltages and currents in the resonant input circuit creating large losses.

For electrically short antennas, this condition can be detected with a voltage probe at the output, such as a pre-ignited neon bulb. The neon discharge tube glows when there is voltage at the output of capacitor C2.

No matter what type of tuner is used, grounding and antenna tuner losses should be avoided as much as possible. Particular attention should be paid to reducing losses in the antenna ground return path by using low-impedance connections and radials, a screen, or a large metal object such as a vehicle, boat, or metal structure such as a railing.

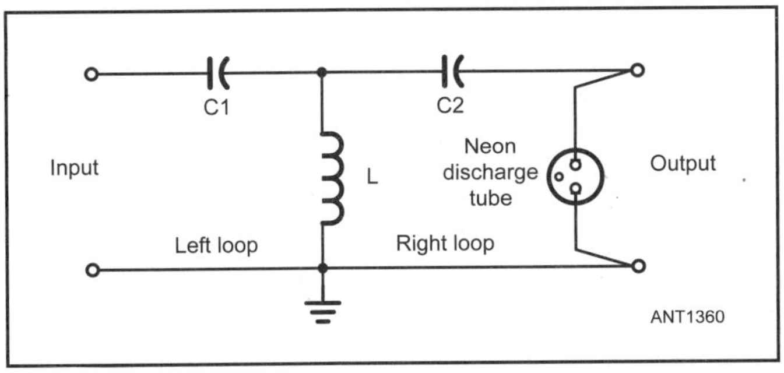

Figure 24.7 — T-configuration antenna tuner configuration showing the resonant circuits formed by LC_1 (left loop) and LC_2 (right loop). The neon discharge tube is connected across the antenna output to indicate relative power output (see text).

24.2.5 The *TLW* (Transmission Line For Windows) Program and Antenna Tuners

The ARRL program *TLW* (Transmission Line for Windows) included with this book's online material does calculations for transmission lines and antenna tuners. *TLW* evaluates four different networks: a low-pass L-network, a high-pass L-network, a low-pass pi-network, and a high-pass T-network. **Figure 24.8** shows the *TLW* output screen for an L-network design example.

Not only does *TLW* compute the exact values for network components, but also the full effects of voltage, current and power dissipation for each component. Depending on the load impedance presented to the antenna tuner, the internal losses in an antenna tuner can be disastrous. See the documentation file TLW.PDF for further details on the use of *TLW*, which some call the "Swiss Army Knife" of transmission line software. Also see the References and Bibliography entry for Birnbaum for another analysis of losses in the popular internal and external automatic L-network tuners.

TLW's author, Dean Straw, N6BV, also wrote the article "A Beginner's Guide to Transmission-Line and Antenna-Tuner

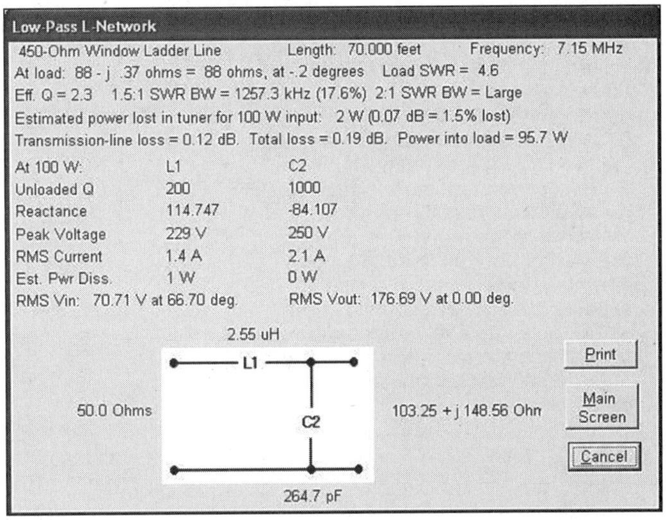

Figure 24.8 — Antenna tuner output screen of *TLW* software. Note the tuner schematic with parts values shown. The data above the schematic provide additional important information.

Modeling," which is included in this chapter's online material. The article provides some examples of how to use *TLW* for common design tasks.

24.2.6 Balanced Antenna Tuners

Modern antenna tuners often include a toroid-wound balun at their output for use with balanced or parallel-conductor feed lines. This allows a transmitter's unbalanced coaxial output to be connected to the balanced feed line. Be aware that at very high or very low impedances, the balun's power rating may be exceeded at high transmitted power levels.

The inductive- or link-coupling circuits seen in **Figure 24.9** are sometimes used but have largely been replaced by the toroid-wound balun. A more detailed discussion on inductive coupling is included with this book's online material, as is a low-power link-coupled tuner project that uses the configuration shown in Figure 24.9D and instructions for building the 100-W "Z-Match" antenna tuner designed by Phil Salas, AD5X. The article "*FilTuners*-a New (Old) Approach to Antenna Matching" by John Stanley, K4ERO (see References and Bibliography) also discusses tuned link-coupling from the standpoint of the matching network providing both filtering and impedance matching.

A fully-balanced tuner has a symmetrical internal circuit with a tuner circuit for each side of the feed line and the balun at the input to the tuner where the impedance is close to 50 Ω. Several examples are shown in **Figure 24.10** that can be recognized as being formed from the unbalanced networks described earlier with a mirror-image of the network being inserted in the "ground" side of the circuit.

A balun is inserted on the 50-Ω side of the circuit to allow connection to unbalanced coaxial feed lines. Some tuners are designed to use a 1:1 balun for this purpose while others transform the load impedance to 200 Ω and use a 4:1 balun. This allows the balun to operate at its design impedances regardless of load impedance. A balun at the output of an unbalanced tuner must operate at whatever load impedance is presented, which can lead to significant losses or arcing in the balun.

A disadvantage of balanced tuners is the higher cost from the additional components and the more complex mechanical arrangements to adjust more than one component at the same time with a single control. The hairpin tuner configuration in **Figure 24.11** is a balanced tuner for use at VHF and UHF where solenoid-wound coils may have too much inductance. The tuner is described in the April 2009 *QST* article "Hairpin Tuners for Matching Balanced Antenna Systems" by John Stanley, K4ERO (the article is included with this book's online material).

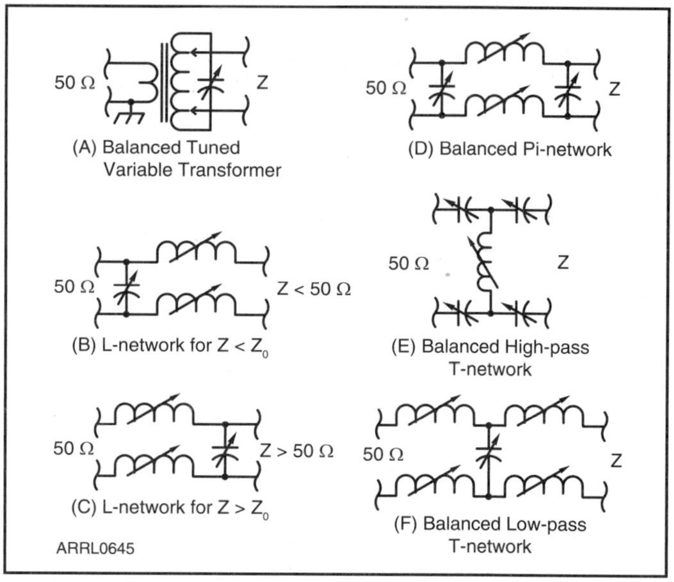

Figure 24.10 — Configurations of balanced antenna tuners.

Figure 24.9 — Simple antenna tuners for coupling a transmitter to a parallel-conductor feed line presenting a load different from the transmitter's design load impedance, usually 50 Ω. A and B, respectively, are series and parallel tuned circuits using variable inductive coupling between coils. C and D are similar but use fixed inductive coupling and a variable series capacitor, C1. A series tuned circuit works well with a low-impedance load; the parallel circuit is better with high impedance loads (several hundred ohms or more).

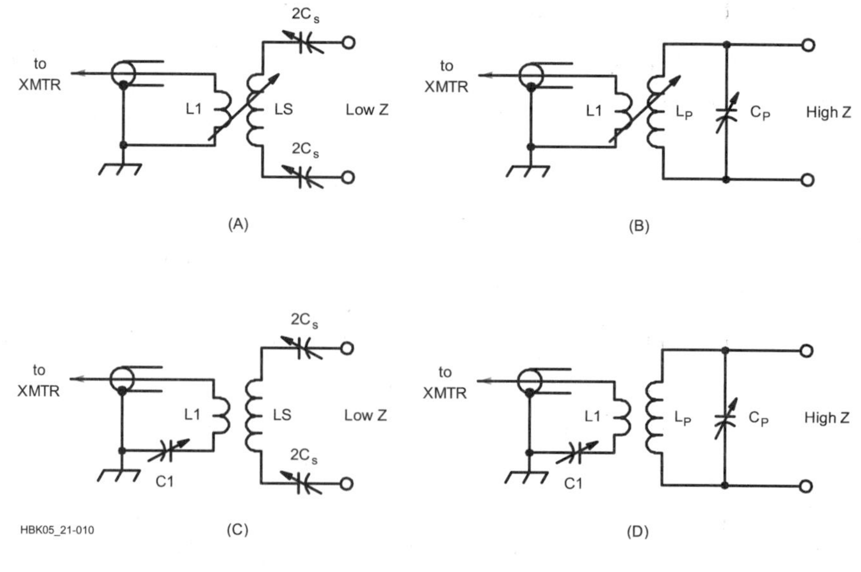

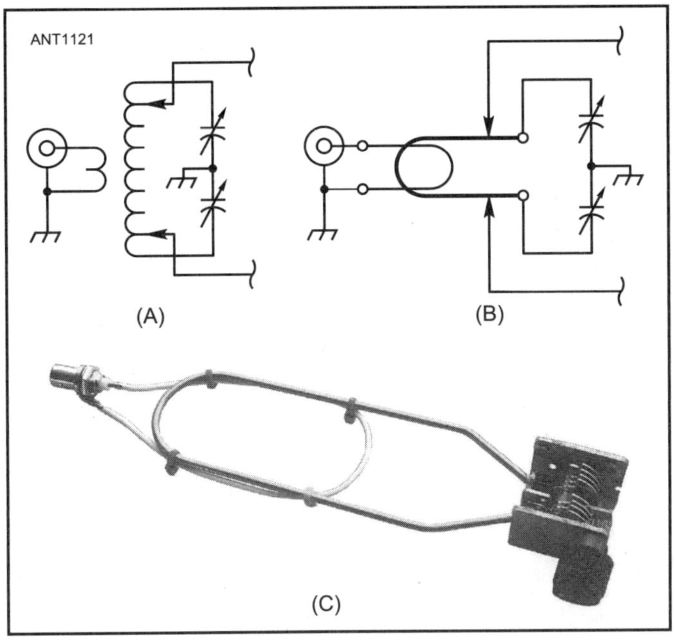

Figure 24.11 — Balanced tuner configurations. At (A) conventional tapped coil based tuner, at (B) the hairpin equivalent. (C) shows a hairpin tuner for 144 MHz. The technique can be used from 10 meters through 70 cm.

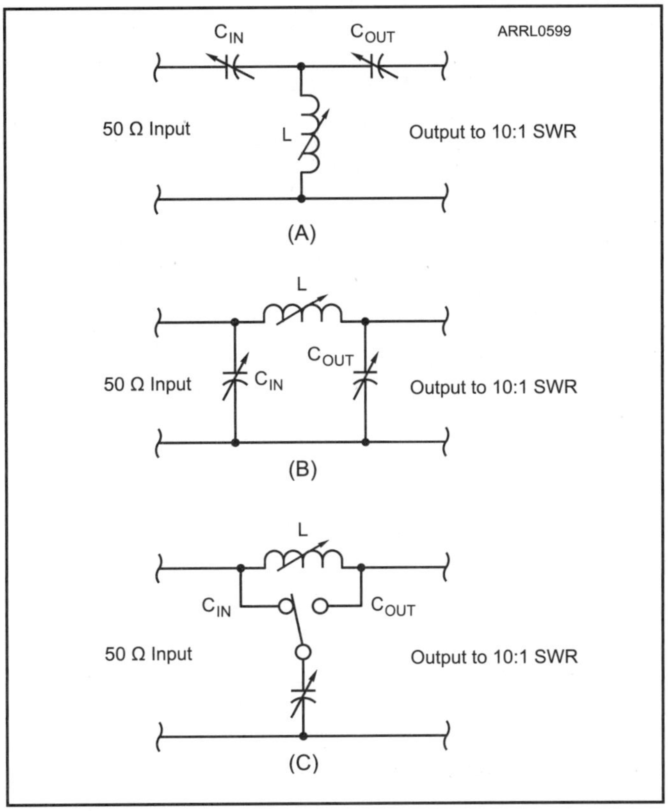

Figure 24.12 — Schematic diagrams of a high-pass T-network (A), pi-network (B), and a low-pass L-network (C). Tables 24.4 to 24.6 give component values at 1.8, 3.5, and 30 MHz to match different values of load impedances to 50 Ω.

24.2.7 General Purpose Tuner Designs

Several antenna tuner designs were created by Joel Hallas, W1ZR, for the book *The ARRL Guide to Antenna Tuners*. The *TLW* program was used to determine component values for a set of common load impedances and three popular antenna tuner circuits shown in **Figure 24.12**. **Tables 24.4** to **24.6** show the required component values to match those load impedances at 1.8, 3.5 and 30 MHz, the extremes of HF operation for antenna tuners.

Former *ARRL Antenna Book* editor, Dean Straw, N6BV, designed a high-power tuner with a 1:1 balun at the input to allow the tuner to work into balanced or unbalanced loads. The tuner has a very wide range and is designed for low losses. See the article "High-Power ARRL Antenna Tuner" that is included in this chapter's online material.

Table 24.4

Component Requirements for High-Pass (Shunt L) T-Network Antenna Tuners at 10:1 SWR

Frequency/Z (Ω)	*Capacitor*		*Inductor (μH)*	*Capacitor Voltage (V_P)*		*Efficiency (%)*
1.8 MHz	*Input (pF)*	*Output (pF)*		*100 W*	*1500 W*	
5	1136	3000	2.1	180	710	96
500	548	500	13.9	323	1250	98
25 + *j*100	343	300	10.3	790	3070	92
25 – *j*100	170	300	20	1040	4030	86
250 + *j*250	308	200	10.5	380	1470	98
250 – *j*250	337	300	16.9	525	2030	96
Frequency/Z (Ω)	*Capacitor*		*Inductor (μH)*	*Capacitor Voltage (V_P)*		*Efficiency (%)*
3.5 MHz	*Input (pF)*	*Output (pF)*		*100 W*	*1500 W*	
5	563	1500	1.1	190	720	96
500	265	200	7.3	343	1330	98
25 + *j*100	275	200	3.5	613	2373	95
25 – *j*100	104	200	8.6	880	3403	88
250 + *j*250	333	100	5.6	381	1475	98
250 – *j*250	136	100	10.8	670	2600	94
Frequency/Z (Ω)	*Capacitor*		*Inductor (μH)*	*Capacitor Voltage (V_P)*		*Efficiency (%)*
30 MHz	*Input (pF)*	*Output (pF)*		*100 W*	*1500 W*	
5	79	200	0.12	160	640	96
500	29	50	0.77	370	1470	97
25 + *j*100	91	30	0.24	400	1560	98
25 – *j*100	24	100	0.46	440	1710	93
250 + *j*250	36	100	0.9	300	1150	98
250 – *j*250	29	100	0.6	360	1410	97

Table 24.5

Component Requirements for Low-Pass (Series L) L-Network Antenna Tuners at 10:1 SWR

Frequency/Z (Ω)	*Capacitor*		*Inductor (μH)*	*Capacitor Voltage (V_P)*		*Efficiency (%)*
1.8 MHz	*Input (pF)*	*Output (pF)*		*100 W*	*1500 W*	
5	5254	n/a	1.34	100	390	98
500	n/a	536	13.5	310	1210	98
25 + *j*100	n/a	1408	12	290	1120	98
25 – *j*100	1760	n/a	11	100	390	97
250 + *j*250	n/a	713	13	310	1210	98
250 – *j*250	n/a	359	13	310	1210	98
Frequency/Z (Ω)	*Capacitor*		*Inductor (μH)*	*Capacitor Voltage (V_P)*		*Efficiency (%)*
3.5 MHz	*Input (pF)*	*Output (pF)*		*100 W*	*1500 W*	
5	2700	n/a	0.69	100	400	98
500	n/a	275	6.8	310	1200	98
25 + *j*100	n/a	720	6.2	290	1120	98
25 – *j*100	926	n/a	5.6	100	390	97
250 + *j*250	n/a	367	6.8	310	1210	98
250 – *j*250	n/a	184	6.8	310	1210	98
Frequency/Z (Ω)	*Capacitor*		*Inductor (μH)*	*Capacitor Voltage (V_P)*		*Efficiency (%)*
30 MHz	*Input (pF)*	*Output (pF)*		*100 W*	*1500 W*	
5	315	n/a	0.08	100	390	98
500	n/a	32	0.79	310	1210	98
25 + *j*100	n/a	85	0.72	290	1120	98
25 – *j*100	140	n/a	0.58	100	390	97
250 + *j*250	n/a	43	0.79	310	1210	98
250 – *j*250	n/a	22	0.79	310	1210	98

Table 24.6
Component Requirements for Low-Pass Pi-Network Antenna Tuners at 10:1 SWR

Frequency/Z (Ω)	*Capacitor*		*Inductor (μH)*	*Capacitor Voltage (V_P)*		*Efficiency (%)*
1.8 MHz	*Input (pF)*	*Output (pF)*		*100 W*	*1500 W*	
5	5256	500	1.4	100	390	98
500	2602	1000	9.6	310	1200	96
25 + *j*100	966	1500	12.5	280	1110	97
25 – *j*100	3410	500	7.5	280	1100	96
250 + *j*250	1931	1000	11.3	310	1210	97
250 – *j*250	1284	500	12.9	310	1210	97
Frequency/Z (Ω)	*Capacitor*		*Inductor (μH)*	*Capacitor Voltage (V_P)*		*Efficiency (%)*
3.5 MHz	*Input (pF)*	*Output (pF)*		*100 W*	*1500 W*	
5	2706	500	0.7	100	390	98
500	1287	500	5.1	310	1200	96
25 + *j*100	643	800	6.2	280	1110	97
25 – *j*100	1886	300	3.7	280	1430	95
250 + *j*250	934	500	6.0	310	1200	97
250 – *j*250	859	300	6.2	310	1200	97
Frequency/Z (Ω)	*Capacitor*		*Inductor (μH)*	*Capacitor Voltage (V_P)*		*Efficiency (%)*
30 MHz	*Input (pF)*	*Output (pF)*		*100 W*	*1500 W*	
5	321	200	0.08	100	390	98
500	118	50	0.7	310	1200	97
25 + *j*100	103	100	0.7	290	1100	97
25 – *j*100	205	30	0.5	285	1100	96
250 + *j*250	71	50	0.8	310	1200	97
250 – *j*250	77	30	0.8	310	1200	97

24.3 Transmission Line System Design

The previous sections of this chapter looked at system design from the point of view of the transmitter, examining what could be done to ensure that the transmitter load is its design load of 50 Ω. In this section, we will look at antenna system design from the point of view of the transmission line.

24.3.1 Transmission Line Impedance Transformation

For the purposes of designing a transmission line system, the line can also be used for its impedance transforming properties. A certain value of load impedance, consisting of a resistance and reactance, at the end of the line is transformed into another value of impedance at the input of the line. The amount of transformation is determined by the electrical length of the line, its characteristic impedance, and by the losses inherent in the line. The input impedance of a real, lossy transmission line is computed using the *Transmission Line Equation*:

$$Z_{in} = Z_0 \times \frac{Z_L \cosh(\eta\ell) + Z_0 \sinh(\eta\ell)}{Z_L \sinh(\eta\ell) + Z_0 \cosh(\eta\ell)} \qquad (9)$$

where

Z_{in} = complex impedance at input of line = $R_{in} \pm j X_{in}$
Z_L = complex load impedance at end of line = $R_l \pm j X_l$
Z_0 = characteristic impedance of line = $R_0 \pm j X_0$
η = complex loss coefficient = $\alpha + j$ b
α = matched line loss attenuation constant, in nepers/unit length (1 neper = 8.688 dB, so multiply line loss in dB per unit length by 8.688)
β = phase constant of line in radians/unit length (multiply electrical length in degrees by 2π radians/360 degrees)
ℓ = electrical length of line in same units of length as used for α.

Solving this equation manually is tedious, since it incorporates hyperbolic cosines and sines of the complex loss coefficient, but it may be solved using a traditional paper Smith chart or software that performs the Smith chart operations. *TLW* can perform this transformation, but without Smith chart graphics.

There are many antenna analyzers available to amateurs that will measure the complex impedance at the input to a transmission line. Given the impedance in the series format, R + *j*X, *TLW* can make the transformations.

Let us go through an example. Use some of the values shown in the table for the 100-foot center-fed dipole in Table 24.5. Suppose we would like to use the antenna on 3.8 MHz and are feeding it with a 100-foot length of 450-Ω window line. The antenna's feed point impedance of 39 – *j*362 Ω creates an SWR of 17.7:1. At the transmitter end of the feed line, using *TLW* shows the impedance is transformed to 233 – *j*1066 Ω for an

Table 24.7
Impedance of Center-Fed 100-Foot Flattop Dipole, 50 Feet High Over Average Ground

Frequency (MHz)	*Antenna Feed point Impedance (Ω)*	*Total Loss for 100 ft 450-Ω Line (dB)*	*Feed Point SWR*
1.83	4.5 – *j* 1673	13.1	390
3.8	39 – *j* 362	1.18	18.3
7.1	481 + *j* 964	0.55	6.7
10.1	2584 – *j* 3292	1.46	16.8
14.1	85 – *j* 123	0.67	5.2
18.1	2097 + *j* 1552	1.05	8.1
21.1	345 – *j* 1073	1.43	10.1
24.9	202 + *j* 367	0.63	3.9
28.4	2493 – *j* 1375	1.26	8.1

SWR of 13.9:1. Line loss would be 1.2 dB due to the high SWR. Remember that the high SWR will be present in the feed line even if an antenna tuner converts the line's input impedance to 50 Ω.

If we were using RG-213 coax to feed this antenna, the situation would be quite different: feed point SWR would be 62.34, impedance at the transmitter would be 6.9 – *j*62.4 Ω for an SWR of 16.7:1, and the feed line loss would be 5.7 dB. Entering the feed point impedance values for the different frequencies and switching feed line types between parallel conductor and coax is very instructive.

Table 24.7 shows a similar set of impedances for a 66-foot inverted-V dipole with the center 50 feet above the ground. This might be a very good 40-meter antenna but when it is fed with 100 feet of 450 Ω window line, the impedance is no longer anywhere close to 50 Ω on the dipole's fundamental frequency. Again, using *TLW* to check the SWR and total line loss is a useful exercise.

SMITH CHART SOFTWARE

The standard way of visualizing transmission line and impedance matching mechanics is by using a Smith chart. (If you are unfamiliar with the Smith chart, the online material for the **Transmission Lines** chapter includes a detailed tutorial on the Smith chart.) Paper charts, however, have been replaced by interactive computer software such as the easy-to-use *jjSmith* (Windows only) by Jim Tonne, W4ENE, available on the *ARRL Handbook's* reference website (**www.arrl.org/arrl-handbook-reference**) and *SimSmith* (**www.ae6ty.com/Smith_Charts.html**) by Ward Harriman, AE6TY. Learning about the Smith chart will be a great aid in understanding the mechanics of transmission lines and impedance matching.

SimSmith includes a number of building blocks, such as lumped-constant circuits and stubs (among other common functions), that allow comprehensive transmission line and antenna system design. It can also work directly with Touchstone format data (see the **Antenna and Transmission Line Measurements** chapter section on antenna analyzers) from measurements. Larry Benko, WØQE, has posted a number of *SimSmith* tutorials and user guides on his website (**w0qe.com/SimSmith.html**) and on his YouTube channel, **youtube.com/@w0qe867**. *SimSmith* is written in Java to run on a number of operating systems and in a variety of web browsers.

24.3.2 Transmission Line Selection

Until you get into the microwave region where waveguides become practical, there are only two practical choices for transmission lines: coaxial cable and parallel-conductor lines such as open wire or ladder line and window line. (Refer to the **Transmission Lines** chapter for information about the different types of feed lines.)

The shielding of coaxial cable offers advantages in incidental radiation and routing flexibility. Coax can be tied or taped to the legs of a metal tower without problem, for example. Some varieties of coax can even be buried underground. Coaxial cable can perform acceptably even with significant SWR. A drawback of coaxial line is its loss, particularly at moderate to high SWR. For example, a 100-foot length of RG-213 coax has 1.1 dB matched-line loss at 30 MHz. If this line were used with a load of 250 + *j*0 Ω (an SWR of 5:1), the total line loss would be 2.2 dB. This represents about a half S unit on most receivers.

On the other hand, open-wire line has the advantage of both lower loss and lower cost compared to coax. At 30 MHz, 600-Ω open-wire line has a matched loss of only 0.1 dB. If you use such open-wire line with the same 5:1 SWR, the total loss would about 0.3 dB. In fact, even if the SWR rose to 20:1, the total loss would be less than 1 dB.

Despite their inherently low-loss characteristics, open-wire lines are not often employed above about 100 MHz. This is because the physical spacing between the two wires begins to become an appreciable fraction of a wavelength, leading to undesirable radiation by the line itself. Some form of coaxial cable is almost universally used in the VHF and UHF amateur bands.

Open-wire line is enjoying a renaissance of sorts with amateurs wishing to cover multiple HF bands with a single-wire antenna. Doublets of various lengths (44, 88, and 105 feet are popular lengths) fed with open-wire line into an antenna tuner have become popular as a simple all-band antenna. The simple 135-foot long 80-meter dipole, fed with 450-Ω window line, is also very popular as an all-band antenna.

So, apart from concerns about convenience and the matter of cost, how do you go about choosing a transmission line for a particular antenna? Let's start with some simple cases.

FEEDING A SINGLE-BAND ANTENNA

If the antenna system is only required to operate on a single band and if the feed point impedance of the antenna doesn't vary too radically across the band, then the choice of transmission line is easy. Most amateurs would opt for convenience — they would use coaxial cable to feed the antenna, usually without an antenna tuner.

An example of such an installation is a half-wave 80-meter dipole fed with 50-Ω coax. The matched-line loss for 100 feet of 50-Ω RG-213 coax at 3.5 MHz is only 0.33 dB. At each end of the 80-meter band, this dipole will exhibit an SWR of about 6:1. The additional loss caused by this level of SWR at this frequency is less than 0.6 dB, for a total line loss of 0.9 dB. Since 1 dB represents an almost undetectable change in signal strength at the receiving end, it does not matter whether the line is "flat" (low SWR) or not for this 80-meter system.

This is true provided that the transmitter can operate properly into the load presented to it by the impedance at the input of the transmission line. Even if the feed line loss is low, an antenna tuner is sometimes required to ensure that the transmitter operates into its design load impedance. On the other amateur bands, where the percentage bandwidth is smaller than that on 75/80 meters, a simple dipole fed with coax will provide an acceptable SWR for most transmitters without an antenna tuner.

If you want a better match at the antenna feed point of a single-band antenna to coax, you can provide some sort of matching network at the antenna. We'll look further into schemes for achieving matched antenna systems later in this chapter, when we'll examine single-band methods of matching feed point and feed line impedances.

FEEDING A MULTIBAND ANTENNA

A multiband antenna is one where special techniques are used to make a single antenna present a consistent feed point impedance on each of several amateur bands. Often, trap circuits are employed. (Information on traps is given in the **Multiband HF Antennas** chapter.) For example, a trap dipole presents a feed point impedance similar to that of a $\lambda/2$ dipole on each of the bands for which it is designed.

Note that "resonance" only means that the self-impedance of the antenna is completely resistive (no reactance) and does not imply that the value of the impedance is low. For example, the 135-foot dipole may be resonant on 3.5 MHz and all harmonics but its feed point impedance will vary from low values at the fundamental and odd harmonics (10.5, 17.5, 24.5 MHz) to very high impedances at even harmonics (7.0, 14.0, 21.0, 28.0 MHz). Yet it may be resonant at all of those frequencies.

Another common multiband antenna is constructed from several dipoles cut for different frequencies and connected in parallel at a common feed point and fed with a single coaxial cable. This arrangement acts as an independent $\lambda/2$ dipole on each band. (Interaction between the individual dipoles is discussed in the **Multiband HF Antennas** chapter.)

Another type of multiband antenna is a log-periodic dipole array (LPDA), which features moderate gain and pattern with a low SWR across a fairly wide band of frequencies. See the **Frequency-Independent Antennas** chapter for more details.

Yet another popular multiband antenna is the trap triband Yagi, or a multiband interlaced quad. On the amateur HF bands, the triband Yagi is almost as popular as the simple $\lambda/2$ dipole. See the **HF Beam Antennas** chapter for more information on this antenna.

A multiband antenna doesn't present much of an antenna system design challenge — you simply feed it with coax that has characteristic impedance close to the antenna's feed point impedance. Usually, 50-Ω cable, such as RG-213, is used.

Using *TLW* to Determine SWR

The program *TLW* can be used in two important ways: to determine SWR and impedance on the "other end" of transmission lines. The first case occurs when you are given a certain load impedance, such as that of an antenna feed point, and wish to know what the SWR and impedance will be at the input of the feed line. This type of information is used to design impedance-matching networks and antenna tuners for use in the station. From the program's main screen, select the feed line type and length. Enter frequency and the load resistance and reactance, specifying **LOAD** for the location of the impedance. The SWR and impedance at the input of the feed line will be displayed at the bottom of the window. The additional loss due to SWR is also calculated.

The second case works in reverse. It occurs when you know the SWR (or impedance) at the input to the feed line and want to know the SWR (or impedance) at the load (antenna) end of the feed line. Enter the cable type and length, frequency, and a value for **RESISTANCE** equal to SWR × Z_0. (If you know the input impedance, enter it instead.) Specify **INPUT** for the location where SWR is specified. The SWR (and impedance) will be displayed at the bottom of the window along with the additional line loss due to SWR.

FEEDING A MULTIBAND NONRESONANT ANTENNA

Let's say that you wish to use a single antenna, such as a 100-foot long doublet, on multiple amateur bands. You know from the **Antenna Fundamentals** chapter that since the physical length of the antenna is fixed, the feed point impedance of the antenna will vary on each band. In other words, except by chance, the antenna will *not* be resonant — or even close to resonant — on multiple bands. This presents special challenges with regard to feed line selection.

For multiband nonresonant antenna systems, the most appropriate transmission line is often a parallel-conductor line, because of the inherently low matched-line loss characteristic of these types of lines. Such a system is called an *unmatched* system, because no attempt is made to match the impedance at the antenna's feed point to the Z_0 of the transmission line. Commercial 450-Ω window ladder line has become popular for this kind of application. It is almost as good as traditional open-wire or ladder-line for most amateur systems.

The transmission line will be mismatched most of the time and on some frequencies it will be severely mismatched. Because of the mismatch, the SWR on the line will vary widely with frequency. As shown in the **Transmission Lines** chapter, such a variation in load impedance has an impact on the loss created in the feed line. Let's look at the losses in a typical multiband nonresonant system.

Table 24.7 summarizes the feed point information over the HF amateur bands for a 100-foot long dipole, mounted as a flattop, 50 feet high over typical ground. In addition, the table shows the total line loss created in 100 feet of 450-Ω ladder line by the SWR at the antenna feed point. As usual, there is nothing particularly significant about the choice of a 100-foot long antenna or a 100-foot long transmission line. Both are practical lengths that could very well be encountered in a real-world situation. At 1.8 MHz, the loss in the transmission line is large — 13.1 dB. This is due to the fact that the SWR at the feed point is a very high 390:1, a direct result of the fact that the antenna is extremely short in terms of wavelength.

Table 24.8 summarizes the same information as in Table 24.7, but this time for a 66-foot long inverted-V dipole, with the apex 50 feet over typical ground and an included angle between its two legs of 120°. The situation at 1.83 MHz is even worse, as might be expected because this antenna is even shorter electrically than its 100-foot flattop cousin. The line loss has risen to 19.7 dB!

Under such severe mismatches, another problem can arise. Transmission lines with solid dielectric have voltage and current limitations. At lower frequencies with electrically short antennas, this can be a more compelling limitation than the amount of power loss. The ability of a line to handle RF power is inversely proportional to the SWR. For example, a line rated for 1.5 kW when matched, should be operated at only 150 W when the SWR is 10:1. At the mismatch on 1.83 MHz illustrated for the 100-foot doublet or the 66-foot inverted-V dipole in Tables 24.7 and 24.7, the line may well arc over, burning the insulation, due to the extremely high SWR. (To calculate the maximum voltage, see the "Line Voltages and Current" section of the **Transmission Lines** chapter.)

To use *TLW* to see the voltage and current along the feed line for 1500 W of input power, select **VOLT/CURRENT** and click **GRAPH**. On 160 meters, where the feed point SWR is highest, the maximum voltage is 6600 V. This would exceed the voltage rating for RG-213 (3700 V) by nearly a factor of two and probably result in a voltage breakdown near the load.

A feed line of 450-Ω window-type ladder line using two #16 AWG conductors should be safe up to the 1500 W level for frequencies where the antenna is at least a half-wavelength long. For the 100-foot dipole, this would be above 3.8 MHz, and for the 66-foot long inverted-V, this would be above 7 MHz. For the very short antennas illustrated above, however, even 450-Ω window line may not be able to take full amateur legal power. Check the line's maximum rated voltage in the table in the **Transmission Lines** chapter and compare with that expected at your maximum power and expected maximum SWR. The article "Don't Blow Up Your Balun" by Dean Straw, N6BV, includes several excellent examples of antenna systems that place a lot of stress on chokes, baluns and antenna tuners. The article is included in the online material.

Table 24.8

Impedance of Center-Fed 66-Foot Inverted-V Dipole, 50-Foot High Apex Over Average Ground

Frequency (MHz)	*Antenna Feed Point Impedance (Ω)*	*Total Loss for 100 ft 450-Ω Line (dB)*	*Feed Point SWR*
1.83	1.6 – *j* 2257	19.7	622
3.8	10 – *j* 879	7.2	153
7.1	65 – *j* 41	0.6	6.3
10.1	22 + *j* 648	4.0	73
14.1	5287 – *j* 1310	1.5	13.9
18.1	198 – *j* 820	1.4	10.8
21.1	103 – *j* 181	0.73	4.8
24.9	269 + *j* 570	0.84	4.9
28.4	3089 + *j* 774	1.3	8.1

24.3.3 Measuring Transmission Line Loss

The most obvious method is to use a calibrated wattmeter and dummy load. With the wattmeter at the input to the line and the dummy load at the output, apply power to the line and measure forward power, P_{IN}. (With the dummy load attached, there should be no reflected power.) Remove power and connect the input of the line directly to the power source. Connect the wattmeter between the output of the line and the dummy load. Apply the same amount of power and read forward power at the dummy load, P_{OUT}. The loss in the line is equal to 10 log (P_{OUT} / P_{IN}).

Without a wattmeter, loss can be measured by using a calibrated mismatch. Assuming a 50-Ω system, select a non-inductive resistor between 150 Ω (3:1 SWR) and 270 Ω (5.4:1 SWR). Convert the resistor's expected SWR to return loss (RL), using **Table 24.9**. For example, a 220-Ω resistive load results in a 4.4:1 SWR which is a return loss of 4.0 dB. Connect the resistor to the output of the line. Make sure the resistor leads are very short so that they do not add a significant amount of inductance. Measure SWR at the input to the line and convert to return loss. The line loss is the difference between return loss at the line input and return loss of the load. For example, with the 220-Ω load (4.0 dB RL) and 100 feet of RG-58 coax at 10 MHz, the input SWR might be 3.0:1 (RL = 6.0 dB). The line loss at this frequency is 6.0 dB – 4.0 dB = 2.0 dB.

Some methods use an open or short circuit at the load end of the line (an infinite SWR and RL = 0) to measure line loss. Most amateur instrumentation is not well-calibrated at high SWR and will give an unreliable reading for SWR and RL. Using a moderate mismatch improves the accuracy of the final result. You can replace the feed line with inline attenuators to check this more accurate method with the known amounts of loss.

24.3.4 Antenna Tuner Location

To meet the goal of presenting a 50-Ω load to the transmitter, in many antenna systems it is necessary to place an antenna tuner between the transmitter and the transmission line going to the antenna. This is particularly true for a single-wire antenna used on multiple amateur bands.

The tuner is usually located near the transmitter in order to adjust it for different bands or antennas. If a tuner is in use for one particular band and does not need to be adjusted once set up for minimum VSWR, it can be placed in a weatherproof container near the antenna. Some automatic tuners are designed to be installed at the antenna, for example. For some situations, placing the tuner at the base of a tower can be particularly effective and eliminates having to climb the tower to perform maintenance on the tuner.

Table 24.9
Reflection Coefficient, Attenuation, SWR, and Return Loss

Reflection Coefficient (%)	*Attenuation (dB)*	*Max SWR*	*Return Loss (dB)*
1.000	0.000434	1.020	40.00
1.517	0.001000	1.031	36.38
2.000	0.001738	1.041	33.98
3.000	0.003910	1.062	30.46
4.000	0.006954	1.083	27.96
4.796	0.01000	1.101	26.38
5.000	0.01087	1.105	26.02
6.000	0.01566	1.128	24.44
7.000	0.02133	1.151	23.10
7.576	0.02500	1.164	22.41
8.000	0.02788	1.174	21.94
9.000	0.03532	1.198	20.92
10.000	0.04365	1.222	20.00
10.699	0.05000	1.240	19.41
11.000	0.05287	1.247	19.17
12.000	0.06299	1.273	18.42
13.085	0.07500	1.301	17.66
14.000	0.08597	1.326	17.08
15.000	0.09883	1.353	16.48
15.087	0.10000	1.355	16.43
16.000	0.1126	1.381	15.92
17.783	0.1396	1.433	15.00
18.000	0.1430	1.439	14.89
19.000	0.1597	1.469	14.42
20.000	0.1773	1.500	13.98
22.000	0.2155	1.564	13.15
23.652	0.2500	1.620	12.52
24.000	0.2577	1.632	12.40
25.000	0.2803	1.667	12.04
26.000	0.3040	1.703	11.70
27.000	0.3287	1.740	11.37
28.000	0.3546	1.778	11.06
30.000	0.4096	1.857	10.46
31.623	0.4576	1.925	10.00
32.977	0.5000	1.984	9.64
33.333	0.5115	2.000	9.54
34.000	0.5335	2.030	9.37
35.000	0.5675	2.077	9.12
36.000	0.6028	2.125	8.87
37.000	0.6394	2.175	8.64
38.000	0.6773	2.226	8.40
39.825	0.75000	2.324	8.00
40.000	0.7572	2.333	7.96
42.000	0.8428	2.448	7.54
42.857	0.8814	2.500	7.36
44.000	0.9345	2.571	7.13
45.351	1.0000	2.660	6.87
48.000	1.1374	2.846	6.38
50.000	1.2494	3.000	6.02
52.000	1.3692	3.167	5.68
54.042	1.5000	3.352	5.35
56.234	1.6509	3.570	5.00
58.000	1.7809	3.762	4.73
60.000	1.9382	4.000	4.44
60.749	2.0000	4.095	4.33
63.000	2.1961	4.405	4.01
66.156	2.5000	4.909	3.59
66.667	2.5528	5.000	3.52
70.627	3.0000	5.809	3.02
70.711	3.0103	5.829	3.01

$$|\rho| = \frac{SWR - 1}{SWR + 1}$$

where $|\rho|$ = 0.01 × (reflection coefficient in %)

$$|\rho| = 10^{-RL/20}$$

where RL = return loss (dB)

$$|\rho| = \sqrt{1 - (0.1^{X})}$$

where X = A/10 and A = attenuation (dB)

$$SWR = \frac{1 + |\rho|}{1 - |\rho|}$$

It is useful to consider the performance of the entire antenna system when deciding where to install the antenna tuner and what types of feed line to use in order to minimize system losses. Here is an example, using the program *TLW*. Let's use the familiar 100-foot doublet described previously. As extreme examples, we will use 3.8 and 28.4 MHz with 200 feet of transmission line. There are many ways to configure this system, but three examples are shown in **Figure 24.13**. A low-pass L-network is assumed for all three systems.

Example 1 in Figure 24.13A shows a 200-foot run of RG-213 going to a 1:1 balun that feeds the antenna. The tuner in the station reduces the VSWR for proper matching in the transmitter. Example 2 (Figure 24.13B) shows a similar arrangement using 450-Ω window line. Example 3 (Figure 24.13C) shows a 50-foot run of 450-Ω line dropping straight down to a remote tuner near the ground and 150 feet of RG-213 going to the station. **Table 24.10** summarizes the losses and the L-network component values required. Balun losses are not included.

Some interesting conclusions can be drawn. First, direct feeding this antenna with coax through a balun is very lossy — a poor solution. If the flattop were λ/2 long — a resonant half-wave dipole — direct coax feed would be a good method. In the second example, direct feed with 450-Ω low-loss line does not give the lowest loss. The combination method in Example 3 provides the best solution. (Note the very high C value at 3.8 MHz and the very low L value at 28.4 MHz in Example 1 and the very low C value at 28.4 MHz in Example 3. A pi- or T-network might be a better choice for these frequencies and impedances.)

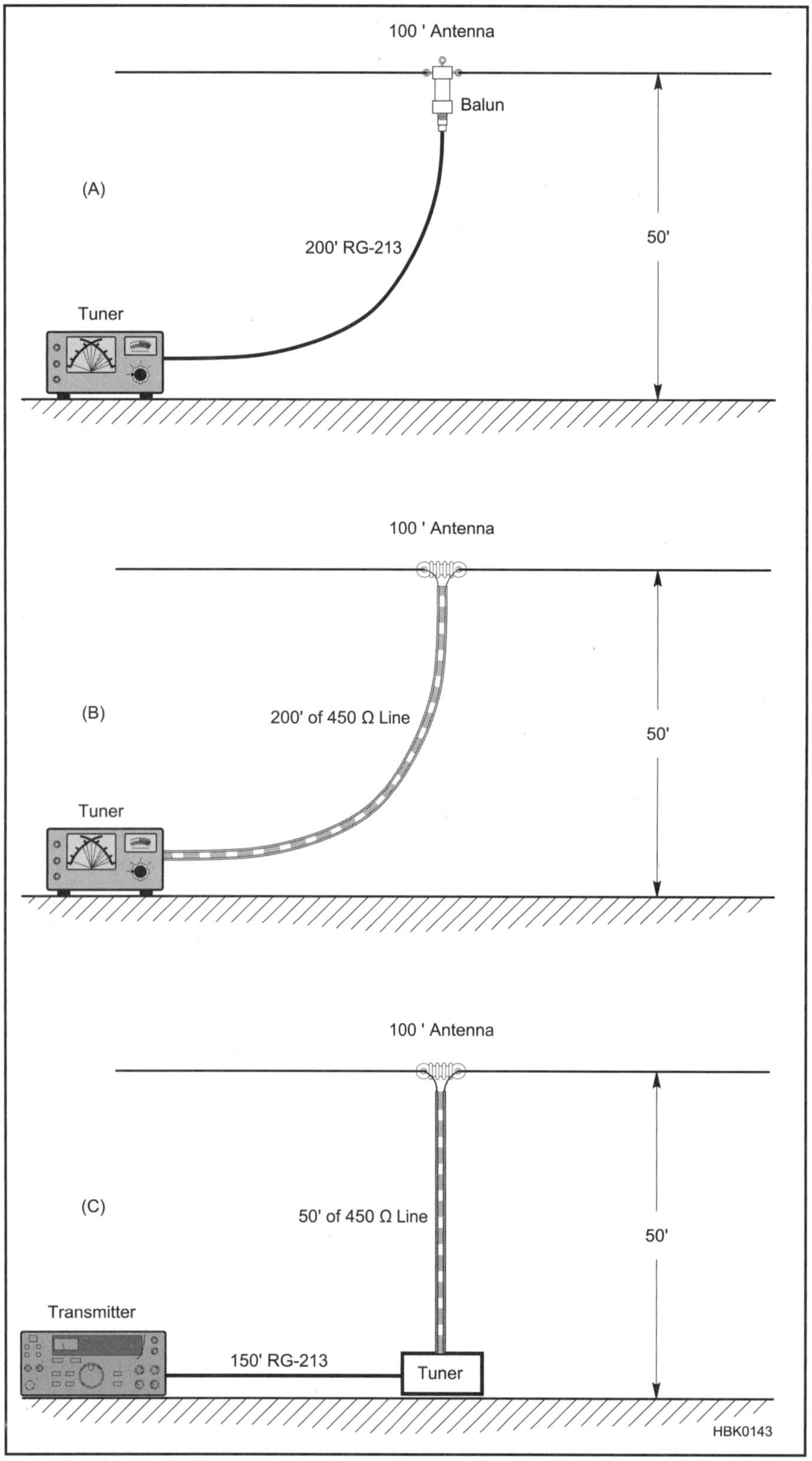

Figure 24.13 — Variations of an antenna system with different losses. The examples are discussed in the text.

Example 3 has some additional advantages. It feeds the antenna in a symmetrical arrangement which is best to reduce common-mode current pickup on the shield of the feed line. The shorter feed line will not weigh down the antenna as much, and the balun's additional weight and expense are also avoided. The coax back to the transmitter can be buried or laid on the ground and it is perfectly matched. Burial of the cable will also prevent any additional common-mode currents from being induced on the coax shield. The tuner is then adjusted for minimum SWR on the cable as measured in the station at the transmitter.

24.3.5 Transmission Line Stubs

The impedance-transformation properties of a transmission line are useful in a number of applications. If the terminating resistance is zero (that is, a short) at the end of a low-loss line with length, $\ell < \lambda/4$, the input impedance is a reactance given by:

$$X_{in} \cong Z_0 \tan \ell \qquad (10)$$

where ℓ is in degrees of electrical length.

If the line termination is an open circuit, the input reactance is given by

$$X_{in} \cong Z_0 \cot \ell \qquad (11)$$

The input of a short (less than λ/4) length of line with a short circuit as a terminating load appears as an inductance, while an open-circuited line appears as a capacitance. This is a useful property of a transmission line, since it can be used as a low-loss inductor or capacitor in matching networks. Such lines are often referred to as stubs.

A line that is electrically λ/4 long is a special kind of a stub. When a λ/4 line is short circuited at its load end, it presents an open circuit at its input. Conversely, a λ/4 line with an open circuit at its load end presents a short circuit at its input. Such a line inverts the impedance of a short or an open circuit at the frequency for which the line is λ/4 long. This is also true for frequencies that are odd multiples of the λ/4 frequency. However, for frequencies where the length of the line is λ/2, or integer multiples thereof, the line will duplicate the termination at its end.

Table 24.10
Low-Pass L-Network Tuner Settings and Performance

Example (Fig 24.10)	*Frequency (MHz)*	*L (μH)*	*C (pF)*	*Line Loss (dB)*	*Tuner Loss (dB)*	*Total Loss (dB)*
1	3.8	1.5	2308	8.4	0.1	8.5
	28.4	0.13	182	12.8	0.1	12.9
2	3.8	20.5	47.5	1.2	0.6	1.8
	28.4	0.8	59	2.3	0.1	2.4
3	3.8	12.5	290	1.0	0.2	1.2
	28.4	1.7	9	0.7	0.2	0.9

BUILDING A COAX STUB

This procedure results in a shorted stub tuned to be λ/2 long because this is the easiest frequency at which to measure an impedance null. The stub will be λ/4 long at one-half the λ/2 frequency. For example, if you want to build a stub that is λ/4 long at 7.1 MHz, tune it to be λ/2 long a 14.2 MHz. The short can either be left in place for a shorted stub or removed for an open stub. If you are unfamiliar with stub building, look up the approximate stub length in a published table such as in the next section. As you begin your measurements, check to be sure the stub will be about the same length as in the table and not off by a factor of two, which indicates a calculation problem.

Begin by installing the desired connector on one end of a piece of coax, cutting the coax about 10% longer than the computed value. Strip ½ inch or so at the far end and short the shield to the center conductor with a direct, minimum-length connection.

Connect the stub to an impedance measuring device and find the lowest frequency at which impedance Z and reactance (X) are minimum, near zero ohms, repeating the termination impedance which is a short. (If you are using an antenna analyzer, ignore the SWR measurement — use only the Z and X values.) At this frequency the stub is λ/2 long. It will be λ/4 long at ½ the measured frequency.

The frequency should be below your desired frequency by about 10%, meaning the stub is too long. Use the actual percentage below your target frequency to tell you how much to cut, then cut about half that much. Repeat until the stub is at the desired frequency. Carefully solder the shorted end and weatherproof it.

TUNING A TRANSMISSION LINE STUB

Because different manufacturing runs of coax will have slightly different velocity factors, a quarter-wave stub is usually cut a little longer than calculated, and then carefully pruned by snipping off short pieces, while using an antenna analyzer or VNA to monitor the response at the harmonic frequency. Velocity factor (VF) also changes a small amount with frequency, enough to be significant when measuring and cutting a stub. VF error can be a fraction of a percent at HF which is enough to move the resonant frequency substantially. For example, the 20-meter band is about 2.5% wide, so a 0.5% error represents about 70 kHz. Either measure VF at the frequency being used or leave enough margin in the initial length to accommodate variations.

Because the end of the coax is an open circuit while pieces are being snipped away, the input of a λ/4 line will show a short circuit exactly at the fundamental frequency. Once the coax has been pruned to frequency, a short jumper is soldered across the end, and the response at the second harmonic frequency is measured. **Figure 24.14** shows how to connect a shorted stub to a transmission line and **Figure 24.15** shows a typical frequency response.

The shorted quarter-wave stub shows low loss at 7 MHz and at 21 MHz where it is 3λ/4 long. It nulls 14 and 28 MHz. This is useful for reducing the even harmonics of a 7 MHz transmitter. It can be used for a 21 MHz transmitter as well and will reduce any spurious emissions such as phase noise and wideband noise which might cause interference to receivers operating on 14 or 28 MHz. (Note that spurious emissions *must* be filtered out *at the transmitter,* or they become in-band signals to a receiver and cannot be removed.)

The open-circuited quarter-wave stub has a low impedance at the fundamental frequency, so a transmitter must operate at two times the frequency for which the stub is cut. For example, a quarter-wave open stub cut for 3.5 MHz will present a high impedance at 7 MHz where it is λ/2 long. It will present a high impedance at those frequencies where it is a multiple of λ/2, or 7, 14 and 28 MHz. It would be connected

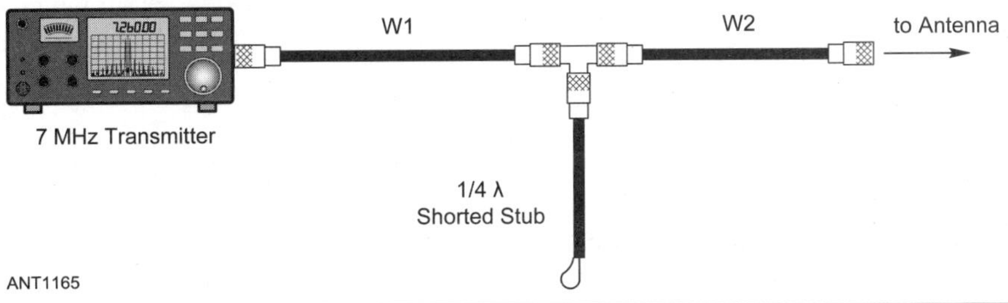

Figure 24.14 — Method of attaching a stub to a feed line.

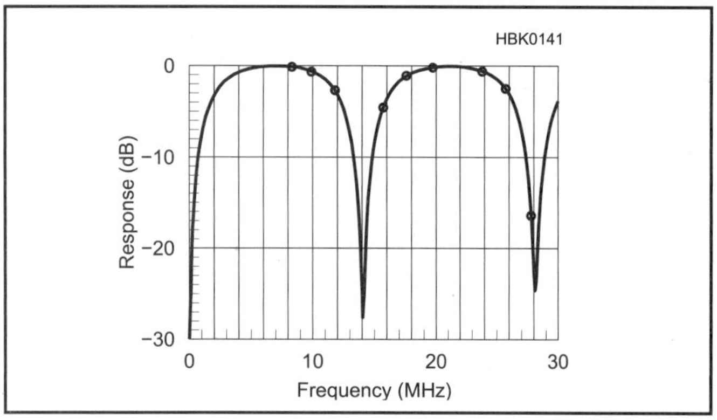

Figure 24.15 — Frequency response of a shorted λ/4 stub cut for 14 MHz.

Table 24.11
Quarter-Wave Stub Lengths for the HF Contesting Bands

Freq (MHz)	*Length (L_e)**	*Remove per 100 kHz*
1.8	90 ft, 10 in	57 3/8 in
3.5	46 ft, 9 in	15 1/2 in
7.0	23 ft, 4 in	4 in
14.0	11 ft, 8 in	1 in
21.0	7 ft, 9 in	7/16 in
28.0	5 ft, 10 in	1/4 in

*Lengths shown are for RG-213 and any similar cable, assuming a 0.66 velocity factor (L_e = 163.5/f).

in the same manner as Figure 24.14 and the frequency plot is shown in **Figure 24.16**.

This open stub can protect a receiver operating on 7, 14, 21 or 28 MHz from interference by a 3.5 MHz transmitter. It also has nulls at 10.5, 17.5 and 24.5 MHz — the 3rd, 5th and 7th harmonics. The length of a quarter-wave stub may be calculated as follows:

$$L_e = \frac{VF \times 983.6}{4f} \qquad (12)$$

where
L_e = length in feet
VF = propagation constant for the coax in use
f = frequency in MHz.

For the special case of RG-213 (and any similar cable with VF = 0.66), equation 11 can be simplified to:

$$L_e = \frac{163.5}{f} \qquad (13)$$

where
L_e = length in feet
f = frequency in MHz.

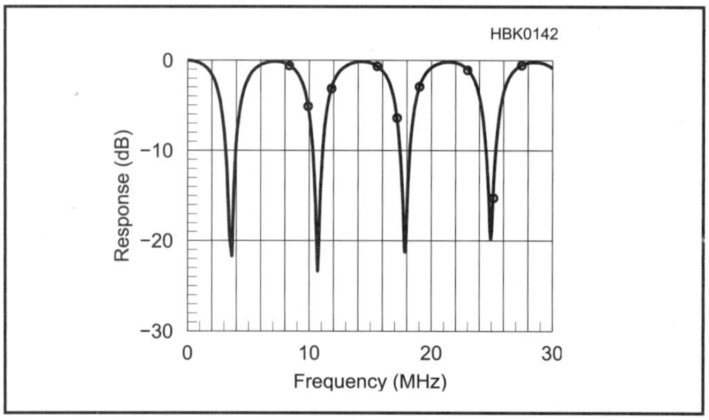

Figure 24.16 — Frequency response of an open λ/4 stub cut for 7 MHz.

Table 24.11 solves this equation for the major contesting bands where stubs are often used. The third column shows how much of the stub to cut off if the desired frequency is 100 kHz higher in frequency. For example: To cut a stub for 14.250 MHz, reduce the overall length shown by 2.5 × 1 inches, or 2.5 inches. There is some variation in dielectric constant of coaxial cable from batch to batch or manufacturer to manufacturer, so it is always best to measure the stub's fundamental resonance before proceeding.

MEASURING STUBS WITH ONE-PORT INSTRUMENTS

Many of the common measuring instruments used by amateurs are one-port devices, meaning they have one connector at which the measurement — typically VSWR — is made. Probably the most popular instrument for this type of work is the antenna analyzer, available from a number of manufacturers.

To test a stub using an antenna analyzer, connect the stub to the meter by itself and tune the meter for a minimum reactance value (or impedance, if reactance is not displayed), ignoring the VSWR display. If practical, tune the stub with one end shorted so as to determine the stub's λ/2 frequency, then dividing the frequency by two to get the λ/4 frequency. This will be easier to read accurately on the analyzer and give more accurate results. It is almost impossible to get an accurate reading on the higher HF bands, particularly with open stubs. For example, when a quarter-wave open stub cut for 20 meters was swept to determine the frequency of the null on an MFJ-259 SWR analyzer, the frequency measured 14.650 MHz, with a very broad null. A recheck with a professional-quality network analyzer measured 14.018 MHz. (Resolution on the network analyzer is about ±5 kHz.) Running the same test on a λ/4 shorted stub gave a measurement of 28.320 MHz on the MFJ-259 and 28.398 MHz on the network analyzer. (These inaccuracies are typical of amateur instrumentation and are meant to illustrate the difficulties of using inexpensive instruments for sensitive measurements.)

Other one-port instruments that measure phase can be used to get a more accurate reading. The additional length added by the required T must be accounted for. If a measurement is made without the T and then with the T, the average value will be close to correct. An alternative is to use a double-female adaptor of the same length as the T connection when making measurements.

MEASURING STUBS WITH TWO-PORT INSTRUMENTS

A two-port measurement is made with a signal generator and a separate detector, such as provided by a vector network analyzer (VNA) as described in the chapter on **Antenna and Transmission Line Measurements**. If a VNA is not available, attach a T connector to the generator with the stub connected to one side. The other side is connected to a cable of any length that goes to the detector. The detector should present a 50-Ω load to the cable. This is how the network analyzer is configured, and it is similar to how the stub is connected in actual use. If the generator is accurately calibrated, the measurement can be very good. There are a number of ways to do this without buying an expensive piece of lab equipment.

An antenna analyzer can be used as the signal generator. Measurements will be quite accurate if the detector has 30 to 40 dB dynamic range. Two setups were tested by W2VJN for accuracy. The first used a digital voltmeter (DVM) with a diode detector. (A germanium diode must be used for the best dynamic range.) Tests on open and shorted stubs at 14 MHz returned readings within 20 kHz of the network analyzer. Another test was run using an oscilloscope as the detector with a 50-Ω load on the input. This test produced results that were essentially the same as the network analyzer.

A noise generator can be used in combination with a receiver as the detector. (An inexpensive noise generator kit is available from Elecraft, **elecraft.com**.) Set the receiver for 2-3 kHz bandwidth and turn off the AGC. An ac voltmeter connected to the audio output of the receiver will serve as a null detector. The noise level into the receiver without the stub connected should be just at or below the limiting level. With the stub connected, the noise level in the null should drop by 25 or 30 dB. Connect the UHF T to the noise generator using any necessary adapters. Connect the stub to one side of the T and connect the receiver to the other side with a short cable. Tune the receiver around the expected null frequency. After locating the null, snip off pieces of cable until the null moves to the desired frequency. Accuracy with this method is within 20 or 30 kHz of the network analyzer readings on 14 MHz stubs.

CONNECTING STUBS

To connect a stub to a coaxial transmission line it is necessary to insert a T adaptor in the line. If the stub is to be connected directly at the transmitter, a female-male-female T is used with the male port connected directly to the transmitter and the antenna feed line and stub connected to the two female ports. If the stub is to be inserted in the feed line, an all-female port T can be used.

It should be noted that the T inserts a small additional length in series with the stub that lowers the resonant frequency. The additional length for an Amphenol UHF T is about 3/8 inch. This length is negligible at 1.8 and 3.5 MHz, but on the higher bands the additional length should be accounted for when measuring the stub.

24.3.6 Transmission Line Stubs as Filters

[Material in this section was adapted from papers and articles by George Cutsogeorge, W2VJN; Jim Brown, K9YC (**audiosystemsgroup.com/publish.htm**); and Ward Harriman, AE6TY (**ae6ty.com/Smith_Charts.html**), which are included with this book's online material and/or online. (See this book's online material information directory and this chapter's References and Bibliography.) ARRL appreciates the contributions of these authors. — Ed.]

The impedance transformation properties of stubs can be put to use as filters. For example, if a shorted line is cut to be λ/4 long at 7.1 MHz, the impedance looking into the input of the line will be an open circuit. The line will have no effect if placed in parallel with a transmitter's output terminals. However, at *twice* the frequency, 14.2 MHz, that same line is now λ/2, and the line looks like a short circuit. This *quarter-wave stub* will act as a filter for not only the second harmonic, but also for higher even-order harmonics, such as the fourth or sixth harmonics. Quarter-wave stubs made of good-quality coax, such as RG-213, can provide 20 to 30 dB of harmonic attenuation or more if located properly in the feed line.

This filtering action is extremely useful in multi-transmitter situations, such as during Field Day, emergency operations centers, portable communications facilities and multioperator contest stations. Transmission line stubs can operate at high power where lumped-constant filters would be expensive. Using stub filters reduces noise, harmonics and strong fundamental signals from the closely-spaced antennas which cause overload and interference to receivers.

One caveat is that there may be other inter-station paths for harmonic energy to get from one radio to another. This coupling is not addressed by adding stubs and may be a reason why applying stubs or bandpass filters may not give the results you expect. Another reason for poor harmonic suppression is that harmonics may be generated by non-linear junctions or devices in the antenna system or in the vicinity of the antenna system. If you suspect these or other sources for harmonic generation or coupling, use test equipment to build and then test the stub. Troubleshoot harmonic generation or coupling separately.

Stub filters can also be used as receive filters to remove a strong fundamental signal received by an antenna system operating at a harmonic of the fundamental. In the following discussion, of stub placement, when placing a stub for receive filtering, reverse the references to transmitter and antenna. Also, do not alter the position of any transmit filter stubs when adding stubs for receive filtering.

POSITIONING A STUB CONNECTION

This discussion will focus on the common application of using a shorted stub to act as a harmonic filter at even integer multiples of a transmitted signal's fundamental frequency. A stub works to suppress a harmonic by placing a short circuit across the line at the harmonic frequency. When a stub is placed in the line somewhere between the transmitter and antenna, the impedance at that point determines how well the stub will work. i.e. – attenuating the harmonic. If the stub is located at a low impedance point in the line, the short circuit is in parallel with the low impedance and so provides little additional attenuation. Additionally, if the length of coax between stub and transmitter output degrades the suppression provided by the transmitter output network, the total suppression (output network plus stub) may be no better than without the stub. ("Transmitter" in this section will refer to either a transceiver or power amplifier, including any filters that will be used.)

It is important to remember that for this application, impedance is measured or calculated at the frequency of the second harmonic, *not* the fundamental. The assumption is made that the antenna is reasonably well-matched to the line at the fundamental (SWR < 2:1) and poorly matched at the harmonic. This procedure is intended to be applied to monoband antenna systems and may be unreliable when the antenna in use is a multiband antenna matched to the line at the fundamental and harmonic(s) in question.

Note also that this procedure does not include the effects of an adjustable antenna tuner, such as an auto-tuner in a transmitter. If a tuner is used, the stub should be located with the tuner adjusted for operation at the fundamental. (This includes any tuning or impedance matching networks or stubs that match the antenna to the line at the fundamental frequency.)

Before beginning, you may not have to undertake a detailed process to achieve acceptable results. Build a stub λ/4 long at the fundamental frequency and prepare to attach it at a convenient point in your transmission line. Measure the strength of the harmonic to be suppressed by either using a receiver S-meter or a spectrum analyzer. Install the stub and determine the amount of attenuation of the harmonic. If you have sufficient attenuation, you need go no further!

Another option is to build the double-stub combination described in the next section as that is nearly guaranteed to provide at least 30 dB of harmonic attenuation at the expense of the extra stub, adaptors, and coupling line.

To optimize the location of the stub in the feed line, each of the three authors mentioned above approach the problem somewhat differently but the basic procedure is as follows:

Step 1: With the antenna connected, measure the complex impedance (at the second harmonic) at the input to the feed line.

Step 2: Use *TLW* or a Smith chart program such as *SimSmith* by AE6TY to find the location of impedance peaks on the line.

Step 3: Break the line at one of those points, insert a coax T (tee) adaptor and add the stub. The length of line from the stub to the antenna corresponds to cable W2 in Figure 24.14. (If you have acceptable results, you can stop here.)

Step 4: Make the line between the stub and the output of the transmitter (cable W1 in Figure 24.14) a length that preserves the harmonic suppression of the transmitter output network. This length of line is relatively non-critical with an error of up to 45° resulting in only 3 dB less attenuation than at the optimum point.

If the element of the transmitter's output matching network (including any filter circuits) nearest the point of connection to the antenna feed line is a series inductor (such as for a Pi-L output network), make the coax as short as possible or some even multiple of λ/2 at the harmonic. If that component is a capacitor, make cable W1 some odd multiple (1, 3, 5, etc.) of λ/4 at the harmonic. If you are using a double stub as below, W1 is the length of coax to the stub closest to the transmitter.

An alternate method is suggested by W2VJN in which the impedance is measured looking back into the transmitter output network through W1. Step 2 from above can then be repeated to find the optimum length of cable that results in a high impedance point at the stub connection point. By optimizing both W1 and W2, W2VJN has observed more than 50 dB of attenuation from a single stub.

STUB COMBINATIONS

A single stub will give 20 to 30 dB attenuation in the null if connected at a high-impedance point in the feed line as described above. A second stub can be added for additional attenuation if separated from the first stub by λ/4 at the frequency of the harmonic to be attenuated. This is shown in **Figure 24.17**. This technique will also provide good attenuation if you are unable to determine an optimum location for the stubs or are required to install the stubs in a non-optimum location. The stubs both force low-impedance points on the line at the harmonic, guaranteeing that at least one stub will have its full effect.

Open and shorted stubs can be combined together to atten-

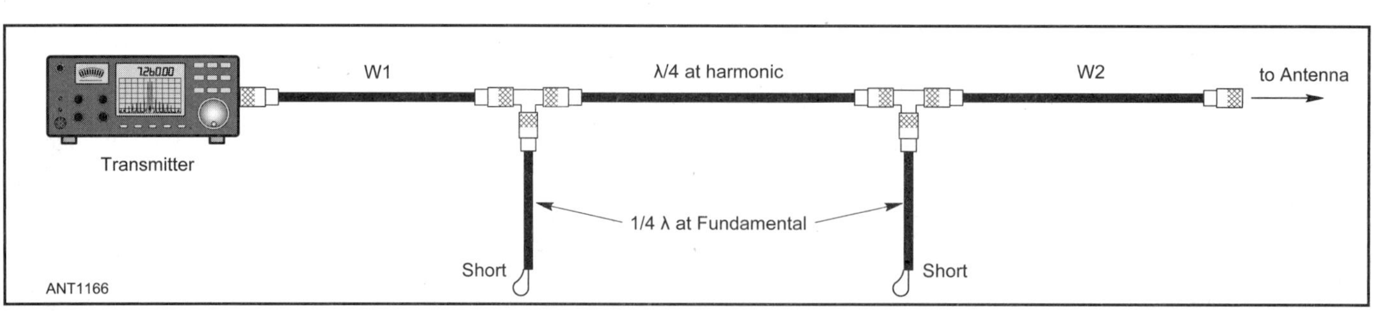

Figure 24.17 — Double λ/4 shorted stubs, placed λ/4 apart at the harmonic, guarantee the full effectiveness of at least one of the stubs, regardless of where the combination is placed in the feed line. If optimally placed, total attenuation is the sum of attenuation from each stub.

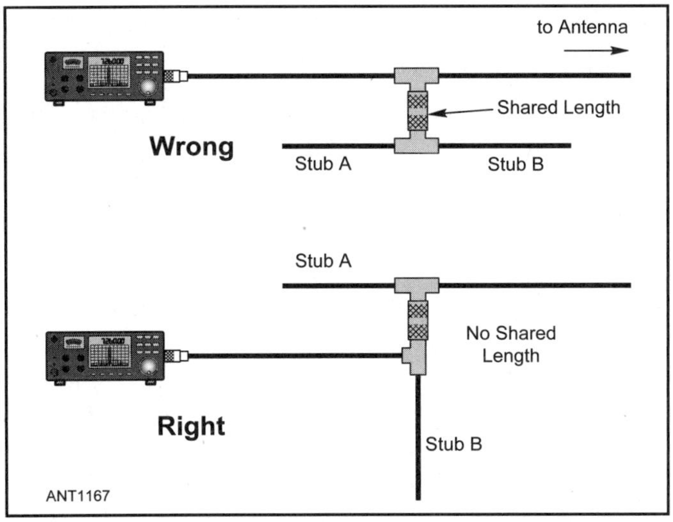

Figure 24.18 — When connecting stubs at a common point, do not connect them so that they share any length. Separate them with a double female or "barrel" adaptor. This avoids interaction between the stubs which would shift the assembly's resonant frequencies.

uate higher harmonics as well as lower frequency bands. The stubs may be cut to the same frequency for maximum attenuation, or to two slightly different frequencies such as the CW and SSB frequencies in one band. Stubs should not be connected together at exactly the same point in the feed line but separated by a very short length of line or a double female adaptor. Stubs should also not share any length. The correct way to connect multiple stubs is shown in **Figure 24.18**.

An interesting combination is the parallel connection of two ⅛ λ stubs, one open and the other shorted. The shorted stub will act as an inductor and the open stub as a capacitor. Their reactance will be equal and opposite, forming a resonant circuit. The null depth with this arrangement will be a bit better than a single quarter-wave shorted stub. This presents some possibilities when combinations of stubs are used in a band switching system. W2VJN's book *Managing Interstation Interference* presents a number of useful combinations. (See the References and Bibliography.)

24.3.7 PROJECT: A Field Day Stub Assembly

Figure 24.19 shows a simple stub arrangement that can be useful in a two-transmitter Field Day station. The stubs reduce out-of-band noise produced by the transmitters that would cause interference to the other stations — a common Field Day problem where the stations are quite close together. This noise cannot be filtered out at the receiver and must be removed at the transmitter. One stub assembly would be connected to each transmitter output and manually switched for the appropriate band.

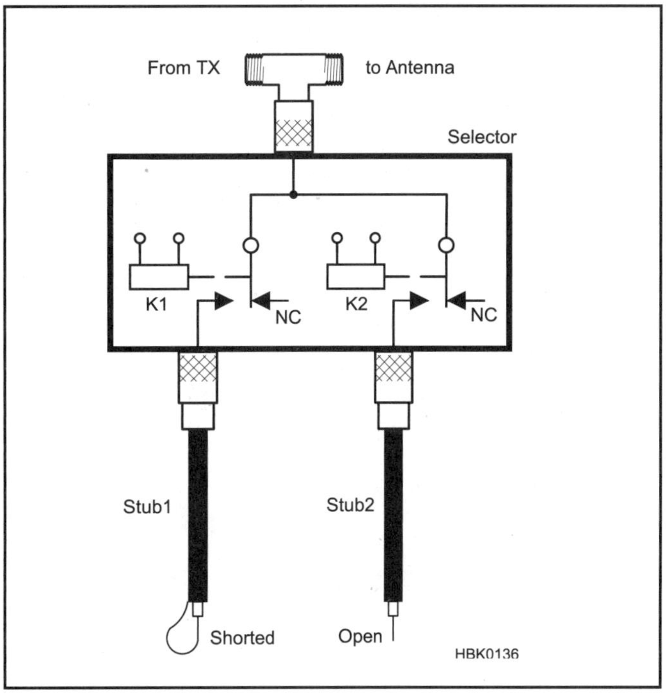

Figure 24.19 — Schematic of the Field Day stub switching relay control box. Table 24.12 shows which relays should be closed or for the desired operating band.

Two stubs are connected as shown. The two-relay selector box can be switched in four ways. Stub 1 is a shorted quarter-wave 40-meter stub. Stub 2 is an open quarter-wave 40-meter stub. Operation is as shown in **Table 24.12**.

The stubs must be cut and tuned while connected to the selector relays. RG-213 may be used for any amateur power level and will provide 25 to 30 dB reduction in the nulls. For power levels under 500 W or so, RG-8X may be used. It will provide a few dB less reduction in the nulls because of its slightly higher loss than RG-213.

Table 24.12
Stub Selector Operation
See Fig 24.16 for circuit details

Relay K1 Position	*Relay K2 Position*	*Bands Passed (meters)*	*Bands Nulled (meters)*
Open	Open	All	None
Energized	Energized	80	40, 20, 15, 10
Energized	Open	40, 15	20, 10
Open	Energized	20, 10	40, 15

24.4 Transmission Line Matching Devices

BALUNS, CHOKES, AND TRANSFORMERS

It is useful to begin with the terminology of this important topic. The term "balun" applies to any device that transfers differential-mode signals between a balanced (*bal-*) system and an unbalanced (*un-*) system while maintaining symmetrical energy distribution at the terminals of the balanced system. The term only applies to the function of energy transfer, not to how the device is constructed. It doesn't matter whether the balanced-unbalanced transition is made through transmission line structures, flux-coupled transformers, or simply by blocking unbalanced current flow. A *common-mode choke*, for example, can perform the balun function by putting impedance in the path of common-mode currents at the load terminals, such as antenna feed point, and is therefore a balun.

A *current balun* forces symmetrical current at the balanced terminals. This is of particular importance in feeding antennas, since antenna currents determine the antenna's radiation pattern. A *voltage balun* forces symmetrical voltages at the balanced terminals. Voltage baluns are less effective in causing equal currents at their balanced terminals, such as at an antenna's feed point.

An *impedance transformer* may or may not perform the balun function. Impedance transformation (changing the ratio of voltage and current) is not required of a balun nor is it prohibited. There are balanced-to-balanced impedance transformers (transformers with isolated primary and secondary windings, for example) just as there are unbalanced-to-unbalanced or *unun* impedance transformers (autotransformer and transmission-line designs). A *transmission-line transformer* is a device that performs the function of power transfer (with or without impedance transformation) by utilizing the characteristics of transmission lines.

Multiple devices are often combined in a single package called a "balun." For example, a "4:1 current balun" is a 1:1 current balun in series with a 4:1 impedance transformer or voltage balun. Other names for baluns are common, such as "line isolator" for a choke balun. Baluns are often referred to by their construction — "bead balun," "coiled-coax balun," "sleeve balun," and so forth. What is important is to separate the function (power transfer between balanced and unbalanced systems) from the construction.

TYPES OF MATCHING DEVICES

There are three types of devices discussed in this section. The first are reflective, in that they perform impedance transformation by setting up a series of reflections in the transmission line. These are called *synchronous transformers* because the reflections have precise phase relationships. The forward and reflected waves combine to create a different ratio of voltage and current, the definition of impedance.

The second type, *transmission line transformers*, isolate the output of short transmission lines from the input by blocking the common-mode signal path with a high impedance created by winding the line on ferrite material. That allows the differential-mode signals from each line to be combined as if they were independent signal sources. The signals can be combined in and out of phase, just as conventional transformer windings can be connected to create different combinations of voltages and current.

Finally, broadband transformers use conventional transformer action, also known as *flux-coupled transformers*, to transform impedances between a primary and secondary winding. Additional windings are used to create flux in the transformer core in some designs. These transformers can have a very wide bandwidth.

24.4.1 Quarter-Wave Transformers

The impedance-transforming properties of a λ/4 transmission line *synchronous transformer* or *Q-section* shown in **Figure 24.20A** can be used to good advantage for matching the feed point impedance of an antenna to the characteristic impedance of the line. As described in the **Transmission Lines** chapter, the input impedance of a λ/4 line terminated in a resistive impedance Z_R is

$$Z_i = \frac{Z_0^{\,2}}{Z_L} \qquad (14)$$

where

Z_i = the impedance at the input end of the line
Z_0 = the characteristic impedance of the line
Z_L = the impedance at the load end of the line

This is called *impedance inversion* because the ratio of Z_L to Z_0 is the same as the ratio of Z_0 to Z_i. Viewed on a Smith chart normalized to Z_0 (the center point represents Z_0), Z_L and Z_I are on opposite sides of and equidistant from the center point.

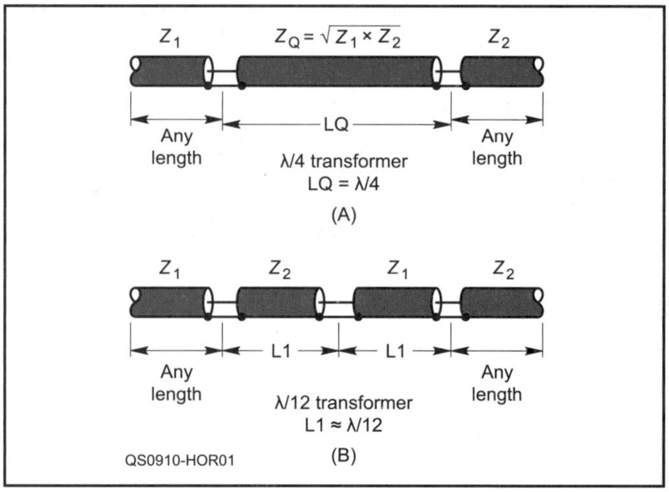

Figure 24.20 — The ¼-wave (A) Q-section and 1/12 wave (B) synchronous transformers.

Rearranging this equation gives

$$Z_0 = \sqrt{Z_i Z_L} \quad (15)$$

This means that any value of load impedance Z_L can be transformed into any desired value of impedance Z_i at the input terminals of a λ/4 line that has a characteristic impedance Z_0 equal to the square root of the product of the other two impedances. The factor that limits the range of impedances that can be matched by this method is the range of values for Z_0 that is physically realizable — approximately 50 to 600 Ω. Practically any type of line can be used for the matching section, including both air-insulated and solid-dielectric lines.

The λ/4 transformer may be adjusted to resonance before being connected to the antenna by following the procedures for determining line length in the chapter **Antenna and Transmission Line Measurements**.

TUNED FEEDERS

Feeding a high-impedance point on an antenna can be made easier by using a quarter-wave transformer. This changes the high feed point impedance to a lower value likely to be easier to transform to 50 Ω with an antenna tuner. For example, if a λ/4 400-Ω line is connected to a 2000-Ω feed point, the output impedance of the line will be $400^2/2000 = 80$ Ω which is much easier to match to 50 Ω. This only works at frequencies for which the feed line is the required electrical length, thus the term "tuned."

Tuned feeders can also create problems due to their length. For example, a feed line some multiple of λ/2 long connected to grounded equipment enclosures at one end also has a low impedance at the other end. That can cause trouble for an end-fed antenna with a high feed point impedance. Resonant feed line lengths (some multiple of λ/4 long) also tend to be effective at picking up energy from the antenna where it creates common-mode currents and re-radiated signals.

YAGI DRIVEN ELEMENTS

Another application for the λ/4 transformer is in matching the low antenna impedance encountered in close-spaced, monoband Yagi arrays to a 50-Ω transmission line. The impedances at the antenna feed point for typical Yagis range from about 8 to 30 Ω. Let's assume that the feed point impedance is 25 Ω. A matching section is needed. Since there is no commercially available cable with a Z_0 of 35.4 Ω, a pair of λ/4-long 75-Ω RG-11 coax cables connected in parallel will have a net Z_0 of 75/2 = 37.5 Ω, close enough for practical purposes.

24.4.2 Twelfth-Wave Transformers

The Q-section is really a special case of series-section matching described below. There's no restriction (other than complexity) that there be just one matching section. In fact, the two-section variation shown in Figure 24.20B is quite handy for matching two different impedances of transmission line, such as 50-Ω coax and 75-Ω hardline. Best of all, special transmission line impedances are not required, only sections of line with the same impedances that are to be matched.

Current Forcing with λ/4 Sections

Current-forcing is an interesting property of λ/4 transmission lines. The magnitude of the *current out* of a λ/4 transmission line is equal to the *input voltage* divided by the characteristic impedance of the line. This is independent of the load impedance. (Note that the power into and out of the line is the same, less losses in the line.) In addition, the phase of the output current lags the phase of the input voltage by 90°, also independent of the load impedance. (See the **Phased Array** chapter's section Recommended Feed Methods for Amateur Arrays for an example of how this property is used.)

If any number of loads are connected to a common driving point through λ/4 lines of equal impedance, the currents in the loads will be *forced* to be equal and in-phase, regardless of the load impedances. Loads that require unequal currents can be fed through λ/4 lines of unequal impedances to achieve other current ratios.

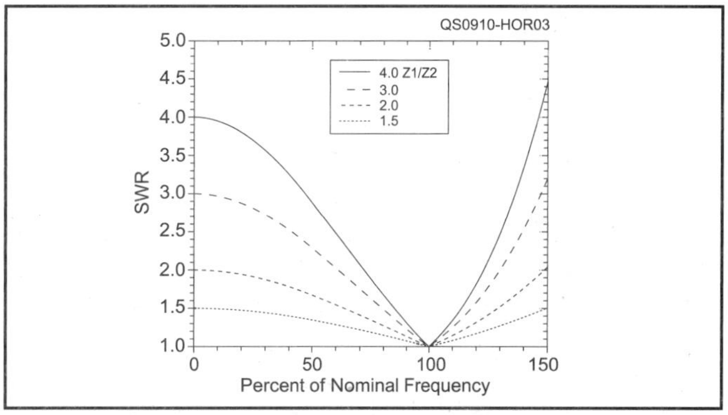

Figure 24.21 — The bandwidth of the λ/12 transformer is fairly broad as shown in this family of curves for different impedance transformation ratios. For 75- and 50-Ω impedances (a ratio of 1.5:1), the points at which an SWR of 1.2:1 are reached are approximately 75% and 125% of the design frequency.

This configuration is referred to as a *twelfth-wave transformer* because when the ratio of the impedances to be matched is 1.5:1 (as is the case with 50- and 75-Ω cables), the electrical length of the two matching sections between the lines to be matched is 0.0815 λ (29.3°), quite close to λ/12 (0.0833 λ or 30°). **Figure 24.21** shows that the SWR bandwidth of the twelfth-wave transformer is quite broad. You can use this technique to make good use of surplus low-loss 75-Ω CATV hardline between 50-Ω antennas and radios.

24.4.3 Series-Section Transformers

The *series-section transformer* has advantages over either stub tuning or the λ/4 transformer. Illustrated in **Figure 24.22**, the series-section transformer bears considerable resemblance to the λ/4 and λ/12 transformers described earlier. (Actually, these are special cases of the series-section transformer.) The important differences are (1) that the matching section need not be located exactly at the load, (2) the matching section

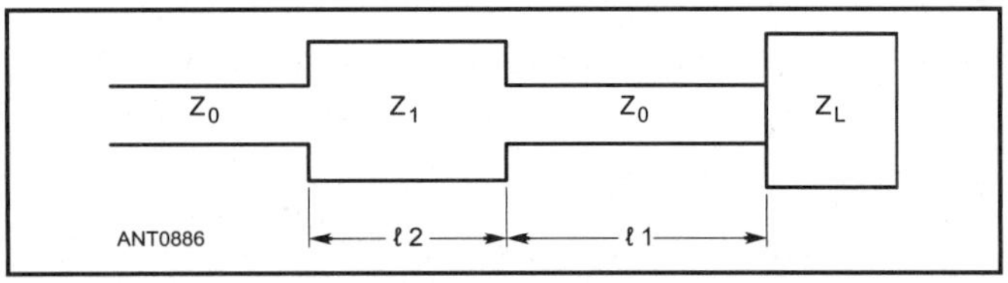

Figure 24.22 — Series section transformer Z_1 for matching transmission line Z_0 to load Z_L.

may be less than a quarter wavelength long, and (3) there is great freedom in the choice of the characteristic impedance of the matching section.

In fact, the matching section can have *any* characteristic impedance that is not too close to that of the main line. Because of this freedom, it is almost always possible to find a length of commercially available line that will be suitable as a matching section. As an example, consider a 75-Ω line, a 300-Ω matching section, and a pure-resistance load. It can be shown that a series-section transformer of 300-Ω line may be used to match *any* resistance between 5 Ω and 1200 Ω to the main line.

Frank Regier, OD5CG, described series-section transformers in the July 1978 *QST* (see References and Bibliography). This information is based on that article. The design of a series-section transformer consists of determining the length L2 of the series or matching section and the distance L1 from the load to the point where the section should be inserted into the main line. Three quantities must be known. These are the characteristic impedances of the main line and of the matching section, both assumed purely resistive, and the complex-load impedance. Either of two design methods may be used. One is a graphic method using the Smith Chart, and the other is algebraic. You can take your choice. (Of course, the algebraic method may be adapted to obtaining a computer solution.) The Smith Chart graphic method is described in an article included with this book's online material.

ALGEBRAIC DESIGN METHOD

The two lengths L1 and L2 are to be determined from the characteristic impedances of the main line and the matching section, Z_0 and Z_1, respectively, and the load impedance $Z_L = R_L + j\,X_L$. The first step is to determine the normalized impedances.

$$n = \frac{Z_1}{Z_0} \qquad (16)$$

$$r = \frac{R_L}{Z_0} \qquad (17)$$

$$x = \frac{X_L}{Z_0} \qquad (18)$$

Next, L2 and L1 are determined from

L2 = arctan B, where

$$B = \pm\sqrt{\frac{(r-1)^2 + x^2}{r\left(n-\frac{1}{n}\right)^2 - (r-1)^2 - x^2}} \qquad (19)$$

L1 = arctan A, where

$$A = \frac{\left(n-\frac{r}{n}\right)B + x}{r + xnB - 1} \qquad (20)$$

Lengths L2 and L1 as thus determined are electrical lengths in degrees (or radians). The electrical lengths in wavelengths are obtained by dividing by 360° (or by 2π radians). The physical lengths (main line or matching section, as the case may be), are then determined from multiplying by the free-space wavelength and by the velocity factor of the line.

The sign of B may be chosen either positive or negative, but the positive sign is preferred because it results in a shorter matching section. The sign of A may not be chosen but can turn out to be either positive or negative. If a negative sign occurs and a computer or calculator is then used to determine L1, a negative electric length will result for L1. If this happens, add 180°. The resultant electrical length will be correct both physically and mathematically.

In calculating B, if the quantity under the radical is negative, an imaginary value for B results. This would mean that Z_1, the impedance of the matching section, is too close to Z_0 and should be changed.

Limits on the characteristic impedance of Z_1 may be calculated in terms of the SWR produced by the load on the main line without matching. For matching to occur, Z_1 should either be greater than $Z_0\sqrt{SWR}$ or less than $Z_0/\sqrt{SWR}$.

AN EXAMPLE

As an example, suppose we want to feed a 29-MHz ground-plane vertical antenna with RG-58 type foam-dielectric coax. We'll assume the antenna impedance to be 36 Ω, pure resistance, and use a length of RG-59 foam-dielectric coax as the series section. See **Figure 24.23**.

Z_0 is 50 Ω, Z_1 is 75 Ω, and both cables have a velocity factor of 0.79. Because the load is a pure resistance, we may determine the SWR to be 50/36 = 1.389. From the above, Z_1 must have an impedance greater than $50\sqrt{1.389}$. From the earlier equations, n = 75/50 = 1.50, r = 36/50 = 0.720, and x = 0.

Further, B = 0.431 (positive sign chosen), and L2 = 23.3° or 0.065 λ. The value of A is –1.570. Calculating L1 yields –57.5°. Adding 180° to obtain a positive result gives L1= 122.5°, or 0.340 λ.

To find the physical lengths L1 and L2 we first find the free-space wavelength.

$$\lambda = \frac{984}{f(MHz)} = 33.93 \text{ feet}$$

Multiply this value by 0.79 (the velocity factor for both

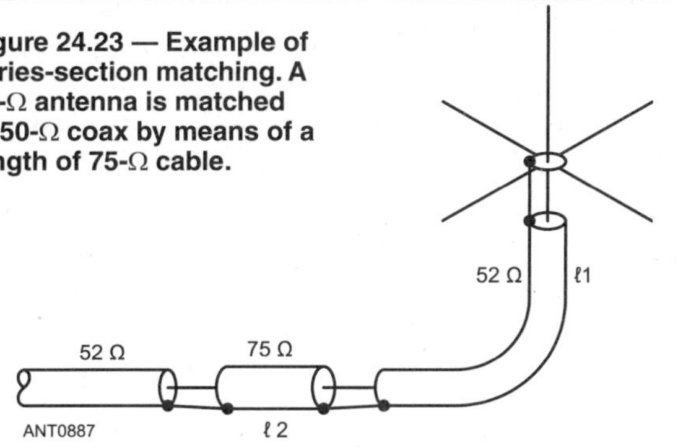

Figure 24.23 — Example of series-section matching. A 36-Ω antenna is matched to 50-Ω coax by means of a length of 75-Ω cable.

types of line), and we obtain the electrical wavelength in coax as 26.81 feet. From this, L1 = 0.340 × 26.81 = 9.12 feet, and L2 = 0.065 × 26.81 = 1.74 feet.

This completes the calculations. Construction consists of cutting the main coax at a point 9.12 feet from the antenna and inserting a 1.74-foot length of the 75-Ω cable.

The antenna in the preceding example could also have been matched by a λ/4 transformer at the load. Such a transformer would use a line with a characteristic impedance of 42.43 Ω. It is interesting to see what happens in the design of a series-section transformer if this value is chosen as the characteristic impedance of the series section.

Following the same steps as before, we find n = 0.849, r = 0.720, and x = 0. From these values we find B = 8 and L2 = 90°. Further, A = 0 and l1 = 0°. These results represent a λ/4 section at the load, and indicate that, as stated earlier, the λ/4 transformer is indeed a special case of the series-section transformer.

24.4.4 Multiple Quarter-Wave Sections

An alternate to the smooth-impedance transformation of the tapered line is provided by using two or more λ/4 transformer sections in series, as shown in **Figure 24.24**. (See article "Tapered Lines" in the online material.) Each section has a different characteristic impedance, selected to transform the impedance at its input to that at its output. Thus, the overall impedance transformation from source to load takes place as a series of gradual transformations. The frequency bandwidth with multiple sections is greater than for a single section. This technique is useful at the upper end of the HF range and at VHF and UHF. Here, too, the total line length that is required may become unwieldy at the lower frequencies.

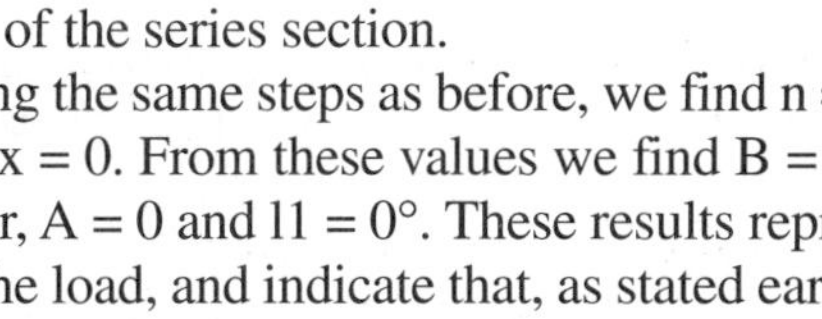

Figure 24.24 — Multiple quarter-wave matching sections approximate the broadband matching transformation provided by a tapered line. Two sections are shown here, but more may be used. The more sections in the line, the broader is the matching bandwidth. Z_0 is the characteristic impedance of the main feed line, while Z_1 and Z_2 are the intermediate impedances of the matching sections. See text for design equations.

A multiple-section line may contain two or more λ/4 transformer sections; the more sections in the line, the broader is the matching bandwidth. Coaxial transmission lines may be used to make a multiple-section line, but standard coax lines are available in only a few characteristic impedances. Open-wire lines can be constructed rather easily for a specific impedance, designed from:

$$S = \frac{d \times 10^{Z_0/276}}{2} \qquad (21)$$

where S is the center-to-center spacing between the conductors, d is the diameter of the conductors (same units as S), and Z_0 is the characteristic impedance in ohms.

The following equations may be used to calculate the intermediate characteristic impedances for a two-section line.

$$Z_1 = \sqrt[4]{R Z_0^{\,3}} \qquad (22A)$$

$$Z_2 = \sqrt[3]{R^2 Z_1} \qquad (22B)$$

where terms are as illustrated in Figure 24.24. For example, assume we wish to match a 75-Ω source (Z_0) to an 800-Ω load. From Eq 21, calculate Z_1 to be 135.5 Ω. Then from Eq 22A, calculate Z_2 to be 442.7 Ω. As a matter of interest, for this example the virtual impedance at the junction of Z_1 and Z_2 is 244.9 Ω. (This is the same impedance that would be required for a single-section λ/4 matching section.)

Multi-section λ/4 transformers are discussed by Randy Rhea in *High-Frequency Electronics* magazine (see References and Bibliography). This technique is related to the "equal delay" transmission line transformers.

DOUBLE QUARTER-WAVE TRANSFORMER

The double λ/4 transformer is a special case of the multi-section λ/4 transformer. If two λ/4 sections of feed line, one with impedance Z_0 followed by another with an impedance of $2Z_0$ as the input impedance as in **Figure 24.25**, the input to the transformer will be the load impedance divided by 4. The transformer can be "turned around" to step up the load impedance. In general, the transformation ratio is the square of the impedance ratio of the two λ/4 sections, and it is independent of the impedances of the input and output. The larger the difference in Z_0 between the sections, the smaller the bandwidth of the impedance transformation.

You are not restricted to the Z_0 of single cables. Paralleled cables with characteristic impedances of Z_0 act as a combined cable with a characteristic impedance of $Z_0/2$. So, for example, a λ/4 section of two 50-Ω cables in parallel (Z_0 = 25 Ω) connected to a λ/4 section of 50-Ω line has an impedance ratio of 2:1 and an impedance transformation ratio of 4:1. This design could match 75-Ω line to a 300-Ω load — using 50-Ω

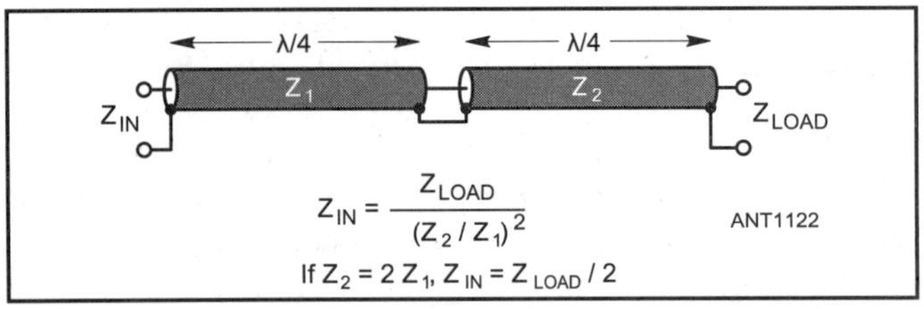

Figure 24.25 — The impedance transformation ratio of the double quarter-wave transformer is the square of the difference between the characteristic impedances of the two λ/4 sections.

cable! If the input section were composed of three cables in parallel, the impedance ratio would be 3:1 and the transformation ratio 9:1 — this could match 50 Ω at the input to 450 Ω at the output.

24.4.5 Transmission Line Transformers (TLT)

From Sevick's paper analyzing TLTs, "A Transmission line transformer transmits the energy from input to output by a transmission line mode and not by flux-linkages as in the conventional transformer" (see References and Bibliography entry for Sevick). The TLT may or may not perform an impedance transformation and may have a balanced-balanced, balanced-unbalanced, or unbalanced-unbalanced configuration.

The basic transmission line transformer, from which other transformers are derived, is the 1:1 *current balun* or *choke balun*, shown in **Figure 24.26A**, first described by Guanella in 1944 (See References and Bibliography). To construct this type of balun, a length of coaxial cable or a pair of close-spaced, parallel wires forming a transmission line are wrapped around a ferrite rod or toroid or inserted through several beads. The ferrite should have a resistive characteristic as discussed in the Current Baluns, Chokes, and Choke Baluns section of this chapter. The Z_0 of the line should equal the load resistance, R. To maintain low attenuation the line length should be much less than one-fourth wavelength at the highest frequency of operation.

The conductors (two close-spaced parallel wires or coaxial cable's braid and center conductor) are tightly coupled by electromagnetic fields and therefore constitute a good conventional transformer with a turns ratio of 1:1. The voltage from A to C is equal to and in-phase with that from B to D. These are *common-mode (CM) voltages*. A *CM current* is one that has the same value and direction in both wires (or on the shield and center conductor).

Because of the ferrite core, a high impedance exists that acts to reduce (choke) the CM current between points A and C and between B and D. The normal *differential-mode* (*DM*) signal does not encounter this CM impedance because the electromagnetic fields due to equal and opposite currents in the two conductors cancel each other in the ferrite, so the magnetic flux in the ferrite due to DM current is virtually zero. This is the main idea of the transmission line transformer: although the CM impedance may be very large, the DM signal is virtually unopposed, especially if the line length is a small fraction of a wavelength. This is true for parallel conductor lines and for coax.

It is also very important to keep in mind that the common-mode voltage across the ferrite winding that is due to DM current is efficiently coupled between both conductors of the transmission line by conventional transformer action, as mentioned before and easily verified. (Note that the ferrite core affects both the coax shield and center conductor equally.) This balancing of CM voltages and CM impedances reduces the conversion of a CM signal to an *undesired* DM signal that can interfere with the *desired* DM signal in both transmitters and receivers. In other words, the undesired CM signal is blocked or "choked."

The CM current, multiplied by the CM impedance due to the ferrite, produces a CM voltage. The CM impedance has L and C reactance and also R. So, L, C and R cause a broad parallel self-resonance at some frequency. The R component also produces some dissipation (heat) in the ferrite. This dissipation is an excellent way to dispose of a small amount of unwanted CM power. (The section on Power Dissipation in Ferrite Transmitting Chokes discusses the effect of large CM voltages across the ferrite material in transmitting applications.)

Because of the high CM impedance, the two output wires of the balun in Figure 24.26A have a high impedance with respect to, and are therefore "isolated" from, the input signal source. This feature is very useful because now any point of R at the output can be grounded. In a well-designed balun circuit almost all of the current in one conductor returns to the generator through the other conductor, despite this ground connection. In a coax balun the return current flows on the inside surface of the braid. Thus, the current balun produces equal and opposite currents in the load terminals.

Note also that the ground connection introduces some CM voltage across the balun cores, and this has to be taken into account. This CM voltage is a maximum if point C is grounded. If point D is grounded and if all "ground" connections are at the same potential, which they often are not, the CM voltage is zero and the balun may no longer be needed.

THE GUANELLA TRANSFORMER

We now look briefly at a transmission line transformer that is based on the current balun. Figure 24.26B shows two identical current baluns whose inputs are in parallel and whose outputs are in series. The output voltage amplitude of each balun is identical to the common input, so the two outputs add in-phase (equal time delay) to produce twice the input voltage. It is the high CM impedance isolating the input and output that makes this voltage addition possible. For the power to remain constant the load current must be one-half the generator current, and the load resistance must be 2 V/0.5 I = 4 V/I = 4 R.

The CM voltage in each balun is V/2, so there is some flux in the cores. The right side floats. This is named the *Guanella transformer* after its inventor who constructed several variations from the basic current balun. If Z_0 of the lines equals 2R

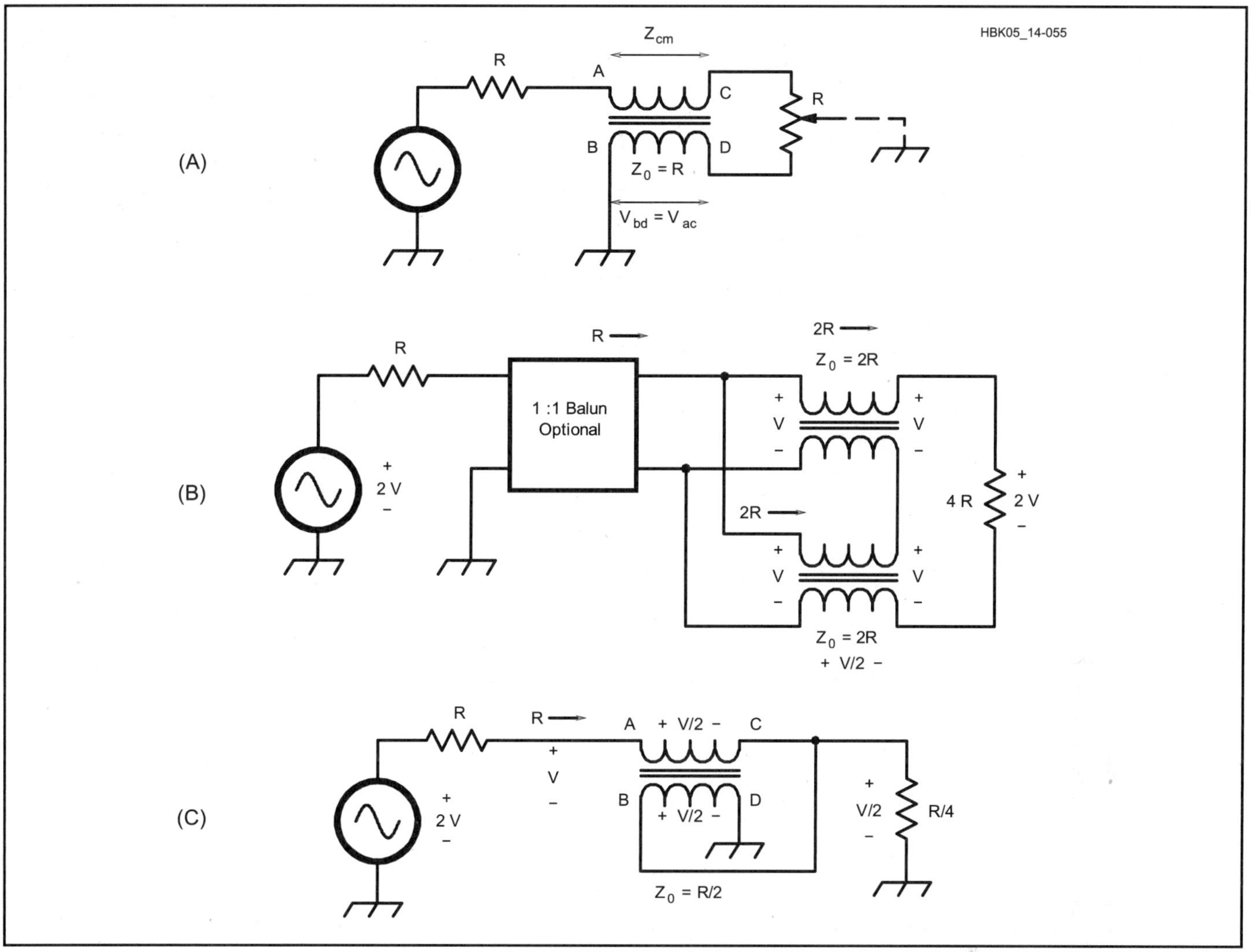

Figure 24.26 — (A) Basic current or choke balun. (B) Guanella 1:4 transformer. (C) Ruthroff 4:1 unbalanced transformer.

and if the load is a pure resistance of 4R then the input resistance R is independent of line length. If the lines are exactly one-quarter wavelength, then $Z_{IN} = (2R)^2 / Z_L$, an impedance inverter, where Z_{IN} and Z_L are complex.

The quality of balance can often be improved by inserting a 1:1 balun (Figure 24.26A) at the left end so that both ends of the 1:4 transformer are floating, and a ground is at the far left side as shown. The Guanella transformer can also be operated from a grounded right end to a floating left end. The 1:1 balun at the left then allows a grounded far left end.

Construction of the 1:1 current balun and 4:1 Guanella transformer wound on toroid cores are shown in **Figure 24.27**.

THE RUTHROFF TRANSFORMER

Figure 24.26C is the *Ruthroff transformer* (named after its inventor) in which the input voltage V is divided into two equal in-phase voltages AC and BD (they are tightly coupled), so the output is V/2. And because power is constant, $I_{OUT} = 2I_{IN}$ and the load is R/4. There is a CM voltage V/2 between A and C and between B and D, so in normal operation the core is not free of magnetic flux. The input and output both return to ground so it can also be operated from right to left for a 1:4 impedance step-up. Since the Ruthroff transformer creates equal voltages at the load terminals, it is referred to as a *voltage balun*. It is important to note that if the impedances connected to the load terminals are not the same, the currents will not be the same. This makes the Ruthroff transformer less effective than the Guanella transformer in creating equal load currents in antennas where impedance imbalances are common.

24.4.6 Broadband Matching Transformers

At low frequencies, where interwinding capacitances can be neglected, these transformers are similar in operation to a conventional transformer. Using higher permeability cores permits fewer turns at the lower frequencies. This improves high-frequency performance since the upper cutoff is limited by leakage inductance. A compensating capacitor across the primary winding is often used to reduce the effect of leakage inductance. For more about the design of these transformers see the tutorial "Wide Band RF Transformers" at **electronics-**

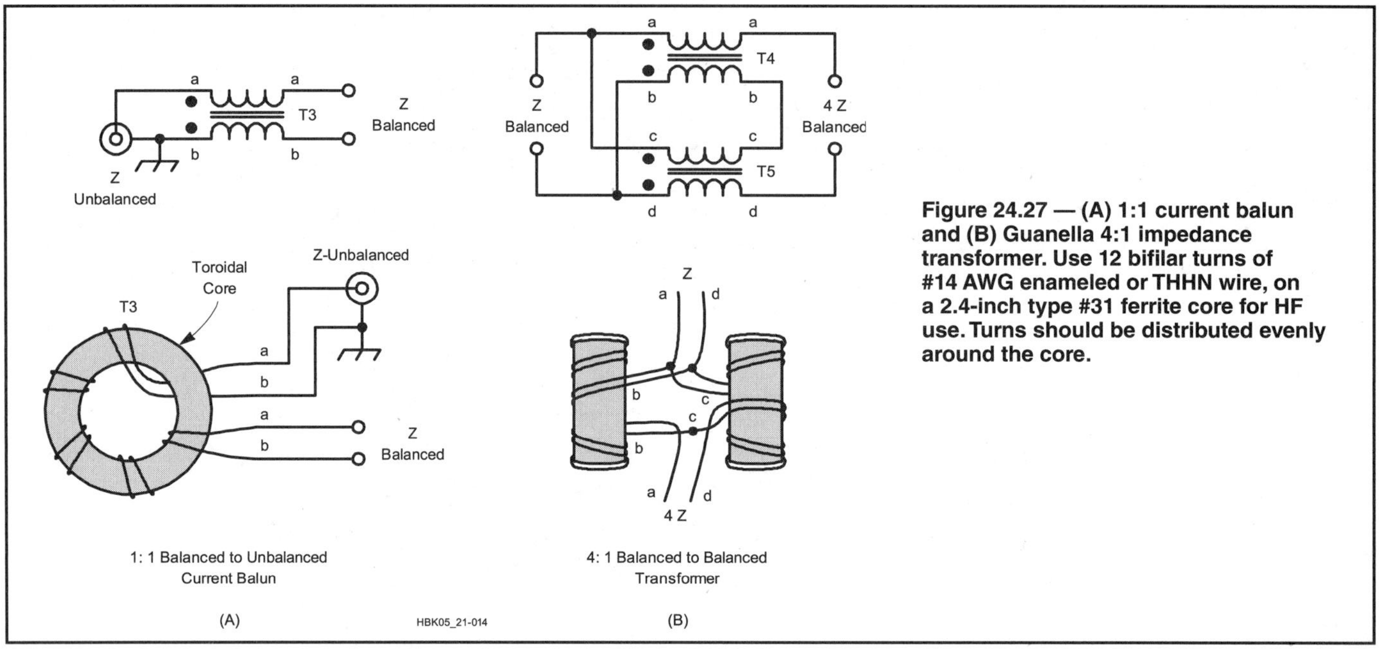

Figure 24.27 — (A) 1:1 current balun and (B) Guanella 4:1 impedance transformer. Use 12 bifilar turns of #14 AWG enameled or THHN wire, on a 2.4-inch type #31 ferrite core for HF use. Turns should be distributed evenly around the core.

tutorials.com/basics/wide-band-rf-transformers.htm and the application note "Use of Ferrites in Broadband Transformers" (**fair-rite.com/wp-content/uploads/2016/06/Use_of_Ferrites_in_Broadband_Transformers1.pdf**).

Cores used in these applications should be ferrites of low-loss type #43 (μ = 800) and #61 material (μ = 125) for use in inductive applications. Transformers wound on these cores can be made to operate over the 1.8 to 28-MHz bands with full power capability and very low loss. Type #61 material requires 10 turns to cover the 1.8-MHz band while type #43 will only require 2 or 3 turns. 1.5-inch OD cores will suffice for 100-W operation and one or two of the larger 2.4-inch OD cores for higher power levels. When you are working with low impedance levels, unwanted parasitic inductances come into play, particularly on 14 MHz and above. In this case lead lengths should be kept to a minimum.

PROJECT: UNUN TRANSFORMERS

Bifilar matching transformers lend themselves to unbalanced operation. That is, both input and output terminals can have a common ground connection. This eliminates the third magnetizing winding required in balanced to unbalanced (*voltage balun*) operation as shown below. These are *unun* transformers, which stands for unbalanced-to-unbalanced.

By adding third and fourth windings, as well as by tapping windings at appropriate points, various combinations of broadband matching can be obtained. **Figure 24.28** shows a 4:1 unbalanced to unbalanced configuration. Using #14 AWG wire it will easily handle 1000 W of power. By tapping at points ¼, ½, and ¾ of the way along the top winding, ratios of approximately 1.5:1, 2:1, and 3:1 can also be obtained. One of the wires should be covered with electrical tape in order to prevent voltage breakdown between the windings. This is necessary when a step-up ratio is used at high power to match antennas with impedances greater than 50 Ω.

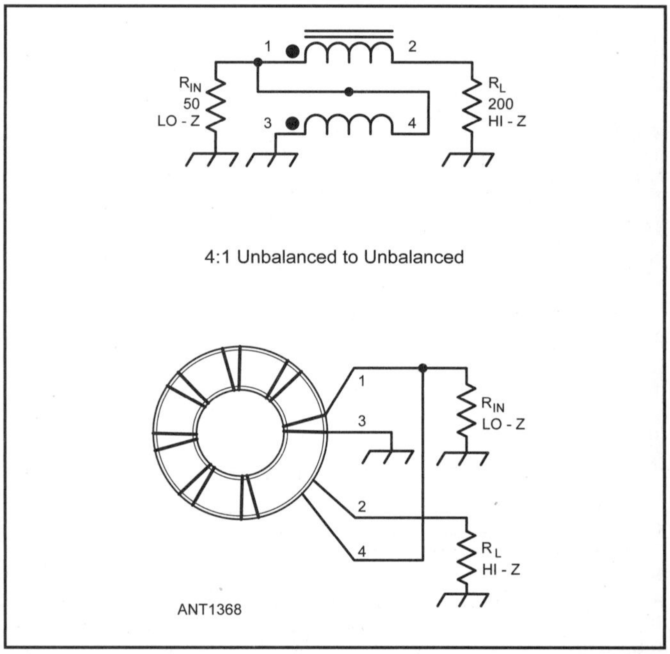

Figure 24.28 — Broadband bifilar transformer with a 4:1 impedance ratio. The upper winding can be tapped at appropriate points to obtain other ratios such as 1.5:1, 2:1, and 3:1.

Figure 24.29 shows a transformer with four windings, permitting wideband matching ratios as high as 16:1. **Figure 24.30** shows this transformer constructed with taps at 4:1, 6:1 (point b in Figure 24.30), 9:1, and 16:1. In tracing the current flow in the windings when using the 16:1 tap, one sees that the top three windings carry the same current. The bottom winding, in order to maintain the proper potentials, sustains a current three times greater. The bottom current cancels out

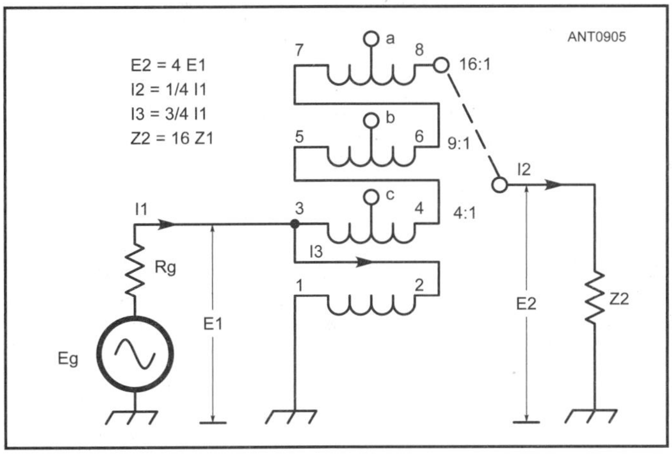

Figure 24.29 — Four-winding, broadband, variable impedance transformer. Connections a, b and c can be placed at appropriate points to yield various ratios from 1.5:1 to 16:1. See Figure 24.26 for an explanation of the wire numbering scheme.

Figure 24.30 — The 4-winding transformer of Figure 24.29 constructed for matching ratios of 4:1, 6:1, 9:1 and 16:1. The 16:1 ratio is the top coaxial connector and, from left to right, 6:1, 9:1 and 4:1 are the others. There are 10 quadrifilar turns of #14 AWG enameled wire on a type #61, 2.5-inch OD ferrite core. (see text for winding taps and numbers of turns on different core materials)

Figure 24.31 — A three-winding 9:1 wideband unun (unbalanced-to-unbalanced) transformer for 160 through 10 meters. Each winding consists of 4 turns of #14 or #16 AWG insulated wire. The core is a Laird 28B1540-000 (1.54-inch OD) or an equivalent size Fair-Rite #43 or #61 core may be substituted. The transformer is rated at 100 W. For higher power use a pair of 2.4-inch OD cores taped together in a stack.

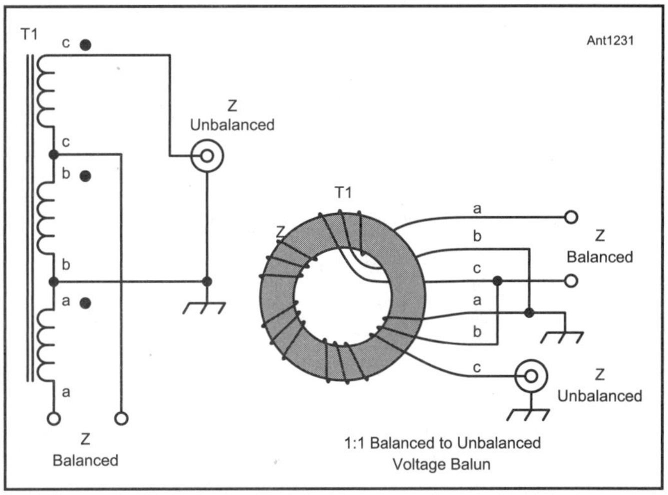

Figure 24.32 — Three-winding 1:1 voltage balun. These have largely been supplanted by the current or choke balun.

the core flux caused by the other three windings. If this transformer is used to match into low impedances, such as 3 to 4 Ω, the current in the bottom winding can be as high as 15 amperes. This value is based on the high side of the transformer being fed with 50-Ω cable handling a kilowatt of power. If one needs a 16:1 match like this at high power, then cascading two 4:1 transformers is recommended. In this case, the transformer at the lowest impedance side requires each winding to handle only 7.5 A. Thus, even #14 AWG wire would suffice in this application.

Figure 24.31 presents a similar 9:1 design if you are only interested in the single impedance ratio. The transformer is for use on 160 through 10 meters at the 100 W level. The complete construction article by Stan Johnson, WØSJ, is included in the online material. (See References and Bibliography) Higher power levels can be accommodated by using a pair of larger toroid cores in a stack.

PROJECT: 1:1 THREE-WINDING VOLTAGE BALUN

The voltage balun shown in **Figure 24.32** is a flux-linked impedance auto-transformer, similar to conventional power transformers. It causes equal and opposite voltages to appear at the two output terminals, relative to the voltage at the ground side of the input.

If the impedances of the two antenna halves are perfectly balanced with respect to ground, the currents flowing from the output terminals will be equal and opposite and no common-mode current will flow on the line. If the line is coaxial, there will be no current flowing on the outside of the shield; if the line is balanced, the currents in the two conductors will be equal and opposite. These are the conditions for a non-radiating line.

Under this condition, the 1:1 voltage balun of Figure 24.32 performs the same function as a current balun since there is no current in winding b. If the antenna isn't perfectly balanced, however, unequal currents will appear at the balun output, causing antenna current to flow on the line, an undesirable condition. Voltage baluns can be used as impedance transformers in this application if a 1:1 current or choke balun is added at the unbalanced input to prevent the common-mode current flow.

Another potential shortcoming of the 1:1 voltage balun is that winding b appears across the line. If this winding has insufficient impedance (a common problem, particularly near the lower frequency end of its range), the impedance transformation ratio will be degraded. In general, voltage baluns are not recommended in favor of a choke or 1:1 current balun. An impedance transformer can then be used on the balanced side of the current balun.

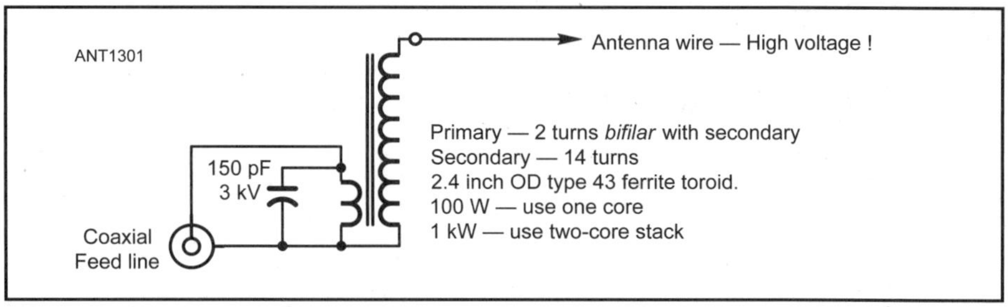

Figure 24.33 — A two-winding 49:1 impedance transformer popular for use with End-Fed Half-Wave (EFHW) antennas as described in the Multiband HF Antennas chapter.

PROJECT: 49:1 END-FED MATCHING TRANSFORMER

The transformer in **Figure 24.33** has a 7:1 turns ratio, resulting in a 49:1 impedance transformation ratio. It is a popular design for matching end-fed half-wave (EFHW) antennas to 50-Ω coax. Transformers with a 6:1 (36:1 impedance ratio) and 8:1 (64:1 impedance ratio) are also used. It is intended for use on 160 through 10 meters. See the **Multiband HF Antennas** chapter for a description of the EFHW antenna.

The two-turn primary wire is loosely twisted with the first two turns of the secondary for maximum coupling of the windings. The 150 pF capacitor compensates for leakage inductance of the windings and extends high-frequency performance through 10 meters. The capacitor should be rated at 3 kV or higher for full power operation. A type #43 core (2.4-inch OD, Fair-Rite 5943003801) is used for power levels up to 1 kW. For higher power, use two cores stacked together and held together with electrical tape. For 100 W, a smaller 1.5-inch OD Fair-Rite 5943002701 core can be used.

24.5 Matching Impedance at the Antenna

Since operating a transmission line at a low SWR requires that the line be terminated in a load matching the line's characteristic impedance, the problem can be approached from two standpoints:

(1) selecting a transmission line having a characteristic impedance that matches the antenna impedance at the point of connection, or

(2) transforming the antenna resistance to a value that matches the Z_0 of the line selected.

The first approach is simple and direct, but its application is obviously limited — the antenna impedance and the line impedance are alike only in a few special cases. Commercial transmission lines come in a limited variety of characteristic impedances while antenna feed point impedances vary over a wide range.

The second approach provides a good deal of freedom in that the antenna and line can be selected independently. The disadvantage of the second approach is that it is more complicated in terms of actually constructing the matching system at the antenna. Further, this approach sometimes calls for a tedious routine of measurement and adjustment before the desired match is achieved.

24.5.1 Antenna Impedance

IMPEDANCE CHANGE WITH FREQUENCY

Most antenna systems show a marked change in impedance when the frequency is changed greatly. For this reason, it is usually possible to match the line impedance only on one frequency. A matched antenna system is consequently a one-band affair, in most cases. It can, however, usually be operated over a fair frequency range within a given band.

The frequency range over which the SWR is low is determined by how rapidly the impedance changes as the frequency is changed. If the change in impedance is small for a given change in frequency, the SWR will be low over a fairly wide band of frequencies. However, if the impedance change is rapid (implying a sharply resonant or high-Q antenna), the SWR will also rise rapidly as the operating frequency is shifted away from antenna resonance, where the line is matched. See the discussion of Q in the **Dipoles and Monopoles** chapter in the section dealing with changes of impedance with frequency.

Material from previous editions in the chapter "Broadband Antenna Matching" by Frank Witt, AI1H, is included for reference with this book's online material. It presents and analyzes various techniques used to increase the bandwidth of antenna feed point impedance.

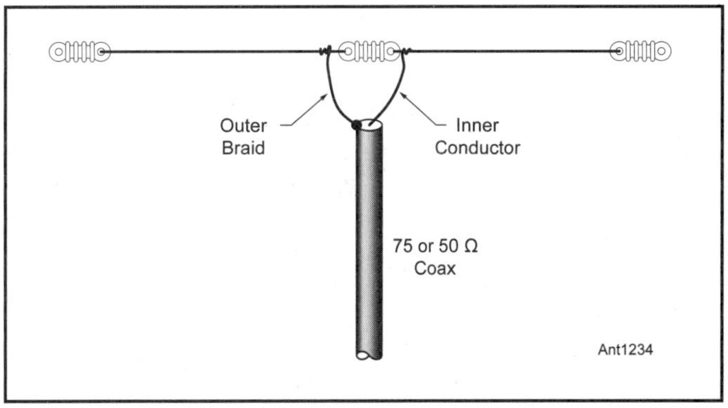

Figure 24.34 — A ½ λ antenna fed with 75-Ω coaxial cable. The outside of the shield of the line acts as a "third wire" connected to the dipole's left leg. A choke balun can be used to reduce current flowing on this conductor.

ANTENNA RESONANCE

In general, achieving a good match to a transmission line means that the antenna is resonant. (Some types of long-wire antennas, such as rhombics, are exceptions. Their input impedances are resistive over a wide band of frequencies, making such systems essentially nonresonant.) Antennas that are not resonant may also be matched to transmission lines, of course, but the additional cancellation of reactance complicates the task.

The higher the Q of an antenna system, the more essential it is that resonance be established before an attempt is made to match the line. This is particularly true of close-spaced parasitic arrays. With simple dipole antennas, the tuning is not so critical, and it is usually sufficient to cut the antenna to the length given by the appropriate equation. The frequency should be selected to be at the center of the range of frequencies (which may be the entire width of an amateur band) over which the antenna is to be used.

24.5.2 Connecting Directly to The Antenna

As discussed previously, the impedance at the center of a resonant λ/2 antenna at heights of the order of λ/4 and more is resistive and is in the neighborhood of 50 to 70 Ω. The dipole may be fed through 75-Ω coaxial cable such as RG-11, as shown in **Figure 24.34**. Cable having a characteristic impedance of 50 Ω, such as RG-213, may also be used. RG-213 may actually be preferable, because at the heights many amateurs install their antennas, the feed point impedance is closer to 50 Ω than it is to 75 Ω.

With a parallel-conductor feed line the system would be symmetrical but with coaxial line it is inherently unbalanced. Stated broadly, the unbalance with coaxial line is caused by the fact that the outside surface of the outer braid is not coupled to the antenna in the same way as the inner conductor and the inner surface of the outer braid. The overall result is that common-mode current will flow on the outside of the outer conductor in the simple arrangement shown in Figure 24.34. The unbalance is small if the line diameter is very small compared with the length of the antenna, a condition that is met fairly well at the lower amateur frequencies. It is not negligible in the VHF and UHF range, however, nor should it be ignored at 28 MHz. If the feed line is oriented asymmetrically with respect to the antenna so that it is closer to one side of the antenna than the other, higher common-mode currents will flow on the outside of the feed line. The system can be detuned for currents on the outside of the line by using a choke.

This system is designed for single-band operation, although it can be operated at *odd* multiples of the fundamental. For example, an antenna that is resonant near the low-frequency end of the 7-MHz band will operate with a relatively low SWR across the 21-MHz band.

At the fundamental frequency, the SWR should not exceed about 2:1 within a frequency range ±2% from the frequency of exact resonance. Such a variation corresponds approximately to the entire width of the 7-MHz band, if the antenna is resonant at the center of the band. A wire antenna is assumed. Antennas having a greater ratio of diameter to length will have a lower change in SWR with frequency.

DIRECT-FEED YAGIS

Direct-feed Yagis are designed to have a feed point impedance of 50- or 75-Ω so that a coaxial feed line can be connected directly to the antenna without additional impedance matching. These have become more common in recent years as antenna modeling has produced designs without the gain and pattern tradeoffs previously required for the higher feed point impedances required for direct-feed.

There is some question as to whether a choke balun is required for direct-feed antennas. The same questions of symmetry and radiation from common-mode current apply to direct-feed Yagis as to dipoles and other types of antennas. If re-radiation is an issue, a choke balun should be used. For commercial antennas, if the manufacturer specifies that a balun be used or makes no recommendation, use a choke balun at the feed point. If the manufacturer specifies that *no* balun be used, that is an indication that the feed line affects antenna performance in some way and the manufacturer's instructions for feed line placement and attachment should be followed exactly.

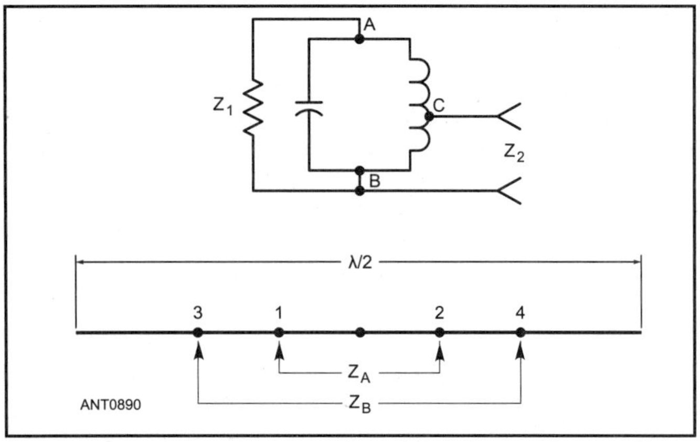

Figure 24.35 — Impedance transformation with a resonant circuit, together with antenna analogy.

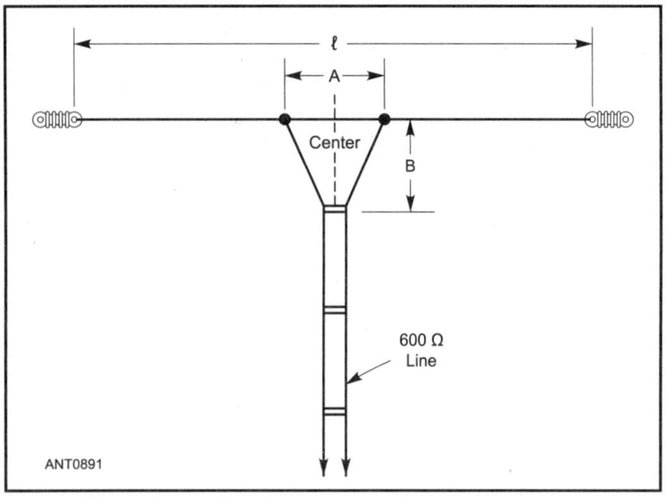

Figure 24.36 — The delta matching system.

24.5.3 The Delta Match

Among the properties of a coil and capacitor resonant circuit is that of transforming impedances. If a resistive impedance, Z_1 in **Figure 24.35**, is connected across the outer terminals AB of a resonant LC circuit, the impedance Z_2 as viewed looking into another pair of terminals such as BC will also be resistive but will have a different value depending on the mutual coupling between the parts of the coil associated with each pair of terminals. Z_2 will be less than Z_1 in the circuit shown. Of course, this relationship will be reversed if Z_1 is connected across terminals BC and Z_2 is viewed from terminals AB.

As stated in the **Antenna Fundamentals** chapter, a resonant antenna has properties similar to those of a tuned circuit. The impedance presented between any two points symmetrically placed with respect to the center of a λ/2 antenna will depend on the distance between the points. The greater the separation, the higher the value of impedance, up to the limiting value that exists between the open ends of the antenna. This is also suggested in Figure 24.31, in the lower drawing. The impedance Z_A between terminals 1 and 2 is lower than the impedance Z_B between terminals 3 and 4. Both impedances, however, are purely resistive if the antenna is resonant.

This principle is used in the *delta matching system* shown in **Figure 24.36**. The center impedance of a λ/2 dipole is too low to be matched directly by any practical type of air-insulated parallel-conductor line. However, it is possible to find, between two points, a value of impedance that can be matched to such a line when a "fanned" section or delta is used to couple the line and antenna. The antenna length ℓ is that required for resonance. The ends of the delta or "Y" should be attached at points equidistant from the center of the antenna. When so connected, the terminating impedance for the line will be resistive. Obviously, this technique is useful only when the Z_0 of the chosen transmission line is higher than the feed point impedance of the antenna.

Based on experimental data for the case of a typical λ/2 antenna coupled to a 600-Ω line, the total distance, A, between the ends of the delta should be 0.120 λ for frequencies below 30 MHz, and 0.115 λ for frequencies above 30 MHz. The length of the delta, distance B, should be 0.150 λ. These values are based on a wavelength in air, and on the assumption that the center impedance of the antenna is approximately 70 Ω. The dimensions will require modifications if the actual impedance is very much different.

The delta match can be used for matching the driven element of a directive array to a transmission line, but if the impedance of the element is low — as is frequently the case — the proper dimensions for A and B must be found by experimentation.

The delta match is somewhat awkward to adjust when the proper dimensions are unknown, because both the length and width of the delta must be varied. An additional disadvantage is that there is always some radiation from the delta. This is because the conductor spacing does not meet the requirement for negligible radiation: The spacing should be very small in comparison with the wavelength.

24.5.4 Folded Dipoles

Basic information on the folded dipole antenna appears in chapter **Dipoles and Monopoles**. The input impedance of a two-wire folded dipole is so close to 300 Ω that it can be fed directly with 300-Ω twinlead or with open-wire line without any other matching arrangement, and the line will operate with a low SWR. The antenna itself can be built like an open-wire line; that is, the two conductors can be held apart by regular feeder spreaders. TV ladder line is quite suitable at low power. It is also possible to use 300-Ω line for the antenna, in addition to using it for the transmission line.

Since the antenna section does not operate as a transmission line, but simply as two wires in parallel, the velocity factor of twinlead can be ignored in computing the antenna length. The reactance of the folded-dipole antenna varies less rapidly with frequency changes away from resonance than a single-wire antenna. Therefore, it is possible to operate over a wider range of frequencies, while maintaining a low SWR on the line, than with a simple dipole. This is partly explained by the fact that the two conductors in parallel form a single conductor of greater effective diameter.

A folded dipole will not accept power at twice the fundamental frequency. However, the current distribution is correct for harmonic operation on odd multiples of the fundamental. Because the feed point resistance is not greatly different for a 3λ/2 antenna and one that is λ/2, a folded dipole can be operated on its third harmonic with a low SWR in a 300-Ω line. A 7-MHz folded dipole, consequently, can be used for the 21-MHz band as well.

Folded dipoles are sometimes used as the driven element of Yagi antennas at VHF and UHF. The low feed point impedance of a Yagi, often less than 20 Ω, when multiplied by four presents a good match to 75-Ω coaxial cable.

24.5.5 The T Match

The current flowing at the input terminals of the T match consists of the normal antenna current divided between the radiator and the T conductors in a way that depends on their relative diameters and the spacing between them, with a superimposed transmission line current flowing in each half of the T and its associated section of the antenna. See **Figure 24.37**. Each such T conductor and the associated antenna conductor can be looked upon as a section of transmission line shorted at the end. Because it is shorter than λ/4 it has inductive reactance. As a consequence, if the antenna itself is exactly resonant at the operating frequency, the input impedance of the T will show inductive reactance as well as resistance. The reactance must be tuned out if a good match to the transmission line is to be obtained. This can be done either by shortening the antenna to obtain a value of capacitive reactance that will reflect through the matching system to cancel the inductive reactance at the input terminals, or by inserting a capacitance of the proper value in series at the input terminals as shown in **Figure 24.38A**.

Analysis shows that the part of the impedance step-up arising from the spacing and ratio of conductor diameters is approximately the same as given for a folded dipole. The actual impedance ratio is, however, considerably modified by the length A of the matching section (Figure 24.37). The trends can be stated as follows:

1) The input impedance increases as the distance A is made larger, but not indefinitely. In general, there is a distance A that will give a maximum value of input impedance, after which further increase in A will cause the impedance to decrease.

2) The distance A at which the input impedance reaches a maximum is smaller as d2/d1 is made larger and becomes smaller as the spacing between the conductors is increased. (d1 is the diameter of the lower T conductor in Figure 24.37 and d2 is the diameter of the antenna.)

3) The maximum impedance values occur in the region where A is 40% to 60% of the antenna length in the average case.

4) Higher values of input impedance can be realized when the antenna is shortened to cancel the inductive reactance of the matching section.

The T match has become popular for transforming the balanced feed point impedance of a VHF or UHF Yagi up to 200 Ω. From that impedance a 4:1 balun is used to transform down to the unbalanced 50 Ω level for the coax cable feeding the Yagi. See the various K1FO-designed Yagis referred to in the **VHF, UHF, and Microwave Antennas** chapter and the section later in this chapter concerning transmission-line baluns. This technique is being replaced by designs such as the OWA and LFA which have a 50-Ω feed point impedance suitable for direct connection to coaxial feed lines.

The structure of the T-match also affects the length of the driven element by increasing the element's electrical diameter. A typical T-match is approximately 5 to 10 times greater in diameter than the element alone. This results in the need to

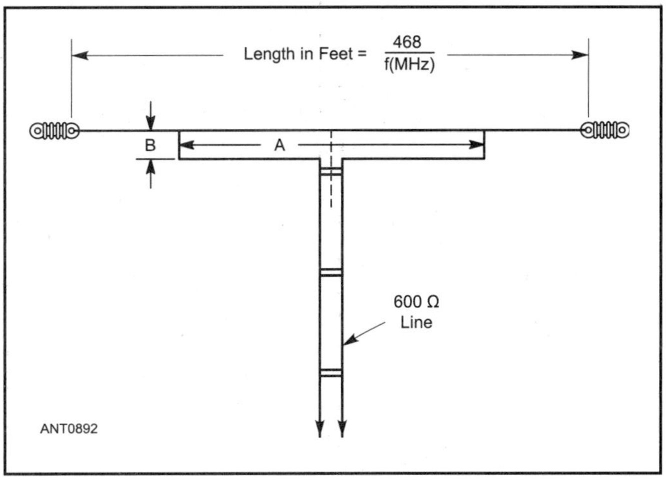

Figure 24.37 — The T matching system, applied to a ½ λ antenna and 600-Ω line.

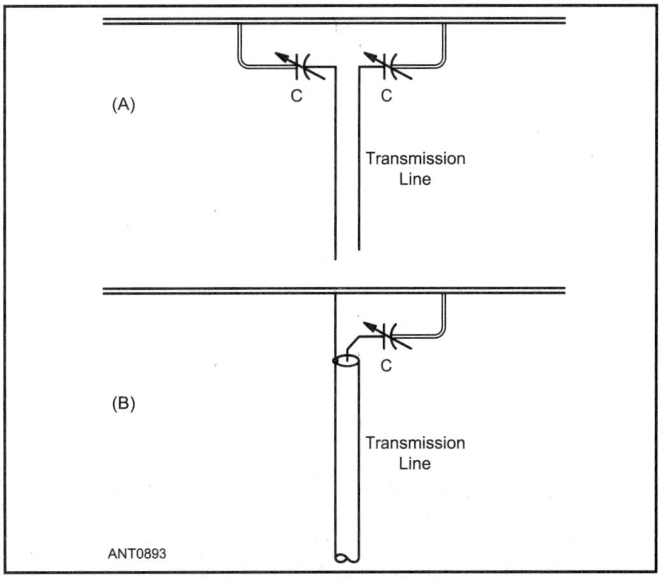

Figure 24.38 — Series capacitors for tuning out residual reactance with the T and gamma matching systems. A maximum capacitance of 150 pF in each capacitor should provide sufficient adjustment range, in the average case, for 14-MHz operation. Proportionately smaller capacitance values can be used on higher frequency bands. Receiving-type plate spacing will be satisfactory for power levels up to a few hundred watts.

extend the length of the driven element by 2-3% to return it to resonance.

24.5.6 The Gamma Match and Shunt Feed

The gamma-match arrangement shown in Figure 24.38B is an unbalanced version of the T, suitable for use directly with coaxial lines. Except for the matching section being connected between the center and one side of the antenna, the remarks above about the behavior of the T apply equally well. The inherent reactance of the matching section can be canceled either by shortening the antenna appropriately or by using the resonant length and installing a capacitor C, as shown in Figure 24.38B.

For years, the gamma match has been widely used for matching coaxial cable to all-metal parasitic beams. Because it is well suited to construction, in which all the metal parts are electrically and mechanically connected, it is quite popular for amateur arrays.

The gamma match technique can also be used to feed grounded towers at MF and HF, referred to as *shunt-feeding*. The "missing" half of the element is replaced by a tower ground system of radials, which is critical to good performance. To use the gamma match design process, it is also important to have an approximate idea of the tower's base impedance. This can usually be estimated by computer modeling. (See the **General Purpose MF and HF Antennas** chapter.)

Because of the many variable factors — driven-element length, gamma rod length, rod diameter, spacing between rod and driven element, and value of series capacitors — a number of combinations will provide the desired match. The task of finding a proper combination can be a tedious one, as the settings are interrelated. A few rules of thumb have evolved that provide a starting point for the various factors. For matching a multielement array made of aluminum tubing to 50-Ω line, the length of the rod should be 0.04 to 0.05 λ, its diameter 1/3 to 1/2 that of the driven element, and its spacing (center-to-center from the driven element), approximately 0.007 λ. The capacitance value should be approximately 7 pF per meter of wavelength. This translates to about 140 pF for 20-meter operation. The exact gamma dimensions and value for the capacitor will depend on the radiation resistance of the driven element, and whether it is resonant. These starting-point dimensions are for an array having a feed point impedance of about 25 Ω, with the driven element shortened approximately 3% from resonance.

CALCULATING GAMMA DIMENSIONS

A starting point for the gamma dimensions and capacitance value may be determined by calculation. H. F. Tolles, W7ITB, has developed a method for determining a set of parameters that will be quite close to providing the desired impedance transformation (see References and Bibliography). The impedance of the antenna must be measured or computed for Tolles's procedure. If the antenna impedance is not accurately known, modeling calculations provide a very good starting point for initial settings of the gamma match.

The math involved in Tolles's procedure is tedious, especially if several iterations are needed to find a practical set of dimensions. The process of calculating the necessary gamma match dimensions and values has been implemented in software by Bill Wortman, N6MW, as *GAMMAMW*. Version 9 is the current version as of early 2023 and is available along with material about gamma matching on his website at **n6mw.jimdofree.com/antenna-matching**. The calculations used for the various versions of *GAMMAMW* are discussed in N6MW's document Gamma Matching Discussion (N6MW-Gamma4.pdf). *GAMMAMW9* is an Excel spreadsheet that takes the same inputs as earlier versions of the program.

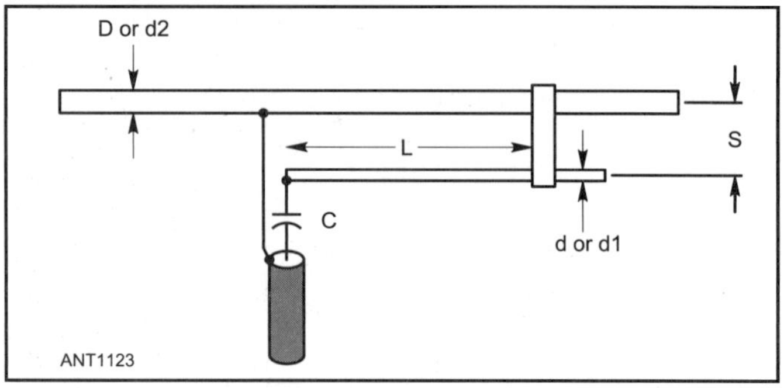

Figure 24.39 — The gamma match, as used with tubing elements. Parameters are those used for the *GAMMAMW4* dimension calculation software. Note that S is a center-to-center value, not surface-to-surface. The transmission line may be either 50-Ω or 75-Ω coax.

Typical inputs to *GAMMAMW* are illustrated in **Figure 24.39**:

Z_a — the complex impedance of the unmatched antenna ($Z_a = R_a + j\,X_a$, normally measured with dipole halves split)

S — center-to-center spacing of the circular antenna element to the circular gamma rod

D — diameter of the circular antenna element

d — diameter of the circular gamma rod

Note that S is a center-to-center dimension, not a surface-to-surface value. The following is a *GAMMAMW* dialog for a 14 MHz antenna with a feed point impedance of 20 + *j*0 Ω, element diameter of 1.5 inches, with a gamma tube diameter of 0.375 inches spaced 2 inches (center to center) from the element. Additional intermediate calculation values are also output but not shown in these examples. (The older version of software is used here because it illustrates the design process more clearly than the spreadsheet version. The results of the calculation are identical.)

```
Gamma Match Design
 N6MW, October 2012

Freq (MHz)? 14

Now input the unmatched antenna impedance
R +jX

Antenna feed point resistance R (ohms)? 20
Antenna feed point reactance X (ohms)? 0
Feed line impedance (ohms)? 50
```

```
Gamma Match Quantities to be input:
 D = Driven element diameter
 d = Gamma rod diameter
 S = Gamma rod spacing (center-to-center)
 The units, such inches or cm, do not matter
but all 3 must be the same
 Gamma rod spacing, S, must be greater than
(D/2 + d/2)

Driven element diameter, D? 1.5
Gamma element diameter, d? 0.375
Gamma rod spacing ( > 0.9) S? 2

Gamma length (deg) 31.81
Gamma length (feet) 6.21
Gamma length (inches) 74.49
Gamma length (cm) 189.19
Gamma capacitor (pF) 125.04
```

GAMMAMW9 also calculates a value, SU, the impedance step-up ratio or "Z ratio" for folded dipoles sometimes used in designing a shunt feed system.

SHUNT-FEED DIMENSIONS

As another example, say we wish to shunt feed a tower at 3.5 MHz with 50-Ω line. The driven element (tower) is 12 inches in diameter, and #12 AWG wire (diameter = 0.0808 inch) with a spacing of 12 inches from the tower is to be used for the "gamma rod." The tower is 50 feet tall with a 5-foot mast and beam antenna at the top. The total height, 55 feet, is approximately 0.19 λ. We assume its electrical length is 0.2 λ or 72°. Modeling shows that the approximate base feed point impedance is $20 - j\,100$ Ω. The computation by *GAMMAMW* says that the gamma rod should be 57.1 feet long, with a gamma capacitor of 32.1 pF.

```
Gamma Match Design
 N6MW, October 2012

Freq (MHz)? 3.5

Now input the unmatched antenna impedance
R +jX

Antenna feed point resistance R (ohms)? 20
Antenna feed point reactance X (ohms)? -100
Feed line impedance (ohms)? 50

 Gamma Match Quantities to be input:
 D = Driven element diameter
 d = Gamma rod diameter
 S = Gamma rod spacing (center-to-center)
 The units, such inches or cm, do not matter
but all 3 must be the same
 Gamma rod spacing, S, must be greater than
(D/2 + d/2)

Driven element diameter, D? 12
Gamma element diameter, d? .0808
Gamma rod spacing ( > 6.0) S? 12

Gamma length (deg) 73.14
Gamma length (feet) 57.10
Gamma length (inches) 685.16
Gamma length (cm) 1740.30
Gamma capacitor (pF) 32.07
```

Immediately we see this set of gamma dimensions is impractical—the rod length (685 inches or 57.1 feet) is greater than the tower height. So, we make another set of calculations, using a spacing of 24 inches between the rod and tower. The results this time are that the gamma rod is 44.2 feet long, with a capacitor of 51 pF. This gives us a practical set of starting dimensions for the shunt-feed arrangement.

The preferred method of building a gamma match is illustrated in **Figure 24.40**. The feed line is connected directly to the center element. This is usually done using a clamp or strap from an RF connector but depends on the physical size of the antenna. The gamma capacitor is created from an insulated wire inside the tube that forms the gamma rod. For ½ inch OD

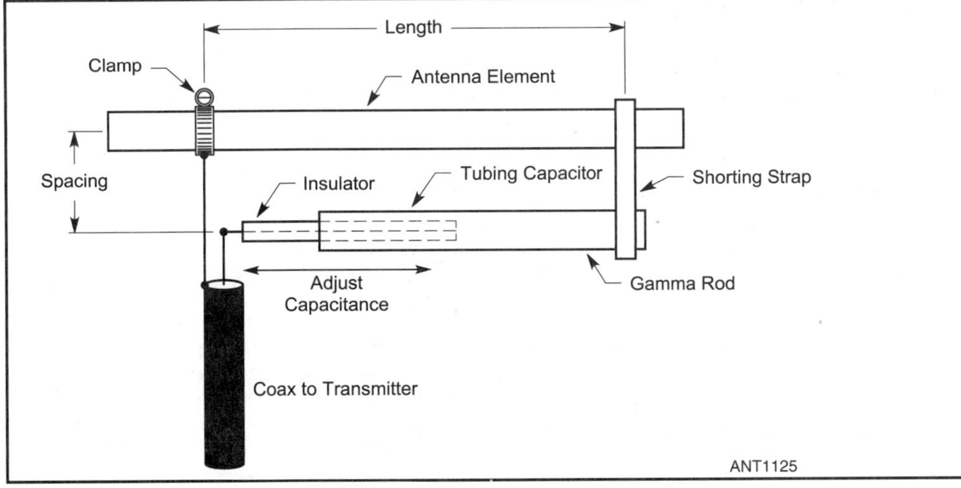

Figure 24.40 — Typical gamma match construction for HF and VHF Yagis.

aluminum tube and the center conductor and insulation from RG-213, the capacitance is approximately 25 pF/ft of wire inserted into the tube. Do not use the center conductor and insulation from foam-dielectric coax as it will absorb water. Seal the end of the wire inserted into the tube to reduce the tendency to arc when wet or if insects or debris are present. After a satisfactory match has been obtained by adjusting the gamma capacitor as described below, the variable capacitor may be replaced with an equivalent length of wire in the gamma rod.

ADJUSTMENT

After installation of the antenna, the proper constants for the T and gamma generally must be determined experimentally. The use of the variable series capacitors, as shown in Figure 24.38, is recommended for ease of adjustment. With a trial position of the tap or taps on the antenna, measure the SWR on the transmission line and adjust C (both capacitors simultaneously in the case of the T) for minimum SWR. If it is not close to 1:1, try another tap position and repeat. It may be necessary to try another size of conductor for the matching section if satisfactory results cannot be brought about. Changing the spacing will show which direction to go in this respect.

24.5.7 The Omega Match

The omega match is a slightly modified form of the gamma match. In addition to the series capacitor, a shunt capacitor is used to aid in canceling a portion of the inductive reactance introduced by the gamma section. This is shown in **Figure 24.41**. C1 is the usual series capacitor. The addition of C2 makes it possible to use a shorter gamma rod or makes it easier to obtain the desired match when the driven element is resonant. During adjustment, C2 will serve primarily to determine the resistive component of the load as seen by the coax line, and C1 serves to cancel any reactance.

24.5.8 The Hairpin and Beta Matches

The usual form of the *hairpin match* is shown in **Figure 24.42**. Basically, the hairpin is a form of an L-matching network in which the feed point's capacitive reactance forms the shunt capacitor. Because it is somewhat easier to adjust for the desired terminating impedance than the gamma match, it is preferred by many amateurs. Its disadvantages, compared with the gamma, are that it must be fed with a parallel-conductor line (a balun may be used with a coax feed line, as shown in Figure 24.42), and the driven element must be split at the center and insulated from the boom. This latter requirement complicates the mechanical mounting arrangement for the element, since the driven element cannot be mounted directly on the boom.

As indicated in Figure 24.42, the center point of the hairpin is electrically neutral. As such, it may be grounded or connected to the remainder of the antenna structure, restoring dc

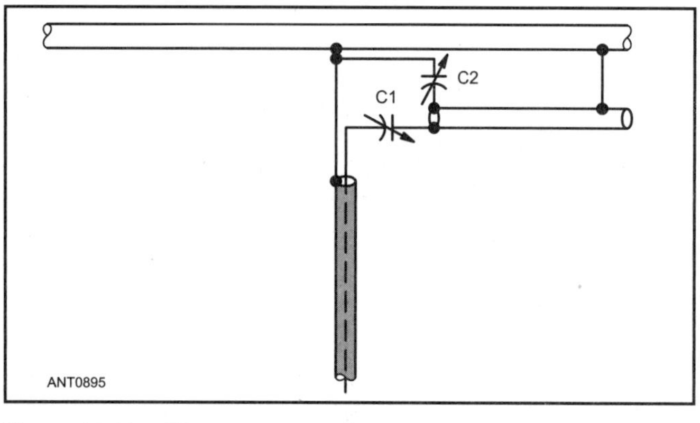

Figure 24.41 — The omega match.

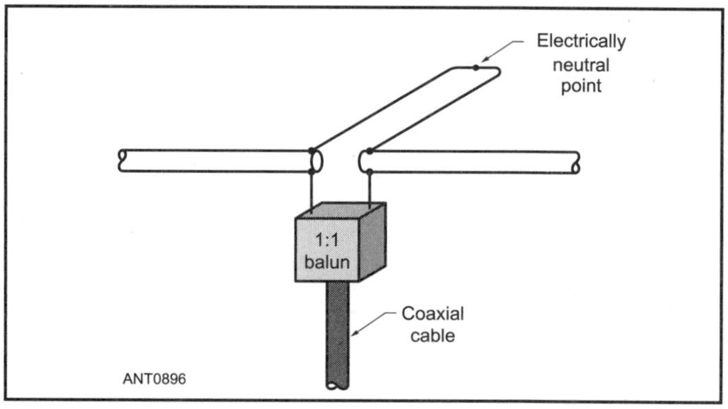

Figure 24.42 — The hairpin match.

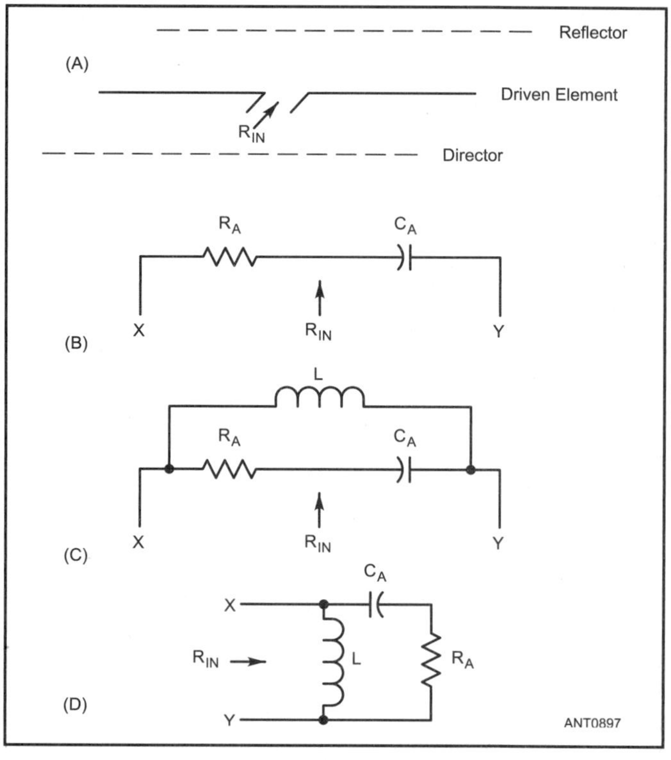

Figure 24.43 — For the Yagi antenna shown at A, the driven element is shorter than its resonant length with a capacitive feed point impedance as represented at B. By adding an inductor, as shown at C, the low value of R_A is made to appear as a higher impedance at terminals XY. At D, the diagram of C is redrawn in the usual L-network configuration.

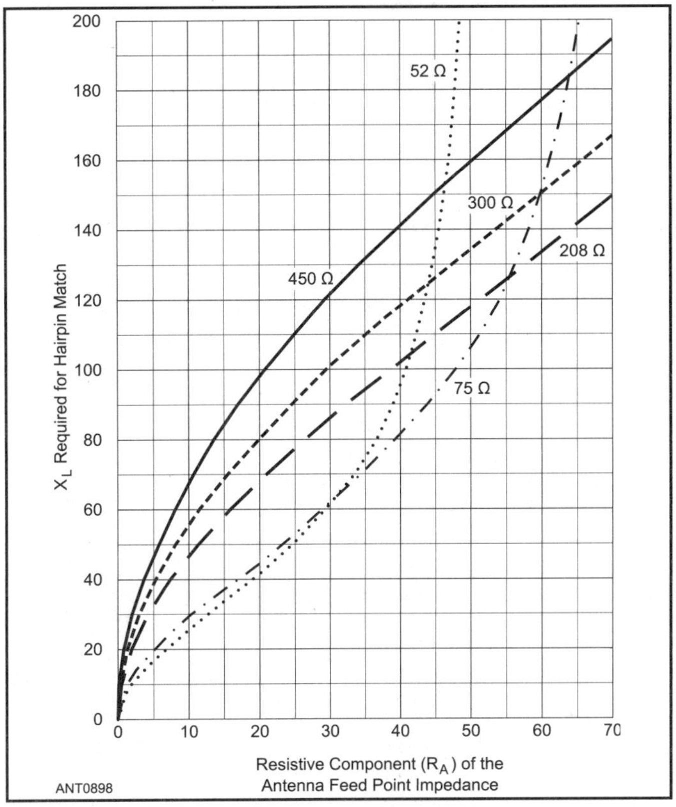

Figure 24.44 — Reactance required for a hairpin to match various antenna resistances to common line or balun impedance. The driven element's feed point impedance must exhibit a specific amount of capacitive reactance as shown in the text.

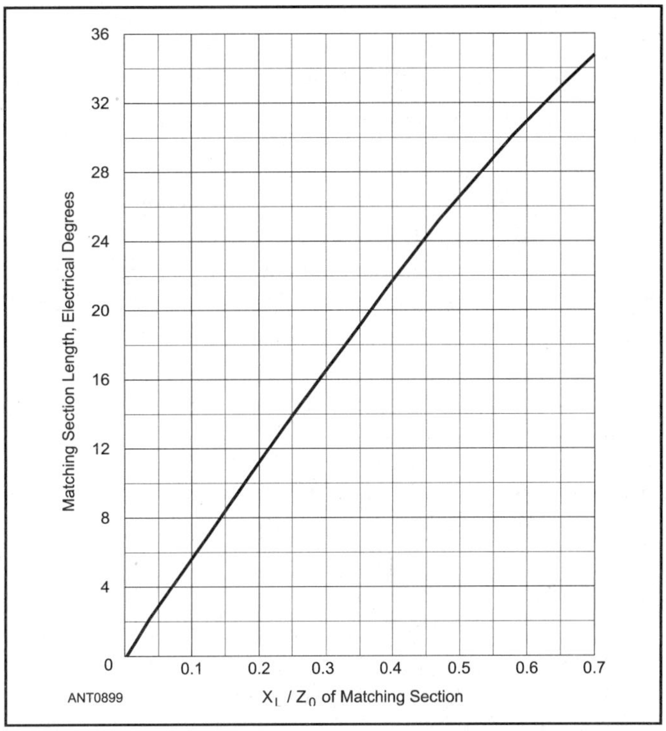

Figure 24.45 — Inductive reactance (normalized to Z_0 of matching section), scale at bottom, versus required hairpin matching section length, scale at left. To determine the length in wavelengths divide the number of electrical degrees by 360. For open-wire line, a velocity factor of 97.5% should be taken into account when determining the electrical length.

ground to the feed line and driven element. The hairpin itself is usually secured by attaching this neutral point to the boom of the antenna array. The Hy-Gain *beta match* is electrically identical to the hairpin match, the difference being in the mechanical construction of the matching section. With the beta match, the conductors of the matching section straddle the Yagi's boom, one conductor being located on either side, and the electrically neutral point consists of a sliding or adjustable shorting clamp placed around the boom and the two matching-section conductors.

The capacitive portion of the L-network circuit is produced by slightly shortening the antenna driven element, shown in **Figure 24.43A**. For a given frequency the impedance of a shortened λ/2 element appears as the antenna resistance and a capacitance in series, as indicated schematically in Figure 24.39B. The inductive portion of the resonant circuit at C is a hairpin of heavy wire or small tubing that is connected across the driven-element center terminals. The diagram of C is redrawn in D to show the circuit in conventional L-network form. R_A, the resistive component of the feed point impedance, must be a smaller value than R_{IN}, the impedance of the feed line, usually 50 Ω.

If the approximate value of R_A for the antenna system is known, **Figures 24.44** and **24.45** may be used to gain an idea of the hairpin dimensions necessary for the desired match. The required value of X_A, the feed point impedance's capacitive reactance component is

$$X_A = -\sqrt{R_A(R_{IN} - R_A)} \tag{23}$$

The curves of Figure 24.44 were obtained from design equations for L-network matching presented earlier in this chapter. Figure 24.45 is based on the equation, $X_L/Z_0 = j \tan \theta$, which gives the inductive reactance as normalized to the characteristic impedance, Z_0, of the hairpin, looking at it as a length of transmission line terminated in a short circuit. For example, if an antenna-system impedance with a resistive component of 20 Ω is to be matched to 50-Ω line, Figure 24.44 shows that the inductive reactance required for the hairpin is +41 Ω. If the hairpin is constructed of 1/4 inch tubing spaced 1½ inches, its characteristic impedance is 300 Ω (from equations in the **Transmission Lines** chapter). Normalizing the required 41-Ω reactance to this impedance, 41/300 = 0.137.

By entering the graph of Figure 24.45 with this value, 0.137, on the scale at the bottom, you can see that the hairpin length should be 7.8 electrical degrees, or 7.8/360 λ. For purposes of these calculations, taking a 97.5% velocity factor into account, the wavelength in inches is 11,508/f (MHz). If the antenna is to be used on 14 MHz, the required hairpin length is 7.8/360 × 11,508/14.0 = 17.8 inches. The length of the hairpin affects primarily the resistive component of the terminating impedance, as seen by the feed line. Greater resistances are obtained with longer hairpin sections — meaning a larger value of shunt inductor — and smaller resistances with shorter sections.

The remaining reactance at the feed point terminals is tuned out by adjusting the length of the driven element, as necessary. If a fixed-length hairpin section is in use, a small range of adjustment may be made in the effective value of the inductance by spreading or squeezing together the conductors of the hairpin. Spreading the conductors apart will have the same effect as lengthening the hairpin, while placing them closer together will effectively shorten it.

Instead of using a hairpin of stiff wire or tubing, this same matching technique may be used with a lumped-constant inductor connected across the antenna terminals. Such a method of matching has been dubbed, tongue firmly in cheek, as the "helical hairpin." The inductor, of course, must exhibit the same reactance at the operating frequency as the hairpin it replaces. A cursory examination with computer calculations indicates that a helical hairpin may offer a very slightly improved SWR bandwidth over a true hairpin.

24.5.9 Matching Stubs

As explained in the **Transmission Lines** chapter, a mismatch-terminated transmission line less than λ/4 long has an input impedance that is both resistive and reactive. The equivalent circuit of the line input impedance at any one frequency can be formed either of resistance and reactance in series, or resistance and reactance in parallel. Depending on the line length, the series resistance component, R_S, can have any value between the terminating resistance Z_R (when the line has zero length) and Z_0^2/Z_R (when the line is exactly λ/4 long).The same thing is true of R_P, the parallel-resistance component.

R_S and R_P do not have the same values at the same line length, however, other than at zero and λ/4. With either equivalent there is some line length that will give a value of R_S or R_P equal to the characteristic impedance of the line. However, there will be reactance along with the resistance. But if provision is made for canceling or tuning out this reactive part of the input impedance, only the resistance will remain. Since this resistance is equal to the Z_0 of the transmission line, the section from the reactance-cancellation point back to the generator will be properly matched.

Tuning out the reactance in the equivalent series circuit requires that a reactance of the same value as X_S (but of opposite kind) be inserted in series with the line. Tuning out the reactance in the equivalent parallel circuit requires that a reactance of the same value as X_P (but of opposite kind) be connected across the line. In practice it is more convenient to use the parallel-equivalent circuit. The transmission line is simply connected to the load (which of course is usually a resonant antenna) and then a reactance of the proper value is connected across the line at the proper distance from the load. From this point back to the transmitter there are no standing waves on the line.

A convenient type of reactance to use is a section of transmission line less than λ/4 long, terminated with either an open circuit or a short circuit, depending on whether capacitive reactance or inductive reactance is called for. Reactances formed from sections of transmission line are called *matching stubs* and are designated as *open* or *closed* depending on whether the free end is open or short circuited. The two types of matching stubs are shown in the sketches in **Figure 24.46**.

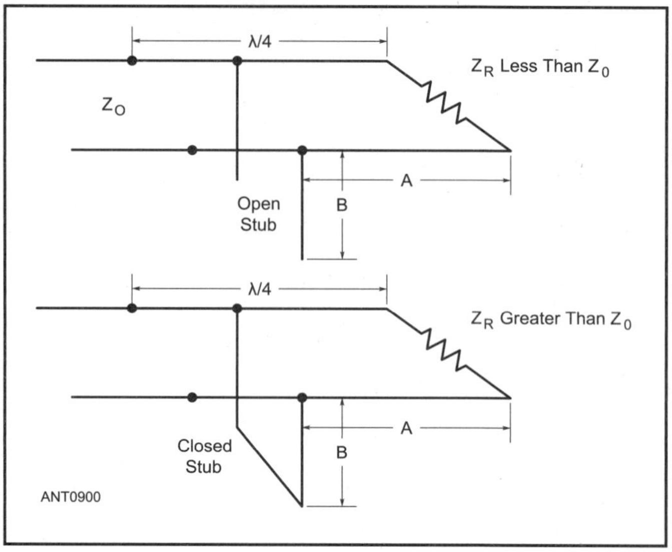

Figure 24.46 — Use of open or closed stubs for canceling the parallel reactive component of input impedance.

The distance from the load to the stub (dimension A in Figure 24.46) and the length of the stub, B, depend on the characteristic impedances of the line and stub and on the ratio of Z_R to Z_0. Since the ratio of Z_R to Z_0 is also the standing-wave ratio in the absence of matching (and with a resonant antenna), the dimensions are a function of the SWR. If the line and stub have the same Z_0, dimensions A and B are dependent on the SWR only. Consequently, if the SWR can

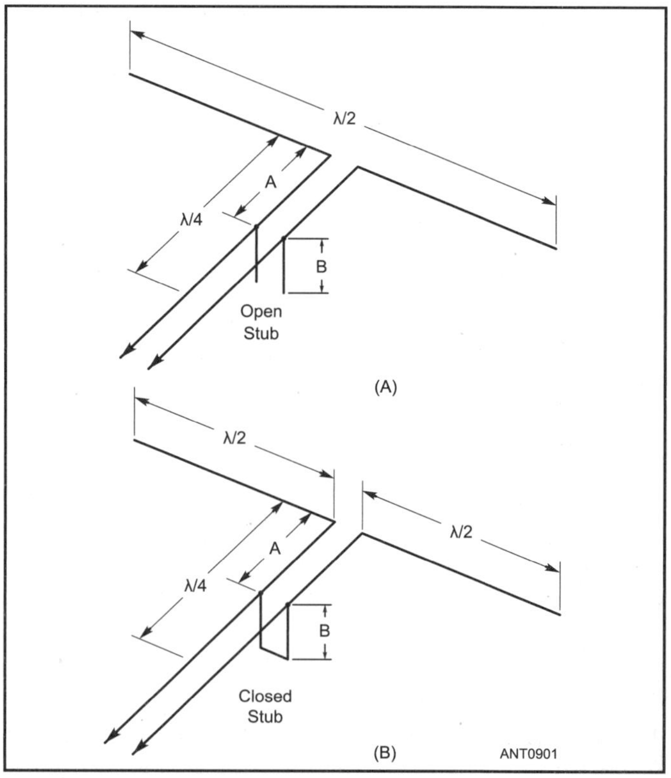

Figure 24.47 — Application of matching stubs to common types of antennas.

be measured before the stub is installed, the stub can be properly located, and its length determined even though the actual value of load impedance is not known.

Typical applications of matching stubs are shown in **Figure 24.47**, where open-wire line is being used. From inspection of these drawings, it will be recognized that when an antenna is fed at a current loop, as in Figure 24.47A, Z_R is less than Z_0 (in the average case) and therefore an open stub is called for, installed within the first $\lambda/4$ of line measured from the antenna. Voltage feed, as at B, corresponds to Z_R greater than Z_0 and therefore requires a closed stub.

A Smith chart may be used to determine the length of the stub and its distance from the load as described on the supplement included with this book's online material or the ARRL program *TLW* (also included) may be used. If the load is a pure resistance and the characteristic impedances of the line and stub are identical, the lengths may be determined by equations. For the closed stub when Z_R is greater than Z_0, they are

$$A = \arctan \sqrt{SWR} \qquad (24)$$

$$B = \arctan \frac{\sqrt{SWR}}{SWR - 1} \qquad (25)$$

For the open stub when Z_R is less than Z_0

$$A = \arctan \frac{1}{\sqrt{SWR}} \qquad (26)$$

$$B = \arctan \frac{SWR - 1}{\sqrt{SWR}} \qquad (27)$$

In these equations the lengths A and B are the distance from the stub to the load and the length of the stub, respectively, as shown in Figure 24.47. These lengths are expressed in electrical degrees, equal to 360 times the lengths in wavelengths.

In using the above equations, it must be remembered that the wavelength along the line is not the same as in free space. If an open-wire line is used the velocity factor of 0.975 will apply. When solid-dielectric line is used, the free-space wavelength as determined above must be multiplied by the appropriate velocity factor to obtain the actual lengths of A and B (see the **Transmission Lines** chapter.)

Although the equations above do not apply when the characteristic impedances of the line and stub are not the same, this does not mean that the line cannot be matched under such conditions. The stub can have any desired characteristic impedance if its length is chosen so that it has the proper value of reactance. Correct lengths can be determined using *TLW* or the Smith Chart for dissimilar types of line.

In using matching stubs, it should be noted that the length and location of the stub should be based on the SWR at the load. If the line is long and has fairly high losses, measuring the SWR at the input end will not give the true value at the load. This point is discussed in the section on attenuation in the **Transmission Lines** chapter.

In the experimental adjustment of any type of matched line it is necessary to measure the SWR with fair accuracy in order to tell when the adjustments are being made in the proper direction. In the case of matching stubs, experience has shown that experimental adjustment is unnecessary, from a practical standpoint, if the SWR is first measured with the stub not connected to the transmission line, and the stub is then installed according to the design data.

REACTIVE LOADS

In this discussion of matching stubs, it has been assumed that the load is a pure resistance. This is the most desirable condition, since the antenna that represents the load preferably should be tuned to resonance before any attempt is made to match the line. Nevertheless, matching stubs can be used even when the load is considerably reactive. A reactive load simply means that the loops and nodes of the standing waves of voltage and current along the line do not occur at integral multiples of $\lambda/4$ from the load. If the reactance at the load is known, the Smith chart or *TLW* may be used to determine the correct dimensions for a stub match.

STUBS ON COAXIAL LINES

The principles outlined in the preceding section apply also to coaxial lines. The coaxial cases corresponding to the open-wire cases shown in Figure 24.47 are given in **Figure 24.48**. The equations given earlier may be used to determine dimensions A and B. In a practical installation the junction of the transmission line and stub would be a T connector.

A special case is the use of a coaxial matching stub, in which the stub is associated with the transmission line in such a way as to form a balun. This is described in detail later on in this chapter. The antenna is shortened to introduce just enough reactance at its feed point to permit the matching stub to be connected there, rather than at some other point along

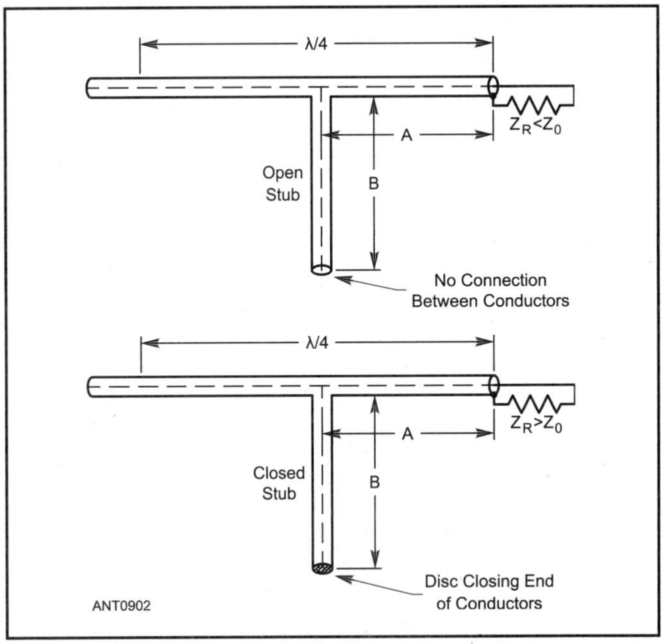

Figure 24.48 — Open and closed stubs on coaxial lines.

the transmission line as in the general cases discussed here. To use this method the antenna resistance must be lower than the Z_0 of the main transmission line, since the resistance is transformed to a higher value. In beam antennas such as Yagis, this will nearly always be the case.

MATCHING SECTIONS

If the two antenna systems in Figure 24.44 are redrawn in somewhat different fashion, as shown in **Figure 24.49**, a system results that differs in no consequential way from the matching stubs described previously, but in which the stub formed by A and B together is called a *quarter-wave matching section.* The justification for this is that a λ/4 section of line is similar to a resonant circuit, as described earlier in this chapter. It is therefore possible to use the λ/4 section to transform impedances by tapping at the appropriate point along the line.

Earlier equations give design data for matching sections, A being the distance from the antenna to the point at which the line is connected, and A + B being the total length of the matching section. The equations apply only in the case where the characteristic impedance of the matching section and transmission line are the same. Equations are available for the case where the matching section has a different Z_0 than the line but

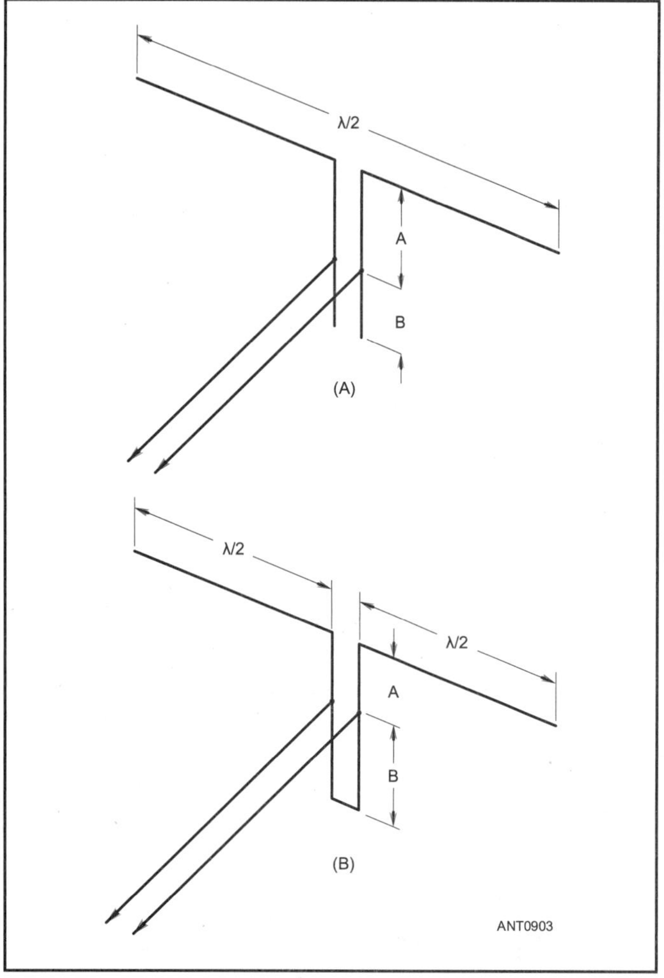

Figure 24.49 — Application of matching sections to common antenna types.

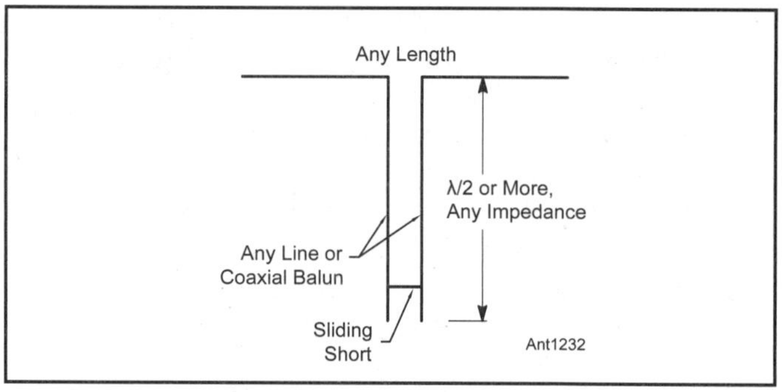

Figure 24.50 —The Universal Stub. An adjustable short on the stub and the points of connection of the transmission line are adjusted for minimum reflected power on the line.

are somewhat complicated. A graphic solution for different line impedances may be obtained with the Smith chart (see the supplement included with this book's online material).

UNIVERSAL STUB

If the stub attached to the antenna is λ/2 long as in **Figure 24.50**, the combination of feed line attachment point and stub are called a *universal stub.* As its name implies, the double-adjustments are useful for many matching purposes. It is most commonly used at VHF and UHF as described in the **VHF, UHF, and Microwave Antenna Systems** chapter.

The stub length is varied to resonate the system by moving the short circuit. The transmission line attachment point is varied until the transmission line and stub impedances are equal. In practice this involves moving both the sliding short and the point of line connection for zero reflected power, as indicated on an SWR bridge connected in the line.

The universal stub allows for tuning out any small reactance present in the driven part of the system. It permits matching the antenna to the line without knowledge of the actual impedances involved. The position of the short yielding the best match gives some indication of the amount of reactance present. With little or no reactive component to be tuned out, the stub must be approximately λ/2 from the load toward the short.

The stub should be made of stiff bare wire or rod, spaced no more than 1/20 λ apart. Preferably it should be mounted rigidly on insulators. Once the position of the short is determined, the center of the short can be grounded, if desired, and the portion of the stub no longer needed can be removed.

It is not necessary that the stub be connected directly to the driven element. It can be made part of a parallel-wire line as a device to match coaxial cable to the line. The stub can be connected to the lower end of a delta match or placed at the feed point of a phased array. Examples of these uses are given later.

24.5.10 Resonant Circuit Matching

Antennas with a high feed point impedance, such as end-fed wires close to λ/2 in length and "voltage-fed" antennas such as the Bobtail Curtain often use a parallel-tuned circuit at the feed point to effect an impedance match. The circuit is adjusted to resonance and then the feed line attached to a tap on the inductor that is moved until an SWR minimum is obtained. The circuit may need a slight retuning following by a final position adjustment of the feed line. (See the chapters **Multiband HF Antennas** and **Broadside and End-Fire Dipole Arrays** for more information on these antennas and typical feed systems.)

The matching bandwidth of this technique is quite narrow, requiring frequent retuning or operation over a narrow bandwidth. In addition, the voltages at the "hot" or ungrounded end of the tank circuit can be very high. Caution must be used in construction to prevent contact with the high voltages and adequately rated components must be used.

24.6 Common-Mode Transmission Line Current

In discussions so far about transmission line operation, it was always assumed that the two conductors carry equal and opposite currents throughout their length. This is an ideal condition that may or may not be realized in practice. In the average case, the chances are rather good that the currents will not be balanced unless special precautions are taken. The degree of imbalance — and whether that imbalance is actually important — is what we will examine in the rest of this chapter, along with measures that can be taken to restore balance in the system.

It is important to note that common-mode current on the shield of a coaxial feed line is not entirely isolated from signals inside the cable. Because of *transfer impedance*, the common-mode current can create differential-mode signals as discussed in the **Transmission Lines** chapter.

There are two common conditions that will cause an imbalance of transmission line currents. Both are related to the symmetry of the system. The first condition involves the lack of symmetry when an inherently *unbalanced* coaxial line feeds a *balanced* antenna (such as a dipole or a Yagi driven element) directly. The second condition involves asymmetrical routing of a transmission line near the antenna or asymmetry in the environment around the antenna and transmission line such as unequal heights or lengths of conductors, ground slope, nearby conducting objects such as other antennas, towers, or buildings. Even trees can affect the fields near an antenna and transmission line.

24.6.1 Unbalanced Coax Feeding a Balanced Antenna

Figure 24.51 shows a coaxial cable feeding a hypothetical balanced dipole fed in the center. The coax has been drawn highly enlarged to show all currents involved. In this drawing the feed line drops at right angles down from the feed point and the antenna is assumed to be perfectly symmetrical. Because of this symmetry, one side of the antenna induces current on the feed line that is completely canceled by the current induced from the other side of the antenna. (See the References and Bibliography entry for Lewallen for a detailed paper about this situation and the use of baluns. The referenced *QST* article by Quick and Siwiak also illustrates the importance of baluns with common amateur antennas.)

Currents I1 and I2 from the transmitter flow on the inside of the coax. I1 flows on the *outer surface* of the coax's inner conductor and I2 flows on the *inner surface* of the shield. Skin effect keeps I1 and I2 inside the transmission line confined to where they are within the line. The field outside the coax is zero, since I1 and I2 have equal amplitudes but are 180° out of phase with respect to each other.

The currents flowing on the antenna itself are labeled I1 and I4, and both flow in the same direction at any instant in time for a resonant half-wave dipole. On Arm 1 of the dipole, I1 is shown going directly into the center conductor of the feed coax. However, the situation is different for the other side of this dipole. Once current I2 reaches the end of the coax, it splits into two components. One is I4, going directly into Arm 2 of the dipole. The other is I3 and this flows down the *outer surface* of the coax shield. Again, because of skin effect, I3 is separate and distinct from the current I2 on the inner surface. The antenna current in Arm 2 is thus equal to the difference between I2 and I3.

The magnitude of I3 is proportional to the relative impedances in each current path beyond the split. The feed point impedance of the dipole by itself is somewhere between 50 to 75 Ω, depending on the height above ground. The impedance seen looking into one half of the dipole is half, or 25 to 37.5 Ω. The impedance seen looking down the outside surface of the coax's outer shield to ground is called the *common-mode impedance*, and I3 is aptly called the *common-mode current*.

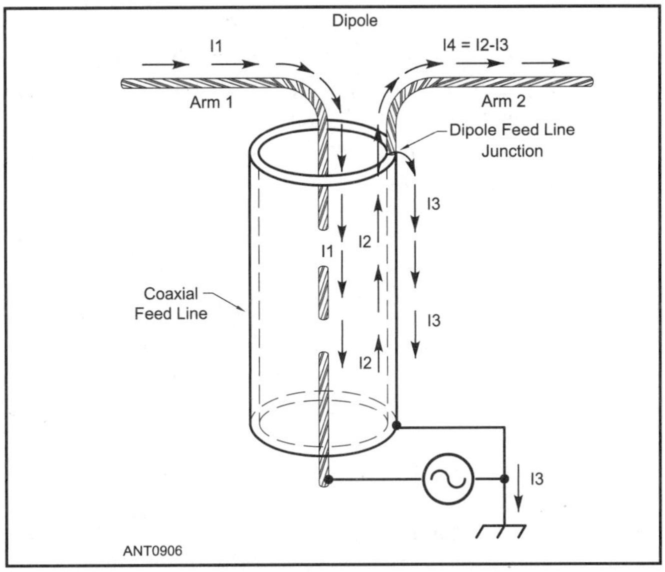

Figure 24.51 — Drawing showing various current paths at feed point of a balanced dipole fed with unbalanced coaxial cable. The diameter of the coax is exaggerated to show currents clearly.

(The term common-mode is more readily appreciated if parallel-conductor line is substituted for the coaxial cable used in this illustration. Current induced by radiation onto both conductors of a two-wire line is a common-mode current, since it flows in the *same direction* on both conductors, rather than in opposite directions as it does for differential-mode transmission line current. The outer braid for a coaxial cable shields the inner conductor from such an induced current, but the unwanted current on the outside braid is still called *common-mode* current.)

The common-mode impedance will vary with the length and diameter of the coaxial feed line, system of conductors and enclosures in the station, and the connection to any ground system. Note that the path from the station equipment to the ground system may go through a ground bus, the transmitter power supply's ac cord, the house wiring and even the power-line service ground. In other words, the overall length of the coaxial outer surface and the other components making up ground can actually be quite a bit different from what you might expect by casual inspection.

The best way to think about the common-mode path is to understand it is really an antenna, and possesses all the properties of an antenna. Voltage and current vary along it according to the conditions along it and its length. As part of the antenna system, it radiates and receives. What it radiates and receives is coupled to and from the "intentional" parts of the antenna.

The worst-case common-mode impedance occurs when the overall effective path length to ground is a multiple of λ/2, making this path half-wave resonant. In effect, the line and ground-wire system acts like a sort of transmission line, transforming the short circuit to ground at its end to a low impedance at the dipole's feed point. This causes I3 to be a significant part of I2.

I3 not only causes an imbalance in the amount of current flowing in each arm of the otherwise symmetrical dipole, but it also radiates by itself. The radiation in Figure 24.51 due to I3 would be mainly vertically polarized, since the coax is drawn as being mainly vertical. However, the polarization is a mixture of horizontal and vertical, depending on the orientation of the ground wiring from the transmitter chassis to the rest of the station's grounding system.

PATTERN DISTORTION FOR A DIPOLE WITH SYMMETRICAL COAX FEED

Figure 24.52 compares the azimuthal radiation pattern for two λ/2-long 14-MHz dipoles mounted horizontally λ/2 above average ground. Both patterns were computed for a 28° elevation angle, the peak response for a λ/2-high dipole. The model for the first antenna, the reference dipole shown as a solid line, has no feed line associated with it — it is as though the transmitter were somehow remotely located right at the center of the dipole. This antenna displays a classical figure-8 pattern. Both side nulls dip symmetrically about 10 dB below the peak response, typical for a 20-meter dipole 33-feet above ground (or an 80-meter dipole placed 137-feet above ground).

The second dipole, shown as a dashed line, is modeled using a λ/2-long coaxial feed line dropped vertically to the ground below the feed point. Now, the azimuthal response of the second dipole is no longer perfectly symmetrical. It is shifted to the left a few dB in the area of the side nulls and the peak response is down about 0.1 dB compared to the reference dipole. Many would argue that this sort of response isn't all that bad! However, do keep in mind that this is for a feed line placed in a symmetrical manner, at a right angle below the dipole. Asymmetry in dressing the coax feed line will result in more pattern distortion.

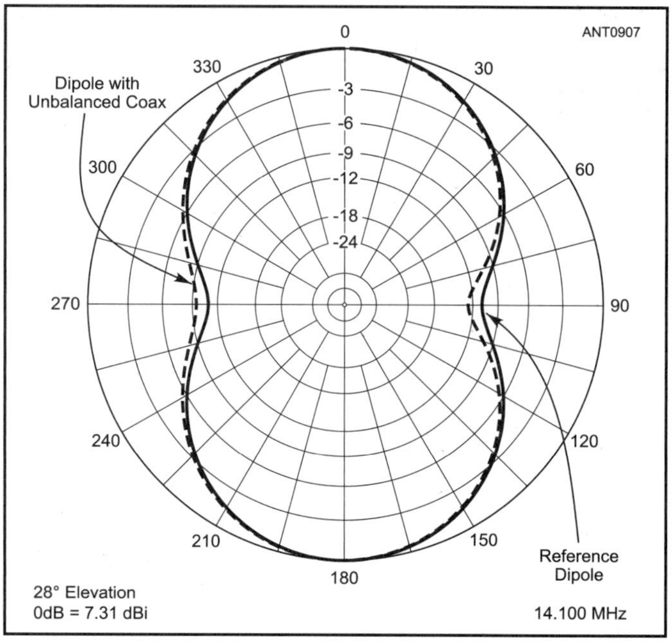

Figure 24.52 — Comparison of azimuthal patterns of two λ/2-long 14-MHz dipoles mounted λ/2 over average ground. The reference dipole without effect of feed line distortion (modeled as though the transmitter were located right at the feed point) is the solid line. The dashed line shows the pattern for the dipole affected by common-mode current on its feed line due to the use of unbalanced coax to feed a balanced antenna. The feed line is dropped directly from the feed point to ground in a symmetrical manner. The feed point impedance in this symmetrical configuration changes only a small amount compared to the reference antenna.

SWR CHANGE WITH COMMON-MODE CURRENT

If an SWR meter is placed at the bottom end of the coax feeding the second dipole, it would show an SWR of 1.38:1 for a 50-Ω coax such as RG-213, since the antenna's feed point impedance is $69.20 + j\,0.69\ \Omega$. The SWR for the reference dipole would be 1.39:1, since its feed point impedance is $69.47 - j\,0.35\ \Omega$. As could be expected, the common-mode impedance in parallel with the dipole's natural feed point impedance has lowered the net impedance seen at the feed point, although the degree of impedance change is miniscule in this particular case with a symmetrical feed line dressed away from the antenna.

In theory at least, we have a situation where a change in the length of the unbalanced coaxial cable feeding a balanced dipole will cause the SWR on the line to change also. This is due to the changing common-mode impedance to ground at the feed point. The SWR may even change if the operator touches the SWR meter, since the path to RF ground is subtly altered when this happens. Even changing the length of an antenna to prune it for resonance may also yield unexpected, and confusing, results on the SWR meter because of the common-mode impedance.

When the overall effective length of the coaxial feed line to ground is not a multiple of a λ/2 resonant length but is an odd multiple of λ/4, the common-mode impedance transformed to the feed point is high in comparison to the dipole's natural feed point impedance. This will cause I3 to be small in comparison to I2, meaning that radiation by I3 itself and the imbalance between I1 and I4 will be minimal. Modeling this case produces no difference in response between the dipole with unbalanced feed line and the reference dipole with no feed line. Thus, a multiple of a half-wavelength for coax and ground wiring represents the *worst case* for this kind of imbalance, when the system is otherwise symmetrical.

If the coax in Figure 24.51 were replaced with parallel-conductor transmission line, the SWR would remain almost constant along the line, no matter what the length. SWR would actually decrease slightly toward the transmitter end because of line loss due to increased SWR. However, the decrease would be slight, because the loss in parallel-conductor transmission line is small, even with relatively high SWR on the line. It is worth noting that window-line can be lossy when wet or covered with ice or snow. (See the **Transmission Lines** chapter for a thorough discussion on additional line loss due to SWR.)

SIZE OF COAX

At HF, the diameter of the coax feeding a λ/2 dipole is only a tiny fraction of the length of the dipole itself. In the case of Figure 24.51 above, the model of the coax used assumed an exaggerated 9-inch diameter, just to simulate a worst-case effect of coax spacing at HF.

However, on the higher UHF and microwave frequencies, the assumption that the coax spacing is not a significant portion of a wavelength is no longer true. The plane bisecting the feed point of the dipole in Figure 24.51 down through the space below the feed point and in-between the center conductor and shield of the coax is the "center" of the system. If the coax diameter is a significant percentage of the wavelength, the center is no longer symmetrical with reference to the dipole itself and significant imbalance will result. Measurements done at microwave frequencies showing extreme pattern distortion for balun-less dipoles may well have suffered from this problem.

24.6.2 Asymmetrical Routing of the Feed Line

Figure 24.51 shows a symmetrically located coax feed line, one that drops vertically at a 90° angle directly below the feed point of the symmetrical dipole. What happens if the feed line is not dressed away from the antenna in a completely symmetrical fashion — that is, not at a right angle to the dipole?

Figure 24.53 illustrates a situation where the feed line goes to the transmitter and ground at a 45° angle from the dipole. Now, one side of the dipole can radiate more strongly onto the feed line than the other half can. Thus, the currents radiated onto the feed line from each half of the symmetrical dipole won't cancel each other. In other words, the antenna itself radiates a common-mode current onto the transmission line. This is a different form of common-mode current from what was discussed above in connection with an unbalanced coax feeding a balanced dipole, but it has similar effects.

Figure 24.54 shows the azimuthal response of a 0.71-λ-high reference dipole with no feed line (as though the transmitter were located right at the feed point) compared to a 0.71-λ-high dipole that uses a 1-λ-long coax feed line, slanted 45° from the feed point down to ground through the transmit-

Balun and Choke Measurements

The techniques for measuring port-to-port isolation and impedance require attention to detail and consistency in the test equipment and workbench setup. The primary reason for poor accuracy and repeatability is parasitic capacitance exhibited by the device (balun or choke) under test (DUT) and the test equipment. Because the measurement is of high impedances and high isolation, it doesn't take much capacitance to affect or even dominate the measurement. For example, 1 pF at 20 MHz creates a reactance of about 8 kΩ. In parallel with a purely resistive 5 kΩ choke, the measured impedance will become 3.6 – j2.25 kΩ or 4.24 kΩ ∠-32°, which is very different from the choke impedance by itself. Measuring high impedance at RF is hard to do properly and consistently. The measurement process and test setups using vector network analyzers are described in Jim Brown, K9YC's presentation slide set *Coaxial Transmitting Chokes* (**audiosystemsgroup.com/CoaxChokesPPT.pdf**) — see slides 114 through 135.

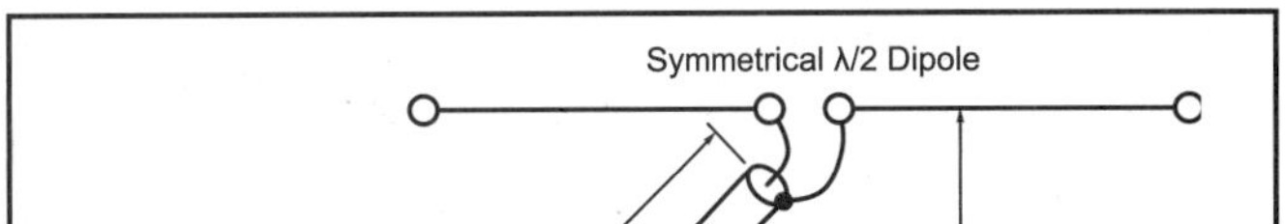

Figure 24.53 — Drawing of λ/2 dipole, placed 0.71 λ above average ground, with a 1-λ long coax feed line connected at far end to ground through a transmitter. Worst-case feed line radiation due to common-mode current induced on the outer shield braid occurs for lengths that are multiples of λ/2.

ter. The 0.71-λ height was used so that the slanted coax could be exactly 1 λ long, directly grounded at its end through the transmitter and so that the low-elevation angle response could be emphasized to show pattern distortion. The feed line was made 1 λ long in this case, because when the feed line length is only 0.5 λ and is slanted 45° to ground, the height of the dipole is only 0.35 λ. This low height masks changes in the nulls in the azimuthal response due to feed line common-mode currents. Worst-case pattern distortion occurs for lengths that are multiplies of λ/2, as before.

The degree of pattern distortion is now slightly worse than that for the symmetrically placed coax, but once again, the overall effect is not really severe. Interestingly enough, the slanted-feed line dipole actually has about 0.2 dB more gain than the reference dipole. This is because the left-hand side null is deeper for the slanted-feed line antenna, adding power to the frontal lobes at 0° and 180°.

The feed point impedance for this dipole with slanted feed line is $62.48 - j\,1.28\ \Omega$ for an SWR of 1.25:1, compared to the reference dipole's feed point impedance of $72.00 + j\,16.76\ \Omega$ for an SWR of 1.59:1. Here, the reactive part of the net feed point impedance is smaller than that for the reference dipole, indicating that detuning has occurred due to mutual coupling to its own feed line. This change of SWR is slightly larger than for the previous case and could be seen on a typical SWR meter.

You should recognize that common-mode current arising from radiation from a balanced antenna back onto its transmission line due to a lack of symmetry occurs for *both* coaxial and balanced transmission lines. For a coax, the inner surface of the shield and the inner conductor are shielded from such radiation by the outer braid. However, the outer surface of the braid carries common-mode current radiated from the antenna and then subsequently reradiated by the line. For a parallel-conductor line, common-mode currents are induced onto both conductors, again resulting in reradiation from the feed line.

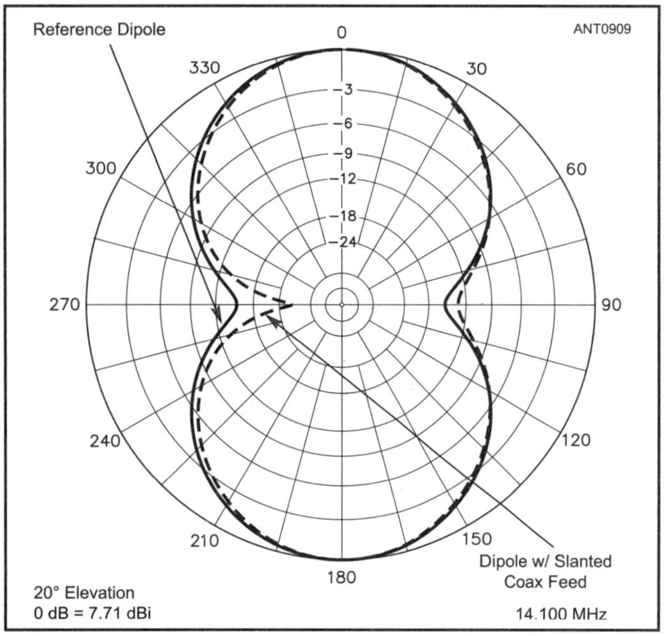

Figure 24.54 — Azimuthal response for two dipoles placed as shown in Figure 24.49. The solid line represents a reference dipole with no feed line (modeled as though the transmitter were located directly at the feed point). The dashed line shows the response of the antenna with feed line slanted 45° down to ground. Current induced on the outer braid of the 1-λ -long coax by its asymmetry with respect to the antenna causes the pattern distortion. The feed point impedance also changes, causing a different SWR from that for the unaffected reference dipole.

If the *antenna or its environment* are not perfectly symmetrical in all respects, there will also be some degree of common-mode current generated on the transmission line, either coax or balanced. Perfect symmetry means that the ground would have to be perfectly flat everywhere under the antenna, and that the physical length of each leg of the antenna would have to be exactly the same. It also means that the height of the dipole must be exactly symmetrical all along its length, and it even means that nearby conductors, such as power lines, must be completely symmetrical with respect to the antenna.

In the real world, where the ground isn't always perfectly flat under the whole length of a dipole and where wire legs aren't cut to the same length, a parallel-conductor line feeding a supposedly balanced antenna is no guarantee that common-mode transmission line currents will not occur! However, dressing the feed line so that it is symmetrical to the antenna will lead to fewer problems in all cases.

Note that the popular End-Fed Half-Wave (EFHW) is an extreme example of asymmetry with the feed line attached at one end of the antenna. (Also see the discussion of vertical half-wave dipoles in the **General Purpose MF and HF Antennas** chapter.) Common-mode current is guaranteed to flow on the feed line because one conductor of the feed line is not attached directly to the antenna. The feed line's common-mode path, whether on both conductors of a parallel-conductor feed line or on the outer shield of coax, is part of the antenna. EFHW designs that depend on this common-mode path as part of the radiating element will not work properly if a choke is placed on the feed line at the antenna.

Some EFHW designs replace the common-mode path with an extra counterpoise wire which is simply the "missing" part of the antenna, allowing an isolation transformer to decouple the feed line from the antenna current.

24.6.3 Common-Mode Current Effects on Directional Antennas

For a simple dipole, many amateurs would look at Figure 24.52 or Figure 24.54 and say that the worst-case pattern asymmetry doesn't look very important, and they would be right. Any minor, unexpected change in SWR due to common-mode current would be shrugged off as inconsequential — if indeed it is even noticed. All around the world, there are many thousands of coax-fed dipoles in use, where no special effort has been made to smooth the transition from unbalanced coax to balanced dipole.

For antennas that are specifically designed to be highly directional, however, pattern deterioration resulting from common-mode currents is a very different matter. Much care is usually taken during design of a directional antenna like a

Yagi or a quad to tune each element in the system for the best compromise between directional pattern, gain and SWR bandwidth. What happens if we feed such a carefully tailored antenna in a fashion that creates common-mode feed line currents?

Figure 24.55 compares the azimuthal response of two five-element 20-meter Yagis, each located horizontally λ/2 above average ground. The solid line represents the reference antenna, where it is assumed that the transmitter is located right at the balanced driven element's feed point without the need for an intervening feed line. The dashed line represents the second Yagi, which is modeled with a λ/2-long unbalanced coaxial feed line going to ground directly under the balanced driven element's feed point.

Minor pattern skewing evident in the case of the dipole now becomes definite deterioration in the rearward pattern of the otherwise superb pattern of the reference Yagi. The side nulls deteriorate from more than 40 dB to about 25 dB. The rearward lobe at 180° goes from 26 dB to about 22 dB. In short, the pattern gets a bit ugly, and the gain decreases as well.

Figure 24.56 shows a comparison at 0.71 λ height between a reference Yagi with no feed line and a Yagi with a 1-λ-long feed line slanted 45° to ground. Side nulls that were deep (at more than 30 dB down) for the reference Yagi have been reduced to less than 18 dB in the common-mode afflicted antenna. The rear lobe at 180° has deteriorated mildly, from 28 dB to about 26 dB. The forward gain of the antenna has fallen 0.4 dB from that of the reference antenna. As expected, the feed point impedance also changes, from $22.3 - j\,25.2\ \Omega$ for the reference Yagi to $18.5 - j\,29.8\ \Omega$ for the antenna with the unbalanced feed. The SWR will also change with line length on the balanced Yagi due to the common-mode path, just as it did for the simple dipole.

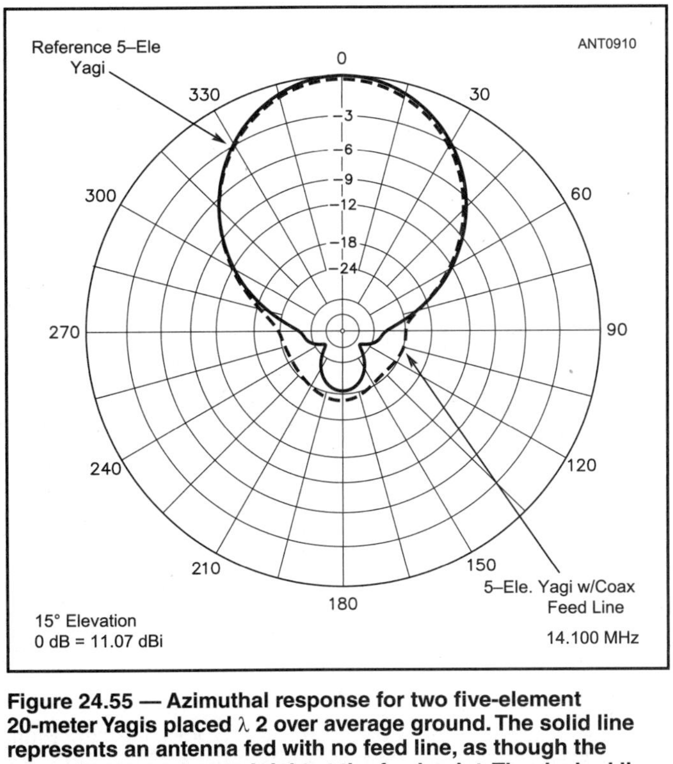

Figure 24.55 — Azimuthal response for two five-element 20-meter Yagis placed λ 2 over average ground. The solid line represents an antenna fed with no feed line, as though the transmitter were located right at the feed point. The dashed line represents an antenna fed with a λ/2 length of unbalanced coax line directly going to ground (through a transmitter at ground level). The distortion in the rearward pattern is evident, and the Yagi loses a small amount of forward gain (0.3 dB) compared to the reference antenna. In this case, placing a common-mode choke of + *j* 1000 Ω at the feed point eliminated the pattern distortion.

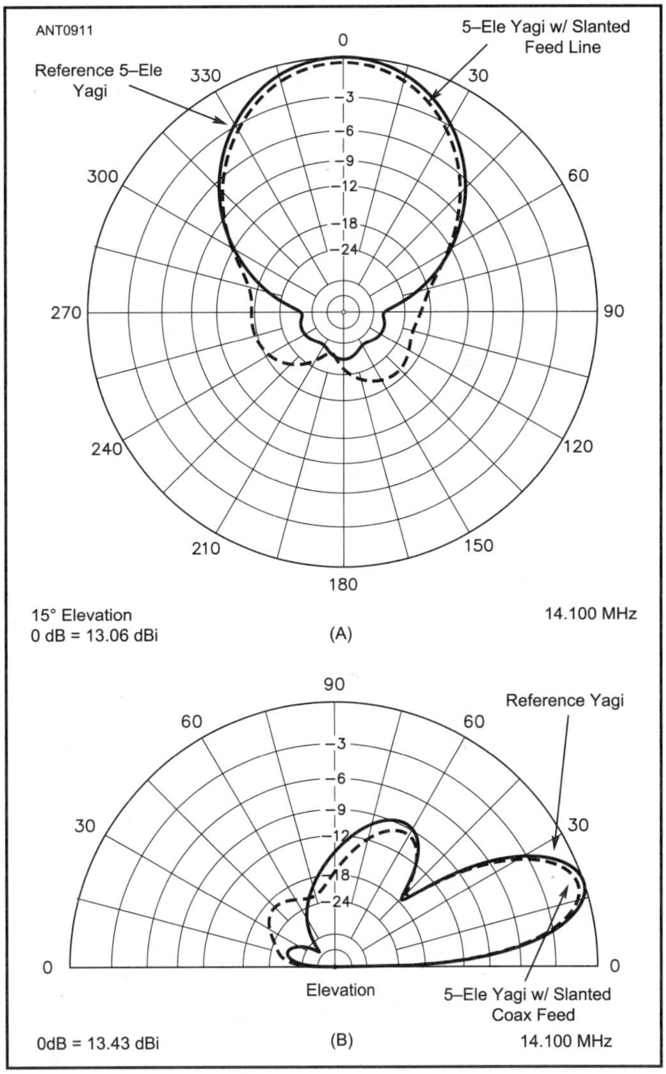

Figure 24.56 — At A, azimuthal response for two five-element 20-meter Yagis placed 0.71 λ over average ground. The solid line represents an antenna fed with no feed line. The dashed line represents an antenna fed with a 1-λ length of unbalanced coax line slanted at 45° to ground (through a transmitter at ground level). The distortion in the rearward pattern is even more evident than in Figure 24.49. This Yagi loses a bit more forward gain (0.4 dB) compared to the reference antenna. At B, elevation response comparison. The slant of the feed line causes more common-mode current due to asymmetry. In this case, placing a common-mode choke of + *j* 1000 Ω at the feed point was not sufficient to eliminate the pattern distortion substantially. Another choke was required λ/4 farther down the transmission line to eliminate common-mode currents of all varieties.

Clearly, the pattern of what is supposed to be a highly directional antenna can be seriously degraded by the presence of common-mode currents on the coax feed line. As in the case of the simple dipole, multiples of $\lambda/2$-long resonant feed line to ground represents the worst-case feed system, even when the feed line is dressed symmetrically at right angles below the antenna. And as found with the dipole, the pattern deterioration becomes even worse if the feed line is dressed at a slant under the antenna to ground, although this sort of installation with a Yagi is not very common. For least interaction, the feed line still should be dressed so that it is symmetrical with respect to the antenna.

In the computer models used to create Figures 24.52, 24.54 and 24.55, placing a common-mode choke (described in the next sections) with a reactance of $+j\ 1000\ \Omega$ at the antenna's feed point removed virtually all traces of the problem. This was always true for the simple case where the feed line was dressed symmetrically, directly down under the feed point. Certain slanted-feed line lengths required additional common-mode chokes which should be placed at $\lambda/4$ intervals beginning $\lambda/2$ down the transmission line from the feed point. (Placing the first choke $\lambda/2$ from the antenna feed point avoids creating a low impedance point on the outside of the coax shield at the feed point.) Remember that the free-space wavelength is used on the *outside* of coax while the VF must be applied *inside* the coax.

24.7 Current Baluns, Chokes, and Choke Baluns

In the preceding sections, problems associated with common-mode currents on transmission lines were described. Common-mode feed line currents have several causes — primarily physical asymmetry of the antenna, direct connection of unbalanced feed lines and balanced antennas, and coupling between the feed line and the antenna due to placement or orientation of the feed line. In addition, noise is picked up by the feed line as common-mode current and signals radiated by current on the feed line can cause interference to appliances and other electronics if they are near the feed line.

In order to reduce common-mode feed line current, *chokes* that create a high impedance in the current's path are used. If the choke is placed at the junction of a coaxial feed line and load, such as an antenna, the choke becomes a *choke balun* between the unbalanced feed line and the balanced load, such as the antenna. Choke and choke baluns come in a variety of forms, which we will explore in this section. See the earlier section Transmission Line Matching Devices for a discussion of the difference between chokes, baluns, and impedance transformers.

It is important to note that a number of the papers and articles referenced in this section were written before the advent of a wide variety of ferrite materials available today, in particular the type #31 mix which is used for EMI suppression in the MF, HF, and VHF ranges. (See **fair-rite.com/materials** for a table of ferrite types and their applications.) In addition, more applications for feed line chokes, such as for reducing received noise and breaking up resonant feed line length, have been developed for amateurs. This does not invalidate the information from those early sources but requires the reader to remember that current usage may have evolved in light of a better understanding of antenna and feed line system behavior and new types of ferrite becoming available.

Material in this section has been updated from earlier editions based on the latest versions of Jim Brown, K9YC's papers "RFI, Ferrites, and Common Mode Chokes For Hams," "A New Choke Cookbook for the 160–10M Bands," are both available for download from **k9yc.com/publish.htm**. See the **Receiving Antennas** chapter for more information about use of chokes with those antennas.

24.7.1 Current Baluns

The *current balun* is a type of transmission line transformer with a high common-mode impedance providing isolation between the input and output terminals. It has the hybrid properties of a tightly coupled transmission line transformer (with a 1:1 transformation ratio) and the common-mode impedance of an inductance or resistance to provide common-mode impedance. (See the previous discussion of Transmission Line Transformers.) The transmission line transformer action forces the current at the output terminals to be equal, and the common-mode impedance blocks common-mode currents. The blocking action is why current baluns are often referred to as choke baluns. The current balun was originally developed for interstage coupling with inductive ferrite materials and not as an antenna system choke component. This causes confusion in amateur circles where the predominant use of baluns is in antenna systems where resistive (lossy) materials are the most useful.

See **Figure 24.57A** for a schematic representation of such a balun. This characterization is attributed to Frank Witt, AI1H. Z_W is the winding impedance that blocks common-mode currents. (This is the Guanella transformer discussed previously.) The winding impedance is determined by the material used for the core on which the transmission line is wound, usually a ferrite rod or toroid.

The *ideal transformer* in this characterization models what happens either inside a coax or for a pair of perfectly coupled parallel wires in a two-wire transmission line. Although Z_W is shown here as a single impedance, it could be split into two equal parts, with one placed on each side of the ideal transformer. The transmission line consists of coaxial cable (such as a small diameter Teflon-insulated cable like RG-303) or tightly coupled (side-by-side) bifilar wires. (Construction

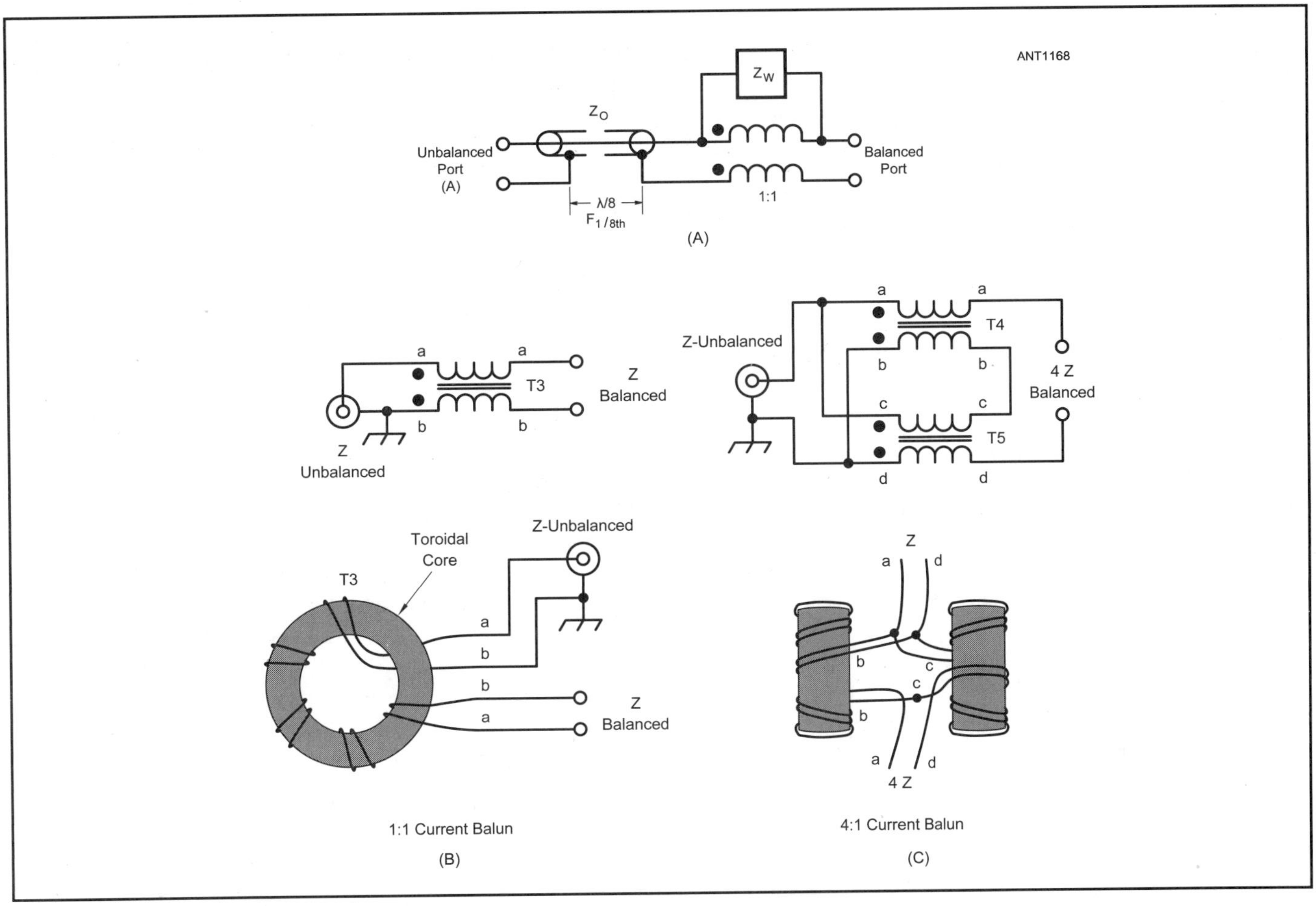

Figure 24.57 — Current or choke baluns. Section A shows the model for a 1:1 current or choke balun by Frank Witt, AI1H. The transformer is an ideal transformer. Z_W is the common-mode winding impedance. Section B shows how to wind a 1:1 version. The 4:1 balun in C is wound on two cores, which are physically separated from each other. Each winding is made from 9 turns of #12 AWG on a 2.4-inch OD type #31 ferrite core.

is discussed later in this section.)

Figure 24.57B and C show two common methods of winding 1:1 and 4:1 current baluns using a ferrite core. Type #31 material is recommended for the core as discussed in the section on Transmitting Ferrite-Core Coaxial Choke Baluns. Each bifilar winding forms a transmission line that is wound around the core which creates the choking impedance, Z_W.

In Figure 24.57C, note that two cores are required. A 4:1 current balun cannot be wound on a single core because of the coupling between the lines that would be created. The transmission lines must be independent and separate cores must be used.

24.7.2 Coiled-Coax Choke Baluns

The simplest method of constructing a feed line choke is simply to wind a length of coaxial cable into a coil (see **Figure 24.58**), creating an inductor from the shield's outer surface. (This construction technique cannot be used with parallel-conductor line because of coupling between the conductors in adjacent turns.) Common-mode current on the outside of the shield encounters the coil's reactance, while differential-mode currents on the inside are unaffected. The reactance creates an RF choke in the common-mode path. If used at the antenna feed point, the choke becomes a type of choke balun by blocking the common-mode current path.

While this type of choke has been used for many years, its performance is hard to control and often over-estimated. Winding style, diameter and organization, and coupling to nearby conductors all affect all affect choke reactance. The impedance of ferrite chokes can be controlled more easily and optimized for specific frequency ranges by selecting the appropriate mix.

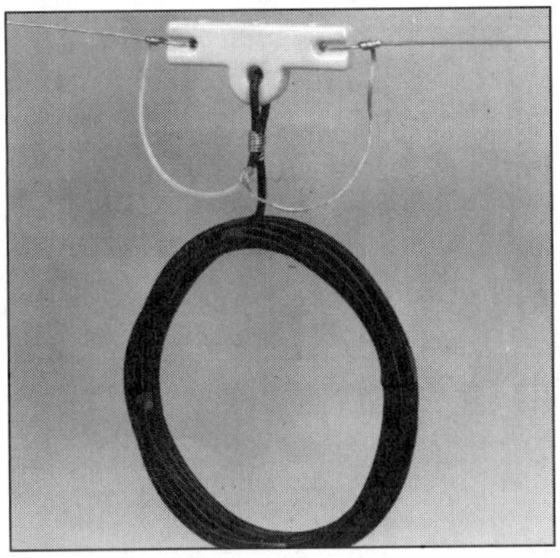

Figure 24.58 — Scramble-wound RF choke formed by coiling the feed line. The reactance of the choke isolates the antenna from the outer surface of the feed line. It is used as a choke balun at the point of connection to the antenna.

How Much Impedance Do I Really Need?

The answer begins with another question, "What are you trying to accomplish?" That will tell you how much impedance is needed on the feed line at the antenna feed point -- if any. For most antennas, lack of a choke will not prevent you from making any contacts, even at VHF. Many stations put up a backyard dipole or simple beam fed directly with coax and make plenty of contacts. If you attach the feed line carefully and arrange it to minimize RF pickup, it will probably work reasonably well. Getting better performance, though, complicates the question.

The necessary choke impedance varies with the intended purpose. Roughly in order from the lowest to highest required impedance:

1. Feed point impedance control (the "third wire" issue) requires about 10x the feed point impedance: for a 50 Ω antenna, a 500 Ω choke is sufficient.
2. Pattern preservation (avoiding re-radiation and pickup by the shield) can lower received noise and reduce interference.
3. RFI from common-mode current being picked up by the shield can be reduced by chokes.
4. Noise ingress (noise current getting into the coax at the feed point) is the most difficult to reduce, especially at VHF where artificial noise is stronger than natural noise. 5 kΩ is often suggested for noise suppression.

A 5 kΩ choke is likely to satisfy all four requirements and might be used as a one-size-fits-all choke in complex and high-performance stations. That said, much lower impedance (and expense) may be sufficient, particularly for applications 2 and 3, if you are willing to experiment or model.

RFI suppression may be more responsive to choke placement than high impedance. Remember that for high-power use, a feed point choke may be subjected to voltages high enough to cause heating.

Ferrite chokes are much less sensitive to winding organization. If a ferrite core designed for EMI suppression is used, the impedance is mostly resistive and thus not affected by line length.

The coiled-coax choke's effectiveness depends on the impedance of the feed line's outer surface at that point: If the impedance is inductive, the choke will likely be effective. Otherwise, the line's capacitive reactance may actually cancel some of the coil's inductive reactance, *increasing* common-mode current on the line. Feed line common-mode impedance is hard to predict or measure accurately, so the antenna system builder must be aware of the possibility of this type of interaction. The G3TXQ web page (**karinya.net/g3txq/chokes**) shows a number of examples in which a choke's reactance combines with that of the feed line. G3TXQ suggests that a choke reactance of at least 1000 Ω is required to avoid this level of interaction. In addition, the feed line and choke impedances will change with frequency, making coiled-coax chokes a poor choice for multiband antennas.

Just as for any inductor, the coiled-coax choke's self-resonance is created by the distributed capacitance between the turns of the coil. At the parallel self-resonant frequency, series impedance is very high. The resonant frequency can be determined with an impedance analyzer or with a dip meter. If using a dip meter, leave the ends of the choke disconnected, couple the coil to the dip meter, and tune for a dip.

SCRAMBLE-WOUND VERSUS SINGLE-LAYER

Scramble-wound chokes (wound like a coil of rope as in Figure 24.58) described in **Table 24.13** were measured by Ed Gilbert, K2SQ, to have a high impedance at the indicated frequencies as measured with an impedance meter. Because the winding order and grouping are uncontrolled, it is unlikely for a choke wound in a slightly different way to have the same resonant frequency and impedance as described in the table. Given the better performance of ferrite chokes, scramble-wound chokes are not recommended for high-performance installations. However, these simple chokes can be created anywhere along the feed line simply by winding it up, adding reactance in order to reduce common-mode current.

The performance of a single-layer coiled-coax choke is

Table 24.13
Coiled-Coax Choke Baluns

Scramble-wound (like a coil of rope) lengths of line are approximate.
Avoid foam-dielectric cable and secure with tape (see sidebar "Minimum Bend Radius")

Single Band, Scramble Wound

Freq (MHz)	*RG-213*	*RG-58*
3.5	22 ft, 8 turns	20 ft, 6-8 turns
7	22 ft, 10 turns	15 ft, 6 turns
10	12 ft, 10 turns	10 ft, 7 turns
14	10 ft, 4 turns	8 ft, 8 turns
21	8 ft, 6-8 turns	6 ft, 8 turns
28	6 ft, 6-8 turns	4 ft, 6-8 turns
50*	4-5 turns, 2$^1/_2$" dia	
144, 222*	2 turns, 2$^1/_2$" dia	
432*	1 turn, 2$^1/_2$" dia	

Multiple Band, Scramble Wound

Freq (MHz)	*RG-58 or RG-213*
3.5 – 30	10 ft, 7 turns
3.5 – 10	18 ft, 9-10 turns
1.8 – 3.5	40 ft, 20 turns
14 – 30	8 ft, 6-7 turns

Multiple Band, Single-layer Solenoid

Freq (MHz)	*RG-213*
7 – 24	12 turns, 4$^1/_4$" dia
14 – 30	6 turns, 4$^1/_4$" dia
14 – 30	4 turns, 6$^5/_8$" dia
7 – 24	8 turns, 6$^5/_8$" dia

*Recommended by Justin Johnson, GØKSC, **g0ksc.co.uk/creatingabalun.html**

Minimum Bend Radius

Chokes made from coaxial cable should be wound with a bend radius sufficiently large that the coax is not deformed. When a line is deformed, the spacing between the center conductor and the shield varies, so voltage breakdown and heating are more likely to occur. Deformation also causes a discontinuity in the impedance; the resulting reflections may cause some waveform distortion and increased loss at VHF and UHF.

Use coaxial cable with solid dielectric insulation, not foamed, to minimize migration of the center conductor through the insulation toward the shield. This is a common problem if the cable will be carrying high power or is heated in any way such as by sunlight or being placed in a hot environment. Keep these chokes away from heat sources and protect them from direct sunlight, if practical.

RG-213 (PE dielectric) or RG-400 (TFE dielectric) are recommended for winding chokes. Even solid PE coax such as RG-213 may experience center conductor migration through the dielectric, leading to eventual short circuits, if wound or bent too tightly. For air-coiled coax, the diameter of the coil should be at least 10 times the cable diameter to avoid mechanically stressing the cable. A good guideline for winding PE-dielectric coax for any coil is a 3-inch minimum radius (6-inch diameter).

To hold a coil together or secure it to a support, use tape instead of cable ties to avoid creating points of high compression or bending of the cable. These cautions also apply to stubs or matching transformer sections that may be coiled. For coiled-coax chokes, wind the cable loosely and support it with small rope or twine so that the coax does not support all the weight of the feed line.

While the turn diameter on toroid cores is smaller than the minimum specified bend radius for RG-400 TFE coax, failures caused by center conductor migration have not been commonly reported. The consensus among experienced builders and manufacturers is that that cable with a TFE dielectric will work as intended as long as it is not operated at its full power rating and flexed repeatedly. This is also discussed in the **Transmission Lines** chapter.

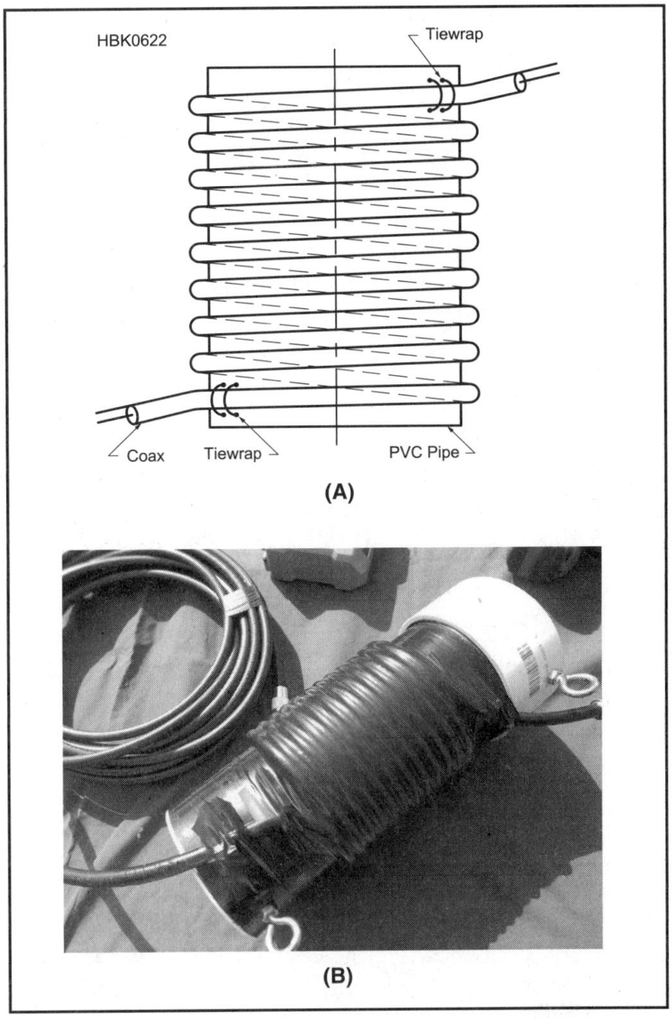

Figure 24.59 — Winding a coaxial choke as a single-layer solenoid (A) controls impedance and self-resonant frequency compared to a scramble-coil choke. The 12-turn 40-meter choke balun wound on a 4¼ inch diameter PVC pipe with eye bolts for attaching the choke to a Yagi boom.

more reproducible. This type of choke is created by winding the cable as a single-layer solenoidal coil on a section of plastic pipe or other suitable cylinder (**Figure 24.59**). The cable is secured with electrical tape as shown in Figure 24.59B. This type of construction reduces the stray capacitance of the coil and makes the coil's construction more consistent. If the choke will be used with a metal-boom Yagi, it is recommended that it not be held directly against the boom which will interact with the choke. As in Figure 24.59B, eye bolts in the form allow the coil to be suspended under the boom, improving electrical performance and giving a measure of mechanical strain relief.

A series of measurements by K2SQ on single-layer coiled-coax chokes determined several useful combinations of turns and diameter listed in Table 24.13. The 12-turn choke in Figure 24.59B, for example, is often used with common 2-element 40-meter Yagis. Although that choke only presents slightly more than 500 Ω of reactance, the low feed-point impedance of the beam over most of the 40-meter band (typical 50-Ω SWR>3:1), makes 500 Ω sufficient to reduce common-mode current to low levels, assuming the feed line impedance at the feed point is not capacitive. If the antenna feed point impedance was higher, a higher choke impedance would be necessary to maintain isolation of the feed line.

The single-layer chokes listed in the table were measured to have greater than 500 Ω of reactance on the bands shown. The measured self-resonant frequency and impedance are also given. While the single-layer chokes are more controlled than scramble-wound, expect a fair amount of variation in choke behavior. (The full table of measurements is included in the online material for this chapter.)

24.7.3 Coax-Wound Ferrite Chokes

Transmitting chokes differ from other common-mode chokes because they must be designed to work well when the feed line they are choking carries high power. Excellent common-mode chokes having very high power-handling capability can be formed simply by winding multiple turns of coax through a sufficiently large ferrite core or multiple cores. (These chokes will be referred to as "coax-wound ferrite chokes" to distinguish them from the air-core coiled-coax chokes of the preceding section.)

Joe Reisert, W1JR, first introduced chokes made with coaxial cable wound on ferrite toroids to amateurs. He used low-loss cores, typically type #61 or #67 material in frequency ranges which produce primarily an inductive reactance. **Figure 24.60** shows that these high-Q chokes are quite effective near their resonance. However, the resonance is narrow and typically covers only one or two bands. Away from resonance, the choke becomes far less effective, as choking impedance falls rapidly and its reactive component interacts with the impedance of the feed line. (An earlier US Army study of ferrite chokes was published in 1996; see the referenced article for Harper.)

Today there are more types of ferrite, including mixes designed for EMI suppression that produce impedances in the MF, HF, and VHF range that are primarily resistive. Chokes made with these materials exhibit broad peaks in impedance that can be used across several amateur bands. Chokes designed for different frequency ranges can be placed in series for even wider frequency coverage. (A procedure for determining the material of an unknown ferrite core was added to the *ARRL Handbook* chapter **RF Techniques** in the 100th edition.)

DESIGN CRITERIA

Traditionally, the rule-of-thumb for a transmission line choke was that the choking impedance needed to be at least 10 Z_0 of the line. I.e., 500 Ω for 50-Ω coax. (See the sidebar "How Much Impedance Do I Need?") At medium power levels (up to 600 W approximately), if the antenna is well-balanced and the feed point impedance reasonably close to Z_0, that would block most of the common-mode current without too much power dissipation. Full power (1500 W) or high duty-cycle operation such as for contesting and some types of digital mode operation, or use with a very unbalanced antenna, can result in high power dissipation in the choke. In such cases, more choking impedance is needed. (See the section Power Dissipation in Ferrite Transmitting Chokes.) A choking imped-

Ferrite Choke Advantages and Caveats

Using ferrite to create feed line chokes and choke baluns has several advantages for antenna system builders:

- Wide frequency range: ferrite components (toroids and beads) operate well over a wide frequency range
- Non-resonant behavior: There is no dependence on velocity factor of coaxial cable and no resonant lengths to calculate
- No extra connectors or "pigtail" connections required for bead designs – the beads are simply placed on the cable.

These advantages come with a few caveats, as well:

- Ferrite components rated for transmitting often cost a few dollars per bead which is more than short pieces of coaxial cable.
- The choice of mix is important to get the expected choking impedance at the frequencies of use.
- Significant common-mode voltage across the choke will heat the ferrite and in extreme cases can cause the ferrite to fracture or alter its impedance. (See the article "Don't Blow Up Your Balun," by Dean Straw, N6BV, in the References and Bibliography.)

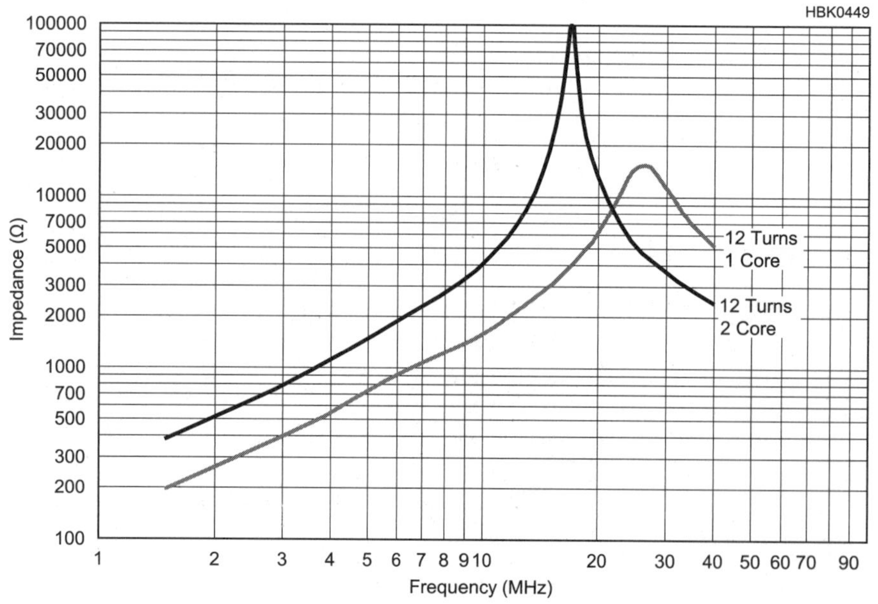

Figure 24.60 — Impedance versus frequency for HF coax-wound ferrite transmitting chokes wound with RG-142 coax on toroid cores of type #61 material.
For the 1-core choke: R = 15.6 kΩ, L = 25 μH, C = 1.4 pF, Q = 3.7.
For the 2-core choke: R = 101 kΩ, L = 47 μH, C = 1.9 pF, Q = 20.

ance (R_S) of 5000 Ω will be enough for most of these situations.

The best way to reduce power dissipation from common-mode current is to increase choking impedance. Doubling choke impedance divides the common-mode current by 2. This divides the power dissipated in the choke's series resistance (R_S) by 4 according to $P = I^2R_S$. Higher impedance can be obtained by winding more turns on a single core or by winding the choke on a stack of two or more cores.

In general, any combination of chokes can be used in series to provide the desired choking impedance over the desired bandwidth. Their combined choking impedance, R_S, will be the sum of their R_S values on each band. Chokes for different frequency ranges can be placed in series to create a choke with a higher impedance across a wider frequency range, as well.

Since the chokes are subjected to only common-mode voltage, the only effect of high SWR on power handling of coax-wound ferrite chokes is to increase the peaks of differential current and voltage along the line established by the mismatch in the antenna system. If SWR is very high, the extra mismatch loss may become an issue.

For receiving applications, a choke impedance of 500-1000 Ω is sufficient to prevent pattern distortion, ordinary cases of RFI, and noise coupling from other sources. These chokes also block strong signals picked up on the feed line shield from nearby transmitters, such as in a multi-transmitter station or broadcast station. Chuck Counselman, W1HIS, correctly observes that radiation and noise coupling from the feed line should be viewed as a form of pattern distortion that fills in the nulls of a directional antenna, reducing its ability to reject noise and interference. (See the **Receiving Antennas** chapter for more information on chokes for receiving antenna feed lines.)

Chokes used to break up a feed line into segments too short to interact with another antenna should have a choking impedance on the order of 1000 Ω to prevent interaction with simple antennas. A value closer to 5000 Ω may be needed if the effects of common-mode current on the feed line are filling the null of directional antenna.

PRACTICAL HF TRANSMITTING CHOKES

Legacy Choke Designs

Legacy designs for coax-wound ferrite chokes from previous editions used RG-8 or RG-11 for full-power operation, and RG-58 for lower power levels. Those chokes were wound on 2.4-inch OD, 1.4-inch ID toroid of type #31 or #43 material, and the 1-inch ID × 1.125-inch long clamp-on of type #31 material. (Note the following section's caveat about material variation for these cores which affects choking performance.)

The resonance curves for these chokes are affected by turn spacing, diameter, and organization, leading to a lot of variation with construction techniques. In addition, the larger minimum bend radius for the PE-insulated coax caused the full-power designs to be rather large and somewhat of a challenge to support at an antenna feed point. **Figure 24.61A** shows examples of the legacy design chokes and **Figures 24.62A – C** are graphs of the magnitude of the impedance for various numbers of turns, type of line, and types of core. These are presented here as reference information although they are not recommended for new installations. **Table 24.14** summarizes legacy designs that meet the 5000-Ω criteria for the 160- through 6-meter ham bands and several practical transmitting choke designs that are "tuned" or optimized for ranges of frequencies. (For VHF and UHF, note that parasitic capacitance makes an effective choke more difficult to create.)

Recommended Choke Designs

Jim Brown, K9YC, and Glen Brown, W6GJB, have built, tested, and measured numerous chokes constructed with RG-8-size coax, RG-400 (Teflon jacket, stranded silver-plated copper center, two silver-plated copper shields, TFE dielectric), #12 and #10 enameled copper wire pairs, THHN #12 and #10 pairs, a #12 Teflon-insulated wire pair (silver-plated stranded copper, 0.109-inch OD), and a pair formed by the black and white conductors removed from #10 and #12 Romex (NM) cable. The transmission characteristics were also measured at MF and HF. The data presented here is a summary of that information and the reader is encouraged to download the entire paper referenced at the beginning of this section (see References and Bibliography).

Their study also discovered wide variations in the fundamental properties of the 2.4-inch cores purchased over a period of 12 years. Variations of ±10% were measured for newly purchased cores. The choke designs in the tables are selected to have sufficient impedance values for average cores but variations at the upper and lower ends of the useful range for the choke will depend on the core characteristics.

K9YC also constructed and tested several chokes using 75-Ω FEP or TFE miniature RG-179 coax wound on 2.4-inch OD #31 ferrite toroids. The turns were wound close-spaced (touching on the inside diameter). This coax has fairly high loss, so the choke should not see more than approximately 300 W (this has not been verified as an upper limit) and even at that power level, it must be exposed to air for cooling.

160 meters	27 turns	12 kΩ Rs
80 meters	24 turns	13.5 kΩ Rs
40 meters	22 turns	10 kΩ Rs

Figures 24.62D-F are graphs of impedance magnitude for

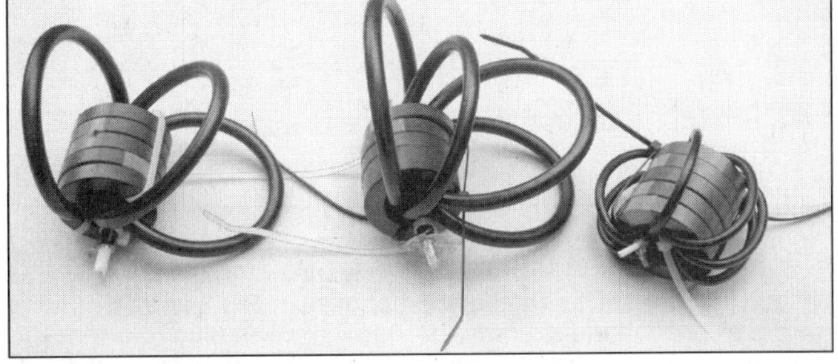

Figure 24.61 — Legacy design coax-wound ferrite transmitting chokes for use on the HF bands. Figure 24.59 shows examples of currently recommended choke construction.

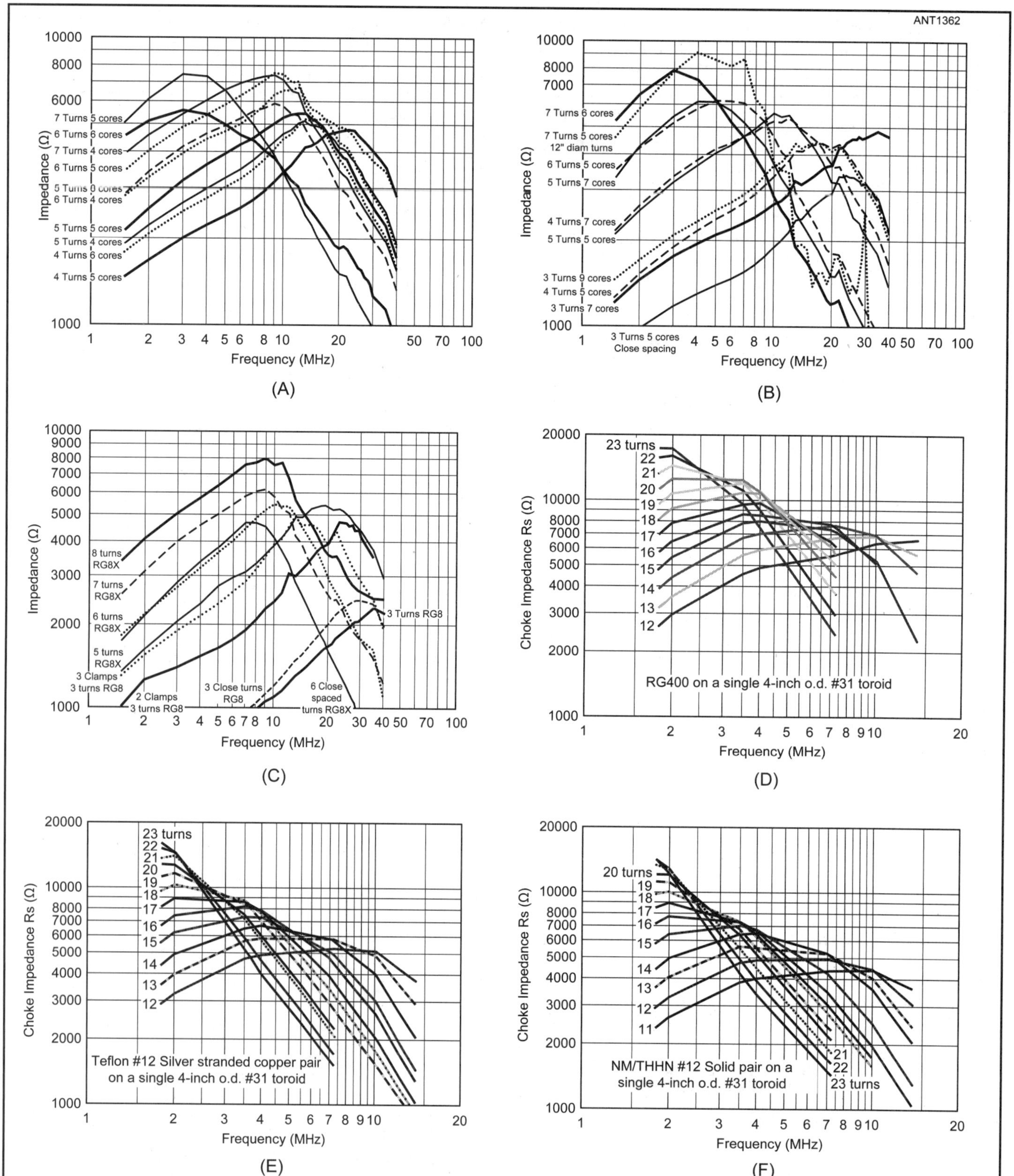

Figure 24.62 — A, Impedance versus frequency for legacy HF coax-wound ferrite transmitting chokes of RG-8X coax wound on 2.4-inch toroid cores of type #31 material. Turns are 5-inch diameter and wide-spaced unless noted. B, Impedance versus frequency for legacy HF coax-wound ferrite transmitting chokes of RG-8 coax wound on 2.4-inch toroid cores of type #31 material. Turns are 5-inch diameter and wide-spaced unless noted. C, Impedance versus frequency for legacy HF coax-wound ferrite transmitting chokes of RG-8X or RG-8 coax wound on big clamp-on cores of type #31 material. Turns are 6-inch diameter, wide-spaced except as noted. D, Impedance versus frequency for currently recommended HF coax-wound ferrite transmitting chokes of RG-400 wound on a single 2.4-inch toroid core of type #31 material. E, Impedance versus frequency for currently recommended HF coax-wound ferrite transmitting chokes Teflon-insulated #12 AWG wire wound on a single 2.4-inch toroid core of type #31 material. F, Impedance versus frequency for currently recommended HF coax-wound ferrite transmitting chokes THHN wire wound on a single 2.4-inch toroid core of type #31 material.

Table 24.14
Legacy Transmitting Choke Designs for Solid PE-insulated Coax (not recommended for new installations)

Freq Band(s) (MHz)	*Mix*	*RG-8, RG-11 Turns*	*RG-8, RG-11 Cores*	*RG-6, RG-8X, RG-58, RG-59 Turns*	*RG-6, RG-8X, RG-58, RG-59 Cores*
1.8, 3.8	#31	7	5 toroids	7 8	5 toroids Big clamp-on
3.5 – 7		6	5 toroids	7 8	4 toroids Big clamp-on
10.1	#31 or #43	5	5 toroids	8 6	Big clamp-on 4 toroids
7 – 14		5	5 toroids	8	Big clamp-on
14		5 4	4 toroids 6 toroids	8 5 – 6	2 toroids Big clamp-on
21		4 4	5 toroids 6 toroids	4 5	5 toroids Big clamp-on
28		4	5 toroids	4 5	5 toroids Big clamp-on
7 – 28, 10.1 – 28, or 14 – 28	#31 or #43	Use two chokes in series: #1 — 4 turns on 5 toroids #2 — 3 turns on 5 toroids		Use two chokes in series: #1 — 6 turns on a big clamp-on #2 — 5 turns on a big clamp-on	
14 – 28		Two 4-turn chokes, each w/one big clamp-on		4 turns on 6 toroids, or 5 turns on a big clamp-on	
50		Two 3-turn chokes, each w/one big clamp-on			
144 – 432	#43	1 – 3 turns on a big clamp-on			

Notes:
"Core" refers to a 2.4-inch OD, 1.4-inch ID toroid
"Big clamp-on" refers to a 1-inch ID, 1.125-inch clamp-on core of type #31 material
Turn diameter is nor critical, but 6 inches is good.

various numbers of turns, type of line, and types of core. **Tables 24.15** and **24.16** summarize designs for the 160 through 6-meter ham bands and several practical transmitting choke designs that are "tuned" or optimized for ranges of frequencies. The tables include designs meeting the 5000-Ω minimum impedance requirement and a higher-impedance design if available. Number of turns are limited on the smaller 2.4-inch OD cores.

An additional compilation of recommended air-core and ferrite-core designs is available from Steve Hunt, G3TXQ, at **karinya.net/g3txq/chokes**. The guidelines correspond roughly with measurements taken by others but should not be taken as guaranteed or representative of all methods of construction or materials. Note that a 500 Ω impedance may be quite inadequate for applications in which the load impedance is high or if high isolation of the load is required. In such cases, a higher-impedance choke is necessary.

SELECTING THE CHOKE TRANSMISSION LINE

Which line is recommended? The best compromise of size and power-handling capability was determined to be a miniature coax with TFE (Teflon) insulation such as RG-400 or a parallel-wire wound choke using TFE-insulated wire. **Table 24.17** was obtained from measured values of S11 (return loss) for short lengths with the far end open and the far end shorted, post-processed using AC6LA's *ZPlots* Excel spreadsheet (**ac6la.com/zplots.html**). Also see the sidebar "Minimum Bend Radius".

Chokes wound with higher Z_0 line (pairs of #12 THHN, NM, Teflon) work quite well at the feed point of various dipoles but may not at the feed point of a complex array. (See the online paper's discussion of 75-Ω chokes for transmitting arrays.) Chokes wound with the #12 Teflon wire pair were found to have the lowest loss and the least dissipation for each band. The wire is expensive and best purchased from surplus vendors or in a quantity group purchase. Remember that for paired-wire lines, Z_0 will vary with insulation thickness and the dielectric properties of the insulation.

The other recommended choices, especially for antennas with feed point Z_0 near 50 Ω, is RG-400, followed by a pair made from the white and black conductors removed from

Table 24.15

Transmitting Choke Designs for TFE Coax and Wire-Pair Lines on 2.4-inch OD Type #31 Toroid

(5 kΩ min impedance design)

See sidebar "Minimum Bend Radius"

Freq Band(s) (MHz)	*RG-400 Turns*	*TFE #12 Pair Turns*	*NM/THHN #12 Pair Turns*
1.8	17	17	16
3.5	13	14	13
7	13	13	13
10	12	13	13-14
14	12	12	11
21	11-12 (4.8 kΩ)	11-12 (4.7 kΩ)	11
28	10 (4.4 kΩ)	10 (4.3 kΩ)	10-11 (4.2 kΩ)
1.8-3.5	17	17	16
3.5-10		15	14
3.5-14	13	13	13
7-21	13	12	

High impedance design, if available, given as"Turns (kΩ)"

1.8	18 (10)	18 (9.5)	18 (9.5)
3.5	16 (8)	15-16 (6.5)	14 (6)
7	14 (6.2)	15 (6.5)	14 (6)
10	14 (6.5)	14 (6)	13-14 (5.5)
14	13 (5.4)	13 (5.5)	12-13 (5)
3.5-14	14 (6, 6, 6, 6)	14 (5.8, 5.8, 6, 5)	

Table 24.16

Transmitting Choke Designs for TFE Coax and Wire-Pair Lines on 4-inch OD Type #31 Toroid

(5 kΩ min impedance)

See sidebar "Minimum Bend Radius"

Freq Band(s) (MHz)	*RG-400 Turns*	*TFE #12 Pair Turns*	*NM/THHN #12 Pair Turns*
1.8	16	15	15
3.5	13	13	20
7.0	12	15	12-14
10	12	13-14	
14	12		
1.8-3.5	16	21	20
1.8-7	16	15	
1.8-10	16		
3.5-7	19	15	13
3.5-10	14	13	

High impedance design, if available, given as "Turns (kΩ)"

1.8	23 (17)	22-23 (15)	21-23 (12.5)
3.5	18-20 (11)	16-18 (7.5)	15-16 (6.7)
7	14 (7.5)	13-14 (5.7)	12-14 (5)
1.8-3.5	21 (13,10)	18 (9.5,8)	17 (8.5,6.5)
1.8-7	17 (7, 9.5, 6)	15 (5.5, 7.2, 5)	
1.8-10	16 (5.5, 8.5, 7.5, 5)		
3.5-7	15 (8.5, 7.5)	14 (6.5, 4.8)	14 (6.5, 5)
3.5-10	16 (8.5,7.5,5)	13 (5.8,5.8,5)	

Notes:
Chokes for 1.8, 3.5 and 7 MHz should have closely spaced turns.
Chokes for 14 – 28 MHz should have widely spaced turns.

Table 24.17

Measured Characteristic Impedance of Paired-Wire Lines

Line Type	*Z_0 @ 5 MHz*	*VF @ 5 MHz*	*10 MHz Loss*
#12 THHN Solid	91.2 Ω	0.725	1.2 dB/100 ft
#10 THHN Stranded	92.4 Ω	0.73	1.5 dB/100 ft
#12 Teflon (Ag/Cu)	96.6 Ω	0.833	76 dB/100 ft
#10 NM	86 Ω	0.725	1.5 dB/100 ft
#12 NM	91 Ω	0.73	1.2 dB/100 ft
#12 Enameled	43.4 Ω	0.77	2.45 dB/100 ft
#10 Enameled	41.3 Ω	0.66	2.36 dB/100 ft
RG-400	50.8 Ω	0.69	1.22 dB/100 ft

Romex (NM) cable.

Previous editions have referred to leakage flux from a parallel-wire (bifilar) winding causing heating in the core. This concern does not appear to be warranted based on measurements. Heating in the core external to the transmission line, coaxial or bifilar, is attributed to flux created by common-mode current only. See the section Power Dissipation in Ferrite Transmitting Chokes for a discussion of heating from common-mode current.

Enameled copper pairs were found to have much greater loss than other paired lines. This is because the magnetic fields produced by currents in very closely spaced pairs used as transmission lines cause the current to be concentrated in the side of the conductors closest to each other. This mechanism, strongly related to skin effect, is called *proximity effect*, and causes differential current to flow on the inside of the coax shield. Just as skin effect forces current to the skin of the conductor, proximity effect forces it to only one half of the skin! Proximity effect rises rapidly as the center-to-center spacing approaches the conductor diameter, which is the case with enameled wire. As can be seen from the table of measured transmission line data in the online paper, the enameled pairs have significantly higher loss (and greater dissipation) than other paired cables. It's also possible for the enamel to be scraped by the ferrite core during winding, shorting to the core at multiple points and significantly degrading choke performance. For both reasons, using enameled wire pairs for ferrite-core chokes are not recommended.

CONSTRUCTION GUIDELINES

Starting The Winding: Wind a cable tie around the cross section of the toroid where you want to start the winding and pull it not quite tight. Feed the cable through the toroid from below and use another cable tie to secure it to the first one, leaving enough free cable to connect the choke when it is complete. Leave enough cable tie for final tightening later. The choke in **Figure 24.63A** starts at 3 o'clock and is wound counterclockwise around the core.

Wind In Sequence: Take care that turns are wound in order around the core — out of sequence turns can cancel. Turns can be continued on a second layer when the first layer is filled by overlaying the starting turns of the winding. In Fig 24.59B, the winding starts at the upper left, completely fills the first

(A)

(B)

Figure 24.63 — At A is a coax-wound ferrite transmitting choke showing RG-400 winding technique. B shows how a wire-pair winding is constructed.

layer around the core, and continues with five more turns overlaying the start of the winding.

Turn Spacing: Measured data are for windings tight to the core, with adjacent windings touching on the inside of the core.

Paired Lines: Take care that pairs are not twisted as they are wound. Twisting can reduce choking impedance. Using different colors for the two conductors makes it easier to see twisting, and also to count turns. Keep the wires parallel and flat against the core. Solid conductors are preferred over stranded because turns tend to stay in place. Stranded wire is much less disciplined. (The choke in the figure has short leads for measurement purposes.)

Maintain polarity between the two ends of the choke — that is, make sure that the same conductor of a parallel pair is connected to the coax shield at both ends of the choke. This is especially important with arrays and can be an issue with lightning protection for a choke added to the line not at the feed point. If the polarity is reversed, the choke will still work but the array won't work as designed and static buildup on a coax shield may not be as well discharged.

Pairing the wire: Loss, VF, and Z_0 data are for the paired conductors touching, held in place every 3-6 inches with Scotch 33 or 35 (thinner than Scotch 88, it can help squeeze an extra turn on 2.4-in chokes for 160 meters). Wider spacing will increase Z_0 and decrease attenuation, especially with enameled pairs (because proximity effect is reduced).

Solid PE-insulated Coax: These legacy designs have been superseded by the RG-400 and paired-wire designs. These chokes are heavier, more expensive, and have greater loss (because they use more cores and more coax). These designs are repeatable only if turns pass through the core(s) sequentially, and if they have the same radius and spacing. Space turns evenly around the toroid to minimize inter-turn capacitance. See the online paper for some suggestions for constructing these chokes.

Supporting the Choke: Ferrite-core chokes can be heavy, even if wound with the lightest line on a single core. This can lead to mechanical failure from wind or other flexing of the antenna and feed line. The referenced paper contains several photos of suggested construction techniques. **Figure 24.64** shows a center insulator assembly of GPO3 fiberglass supporting two chokes in series (see the paper or series performance tables), an SO-239 receptacle for convenient feed line attachment, and sturdy attachment points for the dipole legs and a support rope or cable. The photo was taken before a waterproofing coating was applied to seal the electrical connections and provide UV resistance. Silicone adhesive was used to waterproof the SO-239. Lexan or some other plastic will also work for the body of the assembly.

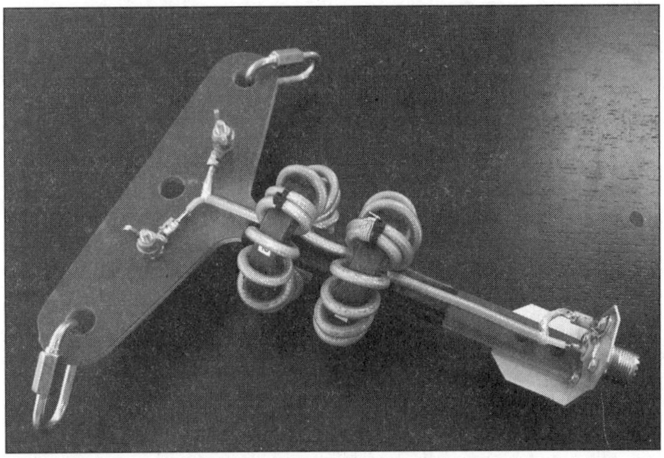

Figure 24.64 — A center insulator assembly designed by W6GJB to support one or two choke baluns in series for a wire antenna. An SO-239 is attached using a small bracket. Waterproofing can be provided by using silicone sealant.

Stray Capacitance: Chokes wound with any large diameter cable have more stray capacitance than those wound with small diameter wire. There are two sources of stray capacitance in a ferrite choke: the capacitance from end-to-end and from turn-to-turn via the core; and the capacitance from turn-to-turn via the air dielectric. Both sources of capacitance are increased by increased conductor size, so stray capacitance will be greater with larger coax. Turn-to-turn capacitance is also increased by larger diameter turns.

TRANSMITTING CHOKES FOR VHF/UHF

This section extends the previous sections to the VHF and low UHF amateur bands. It is excerpted from the paper "Transmitting Chokes for VHF/UHF" by Jim Brown, K9YC, available at **k9yc.com/publish.htm**.

The primary function of these chokes is to suppress common-mode current on the feed line that in receive mode can couple to the antenna, filling in nulls in the pattern from off-axis signals and noise. For noise reduction on the HF bands, 5 kΩ of resistive impedance at the working frequency is a good starting point, with twice that value to provide greater power handling. Noise levels at VHF and UHF are usually lower than at HF, so lower values of choking impedance may be sufficient.

(A)

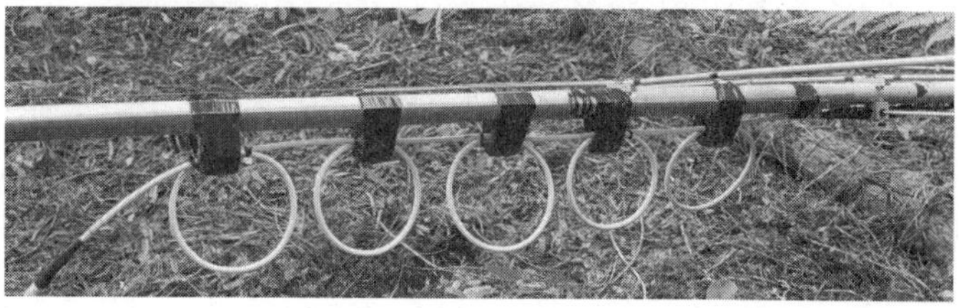

(B)

Figure 24.65 — At A, the 6-meter chokes are shown prior to installation and attached to the antenna boom at B. The elements are not yet attached in the second photo. (Photos courtesy of Jim Brown, K9YC)

Chokes For 6 Meters

RG8-Size coax: Two 6-inch diameter turns through one 1-inch ID type #31 clamp-on (Fair-Rite 0431177081) yields about 1 kΩ of resistive impedance. Use multiple chokes in series as in **Figure 24.65A** to achieve the desired choking impedance.

RG58, RG400-size coax: Two turns through two 0.75-inch ID type #31 clamp-ons (Fair-Rite 0431173551) yields about 1.2 kΩ resistive impedance. Use multiple chokes in series to achieve the desired choking impedance.

Remember that each pass of the cable through a ferrite core counts as one turn, so each loop of cable in the figure counts as *two* turns.

Chokes should be placed along the feed line starting as close as possible to the antenna's feed point with a few inches between cores. Coax and cores should be spaced from the boom so that capacitance to the boom does not add stray capacitance and lower the parallel resonance of the ferrite core. An insulating spacer about ½-in thick should be sufficient. In Figure 24.65B, the cores are lashed under the antenna's boom (elements had not yet been attached), with the spacer in place and turns hanging below the boom. The spacer is made of nested sections of 1½-inch or 2-inch UV-resistant PVC conduit.

The coax in the figure is a PTFE-insulated cable comparable to LMR-400. The cores are clamped tightly closed to minimize any air gap where their two halves meet, and the turns are also held in place on both sides of each core. Cable ties are protected with UV-resistant Scotch 88 tape.

Chokes For 144 MHz and 220 MHz

RG58, RG400-Size coax: Apply enough Fair-Rite #31 clamp-ons to achieve the desired choking impedance. Each Fair-Rite 0431164951 core provides about 300 Ω of resistive impedance on 144 MHz and a bit less on 220 MHz.

RG213-Size coax: Apply enough Fair-Rite #31 clamp-ons to achieve the desired choking impedance. Each Fair-Rite 0431164181 core provides about 360 Ω resistive impedance and a bit less on 220 MHz.

Chokes For 430 MHz

Apply enough Fair-Rite #61 clamp-ons to achieve the desired choking impedance. Each Fair-Rite 0431164951 core provides about 280 Ω resistive impedance.

24.7.4 Using Ferrite Beads in Choke Baluns

The ferrite bead current baluns developed by Walt Maxwell, W2DU, formed simply by stringing multiple beads in series on a length of coax to obtain the desired choking impedance, are really common-mode chokes. Maxwell's designs utilized 50, 100, and 200 very small beads of type #73 material as shown in **Figure 24.66**. Product data sheets show that a single type #73 bead has a very low-Q resonance around 20 MHz, and has a predominantly resistive impedance of 10-20 Ω on all HF ham bands. Stringing 50 beads in series simply multiples the impedance of one bead by 50, so the W2DU balun has a choking impedance of 500-1000 Ω and because it is strongly resistive, any resonance with the feed line is minimal.

This is a fairly good design for moderate power levels, but suitable beads are too small to fit most coax. A specialty coaxial cable such as RG-303 must be used for high-power applications. Even with high-power coax, the choking impedance is often insufficient to limit current to a low enough value

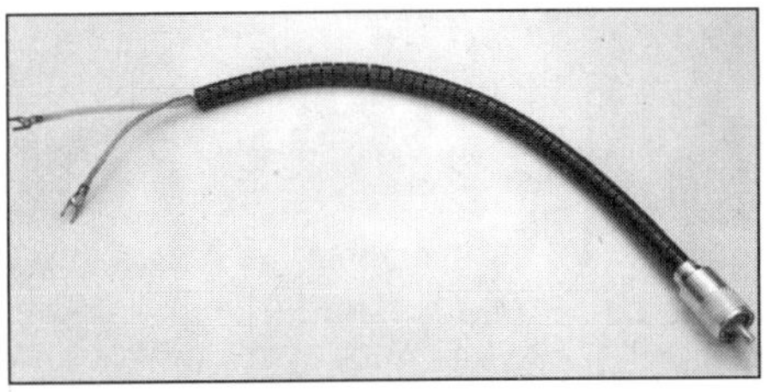

Figure 24.66 — W2DU bead balun consisting of 50 FB-73-2041 ferrite beads over a length of RG-303 coax. See text for details.

to prevent overheating. Equally important — the lower choking impedance is much less effective at rejecting noise and preventing the filling of nulls in a radiation pattern.

Newer bead balun designs use type #31 and #43 beads that are resonant around 150 MHz, are inductive below resonance, and have only a few tens of ohms of strongly inductive impedance on the HF bands. Even with 20 of the type #31 or #43 beads in the string, the choke is still resonant around 150 MHz, is much less effective than a wound coaxial ferrite choke, and is still inductive on the HF bands (so it will be ineffective at frequencies where it resonates with the line). Be aware that the heat-dissipating capability of small-diameter ferrite beads can be exceeded where there is a serious imbalance that results in large common-mode currents. Beads nearest the feed point can become very warm and can even shatter under extreme conditions of imbalance. Use enough beads to provide the necessary choking impedance to keep power dissipation at safe levels. The original W2DU designs should be limited to use at 100 W power levels if there is significant imbalance in the antenna system.

24.7.5 Measuring Choke Balun Impedance

A ferrite RF choke creates a parallel resonant circuit from inductance and resistance coupled from the core and stray capacitance resulting from interaction of the conductor that forms the choke with the permittivity of the core. If the choke is made by winding turns on a core (as opposed to single-turn bead chokes) the inter-turn capacitance also becomes part of the choke's circuit.

These chokes are very difficult to measure for two fundamental reasons. First, the stray capacitance forming the parallel resonance is quite small, typically 0.4-5 pF, which is often less than the stray capacitance of the test equipment used to measure it. The key to accurate measurement of high impedance ferrite chokes is to set up the choke as the series element, Z_X, of a voltage divider with a calibrated load.

The coax-wound ferrite chokes in this section were measured with a two-port vector network analyzer (VNA) using a test fixture built by K9YC and W6GJB that places the choke in series between the input and output of the VNA, forming a voltage divider between the choke and the 50-Ω input impedance of the VNA. The VNA was calibrated to a measurement plane at the point where the choke is inserted, and S21 (the gain from output to input) is measured. See the **Antenna and Transmission Line Measurements** chapter for information about using VNAs.

In a vector network analyzer, S21 is complex — that is, the result contains both magnitude and phase data. Math functions built into the VNA operating and display software solves the voltage divider equation to convert S21 (the voltage divider ratio) to Z_{MAG}, R_S, and X_S. See the online paper "A New Choke Cookbook for the 160-10M Bands" for more information about the VNA test fixture.

OBTAINING R, L, AND C VALUES

The VNA will provide a data file including Z_{MAG}, R_S, and X_S. In a spreadsheet worksheet, create columns that compute parallel L and C values from the VNA data. (The required equations can be found in the section Parallel Circuits of Moderate to High Q of the **Electrical Fundamentals** chapter in the *ARRL Handbook*.)

The spreadsheet should also plot impedance of the same range of frequencies as the measurements and with the same plotted scale as the measurements.

1) R is equal to the resonant peak of the measured impedance.

2) At a point on the resonance curve below the resonant frequency with approximately one-third of the impedance at resonance compute L for that value of inductive reactance ($L = X_L / 2pf$).

3) Calculate a value for C that produces the same resonant frequency of the measurement.

The resulting values for R, L, and C form the equivalent circuit for the choke. The values can then be used in circuit modeling software (*NEC*, *SPICE*) to predict the behavior of circuits using ferrite chokes.

ACCURACY

The test fixture can be constructed so that its stray capacitance is small but it won't be zero. A first approximation of the stray capacitance can be obtained by substituting for the unknown a noninductive resistor whose resistance is in the same general range as the chokes being measured, then sweeping through the VNA range to find the -3 dB point where $X_C = R$. This test for the author's setup yielded a stray capacitance value of 0.4 pF. A thin-film surface-mount or chip resistor will have the lowest stray reactances and devices with <0.1 pF capacitance are available.

Since the measured curve includes stray capacitance, the actual capacitance of the choke will be slightly less than the computed value. If you have determined the value of stray capacitance for your test setup, subtract it from the computed value to get the actual capacitance. You can also use this corrected value in the theoretical circuit to see how the choke will actually behave in a circuit — that is, without the stray capacitance of your test setup. You won't see the change in your measured data, only in the theoretical RLC equivalent.

DUAL RESONANCES

In NiZn ferrite materials (type #61, #43), there is only circuit resonance, but MnZn materials (#77, #78, #31) have both circuit resonance and dimensional resonance. (See the **RF Techniques** chapter of the *ARRL Handbook* for a discussion of ferrite resonances.) The dimensional resonance of type #77 and #78 material is rather high-Q and clearly defined, so

R, L, and C values can often be computed for both resonances. (Type #77 and #78 material are not recommended for common-mode chokes. Those materials are intended for low-frequency magnetic circuits.)

This is not practical with chokes wound on type #31 cores because the dimensional resonance occurs below 5 MHz, is very low-Q, is poorly defined, and blends with the circuit resonance to broaden the impedance curve. The result is a dual-sloped resonance curve — that is, curve fitting will produce somewhat different values of R, L, and C when matching the low-frequency slope and high frequency slope. When using these values in a circuit model, use the values that most closely match the behavior of the choke in the frequency range of interest.

24.7.6 Power Dissipation in Ferrite Transmitting Chokes

Current through a choke is caused by the voltage across the choke from the load to the common-mode path on the feed line. The resistive component of a choke's impedance will dissipate power like any resistor but tends to be fairly broadband. The reactive component will not dissipate power but tends to be highest in a narrower bandwidth than resistive chokes. (The following discussion refers only to power dissipation caused by common-mode current. Differential-mode losses in the short transmission line windings can become significant above 20 MHz and at high values of SWR.)

Ferrites used in chokes exhibit both resistive and inductive components that change with frequency so the type or mix and the frequency both affect choke impedance. (See *The ARRL Handbook's* **RF Techniques** chapter and K9YC's ferrite tutorials at **k9yc.com/publish.htm** for more information on ferrites.)

If the choke's impedance is primarily inductive reactance, such as for an air-core choke, there is little power dissipation. This is the case for wound-coax chokes and chokes made with ferrites designed for inductive applications. Feed line impedance at the choke can also affect the net choking impedance by adding to or subtracting from the choke's impedance.

Inductive chokes, such as air-core coiled coax chokes and chokes wound on high-Q ferrite materials (#43, #52, #61, #67), tend to have limited bandwidths over which choking impedance is high. These chokes work best on the one or two bands containing the self-resonant frequency, but impedance drops quickly above and below that range. As impedance decreases, the choke is not as effective.

For ferrite chokes with an impedance that is primarily resistive, choking impedance is less dependent on frequency and feed line reactance but power is dissipated by the choke's resistance. If the choke's impedance is high enough, current through the choke can be reduced to a safe level of power dissipation.

The antenna's feed point impedance also changes with frequency as does the impedance of the feed line's common-mode path. Determining the voltage a choke will have to withstand thus requires analyzing the whole antenna system, a job best done with careful modeling. The variability of antenna system impedance is why a choke might work properly on some bands and overheat on others. This problem is addressed in Zack Lau, W1VT's article, "Why Do Baluns Burn Up?" which is included with this chapter's online material, and in Jim Brown K9YC's online paper "A New Choke Cookbook for the 160–10M Bands" at **k9yc.com/2018Cookbook.pdf**. The article "Don't Blow Up Your Balun" by Dean Straw, N6BV, includes several excellent examples of antenna systems that place a lot of stress on ferrite chokes and antenna tuners. The article is included in the online material.

Determining the voltage across the choke is done by modeling the system with various impedances inserted in the common-mode current path. A wire representing the common-mode current path is connected to one side of the antenna and follows the geometry of the feed line. (The feed line is not always connected to ground, such as in a link-coupled tuner.) The added wire should be the diameter of the coax shield or twice the diameter of the paired conductors, and with insulation corresponding to the outer jacket of the coax. Modeling software then determines the current at the choke. (See Lau's article for a description of how this is done in *EZNEC*.)

For example, Lau modeled an 80-meter dipole operating on both 20 meters and 80 meters with 1500 W. **Table 24.18** provides examples of different choke impedances, the resulting common-mode current, and loss in the choke in both watts and decibels. (Note that the paper does not evaluate power dissipation for a variety of ferrite materials. Using different materials would result in different common-mode impedance and power dissipation values.)

On 20 meters, where the feed point impedance is 2834 + *j*1214 Ω, almost all of the chokes dissipate significant power. The 12-turn wound-coax choke dissipates the least amount of power but that frequency is near the choke's self-resonance where it presents a very high resistive impedance. That choke will not present the same impedance on other bands. Con-

Table 24.18
Balun Impedance and Loss

Balun Impedance (Ω)	Common-Mode Current (A)	Balun (W)	Loss (dB)
80-meter dipole operated on 20 meters			
1000	0.5	253	1.3
4000	0.2	144	0.7
10000	0.08	72	0.3
1300 – *j*4001	0.44	258	1.3
449 + *j*58332	0.14	9	0.04
80-meter dipole operated on 80 meters			
Balun Impedance (Ω)	*Common-Mode Current (A)*	*Balun Loss (W)*	*(dB)*
50	0.02	0.022	0.0
2000	0.015	0.45	0.002
5 + *j*5611	0.022	0.0024	0.0
No balun	0.021	0.000	0.0

Notes
1. W2DU bead balun
2. 12 turns of RG-213 on 4¼-inch form

versely, on 80 meters, where feed point impedance in this example is less than 100 Ω, almost any of the chokes will work without significant temperature rise — because of the low feed point impedance, feed line shield current is minimal even with no choke at all!

A high value of resistance increases the ability of a resistive choke to handle higher transmit power. Dissipation due to common-mode current is $I_{CM}^2 R_S$ where R_S is the series equivalent resistance of the choke and I_{CM} is the common-mode current. Because power is proportional to the square of current, power dissipation is greatly reduced with very high R_S.

The power dissipated by a ferrite bead or core can result in a significant amount of heat buildup. Heat builds up throughout the material, so the problem is getting the heat out through its surface area. Lau also developed the following formula for temperature rise of ferrite components in free air (see his referenced entry):

$$\Delta T = \left(\frac{P_{dis}}{A}\right)^{0.833} \quad (28)$$

where

ΔT = Temperature rise in °C

P_{dis} = Power dissipation in milliwatts

A = Surface area in cm^2

As Lau determined, even a small amount of power can, over time, lead to a large amount of temperature rise. For example, 4 W of continuous power dissipation in a large 2-inch toroid creates a 25°C temperature rise. Putting the toroid in an enclosure can make the temperature rise even greater. See K9YC's updated choke cookbook for a discussion of power dissipation and enclosure ventilation. Chokes can be wound on multiple cores to reduce power dissipation in a single core and create more surface area.

You can compute an estimate the amount of power lost in a choke by transforming the polar representation of the winding impedance (impedance magnitude and phase angle) to its equivalent parallel form (R_p resistance and X_p shunt reactance). This procedure assumes the full feed point voltage appears across the choke impedance.

Power dissipated in the choke is estimated as the square of half the voltage across the feed point divided by the choke's equivalent parallel resistance: $(E/2)^2/R_p$. For example, a choke made with 8 turns of RG-213 on a 6-5/8 inch diameter coil form has a series impedance at 14 MHz of 262 ∠–86.9°. (See the K2SQ table of coiled-coax choke impedances in this chapter's online material.) Converting polar to rectangular form, this is equal to $14.17 - j\,261.62$ Ω, then converting series to parallel, we have $4844 - j\,262.38$ Ω. For an RF power of 1500 W in the antenna, one-half the feed point voltage is 273.9 V RMS. Thus, an estimate of the power lost in the choke is $(273.9/2)^2/(4844.8) = 3.9$ W, while for a 50-Ω load the power is $273.9^2/50 = 1500$ W.

The articles and papers by Lau and Brown go into considerably more detail than this short summary but it is clear that choke selection should be done carefully, with a good understanding of feed point impedance If the antenna will be used on several bands, the analysis should be done for each band.

24.7.7 Determining Balun Polarity

Many baluns, impedance transformers, chokes (a.k.a. "line isolators"), and other similar items are manufactured as sealed units and markings for output polarity with respect to the input connector are not often clear. For designs in which one or more continuous coaxial cables or parallel-wire lines are connected between the input and output terminals, a resistance measurement will suffice to determine polarity. In flux-coupled designs there is no continuity between the input and output terminals at dc so a resistance measurement cannot be used. Similarly, for autotransformer designs there may be a low resistance across the input or output terminals. In these cases, it is necessary to test the units at RF.

The first method is to test the unit using a dual-trace oscilloscope. Analog scopes should be in "Chop" mode so that both traces show display waveforms synchronized in time. Digital scopes must also sample both waveforms at the same time. Do not use "Alt" or an alternating waveform display. Drive the input to the unit with a signal generator's output in the unit's specified operating frequency range. Connect one scope channel to the unit's input and the other channel to the output. If the waveforms are displayed in-phase, the connections to the scope have the same polarity.

The following procedure requires only a signal generator and RF voltmeter (see the **Test Equipment and Measurements** chapter in *The ARRL Handbook*) and is used to check two identical units. If the units are substantially different, the test may not be conclusive or reliable. The procedure assumes a 50-Ω system impedance. If the units operate at an impedance very different from 50 Ω, such as for 300-, 450-, or 600-Ω open-wire line, use a 6-10 dB attenuator in the generator output to isolate the generator from the mismatch.

Connect the signal generator output to the input of both units using a T connector and identical lengths of feed line. Connect one output terminal of unit "A" to an output terminal of unit "B" and measure the RF voltage across the combined balun outputs. Swap the output terminal connections on one of the units and measure the RF voltage again. One arrangement of connections should show a substantially higher output voltage — this is the arrangement with the same polarity for both units.

24.8 Transmission-Line Baluns and Matching Devices

The properties of transmission lines, explored in the **Transmission Lines** chapter can be put to work isolating loads and transforming impedances. Here are a few useful designs for use with your antenna projects. Additional suggestions and construction ideas for VHF and UHF antennas are given by DG7YBN at **dg7ybn.de/Symmetrising/Symmetrising.htm**.

24.8.1 Detuning Sleeves

The detuning sleeve shown in **Figure 24.67B** is essentially an air-insulated λ/4 line, but of the coaxial type, with the sleeve constituting the outer conductor and the outside of the coax line being the inner conductor. Because the impedance at the open end is very high, the unbalanced voltage on the coax line cannot cause much current to flow on the outside of the sleeve. Thus, the sleeve acts just like a choke to isolate the remainder of the line from the antenna. (The same viewpoint can be used in explaining the action of the λ/4 arrangement shown at Figure 24.67A but is less easy to understand in the case of baluns less than λ/4 long.)

A sleeve of this type may be resonated by cutting a small longitudinal slot near the bottom, just large enough to take a single-turn loop which is, in turn, link-coupled to a dip meter. If the sleeve is a little long to start with, a bit at a time can be cut off the top until the stub is resonant.

The diameter of the coaxial detuning sleeve in Figure 24.67B should be fairly large compared with the diameter of the cable it surrounds. A diameter of two inches or so is satisfactory with half-inch cable. The sleeve should be symmetrically placed with respect to the center of the antenna so that it will be equally coupled to both sides. Otherwise, a current will be induced from the antenna to the outside of the sleeve. This is particularly important at VHF and UHF.

In both the balancing methods shown in Figure 24.67 the λ/4 section should be cut to be resonant at exactly the same frequency as the antenna itself. These sections tend to have a beneficial effect on the impedance-frequency characteristic of the system, because their reactance varies in the opposite direction to that of the antenna. For instance, if the operating frequency is slightly below resonance the antenna has capacitive reactance, but the shorted λ/4 sections or stubs have inductive reactance. Thus, the reactances tend to cancel, which prevents the impedance from changing rapidly and helps maintain a low SWR on the line over a band of frequencies.

The *Pawsey stub* in **Figure 24.68A** is similar to a sleeve balun but consists only of the single λ/4 wire which is attached to one terminal of the load and the shield of the feed line. This creates a λ/4-wave shorted stub that creates a high impedance in the common-mode current path at the connection of the feed line and the load. The stub creates a dc short-circuit at the load which is a disadvantage in some applications. The Pawsey stub is useful from UHF through microwave frequen-

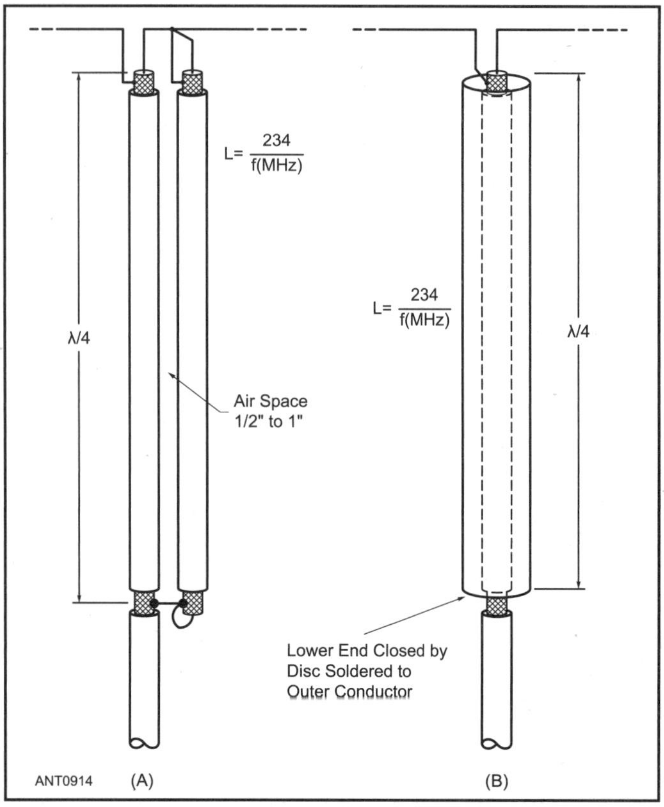

Figure 24.67 — Fixed-balun methods for balancing the termination when a coaxial cable is connected to a balanced antenna. These baluns work at a single frequency. The balun at B is known as a "sleeve balun" and is often used at VHF. Adding one or more ferrite cores to the balun at A at the load will improve performance.

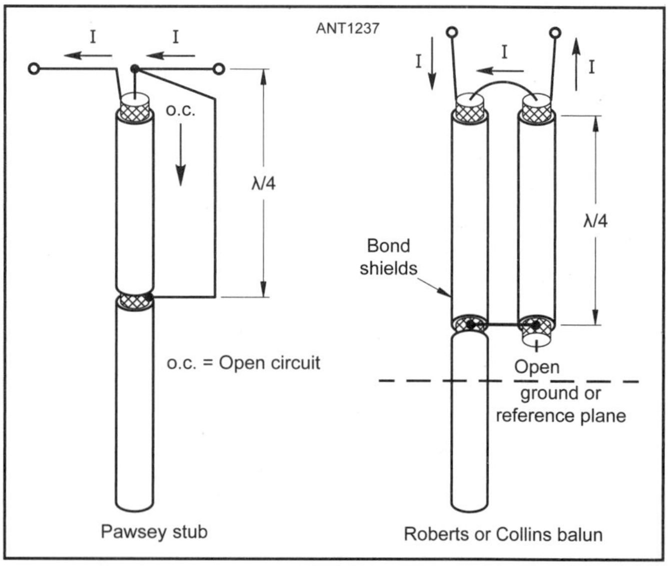

Figure 24.68 — The Pawsey stub (A) and Roberts or Collins baluns (B). See text for a description of how they function.

cies where the length of the connections at the load terminals becomes significant.

The *Roberts* or *Collins balun* in Figure 24.68B is similar to the Pawsey stub but does not place a dc short-circuit across the load terminals. The λ/4 open stub presents a low impedance to RF at the other end of the stub, allowing the same RF current to flow in both load terminals. It is most useful from 2 meters where the length of the stub starts to become unwieldy to above 23 cm where connection lengths start to become significant.

The length of the open stub can be varied to act as a matching element or extend the bandwidth of the antenna. The stub can also act as a quarter-wave transformer for the load impedance. The usual construction is for a ground plane to create the bond between the stub and the feed line. A complete analysis is available from the MIT Haystack Observatory at **haystack.mit.edu/ast/arrays/Edges/EDGES_memos/087.pdf**.

24.8.2 Quarter/Three-Quarter-Wave Balun

The coaxial balun in **Figure 24.69** is a 1:1 decoupling balun made from two pieces of coaxial cable. One leg is λ/4 long and the other 3λ/4 long. The two coaxes and the feed line are joined together with a T connector. At the antenna, the shields of the cables are connected together, and the center conductors connected to the terminals of the antenna feed point. The balun has very little loss and is reported to have a bandwidth of more than 10%.

The balun works because of the current-forcing function of a transmission line an odd number of λ/4 long. The current at the output of such a transmission line is V_{IN} / Z_0 regardless of the load impedance, similarly to the behavior of a current source. Because both lines are fed with the same voltage, being connected in parallel, the output currents will also be equal.

The current out of the 3λ/4 line is delayed by λ/2 from the current out of the λ/4 line (and so is out of phase). The result is that equal and opposite currents are forced into the terminal of the load.

24.8.3 Combined Balun and Matching Stub

In certain antenna systems the balun length can be considerably shorter than λ/4; the balun is, in fact, used as part of the matching system. This requires that the radiation resistance be fairly low as compared with the line Z_0 so that a match can be brought about by first shortening the antenna to make it have a capacitive reactance, and then using a shunt inductor across the antenna terminals to resonate the antenna and simultaneously raise the impedance to a value equal to the line Z_0. This is the same principle used for hairpin matches. The balun is then made the proper length to exhibit the desired value of inductive reactance.

The basic matching method is shown in **Figure 24.70A** for parallel-conductor line, and the balun adaptation to coaxial feed is shown in Figure 24.70B. The matching stub in Figure 24.71B is a parallel-line section, one conductor of which is the outside of the coax between point X and the antenna; the other stub conductor is an equal length of wire. (A piece of coax may be used instead, as in the balun in Figure 24.67A.) The spacing between the stub conductors can be 2 to 3 inches. The stub of Figure 24.70 is ordinarily much shorter than λ/4, and the impedance match can be adjusted by altering the stub length along with the antenna length. With simple coax feed, even with a λ/4 balun as in Figure 24.67, the match depends entirely on the actual antenna impedance and the Z_0 of the cable; no adjustment is possible.

ADJUSTMENT

When a λ/4 balun is used it is advisable to resonate it before connecting the antenna. This can be done without much difficulty if a dip meter or impedance analyzer is available. In the system shown in Figure 24.67A, the section formed by the two parallel pieces of line should first be made slightly longer than the length given by the equation. The shorting connection at the bottom may be installed permanently. With the dip meter coupled to the shorted end, check the frequency and cut off small lengths of the shield braid (cutting both lines equally) at the open ends until the stub is resonant at the desired frequency. In each case leave just enough inner conductor

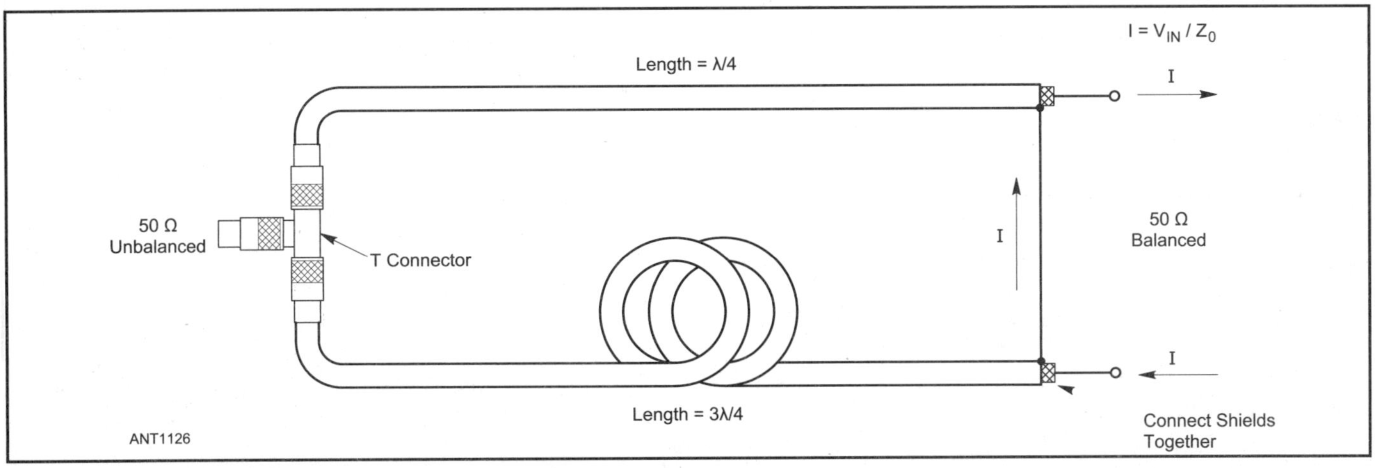

Figure 24.69 — The λ/4 – 3λ/4 balun uses the current-forcing function of odd-λ/4 feed lines and the λ/2 delay of the longer line to cause equal and opposite currents to flow in the antenna terminals.

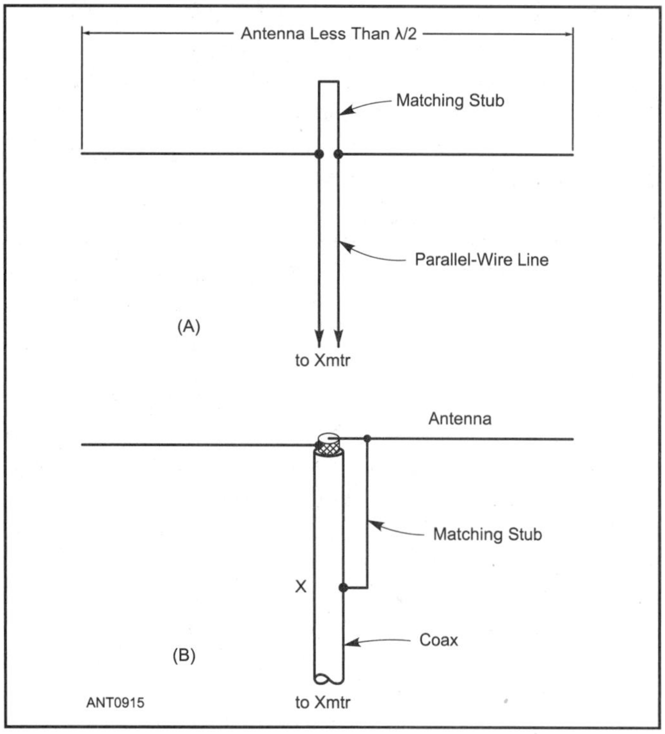

Figure 24.70 — Combined matching stub and balun. The basic arrangement is shown at A. At B, the balun arrangement is achieved by using a section of the outside of the coax feed line as one conductor of a matching stub.

remaining to make a short connection to the antenna. After resonance has been established, solder the inner and outer conductors of the second piece of coax together and complete the connections indicated in Figure 24.67A.

Another method is to first adjust the antenna length to the desired frequency, with the line and stub disconnected, then connect the balun and recheck the frequency. Its length may then be adjusted so that the overall system is again resonant at the desired frequency.

CONSTRUCTION

In constructing a balun of the type shown in Figure 24.67A, the additional conductor and the line should be maintained parallel by suitable spacers. It is convenient to use a piece of coax for the second conductor; the inner conductor can simply be soldered to the outer conductor at both ends since it does not enter into the operation of the device. The two cables should be separated sufficiently so that the vinyl covering represents only a small proportion of the dielectric between them. Since the principal dielectric is air, the length of the λ/4 section is based on a velocity factor of 0.95, approximately.

24.8.4 Impedance Step-Up/Step-Down Balun

A coax-line balun may also be constructed to give an impedance step-up ratio of 4:1. This form of balun is shown in **Figure 24.71**. If 75-Ω line is used, as indicated, the balun will provide a match for a 300-Ω terminating impedance. If 50-Ω line is used, the balun will provide a match for a 200-Ω terminating impedance. The U-shaped section of line must be an electrical length of λ/2 long, taking the velocity factor of the line into account. Note that this type of balun is a voltage balun and does not force equal currents into each load terminal.

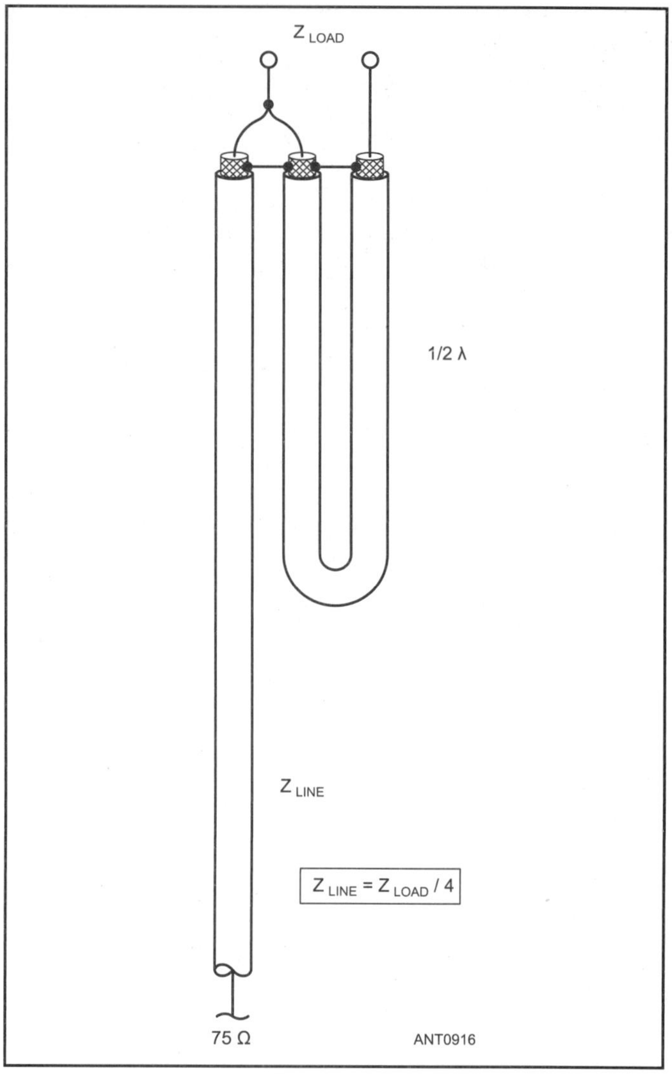

Figure 24.71 — A balun that provides an impedance step-up ratio of 4:1. The electrical length of the U-shaped section of line is λ/2. This will match 75 Ω line to a 300 Ω load or a 50 Ω line to a 200 Ω load. The load is often a folded dipole driven element.

In most installations using this type of balun at HF, it is customary to roll up the length of line represented by the U-shaped section into a coil of several inches in diameter. The coil turns may be bound together with electrical tape. At VHF and UHF, the λ/2 section is formed into a small circular loop and the shields soldered directly together as shown by DG7YBN on the web page referenced at the beginning of this section.

Because of the bulk and weight of the balun at HF, this type is seldom used with wire-line antennas suspended by insulators at the antenna ends. More commonly it is used with multielement Yagi antennas, where its weight may be supported by the boom of the antenna system. See the K1FO designs in the **VHF, UHF and Microwave Antennas** chapter, where 200-Ω T-matches are used with such a balun.

24.8.5 Matching with Parallel Line Sections

Two sections of coax can also be connected in parallel to create a section with a characteristic impedance equal to half that of either section. This creates a quarter-wave transformer for values of load impedance less than the main feed line characteristic impedance which is usually 50 Ω. **Figure 24.72** shows two examples. Note that RG-83 coax has a characteristic impedance of 35-Ω coax and can be used in place of the parallel 75-Ω lines, providing an exact match between 25 and 50 Ω. Adding a ferrite choke at the load improves performance by decoupling the matching section shields.

Because the parallel lines are usually close together, the shields may couple and add some inductance that increases the difference between internal electrical length and outer surface electrical length. Foam-dielectric cables with their higher velocity of propagation will reduce the electrical difference between the internal and external electrical lengths.

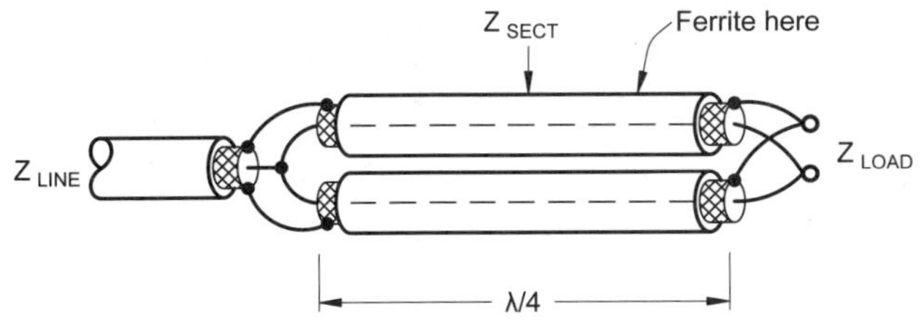

Z LINE	Z SECT	Z LOAD
50 Ω	75 Ω	28 Ω
50 Ω	50 Ω	12.5 Ω

ANT1363

Figure 24.72 — Using parallel λ/4 lines creates different transformation ratios.

24.9 References and Bibliography

Source material and more extended discussion of topics covered in this chapter can be found in the references given below and in the textbooks listed at the end of the **Antenna Fundamentals** chapter.

G. Barrere, "Magnetic Coupling in Transmission Lines and Transformers," *QEX*, Sep./Oct. 2006, pp. 28-36.

D. K. Belcher, "RF Matching Techniques, Design and Example," *QST*, Oct. 1972, pp. 24-30.

D. Birnbaum, "Direct Calculation of Antenna Tuner Losses," *QEX*, Nov./Dec. 2018, pp. 23-25.

J. Brown, "RFI, Ferrites, and Common Mode Chokes For Hams," April 2019, **k9yc.com/publish.htm**.

J. Brown, "A New Choke Cookbook for the 160–10M Bands," Dec 2018, **k9yc.com/publish.htm**.

J. Brown, "Optimizing the Location of Stubs For Harmonic Suppression," **audiosystemsgroup.com/publish.htm**.

W. Bruene, "Introducing the Series-Parallel Network," *QST*, June 1986, pp. 21-23.

W. Caron, *Antenna Impedance Matching* (Newington: ARRL, 1989). [out of print]

G. Cutsogeorge, *Managing Interstation Interference, 2nd edition*, International Radio, 2009.

T. Dorbuck, "Matching-Network Design," *QST*, Mar. 1979, pp. 26-30.

B. A. Eggers, "An Analysis of the Balun," *QST*, Apr. 1980, pp. 19-21.

D. Emerson, "Try a Twelfth-Wave Transformer," *QST*, June 1997, pp. 43-44.

J. Garland, "The EZ Tuner — Parts 1, 2, and 3," *QST*, Apr. 2002, pp 40-43, May 2002, pp. 28-34 and June 2002, pp. 89-96.

D. Geiser, "Resistive Impedance-matching with Quarter-Wave Lines," *QST*, Feb. 1963, pp. 63-67.

J. D. Gooch, O. E. Gardner, and G. L. Roberts, "The Hairpin Match," *QST* , Apr. 1962, pp. 11-14, 146, 156.

G. Grammer, "Simplified Design of Impedance-Matching Networks," *QST*, Part 1, Mar. 1957, pp. 38-42; Part 2, Apr. 1957, pp. 32-35; Part 3, May 1957, pp. 29-34.

G. Guanella, "New Method of Impedance Matching in Radio-Frequency Circuits," Sep. 1944, Brown Boveri Review, pp. 125-127.

J. Hallas, *The ARRL Guide to Antenna Tuners* (Newington: ARRL, 2010).

E. Harper, "Ferrite Cable Chokes", US Army, March 1966.

W. Harriman, "Second Harmonic Suppression Using a Coax Stub," **ae6ty.com/Smith_Charts.html**.

D. J. Healey, "An Examination of the Gamma Match," *QST*, Apr. 1969, pp. 11-15, 57.

S. Johnson, "Build a 9 to 1 Unun Transformer," *QST*, Mar. 2019, pp. 34-35.

J. D. Kraus and S. S. Sturgeon, "The T-Matched Antenna," *QST*, Sep. 1940, pp. 24-25.

Z. Lau, "Why Do Baluns Burn Up?" *QEX*, Jan./Feb. 2004, pp. 55-58.

Z. Lau, "RF: Calculating the Power Limit of Circuits with Toroids," *QEX*, Mar./Apr. 1995, pp. 24-30.

R. W. Lewallen, "Baluns: What They Do and How They Do It," *The ARRL Antenna Compendium, Vol 1* (Newington: ARRL, 1985), pp. 157-164.

R. Lindquist, "*QST* Compares: Four High-Power Antenna Tuners," Product Review, *QST*, Mar. 1997, pp. 73-77.

M. W. Maxwell, "Some Aspects of the Balun Problem," *QST*, Mar. 1983, pp. 38-40.

M. W. Maxwell, *Reflections III* (New York: CQ Communications, 2010).

R. A. Nelson, "Basic Gamma Matching," *Ham Radio*, Jan. 1985, pp. 29-31, 33.

B. Pattison, "A Graphical Look at the L Network," *QST*, Mar. 1979, pp. 24-25.

R. Quick and K. Siwiak "Does Your Antenna Need a Choke or a Balun?," *QST*, Mar., 2017, pp. 30-33.

F. A. Regier, "Series-Section Transmission line Impedance-matching," *QST*, July 1978, pp. 14-16.

R. Rhea, "Yin-Yang of Matching, Parts 1 and 2," *High Frequency Electronics,* Mar and Apr 2006. Also available from Keysight Technologies (**keysight.com**) as application notes 5989-9012EN and 5989-9015EN. Go to the Services & Support section, then Technical Support, and use the Search function.

W. Sabin, "Understanding the T-tuner (C-L-C) Transmatch," *QEX*, Dec. 1997, pp. 13-21.

J. Sevick, *Understanding, Building, and Using Baluns and Ununs*, (New York: CQ Communications, 2003).

J. Sevick, *Transmission Line Transformers, 4th edition,* Noble Publishing, 2001.

J. Sevick, "Simple Broadband Matching Networks," *QST*, Jan. 1976, pp. 20-23.

J. Sevick, "A Simplified Analysis of the Broadband Transmission Line Transformer," *High Frequency Electronics*, Feb. 2004, pp. 48-53.

J. Sevick, "Magnetic Materials for Broadband Transmission Line Transformers," *High Frequency Electronics*, Jan. 2005, pp. 46-52.

W. Silver, ed., *ARRL Handbook*, (Newington: ARRL, 2019).

W. Silver, "Hands-On Radio: Experiment #157 — Matching Network Design and Build," *QST*, Feb. 2016, pp. 65-66.

J. Stanley, "Hairpin Tuners for Matching Balanced Antenna Systems," *QST,* Apr. 2009, pp. 34-35.

J. Stanley, "*FilTuners* — a New (Old) Approach to Antenna Matching," *The ARRL Antenna Compendium, Vol. 6* (Newington: ARRL, 1999), pp. 168-173.

R. E. Stephens, "Admittance Matching the Ground-Plane Antenna to Coaxial Transmission Line," Technical Correspondence, *QST*, Apr. 1973, pp. 55-57.

D. Straw, "A Beginner's Guide to Transmission-Line and Antenna-Tuner Modeling," *QST*, May 2001, pp 34-37.

D. Straw, "Don't Blow Up Your Balun," *QST*, June 2015, pp. 30.

H. F. Tolles, "How to Design Gamma-Matching Networks," *Ham Radio*, May 1973, pp. 46-55.

E. Wingfield, "New and Improved Formulas for the Design of Pi and Pi-L Networks," *QST*, Aug. 1983, pp. 23-29.

F. Witt, "Baluns in the Real (and Complex) World," *The ARRL Antenna Compendium, Vol 5* (Newington: ARRL, 1997), pp. 171-181.

F. Witt, "How to Evaluate Your Antenna Tuner," *QST*, Part 1, Apr. 1995, pp. 30-34 and May 1995, pp. 33-37.

B. S. Yarman, *Design of Ultra Wideband Antenna Matching Networks*, (New York: Springer, 2008).

Notes

Notes

Notes

Notes

Notes